Analytic Geometry and Calculus

ANALYTIC
GEOMETRY
AND
CALCULUS

Second Edition

William L. Hart, PH.D.

University of Minnesota

D. C. HEATH AND COMPANY BOSTON

Copyright © 1963 by D. C. HEATH AND COMPANY

Printed in the United States of America (6 в 3)

Library of Congress Catalog Card Number: 63-12326

Preface

This text should be considered as an essentially new presentation of the subject, because of the major alterations and additions which occurred in the rewriting of substantial parts of the first edition. Brief remarks about points of similarity of the two editions will be made later. Priority now will be given to comments concerning the present book.

Prerequisites. The student should have had substantial training in trigonometry and college algebra (or fourth semester algebra in a secondary school).

Concerning the analytic geometry. No formal acquaintance with the subject is assumed, but moderate previous study of analytic geometry would permit the student to cover Chapter One quickly as a review. Aside from the basic analytic geometry presented in Chapters One and Two, the remainder of the plane analytic geometry, where possible, is presented in association with related calculus.

Function concept. The book consistently restricts "function" to mean *single-valued function*. Classical functional notation is employed. The single-valued feature is exploited somewhat uniquely to create simplicity in considering inverse and implicit functions and related calculus.

Basic theoretical level.* The logical structure is emphasized by formal exhibition of major definitions, theorems, and their proofs. The book does *not* subscribe to the opinion that proof, in a first course in calculus, means solely *analytic proof*, frequently of the classical (ϵ, δ) type. Intuitional arguments are used frankly where appropriate. In cases where analytic proof seems undesirable, the text aims to attain equivalent verbal rigor, when feasible. A few important theorems of an advanced nature are stated and used without proof (some of the proofs are given in the Appendix).

Simplification of classical content. The fundamental definitions, theorems, and related exposition are arranged to create a simplified setting for those students who will not study optional material.

Treatment of vectors. The emphasis on vectors in association with calculus in applied mathematics and the utility of vector methods in pure mathematics justify

---

* With a higher level in the chapter supplements and the Appendix.

the presence of substantial content about vectors, arranged to facilitate various stages of emphasis.

- *Vectors are introduced geometrically;* an abstract algebraic foundation is suggested as a supplementary procedure.

- *The minimum content about vectors* leads through the stage of the scalar product; includes a foundation for treatment of directions, direction angles, their cosines, and direction numbers in space or in a plane; permits a satisfying discussion of gradients later; provides an elegant basis for discussing the forward tangent to a curve.

- *Supplementary content on vectors* includes a thorough discussion of the tangential and normal components of the velocity and acceleration vectors in motion on a plane curve; the connection of the normal component of the acceleration with the circle of curvature; limits, continuity, and derivatives for vector-valued functions of a single variable; the vector product; the scalar triple product and certain applications of it connected with solid analytic geometry; vector derivation of the normal forms for a line in a plane and a plane in space.

Supplementary content. To assist superior students in obtaining deeper than normal appreciation of the content, an unusual amount of supplementary material is provided.* It is arranged to avoid interference with normal progress through the text.

- *A supplement occurs at the end of each chapter,* presenting either problems alone or problems preceded by supplementary sections.

- *Various analytic proofs* above the basic theoretical level of the text are presented in the Appendix.

- *A substantial introduction to analytic proof* of the $(\epsilon, \delta_\epsilon)$ or (ϵ, N_ϵ) type and proofs of limit theorems are provided in the Appendix, with associated problems in several chapter supplements.

- *The problems in the chapter supplements* not only demand special skill in routine applications but also present new aspects of previous content, and some extensions of the theory. For instance, in the supplements, the student will meet the intriguing Schwarz example relating to definitions of surface area; the method of Lagrange multipliers for investigating extrema; Newtonian attraction; problems concerning absolute extrema; extended use of vector methods in plane and solid analytic geometry; line and surface integrals.

Sets. The concept of a set of elements is introduced at the very start, and is emphasized as an indispensable part of the technical vocabulary, to be used fre-

* All marked with a black star.

quently. However, functions are not described in set theoretic notations. Also, no algebra of sets is met in the text, except for a brief description of set operations in the Appendix.

Role of applications. At every opportunity, the calculus content is motivated by appropriate applications, which are taken from social science and statistics, as well as from physical science, technology, and parts of pure mathematics. Also, the needs of students of applied mathematics in their early courses strongly influenced the location of certain content in the book.

Skills of calculus. This text emphasizes illustrative examples, graphical aids (472 figures in the book), and systematic training in differentiation and integration to develop proficiency in techniques. The exercises contain quantities of problems, with a sensible balance between routine examples and those of increasing difficulty. Thirteen review exercises occur in strategic locations.

Features of the Exposition and Arrangement

●Preliminary treatment of basic analytic geometry, with moderate total length, and integration of many of its topics later with calculus.

●Certain simplifications in the connection between derivatives and their applications in graphing, with emphasis on symmetry with respect to "x and y," or "horizontal and vertical" in discussion of an equation $f(x, y) = 0$.

●Early location of the fundamental first chapter on integration, particularly for a class which can consider Chapter 1 as mere review.

●Brevity of the intermission between the first chapter on integration and the main body of the integral calculus for simple integrals.

●Considerable elementary use of vectors, particularly in connection with direction angles and their cosines in a plane as well as in space.

●Introduction of the definite integral first, with moderate numerical integration, and then definition of the indefinite integral as a species of definite integral.

●Arrangements permitting a teacher to include content on a higher level without disturbing a continuous development of the normal course.

●Destruction of the artificial wall between calculus for functions of *one* variable and for functions of *more than one* variable, wherever possible.

●Relatively early location of multiple integrals and their applications.

●Frequent appearances of content involving the use of differentials.

●Use of right-handed coordinates in space.

•Definitions of multiple integrals by use of rectangular meshes, not only for simplicity but also to establish a logical order for introduction of the concepts of area in a plane and volume in space as integrals.

•Division of the work on partial differentiation into three separated parts, with a substantial elementary part appearing somewhat early.

•The key role played by parametric form in considering arc length.

•Emphasis on parametric form, with θ as the parameter, for a curve in an $r\theta$-system of polar coordinates.

•Repeated elementary contacts with differential equations at several places outside of the final chapter.

•Natural approach to Taylor's formula through integration by parts, and emphasis on its applications.

•Answers to almost all odd-numbered problems are included in the text; answers to even-numbered problems are available in a separate pamphlet. In chapter supplements, many answers of a theoretical nature are provided in the statements of problems. Otherwise, answers are omitted in order to develop self-criticism by the superior student.

Comparison with First Edition

The most noticeable alterations in this text as compared with the original edition are as follows: addition of a substantial treatment of vectors; inclusion of new content at a higher level in chapter supplements and the Appendix; a major re-ordering of content in the early part of the book to shorten the intermission between the first and second appearances of integration; the considerable increase in the extent and number of review exercises; inclusion of more content on differential equations early in the book. Less noticeable, but important, changes occurred in the rewriting of major parts of the discussion in the first five hundred pages and in minor alterations of the exposition and arrangement beyond that point. The added content on vector analysis affected certain advanced sections in the text. The exercises were revised but, on the whole, routine problems were taken from the first edition.

The author expresses his deep appreciation of suggestions for alteration of the first edition from teachers who have used it. In particular, he is very grateful for comments received from his colleagues at the University of Minnesota. Also, he thanks the staff of D. C. Heath and Company, and especially its College Editor for Mathematics, Miss Barbara B. Betts, for the manner in which the details of publication were carried out.

William L. Hart
University of Minnesota

Contents

* Can be omitted; included in later treatment by double integrals.

CHAPTER FIFTEEN
Advanced Integration
368

CHAPTER SIXTEEN
Length of Arc and Applications
387

CHAPTER SEVENTEEN
Vectors and Direction Cosines
406

* The remainder of the chapter may be omitted.

CHAPTER TWENTY–SIX

Envelopes, Space Curves, and Surfaces   *594*

CHAPTER TWENTY–SEVEN

Applications of Partial Derivatives   *615*

CHAPTER TWENTY–EIGHT

Hyperbolic Functions   *633*

CHAPTER TWENTY–NINE

Differential Equations   *642*

Appendix   *673*

Tables   *691*

Answers to Exercises   *715*

Index   *746*

Analytic Geometry and Calculus

CHAPTER ONE

Review of Basic Terminology

1. INTRODUCTION

Calculus is a field of mathematics whose fundamental notions arose through the study of various problems of physics and geometry. The subject matter of calculus is concerned mainly with the theory and applications of two major concepts, the notions of a *derivative* and an *integral*, whose definitions involve the idea of a *limit* as a basic feature. A derivative is a *rate of change* in value, illustrated in physics by the instantaneous velocity of a moving body. An integral is *the limit of a set of finite sums* and, in one setting, can be identified with the value of a certain area. The first use of integration is credited to the Greek mathematician ARCHIMEDES (287–212 B.C.) in his computation of lengths of curves, areas, volumes, and centroids. His work had little influence until late in the 16th century. The first clear recognition of the connection between differentiation and integration is credited to the English mathematician ISAAC BARROW (1630–1677), who was the principal mathematical teacher of Sir ISAAC NEWTON (1642–1727). In the late 17th century, Newton and GOTTFRIED WILHELM LEIBNIZ (1646–1716) independently formulated the fundamental concepts of calculus as an effective discipline, and hence usually are referred to as the founders of calculus.*

The rapid development of calculus in the 17th century was preceded by and assisted by achievements of the French mathematician and philosopher RENÉ DESCARTES (1596–1650). In the year 1637, he established a landmark in the field of mathematics by publishing a book entitled *la Géométrie*, which introduced the notion of the equation of a curve and related analytical methods into the study of geometry. The resulting combination of analysis and geometry is referred to now as **analytic geometry.** For contrast, the study of geometry by purely geometric methods, as in high school geometry, is called **synthetic geometry.** The first two chapters of this text are concerned mainly with analytic geometry. Other parts of the subject are treated later in the text.

* For interesting historical facts, see *The History of Calculus* by Arthur Rosenthal, *American Mathematical Monthly*, Volume 58 (1951), pages 75–86.

2. REAL NUMBERS AND DIRECTED LINE SEGMENTS

When we mention a *number*, we shall mean a **real number** unless otherwise specified, because imaginary numbers will occur rarely. Any single letter, say x, introduced hereafter without a previous description will be a symbol for a number. A real number is called a **rational number** if it can be represented as a fraction p/q where p and q are integers and $q \neq 0$. Any real number which is not a rational number is called an **irrational number.**

ILLUSTRATION 1. The student has met the irrational numbers $\sqrt{2}$ and π, a symbol for the endless nonrepeating decimal $3.14159 \cdots$.

The **absolute value** of a real number b is defined as b *itself* if b is *nonnegative*, and as $-b$ if b is *negative*. The absolute value of b is represented by the symbol $|b|$. We say that two numbers b and c are **numerically equal** if $|b| = |c|$; then, b and c differ at most in sign. We observe that

$$|b|^2 = b^2; \quad |bc| = |b| \cdot |c|;$$

$$\left| \frac{b}{c} \right| = \frac{|b|}{|c|}, \; if \; c \neq 0.$$

ILLUSTRATION 2. $|5| = |-5| = 5$; 5 and -5 are numerically equal.

Knowledge of the fundamentals of analytic geometry is essential for commencing the study of calculus. Then, calculus will be found very useful in the treatment of various advanced parts of analytic geometry. Hence, a large part of the first two chapters of this text will be devoted to topics dealing with analytic geometry on a given line (meaning a straight line), or in a given plane. Let us assume that a unit of length has been specified. Then, in this book, the word *length* or the unqualified word *distance* will refer to a *nonnegative number* which is the measure of some distance in terms of the given unit of length. By the *distance between two points*, we mean the length of the line segment joining them.

A line l is said to be a *directed line* if it is agreed that one direction on l is called positive, with the opposite direction negative, as in Figure 1. Also, directed distances on l in the corresponding directions will be taken positive and negative, respectively, and a direction is assigned to each line segment on l. To indicate that a segment is directed or traced from a point A to B on l, the segment is named AB. Then, we shall let $\overline{AB}$ represent the *directed distance* from A to B, and may call $\overline{AB}$ the *value* of AB. Thus, if A and B coincide, $\overline{AB} = 0$. If AB has positive direction, then $\overline{AB}$ is positive and is the length of the segment. If AB has negative direction, then $\overline{AB}$ is the negative of the length of AB. In any case, the *absolute value* of $\overline{AB}$ is the length of AB:

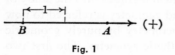

Fig. 1

$$|\overline{AB}| = (\text{length of segment } AB). \tag{1}$$

If a segment is directed from B to A, we refer to the segment as BA. Since AB and BA have opposite directions,

$$\overline{AB} = -\overline{BA} \quad or \quad \overline{AB} + \overline{BA} = 0. \tag{2}$$

ILLUSTRATION 3. In Figure 1, the positive direction is indicated on the line by an arrowhead (a common usage); then

$$\overline{AB} = -2; \quad \overline{BA} = 2; \quad |\overline{AB}| = |\overline{BA}| = 2.$$

The student already has met directed line segments in the familiar representation of real numbers on a linear scale, as in Figure 2. If x is any real number, we associate it with that point P on the scale for which $x = \overline{OP}$, where $\overline{OP}$ is positive or negative according as P is to the right or the left, respectively, from O. On the real number scale in Figure 2, we call O the **origin** and x the **coordinate** of P. We shall use "$P{:}(x)$" to abbreviate "*point P with coordinate x.*"

Fig. 2

For any three points A, B, and C on a directed line, as in Figures 3 and 4,

$$\overline{AB} + \overline{BC} = \overline{AC}. \tag{3}$$

In (3), if we think of the *value* of each segment as *the measure of travel in a specified direction*, then (3) simply states the fact that travel *from A to B*, followed by travel *from B to C*, is equivalent to travel *from A to C*.

A   B   C   B   C   A

Fig. 3   Fig. 4

ILLUSTRATION 4. In Figure 2 above, $\overline{AB} = 7$, $\overline{BC} = -5$, and $\overline{AC} = 2$. We verify that $7 + (-5) = 2$, as stated in (3).

Theorem I. *If $P_1{:}(x_1)$ and $P_2{:}(x_2)$ are on a number scale, then*

$$\overline{P_1P_2} = x_2 - x_1; \tag{4}$$

$$\textbf{(length of } P_1P_2) = |\overline{P_1P_2}| = |x_2 - x_1|. \tag{5}$$

Proof of (4). In Figure 2 above, $\overline{OP_1} = x_1$, $\overline{OP_2} = x_2$, and $\overline{P_1O} = -\overline{OP_1}$. On applying (3) to (P_1, O, P_2) in that order, we obtain

$$\overline{P_1P_2} = \overline{P_1O} + \overline{OP_2} = \overline{OP_2} - \overline{OP_1} = x_2 - x_1.$$

ILLUSTRATION 5. In Figure 2 above, the coordinates of B and C are 2 and -3, respectively. From (4), $\overline{BC} = -3 - 2 = -5$; the distance between 2 and -3 is $|\overline{BC}| = |-3 - 2| = 5$.

We use the number scale as a background for geometrical language where each *number* may be talked of as a *point*. Thus, to remark that *b is close to c* will mean that *the scale distance $|b - c|$ is small.*

If no agreement is made as to positive and negative directions on a line l, it is said to be *undirected*. Then, all distances measured on l are positive, and we may use either AB or BA for a segment of l with A and B as end points. In this case, either $\overline{AB}$ or $\overline{BA}$ is the length of AB.

Note 1. If a line segment or distance is *directed* (and thus possibly is *negative*), this will be stated. If we refer to a directed segment AB on a line where, previously, no positive direction has been assigned, we agree that AB has positive direction.

If b and c are real numbers, we say that b *is less than* c, or c *is greater than* b, if b is to the *left* of c on the number scale. We use the inequality signs "$<$" to abbreviate "*less than*" and "$>$" for "*greater than*." We refer to "$b < c$," or to "$b \leqq c$," as an *inequality*.

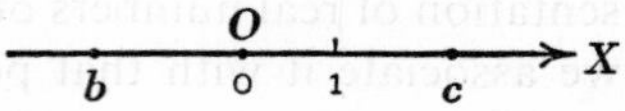

Fig. 5

If $b < c$, as in Figure 5, the directed segment from b to c on the scale has the value $(c - b)$, which is *positive* because b is to the left of c. Hence,

$$\text{``}b < c\text{'' means that } (c - b) \text{ is positive.} \tag{6}$$

ILLUSTRATION 6. $- 5 < 2$ because $- 5$ is to the left of 2 on the number scale, and also because $2 - (- 5) = 7$, which is *positive*.

Let any number x_1 be represented on a number scale by point P_1, as in Figure 2 on page 5. We note that $| x_1 |$ is the measure of the *length of segment* OP_1, or $| x_1 | = | \overline{OP_1} |$. Then, if x_1 and x_2 are any two numbers, the student should verify with the aid of Figure 2 that

$$| x_1 + x_2 | \leqq | x_1 | + | x_2 |. \tag{7}$$

To check (7), the following mutually exclusive possibilities should be considered: (*a*) *neither* x_1 *nor* x_2 *negative;* (*b*) *neither positive;* (*c*) x_1 *and* x_2 *of opposite signs.* In (7), the *equality* sign applies in (*a*) and (*b*) and the *inequality* sign in (*c*).

EXERCISE 1

Read the symbol in words and find its value.

1. $| 3 |$.   **2.** $| - 4 |$.   **3.** $| - 2 |$.   **4.** $| - 6 |^2$.   **5.** $| - 2 |^3$.

6. Mark $A:(2)$, $B:(- 3)$, $C:(- 6)$, and $D:(- 8)$ on a number scale and compute $\overline{AB}$, $\overline{CD}$, $| \overline{BC} |$, and $\overline{DA}$.

Plot the points on a scale. Find $\overline{AB}$, $\overline{BC}$, *and* $\overline{AC}$ *by use of Section 2, and check* $\overline{AB} + \overline{BC} = \overline{AC}$. *Also, compute* $| \overline{AB} | + | \overline{BC} |$ *and* $| \overline{AC} |$.

7. $A:(- 7)$; $B:(- 3)$; $C:(- 1)$.   **8.** $A:(9)$; $B:(- 1)$; $C:(- 5)$.
9. $A:(- 2)$; $B:(- 6)$; $C:(0)$.   **10.** $A:(8)$; $B:(- 6)$; $C:(- 3)$.
11. $A:(- 5)$; $B:(7)$; $C:(2)$.   **12.** $A:(9)$; $B:(- 8)$; $C:(0)$.

Insert the proper sign, $<$ or $>$, between the numbers.

13. 2 and 5.   **14.** $- 12$ and 3.   **15.** $- 3$ and 0.   **16.** $- 4$ and $- 7$.

Think of the number x on a number scale and state the given fact by an inequality.

17. x is positive; negative.   **18.** x is to the left of $- 4$.
19. x is to the right of 6.   **20.** x is to the right of $- 3$.

Verify (7) on this page for the indicated numbers x_1 and x_2.

21. $x_1 = 5$; $x_2 = 7$.   **22.** $x_1 = - 3$; $x_2 = - 5$.
23. $x_1 = - 4$; $x_2 = 6$.   **24.** $x_1 = - 4$; $x_2 = 7$.

3. SETS, VARIABLES, AND CONSTANTS

In referring to a *set* of things, we take **"set"** as an undefined term. Each object in a set will be called an **element** or a **member** of it. For any set A, we imply that we have the means to recognize whether or not any specified object belongs to A. A **subset** S of a set A is a set consisting of some (possibly all) of the members of A. If a set T has just n elements, where n is a nonnegative integer, we call T a *finite set*. If T is not a finite set, T is said to be an *infinite set*. Then, corresponding to any positive integer n, there exist *more than n elements* in T.

ILLUSTRATION 1. We may refer to the set, T, of members of the United States Senate. The two senators from Illinois form a subset of T.

ILLUSTRATION 2. The set, T, of all integers, and the set, R, of all real numbers are infinite sets. The set, P, of all positive integers is a subset of T, and of R. The set, A, of all rational numbers and the set, L, of all irrational numbers are infinite sets.

If S is a subset of the set T, we say that S is *included* in T, and write "$S \subset T$," read "*S is included in T*." We have $T \subset T$. If all members of S are members of T, and if all members of T also are members of S, then S and T consist of the *same members* and we write $S = T$. Above, with $n = 0$, we implicitly introduced the so-called **empty set,** or **null set,** with *no* members, to be represented by $\emptyset$. We agree to say that $\emptyset$ is a subset of every set. If $S \subset T$ and $S \neq T$, we say that S is a **proper subset** of T. Then, there is *at least one element* of T which is *not* in S.

ILLUSTRATION 3. In Illustration 2, $P \subset T$ and P is a proper subset of T. If H is the set $\{1, 2, 3, 4, 5, 6, 7, 8, 9, 10, 11, 12\}$, then the set $\{1, 2, 3\}$ is a proper subset of H.

Note 1. In this text, we shall mention sets frequently. The objective of the present section is to alert the student to the fact that the notion of a set of elements is fundamental in mathematics. In Note 3 of the Appendix, various operations on sets are described. There will be no necessity for employing these operations in the main body of the text.

A **variable** is a symbol, such as x, which may represent any particular element of a *specified set*, S, of elements (not necessarily numbers). We call S the **domain** of the variable x; each element of S is called a *value* of x, where value does not necessarily refer to a number. In this text, unless otherwise specified, the domain of any variable will be a set of numbers.

ILLUSTRATION 4. We may use y to represent any person in the United States. Then, its population is the domain of the variable y.

ILLUSTRATION 5. Let S be the set of all numbers $x < 2$. We could also define S as the set of all numbers $u < 2$. Thus, the letter, x or u, chosen as the symbol for an arbitrary number in S is of no importance.

In a given discussion, a **constant** is a number symbol representing a fixed number. A letter, such as b, which is a constant also may be called a variable whose domain consists of *just one number*. When a variable is mentioned, we shall infer that it is not a constant, unless otherwise specified.

In this text, except where otherwise implied, any literal number symbol, such as x, is understood to be a variable whose domain is the set of *all real numbers x* for which the expression involved has meaning.

ILLUSTRATION 6. In the formula $A = \pi r^2$ for the area,* A, of a circle of radius r, if we think of all circles, then A and r are variables and π is a constant.

4. CONCERNING EQUATIONS AND INEQUALITIES

In order to present certain terminology for *equations* and *inequalities* in a unified fashion, let us define a **numerical statement** as an assertion concerning *equality* or *inequality* about various number expressions. We define an **open numerical statement** as a statement involving *at least one variable*.

ILLUSTRATION 1. A numerical statement may be an equation, or a system of equations, an inequality, etc. The equation $4 = \sqrt{25}$ is a false statement. If x is a variable, then $3 + 2x = 4$ is an open statement, true only when $x = \frac{1}{2}$.

Definition I. *A* **solution** *of an open numerical statement is a set of numbers, consisting of a value of each variable, such that the statement is true when each variable is assigned the specified value. Then, the set of values of the variables is said to* **satisfy** *the statement.*

Note 1. A solution of an equation in a single variable also is called a **root** of the equation. Any reference to a solution of a numerical statement will imply that it is an open statement. For brevity, the *set of all solutions* of a statement may be called its **solution set.**

ILLUSTRATION 2. The equation $2x^2 - x = 1$, or $(2x + 1)(x - 1) = 0$, has the solutions $x = -\frac{1}{2}$ and $x = 1$; the solution set consists of $\{-\frac{1}{2}, 1\}$.

ILLUSTRATION 3. If x and y are variables, a solution of $x + y = 3$ is a pair of corresponding values of x and y which satisfy the equation. Thus, $(x = 2, y = 1)$ is a solution. If x takes on any value in the given equation, it determines a corresponding number y so that (x, y) is a solution. Hence, the equation has *infinitely many solutions.*

ILLUSTRATION 4. The inequality $x < 2$ has infinitely many solutions, consisting of all numbers represented by the points on a number scale, as in Figure 2 on page 5, to the left of the point B representing 2.

A numerical statement (for instance, an equation or an inequality) is said to be **inconsistent** if it has *no solution*, and otherwise is said to be **consistent.** The statement is said to be a **conditional statement** if it is not satisfied by *all* sets of values of the variables. If the statement is satisfied by *all* sets of values of the variables, it is called an **identical statement.** Two numerical statements in the same variables are said to be **equivalent** if the statements have the same solutions.

ILLUSTRATION 5. An identical equation is called simply an *identity.* Thus,

$$x^2 - 4 = (x - 2)(x + 2)$$

is an identity. An identical inequality sometimes is called an *absolute inequality.* Thus, $x^2 \geq 0$ is an absolute inequality because x^2 cannot be negative.

---

* Whenever we use a symbol for a concrete quantity, in agreement with common practice the symbol will represent a number which is the measure of the quantity in terms of an appropriate unit.

ILLUSTRATION 6. The equations $x + 3 = 2$ and $x(x + 3) = 2x$ are *not* equivalent because the second equation has the root $x = 0$, which does not satisfy $x + 3 = 2$.

Let A, B, h, p, and N be number symbols, where p is positive and N is negative. Then, in algebra as met before this course, it is proved that the inequality $A < B$ is equivalent to each of the following inequalities, where the inequality sign is reversed by the negative multiplier N:

$$A + h < B + h; \quad pA < pB; \quad NA > NB. \tag{1}$$

To solve an inequality in a single variable, x, means to obtain a simple description of the solution set. To solve an inequality equivalent to $ax + b < 0$, where a and b are constants and $a \neq 0$, we use (1) to obtain an equivalent inequality $x < c$ or $c < x$.

ILLUSTRATION 7. To solve $\qquad \frac{3}{2}x - 1 < \frac{2}{3}x + 4, \tag{2}$

we obtain in sequence the following equivalent inequalities by multiplying by 6; by adding $(6 - 4x)$; by dividing by 5:

$$9x - 6 < 4x + 24; \quad 5x < 30; \quad x < 6. \tag{3}$$

Hence, the solution set for (2) consists of *all numbers $x < 6$*.

If M is a set of real numbers, we define the **graph of M** on a real number scale as the set of points on the scale representing the numbers of M. Now, let x be a variable and let S be the solution set for a numerical statement involving only the single variable x. Then, we define **the graph of the statement** on a number scale to be **the graph of the solution set S.**

ILLUSTRATION 8. From Illustration 2, the graph of $2x^2 - x - 1 = 0$ on a number scale would consist of the points $P:(-\frac{1}{2})$ and $Q:(1)$. The graph, in Figure 6, of inequality (2) is the half-line of the scale to the left of the point representing 6.

Fig. 6

The statement $A < B < C$, which we read "$A < B$ and $B < C$," forms an illustration of a compound numerical statement. The statement

$$A = B \quad or * \quad C < D \tag{4}$$

also is a compound statement. The terminology about statements in Definition I, and related remarks above, apply to *compound* statements.

If b and c are distinct numbers, the set of all numbers x on the real number scale from b to c, with one, both, or neither of the end points b and c included, is called an **interval of numbers.** If b and c are not included, the interval is said to be **open.** If both b and c are included, the interval is said to be **closed.** If just one of b and c is included, the interval is said to be **half-open** or **half-closed.** Any interval can be described as the solution set for a certain compound statement involving inequalities and possibly equalities.

---

* In this text, if we say that "H or K is true," where H and K separately have meaning, we shall mean that one of the following mutually exclusive possibilities is true: (1) *H alone is true;* (2) *K alone is true;* (3) *both H and K are true.*

ILLUSTRATION 9. We read the compound statement $-2 < x < 6$ as follows:

$$-2 < x \quad and \quad x < 6, \tag{5}$$

which is a system of simultaneous inequalities. The graph, M,* of (5) in Figure 7 consists of the open interval between -2 and 6 where the graphs of $-2 < x$ and $x < 6$ overlap.* Similarly, $a < x < b$ means that x is between a and b on the scale, or the graph of $a < x < b$ is the open interval with end points a and b.

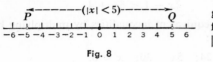

Fig. 7

ILLUSTRATION 10. The graph of $2 \leqq x \leqq 6$ is the closed interval with end points 2 and 6. The graph of $2 < x \leqq 6$ is a half-open interval because P:(2) is excluded.

ILLUSTRATION 11. The statement $|x| < 5$ is equivalent to $-5 < x < 5$, read "$-5 < x$ and $x < 5$." In Figure 8, the graph of $|x| < 5$ is the open interval from P:(-5) to Q:(5). The inequality $|x| > 5$ is equivalent to

Fig. 8

$$x < -5 \quad or \quad 5 < x. \tag{6}$$

In Figure 8, the graph of $x < -5$ is the half-line M_1 to the left of P:(-5); the graph of $5 < x$ is the half-line M_2 to the right of Q:(5). Thus, the graph, N, of $|x| > 5$ consists of all points in M_1 or M_2.†

EXERCISE 2

Solve each equation or inequality. Obtain a simple description, without use of absolute values, of the solution set wherever an inequality is involved. Graph each solution set.

1. $x^2 - 2x = 8$.   2. $2x^2 - 5x = 3$.   3. $x^2 + 2x + 2 = 0$.
4. $2 - x < 3x + 6$.   5. $|x| \leqq 2$.   6. $2x + 7 > 15$.
7. $\frac{2}{3}x - 7 < 4$.   8. $7 - 2x > 3x$.   9. $\frac{1}{4}x - 3 < 2x$.
10. $|x - 2| < 3$.   11. $|x + 4| < 2$.   12. $|x| \geqq 3$.

Hint for Problem 10. $-3 < x - 2 < 3$, or $-1 < x < 5$.

13. $|x + 3| < 1$.   14. $|x - 3| > 2$.   15. $|x + 1| > 3$.

16. Verify that, if b and d are constants, the graph of $|x - b| < d$ on a number scale is the open interval with center b and length $2d$.

17. If T represents the set $\{1, 2, 3, 4, 5, 6\}$, write out all subsets of T consisting of three integers.

Describe the interval by means of inequalities.

18. The open interval with end points -2 and 4.

19. The closed interval with end points -3 and 5.

20. The half-open interval with end points 1 and 7, where the interval is open at 1 but closed at 7.

21. The half-open interval from -4, inclusive, to 5, excluding 5.

---

* Let S_1 be the graph of $2 < x$ and S_2 be the graph of $x < 6$. Then, in terminology from page 674, $M = S_1 \cap S_2$.
† In set terminology from page 674, $N = M_1 \cup M_2$.

5. COORDINATES IN A PLANE

A pair of elements * x and y is said to be an **ordered pair** in case each symbol is assigned to a specific place in two available locations. If the symbols are written with a comma between them, we shall call the corresponding symbols the first and second *components* of the pair. Two ordered pairs of symbols (a, b) and (c, d) are considered *identical* if and only if a and c represent the same element and b and d represent the same element. Thus, the ordered pairs of numbers (a, b) and (c, d) are identical if and only if $a = c$ and $b = d$. To initiate analytic geometry in a plane, we shall associate an ordered pair of numbers, called *coordinates*, with each point in the plane.

Consider a given plane subject to any one of the customary sets of postulates involved in Euclidean geometry at the high school level. In this plane, we draw two perpendicular lines, each called a *coordinate axis*, with one axis, OX, horizontal and the other, OY, vertical in the typical Figure 9. We agree that the axes and lines parallel to them will be *directed lines*, with the positive direction to the right on lines parallel to OX and *upward* on lines parallel to OY. On each axis, we establish a number scale with O as the origin. In doing this, we choose *arbitrarily* a unit for scale distance on OX, and a unit for scale distance on OY, where these units are *not necessarily equal*. For coordinate purposes, distances in the plane along lines parallel to OX will be measured in terms of the scale unit on OX, and along lines parallel to OY in terms of the scale unit on OY. Let P be any point in the given plane. Then, we present the following terminology.

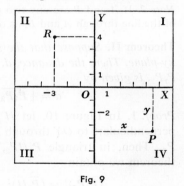

Fig. 9

I. *The horizontal coordinate, or* **abscissa,** *of P is the directed distance x, measured parallel to OX, from the vertical axis OY to P.*

II. *The vertical coordinate, or* **ordinate,** *of P is the directed distance y, measured parallel to OY, from the horizontal axis OX to P.*

The abscissa and ordinate of P together are called its **rectangular coordinates.** We shall use "P:(x, y)" to mean "P *with coordinates* (x, y)," and read "P:(x, y)" as "P, x, y." In (I) and (II) we have established a one-to-one correspondence between all ordered pairs of real numbers and the points in the plane. The intersection, O:$(0, 0)$, of the axes is called the **origin** of coordinates. The axes divide the plane into four **quadrants,** numbered I, II, III, and IV, counterclockwise from OX.

ILLUSTRATION 1. To plot R:$(- 3, 4)$, erect a perpendicular to OX at $x = - 3$ and go 4 units upward to reach R, in Figure 9.

Recall that a geometric *locus* is a set of all points satisfying a specified condition.

* The elements are not necessarily numbers.

ILLUSTRATION 2. The locus of all points $P:(x, y)$ with $x = 5$ is the line perpendicular to OX and 5 units to the right of OY.

Note 1. "To find a point" usually means *"to find its coordinates."*

Hereafter in this text, unless otherwise specified, in any reference to an xy-plane, it will be implied that the scale units on the axes possibly are unequal. We make the following agreement.

$$\left\{ \begin{array}{l} \textit{If the scale units on the coordinate axes in an} \\ \textit{xy-plane are equal, this unit also applies in} \\ \textit{measuring distance in any direction in the plane.} \end{array} \right\} \qquad (1)$$

The **projection** of a point P on a line l is defined as the foot of the perpendicular from P to l.

ILLUSTRATION 3. In Figure 9 on page 11, the projection of $R:(-3, 4)$ on OX is $(-3, 0)$ and on OY is $(0, 4)$. The projection of any point $P:(x, y)$ on OX is $(x, 0)$ and on OY is $(0, y)$.

Note 2. If A and B are any two points, at present *"AB"* will refer to the segment AB of the line through A and B, as on page 4.

Theorem II. *Suppose that the scale units on the coordinate axes are equal in an xy-plane. Then, the distance, d, between $P_1:(x_1, y_1)$ and $P_2:(x_2, y_2)$, or the length of P_1P_2, is given by*

$$d = |\overline{P_1P_2}| = \sqrt{(x_2 - x_1)^2 + (y_2 - y_1)^2}. \qquad (2)$$

Proof. 1. In Figure 10, let H be the intersection of perpendiculars to OY through P_1, and to OX through P_2. Then, in triangle P_1HP_2, by the Pythagorean theorem we obtain

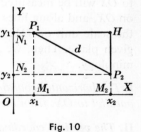

Fig. 10

$$(\overline{P_1P_2})^2 = (\overline{P_1H})^2 + (\overline{HP_2})^2.$$

2. From (4) on page 5,

$$\overline{P_1H} = \overline{M_1M_2} = x_2 - x_1;$$

$$\overline{HP_2} = \overline{N_1N_2} = y_2 - y_1.$$

Hence, $\qquad\qquad d^2 = (\overline{P_1P_2})^2 = (x_2 - x_1)^2 + (y_2 - y_1)^2.$

On extracting square roots we obtain (2).

Since $|\overline{P_1P_2}| = |\overline{P_2P_1}|$, and also because (2) involves *squares* of differences, the *order* of P_1, P_2 in (2) is immaterial. In (2), $|\overline{P_1P_2}|$ can be rewritten merely $\overline{P_1P_2}$ if P_1P_2 is undirected, and hence has a nonnegative value.

ILLUSTRATION 4. From (2) with $x_1 = 2$, $x_2 = -3$, etc., the distance between $A:(2, -8)$ and $B:(-3, 4)$ is

$$\overline{AB} = \sqrt{(-3 - 2)^2 + [4 - (-8)]^2} = \sqrt{25 + 144} = 13.$$

The distance d of $P:(x, y)$ from the origin $O:(0, 0)$ is called the **radius vector** of P and is found from (2):

$$d = \sqrt{x^2 + y^2}. \qquad (3)$$

EXERCISE 3

Find the other vertex of a rectangle with the given vertices.

1. $(3, 4)$; $(-5, 4)$; $(3, -1)$.   **2.** $(-2, -1)$; $(3, -1)$; $(3, 2)$.

3. A line l through $(2, -3)$ is perpendicular to OY. What is true about the ordinates of all points on l?

Describe and construct the locus of a point P:(x, y) satisfying the condition.

4. The abscissa is -3.   **5.** The ordinate is -4.

Plot the point and its projections M and N on OX and OY, respectively. Find the coordinates of M and N.

6. $(3, 7)$.   **7.** $(-2, 4)$.   **8.** $(-2, -5)$.   **9.** $(8, -7)$.

If A represents the first point and B the second, find $\overline{AB}$ and $|\overline{AB}|$, by projecting A and B on one of the coordinate axes.

10. $(0, 8)$; $(0, 5)$.   **11.** $(8, 4)$; $(2, 4)$.   **12.** $(-1, 3)$; $(-1, 5)$.

13. $(2, 2)$; $(9, 2)$.   **14.** $(3, 4)$; $(3, -12)$.   **15.** (x_1, y_1); (x_1, y_2).

The following problems refer to an xy-plane where the scale units on the coordinate axes are equal. Use the distance formula in each problem.

Find the distance between the points, or an expression for it.

16. $(1, 2)$; $(3, 6)$.   **17.** $(5, 0)$; $(0, 12)$.   **18.** $(3, 7)$; $(-6, 7)$.

19. $(7, 2)$; $(2, 14)$.   **20.** $(-1, -3)$; $(2, 1)$.   **21.** $(0, 0)$; $(4, 7)$.

22. $(0, 3)$; $(4, 0)$.   **23.** $(-2, 5)$; $(-2, -1)$.   **24.** (x, y); $(3, -4)$.

Prove that the triangle with the given vertices is isosceles.

25. $(-2, 8)$; $(-1, 1)$; $(3, 3)$.   **26.** $(3, -1)$; $(3, -3)$; $(7, -2)$.

Prove that the triangle with the given vertices is equilateral.

27. $(-2, 0)$; $(8, 0)$; $(3, 5\sqrt{3})$.   **28.** $(0, 2)$; $(0, -6)$; $(4\sqrt{3}, -2)$.

Prove that the points are the vertices of a right triangle.

29. $(-1, -1)$; $(1, 0)$; $(-2, 6)$.   **30.** $(3, 2)$; $(5, 3)$; $(0, 8)$.

6. INCLINATION AND SLOPE

Let l be a nonhorizontal line in an xy-plane. Then, regardless of the scale units chosen on the coordinate axes, we define the **inclination** of l as that angle ψ, less than $180°$, through which the x-axis must be rotated counterclockwise about its intersection with l in order to coincide with l. If l is horizontal, its inclination is defined as $\psi = 0°$. Thus, in any case, we have $0° \leqq \psi < 180°$, as illustrated in Figures 11 and 12 on page 14.

Note 1. The *whole line* through two points A and B will be referred to as AB when there is no danger of confusion with the *segment* AB.

Theorem III. *Let P_1:(x_1, y_1) and P_2:(x_2, y_2) be distinct points on a nonvertical line l in an xy-plane with equal scale units on the axes. Then, if ψ is the inclination of l,*

$$\left\{ \begin{array}{l} \text{the scale units are} \\ \textbf{equal } \textit{on } OX \textit{ and } OY \end{array} \right\} \qquad \tan \psi = \frac{y_2 - y_1}{x_2 - x_1}. \qquad (1)$$

Proof. 1. The order in which we label P_1 and P_2 is immaterial in (1). Hence, we assign subscripts to P_1 and P_2 so that $x_1 < x_2$ if $\psi < 90°$ and $x_2 < x_1$ if $\psi > 90°$, as in Figures 11 and 12. Then, the following discussion applies to either figure.

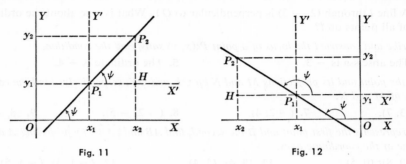

Fig. 11   Fig. 12

2. With respect to the lines P_1X' and P_1Y' as *new x'y'-axes*, and with the same unit for distance as in the *xy*-system, the coordinates of P_2 are

$$x' = \overline{P_1H} = x_2 - x_1 \quad and \quad y' = \overline{HP_2} = y_2 - y_1. \tag{2}$$

Hence, by the definition of the tangent function on page 676, $\tan \psi = y'/x'$, which gives (1).

Note 2. If the scale unit for x is v inches and for y is w inches, possibly with $v \neq w$, in Figure 11 we obtain, in inches, $\overline{P_1H} = v(x_2 - x_1)$ and $\overline{HP_2} = w(y_2 - y_1)$, so that

$\begin{cases} x\text{-unit, } v \text{ inches;} \\ y\text{-unit, } w \text{ inches} \end{cases}$ $\qquad \tan \psi = \dfrac{w}{v} \cdot \dfrac{y_2 - y_1}{x_2 - x_1}. \tag{3}$

From (1) or (3), $(y_2 - y_1)/(x_2 - x_1)$ is a constant for all choices of P_1 and P_2 on l because ψ is a constant. Then, we give the fraction a name as follows.

Definition II. *The* **slope,** *m, of a nonvertical line l in any xy-plane is the ratio of the change in the vertical coordinate to the change in the horizontal coordinate as we move on l from any point $P_1:(x_1, y_1)$ to a distinct point $P_2:(x_2, y_2)$, or*

$\begin{cases} in \textbf{ any} \\ xy\text{-plane} \end{cases}$ $\qquad$ **slope** $= m = \dfrac{y_2 - y_1}{x_2 - x_1}. \tag{4}$

From (1) and (4),

(equal *scale units on axes*)$\qquad\qquad\qquad\qquad m = \tan \psi. \tag{5}$

ILLUSTRATION 1. To find the slope of the line through $A:(2, -5)$ and $B:(-3, 4)$, use (4) with A as P_1 and B as P_2, or with B as P_1, etc.:

$$m = \frac{4 - (-5)}{-3 - 2} = -\frac{9}{5} \quad or \quad m = \frac{-5 - 4}{2 - (-3)} = -\frac{9}{5}.$$

Recall that $\tan \psi > 0$ if $0° < \psi < 90°$; $\tan \psi < 0$ if $90° < \psi < 180°$.

Note 3. In the remainder of this section, we restrict the major discussion to an *xy*-plane where the scale units on the axes are *equal*, so that (1) and (5) are true. The discussion applies with minor alterations to *any xy*-plane if (3) is employed in place of (1).

From (5), $\tan \psi > 0$ or the slope of a line l is *positive* if and only if $0° < \psi < 90°$, and is *negative* if and only if $90° < \psi < 180°$. If $\psi = 90°$ so that l is vertical, we have not defined the notion of slope for l, or **a vertical line has no slope;** this corresponds to the fact that $\tan 90°$ does not exist. If l varies so as to approach a limiting vertical position, then $|m|$ grows large without bound or, briefly, m *becomes infinite*, because $|\tan \psi|$ becomes infinite as ψ approaches 90° as a limit. On account of the preceding remarks, although a vertical line has no slope in the ordinary sense, it is sometimes said that *a vertical line has infinite slope.*

ILLUSTRATION 2. The slope of l is positive if, colloquially, l slopes upward to the right ($\psi < 90°$), and is negative if l slopes downward to the right ($\psi > 90°$). If l is horizontal, the slope of l is zero. If l is vertical, l has no slope.

ILLUSTRATION 3. From (5), if $\psi = 45°$, the slope is $m = \tan 45° = 1$. If $\psi = 117°$, from Table VI we find

$$m = \tan 117° = -\tan 63° = -1.963.$$

If $m = -.8$, then $\tan \psi = -.800$ and hence ψ is obtuse. From Table VI, by interpolation we obtain

$$\tan 38.7° = .800; \quad hence \quad \psi = 180° - 38.7° = 141.3°.$$

Note 4. From (4), in the language of a surveyor,

$$(slope \ of \ a \ nonvertical \ line \ l) = \frac{rise}{run}, \tag{6}$$

where the *rise*, $(y_2 - y_1)$, and the *run*, $(x_2 - x_1)$, are measured from any point $P_1:(x_1, y_1)$ to any distinct point $P_2:(x_2, y_2)$ on l.

Theorem IV. *In any xy-plane, two lines l_1 and l_2 with slopes m_1 and m_2, respectively, are parallel if and only if $m_1 = m_2$.*

Proof. Let ψ_1 and ψ_2 be the inclinations of l_1 and l_2, respectively. Lines l_1 and l_2 are parallel if and only if $\psi_1 = \psi_2$. This is equivalent to $\tan \psi_1 = \tan \psi_2$, which is equivalent to $m_1 = m_2$.

EXAMPLE 1. With $A:(2, 3)$, $B:(4, 6)$, $C:(-3, 1)$, and $D:(-1, 4)$, determine whether or not line AB is parallel to line CD.

Solution. The slopes m_1 and m_2 of AB and CD, respectively, are

$$m_1 = \frac{6-3}{4-2} = \frac{3}{2}; \quad m_2 = \frac{4-1}{-1+3} = \frac{3}{2} = m_1.$$

Hence, AB is parallel to CD.

Theorem V. *In any xy-plane, if A, B, and C are distinct points where the lines AB and BC have the slopes m_1 and m_2, respectively, then A, B, and C are collinear (lie on a line) if and only if $m_1 = m_2$.*

Proof. To say that A, B, and C lie on a line is equivalent to stating that lines AB and BC *coincide*, which means that they are *parallel*. By Theorem IV, AB and BC coincide if and only if $m_1 = m_2$, which proves Theorem V.

ILLUSTRATION 4. To prove that $A:(2, 3)$, $B:(5, 1)$, and $C:(11, -3)$ are collinear, we compute

$$(slope\ of\ AB) = \frac{3-1}{2-5} = -\frac{2}{3}; \quad (slope\ of\ BC) = -\frac{3+1}{11-5} = -\frac{2}{3}.$$

Hence, the points are collinear.

In considering an angle formed by two lines in an xy-plane, for simplicity we agree that the scale units on the coordinate axes will be taken *equal*, so that $\tan \psi = m$ as in (5) on page 14. This agreement will apply also in any discussion about perpendicularity of two lines in this text.

Theorem VI. *If lines l_1 and l_2 have slopes m_1 and m_2, respectively, then l_1 and l_2 are perpendicular if and only if the slopes are negative reciprocals, or*

$$m_1 = -\frac{1}{m_2} \quad or \quad m_2 = -\frac{1}{m_1} \quad or \quad m_1 m_2 = -1. \tag{7}$$

Proof. We are given that l_1 and l_2 have slopes. Let the inclinations of l_1 and l_2 be ψ_1 and ψ_2, respectively, where the notation is chosen so that $\psi_1 \leqq \psi_2$. To say that "l_1 *and* l_2 *have slopes and are perpendicular*" is equivalent to saying that "$\psi_2 = \psi_1 + 90°$ and $\psi_1 \neq 0$," as in Figure 13. Since ψ_2 and $(\psi_1 + 90°)$ both lie on the domain from 90° to 180°, we have $\psi_2 = \psi_1 + 90°$ if and only if

$$m_2 = \tan \psi_2 = \tan (\psi_1 + 90°),\ or\ *$$

$$m_2 = -\cot \psi_1 = -\frac{1}{\tan \psi_1} = -\frac{1}{m_1}.$$

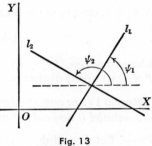

Fig. 13

Hence, l_1 and l_2 are perpendicular if and only if $m_2 = -1/m_1$.

ILLUSTRATION 5. Line l_1 through $(-2, 1)$ and $(2, 3)$ is perpendicular to line l_2 through $(-1, 4)$ and $(2, -2)$ because

$$m_1 = \frac{3-1}{2+2} = \frac{1}{2}; \quad m_2 = \frac{-2-4}{2+1} = -2 = -\frac{1}{m_1}.$$

EXERCISE 4

Wherever inclination or perpendicularity is mentioned, assume that the scale units are equal on the coordinate axes.

Find the slope of the line with the given inclination.

1. 73°.　　　**2.** 96°.　　　**3.** $\frac{3}{4}\pi$.†　　　**4.** $\frac{2}{3}\pi$.　　　**5.** $\frac{1}{4}\pi$.　　　**6.** $\frac{5}{6}\pi$.

Find the inclination, in degrees, corresponding to the given slope.

7. $m = 3$.　　　**8.** $m = .554$.　　　**9.** $m = -2$.　　　**10.** $m = -.325$.

* Recall the trigonometric identity $\tan (\theta + 90°) = -\cot \theta$.
† When there is no indication of degree measure for an angle, the value is understood to be stated in radian measure. See page 677.

Find the slope of the line through the given points.

11. (2, 3); (7, 10).   **12.** (− 2, 4); (4, − 3).   **13.** (− 4, − 7); (− 3, − 4).

14. (1, 4); (5, 6).   **15.** (0, − 3); (− 2, 5).   **16.** (6, − 4); (2, − 3).

Prove that lines AB and CD are parallel, or that they are perpendicular if the scale units on the coordinate axes are equal.

17. A:(3, 5); B:(1, 1); C:(− 2, 1); D:(− 1, 3).

18. A:(− 1, − 2); B:(− 2, − 4); C:(2, − 3); D:(0, − 2).

19. A:(1, 5); B:(1, 2); C:(2, − 4); D:(3, − 4). •

Prove that the points are collinear.

20. (2, 3); (3, 5); (1, 1).   **21.** (− 2, 1); (0, 2); (4, 4).

22. (0, 3); (1, 6); (− 1, 0).   **23.** (− 3, − 5); (1, − 6); (− 7, − 4).

Prove the result if the scale units on the axes are equal.

24. (− 4, 1), (2, 4), (5, − 2), and (− 1, − 5) are vertices of a square.

25. (1, 0), (− 2, 6), and (− 1, − 1) are vertices of a right triangle.

Find x, or y, if the points are collinear.

26. (3, 4); (2, 6); (x, 3).   **27.** (3, − 2); (1, − 3); (2, y).

7. GRAPH OF AN EQUATION IN TWO VARIABLES

A **monomial** in certain variables x, y, z, ... is defined as a nonzero constant, called the **coefficient** of the monomial, multiplied by powers of the variables where the exponents are nonnegative integers. If each exponent is zero, the monomial is merely a *constant, not zero*. A sum of monomials in the variables is called a **polynomial** in them. A polynomial is called a **binomial** or a **trinomial** according as the polynomial is the sum of two or of three monomials, respectively. The **degree of a monomial** in a set of variables is the sum of the exponents of their powers which are factors of the monomial. The **degree of a polynomial** in the variables is the degree of the monomial of *highest degree* in the polynomial. A polynomial of the *first degree* in any set of variables is said to be **linear** in them.

ILLUSTRATION 1. Let a, b, and c be constants, not zero, and all other letters represent variables. Then $7ax^3y^2$ is a monomial of degree 5 in x and y, with the coefficient $7a$. The polynomial $5a + 3bxy^2 + 2cy^3z^2$ is of degree 5 in x, y, and z; if we decide temporarily to consider x and z also as constants, the polynomial then is said to be of degree 3 in y alone. Since $x^0 = 1$ if $x \neq 0$, any constant $b \neq 0$ can be thought of as being of degree zero in x, because $b = bx^0$.

Consider an equation in two variables, x with the domain H and y with the domain K, where H and K possibly do not consist entirely of real numbers. By Definition I on page 8, a *solution* of the equation is a *pair of corresponding values of x and y*, or is an *ordered pair* of numbers (x, y), which satisfy the equation. Hereafter in this chapter, we shall assume that the domain of any variable consists of real numbers. Then, the solution set for an equation in two variables is a set of *ordered pairs of real numbers*. At present, in any equation which we consider, each member will be a polynomial in the variables.

ILLUSTRATION 2. In $3x - 5y = 15$, if $x = 0$ then $y = 5$ in order to satisfy the equation; thus $(0, 5)$ is a solution of it. Another solution is $(8\frac{1}{3}, 2)$, obtained by placing $y = 2$. The given equation has infinitely many solutions obtained similarly.

Suppose that each solution (x, y) of an equation in x and y is taken as the coordinates of a point in an xy-plane. This leads to the following terminology.

Definition III.* *The* **graph** *or* **locus** *of an equation in two variables x and y is the set of points whose coordinates (x, y) satisfy the equation.*

Suppose that T is *any* set of ordered pairs of real numbers (x, y), and let us define the *graph of T* as the set of points in an xy-plane whose coordinates are number pairs in T. Then, in place of Definition III, we may say that **the graph of an equation in the variables x and y is the graph of the solution set for the equation.**

To graph an equation, we may form a table of solutions (x, y). The graph then is drawn through the points representing these solutions.

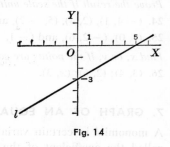

ILLUSTRATION 3. To graph $3x - 5y = 15$, we compute the following solutions. The graph, in Figure 14, is seen to be a straight line, l.

Fig. 14

$x =$	-5	-2	0	5	6
$y =$	-6	$-4\frac{1}{5}$	-3	0	$\frac{3}{5}$

To say that an equation is **linear,** or of the *first degree* in x and y, means that the equation is equivalent to one of the form $Ax + By + C = 0$, where A and B are constants not both zero. In Figure 14, we illustrated the fact (to be proved later) that *the graph of a linear equation in x and y is a line.*

The **x-intercepts** of a graph in an xy-plane are the values of x at the points where the graph meets the x-axis; the **y-intercepts** are the values of y where the graph meets the y-axis. Intercepts are useful in graphing.

Summary. *To obtain the intercepts of the graph of an equation in x and y.*
1. *To find the x-intercepts, place $y = 0$ and solve for x.*
2. *To find the y-intercepts, place $x = 0$ and solve for y.*

ILLUSTRATION 4. To graph $3x - 5y = 15$, we place $x = 0$ and find $y = -3$, the y-intercept. The x-intercept is $x = 5$. The graph is in Figure 14.

ILLUSTRATION 5. We may look upon $x - 8 = 0$ as a linear equation in x and y where y has the coefficient zero. Then, the graph of $x - 8 = 0$ in an xy-plane has an x-intercept, $x = 8$, but no y-intercept because we cannot have $x = 0$. Hence, the graph is the line perpendicular to the x-axis where $x = 8$.

ILLUSTRATION 6. The equation $x^2 + 5y^2 = -6$ has no real solution (x, y) because $x^2 \geqq 0$ and $y^2 \geqq 0$ for all real x and y, and hence $x^2 + 5y^2 \neq -6$ for any real point (x, y). Therefore, the equation has no graph.

---

* This definition extends without alteration if the word *equation* is replaced by *any numerical statement*, in two variables. See Section 4 on page 8.

ILLUSTRATION 7. To graph $y - x^2 + 2x + 1 = 0$, we first solve for y to obtain $y = x^2 - 2x - 1$; then we assign values to x and compute y to form a table of solutions (x, y). The graph, in Figure 15, is called a **parabola**. Sometimes we refer to an equation by giving it the name of its graph. In Figure 15, we observe the *parabola* $y = x^2 - 2x - 1$.

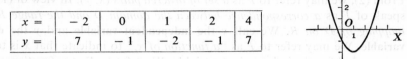

$x =$	-2	0	1	2	4
$y =$	7	-1	-2	-1	7

Fig. 15

An equation of a locus in an xy-plane is an equation in x and y whose graph is the given locus.

If we can find one equation for a locus, then we can write infinitely many equivalent equations for it. As a rule, we refer to the particular one of these equations with which we deal as **THE** equation of the locus.

ILLUSTRATION 8. The locus of $3x - 5y = 15$ is the line l in Figure 14, page 18. This line also is the locus of the equivalent equation $6x - 10y = 30$.

Either the *equation of a locus* in an xy-plane or the *locus of an equation* in x and y is determined by the following conditions.

I. *If P:(x, y) is on the locus, the coordinates (x, y) of P satisfy the equation.*

II. *If P:(x, y) is not on the locus, the coordinates (x, y) of P do not satisfy the equation.*

EXERCISE 5

Graph each equation in an xy-plane.

1. $3x + 2y = 6.$ **2.** $3y - 4x - 12 = 0.$ **3.** $3x + 7y = 0.$
4. $x - 5 = 0.$ **5.** $y = -7.$ **6.** $x + y = 0.$ **7.** $3x - 4 = 0.$

Graph the equation with $x = 2$ used in the table of values.

8. $y = x^2 - 4x - 5.$ **9.** $y = 3 + 4x - x^2.$ **10.** $y = 3 - 8x + 2x^2.$

Graph the equation with $y = -2$ used in the table of values.

11. $x = y^2 + 4y - 5.$ **12.** $x = 7 - 8y - 2y^2.$ **13.** $2x - 8y = 2y^2 + 5.$

14. Make verbal statements to prove that $3x^2 + y^2 = -5$ has no graph.

15. Prove that the graph of $x^2 + (y - 2)^2 = 0$ consists of just one point.

8. FUNCTION CONCEPT

Definition IV. *Let D be a given set of numbers. Suppose that, for each number x in D, some rule specifies* **just one** *corresponding number y, and let R be the set of all of these values of y. Then,*

$$\left. \begin{array}{l} \textit{this } \textbf{correspondence } \textit{between the numbers of } D \textit{ and} \\ \textit{those of } R \textit{ is called a } \textbf{function, } F, \textit{ from } D \textit{ to } R, \end{array} \right\} \textit{ or} \tag{1}$$

$$\left. \begin{array}{l} \textbf{the whole set of ordered pairs} \\ (x, y) \textit{ is called a } \textbf{function, } F. \end{array} \right\} \tag{2}$$

The *correspondence* in (1) determines the *ordered pairs* in (2); conversely, *these pairs* create the *correspondence*. Hence, mere personal preference is involved in deciding which of (1) and (2) is to be emphasized at any time. In Definition IV, each value of *y* is called a *value of the function.* The set *D* of values of *x* is referred to as the **domain** (of definition) of *F*, and *R* is called the **range** (of values) of *F*. From (2), we may refer to *F* as *a set of ordered pairs* (*x, y*). In view of (1), we may speak of *F* as *a correspondence between the domain D and the range R,* or as *a mapping of D on R.* We call *x* the **independent variable** and *y* the **dependent variable.** We may refer to *F* as "*a function of x,*" to indicate that *x* is to be used as a symbol for the independent variable. We refer to *F* as a *function of a single variable* because the domain *D* consists of *single numbers.*

ILLUSTRATION 1. Let *D* be the set of all *x* such that $1 \leqq x \leqq 3$, and let $y = 2x + 3$. If $x = 1$ then $y = 5$; if $x = 2$ then $y = 7$; etc. Thus, with *x* in *D*, the values of *y* make up the interval *R*, $5 \leqq y \leqq 9$, on *OY* in Figure 16, where the correspondence between *x* and *y* is indicated by representative arrows. This *correspondence* is a function, *F*, mapping *D* on *R*; we say that *F* is *defined as a function of x* by the equation $y = 2x + 3$.

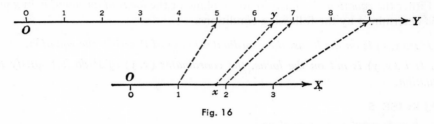

Fig. 16

Any formula in a variable *x*, specifying a single value for each value of *x*, defines a function whose values are given by substitution in the formula. However, a function may be defined merely by its tabulated values, or other means, without use of a formula. If a function is defined by a formula, the function frequently is named on the basis of the nature of its formula. Thus, previous mathematics has dealt with algebraic, trigonometric, logarithmic, and exponential functions, which are called the *elementary functions of mathematical analysis.*

ILLUSTRATION 2. In Definition IV, if $y = k$, a constant, for all values of *x*, we say that *F* is a **constant function.**

Definition V. *In an xy-plane, the* **graph of a function** *of a single variable, x, is the set of all points whose coordinates* (*x, y*) *form pairs of corresponding values of x and the function.*

On the basis of Definition V, we are led to the following procedure to graph a function defined by a formula in a variable *x*: *place y equal to the formula and graph the resulting equation.*

ILLUSTRATION 3. To graph the function whose value is ($x^2 - 2x - 1$) at any value of the variable *x*, we let $y = x^2 - 2x - 1$ and graph this equation. The graph is the parabola in Figure 15 on page 19.

ILLUSTRATION 4. Let D be $\{0, 1, 2, 3, 4, 5, 6, 7, 8, 9, 10, 11, 12, 13\}$. Let F be the function such that, for any x in D, the value, y, of F is the largest integral multiple of 2 which is at most equal to x. Thus, if $x = 0$ then $y = 0$; if $x = 5$ then $y = 4$, etc. The range, R, of F is $\{0, 2, 4, 6, 8, 10, 12\}$. In Figure 17, the correspondence between D and R is shown by arrows. F consists of fourteen pairs $(0, 0)$, $(1, 0)$, $(2, 2)$, $(3, 2)$, $\cdots$, $(11, 10)$, $(12, 12)$, $(13, 12)$. A graph of F would consist of fourteen points.

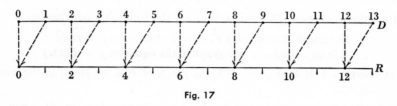

Fig. 17

Note 1. Usually, in graphing a function in a coordinate plane, we use the horizontal axis for plotting values of the independent variable.

In the description of a function F, the letters used for the independent and dependent variables are of no importance. Thus, suppose that F is defined by stating that, for every number x in the domain, the value, y, of F is $y = 3x - 5$. The same function is defined by saying that, for every number u in the domain, the value, r, of F is $r = 3u - 5$.

★*Note 2.* In Definition IV, since *just one* value of y corresponds to each value of x, sometimes it is said that a function, as thus defined, is *single-valued*. If n is a positive integer greater than 1, and if Definition IV were altered to read that n values of y correspond to each value of x, a function as thus defined would be called *n-valued*. We shall not use the concept of an n-valued function.

★*Note 3.* In Definition IV, if we change the word *number* to *element*, the definition describes a function F whose domain D is a set of *elements, of any specified variety*, and whose range is a second set of *elements*. Thus, D might consist of a *set of people*, and y, with range R, might be the *color of the eyes of the person x of D*. Functions of this nature are important but, in this book, except when otherwise indicated, the domain and range of any function will consist of *numbers*, as specified in Definition IV.

Let F be a function with the domain D. Then, it frequently is convenient to represent the *value* of F corresponding to the number x in D by the symbol "$F(x)$," read "F *of* x" or "F *at* x." Thus,

$$\left\{ \begin{array}{l} F(x) \text{ represents the } \textbf{value} \text{ of } F \text{ cor-} \\ \text{responding to any number } x \text{ in } D. \end{array} \right\} \tag{3}$$

We then say that $F(x)$ is a symbol in functional notation. We use symbols like F, G, H, f, g, h, etc., to represent functions.

ILLUSTRATION 5. If we write $F(x) = 3x^2 + x - 5$, this assigns F as a symbol for the function, and gives a formula, $3x^2 + x - 5$, for the *values* of F. Thus, the values of F at $x = -1$ and $x = 2 + h$ are

$$F(-1) = 3 - 1 - 5 = -3; \qquad F(2 + h) = 3(2 + h)^2 + (2 + h) - 5.$$

ILLUSTRATION 6. If $f(x) = 5x^2 + 2$ and $g(y) = 4/y$, then

$$[f(3)]^2 = [5(9) + 2]^2 = 47^2 = 2209; \quad f(x)g(x) = (5x^2 + 2)\left(\frac{4}{x}\right) = 20x + \frac{8}{x};$$

$$f(g(y)) = 5(g(y))^2 + 2 = 5\left(\frac{4}{y}\right)^2 + 2 = \frac{80}{y^2} + 2;$$

$$f(x + 3) = 5(x + 3)^2 + 2 = 5x^2 + 30x + 47; \quad f(3x) = 5(3x)^2 + 2 = 45x^2 + 2.$$

In functional notation, Definition V yields the following conclusion.

$$\left\{ \begin{array}{l} \textit{The } \textbf{graph of a function } \textit{F, with the independent variable} \\ \textit{x, in an xy-plane, is the } \textbf{graph of the equation } \textit{y} = \textbf{F(x).} \end{array} \right\} \tag{4}$$

ILLUSTRATION 7. If $F(x) = 3x^2 + 5$, the graph of F is the graph of the equation $y = 3x^2 + 5$.

Suppose that the functions f and g have a common domain, D. Then, for f and g, we define their *sum function,* H, *product function,* K, and *quotient function,* Q, for f divided by g, as those functions with the following values:

$$H(x) = f(x) + g(x); \quad K(x) = f(x)g(x); \quad Q(x) = \frac{f(x)}{g(x)}.$$

The domain for both H and K is the common domain D for f and g. The domain for Q consists of all numbers x in D such that $g(x) \neq 0$. If c is any constant, the product function cf is defined as that function W for which $W(x) = cf(x)$. Above, we might write $H = f + g$, $K = f \cdot g$, $Q = f/g$, and $W = cf$. However, it must be remembered that these statements are abbreviations for the definitions of the functions H, K, Q, and W, and are *not* equalities involving numbers.

ILLUSTRATION 8. Let $f(x) = x^2 + 1$ and $g(x) = 2x - 5$. Then, for f and g, their sum, H, product, K, and quotient, Q, for f/g, have the values

$$H(x) = (x^2 + 1) + (2x - 5); \quad K(x) = (x^2 + 1)(2x - 5); \quad Q(x) = \frac{x^2 + 1}{2x - 5}.$$

The function f^2 has the values

$$f^2(x) = [f(x)]^2 = (x^2 + 1)^2.$$

Let x and y be variables which are free to assume any ordered pair of values (x, y) in a certain set, D, of pairs of numbers. We may represent D as a corresponding set of points (x, y) in an xy-plane. Suppose that, to each point (x, y) in D, there corresponds just one number z, and let R be the set of all values thus obtained for z. Then,

$$\left\{ \begin{array}{l} \textit{this correspondence between pairs in D and numbers} \\ \textit{in R is called a function, F, from D to R,} \end{array} \right\} \textit{ or} \tag{5}$$

$$\left\{ \begin{array}{l} \textit{the whole set of ordered triples of numbers} \\ \textit{(x, y, z) is called a function, F.} \end{array} \right\} \tag{6}$$

In (5) and (6), F is said to be a function of two independent variables, x and y, because D consists of *pairs of numbers*, (x, y). We refer to D as the **domain** of F, and to R as the **range** of F. We write $z = F(x, y)$, meaning that $F(x, y)$, as well

* The word *function* frequently will be omitted in such a case.

as z, represents the value of F at the point (x, y) in the domain of F. Similarly, we may have a function of three or more variables. Thus, $F(x, y, w)$ would represent the value of a function F of three independent variables at the point (x, y, w) in the domain of F.

ILLUSTRATION 9. If $F(x, y) = 3x^2y + 8x + 5y^2$, then
$$F(2, -3) = -36 + 16 + 45 = 25.$$

Note 4. Hereafter, unless otherwise stated, in any reference to a *function* we shall mean a *function of a single variable*.

EXERCISE 6

State the range R of the function F and write the complete set of ordered pairs of numbers which form F. Construct a graph of F in an xy-plane. Also, prepare a diagram like Figure 16 on page 20 to show how F maps its domain on the range.

1. F has the domain $\{-4, -3, -2, -1, 0, 1, 2, 3, 4\}$ and the value of F for any number x in the domain is x^2.
2. The domain, D, of F consists of the integers $\{1, 2, 3, \ldots, 15\}$. The value of F corresponding to any number x in D is the largest integral multiple of 3 which is less than or equal to x.

Graph the function whose values are given by the formula.

3. $3x - 2$.   4. $-2x + 5$.   5. 10.   6. $x^2 + 6x - 5$.

If $f(x) = 2x + 3$, find the value of the symbol.

7. $f(2)$.   8. $f(-3)$.   9. $f(-2)$.   10. $f(\frac{1}{2})$.   11. $|f(-4)|^2$.

If $g(z) = 2z^4 - 3z^2$, find the value of the symbol.

12. $g(-3)$.   13. $3g(5)$.   14. $g(-\frac{1}{2})$.   15. $g(2c)$.   16. $g(\sqrt{x + y})$.

If $F(x, y) = 3y^2 + 2x - xy$, find the value of the symbol.

17. $F(3, 2)$.   18. $F(-1, 3)$.   19. $F(a, b)$.   20. $F(c, d^2)$.

21. If $h(u) = 2u + 3$ and $g(v) = v^3 - 2$, find $h(2)g(3)$; $h(3)$; $h(2)/g(-1)$; $h(g(x))$; $3h(x) + g(x)$.
22. If $f(x) = x^2 + 2x - 1$, find $f(h)$; $f(3h)$; $f(x + 2)$; $f(x + h)$; $f(4x)$.
23. If $H(x) = x^3$, find $H(2 + k)$; $H(2x)$; $H(x - 3)$.
24. If $F(x) = x^2$ and $G(x) = 2x - 1$, and if x is a variable with the domain $\{1, 2, 3, 4, 5\}$,
   (a) write the complete set of ordered pairs of numbers which form the function G;
   (b) write the set which forms the sum function, H, and the product function, K, for F and G.
25. Let $f(x) = 2x + 3$ and $g(x) = x + 5$. (a) If H, K, and Q are, respectively, the sum function and the product function for f and g, and the quotient function for f divided by g, find $H(3)$; $K(-1)$; $Q(2)$. (b) Describe the domain of Q. (c) If M represents f^2, find $M(3)$.

Unless otherwise implied, the domain of any variable x consists of all real numbers. Graph the function whose values are defined.

26. $f(x) = \sqrt{4 - x^2}$.   27. $f(x) = |x|$.   28. $f(x) = [x]$.*

* $[x]$ represents the *greatest integer at most equal to x*.

9. RELATIONS DEFINED BY EQUATIONS

Frequently hereafter, when $y = f(x)$, we shall use the following widely accepted phraseology:

$$y \text{ is a function of } x. \tag{1}$$

Thus, (1) means that there exists *some function f* where we shall use $y = f(x)$.

ILLUSTRATION 1. If an object P is moving along an s-axis, with s as the coordinate of P at an arbitrary value, t, of the time, then we may say that s *is a function of t*.

Suppose that x and y are variables, and that T is any *nonempty set* of ordered pairs of numbers (b, c), where b is a value of x and c is a value of y. Then, we shall refer to T as a **relation** in (or, between) x and y, and may speak of x and y as *related variables*. In particular, any consistent equation in x and y defines a relation, S, in x and y, where S is the set of all solutions (x, y) of the equation; then, we shall say that x and y are related by the equation.* Also, from (2) on page 19, *any function, F, is a relation* between the independent variable x and the dependent variable y, with the special characteristic that *just one value of y* corresponds to each value of x. In contrast, *a relation T* between x and y *is a function* with x as the independent variable *when and only when the special characteristic just mentioned is true*. Thus, some relations are *not* functions.

ILLUSTRATION 2. The following table of corresponding values of x and y describes a relation, T, in x and y. We see that T is *not* a function with x as *the independent*

$x =$	1	1	2	3	2
$y =$	2	-4	1	2	3

variable because there are *two* pairs $(1, 2)$ and $(1, -4)$ with $x = 1$. Also, T is *not* a function with y *as the independent variable* because there are *two* pairs $(1, 2)$ and $(3, 2)$ with $y = 2$. A graph of T in the xy-plane would consist of just five points.

Consider an equation

$$h(x, y) = 0, \tag{2}$$

whose solution set is S. Assume that there exists a function, f, with values $y = f(x)$, and domain D so that, for each number x in D, the pair (x, y) is a solution of (2), and thus is an element in S. That is, we have

$$h(x, y) = 0 \text{ when } y = f(x), \quad or \quad h(x, f(x)) = 0, \tag{3}$$

when x is in D. Then, we shall refer to f as a **solution function** of (2) *for y as a function of x*. If S contains *just one* solution (x_0, y_0) for any assigned value $x = x_0$, then S *itself is a solution function* for y as a function of x, and we may say that (2) **defines y as a function of x**. If any solution function f, with $y = f(x)$, is considered as a set of ordered pairs of numbers, then f *is a subset of S*. If (2) is sufficiently simple, by solving (2) for y in terms of x we may be able to obtain the values $y = f(x)$ of one or more solution functions, f, giving all solutions in S. On reversing the preceding roles of x and y, we may refer to a function g, with

* On page 66, we shall meet relations defined by inequalities.

$x = g(y)$, which is a *solution function* of (2) for x *as a function of* y, so that $h(g(y), y) = 0$. And, S itself is a *solution function*, for x *as a function of* y, in case there is just one solution (x_0, y_0) in S for each permissible number $y = y_0$. Then, we may say that (2) **defines x as a function of y.**

ILLUSTRATION 3. From $3x - 5y = 15$, we obtain

$$y = \tfrac{3}{5}x - 3, \quad and\ similarly, \quad x = \tfrac{5}{3}y + 5.$$

Hence, the equation $3x - 5y = 15$ defines y as a function of x, and also x as a function of y. The graph of either of these functions in an xy-plane is identical with the graph of $3x - 5y = 15$.

In Illustration 3, we observed a special case of the fact that, if (2) defines y as a function of x (or, x as a function of y), *the graph of this function in an xy-plane is identical with the graph of* (2).

ILLUSTRATION 4. From $x^2 + y^2 = 25$, we obtain

$$y = +\sqrt{25 - x^2} \quad or \quad y = -\sqrt{25 - x^2}.$$

Let $f(x) = \sqrt{25 - x^2}$ and $g(x) = -\sqrt{25 - x^2}$. Then, f and g are solution functions of the equation $x^2 + y^2 = 25$ for y as a function of x. The graph of $y = f(x)$ is the upper semicircle and of $y = (gx)$ is the lower semicircle in Figure 18. The whole circle is the graph of $x^2 + y^2 = 25$. The graph of $y = f(x)$ passes through $(3, 4)$.

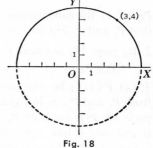

Fig. 18

EXERCISE 7

By solving for y in terms of x, obtain formulas for the values of one or more solution functions of the equation for y as a function of x. Also, obtain formulas for the values of one or more solution functions of the equation for x as a function of y.

1. $2x + 3y = 6$.   **2.** $5 - 3y = 2x$.   **3.** $x^2 - 2y = 5$.

4. $x^2 + y^2 = 4$.   **5.** $4x^2 - y^2 = 1$.   **6.** $4x^2 + 9y^2 = 36$.

Draw a graph of the relation, T, between the variables x and y defined by the table of pairs (x, y). Is T a function (a) with x as the independent variable or (b) with y as the independent variable? Why?

7.

$x =$	3	2	0	3	-1
$y =$	1	4	-2	-2	3

8.

$x =$	0	1	2	3	6
$y =$	-3	2	1	-3	4

The equation defines y as a function of x, or x as a function of y. Obtain a formula for the values of this function and draw its graph.

9. $2y - 3x^2 = 0$.   **10.** $3x + y^2 = 2$.   **11.** $y - x^2 = 3 - x$.

12. Graph the function f defined as follows for $-2 \leqq x \leqq 4$:

$$f(x) = x + 2 \ if - 2 \leqq x \leqq 2; \quad f(x) = 6 - 2x \ if\ 2 < x \leqq 4.$$

10. EQUATIONS FOR A LINE IN AN xy-PLANE

In the study of loci of a given type in analytic geometry, it is desirable to derive standard equations for the typical locus, corresponding to special features of its situation. At present, we illustrate this procedure for lines.

ILLUSTRATION 1. If the x-intercept of a vertical line l is a, the equation of l is $x = a$. If the y-intercept of a horizontal line l is b, the equation of l is $y = b$. Thus we have the following standard forms.

Line parallel to OX: $y = b$.   **Line parallel to OY: $x = a$.**

Two-point form. *The line l through two distinct points P_1:(x_1, y_1) and P_2:(x_2, y_2), not on a vertical line, has the equation*

$$y - y_1 = \frac{y_2 - y_1}{x_2 - x_1}(x - x_1). \tag{1}$$

Proof. 1. By substitution, $(x = x_1, y = y_1)$ and $(x = x_2, y = y_2)$ satisfy (1), so that P_1 and P_2 are on the graph of (1).

2. By page 14, segment P_1P_2 and l have the slope $(y_2 - y_1)/(x_2 - x_1)$.

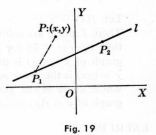

Fig. 19

3. Let P:(x, y) be *any* point in the plane distinct from P_1 and P_2, as in Figure 19. By Theorem V on page 15, P is on l, or P_1, P_2, and P are *collinear, if and only if* line segment P_1P has a *slope* which is equal to the slope of segment P_1P_2. Then $x \neq x_1$ and the slope of P_1P is $(y - y_1)/(x - x_1)$. Hence, P is on l if and only if

$$\frac{y - y_1}{x - x_1} = \frac{y_2 - y_1}{x_2 - x_1}, \quad or \quad y - y_1 = \frac{y_2 - y_1}{x_2 - x_1}(x - x_1). \tag{2}$$

Therefore (1) is the equation of l, because (1) is *not true* if P:(x, y) is *not* on l, and *is true* if P is P_1, P_2, or any other point on l.

In (1), we may refer to $(y_2 - y_1)/(x_2 - x_1)$ as *the slope, m, of l*. Then, (1) gives the following result.

Point-slope form. *The line through P_1:(x_1, y_1) with slope m has the equation*

$$y - y_1 = m(x - x_1). \tag{3}$$

Because of conditions (I) and (II) on page 19, a result such as (3) applies in two senses: *First*, the specified line has (3) as its equation. *Second*, the graph of any equation of the form (3) is *a line of the indicated character.*

ILLUSTRATION 2. By (3), the graph of $y - 1 = 2(x - 3)$ is a line with slope 2 through P_1:$(3, 1)$.

ILLUSTRATION 3. The equation of the line through $(2, 3)$ and $(-3, 5)$ is obtained from (1) with $(2, 3)$ as P_1 and $(-3, 5)$ as P_2 (or vice versa):

$$y - 3 = \frac{5 - 3}{-3 - 2}(x - 2) \quad or \quad 5y + 2x = 19.$$

ILLUSTRATION 4. The equation of the line with slope 3 through $(2, -5)$ is obtained from (3) with $m = 3$, $x_1 = 2$, and $y_1 = -5$:

$$y + 5 = 3(x - 2) \quad or \quad y - 3x = -11.$$

If $x_1 = x_2$, equation (1) does not apply, and P_1P_2 is vertical; then, without (1), the equation of P_1P_2 is $x = x_1$.

ILLUSTRATION 5. The line through $(3, -5)$ and $(3, 8)$ is $x = 3$.

Note 1. To find a line will mean *to find an equation of the line.*

EXAMPLE 1. Find the line through $(2, -3)$ with the y-intercept -1.

Solution. The line l goes through $(0, -1)$ on the y-axis. From (1) with $P_1:(2, -3)$ and $P_2:(0, -1)$, the line l has the equation

$$y + 3 = \frac{-1 + 3}{0 - 2}(x - 2) \quad or \quad y + x + 1 = 0.$$

The intercept form. *If $a \neq 0$ and $b \neq 0$, the line with x-intercept a and y-intercept b has the equation*

$$\frac{x}{a} + \frac{y}{b} = 1. \tag{4}$$

Proof. Points $A:(a, 0)$ and $B:(0, b)$ are on the specified line. From the two-point form, the equation of AB is

$$y - 0 = \frac{b - 0}{0 - a}(x - a) = -\frac{b}{a}(x - a); \quad or \quad \frac{b}{a}x + y = b. \tag{5}$$

On dividing both sides in (5) by b we obtain (4).

ILLUSTRATION 6. The equation of the line with x-intercept 3 and y-intercept -5 is

$$\frac{x}{3} + \frac{y}{-5} = 1 \quad or \quad 5x - 3y = 15.$$

Slope-intercept form. *The line with slope m and y-intercept b has the equation*

$$y = mx + b. \tag{6}$$

Proof. Point $B:(0, b)$ is on the line. From (3), the equation of the line through B with slope m is

$$y - b = m(x - 0) \quad or \quad y = mx + b. \tag{7}$$

ILLUSTRATION 7. The line with slope -3 and y-intercept 5 is $y = -3x + 5$.

In an equation $Ax + By + C = 0$, where $B \neq 0$, we can always change the equation to the form (6) *on solving for y in terms of x,* and then *by inspection* obtain the slope and y-intercept of the graph of the given equation.

ILLUSTRATION 8. By inspection, and comparison with (6), we see that the graph of $y = 3x - 7$ is a line with slope 3 and y-intercept -7.

ILLUSTRATION 9. To obtain the slope-intercept form of $3x + 2y - 8 = 0$, solve for y in terms of x:

$$2y = -3x + 8 \quad or \quad y = -\tfrac{3}{2}x + 4.$$

Hence, $3x + 2y - 8 = 0$ is a line with slope $-\tfrac{3}{2}$ and y-intercept 4.

ILLUSTRATION 10. If a line l in an xy-plane has the inclination* $120°$ and y-intercept
-8, the slope of l is $m = \tan 120° = -\sqrt{3}$, and
the equation of l is

$$y = -\sqrt{3}x - 8.$$

EXAMPLE 2. Find the equation of the line l through
the point A:$(2, 2)$ perpendicular to the line s
through B:$(1, -2)$ and C:$(5, 1)$.

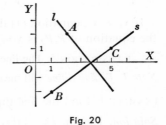

Fig. 20

Solution. In Figure 20, the slope of s is $(1 + 2)/(5 - 1)$
or $\frac{3}{4}$. Since l is perpendicular to s, the slope m of l
is the *negative reciprocal* of $\frac{3}{4}$, or $m = -\frac{4}{3}$. Hence,
the equation of l is

$$y - 2 = -\frac{4}{3}(x - 2) \quad or \quad 4x + 3y = 14.$$

A function P is called a **polynomial function** of degree n in certain variables,
say x and y, if $P(x, y)$ is given by a polynomial of degree n in the variables. An
equation in the variables, say x and y, is called a **polynomial equation** of degree
n if the equation is of the form $f(x, y) = g(x, y)$ where $f(x, y)$ and $g(x, y)$ are
polynomials, and $[f(x, y) - g(x, y)]$ is of degree n in the variables. We sometimes
drop the word *polynomial* in the preceding terminology and refer simply to a
function of degree n, or an *equation* of degree n. The values of any polynomial
function P of degree n in x are given by a polynomial of the form

$$P(x) = a_0 + a_1 x + a_2 x^2 + \cdots + a_n x^n, \tag{8}$$

where $a_0, a_1, \cdots, a_n$ are constants and $a_n \neq 0$. If $n = 0$, then $P(x) = a_0$, where†
$a_0 \neq 0$. Polynomial functions (or, equations) of degrees 1, 2, 3, and 4 are called,
respectively, *linear*, *quadratic*, *cubic*, and *quartic* functions (or, equations) in the
variables. With the degree $n > 4$, usually we do not use a special name, but
merely state the degree.

If f is a constant function, so that $f(x) = b$, a constant, at all values of x, the
graph of f in an xy-plane is the line $y = b$, or $y = 0 \cdot x + b$, whose slope is zero
and y-intercept is b. If f is a *linear function* of a single variable, x, then $f(x)$ is
of the form

$$f(x) = mx + b, \quad where \quad m \neq 0, \tag{9}$$

and the graph of f in an xy-plane is the line $y = mx + b$, with slope $m \neq 0$ and
y-intercept b. Thus, from (6) on page 27 and the preceding remarks, we arrive
at the following conclusion.

$$\left\{ \begin{array}{l} \textit{If } f(x) = mx + b, \textit{ the graph of the linear or constant function} \\ f \textit{ in an } xy\text{-plane is the line with slope } m \textit{ and } y\text{-intercept } b. \end{array} \right\}$$

---

* Recall that when *inclination* or *perpendicularity* is mentioned, we assume that the scale units
on the axes are *equal*.
† The constant function P, where $P(x) = 0$ at all values of x, is not referred to as a polynomial
of degree *zero*, but sometimes is called the *zero polynomial*.

EXERCISE 8

Write the equation of the line satisfying the conditions.

1. Horizontal; y-intercept -5.

2. Vertical; x-intercept 3.

3. Slope 3; y-intercept 2.

4. Slope -2; y-intercept -3.

5. x-intercept 2; y-intercept 3.

6. x-intercept -1; y-intercept 4.

7. Slope $-\frac{2}{3}$; y-intercept 4.

8. Slope $\frac{13}{5}$; y-intercept -2.

9. Inclination 30°; y-intercept 2.

10. Inclination 135°; y-intercept 4.

11. Inclination $\frac{1}{4}\pi$; y-intercept 3.

12. Inclination $\frac{1}{3}\pi$; y-intercept 3.

Write the equation of the line through the given points; or through the given point with slope m, inclination ψ, x-intercept a, or y-intercept b; or satisfying other data as given.

13. $(2, -4)$; $m = 5$.

14. $(1, 3)$; $m = -2$.

15. $(3, 0)$; $m = -\frac{1}{4}$.

16. $(-1, 3)$; $m = 0$.

17. $(5, -2)$; $\psi = \frac{1}{2}\pi$.

18. $(0, 0)$; $m = \frac{2}{3}$.

19. $(1, 5)$; $(3, 7)$.

20. $(0, 3)$; $(-1, 3)$.

21. $(-2, 3)$; $(1, 4)$.

22. $(3, -2)$; $(5, 0)$.

23. $(-1, 3)$; $(-1, 7)$.

24. $(3, 5)$; $\psi = 135°$.

25. $(-1, 3)$; $b = -3$.

26. $a = 6$; $b = -2$.

27. $b = 6$; $\psi = \frac{2}{3}\pi$.

28. $\psi = 45°$; $b = -3$.

29. $\psi = \frac{3}{4}\pi$; $b = 5$.

30. $(-1, 3)$; $\psi = \frac{1}{2}\pi$.

Write the equations of the lines through C which are, respectively, parallel to AB, and perpendicular to AB, in a coordinate plane having equal units on the axes. Check in a figure.

31. $A:(2, 5)$; $B:(1, 3)$; $C:(-2, 7)$.

32. $A:(1, -2)$; $B:(4, 7)$; $C:(5, 9)$.

Prove that the points lie on a line and find its equation.

33. $(2, 3)$; $(3, 5)$; $(1, 1)$.

34. $(1, -6)$; $(-3, -5)$; $(-7, -4)$.

Write the line in the slope-intercept form to find the slope and y-intercept.

35. $2x + 3y = 6$.

36. $3x + 4y = -2$.

37. $5x = 12y + 6$.

38. $3x - 5y = 15$.

39. $6x + 10 = 5y$.

40. $x = 4y - 5$.

Graph the linear function whose values are given by the polynomial.

41. $3x - 5$.

42. $3 - 2x$.

43. $-6x$.

44. $-x - 4$.

11. GENERAL EQUATION OF THE FIRST DEGREE IN TWO VARIABLES

Any equation of the first degree in two variables x and y can be written in the equivalent form $Ax + By + C = 0$, where A and B are not both zero, which we call the *general linear equation* in x and y.

Theorem VII. *The graph of any linear equation in x and y is a line.*

Proof. 1. If $B \neq 0$, we can solve $Ax + By + C = 0$ for y:

$$y = -\frac{A}{B}x - \frac{C}{B}. \tag{1}$$

This is the equation of a line with slope $-A/B$ and y-intercept $-C/B$.

2. If $B = 0$, then $A \neq 0$ and $Ax + By + C = 0$ becomes $Ax = -C$, from which we obtain $x = -C/A$. This is the equation of a vertical line. Hence, in *all* cases the locus of the equation $Ax + By + C = 0$ is a *line*.

Theorem VIII. (*Converse of Theorem VII.*) *Any line in the xy-plane has an equation linear in x and y.*

Proof. If a line l is vertical, with x-intercept a, the equation of l is $x = a$, which is linear in x and y. If l is not vertical, it has a slope m and y-intercept b. Then, the equation of l is $y = mx + b$. Hence, any line has an equation linear in x and y.

Note 1. The names *linear function* and *linear equation* may be associated with the fact that the corresponding graphs are straight lines.

Note 2. The nonlinear equation

$$(x^2 + 5)(x + 2y) = 0, \quad or \quad x^3 + 2x^2y + 5x + 10y = 0, \tag{2}$$

is satisfied if and only if $\qquad x^2 + 5 = 0 \quad or \quad x + 2y = 0.$

But, $x^2 + 5 \neq 0$ for any real x. Hence, (2) is satisfied by a real pair (x, y) if and only if $x + 2y = 0$, whose graph is a line. Similarly, *nonlinear equations may be written for any given line*, although usually this is not done.

Hereafter, in referring to any equation for a line, we shall mean an equation *linear* in the variables. For brevity, we shall refer to "*the line $Ax + By + C = 0$*" instead of to "*the line which is the graph of $Ax + By + C = 0$.*"

EXAMPLE 1. Find the line l through $(-2, 3)$ perpendicular to the line $3x - 4y = 5$, in an xy-plane having equal units on the axes.

Solution. 1. Change $3x - 4y = 5$ to the slope-intercept form:

$$4y = 3x - 5; \quad y = \tfrac{3}{4}x - 5; \quad hence, \ slope \ is \ \tfrac{3}{4}.$$

2. The slope of l is the negative reciprocal of $\tfrac{3}{4}$, or $-\tfrac{4}{3}$. Hence, by the point-slope form, the equation of l is

$$y - 3 = -\tfrac{4}{3}(x + 2), \quad or \quad 3y + 4x = 1.$$

12. THE ACUTE ANGLE FORMED BY TWO LINES

Since we wish to discuss angles between lines in a plane, we agree that, for the purposes of this section and its later applications, the plane will be provided with an xy-system of coordinates where *the scale units on the axes are equal.*

Let θ be the positive angle, at most $90°$, formed by two intersecting lines l_1 and l_2, whose inclinations are ψ_1 and ψ_2, respectively. If $\theta = 90°$, this fact can be learned by elementary means considered previously. Suppose, now, that neither l_1 nor l_2 is vertical and that θ is acute. Then, with m_1 and m_2 as the slopes of l_1 and l_2, respectively, we shall prove that

$$\left\{ \begin{array}{c} acute\ angle\ \theta \\ between\ two\ lines \end{array} \right\} \qquad \tan \theta = \left| \frac{m_2 - m_1}{1 + m_1 m_2} \right|. \tag{1}$$

Proof. 1. Suppose that l_2 is the line with the *greater inclination;* then $\psi_1 < \psi_2$, as in Figure 21 on page 31. Let $\phi = \psi_2 - \psi_1$. From (V) on page 679,

$$\tan \phi = \tan (\psi_2 - \psi_1) = \frac{\tan \psi_2 - \tan \psi_1}{1 + \tan \psi_1 \tan \psi_2} = \frac{m_2 - m_1}{1 + m_1 m_2}. \tag{2}$$

2. If ϕ is acute, then $\tan \theta = \tan \phi$, and (1) is true without use of the absolute value bars because $\tan \phi$ and $\tan \theta$ are positive. If $\phi > 90°$, as in Figure 21, then the right-hand side of (2) is seen to be negative, $\theta = 180° - \phi$, and $\tan \theta = -\tan \phi$. Hence, $\tan \theta$ is equal to the negative of the fraction in (2), or *is equal to its absolute value*, as given in (1).

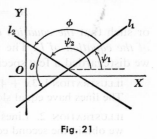

Fig. 21

★*Note 1.* If l_1 and l_2 are intersecting lines, "*the angle from l_1 to l_2*" is defined as "*that angle less than 180° through which l_1 must be rotated counterclockwise about its intersection with l_2 to bring l_1 into coincidence with l_2.*" If ϕ is the angle *from l_1 to l_2*, it is found that

$$\left\{ \begin{matrix} angle\ \phi \\ from\ l_1\ to\ l_2 \end{matrix} \right\} \qquad \tan \phi = \frac{m_2 - m_1}{1 + m_1 m_2}. \tag{3}$$

The student may desire to prove (3) either by use of (1) and an analysis of possible cases, or directly by use of the method employed in proving (1).

Formula (1) does not hold when $\theta = 90°$, because then $\tan \theta$ does not exist; in this case $m_1 m_2 = -1$, which alone shows that $\theta = 90°$. Also, (1) does not hold if l_1 or l_2 is vertical; then, θ is obtained by finding the inclinations ψ_1 and ψ_2.

Note 2. Let us use the notation "l:$[Ax + By + C = 0]$" to mean "*line l whose equation is $Ax + By + C = 0$.*"

EXAMPLE 1. Find the acute angle θ formed by the lines

$$l_1:[2x + 3y - 12 = 0] \quad and \quad l_2:[3x - 4y - 12 = 0].$$

Solution. 1. Write the lines in the slope-intercept form:

$$l_1:[y = -\tfrac{2}{3}x + 4]; \quad m_1 = -\tfrac{2}{3}. \qquad l_2:[y = \tfrac{3}{4}x - 3]; \quad m_2 = \tfrac{3}{4}.$$

2. Hence, $\qquad \tan \theta = \left| \dfrac{\tfrac{3}{4} + \tfrac{2}{3}}{1 - \tfrac{2}{3} \cdot \tfrac{3}{4}} \right| = \dfrac{17}{6} = 2.833; \quad \theta = 70.5°.$

Consider two lines l_1 and l_2 and their slope-intercept forms: *

$$l_1:[A_1 x + B_1 y + C_1 = 0]; \quad l_2:[A_2 x + B_2 y + C_2 = 0]; \quad or \tag{4}$$

$$l_1: \left[y = -\frac{A_1}{B_1}x - \frac{C_1}{B_1} \right]; \quad l_2: \left[y = -\frac{A_2}{B_2}x - \frac{C_2}{B_2} \right]. \tag{5}$$

We observe the following facts by checking slopes and intercepts in (5).

Lines l_1 and l_2 are parallel if and only if $\qquad \dfrac{A_1}{B_1} = \dfrac{A_2}{B_2}.$ $\qquad$ (6)

Lines l_1 and l_2 coincide if and only if $\qquad \dfrac{A_1}{B_1} = \dfrac{A_2}{B_2}$ *and* $\dfrac{C_1}{B_1} = \dfrac{C_2}{B_2}.$ (7)

If, for convenience, we disregard certain simple special cases where some denominator below is zero, from (7) we obtain

$$\frac{A_1}{A_2} = \frac{B_1}{B_2} = \frac{C_1}{C_2}. \tag{8}$$

* Assume that $B_1 \neq 0$ and $B_2 \neq 0$. Special cases thus omitted are easily treated separately.

Let k be the common value of the fractions in (8). Then, from (8), l_1 and l_2 of (4) **coincide if and only if there exists a constant $k \neq 0$ such that**

$$A_1 = kA_2, \qquad B_1 = kB_2, \qquad C_1 = kC_2, \tag{9}$$

or such that *the equation of l_1 can be obtained by multiplying by k on both sides of the equation of l_2.* The preceding results hold for all lines l_1 and l_2, although we disregarded a few special cases, such as $A_2 = 0$ or $C_2 = 0$.

ILLUSTRATION 1. $3x + 4y = 5$ is parallel to $6x + 8y + 3 = 0$ because $3 : 4 = 6 : 8$. The lines have equal slopes, $-\frac{3}{4}$ and $-\frac{6}{8}$.

ILLUSTRATION 2. Lines $3x - 2y = 5$ and $-6x + 4y = -10$ coincide because we obtain the second equation on multiplying both sides of the first by -2.

★*Note 3.* From (6), $A_1B_2 = A_2B_1$, or $A_1B_2 - A_2B_1 = 0$. That is, the determinant

$$\begin{vmatrix} A_1 & B_1 \\ A_2 & B_2 \end{vmatrix} = 0. \tag{10}$$

EXERCISE 9

Assume that the scale units on the coordinate axes are equal wherever perpendicularity or an angle between lines is mentioned.

Find the line through the given point parallel to, and perpendicular to, the given line.

1. $(2, -4)$; $3x - y = 6$. **2.** $(6, 3)$; $2x - 6y - 9 = 0$.

3. $(0, 5)$; $3y - 4x + 7 = 0$. **4.** (a, b); $hx + ky = 4$, $hk \neq 0$.

5. $(0, 0)$; $y = 7$. **6.** $(2, 4)$; $x = -5$.

7. Prove that the lines intersect to form a parallelogram:
$$2x - 3y = 5; \quad 4x + 5y = 1; \quad 6y - 4x = 3; \quad 3 - 8x - 10y = 0.$$

8. Write $y = mx + b$ in the intercept form, if $mb \neq 0$.

9. If $Ax + By + C = 0$ is a vertical line, prove that $B = 0$.

10. Under what conditions on A, B, and C will the line $Ax + By + C = 0$ pass through the origin; have no x-intercept; have no y-intercept?

11. If $AB \neq 0$, find the intercepts of the line $Ax + By + C = 0$.

Find the positive angle at most $90°$ formed by lines l_1 and l_2 having the given slopes m_1 and m_2, or the given equations.

12. $m_1 = -2$; $m_2 = 2$. **13.** $m_1 = \frac{1}{2}$; $m_2 = -\frac{3}{2}$. **14.** $m_1 = 4$; $m_2 = -\frac{1}{4}$.

15. $\begin{cases} 2x - y = 5. \\ 4x + y = 2. \end{cases}$ **16.** $\begin{cases} 2y + 8 = 0. \\ 2x + 4y = 5. \end{cases}$ **17.** $\begin{cases} 3x - 2y = 0. \\ 2x + 3y = 0. \end{cases}$

Draw line l through the first two points and line s through the last two. Then find the acute angle formed by l and s.

18. $(2, 1)$; $(4, 9)$; $(3, 3)$. **19.** $(1, 1)$; $(4, 5)$; $(5, -2)$.

Find the constant h if the lines are (a) parallel; (b) perpendicular.

20. $\begin{cases} 3x + 5y = 7, \\ hx + 2y = 4. \end{cases}$ **21.** $\begin{cases} 2x - 3y = 4, \\ hx - 2y = 5. \end{cases}$ **22.** $\begin{cases} 3x + 4y = 7. \\ 6x + hy = 5. \end{cases}$

★*Find the angles of the triangle with the given vertices, or formed by the lines.*

23. $(-2, 0)$; $(1, 1)$; $(-1, 5)$. **24.** $(-1, 0)$; $(2, -1)$; $(4, 1)$.

25. $-x + y - 2 = 0$; $2x + 3y = 6$; $x - 4y = 2$.

13. PARAMETRIC EQUATIONS FOR A LINE

Let l be the line through two distinct points $P_1:(x_1, y_1)$ and $P_2:(x_2, y_2)$ in an xy-plane. Let t be a variable whose domain consists of *all real numbers*. Then, we shall prove that, *for each value of t, the following equations* (1) *give the coordinates of a point $P:(x, y)$ on l* and, conversely, that *each point P is given by* (1) *for just one value of t*. We refer to (1) as *parametric equations for l*, and call the variable t the *parameter* in these equations.

$$x = x_1 + t(x_2 - x_1); \quad y = y_1 + t(y_2 - y_1). \tag{1}$$

Proof. 1. For our proof,* designate l to be a *directed* line, with the positive direction *from P_1 to P_2*, and with distance on l to be measured in terms of *any* specified unit. If $P:(x, y)$ is any point on l, with $\overline{P_1P}$ and $\overline{P_1P_2}$ as the values of directed line segments, let a variable t be defined by

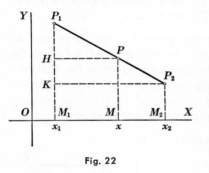

Fig. 22

$$\frac{\overline{P_1P}}{\overline{P_1P_2}} = t \quad so\ that \quad \overline{P_1P} = t(\overline{P_1P_2}). \tag{2}$$

For each point P, a single value of t is determined by (2). Conversely, for each value of t, just one value of $\overline{P_1P}$, and hence just one point P, is determined by (2). Thus, (2) establishes a *one-to-one correspondence* between the points P on l and all real values of t. From (2), P is in the direction of P_2 from P_1 when $t > 0$, and in *the opposite direction when $t < 0$.*

2. Equations (1) are true when $t = 0$, with $P:(x, y)$ given as P_1. Suppose, now, that P is not P_1, and that l is *not vertical*, as in Figure 22.† From the similar triangles P_1HP and P_1KP_2, and (2), we obtain

$$\frac{\overline{HP}}{\overline{KP_2}} = \frac{\overline{P_1P}}{\overline{P_1P_2}}, \quad or \quad \frac{x - x_1}{x_2 - x_1} = t. \tag{3}$$

We note that (3) is true *regardless of the units of length used on OX and l*, because the value of each fraction in (3) is independent of the unit of length. From (3), $x = x_1 + t(y_2 - y_1)$. If l is vertical, then $x_2 = x_1$ and (1) gives $x = x_1$, which is true. Thus, (1) has been proved for x. Similarly, we may prove (1) for y.

If $t = \frac{1}{2}$ in (2), then P is the **mid-point** of segment P_1P_2, and (1) becomes

(mid-point of P_1P_2) $\qquad x = \frac{1}{2}(x_1 + x_2); \quad y = \frac{1}{2}(y_1 + y_2). \tag{4}$

The coordinates of that point $P:(x, y)$ dividing the segment P_1P_2 in any given ratio can be found from (1) with the proper value for t, as illustrated in (4). Hence, equations (1) sometimes are called **point of division formulas.**

* And frequently in applications of (1).

† In Figure 22, P_1P and P_1P_2 have the same direction. The student may construct a corresponding figure and check the proof for a case where P_1P and P_1P_2 have opposite directions.

EXAMPLE 1. Write parametric equations for the line l through P_1:(2, 3) and P_2:(− 4, 5). Then, find the mid-point of P_1P_2; the points trisecting P_1P_2; the point P dividing P_1P_2 internally in the ratio 3 : 5.

Solution. 1. From (1), parametric equations for l are

$$x = 2 - 6t; \quad y = 3 + 2t. \tag{5}$$

2. *Mid-point:* use $t = \frac{1}{2}$ in (5), or use (4), to obtain P:(− 1, 4).

3. *Points of trisection:* use $t = \frac{1}{3}$ and $t = \frac{2}{3}$ in (5) to obtain P so that, respectively, $\overline{P_1P} = \frac{1}{3}\overline{P_1P_2}$ and $\overline{P_1P} = \frac{2}{3}\overline{P_1P_2}$:

When $t = \frac{1}{3}$, $(x = 0, y = \frac{11}{3})$.

When $t = \frac{2}{3}$, $(x = -2, y = \frac{13}{3})$.

Fig. 23

4. If P divides $\overline{P_1P_2}$ internally in the ratio 3 : 5, as in Figure 23, then $\overline{P_1P}/\overline{PP_2}$ is equal to $\frac{3}{5}$, or $\overline{P_1P} = \frac{3}{8}\overline{P_1P_2}$. With $t = \frac{3}{8}$ in (5), we find P:(− $\frac{1}{4}$, $\frac{15}{4}$).

Some of the familiar theorems of elementary geometry can be proved by use of analytic geometry. Usually, as a first step in such a proof, we place the figure conveniently on a coordinate system. Next, we introduce as few variables as possible in terms of which we can write the coordinates of all points which concern us. Our analytic proof then consists of establishing relations between these variables which are equivalent to the conclusion of the theorem.

★EXAMPLE 2. Prove that the diagonals of a parallelogram bisect each other.

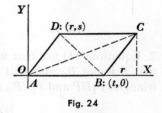

Fig. 24

Proof. 1. In Figure 24, place parallelogram $ABCD$ with A at (0, 0), B on the positive side of OX, and DC above OX. Let the coordinates of D be (r, s) and of B be $(t, 0)$. Since $\overline{AB} = \overline{DC}$ and AB is parallel to DC, then C is $(r + t, s)$.

2. The mid-point of AC is $[\frac{1}{2}(r + t), \frac{1}{2}s]$; this is also found to be the mid-point of BD. Hence, AC and BD intersect at a common mid-point.

Note 1. In proving theorems of plane Euclidean geometry by use of a coordinate system, usually it will be best to use equal scale units on the axes.

EXERCISE 10

Write parametric equations for the line through the points. Then, find the mid-point and the points of trisection of the line segment joining the points.

1. (2, 4); (8, 10).   **2.** (0, 6); (12, 0).   **3.** (− 2, 3); (− 8, − 3).

4. (3, 5); (9, 8).   **5.** (− 4, 5); (− 10, − 2).   **6.** (2, 3); (6, 11).

7. Find the points for division into four equal parts in Problem 1.

On the line through A:(− 3, 4) *and* B:(5, − 2), *find* C.

8. C divides AB internally in the ratio 2 : 3.

9. AB is directed; $\overline{AC} = 3(\overline{AB})$.   **10.** AB is directed; $\overline{AC} = -3(\overline{AB})$.

11. A:(2, 3) is an end point and (4, 7) is the mid-point of segment AC; find C.

12. If $(3, \frac{1}{2})$ is the center of a circle which passes through (1, 2), find another point on the circle by use of Section 13.

13. If (2, 2), (3, − 3), (6, 4) are vertices of a parallelogram in counterclockwise order, find the other vertex by use of Section 13.

Note 1. A **median** of a triangle is a line segment from a vertex to the mid-point of the opposite side. A proof of the following theorem is requested in Problem 40 on page 38: *The medians of a triangle meet in a point which is $\frac{2}{3}$ of the way from any vertex to the mid-point of the opposite side.*

14. Verify the result stated in Note 1 for the triangle with the vertices A:(1, 1), B:(7, 9), and C:(3, 5), by finding the specified point on each median by use of Section 13.

★15. Obtain the coordinates of P:(x, y) on the line through P_1 and P_2 of Figure 22 on page 33, with $\overline{P_1P}/\overline{PP_2} = k_1/k_2$.

★Prove the stated result by an analytic method.

16. An isosceles triangle has two equal medians.

17. The line segment joining the mid-points of opposite sides of a parallelogram is parallel to and has the same length as the other sides.

18. The line segment joining the mid-points of two sides of a triangle is one-half as long as the third side and parallel to it.

19. A triangle having two equal medians is isosceles.

14. SYSTEMS OF LINEAR EQUATIONS

With f, g, h, and k as functions of the variables x and y, consider the system of equations (a compound statement)

$$f(x, y) = g(x, y) \quad and \quad h(x, y) = k(x, y). \tag{1}$$

From page 8, a solution of (1) is an ordered pair of numbers (x, y) which is a solution of both equations. In solving a system (1), we sometimes say that the equations are being solved *simultaneously*. If (1) has a solution, then (1) is said to be *consistent*. Otherwise, (1) is said to be *inconsistent*.

Suppose that u and v are constants, with $u \neq 0$ and $v \neq 0$. On multiplying both sides of $f(x, y) = g(x, y)$ by u, and of $h(x, y) = k(x, y)$ by v, we obtain

$$uf(x, y) = ug(x, y) \quad and \quad vh(x, y) = vk(x, y). \tag{2}$$

Then, on adding corresponding sides in (2), we obtain (4) below. In algebra, the student had experience with use of the following result:

$$\left\{ \begin{array}{l} \textit{System (1) is equivalent to (has the same solutions} \\ \textit{as) the new system obtained on replacing either} \\ \textit{one of the given equations by the new equation} \\ uf(x, y) + vh(x, y) = ug(x, y) + vk(x, y). \end{array} \right\} \tag{3}$$

Result (3) extends to systems of three or more equations in any number of variables. Without further comment, we shall use (3) in the familiar methods for solution of systems of linear equations.

EXAMPLE 1. Solve algebraically: $\begin{cases} x - y = 5, \text{ and} & (4) \\ x + 2y = 2. & (5) \end{cases}$

Solution. On subtracting corresponding sides of the equations, in the order (5) − (4), we find $3y = -3$ or $y = -1$. From (4) with $y = -1$, we obtain $x = 4$. Hence, the solution of the system is $(x = 4, y = -1)$.

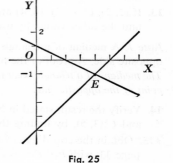

Fig. 25

To solve a system (1) graphically, we graph the equations in the same xy-plane. Then, the coordinates of any common point of the graphs form a solution of the system.

    ILLUSTRATION 1. In Figure 25, E:(4, −1) gives the solution of [(4), (5)].

    ILLUSTRATION 2. The system $\begin{cases} 3x - 2y - 4 = 0, \text{ and} & (6) \\ 4y - 6x + 8 = 0, & (7) \end{cases}$

has infinitely many solutions because the graphs of the equations are the same line. The equations are equivalent because (7) can be obtained by multiplying both sides of (6) by −2. If an algebraic solution is attempted, an identity like 0 = 0 results.

EXAMPLE 2. Discuss the system: $\begin{cases} 3x + 2y + 7 = 0, \text{ and} & (8) \\ 6x + 4y - 9 = 0. & (9) \end{cases}$

Discussion. The slope and y-intercept are $-\frac{3}{2}$ and $-\frac{7}{2}$ for (8), and $-\frac{3}{2}$ and $\frac{9}{4}$ for (9). Hence, the graphs of (8) and (9) are parallel and distinct. The system has no solution, or the equations are inconsistent. In an algebraic solution, a contradiction such as 23 = 0 would be obtained.

    If all of a set of lines pass through a point, they are called **concurrent lines.** Three lines are concurrent if and only if their equations are consistent. To investigate their consistency, solve any two of them simultaneously and test the solution, if any, in the third equation.

EXAMPLE 3. If the graphs of $3x + 4y - 5 = 0$ and $9x + hy + p = 0$ coincide, find h and p.

Solution. 1. From (9) on page 32, there exists a constant $k \neq 0$ so that

$$9 = 3k; \quad h = 4k; \quad p = -5k.$$

2. From $9 = 3k$ we find $k = 3$. Then, $h = 12$ and $p = -15$.

EXERCISE 11

Solve graphically and also by any algebraic method. If the equations are inconsistent or equivalent, prove this by use of (6) or (7) on page 32.

1. $\begin{cases} x - y = 1, \text{ and} \\ y + 2x = -3. \end{cases}$ 2. $\begin{cases} y + x = 2, \text{ and} \\ 2y - x = -5. \end{cases}$ 3. $\begin{cases} 3x + 8 = 0, \text{ and} \\ 6x + 7y = 5. \end{cases}$

4. $\begin{cases} x - 5y = 2, \text{ and} \\ 10y - 2x = 9. \end{cases}$ 5. $\begin{cases} x + y = 1, \text{ and} \\ 2x + 2y = 7. \end{cases}$ 6. $\begin{cases} 3x - 4y = 5, \text{ and} \\ 6x - 10 = 8y. \end{cases}$

Find g and h if the two lines coincide.

7. $\begin{cases} 3x - 5y = 2; \\ hx + 10y = g. \end{cases}$ **8.** $\begin{cases} 2x + hy = 3; \\ gx + 3y = 6. \end{cases}$ **9.** $\begin{cases} hx - 3y = 2; \\ 2x + gy = 8. \end{cases}$

Find the intersection of the lines or prove them not concurrent.

10. $\begin{cases} 7x - 2y = 8; \\ 5x + 2 = 4y; \\ 5x - y = 7. \end{cases}$ **11.** $\begin{cases} 2x - 3y = 8; \\ 3x - y = 5; \\ 2x + 5y = -8. \end{cases}$ **12.** $\begin{cases} x + y = 6; \\ 2x - 3y = 11; \\ 2x + 7y = 1. \end{cases}$

Note 1. In an xy-plane, a set of all curves satisfying a specified condition sometimes is called a **family of curves.** An equation involving x, y, and a third variable k is called an *equation for the family* in case: (1) for each value of k (with perhaps negligible exceptions) the locus of the equation is a curve of the family; (2) each curve of the family is the graph of the equation for just one value of k. We then refer to k as a *parameter* or *arbitrary constant*, and call the family a *one-parameter family of curves*. Thus, an equation for the family of lines with slope $-\frac{2}{3}$ is seen to be $y = -\frac{2}{3}x + b$, where b is a parameter whose domain is all real numbers.

Write an equation for the specified one-parameter family of lines. Mention any exceptional lines excluded by your equation.

13. With x-intercept 4.   **14.** With slope $\frac{3}{4}$.   **15.** Through $(2, -4)$.
16. Parallel to $3x - 5y = 7$.   **17.** Perpendicular to $x - 2y = 3$.

★*Without finding the intersection of the given lines, find the line through their intersection satisfying the given condition.*

18. $2x - y - 6 = 0$; $4x + 3y - 5 = 0$. Through $(3, -1)$.

Hint. An equation for the family of lines (with one exception) through the intersection of two nonparallel lines

$$A_1x + B_1y + C_1 = 0 \quad and \quad A_2x + B_2y + C_2 = 0,$$

is $$A_1x + B_1y + C + k(A_2x + B_2y + C_2) = 0.$$

(Why is this true, and what line is the exception?) First find k.

19. $2x + 3y - 5 = 0$; $3x + y - 2 = 0$. Through $(1, 3)$.
20. $2x - 5y + 3 = 0$; $x - y + 2 = 0$. With slope 2.

★*SUPPLEMENT FOR CHAPTER ONE*

Graph the function f in an xy-plane.

21. $f(x) = |x + 1|$.   **22.** $f(x) = |x|/x$ if $x \neq 0$; $f(0) = 0$.
23. If $f(x) = 3x^2 + 2$ and $g(u) = 3u + 5$, find $g(f(y))$.

Graph the statement in the variable x on a number scale, if the statement is consistent. Describe the solution set of the statement simply.

24. $1 < 3x - 5 \leq 4$.   **25.** $4 - x < 3x - 2 \leq x + 4$.
26. $5 < 3 - 2x < 4$.   **27.** $7 < 2x - 1 < 2 - x$.

28. Prove that the equation of the line through two distinct points $P_1:(x_1, y_1)$ and $P_2:(x_2, y_2)$ can be written in the form at the right: $\begin{vmatrix} x & y & 1 \\ x_1 & y_1 & 1 \\ x_2 & y_2 & 1 \end{vmatrix} = 0.$

29–31. Solve Problems 19–21 on page 29 by use of Problem 28.

32. In an xy-plane, the scale units are h inches on the x-axis and k inches on the y-axis. For points $P_1:(x_1, y_1)$ and $P_2:(x_2, y_2)$, obtain a formula for $|\overline{P_1P_2}|$, in inches, in terms of the coordinates.

Note 2. In a given plane, let OX and OY be two nonparallel directed lines, called *axes*, intersecting at O, called the *origin*, and not necessarily perpendicular. On each axis, assign a unit of length for a number scale. Let OX be horizontal, with the positive direction to the right, and OY be directed upward, at some angle. Any line, L, parallel to an axis will be considered directed, with the same positive direction as this axis, and with segments on L measured in terms of the scale unit on this axis. Let the coordinates (x, y) of any point P be the directed distance x, from OY to P measured *parallel to OX*, and y, from OX to P measured *parallel to OY*. In honor of Descartes, any system of coordinates as just described is called a **Cartesian system.** Hereafter, unless the preceding coordinate system is specified for use, the axes will be perpendicular in any system which we use.

33. For a line l in the xy-plane of Note 2, define the slope of l, by (4) on page 14. Prove Theorems IV and V in Section 6 for the present xy-plane. Then check the results in Sections 10, 11, and 13, for this plane.

34. Let $P_1:(x_1, y_1)$ and $P_2:(x_2, y_2)$ be points in the plane of Note 1, where one inch is used as the unit for length in any direction, and on the scales on OX and OY. Let θ be the smallest positive angle generated by rotating OX to OY about O in the xy-plane. Obtain a formula for $|\overline{P_1P_2}|$ in inches.

35. If A and B are any complex numbers, plotted in an Argand diagram in an xy-plane, prove that $|A + B| \leqq |A| + |B|$.

36. If A, B, and C are on a line, we say that C divides AB *externally* in the ratio $r_1 : r_2$ if C is outside AB and $|\overline{AC}| : |\overline{CB}| = r_1 : r_2$. Find C with $A:(2, -4)$ and $B:(-4, 6)$ if C divides AB externally in the ratio (*i*) $2 : 3$; (*ii*) $3 : 2$.

37. Prove that all lines having the equation $6x + ky + 8 + 3k = 0$, where k is any number, pass through a common point.

38. Suppose that k is a fixed constant, not zero, and that the x-intercept, a, and y-intercept, b, of a line in the xy-plane satisfy $a^{-1} = b^{-1} + k$. Prove that all lines with this property pass through a common point.

39. In the triangle formed by the lines, find the equations of the altitudes from the vertices to the opposite sides, without finding the vertices:

$$2x + 3y = 5; \quad x + 2y = 7; \quad 5x + 2y = 2.$$

40. In any triangle, prove that (*i*) the medians are concurrent; (*ii*) the perpendicular bisectors of the sides are concurrent; (*iii*) the altitudes from the vertices to the opposite sides are concurrent; (*iv*) the intersections in (*i*), (*ii*), and (*iii*) are collinear, with (*i*) giving a trisection point of the segment joining the points from (*ii*) and (*iii*). Before carrying out the general proof, verify the facts for the triangle with the vertices $(-4, -3)$, $(4, 1)$, and $(3, 4)$.

Note 3. In Problem 40, the intersections of the lines in (*i*), (*ii*), and (*iii*) are called, respectively, the *centroid*, the *circumcenter* (center of the circumscribed circle), and *orthocenter* of the triangle. In a later problem, the student may prove, also, that the bisectors of the interior angles of the triangle are concurrent. This point of intersection is called the *incenter* (center of the inscribed circle) of the triangle.

CHAPTER TWO

Introduction to Common Curves *

15. SOME BASIC PRINCIPLES IN GRAPHING

We recall that the product of two or more numbers is zero if and only if one or more of the factors is zero. This result may be useful in graphing an equation $f(x, y) = 0$ if it is found that $f(x, y)$ can be factored conveniently.

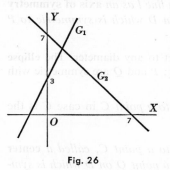

Fig. 26

ILLUSTRATION 1. The equation

$$(2x - y + 3)(x + y - 7) = 0 \qquad (1)$$

is satisfied if and only if

$$2x - y + 3 = 0 \quad or \quad x + y - 7 = 0. \qquad (2)$$

Hence, a point (x, y) satisfies (1), or is on the graph, G, of (1) if and only if (x, y) is on the graph, G_1, of $2x - y + 3 = 0$ or on the graph, G_2, of $x + y - 7 = 0$. Thus, G consists of the *two lines* G_1 and G_2 in Figure 26.†

Suppose, now, that a polynomial $f(x, y)$ is expressed as a product of various factors. Then, as illustrated with (1), the graph of $f(x, y) = 0$ consists of the *graphs of the new equations* obtained by placing each of the specified factors equal to zero.

ILLUSTRATION 2. In order to graph

$$4x^2 - 4xy + y^2 = 9, \qquad (3)$$

we first arrange to have one member zero, and then factor:

$$(2x - y)^2 - 9 = 0 \quad or \quad (2x - y - 3)(2x - y + 3) = 0. \qquad (4)$$

Equation (4) is satisfied if and only if

$$2x - y - 3 = 0 \quad or \quad 2x - y + 3 = 0. \qquad (5)$$

The graph of (3) consists of the two lines which are the graphs of the linear equations in (5).

---

* Unless otherwise specified, any point, line, or curve which we mention is assumed to lie in some given plane.

† In terminology from page 674, G is the *union* of G_1 and G_2; $G = G_1 \cup G_2$.

ILLUSTRATION 3. To graph $4x^2 = 9y^2$, we first obtain $2x = \pm \sqrt{9y^2}$:

$$x = \tfrac{3}{2}y \quad or \quad x = -\tfrac{3}{2}y. \tag{6}$$

Hence, the graph of $4x^2 = 9y^2$ consists of the *two lines* which are the graphs of the equations in (6). We could have written, first, $4x^2 - 9y^2 = 0$ and

$$(2x - 3y)(2x + 3y) = 0.$$

This also leads to (6).

Two points P and Q are said to be symmetric *with respect to a line l* if l is the perpendicular bisector of the segment PQ, as in Figure 27.

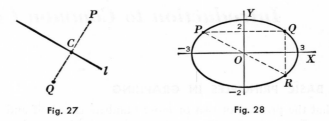

Fig. 27   Fig. 28

Definition I. *A curve D is symmetric with respect to a line l as an* **axis of symmetry** *in case, for each point P on D, there is a point Q on D which is symmetric to P with respect to l.*

ILLUSTRATION 4. A circle is symmetric with respect to any diameter. The **ellipse** in Figure 28 has OX and OY as axes of symmetry; P and Q are symmetric with respect to OY, and Q and R are symmetric to OX.

Two points P and Q are symmetric *with respect to a point C* in case C is the mid-point of the segment PQ, as in Figure 27.

Definition II. *A curve D is symmetric with respect to a point C, called a* **center of symmetry**, *in case, for each point P on D, there is a point Q on D which is symmetric to P with respect to C.*

ILLUSTRATION 5. From Definition II, for the curve D, every chord PQ through C is bisected by C. In Figure 28 above, the origin is a center of symmetry for the ellipse; P and R are symmetric with respect to the origin.

ILLUSTRATION 6. The following facts are exhibited in Figure 29.

I. (x, y) and $(x, -y)$ are symmetric with respect to the x-axis.

II. (x, y) and $(-x, y)$ are symmetric with respect to the y-axis.

III. (x, y) and $(-x, -y)$ are symmetric with respect to the origin.

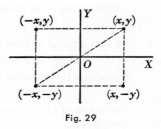

Fig. 29

As a rule, a reference to *symmetry* will mean symmetry of the *preceding types.* Each of the following tests involves showing that, if a point (x, y) satisfies the equation, the symmetric point of (I), (II), or (III) above also satisfies it.

Summary. *The graph of $f(x, y) = 0$ has the indicated symmetry if and only if an equivalent equation is obtained by the specified change.*

1. **Symmetry to x-axis:** *replace y by $-y$.*

2. **Symmetry to y-axis:** *replace x by $-x$.*

3. **Symmetry to the origin:** *replace x by $-x$ and y by $-y$.*

ILLUSTRATION 7. To test the graph of $xy = 8$ for symmetry, we replace x by $-x$ and obtain $-xy = 8$, *not equivalent to* $xy = 8$. Hence, its graph is *not* symmetric to OY and, similarly, is *not* symmetric to OX. If we replace x by $-x$ and y by $-y$ we obtain $(-x)(-y) = 8$ or $xy = 8$, the original equation. Hence, if (x, y) is on its graph, the point $(-x, -y)$ also is on the graph, and it is symmetric to the origin. The graph of $xy = 8$ is in Figure 30 and is called a **hyperbola**.

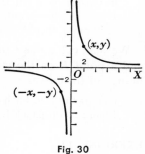

Fig. 30

In graphing an equation $f(x, y) = 0$, we exclude any value of x or y for which the other variable is *imaginary* or *undefined*. To determine excluded values, we inspect $f(x, y)$ itself, and also any expression obtained in solving $f(x, y) = 0$ for x or for y, if this operation is convenient. After such exclusions, the remaining values for x, or y, are taken as the *domain* for the variable. If no real values (x, y) satisfy the equation, its locus is said to be *imaginary*.

EXAMPLE 1. Graph the equation
$$4x^2 + 9y^2 = 36. \tag{7}$$

Solution. 1. *Types of symmetry.* Since $(-x)^2 = x^2$ and $(-y)^2 = y^2$, equation (7) is unaltered if we replace x by $-x$, or y by $-y$, or both x by $-x$ and y by $-y$. Hence, the graph is symmetric to OX, OY, and the *origin*.

2. *Domains for x and y.* On solving (7) for x and for y, we find
$$x = \pm \tfrac{3}{2}\sqrt{4 - y^2} \quad and \quad y = \pm \tfrac{2}{3}\sqrt{9 - x^2}. \tag{8}$$
From (8), x is imaginary if $|y| > 2$. Thus, the domain for y is $|y| \leq 2$, and for x is $|x| \leq 3$. By using $x = 0$ in (7), we find the y-intercepts $y = \pm 2$; the x-intercepts are $x = \pm 3$; if $x = \pm 2$, then $y = \pm 1.5$. The graph is in Figure 28 on page 40.

$x =$	-3	-2	0	2	3
$y =$	0	± 1.5	± 2	± 1.5	0

In Example 1, we illustrated the fact that the graph of an equation in x and y is symmetric to OX if y is involved just with *even* exponents. Also, if the graph is symmetric to both OX and OY, then the graph *also has the origin as a center of symmetry*. The converse of the last statement is not true, as seen in Figure 30 above, where the origin is a center of symmetry but neither OX nor OY is an axis of symmetry. If we now think of OX and OY as *any two perpendicular axes of symmetry*, we have the following result.

$$\left\{ \begin{array}{l} \textit{If a plane curve has two perpendicular axes of symmetry, the in-} \\ \textit{tersection of these axes is a center of symmetry for the curve.} \end{array} \right\} \tag{9}$$

Note 1. If b is a constant, the set of all numbers $x > b$ is called an *infinite interval* of the number scale. Similarly, "*all* $x < b$," "*all* $x \leqq b$," "*all* $x \geqq b$," and "*all real numbers* x" define infinite intervals. The domain of a variable is said to be *infinite* if the domain includes an infinite interval.

A set of points, in a plane or in space, is said to have *infinite extent,* or *to extend to infinity,* if the distance from a fixed point to a point P of the set can be made to exceed any value, however large,* by properly selecting P. A variable point P:(x, y) is said *to recede to infinity* on a curve in the xy-plane if the distance from the origin to P grows large without bound as x, or y, grows large without bound.

ILLUSTRATION 8. In Illustration 7, the domains of both x and y are infinite. If P:(x, y) varies on either branch of the curve so that $|x|$, or $|y|$, grows large without bound, then P recedes to infinity and approaches a coordinate axis.

We shall call a line l an **asymptote** of a curve if the shortest distance between l and a point P on the curve approaches zero if P recedes to infinity on some branch of the curve.

ILLUSTRATION 9. Each of the coordinate axes is an asymptote for the hyperbola in Figure 30 on page 41.

EXERCISE 12

Graph the equation by use of factoring.

1. $(2x - y + 4)(x + y) = 0$. **2.** $(3x - 4 + y)(x - y) = 0$.
3. $(x + 2)(x + y - 1) = 0$. **4.** $(y - 3)(2x - y - 1) = 0$.
5. $x^2 - 4y^2 = 0$. **6.** $4y^2 - 9x^2 = 0$. **7.** $4x^2 = 25y^2$.
8. $(x - 3)(x - 5) = 0$. **9.** $(x - 3)(y + 5) = 0$. **10.** $(x - 1)^2 = 0$.
11. $2x^2 - x = 1$. **12.** $3y^2 + 5y = 2$. **13.** $x^2 + 6y^2 = 5xy$.

For each point, give the symmetric points with respect to the coordinate axes and the origin, and plot all points.

14. $(2, 3)$. **15.** $(-3, 5)$. **16.** $(-2, -3)$. **17.** $(0, -4)$. **18.** (a, b).

For each equation, without graphing, test for the symmetry of its graph with respect to the coordinate axes and the origin.

19. $4x^2 - 9y^2 = 0$. **20.** $9x^2 + 4y^2 = 36$. **21.** $x^2 - y^2 = 9$.
22. $xy = 6$. **23.** $xy = -5$. **24.** $y^2 = -8x$.

Graph each equation which has a real locus.

25. $y^2 = 4$. **26.** $x^2 = -9$. **27.** $y^2 = 0$.
28. $x^2 + 4y^2 = 0$. **29.** $4x^2 + y^2 = -2$. **30.** $(y - 3)^2 = 0$.
31. $xy = -6$. **32.** $x^2 = y$. **33.** $(x - 2y)^2 = 4$.

34. In an xy-plane where the scale-units on the axes are equal, a line l bisects the angle in quadrant I between the axes. What point is symmetric to P:(x, y) with respect to l? Test the graphs of each of the equations in Problems 31, 32, and 33 for this type of symmetry.

* We are using the language of *limits* intuitively at several places in this section.

16. EQUATIONS FOR A CIRCLE

In this section, we stipulate that *equal units* are to be used on the axes. Then, the distance formula (2) of page 12 is available.

Suppose that a locus in an xy-plane is defined geometrically. Then, to obtain an equation for the locus, we apply its definition to obtain an equation satisfied by the coordinates of P if and only if P is on the locus.

Consider the circle T with center $C{:}(h, k)$ and radius r, in Figure 31. If $P{:}(x, y)$ is any point in the plane, from page 12 we obtain

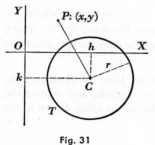

Fig. 31

$$| \overline{CP} | = \sqrt{(x - h)^2 + (y - k)^2}.$$

If $| \overline{CP} | = r$, or $(\overline{CP})^2 = r^2$, then P *is on the circle* T. If $(\overline{CP})^2 \neq r^2$, P *is not on* T. Hence, we obtain the equation of T by writing $(\overline{CP})^2 = r^2$, or

$$(x - h)^2 + (y - k)^2 = r^2. \tag{1}$$

We call (1) the **center-radius form** for the equation of a circle. If the center is $(0, 0)$, then (1) becomes

$$x^2 + y^2 = r^2. \tag{2}$$

ILLUSTRATION 1. The equation of the circle with center $(2, -3)$ and radius 5 is $(x - 2)^2 + (y + 3)^2 = 25$.

In (1) or (2), we permit $r = 0$. Such a circle is just a point, a *point-circle*. If $r = 0$ in (1), the only solution is $(x = h, y = k)$.

When we expand the center-radius form (1), we obtain

$$x^2 + y^2 - 2hx - 2ky + (h^2 + k^2 - r^2) = 0. \tag{3}$$

In (3), let $$D = -2h; \quad E = -2k; \quad F = h^2 + k^2 - r^2.$$

Then, from (3),

$$x^2 + y^2 + Dx + Ey + F = 0. \tag{4}$$

Thus, every circle has an equation of type (4). Conversely, for any values of the constants D, E, and F, (4) can be changed to the center-radius form and therefore represents a circle, real or imaginary. We call (4) the **general form** for the equation of a circle. To obtain the center and radius of a circle whose equation is given in this form, group the terms in x and, separately, those in y, and *complete a square in each set of terms*; then rewrite the equation in the center-radius form.

Note 1. To make $(x^2 + cx)$ a perfect square, we add $(\tfrac{1}{2}c)^2$ or $c^2/4$.

EXAMPLE 1. Obtain the center and radius of

$$x^2 + y^2 - 4x + 6y - 12 = 0. \tag{5}$$

Solution. 1. Add 4 and 9 to complete squares:

$$(x^2 - 4x + 4) + (y^2 + 6y + 9) = 12 + 4 + 9 = 25; \text{ or}$$

$$(x - 2)^2 + (y + 3)^2 = 5^2. \tag{6}$$

2. From (6), the center is $(2, -3)$ and radius is 5.

ILLUSTRATION 2. The equation $(x - 1)^2 + (y - 3)^2 = -25$ has no graph, because the left-hand side is positive or zero for all values of x and y, while the right-hand side is negative. Such an equation may be said to represent an *imaginary circle*.

If $a \neq 0$, any equation of the form

$$ax^2 + ay^2 + bx + cy + d = 0 \qquad (7)$$

can be changed to the general form (4) by dividing both sides in (7) by a. Hence, we reach the following conclusion.

If an equation of the second degree in x and y is of the form (7), *where the coefficients of x^2 and y^2 are equal and there is no term involving xy, the graph of the equation is a circle, real or imaginary, in an xy-plane where the units on the axes are* **equal.**

Note 2. A formal discussion of tangents to curves will be met later. At present, from elementary geometry, we accept the notion of a tangent to a circle, and assume the well-known fact that *the tangent is perpendicular to the radius* of the circle drawn to the point of tangency.

EXERCISE 13

In this exercise, it is understood that **equal scale units** *are used on the axes in the coordinate plane.*

Write an equation of the circle with center C and radius r.

1. C:(3, 4); $r = 2$.   2. C:(-2, 5); $r = 3$.   3. C:(3, -2); $r = 4$.
4. C:(-2, -4); $r = 3$.   5. C:(0, 0); $r = 4$.   6. C:(0, 3); $r = 3$.
7. C:(-2, 0); $r = 2$.   8. C:(a, 0); $r = a$.   9. C:(0, b); $r = b$.

If the graph is a real circle, find its center and radius.

10. $x^2 + 2x + y^2 - 4y = 4$.   11. $x^2 - 6x + y^2 - 4y = 3$.
12. $x^2 + y^2 + 4x + 2y = -1$.   13. $x^2 + y^2 + 6x + 3 = 4y$.
14. $x^2 + y^2 + 8y + 19 = 0$.   15. $x^2 + y^2 - 6x - 11 = 0$.
16. $x^2 + y^2 + 6x + 9 = 4y$.   17. $x^2 + y^2 + 6x + 13 = 4y$.
18. $x^2 + y^2 + 5x + \frac{9}{4} = 6y$.   19. $x^2 + y^2 + 3y + 3 = x$.

Obtain the equations of the circles satisfying the conditions.

20. Center (3, 0); tangent to the y-axis.
21. Tangent to the y-axis at (0, -3); radius 4.
22. Tangent to the line $y = 4$; center (2, 7).
23. Tangent to the line $x = -3$; center (-5, 4).
24. With (-2, 3) and (4, 3) as end points of a diameter.
25. Center (2, -3) and passing through (3, 1).

★*Note 1.* Either the center-radius form

$$(x - h)^2 + (y - k)^2 = r^2, \qquad (1)$$

or the general form $x^2 + y^2 + Dx + Ey + F = 0$,   (2)

for the equation of a circle involves *three constants*. Hence, to obtain the equation of a circle, we need enough information to write three equations involving the constants, when none of them are given.

★*Find the equation of the circle through the points, or satisfying the various conditions.*

26. $(7, 5); (-1, -1); (0, -2)$.　　　　**27.** $(-2, 4); (-2, 0); (4, 4)$.

　Hint. Substitute the coordinates of the points in (2) to obtain three equations for D, E, and F, and then solve for their values.

28. Through $(2, 1)$ and $(2, 7)$ with radius 5.

29. Through $(3, 6)$ tangent to the y-axis at $(0, -3)$.

★*Note 2.* Let $S_1 = 0$ and $S_2 = 0$ abbreviate the equations of two nonconcentric circles C_1 and C_2, respectively, written in the form (2). Then, if $k \neq -1$, the equation

$$S_1 + kS_2 = 0$$

is the equation of *the set of circles* (except for C_2) *through the intersections, if any, of C_1 and C_2.* If $k = -1$, then $S_1 + kS_2 = 0$ is *linear* in x and y and hence represents a *line*. This line, l, is the common chord of C_1 and C_2 if they intersect. In any case, l is called the **radical axis** of C_1 and C_2. The equation of l, with $k = -1$ as above, is obtained by eliminating x^2 and y^2 between the equations of C_1 and C_2. The equation of l arises naturally if the equations of C_1 and C_2 are solved simultaneously, in an effort to find their intersections.

★*Find the equation of the circle through the intersections of the given circles and the given point. Also, find the intersections of the given circles algebraically.*

30. $\begin{Bmatrix} x^2 + y^2 + 2x + 4y - 5 = 0 \\ x^2 + y^2 - 8x - 6y + 5 = 0 \end{Bmatrix}$; given point $(-4, 1)$.

31. $\begin{Bmatrix} x^2 + 2x + y^2 + 4y - 4 = 0 \\ x^2 + y^2 - 6x - 4y - 4 = 0 \end{Bmatrix}$; given point $(1, 5)$.

★**32.** In Problem 30, prove that the line of centers and the radical axis of the given circles are perpendicular.

★**33.** Prove that the line of centers of any two nonconcentric circles is perpendicular to their radical axis.

★**34.** Prove that the length, t, of the tangent from a point (x_1, y_1) to a circle in the form (4), page 43, is given by $t^2 = x_1^2 + y_1^2 + Dx_1 + Ey_1 + F$. Also, if we let

$$f(x, y) = x^2 + y^2 + Dx + Ey + F,$$

prove that $f(x, y) < 0$ if $P:(x, y)$ is *interior* to the circle, and $f(x, y) > 0$ if P is *exterior* to the circle.

17. SIMPLE STANDARD EQUATIONS FOR A PARABOLA

At the center of a circle T, erect a line m perpendicular to the plane in which T lies. Select any point V on m, not in the plane of T, as in Figure 32 on page 46. From any point Q on T, draw a line l through V. Then, the locus of all points swept out by l, as Q moves around T, is a surface of infinite extent called a *right circular cone*, whose *vertex* is V and *axis* is m. Each position of l is called a *ruling* of the cone. V divides the cone into two *nappes;* in Figure 33 on page 46, each nappe is cut off above and below V by a plane perpendicular to the cone's axis.

If a plane cuts the cone, the curve of intersection is called a **conic section,** or simply a *conic.* First, suppose that the plane does not pass through V. Then, if the plane cuts just one nappe and is not parallel to a ruling (Figure 34), the conic section AB is called an **ellipse;** the ellipse is a *circle* if the plane is perpendicular to the axis of the cone. If the plane cuts just one nappe and is parallel to a ruling (Figure 34), the conic *CDE* is called a **parabola**, which has infinite extent. If the plane cuts both nappes in any fashion (Figure 33), the conic, *ABC* and *DEF*, is called a **hyperbola**, which has a separate piece or *branch* of infinite extent on each nappe.

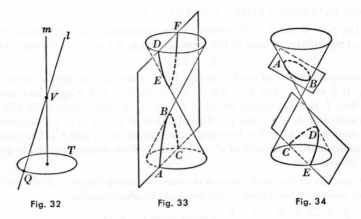

Fig. 32   Fig. 33   Fig. 34

If a cone is cut by a plane through *V*, the only point of intersection may be *V*, so that the conic section is *just this point*. Or, the plane may touch the cone merely along one ruling, in which case the conic is *just this line*. Or, the plane may cut the cone along two rulings, so that the conic consists of these *two lines* intersecting at *V*. Such sections through *V* are called **degenerate conics.** We may think of a conic which is a single point as a limiting case of an ellipse or circle as the cutting plane approaches *V*. A conic which is two intersecting lines may be considered as a limiting case of a hyperbola as a variable plane cutting both nappes approaches the vertex *V*.

In the future, unless otherwise specified, we shall include under the name *conic sections* all curves mentioned in (I) and (II) below. Notice that two parallel lines are listed in (II). This is done for later convenience, although two parallel lines cannot be obtained as a plane section of a cone of two nappes.

I. The nondegenerate conics: *parabola; ellipse, including a circle as a special case; hyperbola.*

II. The degenerate conics: *a single point; two lines in the same plane, where the lines may intersect in just one point, or may be coincident, or may be parallel.*

For simplicity, we shall define each of the nondegenerate conics by means of certain of its geometric properties. Proof of the equivalence of these new definitions and the preceding definition of the curves as plane sections of a cone is beyond the scope of this text. As a first step in our program, we shall define a *parabola*, and obtain certain standard equations for it.

Note 1. In Sections 17–19, in any *xy*-plane, we assume that the scale units are equal on the axes, with the agreement (1) of page 12 in force.

Definition III. *A **parabola** is the locus of a point P whose undirected distance from a fixed point F, called the **focus**, is equal to the undirected distance of P from a fixed line D, called the **directrix**, which does not go through F.*

EXAMPLE 1. Find the equation of the parabola with focus $F:(-3, 0)$ and directrix $D:[x = 3]$.

Solution. 1. In Figure 35, let $P:(x, y)$ be any point not on D, and let MP be perpendicular to D from P. Then M is the point $(3, y)$.

2. Let h be the length of PF; then

$$h = \sqrt{(x + 3)^2 + y^2}.$$

3. From (4) on page 5, we have $\overline{PM} = 3 - x$. Let $d = |\overline{PM}|$; then $d^2 = (3 - x)^2$.

4. P is on the locus if and only if $h = d$. Since h and d are positive, the equation $h = d$ is equivalent to $h^2 = d^2$, which becomes

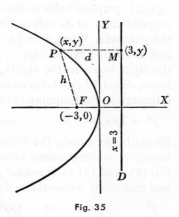

Fig. 35

$$(3 - x)^2 = (x + 3)^2 + y^2 \quad or \quad y^2 = -12x. \tag{1}$$

Derivation of a standard equation for a parabola

1. Refer to Figure 36. Let p be the distance from the directrix D to the focus F, where $p > 0$. Designate the x-axis as the line through F perpendicular to D, with the origin midway between F and D, and F in the positive direction from O. Then, F is the point $(\frac{1}{2}p, 0)$ and D is the line $x = -\frac{1}{2}p$.

2. Let $P:(x, y)$ be any point in the plane, and let the undirected distance of P from F be h, and from D be d. In Figure 36, M is the point $(-\frac{1}{2}p, y)$. Hence, from (4) on page 5, $\overline{MP} = x - (-\frac{1}{2}p)$;

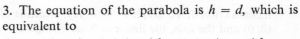

$$h = |\overline{PF}| = \sqrt{\left(x - \frac{p}{2}\right)^2 + y^2};$$

$$d = |\overline{MP}| = \left| x + \frac{p}{2} \right|. \tag{2}$$

3. The equation of the parabola is $h = d$, which is equivalent to

$$h^2 = d^2 \quad or \quad \left(x - \frac{p}{2}\right)^2 + y^2 = \left(x + \frac{p}{2}\right)^2.$$

On expanding and simplifying, we obtain

$$y^2 = 2px, \tag{3}$$

$y^2 = 2px$

Fig. 36

whose graph is shown in Figure 36.

Discussion of $y^2 = 2px$. The graph is symmetric to the x-axis because y occurs only with an *even* exponent. Thus, the line perpendicular to the directrix through the focus is an axis of symmetry, called the **axis of the parabola.** The intersection of this axis and the parabola is called its **vertex,** the origin in Figure 36. Since $y = \pm \sqrt{2px}$, negative values of x are excluded; or, the domain for x is all numbers $x \geqq 0$. Later, we shall prove that the tangent to the parabola at its vertex is perpendicular to the axis of the parabola. The chord KL of the parabola perpendicular to its axis at the focus is called the **focal chord,** or **latus rectum** of the parabola. When $x = \frac{1}{2}p$, at F, we find that $y^2 = p^2$ or $y = \pm p$. Hence, K and L are the points $(\frac{1}{2}p, \pm p)$ and $|\overline{KL}| = 2p$. The parabola is *concave* * to the right (*open* to the right). In our primary applications, the location of the focus, directrix, and latus rectum will be of negligible interest. Hence, our essential information for graphing (3) is as follows:

$$y^2 = 2px, p > 0: \qquad (axis, y = 0; vertex, (0, 0); concave\ to\ right) \qquad (4)$$

Similarly, we obtain the following additional standard equations for a parabola having p as the distance between the focus F and directrix D. We refer to (4), (5), (6), and (7) as *standard forms* for a parabola with its *vertex at the origin* and *axis along a coordinate axis.*

$$y^2 = -2px, p > 0: \qquad (axis, y = 0; vertex, (0, 0); concave\ to\ left). \qquad (5)$$

$$x^2 = 2py, p > 0: \qquad (axis, x = 0; vertex, (0, 0); concave\ upward). \qquad (6)$$

$$x^2 = -2py, p > 0: \qquad (axis, x = 0; vertex, (0, 0); concave\ downward). \qquad (7)$$

The corresponding *standard positions* are in Figures 36, 37, 38, and 39.

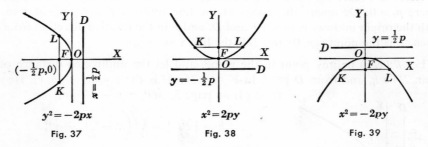

$$y^2 = -2px \qquad\qquad x^2 = 2py \qquad\qquad x^2 = -2py$$

Fig. 37   Fig. 38   Fig. 39

Note 2. For (5), the focus is $F:(-\frac{1}{2}p, 0)$ and directrix is the line $x = \frac{1}{2}p$. For (6), the focus is $F:(0, \frac{1}{2}p)$ and directrix is the line $y = -\frac{1}{2}p$. Etc. for (7).

ILLUSTRATION 1. To graph $x^2 = -12y$, which is of type (7), we locate the vertex $(0, 0)$ and the axis, the line $x = 0$, as in Figure 39. By using $y = -3$ we obtain $x = \pm 6$, and the two points $(\pm 6, -3)$ on the curve. Other points could be found similarly.

ILLUSTRATION 2. To change $3x^2 = 7y$ to a standard form, divide by 3 to obtain $x^2 = \frac{7}{3}y$. Hence, $3x^2 = 7y$ is of type (6), with the vertex of the graph at $(0, 0)$ and the line $x = 0$ as the axis.

The method of Illustration 2 shows that each equation of types (8) and (9) on page 49 is equivalent to one of the standard forms (4)–(7). These remarks justify the following conclusions.

* Concavity will be discussed in detail later in the text.

Any **parabola** whose vertex is the origin and whose axis of symmetry is a coordinate axis has an equation as follows. Conversely, the graph of any equation of this nature is a parabola of the specified type:

(With $A \neq 0$, $C \neq 0$, $D \neq 0$, and $E \neq 0$)

Parabola with OY as the axis:	$Ax^2 + Ey = 0.$	(8)
Parabola with OX as the axis:	$Cy^2 + Dx = 0.$	(9)

EXERCISE 14

By the locus method of Example 1 on page 47, obtain the equation of the parabola with the given focus and equation for the directrix.

1. Focus $(4, 0)$; directrix, $x = -4$.   2. Focus $(0, -3)$; directrix, $y = 3$.

Plot the parabola by use of its vertex and two pairs of points symmetric to the parabola's axis. Describe the parabola's axis.

3. $y^2 = -12x$.   4. $y^2 = 8x$.   5. $x^2 = 8y$.   6. $x^2 = -8y$.

7. $y^2 = -8x$.   8. $y^2 = -6x$.   9. $x^2 = 4y$.   10. $x^2 = -6y$.

11. $y^2 = 2x$.   12. $2x^2 = 9y$.   13. $3y^2 = -10x$.   14. $y^2 = -x$.

15. $x^2 + y = 0$.   16. $4x^2 + y = 0$.   17. $2y^2 - 7x = 0$.

By use of a standard form, find the equation of a parabola whose axis is a coordinate axis and whose vertex is $(0, 0)$, if the parabola passes through the given point.

18. $(\frac{2}{3}, -2)$.   19. $(-6, -6)$.   20. $(-16, -8)$.   21. $(-6, 18)$.

★Graph the equation, showing the focus, directrix, and focal chord.

22. $2x^2 = 5y$.   23. $x^2 = -3y$.   24. $y^2 = -2x$.   25. $y^2 = -10x$.

★26. By use of a standard form of Section 17, find an equation for a parabola in standard position where (a) the focus is $F:(-2, 0)$; (b) the directrix is the line $y = -3$.

★27. A parabola has the line $x + y + 3 = 0$ as directrix, and the focus $F:(-4, -5)$. By a geometric construction, find the vertex and axis of the parabola. Construct enough points on it to draw it, by use of lines perpendicular to the axis, and arcs of circles with F as a center. Finally state a clear rule for constructing points on a parabola with given focus and directrix.

★28. By the method used to obtain (3) on page 47, derive (7) on page 48 by use of the focus $F:(0, -\frac{1}{2}p)$, with the line $y = \frac{1}{2}p$ as the directrix.

18. ELLIPSE DEFINED BY FOCAL RADII

Recall that Note 1 of page 46 applies in the present section.

Definition IV. *An ellipse is the locus of a point for which the sum of the undirected distances to two fixed points * F and F', called the **foci**, is a constant greater than the distance between F and F'.*

Note 1. In the definitions of a parabola and an ellipse, we have introduced points called *foci*. Likewise, we shall define a hyperbola by use of foci. If a point P is on any conic with a focus, let the undirected distance from a focus to P be called a **focal radius** of P.

* We allow for the possibility that F and F' coincide.

EXAMPLE 1. Find the equation of the ellipse with foci F:(4, 0) and F':(− 4, 0), if the sum of the focal radii for any point on the ellipse is 10.

Solution. 1. Let P:(x, y) be any point in the plane. If the lengths of PF and PF' in Figure 40 are h and h', respectively, then P is on the ellipse if and only if $h + h' = 10$. That is, by use of the distance formula from page 12, an equation for the ellipse is

$$\sqrt{(x - 4)^2 + y^2} + \sqrt{(x + 4)^2 + y^2} = 10; \ or, \tag{1}$$

$$\sqrt{(x - 4)^2 + y^2} = 10 - \sqrt{(x + 4)^2 + y^2}. \tag{2}$$

Square and simplify:

$$5\sqrt{(x + 4)^2 + y^2} = 25 + 4x. \tag{3}$$

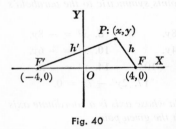

Fig. 40

Square and simplify:

$$9x^2 + 25y^2 = 225. \tag{4}$$

2. If (1) is satisfied by P:(x, y), then (3) is satisfied, and then (4), because the squares of equal numbers are equal. Conversely, as proved below, if P:(x, y) satisfies (4), then (1) also is satisfied. Hence, (4) is our final equation for the ellipse. The graph of (4) is shown in Figure 42 on page 51, if the distance unit is chosen in that figure so that $\overline{OF} = 4$.

★*Comment.* The solution set for (4) is the *union* (see page 674) of the solution sets for the four equations obtained by using all possible combinations of the ambiguous signs $\pm$ in $[\pm h \pm h' = 10]$. This is true because (*a*) if (x, y) satisfies any one of these equations, the squaring operations above would yield a true statement in (4); (*b*) by two successive extractions of square roots (reversing steps), if (x, y) satisfies (4) then (x, y) satisfies *at least one* of the four equations just mentioned. However, the only possible combination of signs is $+ h + h' = 10$, because h, h', and 8 are the lengths of the sides of triangle PFF' in Figure 40, and therefore $|h - h'| < 8$. Hence, (4) is equivalent to the *single* equation $h + h' = 10$, in (1). Such reasoning will be omitted hereafter in rationalizing as in (1). The interested student may repeat the reasoning in such cases.

Derivation of a standard equation for an ellipse

1. Let the distance between the foci F and F' be $2c$, let the line through F and F' be the *x*-axis, and place the origin at the mid-point of $F'F$, as in Figure 41. Then, the foci are $(\pm c, 0)$. Let the constant referred to in Definition IV on page 49 be $2a$, where $a > c$.

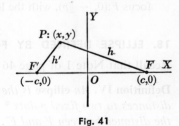

Fig. 41

2. If P:(x, y) is any point, let h and h' be the lengths of PF and PF', as in Figure 41. P is on the ellipse if and only if $h + h' = 2a$, or an equation for the ellipse is

$$\sqrt{(x - c)^2 + y^2} + \sqrt{(x + c)^2 + y^2} = 2a. \tag{5}$$

3. On rationalizing in (5), we obtain

$$(a^2 - c^2)x^2 + a^2y^2 = a^2(a^2 - c^2).$$ (6)

Define a positive number $b \leq a$ as follows: $\qquad\qquad b^2 = a^2 - c^2.$ (7)

Then, (6) becomes $b^2x^2 + a^2y^2 = a^2b^2$, or

[*foci* $(\pm\ c, 0)$, $c^2 = a^2 - b^2$] $\qquad\qquad\qquad \dfrac{x^2}{a^2} + \dfrac{y^2}{b^2} = 1,$ (8)

whose graph is in Figure 42.

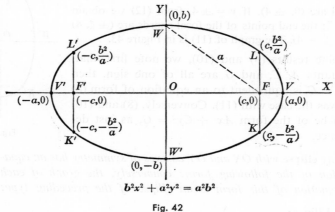

$$b^2x^2 + a^2y^2 = a^2b^2$$

Fig. 42

Discussion of (8). Since x and y occur only with *even* exponents in (8), its graph is symmetric to OX and to OY, and hence also has *the origin as a center of symmetry*, called the *center* of the ellipse. Its x-intercepts are $\pm\ a$; the y-intercepts are $\pm\ b$. From (8),

$$y = \pm\frac{b}{a}\sqrt{a^2 - x^2} \quad and \quad x = \pm\frac{a}{b}\sqrt{b^2 - y^2}.$$ (9)

Thus, to give real values for y, the domain for x is $|\ x\ | \leq a$; for y, the domain is $|\ y\ | \leq b$. Since $b \leq a$, in Figure 42 we call $V'V$, with length $2a$, the **major axis;** we call $W'W$, with length $2b$, the **minor axis** of the ellipse. Points V and V' are called the **vertices** of the ellipse. Each of the chords KL and $K'L'$ through a focus perpendicular to the major axis is called a **focal chord,** or **latus rectum** of the ellipse. By substituting $x = c$ in (8) we find that $y = b^2/a$ at L.

Similarly, with the roles of x and y in (8) interchanged, by the method leading to (8) we may obtain

[*foci* $(0, \pm\ c)$, $c^2 = a^2 - b^2$] $\qquad\qquad\qquad \dfrac{y^2}{a^2} + \dfrac{x^2}{b^2} = 1$ (10)

as the equation of an ellipse with its foci on the y-axis, as in Figure 43 on page 52. We refer to (8) and (10) as *standard forms*, and call the corresponding locations of the ellipse, in Figures 42 and 43, *standard positions* for an ellipse with its axes along the coordinate axes.

ILLUSTRATION 1. To graph $25x^2 + 9y^2 = 225,$ (11)

we divide both sides by 225 to change to the standard form

$$\frac{x^2}{9} + \frac{y^2}{25} = 1.$$ (12)

Since $25 > 9$, the ellipse (12) is of type (10), with the foci on OY. The vertices are
$(0, \pm 5)$. The end points of the minor axis are $(\pm 3, 0)$.
From (10),

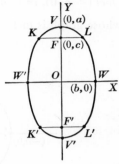

$$c^2 = 25 - 9 = 16;$$

the foci are $(0, \pm 4)$. If $y = \pm 4$, from (12) we obtain
$x = \pm \frac{9}{5}$; the end points of the focal chords are $(\pm \frac{9}{5}, 4)$
and $(\pm \frac{9}{5}, -4)$. The graph of (11) is in Figure 43.

To combine results (8) and (10), we note first that,
if the constants A, C, and G are all of one sign, then
$Ax^2 + Cy^2 = G$ is equivalent to an equation of form (8)
or (10), as was the case with (11). Conversely, (8) and (10)
are seen to be of the form $Ax^2 + Cy^2 = G$, as just described. Hence,

Fig. 43

$$\left\{ \begin{array}{l} \textit{any } \textbf{ellipse } \textit{with OX and OY as axes of symmetry has an equa-} \\ \textit{tion of the following form; conversely, the graph of each} \\ \textit{equation of this form is an ellipse of the preceding type:} \end{array} \right\}$$ (13)

$$\left\{ \begin{array}{c} \textbf{Ellipse:} \\ A, \ C, \textit{ and } G \textit{ of } \textbf{same sign,} \end{array} \right\} \qquad \boldsymbol{Ax^2 + Cy^2 = G.}$$ (14)

In our main applications of ellipses, with equations as in (8) or (10), we shall
be interested in obtaining graphs *quickly, without interest in the location of the
foci, or specification of the major and minor axes.** Then, we may eliminate (10)
from our thoughts and concentrate on (8) as an ellipse with *OX and OY as axes
of symmetry, x-intercepts* $\pm a$, *and y-intercepts* $\pm b$, even when $a < b$. Thus, (8)
may be thought of as the *intercept form* of (14).

Summary. *To graph an* **ellipse** *of type* (14), *find its x-intercepts and y-intercepts; then
sketch the ellipse through its intercept points with recollection of the nature of the
curve. To improve on such a graph, compute solutions* (x, y) *of* (14) *as desired.*

ILLUSTRATION 2. The ellipse of type (14), or (8), with x-intercepts ± 3 and y-inter-
cepts ± 5 has the equation

$$\frac{x^2}{9} + \frac{y^2}{25} = 1.$$

Note 2. Construction of an ellipse. With a and c given, prepare a loop of string with
length $(2c + 2a)$. Pass the loop around tacks placed at the foci F and F' on paper. With
a pencil point, stretch the string tightly, anchored by the tacks. Then, as the pencil point
moves through all possible positions, the point traces the ellipse continuously.

* This will be particularly true later when we graph (8) or (10) in an xy-plane where the scale
units on the coordinate axes are *unequal.*

EXERCISE 15

1. Write the equation of an ellipse with axes along OX and OY, semi-major axis of length 4, and semi-minor axis of length 3, if the foci are (*i*) on OX; (*ii*) on OY.

Graph the ellipse by use of eight accurate points.

2. $16x^2 + 25y^2 = 400$.

3. $4x^2 + y^2 = 16$.

4. $4x^2 + 9y^2 = 36$.

5. $5x^2 + 9y^2 = 45$.

6. $\dfrac{x^2}{64} + \dfrac{y^2}{289} = 1$.

7. $\dfrac{x^2}{289} + \dfrac{y^2}{225} = 1$.

8. $\dfrac{x^2}{25} + \dfrac{y^2}{169} = 1$.

9. $x^2 + 2y^2 = 8$.

10. $9x^2 + 5y^2 = 45$.

11. $5x^2 + y^2 = 5$.

12. $2x^2 + 3y^2 = 6$.

13. $5x^2 + 2y^2 = 10$.

14. $3x^2 + 4y^2 = 12$.

Write the equation of the ellipse with axes along OX and OY satisfying the specified condition.

15. x-intercepts ± 6; y-intercepts ± 5.

16. x-intercepts ± 3; y-intercepts ± 6.

17. x-intercepts ± 2; y-intercepts ± 1.

18. Vertices $(\pm 5, 0)$; semi-minor axis of length 2.

★19. Foci $(\pm 4, 0)$; vertices $(\pm 6, 0)$.

★20. End points of minor axis $(\pm 2, 0)$; foci $(0, \pm 4)$.

★By use of Definition IV on page 49, and the locus method of Example 1 on page 50, derive the equation of the ellipse with the given foci and specified sum, 2a, for the focal radii of any point.

21. Foci $(\pm 2, 0)$; $2a = 6$.

22. Foci $(2, 3)$ and $(2, 9)$; $2a = 8$.

19. HYPERBOLA DEFINED BY FOCAL RADII

Recall that Note 1 of page 46 applies at present.

Definition V. *A **hyperbola** is the locus of a point for which the **absolute value** of the difference of the undirected distances to two fixed points F and F', called the **foci**, is a positive constant which is less than the distance FF'.*

Derivation of a standard equation for a hyperbola

1. Let the distance between the foci F and F' be $2c$; let the line through F and F' be the x-axis, with the origin O at the mid-point of $F'F$, and F in the positive direction from O. Then the foci are $(\pm c, 0)$. Let the constant referred to in Definition **V** be $2a$, where $a < c$.

2. If $P:(x, y)$ is any point in the plane, let h and h' be the lengths of PF and PF', as in Figure 44, where $(h - h')$ is positive for one position of P, and negative for the other position. P is on the hyperbola if and only if $|h - h'| = 2a$; this is true if and only if the coordinates of P satisfy

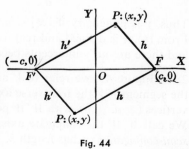

Fig. 44

$$h - h' = 2a \quad or \quad h' - h = 2a. \tag{1}$$

3. The equation $h - h' = 2a$, or $h = h' + 2a$, becomes

$$\sqrt{(x - c)^2 + y^2} = \sqrt{(x + c)^2 + y^2} + 2a. \tag{2}$$

On rationalizing in (2) we obtain

$$(c^2 - a^2)x^2 - a^2y^2 = a^2(c^2 - a^2). \tag{3}$$

If the equation $h' - h = 2a$ is discussed similarly, we again obtain (3). Thus, we conclude that (3) is equivalent to (1), or (3) is an equation for the hyperbola. Define a positive number b by the equation

$$b^2 = c^2 - a^2. \tag{4}$$

Then, (3) becomes $b^2x^2 - a^2y^2 = a^2b^2$, or

$$[foci \ (\pm \ c, \ 0), \ where \ c^2 = a^2 + b^2] \qquad \frac{x^2}{a^2} - \frac{y^2}{b^2} = 1, \tag{5}$$

whose graph consists of the two branches in Figure 45.

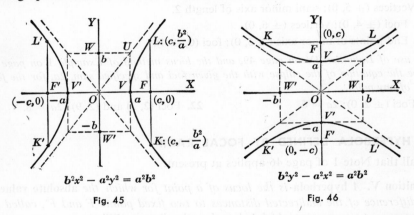

$$b^2x^2 - a^2y^2 = a^2b^2 \qquad\qquad b^2y^2 - a^2x^2 = a^2b^2$$

Fig. 45   Fig. 46

Discussion of (5). 1. The hyperbola has the *x*-axis and the *y*-axis as axes of symmetry and the origin as a center of symmetry, called the *center* of the hyperbola. On solving (5) for *x* and for *y*, we obtain

$$y = \pm \frac{b}{a}\sqrt{x^2 - a^2} \quad and \quad x = \pm \frac{a}{b}\sqrt{y^2 + b^2}. \tag{6}$$

Thus, *y* is imaginary if $|x| < a$, and the domain for *x* is $x \le -a$ and $x \ge a$. From (6), *x* is defined and real for all values of *y*. The *x*-intercepts are $x = \pm a$, and there are no *y*-intercepts because *y* is imaginary when $x = 0$.

2. In Figure 45, we refer to *V* and *V'* as the **vertices** of the hyperbola and call the segment *V'V* the **transverse axis**. We complete the **associated rectangle** having vertices $(\pm a, \pm b)$, with *W'W* perpendicular to the transverse axis at the origin. We call *W'W* the **conjugate axis**. The *semi-transverse* axis has length *a* and the *semi-conjugate* axis has length *b*. Without proof at this time, we mention that the

diagonals, extended, of the associated rectangle are *asymptotes* for the hyperbola. The equations of the asymptotes are $y = \pm bx/a$, or

$$\frac{x}{a} - \frac{y}{b} = 0 \quad and \quad \frac{x}{a} + \frac{y}{b} = 0, \tag{7}$$

which are equivalent to the single equation

$$\frac{x^2}{a^2} - \frac{y^2}{b^2} = 0 \quad or \quad b^2x^2 - a^2y^2 = 0. \tag{8}$$

3. Each of the chords KL and $K'L'$, perpendicular to the transverse axis at F and F', is called a **focal chord,** or **latus rectum,** of the hyperbola. With $x = c$ in (5), we find that the ordinate of L is b^2/a, or $KL = 2b^2/a$.

In the work leading to (5), if we had let the line FF' be the y-axis, we would have obtained the hyperbola as in Figure 46 on page 54 with the equation

$$[foci\ (0, \pm c);\ c^2 = a^2 + b^2] \qquad \frac{y^2}{a^2} - \frac{x^2}{b^2} = 1. \tag{9}$$

We refer to (5) and (9) as *standard forms*, and call the corresponding locations of the hyperbola, in Figures 45 and 46, *standard positions* for a hyperbola with its axes along the coordinate axes.

ILLUSTRATION 1. The equation $\qquad 16x^2 - 9y^2 = 144 \qquad$ (10) can be changed to the standard form (5) by dividing both sides by 144,

$$\frac{x^2}{9} - \frac{y^2}{16} = 1. \tag{11}$$

A graph of (11) is in Figure 45 on page 54, if $OV = 3$.

Similarly, as in Illustration 1, when A and C are of *opposite signs* and $G \neq 0$, the equation $Ax^2 + Cy^2 = G$ is equivalent to form (5), or (9), and hence represents a hyperbola. *Conversely*, (5) and (9) are of the form $Ax^2 + Cy^2 = G$ as just described. Moreover, we note that (8), and the corresponding equation $b^2y^2 - a^2x^2 = 0$ for (9), can be obtained from (5), or (9), on replacing the constant term "1" by "0" on the right. Hence,

$\left\{\begin{array}{l} any \text{ \textbf{hyperbola}} \ with \ OX \ and \ OY \ as \ axes \ of \ symmetry \ has \ an \\ equation \ of \ the \ following \ form \ and, \ conversely, \ the \ graph \ of \\ such \ an \ equation \ is \ a \ hyperbola \ of \ the \ preceding \ nature: \end{array}\right\}$ (12)

$\left\{\begin{array}{c} \textbf{Hyperbola:} \\ A \ and \ C \ of \textbf{ opposite signs;} \ G \neq 0 \end{array}\right\}$ $\qquad Ax^2 + Cy^2 = G.$ (13)

Asymptotes for (13): $\qquad\qquad\qquad\qquad Ax^2 + Cy^2 = 0.$ (14)

In applications of (5) and (9), we shall be interested mainly in obtaining a graph of any equation (13) without reference to (5) or (9).

Summary. *To graph a* **hyperbola** $Ax^2 + Cy^2 = G$, *obtain its intercepts on that coordinate axis which intersects the curve; draw the asymptotes by graphing* (14); *sketch each branch of the hyperbola through an intercept point (a vertex) to approach the asymptotes smoothly.*

ILLUSTRATION 2. To graph $16y^2 - 9x^2 = 144,$ (15)

first place $y = 0$, and obtain $x^2 = -16$; the x-intercepts are *imaginary*, or there are no x-intercepts. Place $x = 0$ and obtain $y^2 = 9$ or $y = \pm 3$, the y-intercepts; the vertices of the hyperbola are $(0, \pm 3)$. An equation for the asymptotes is $16y^2 - 9x^2 = 0$, or

$$y = \tfrac{3}{4}x \quad and \quad y = -\tfrac{3}{4}x.$$ (16)

If the distance unit is such that $OV = 3$ in Figure 46 on page 54, the graphs of (16) are the broken lines. Then, we draw each branch of the hyperbola through a vertex, $(0, 3)$ or $(0, -3)$, to approach the asymptotes smoothly. If desired, the vertices of the associated rectangle in Figure 46 could be located by using $y = +3$ and $y = -3$ in (16). If greater accuracy is desired, we may find two pairs of symmetrical points on the hyperbola by substituting any numbers $\pm y$ such that $|y| > 3$ in (15). Thus, if $y = \pm 5$ in (15), we find $x^2 = \tfrac{256}{9}$ or $x = \pm \tfrac{16}{3}$.

EXERCISE 16

Graph the hyperbola, showing its asymptotes; give their equations.

1. $\dfrac{x^2}{16} - \dfrac{y^2}{9} = 1.$ **2.** $\dfrac{y^2}{144} - \dfrac{x^2}{25} = 1.$ **3.** $\dfrac{y^2}{64} - \dfrac{x^2}{225} = 1.$

4. $4x^2 - 9y^2 = 144.$ **5.** $4y^2 - x^2 = 4.$ **6.** $x^2 - 9y^2 = 9.$

7. $3y^2 - 12 = x^2.$ **8.** $x^2 - y^2 = 25.$ **9.** $9x^2 + 63 = 7y^2.$

Note 1. An **equilateral** or **rectangular hyperbola** is one whose transverse and conjugate axes are equal, so that the associated rectangle is a square and the asymptotes are perpendicular. The hyperbola in Problem 8 is equilateral.

10. $225 + 9x^2 = 25y^2.$ **11.** $9x^2 - 144 = 4y^2.$

Note 2. The hyperbolas $b^2x^2 - a^2y^2 = a^2b^2$ and $a^2y^2 - b^2x^2 = a^2b^2$ are called **conjugate hyperbolas.** They have the same asymptotes.

Graph the pair of conjugate hyperbolas on one coordinate system.

12. $\begin{cases} 9x^2 - 4y^2 = 36. \\ 4y^2 - 9x^2 = 36. \end{cases}$ **13.** $\begin{cases} 4x^2 - y^2 = 16. \\ y^2 - 4x^2 = 16. \end{cases}$ **14.** $\begin{cases} x^2 - y^2 = 16. \\ y^2 - x^2 = 16. \end{cases}$

Note 3. In Problem 40 on page 66, the student may prove that the graph of $xy = k$, where $k \neq 0$, represents an equilateral hyperbola whose asymptotes are the coordinate axes, and whose transverse axis makes an angle of $45°$ with OX.

Graph by use of the asymptotes and a few accurate points.

15. $xy = 4.$ **16.** $xy = -6.$ **17.** $3xy + 7 = 0.$ **18.** $2xy = 9.$

★*By use of* (5) *or* (9) *of Section* 19, *find the equation of the hyperbola with OX and OY as axes of symmetry, to satisfy the data, and graph the equation.*

19. Transverse axis of length 8; conjugate axis of length 10; foci on OX.

20. Vertices $(\pm 3, 0)$; foci $(\pm 4, 0)$.   **21.** Vertices $(0, \pm 5)$; foci $(0, \pm 8)$.

22. Ends of conjugate axis $(\pm 5, 0)$; foci $(0, \pm 7)$.

★*By use of the locus method of Example* 1, *page* 50, *derive the equation of the hyperbola to satisfy the data, and graph the equation.*

23. Foci $(0, \pm 5)$; absolute value of difference of the focal radii is 6.

24. Foci $(\pm 5, 0)$; absolute value of difference of the focal radii is 8.

20. CONICS SYMMETRIC TO OX AND OY

Consider two coordinate systems superimposed on the same plane, an xy-system, which we shall call the *original system*, and a *new $x'y'$-system*. Then, each point P in the plane has two sets of coordinates, (x, y) and (x', y'). Any locus with an equation $f(x, y) = 0$ also will have a related equation $F(x', y') = 0$ in the new system. The process of obtaining (x', y') for any point $P:(x, y)$, or the new equation $F(x', y') = 0$ for any locus, is called a *transformation of coordinates*.

We now return to the viewpoint that, *unless otherwise specified*, the scale units on the coordinate axes in an xy-plane are not necessarily equal. However, as usual, there is a unit specified for measuring any distance in the Euclidean plane with which we are involved. Then, let h and k be positive constants, and define a transformation from an xy-system to a new $x'y'$-system of coordinates by

$$x' = hx \quad and \quad y' = ky, \text{ or} \tag{1}$$

$$x = \frac{1}{h}x' \quad and \quad y = \frac{1}{k}y'. \tag{2}$$

Transformation (1), or (2), gives a new $x'y'$-system with the same origin, axes, and positive directions on the axes as in the xy-system. However, the scale unit for x' is $1/h$ times the scale unit for x, because $x' = h$ when $x = 1$ in (1); the scale unit for y' is $1/k$ times the scale unit for y. Thus, if the scale units are h *inches* (or, h times *any* specified unit for length) for x, and k *inches* for y, the scale unit is *1 inch* for both x' and y'. That is, for *any* xy-system, by (1) we can transform to a new $x'y'$-system having *equal units* on the axes, with this unit the same as the unit of length in the Euclidean plane.

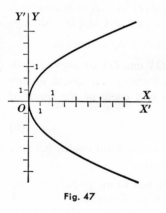

Fig. 47

ILLUSTRATION 1. Let the scale units be 2 inches for x and 3 inches for y, as shown proportionately in Figure 47. To obtain an $x'y'$-system with the scale unit 1 inch on both axes, we use equations (1) with $h = 2$ and $k = 3$:

$$x' = 2x \quad and \quad y' = 3y. \tag{3}$$

Then, from (3), $P:(x = 1, y = 1)$ is seen to become $P:(x' = 2, y' = 3)$; $Q:(x = 2, y = -3)$ becomes $Q:(x' = 4, y' = -9)$. The graph of

$$9y^2 = 10x \tag{4}$$

has a new $x'y'$-equation, obtained by using $x = \frac{1}{2}x'$ and $y = \frac{1}{3}y'$ from (3) in (4):

$$9(\tfrac{1}{9}y'^2) = 10(\tfrac{1}{2}x'), \quad or \quad y'^2 = 5x'. \tag{5}$$

From (9) on page 49, where the scale units on the axes were assumed to be equal, the graph of (5), and hence of (4), is a *parabola* whose vertex is at O', which is O, and whose axis is the line $y' = 0$, which also is the line $y = 0$. The graph is in Figure 47. Thus, although the scale units on the axes in the xy-system are *unequal*, the remarks concerning (9) on page 49 are true for (4).

The method of Illustration 1 can be applied to the general equations previously obtained for conic sections, and leads to the following results.

Theorem I. *The statements about parabolas in* (8) *and* (9) *on page* 49, *about ellipses in* (13) *and* (14) *on page* 52, *and about hyperbolas in* (12), (13), *and* (14) *on page* 55 *remain true in any xy-plane, where the scale units on the axes may be unequal.*

Recall that we name a locus a *degenerate conic* if it consists of a *single point* or of *two lines*. We shall observe that a degenerate conic has at least one pair of perpendicular axes of symmetry, and hence at least one center of symmetry.

ILLUSTRATION 2. If a locus consists of *two intersecting lines*, the bisectors of the angles which they form are perpendicular axes of symmetry. In any *xy*-plane, a general equation for such a locus with OX and OY as axes of symmetry is

$$Ax^2 + Cy^2 = 0,$$

where $AC < 0$. Thus, $4x^2 - 9y^2 = 0$, or $2x = \pm 3y$ gives two lines of the specified character.

ILLUSTRATION 3. If a locus is a *single point*, then any two perpendicular lines through the point are axes of symmetry. An equation for a single point, the origin, with OX and OY as axes of symmetry is $Ax^2 + Cy^2 = 0$ where A and C have the same sign. Thus, the graph of $x^2 + 3y^2 = 0$ is just the point $(0, 0)$.

ILLUSTRATION 4. If a locus consists of *two parallel lines*, the line parallel to them and equidistant from them is an axis of symmetry; any line perpendicular to this axis is a second axis of symmetry. In an *xy*-plane, a general equation for such a locus with OX and OY as axes of symmetry is $Ax^2 = G$, where A and G have the same sign, or where $A \neq 0$ and $G = 0$. Thus, $4x^2 = 9$ gives the parallel lines

$$2x = \pm 3, \quad and \quad 4x^2 = 0$$

gives the line $x = 0$ twice. A similar locus with OX and OY as axes of symmetry is given by $Cy^2 = G$, where C and G have the same sign, or $C \neq 0$ and $G = 0$.

Illustrations 2, 3, and 4, and Theorem I justify the following statement.

Any **ellipse, hyperbola,** *or* **degenerate conic** *with OX and OY as axes of symmetry has an equation of the following form. Conversely, the graph of any equation of this form with A and C not both zero is a conic of the specified type or is imaginary:*

$$Ax^2 + Cy^2 = G. \tag{6}$$

We call ellipses, hyperbolas, and degenerate conics the **central conics** because each locus of this sort has at least one center of symmetry.

ILLUSTRATION 5. If the equation $x^2 + y^2 = 25$ is graphed in an *xy*-plane having equal scale units on the axes, the graph is a circle. If the scale unit on OX is $\frac{3}{5}$ inch and on OY is 1 inch, the graph becomes an ellipse with its major axis along OY. If the preceding scale units are interchanged, the graph is an ellipse with its major axis along OX. The student should sketch these graphs.

When we do not require the scale units on the coordinate axes to be equal, from Illustration 5 we infer that no importance should be attached to the notions of the major and minor axes of an ellipse, or to the location of any focus of a conic. We emphasize that the Summaries of pages 52 and 55 for graphing an ellipse or hyperbola given by (6) still apply.

EXERCISE 17

Use unequal scale units on the coordinate axes unless otherwise specified. Graph by rapid methods without finding any focus. Use the vertex and axis of any parabola, and the asymptotes of any hyperbola, and any x-intercept or y-intercept.

1. $3x^2 + 4y^2 = 12$. **2.** $2y^2 = 9x$. **3.** $3x^2 = 8y$.

4. $4x^2 - y^2 = 100$. **5.** $y^2 - 25x^2 = 49$. **6.** $2x^2 = -7y$.

7. $x^2 - 49y^2 = 0$. **8.** $2x^2 + y^2 = 0$. **9.** $4x^2 - 25 = 0$.

10. Graph $x^2 + y^2 = 16$ with (*a*) equal scale units on the axes; (*b*) the scale unit for x twice as long as the scale unit for y; (*c*) the units of part (*b*) interchanged. Use a separate cross-section grid for each graph.

11. Graph $4x^2 + 9y^2 = 36$ with (*a*) equal scale units on the axes; (*b*) the scale unit for x as $\frac{2}{3}$ of the scale unit for y. (*c*) In the xy-plane of part (*b*), use the transformation $x = 3x'$ and $y = 2y'$ to obtain a new $x'y'$-equation for the curve. What is true about the scale units for x' and y'?

A hyperbola is symmetric to the coordinate axes and satisfies the specified condition. Write an equation for the hyperbola and draw it.

12. Transverse axis along OX, with length 8 x-units; conjugate axis with length 6 y-units.

13. Transverse axis along OY, with length 10 y-units; conjugate axis with length 6 x-units.

14. Transverse axis along OX, with length 8 x-units; asymptotes $y = \pm \frac{5}{4}x$.

15. Transverse axis along OY, with length 10 y-units; asymptotes $y = \pm \frac{5}{12}x$.

★16. Prove that part of Theorem I on page 58 referring to hyperbolas.

21. TRANSLATION OF AXES

In Figure 48, let OX and OY be original axes; let $O'X'$ and $O'Y'$ be new axes, respectively parallel to OX and OY, with the same positive directions, the same scale unit on OX as on $O'X'$, and the same unit on OY as on $O'Y'$. A change of this nature is called a **translation of axes to the new origin O'.** If O' has original coordinates $(x = h, y = k)$, we shall prove that the coordinates (x, y) and (x', y') of any point P satisfy

$$x = x' + h; \quad y = y' + k. \tag{1}$$

Or,

$$x' = x - h; \quad y' = y - k. \tag{2}$$

Proof. Let the projection of $P:(x,y)$ on $O'X'$ be M' and on OX be M, and the projection of O' on OX be N. Since all line segments to be mentioned in Figure 48 are directed, for any position of P we obtain the following relations:

$$h = \overline{ON}; \quad x' = \overline{O'M'} = \overline{NM};$$
$$x = \overline{OM} = \overline{ON} + \overline{NM} = h + x'.$$

Similarly, by projecting P on $O'Y'$ and OY, we would obtain $y = k + y'$.

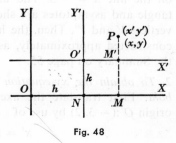

Fig. 48

ILLUSTRATION 1. Let the new origin be $O':(x = 2, y = -3)$. Then, from (2), the point $(x = -1, y = 4)$ has new coordinates

$$x' = -1 - 2 = -3 \quad and \quad y' = 4 - (-3) = 7.$$

A major objective in transformation of coordinates is the simplification of equations in terms of the new coordinates.

EXAMPLE 1. Transform the following equation by translating axes to the new origin $(x = 2, y = -3)$:

$$2x^2 - 8x + y^2 + 6y + 11 = 0. \tag{3}$$

Solution. 1. From (1), substitute $x = x' + 2$ and $y = y' - 3$ in (3):

$$2(x' + 2)^2 - 8(x' + 2) + (y' - 3)^2 + 6(y' - 3) + 11 = 0, \ or$$
$$2x'^2 + y'^2 = 6. \tag{4}$$

2. The locus of (4) is an ellipse with center $(x' = 0, y' = 0)$, with $O'X'$ and $O'Y'$ as axes of symmetry, x'-intercepts $\pm \sqrt{3}$ and y'-intercepts $\pm \sqrt{6}$. The graph of (4), with reference to $O'X'$ and $O'Y'$, is in Figure 49. Hence, the locus of (3) is an ellipse with center $(x = 2, y = -3)$, and with the lines $x = 2$ and $y = -3$ as axes of symmetry.

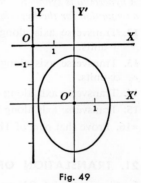

We may use (1) to transform an equation from an xy-system to the $x'y'$-system, and use (2) for the *inverse* transformation from the $x'y'$-system to the xy-system. Thus, in Example 1, if we use $x' = x - 2$ and $y' = y + 3$ in (4), we obtain the original equation (3). Since (1) and (2) are *linear* in $x, y, x',$ and y', *the degree of an equation is unchanged by translating axes.*

Fig. 49

22. CONIC WITH AN AXIS OF SYMMETRY PARALLEL TO OX OR OY

EXAMPLE 1. Obtain an equation for the hyperbola with center $(-3, 2)$, semi-transverse axis horizontal and 4 x-units long; semi-conjugate axis 3 y-units long.

Solution. 1. In Figure 50, the transverse axis is on the line $y = 2$; the conjugate axis is on the line $x = -3$. The associated rectangle and asymptotes are shown, with the vertices V and V'. Then, the hyperbola was constructed approximately, as described in the Summary on page 55.

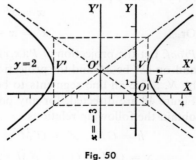

2. *To obtain the xy-equation of the hyperbola:* First translate the axes to the new origin $O':(-3, 2)$ by use of

Fig. 50

$$x' = x + 3 \quad and \quad y' = y - 2. \tag{1}$$

In the $x'y'$-system, by use of (5) on page 54, the equation of the hyperbola is

$$\frac{x'^2}{16} - \frac{y'^2}{9} = 1. \tag{2}$$

On using (1) in (2), we obtain $\qquad \dfrac{(x+3)^2}{16} - \dfrac{(y-2)^2}{9} = 1. \tag{3}$

In any xy-plane, the method of Example 1 can be applied to any central conic with center (h, k), or any parabola with vertex (h, k), if an axis of symmetry of the conic is parallel to OX or OY. Thus, the axes can be translated to the new origin $O':(x = h, y = k)$ by use of

$$x' = x - h \quad and \quad y' = y - k. \tag{4}$$

Then, the $x'y'$-equation of the conic can be written by use of (8) or (9) on page 49 for a parabola, or (6) on page 58 for a central conic. In the resulting equation, we would use (4) to arrive at an xy-equation. We obtain the following forms, where A, C, D, E, and G are constants.

I. Parabola *with vertex (h, k) and axis parallel to OX or OY.*

$$(A \neq 0, \quad C \neq 0, \quad D \neq 0, \quad E \neq 0)$$

Axis, the line $y - k = 0$: $\qquad C(y - k)^2 + D(x - h) = 0. \tag{5}$

Axis, the line $x - h = 0$: $\qquad A(x - h)^2 + E(y - k) = 0. \tag{6}$

II. Ellipse, hyperbola, *or* **degenerate conic** *with axes parallel to OX and OY, and center (h, k).*

(A and C not both zero): $\qquad A(x - h)^2 + C(y - k)^2 = G. \tag{7}$

ILLUSTRATION 1. To graph $\qquad (x - 2)^2 = -8(y + 4), \tag{8}$

which we recognize as a special case of (6), first translate the axes to the new origin $O':(x = 2, y = -4)$ by use of

$$x' = x - 2 \quad and \quad y' = y - (-4) = y + 4. \tag{9}$$

Then, (8) becomes $\qquad x'^2 = -8y'. \tag{10}$

The graph of (10) is a parabola with vertex O' and axis $O'Y'$. Thus, in the xy-system, the graph of (8) is a parabola concave downward with vertex $(2, -4)$ and with the line $x - 2 = 0$ as the axis of symmetry.

ILLUSTRATION 2. To graph $\qquad \dfrac{(x - 2)^2}{25} + \dfrac{(y - 3)^2}{9} = 1, \tag{11}$

we translate the origin to $O':(x = 2, y = 3)$ by use of $x' = x - 2$ and $y' = y - 3$. Then, (11) becomes

$$\frac{x'^2}{25} + \frac{y'^2}{9} = 1, \tag{12}$$

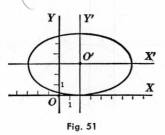

Fig. 51

whose graph is an ellipse with center O', x'-intercepts $x' = \pm 5$, and y'-intercepts $y' = \pm 3$, as shown in Figure 51. Thus, (11) represents an ellipse with center O', and the lines $x - 2 = 0$ and $y - 3 = 0$ as axes of symmetry.

Any equation of the second degree in x and y which does not involve the product xy is equivalent to an equation of the form

$$Ax^2 + Cy^2 + Dx + Ey + F = 0, \qquad (13)$$

where A, C, D, E, and F are constants and A and C are not both zero. Any one of equations (5), (6), and (7) is equivalent to the form (13) when expanded. Conversely, by completing a square in the x-terms when $A \neq 0$, and in the y-terms when $C \neq 0$, any equation (13) can be written in one of the forms (5), (6), and (7), with A and C having the *same values* there as in (13). Our information about central conics in (14) on page 52, (13) on page 55, and (6) on page 58, and about parabolas in (5) and (6), then gives us the following results for rapid diagnosis of the nature of the graph of any equation (13).

Theorem II. *Any conic with an axis of symmetry parallel to a coordinate axis has an equation of form* (13) *with A and C not both zero. Conversely, if A and C are not both zero, the locus of* (13) *is imaginary, or is a conic of the preceding type, with possibilities as follows:*

A **or** C **is zero:** *a parabola, two parallel lines, or imaginary.* $\qquad (14)$

A **and** C **of same sign:** *an ellipse, a single point, or imaginary.* $\qquad (15)$

A **and** C **of opposite signs:** *a hyperbola or two intersecting lines.* $\qquad (16)$

EXAMPLE 2. Remove linear terms by translating axes and graph

$$9x^2 - 36x + 25y^2 - 150y + 36 = 0.$$

Solution. By (15), the graph is an ellipse, a point, or imaginary. On completing squares, we obtain

$$9(x^2 - 4x + 4) + 25(y^2 - 6y + 9) = -36 + 225 + 36, \text{ or}$$
$$9(x - 2)^2 + 25(y - 3)^2 = 225, \qquad (17)$$

which is equivalent to (11) on page 61. The graph of (17) then is obtained as on page 61, in Figure 51.

EXAMPLE 3. Graph the equation $\qquad x^2 - 4x + 8y = -36.$

Solution. By (14), the graph is a parabola, two parallel lines, or imaginary. We complete a square with the terms in x:

$$(x^2 - 4x + 4) = -8y - 36 + 4, \text{ or}$$
$$(x - 2)^2 = -8(y + 4),$$

which is (8) on page 61. The parabola with vertex $(2, -4)$ and axis as the line $x - 2 = 0$ then is obtained as in Figure 52, with $x' = x - 2$ and $y' = y + 4$ in the background equation $x'^2 = -8y'$.

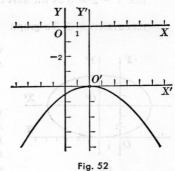

Fig. 52

As a special case of the method applied to (13), consider the graph of a quadratic function $f(x) = ax^2 + bx + c$, where $a \neq 0$. That is, consider the graph of

$$y = ax^2 + bx + c. \tag{18}$$

On dividing by a, and then adding $b^2/4a^2$ to complete a square, we obtain

$$\left(x + \frac{b}{2a}\right)^2 = \frac{1}{a}(y - k), \quad or \quad \left[x - \left(-\frac{b}{2a}\right)\right]^2 = \frac{1}{a}(y - k), \tag{19}$$

where $k = (4ac - b^2)/4a$. With

$$x' = x - \left(-\frac{b}{2a}\right) \quad and \quad y' = y - k,$$

equation (19) becomes $x'^2 = y'/a$, which represents a parabola whose vertex is $(x' = 0, y' = 0)$ and axis is the line $x' = 0$, or $x - (-b/2a) = 0$. By reference to Figures 38 and 39 on page 48, we see that the parabola is concave *upward* or *downward* according as $a > 0$ or $a < 0$. Our conclusions justify the following statement.

> If $f(x) = ax^2 + bx + c$ *where* $a \neq 0$, *the graph of* f, *or of*
> *the equation* $y = f(x)$, *is a* **parabola** *with the following char-*
> *acteristics: it is concave in the* **positive** *y-direction when* (20)
> $a > 0$, *and in the* **negative** *y-direction when* $a < 0$; *at*
> *the* **vertex,** $x = -b/2a$; *the* **axis** *is the line* $x = -b/2a$.

If $A \neq 0$, $C = 0$, and $E \neq 0$ in (13) on page 62, the equation is linear in y. Then, on solving for y in terms of x, we find that the equation defines y as a quadratic function of x. To graph the equation, instead of completing a square to change to a standard form, it frequently is more convenient to use (20). Similarly, if $A = 0$, $C \neq 0$, and $D \neq 0$ in (13), we solve for x, note that the equation defines x as a quadratic function of y, and use (20) with the roles of x and y interchanged. Thus, with $a \neq 0$, the graph of

$$x = ay^2 + by + c \tag{21}$$

is a parabola at whose vertex $y = -b/2a$; the axis is the line $y = -b/2a$.

EXAMPLE 4. Graph $\qquad 2y - 2x^2 + 4x + 6 = 0. \tag{22}$

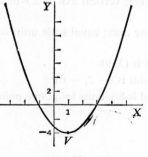

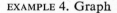

Fig. 53

Solution. 1. Solve (22) for y:

$$y = x^2 - 2x - 3. \tag{23}$$

Hence, y is a quadratic function of x, and the graph will be a parabola.

2. From (20), at the vertex of the parabola, $x = -(-2)/2 = 1$; with $x = 1$ in (23), $y = -4$ and the vertex is $(1, -4)$. A few more points on the graph were found by substituting values of x in (23). The axis of the parabola is the line $x = 1$. The graph is in Figure 53.

EXERCISE 18

1. Find the new coordinates of $(3, 7)$, $(- 4, 6)$, $(- 1, - 2)$, and $(0, 0)$, if the axes are translated to the new origin $O'{:}(2, 4)$. Plot all points and both sets of axes in the same plane.

2. If the axes have been translated to $O'{:}(- 2, 3)$, find the old coordinates of the points whose new coordinates are $(- 1, 2)$, $(2, - 3)$, $(0, 0)$, and $(- 4, 3)$. Plot all points and both sets of axes.

3. Transform the equation by translating the axes to the specified new origin O'; then graph the equation with both sets of axes shown.

$$O'{:}(x = 2, y = 4){:}\quad y^2 - 8y - 4x + 24 = 0.$$

Graph the equation by first translating the origin conveniently. Draw the asymptotes for any hyperbola.

4. $(y - 2)^2 = 4(x - 3)$.

5. $25(x - 4)^2 + 9(y - 5)^2 = 225$.

6. $\dfrac{(x - 3)^2}{9} - \dfrac{(y + 5)^2}{16} = 1$.

7. $\dfrac{(y + 3)^2}{144} - \dfrac{(x + 6)^2}{25} = 1$.

First specify the possible nature of the graph of the equation. Then, after completing one or more squares, translate the origin conveniently and draw the graph, showing any asymptotes. Also, give the xy-coordinates of the vertex of any parabola, or center of any ellipse, and the equations of any asymptotes.

8. $x^2 - 2x + y^2 - 6y + 6 = 0$.

9. $y^2 - 8y - 6x + 28 = 0$.

10. $9x^2 + 36x + 4y^2 - 24y + 36 = 0$.

11. $4x^2 + 9y^2 + 24x = 0$.

12. $y^2 + 6x - 4y = 14$.

13. $2x^2 - 8x - 15y = - 53$.

14. $4y^2 + 24y = x^2 - 20$.

15. $25x^2 - 100x - 4y^2 - 32y = 64$.

16. $y^2 + 4x^2 + 10y + 32x + 25 = 0$.

17. $3x^2 + 4y^2 - 12x + 8y + 19 = 0$.

18. $4x^2 - 25y^2 - 8x + 50y - 9 = 0$.

19. $x^2 + 4y^2 = 4y - 1$.

20. $4x^2 - 4x = 3 - 12y + 9y^2$.

21. $5x^2 + 20x - 4y^2 - 40y - 160 = 0$.

Graph by the method based on (20) on page 63.

22. $y = x^2 - 4x + 7$.

23. $4x - 2x^2 = y - 3$.

24. $x = 8y - 2y^2 - 6$.

25–26. The equations in Problems 9 and 12, respectively.

In a given xy-coordinate system, obtain the equation of the specified conic by first writing its equation in a related x'y'-system.

27. *Ellipse:* center $(2, - 5)$; horizontal axis is 3 x-units long; vertical axis is 2 y-units long.

28. *Hyperbolas:* center $(- 4, 6)$; axes parallel to coordinate axes; equal scale units on axes; transverse axis 6 and conjugate axis 8.

29. *Parabola:* vertex $(1, 5)$; axis parallel to OX; one point is $(3, 9)$.

30. *Parabola:* vertex $(2, - 4)$; axis parallel to OY; one point is $(- 2, - 6)$.

31. *Hyperbola:* center $(5, 8)$; transverse axis is vertical, and is 8 y-units long; one point on hyperbola is $(6, 16)$.

32. *Parabola:* vertex $(1, 5)$; focus $(3, 5)$.

33. *Parabola:* vertex $(2, - 4)$; focus $(2, - 6)$.

34. *Ellipse:* foci $(2, -1)$ and $(2, 7)$; one vertex $(2, - 2)$; equal units on axes.

EXERCISE 19 (*Review of Chapters One and Two*)

1. With $A:(3, 6)$ and $B:(1, -2)$, find the mid-point of segment AB; the points of trisection of AB; the point P on the line AB where $AP = \frac{3}{4}AB$, with the line considered as a directed line.

2. With $A:(1, -2)$ and $B:(-2, -4)$, write parametric equations for the line AB; from these equations, find two other points on AB and plot all of these points; eliminate the parameter t by use of the parametric equations to find an xy-equation for the line, and check by use of the two-point form for the line.

3. If $f(x) = 6x + 5 - x^2$, find $f(3)$, $f(2)$, and $f(-2)$.

4. Find k if $(2, k)$ is on the graph of $3x^2 + 5x - 3y = 1$.

5. Find the equation of the line with slope 4 through the intersection of
$$2x + 3y - 5 = 0 \quad \text{and} \quad 3x - 4y + 3 = 0.$$

6. Determine analytically whether or not the lines are concurrent:
$$2x + 5y - 3 = 0; \quad 3x + 2y + 5 = 0; \quad x - y + 7 = 0.$$

7. Find h and k if the equations $3x - 2y + k = 0$ and $4x - hy + 3 = 0$ represent coincident lines.

In the following problems, the scale units are equal in the xy-plane.

8. Write the equation $3x - 4y - 7 = 0$ in the slope-intercept form, and state the slope and y-intercept; in the intercept form, and state the intercepts. Also, find the inclination of the line.

9. Find the inclination of a line whose slope is (*a*) 2.904; (*b*) $-.368$.

10. Find the slope of a line whose inclination is (*a*) $27°$; (*b*) $139°$.

11. Give two proofs of the fact that the quadrilateral with the vertices $(-1, 5)$, $(10, 7)$, $(2, 1)$, and $(7, 11)$ is a rectangle.

12. Find k so that the following lines are (*a*) parallel; (*b*) perpendicular:
$$3x - ky + 3 = 0; \quad 5x + 2y = 4.$$

13. Find the acute angle formed by two lines with slopes $\frac{1}{3}$ and -2.

14. Write the equations of the lines through $(3, -2)$ parallel and perpendicular to $3x - 5y + 2 = 0$.

With the x-axis horizontal in an xy-plane, graph the function defined by the formula, or graph the given equation, if its locus is not imaginary. State the coordinates of the vertex of any parabola, and the center of any central conic. Show any asymptotes.

15. $3x + 5$.   16. $-2x^2 - 8x + 3$.   17. $x = y^2 - 4y - 2$.   18. $y^2 = 10x$.

19. $y^2 = -7x$.   20. $x^2 = -5y$.   21. $x^2 - 6y = 0$.

22. $x^2 + 4y^2 = 4$.   23. $x^2 - 4y^2 = 4$.   24. $x^2 + 4y^2 = 0$.

25. $x^2 - 2x + 4y - 7 = 0$.

26. $y^2 + 4y - 6x + 22 = 0$.

27. $x^2 + 9y^2 - 4x + 18y + 12 = 0$.

28. $9x^2 - 4y^2 + 36x + 8y + 31 = 0$.

29. $x^2 + y^2 - 4x + 8y + 6 = 0$.

30. $3x^2 + 3y^2 - 6x - 10y + 53 = 0$.

31. Transform coordinates by translation of axes to the new origin $O':(1, -2)$ and obtain the $x'y'$-form of the equation $4x^2 - 5y^2 = 20$.

The specified conic has an axis of symmetry parallel to a coordinate axis. Write an equation for each conic satisfying the data.

32. *Parabola:* vertex $(0, 0)$; through point $(2, -3)$.

33. *Ellipse:* x-intercepts ± 4; y-intercepts ± 2.

34. *Hyperbola:* center $(0, 0)$; transverse axis horizontal and 10 x-units long; conjugate axis 6 y-units long.

35. *Hyperbola:* center $(2, 3)$; transverse axis vertical and 6 y-units long; conjugate axis 8 x-units long.

36. *Ellipse:* center $(-2, -3)$; horizontal axis of symmetry 10 x-units long; vertical axis of symmetry 8 y-units long.

By direct use of the locus method, obtain the equation of the conic, if the scale units on the coordinate axes are equal.

37. *Parabola:* focus $(2, 0)$; directrix is line $x = 5$.

38. *Ellipse:* foci $(3, 0)$ and $(11, 0)$; sum of focal radii is 10.

39. *Hyperbola:* foci $(2, -8)$ and $(2, 0)$; absolute value of the difference of the focal radii is 6.

★*SUPPLEMENT FOR CHAPTER TWO*

40. If the scale units on the coordinate axes in an xy-plane are equal, and $h > 0$, find an equation for the hyperbola with foci (h, h) and $(-h, -h)$ if the absolute value of the difference of the focal radii is $2h$. Thus, show that, if $k > 0$, the graph of $xy = k$ is a hyperbola whose asymptotes are the coordinate axes and foci are $(\sqrt{2k}, \sqrt{2k})$ and $(-\sqrt{2k}, -\sqrt{2k})$. Prove that this hyperbola is equilateral, or that $a = b$ in the standard notation of Section 19 on page 53. Similar results may be obtained for $xy = k$ where $k < 0$.

Graph the equation.

41. $|x| + |y| = 4$.   **42.** $|x| - |y| = 5$.   **43.** $[x] = [y]$.

Note 1. Let f and g be functions of two independent variables, (x, y). Then, the graph of the inequality $f(x, y) < g(x, y)$ or of $f(x, y) \leqq g(x, y)$ is defined as the set of all points in the xy-plane satisfying the given numerical statement. Assume that f is a continuous * function. Then, $f(x, y) = 0$ on the curve C which is the graph of the equation (illustrated by the circle as the graph of $f(x, y) = x^2 + y^2 - 4 = 0$ in Figure 54). Let $P_0:(x_0, y_0)$ be any point where $f(x_0, y_0) > 0$. Suppose that $P_1:(x_1, y_1)$ can be joined to P_0 by a continuous curve D, as in Figure 54, not crossing C. If $Q:(x, y)$ moves on D from P_0 to P_1, the function value $f(x, y)$ changes continuously from $f(x_0, y_0)$, which is *positive*, to $f(x_1, y_1)$ at P_1, and $f(x, y)$ *does not assume the value zero because D does not meet C.* Hence, $f(x_1, y_1)$ *also is positive*, because $f(x, y)$

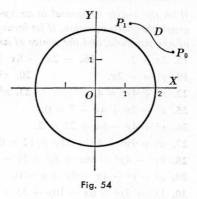

Fig. 54

* Intuitively at present, we take this to mean that $f(x, y)$ changes continuously if $P:(x, y)$ moves continuously in the xy-plane.

could not change continuously from $f(x_0, y_0) > 0$ to a *negative value* without passing through the value zero. Reasoning of this nature will justify the following procedure in all usual problems.

> **Summary.** *To graph $f(x, y) < 0$ and $f(x, y) > 0$ in an xy-plane, first draw the graph, C, of $f(x, y) = 0$. Select a point inside each of the regions into which (we assume) C divides the plane. Then, the value of $f(x, y)$ at the chosen point in any region determines the nature, positive or negative, of $f(x, y)$ at all points in the region.*

The preceding remarks remain valid if $f(x, y) = F(x)$, not involving y, or $f(x, y) = G(y)$,
not involving x. Thus, $x - 2 < 0$ has a *one-dimensional* graph, as on page 9, and also a *two-dimensional* graph in an xy-plane. By the Summary, the graph of

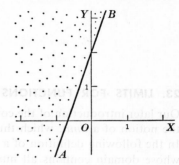

$$f(x, y) = x^2 + y^2 - 4 < 0$$

is the set of points *inside* the circle in Figure 54 on page 66 because $f(0, 0) = -4$. The graph of

$$g(x, y) = y - 3x - 2 > 0$$

is the *half-plane* above line AB in Figure 55, because $g(-2, 0) = 6 - 2 > 0$.

Fig. 55

In an xy-plane, first graph an equation. Then, by substituting the coordinates of a point in each of the regions into which the graph divides the plane, find the graph of the given statement.

44. $x - 2 < 0$. **45.** $(x + 1)(x - 3) > 0$. **46.** $|x + 2| \geq 0$.

47. $x + y - 1 < 0$. **48.** $2x - 3y - 6 > 0$. **49.** $x^2 + y^2 < a^2$.

50. $y^2 - 4x < 0$. **51.** $4x^2 + 9y^2 < 36$.

52. $9x^2 - 25y^2 \leq 225$. **53.** $|x| + |y| \geq 1$.

Prepare a figure showing the solutions of the system of inequalities. (If sets of points A and B, respectively, represent the graphs of the two inequalities, the solution set of the system is the intersection of A and B, or $A \cap B$; see page 674.)

54. $\begin{cases} x - y > 0, \text{ and} \\ 2x + y - 2 < 0. \end{cases}$ **55.** $\begin{cases} y^2 < 4x, \text{ and} \\ x - 2y - 2 < 0. \end{cases}$ **56.** $\begin{cases} x^2 - 8y < 0, \text{ and} \\ x^2 + y^2 - 4 < 0. \end{cases}$

57. Sketch the points in the xy-plane where $\sqrt{x^2 + 4y^2 - 16}$ is real.

58. Prove that, for every number k, the graph of $x^2 + kxy - y^2 = 0$ consists of a pair of perpendicular lines (units equal on the axes).

59. Prove that, if a, b, and k are constants and $(a + b) \neq 0$, with $ab < k^2$, the graph of the equation $ax^2 + 2kxy + by^2 = 0$ consists of two lines, and that they form an angle ϕ for which $\tan \phi = 2\sqrt{k^2 - ab}/|a + b|$ (units equal on the axes).

60. Suppose that the scale units on the coordinate axes in an xy-plane are unequal and that W is a nonzero constant. By use of Problem 40, prove that the graph of $xy = W$ is a hyperbola whose asymptotes are the coordinates axes, and whose transverse axes makes an angle of $45°$ with the x-axis.

CHAPTER THREE

Limits and the Derivative

23. LIMITS FOR FUNCTIONS OF A CONTINUOUS VARIABLE

Our later introduction of the concepts of a derivative and an integral will involve the notion of a *limit*, which thus takes on fundamental importance in calculus. In the following definition of a certain variety of limit, we consider a function f whose domain contains all numbers x on some interval of the number scale, except perhaps the number c on the interval. Any value of x to which we shall refer is on the specified interval, and c may be one of its end points.

Note 1. We shall refer to a variable x as a **continuous variable** if and only if the domain of x consists of one or more intervals of numbers.

Definition I. *To state that "the limit of $f(x)$ is L as x approaches c," or to write*

$$\lim_{x \to c} f(x) = L, \tag{1}$$

means that,* for $x \neq c$, $|f(x) - L|$ will be as small as we please at all values of x such that $|x - c|$ is sufficiently small.

In place of (1), we sometimes write "$f(x) \to L$ as $x \to c$." Statement (1) means that, if $x \neq c$, $f(x)$ is *as near L as we please at all values of x sufficiently near c.* When (1) is true, we may say that *the function f has a limit at $x = c$.*

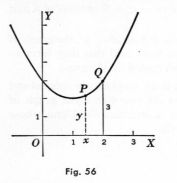

Fig. 56

ILLUSTRATION 1. Consider the function f where

$$f(x) = (x - 2)^2 + 2(x - 2) + 3.$$

If $x \to 2$, then $(x - 2) \to 0$, $(x - 2)^2 \to 0$, and $f(x)$ will be as near 3 as we please if x is sufficiently near 2. Hence, $\lim_{x \to 2} f(x) = 3$. We observe that $f(2) = 3$, so that

$$\lim_{x \to 2} f(x) = f(2). \tag{2}$$

Thus, if $P:(x, y)$ is on the graph of $y = f(x)$, in Figure 56, and if $x \to 2$, the ordinate y of P approaches $f(2)$, which is the ordinate of $Q:(2, 3)$.

* In Definition I, "$\to$" abbreviates "*approaches*"; also, even if $f(c)$ exists, it is not involved.

ILLUSTRATION 2. Suppose that $$f(h) = \frac{7h^2 - 2h + 5}{2 - 3h^3}.\qquad(3)$$

If $h \to 0$, then $7h^2 \to 0$, $2h \to 0$, and $3h^3 \to 0$. Hence, the numerator in (3) will be as near 5, the denominator will be as near 2, and the fraction will be as near $\frac{5}{2}$ as we please for all values of h sufficiently near zero. That is,

$$\lim_{h \to 0} f(h) = \frac{0 - 0 + 5}{2 - 0} = \frac{5}{2}.$$

ILLUSTRATION 3. The fraction $(5h^2 + 6h)/(2h^2 + 3h)$ is not defined when $h = 0$, but $h = 0$ is not involved in a limit as $h \to 0$. Hence,

$$\lim_{h \to 0} \frac{5h^2 + 6h}{2h^2 + 3h} = \lim_{h \to 0} \frac{5h + 6}{2h + 3} = \frac{6}{3} = 2.$$

ILLUSTRATION 4. Let $f(x)$ be the cost in cents of mailing a letter of weight x ounces at 5 cents per ounce or fraction thereof. For instance, $f(1) = 5$; $f(1.01) = 10$; etc. The graph of the function f, in Figure 57, has breaks at $x = 0, 1, 2, \cdots$. In particular, there is no number L such that $f(x)$ is as near L as we please at all values of x sufficiently near 2, with both sides, $x > 2$ and $x < 2$, considered. The open dot at C in Figure 57 indicates that C is not on the graph. When $x = 2$, we obtain D on the graph. Thus, $\lim_{x \to 2} f(x)$ does not exist. However, $f(x) \to 10$ as "x *approaches* 2 *from the left*," abbreviated "$x \to 2-$," and $f(x) \to 15$ as "x *approaches* 2 *from the right*," abbreviated "$x \to 2+$." We then say that, at $x = 2$, the *left-hand limit* of f is 10, and the *right-hand limit* is 15, and write

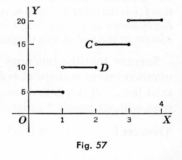

Fig. 57

$$\lim_{x \to 2-} f(x) = 10; \quad \lim_{x \to 2+} f(x) = 15.\qquad(4)$$

In contrast to *one-sided limits*, such as (4), we may refer to $\lim_{x \to c} f(x)$ as the *unrestricted limit as* $x \to c$, to emphasize that values on *both sides*, $x < c$ and $x > c$, are in mind in Definition I.

We call attention to the useful fact that

$$\lim_{x \to c} f(x) = L \quad \text{is equivalent to} \quad \lim_{x \to c} [f(x) - L] = 0.\qquad(5)$$

Also, if $f(x) = x$, we observe that $\lim_{x \to c} f(x) = c$; or, $\lim_{x \to c} x = c$.

ILLUSTRATION 5. If k is a constant and $f(x) = k$ for all values of x, then $f(x) \to k$ when $x \to c$, for any value of c.

To say that "$\lim_{x \to c} f(x) = 0$" means that $|f(x)|$ is as near zero as we please at all values of x sufficiently near c, except perhaps at $x = c$. Hence, by Definition I, it follows that

$$\mathbf{\lim_{x \to c} f(x) = 0} \quad \textit{if and only if} \quad \mathbf{\lim_{x \to c} |f(x)| = 0.}\qquad(6)$$

ILLUSTRATION 6. If $0 \leq |g(x)| \leq f(x)$ and $\lim_{x \to c} f(x) = 0$, then we find that $\lim_{x \to c} g(x) = 0$, because $|f(x)|$, and hence $|g(x)|$ will be as small as we please at all values of x sufficiently near c, except perhaps at $x = c$.

★*Note 2. The (ϵ, δ)-definition of a limit.* Suppose that $\lim_{x \to c} f(x) = L$, and consider the graph of $y = f(x)$ in Figure 58. Assign any number $\epsilon > 0$. Then, Definition I states that, if $x \neq c$, the graph of $y = f(x)$ is between the lines $y = L - \epsilon$ and $y = L + \epsilon$ at all values of x sufficiently near $x = c$, say between $x = c - \delta$ and $x = c + \delta$, where δ is sufficiently small. We leave a hole at $Q:(c, L)$ in Figure 58 because the definition of "$\lim_{x \to c} f(x) = L$" includes no stipulation about $f(x)$ when $x = c$. The preceding remarks are true for any $\epsilon > 0$, but are of greatest interest if ϵ is thought of as arbitrarily small. In terms of ϵ and δ, Definition I can be restated as follows:

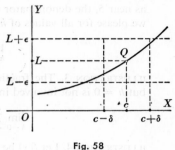

Fig. 58

The limit of $f(x)$ as x approaches c is L if and only if, for every $\epsilon > 0$, there exists a corresponding $\delta > 0$, such that

$$\text{when} \quad 0 < |x - c| < \delta \quad \text{then} \quad |f(x) - L| < \epsilon. \tag{7}$$

In (7), ϵ is the arbitrarily small measure of closeness of $f(x)$ to L, as mentioned in Definition I; δ is the corresponding measure of closeness of x to c which insures $|f(x) - L| < \epsilon$. Applications of (7) are found in Note 5 of the Appendix, and in the supplementary content at the end of this chapter.

Suppose that the functions f and g are defined on some common interval of numbers except perhaps at point c on the interval. It is assumed below that there exist $\lim_{x \to c} f(x) = L$ and $\lim_{x \to c} g(x) = M$. We shall accept the following theorems without proofs * as intuitively plausible at this stage.

Theorem I. $\qquad \lim_{x \to c} [f(x) + g(x)] = \lim_{x \to c} f(x) + \lim_{x \to c} g(x) = L + M.$

Theorem II. *If k is any constant,*

$$\lim_{x \to c} kf(x) = k \left(\lim_{x \to c} f(x) \right) = kL.$$

Theorem III. $\qquad \lim_{x \to c} f(x) \, g(x) = \left(\lim_{x \to c} f(x) \right)\left(\lim_{x \to c} g(x) \right) = LM.$

Theorem IV. *If $\lim_{x \to c} g(x) \neq 0$, then*

$$\lim_{x \to c} \frac{f(x)}{g(x)} = \frac{\lim_{x \to c} f(x)}{\lim_{x \to c} g(x)} = \frac{L}{M}.$$

Note 3. For quick recollection, we summarize Theorems I–IV verbally as follows: (I) *the limit of a sum of two (or more) functions is the sum of their limits;* (II) *the limit of a constant times a function is equal to the constant times the limit of the function;* (III) *the limit of a product of two (or more) functions is the product of their limits;* (IV) *the limit of a quotient of two functions is the quotient of their limits, provided that the limit of the divisor is* **not zero.**

We observe that Theorem II is the special case of Theorem III where one function is a constant function.

By use of Theorem I, and then Theorem II with $k = -1$, we prove that

* For proofs, on the basis of Note 2 above, see Note 5 in the Appendix.

the limit of a difference is equal to the difference of the limits:

$$\lim_{x \to c} [f(x) - g(x)] = \lim_{x \to c} f(x) + \lim_{x \to c} [-g(x)] = \lim_{x \to c} f(x) - \lim_{x \to c} g(x) = L - M.$$

ILLUSTRATION 7. From Theorems II and III, since $\lim_{x \to c} x = c$,

$$\lim_{x \to c} 5x^3 = 5 \left[\lim_{x \to c} (x \cdot x \cdot x) \right] = 5c \cdot c \cdot c = 5c^3.$$

Similarly, if k is a constant, and m is a positive integer,

$$\lim_{x \to c} kx^m = kc^m. \tag{8}$$

ILLUSTRATION 8. By use of Theorem IV, and then Theorems I and II,

$$\lim_{x \to 3} \frac{2x^2 + x - 5}{3x - 7} = \frac{\lim_{x \to 3} (2x^2 + x - 5)}{\lim_{x \to 3} (3x - 7)} = \frac{18 + 3 - 5}{9 - 7} = \frac{16}{2} = 8.$$

If n is a positive integer and $\lim_{x \to c} f(x) = L$, we accept the fact that

$$\lim_{x \to c} \sqrt[n]{f(x)} = \sqrt[n]{L}. \tag{9}$$

ILLUSTRATION 9. $\qquad \lim_{x \to 4} \sqrt[3]{3 + 6x} = \sqrt[3]{3 + \lim_{x \to 4} 6x} = \sqrt[3]{27} = 3.$

Theorem V. *Suppose that* $f(x) = N(x)/D(x)$, *where* $D(x) \neq 0$ *near* c, *except possibly when* $x = c$. *Then, if* f *has a limit at* $x = c$ *and if* $D(x) \to 0$ *as* $x \to c$, *it is also true that* $N(x) \to 0$ *as* $x \to c$.

Proof. Let $\lim_{x \to c} f(x) = L$. If $x \neq c$, then $N(x) = f(x)D(x)$ and

$$\lim_{x \to c} N(x) = \left[\lim_{x \to c} f(x) \right] \left[\lim_{x \to c} D(x) \right] = L \cdot 0 = 0.$$

A fraction of the type met in Theorem V tends to the meaningless form, or so-called *indeterminate form*, 0/0 as $x \to c$. This form is important in the development of calculus. To evaluate the limit of a particular fraction $N(x)/D(x)$ of this nature, first try to alter it in order to avoid the form 0/0.

EXAMPLE 1. Investigate $\qquad\qquad \lim_{x \to 2} \dfrac{2x^2 + x - 10}{3x - 6}. \tag{10}$

Solution. Let $f(x)$ represent the fraction in (10). As $x \to 2$, $f(x)$ tends to the form 0/0. In fact, at $x = 2$, both numerator and denominator are zero, and the fraction in (10) is meaningless. However, by the factor theorem * of algebra, both numerator and denominator have the factor $(x - 2)$, which we divide out:

$$\lim_{x \to 2} f(x) = \lim_{x \to 2} \frac{(x - 2)(2x + 5)}{3(x - 2)} = \lim_{x \to 2} \frac{2x + 5}{3} = 3.$$

Theorem VI. *If there exists* $\lim_{x \to c} f(x)$, *then this limit is unique. Or,*

$$\text{if } \lim_{x \to c} f(x) = L_1 \text{ and } \lim_{x \to c} f(x) = L_2, \text{ then } L_1 = L_2. \tag{11}$$

* If a polynomial $f(x)$ is zero when $x = c$, then $(x - c)$ is a factor of $f(x)$.

Proof. 1. From (7) on page 6,

$$0 \leq |L_1 - L_2| = |[L_1 - f(x)] + [f(x) - L_2]|, \; or$$
$$0 \leq |L_1 - L_2| \leq |L_1 - f(x)| + |L_2 - f(x)|. \tag{12}$$

2. From (5) on page 69, each absolute value on the right in (12) has the limit zero as $x \to c$. Then, by Theorem I, the right-hand side in (12) has the limit zero. Hence, by Illustration 6 on page 69, the *constant* $|L_1 - L_2|$ has the limit *zero* as $x \to c$, and therefore $|L_1 - L_2| = 0$, or $L_1 = L_2$.

EXERCISE 20

Evaluate the limit by use of theorems on limits.

1. $\lim\limits_{x \to 3} [(x - 3)^2 + 4]$.   **2.** $\lim\limits_{h \to -2} (2h^2 - 3h)$.   **3.** $\lim\limits_{x \to 3} \sqrt[2]{2x + 2}$.

4. $\lim\limits_{x \to 4} \dfrac{x^2 - 6x + 9}{x^2 + 3x}$.   **5.** $\lim\limits_{x \to 2} \dfrac{2x^2 - x - 6}{4x + 8}$.

6. $\lim\limits_{x \to 3} \dfrac{2x^2 - 7x + 3}{2x - 6}$.   **7.** $\lim\limits_{x \to -2} \dfrac{3x^2 + x - 10}{x^2 - 4}$.

8. $\lim\limits_{x \to -3} \dfrac{x^3 + 27}{2x + 6}$.   **9.** $\lim\limits_{h \to 0} \dfrac{3h^3 + 2h^2 + 5h}{3h^2 + 2h}$.

10. Graph the function f which is defined on $0 \leq x \leq 4$ by

$$f(x) = 2x \; when \; 0 \leq x \leq 2, \quad and \quad f(x) = 9 - 2x \; when \; 2 < x \leq 4.$$

What can be said about $\lim_{x \to 2} f(x)$; $\lim_{x \to 2-} f(x)$; $\lim_{x \to 2+} f(x)$?

Evaluate the limit.

11. $\lim\limits_{x \to 4} \dfrac{3\sqrt{x} - 6}{x - 4}$.   **12.** $\lim\limits_{x \to 3} \dfrac{\sqrt{3 + 2x} - 3}{x - 3}$.

Hint for Problem 11. Avoid 0/0 by multiplying both numerator and denominator by $(3\sqrt{x} + 6)$, and simplifying.

★**13.** Let $f(x) = \sin (1/x)$. Is $f(x)$ defined at $x = 0$? If x is on the interval $.01 \leq x \leq .1$, between what values does $f(x)$ vary? Draw curves showing, roughly, the nature of the graph of f for positive values, and for negative values of x near $x = 0$. What can be said about

$$\lim_{x \to 0} f(x); \quad \lim_{x \to 0-} f(x); \quad \lim_{x \to 0+} f(x)?$$

24. CONTINUITY

Consider a function f, with values $f(x)$, where the domain of f contains all numbers x on some interval except possibly the number c on this interval.

Definition II. *To state that a function f is* **continuous** *at a point $x = c$ means that (i) c is in the domain of f, or $f(c)$ is defined, (ii) f has a limit at $x = c$, and (iii)*

$$\lim_{x \to c} f(x) = f(c). \tag{1}$$

Definition III. *To state that a function f is* **discontinuous** *at a point $x = c$ means that f is not continuous at $x = c$.*

Let the graph of $y = f(x)$ be the curve in Figure 59. Then, (1) states that the ordinate $f(x)$ at a variable point $P{:}(x, y)$ on the graph approaches the ordinate $f(c)$ at the fixed point $Q{:}(c, f(c))$ on the curve as $x \to c$.

If a function f is continuous at all values of x on some interval of the domain of f, we say that f is *continuous on the interval*. If we state simply that f is *continuous*, we shall mean that f is continuous at *all* points x in the domain of f.

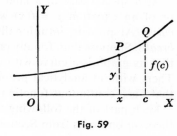

ILLUSTRATION 1. If $f(x) = 3x^2 + x - 4$, then $f(2) = 10$, and

$$\lim_{x \to 2} f(x) = 3 \lim_{x \to 2} x^2 + \lim_{x \to 2} x - \lim_{x \to 2} 4$$
$$= 12 + 2 - 4 = 10.$$

Fig. 59

Or, $\lim_{x \to 2} f(x) = f(2)$. Thus, by (1), f is continuous at $x = 2$.

ILLUSTRATION 2. Let
$$f(x) = \frac{x^2 - x - 6}{x - 3}. \tag{2}$$

Then $f(x)$ is undefined when $x = 3$; hence f is discontinuous at $x = 3$. However,

$$\lim_{x \to 3} f(x) = \lim_{x \to 3} \frac{(x - 3)(x + 2)}{x - 3} = \lim_{x \to 3} (x + 2) = 5. \tag{3}$$

The graph of $y = f(x)$, in Figure 60, is line AB with a hole at P, because $f(x)$ is not defined at $x = 3$. The line AB, with the hole filled, is the graph of the continuous function g where $g(x) = x + 2$, and $g(x) = f(x)$ when $x \neq 3$. The hole in the graph of f would be filled and f would become g if we should define $f(x)$ by (2) when $x \neq 3$ and, separately, define $f(3) = 5$. Hence, we say that f has a **removable discontinuity** at $x = 3$.

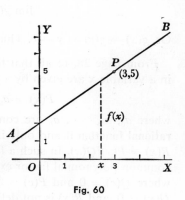

ILLUSTRATION 3. In Illustration 4, page 69, the function f is discontinuous at all positive integral values of x. There is a jump of five units in the graph of f at each discontinuity, as shown in Figure 57, page 69.

Fig. 60

It is convenient to use (1) with changes in notation. Thus, if we replace x by $(c + h)$, then $x \to c$ is equivalent to $h \to 0$, and (1) becomes

$$\lim_{h \to 0} f(c + h) = f(c). \tag{4}$$

Or, if we take $c = x$, then (4) becomes

$$\lim_{h \to 0} f(x + h) = f(x), \quad or \quad \lim_{h \to 0} [f(x + h) - f(x)] = 0. \tag{5}$$

Now, let $y = f(x)$, and let $h = \Delta x$, to be read "*delta x*," meaning an *increment* in the value of x. Then, let

$$y + \Delta y = f(x + \Delta x), \quad so \ that \quad \Delta y = f(x + \Delta x) - f(x). \tag{6}$$

With this notation, from (5), f is continuous at the point x if and only if

$$\lim_{\Delta x \to 0} f(x + \Delta x) = f(x), \quad \text{or} \quad \lim_{\Delta x \to 0} \Delta y = 0. \tag{7}$$

As a special case of a later definition, the graph of a continuous function f, or of an equation $y = f(x)$ where f is continuous, is said to be a *continuous curve*. At present, intuitively, we take this to mean that *the graph has no breaks*. Suppose that, for any particular function f, we are convinced geometrically that its graph is a curve without breaks if x lies on a certain interval of values. Then, without analytical proof based on Definition II, we permit the inference that f is a continuous function at these values of x.

Each part of the following theorem can be proved by use of a corresponding theorem on limits from Section 23.

Theorem VII. *A sum, a difference, or a product of continuous functions is continuous, and a quotient of two continuous functions is continuous wherever the divisor is not zero.*

Proof (for a quotient). Let the functions f and h be continuous at $x = c$, where $h(c) \neq 0$. Then, by Definition II, $f(x) \to f(c)$ and $h(x) \to h(c)$ when $x \to c$. Let $g(x) = f(x)/h(x)$. Hence, by Theorem IV on page 70,

$$\lim_{x \to c} g(x) = \frac{\lim_{x \to c} f(x)}{\lim_{x \to c} h(x)} = \frac{f(c)}{h(c)}.$$

Or, $g(x) \to g(c)$ as $x \to c$. Thus, g is continuous at $x = c$.

From page 28, recall that the values of a polynomial function P of degree n in a variable x are given by a polynomial of the form

$$P(x) = a_0 + a_1 x + a_2 x^2 + \cdots + a_n x^n, \tag{8}$$

where $a_0, a_1, \cdots, a_n$ are constants and $a_n \neq 0$. A function R is said to be a **rational function** if and only if there exist polynomials $P(x)$ and $Q(x)$ such that $R(x) = P(x)/Q(x)$. In such a form, we shall assume that $P(x)$ and $Q(x)$ have no common polynomial factor except for constants, so that there is no value $x = c$ where $Q(c) = 0$ and $P(c) = 0$. Then, $R(x)$ is defined at all values of x where $Q(x) \neq 0$, and $R(x)$ is not defined where $Q(x) = 0$.

ILLUSTRATION 4. If $f(x) = (3x^2 + 5)/(x - 2)$, the rational function f is not defined when $x = 2$; or, 2 is not a point in the domain of f because the denominator is zero at $x = 2$.

Theorem VIII. *If k is a constant, m is a positive integer, x is a variable, and*

$$f(x) = kx^m,$$

then the monomial function f is continuous at all values of x.

Proof. At any point $x = c$, from (8) on page 71,

$$\lim_{x \to c} f(x) = kc^m = f(c).$$

Hence, f is continuous at $x = c$, for all values of c.

Theorem IX. *If $P(x)$ is a polynomial, then P is continuous at all values of x.*

Proof. By Theorem VIII, each monomial of $P(x)$ in (8) defines a continuous function. Hence, by Theorem VII on page 74, the sum on the right in (8) represents the values of a continuous function.

Theorem X. *A rational function f where $f(x) = P(x)/Q(x)$, and P and Q are polynomial functions, is continuous at all values of x where $Q(x) \neq 0$.*

Proof. By Theorem IX, P and Q are continuous functions. Hence, by Theorem VII on page 74, the function f is continuous at all values of x where $Q(x) \neq 0$.

Note 1. To say that a function R is a rational function of two independent variables means that $R(x, y) = P(x, y)/Q(x, y)$ where $P(x, y)$ and $Q(x, y)$ are polynomials in x and y. Rational functions of any number of variables are defined similarly.

If a function f is continuous at $x = c$, then $f(x) \to f(c)$ as $x \to c$. This permits the following method for evaluating certain limits.

$$\left. \begin{array}{c} \textit{If a function } f \textit{ is continuous at a point } c \textit{ in the domain} \\ \textit{of } f, \textit{ we may substitute } x = c \textit{ in } f(x) \textit{ to find } \lim_{x \to c} f(x): \\ \lim_{x \to c} f(x) = f(c). \end{array} \right\} \qquad (9)$$

ILLUSTRATION 5. If $f(x) = (2x^2 - 5x)/(x^3 - 2)$, then f is continuous at $x = 3$, where $x^3 - 2 \neq 0$. Hence, we substitute $x = 3$ in the fraction to obtain

$$\lim_{x \to 3} \frac{2x^2 - 5x}{x^3 - 2} = \frac{2(3^2) - 5(3)}{3^3 - 2} = \frac{3}{25}.$$

Whenever common knowledge of the graph of a function f convinces us that f is continuous, we shall permit use of (9) without demanding analytic proof of the continuity of f.

EXERCISE 21

Evaluate the limit, by use of continuity in the final stage.

1. $\lim\limits_{x \to 3} \dfrac{x^2 + 5}{3x + x^3}$.

2. $\lim\limits_{x \to \frac{1}{4}\pi} \dfrac{\cos x + \sin x}{3 + \csc^2 x}$.

3. $\lim\limits_{x \to \frac{1}{4}\pi} \dfrac{\tan^2 x - \sin x}{\cos x}$.

4. $\lim\limits_{x \to 2} \dfrac{3x + 5}{2x + 7}$.

5. $\lim\limits_{x \to -4} \dfrac{x^2 + 2x - 8}{2x + 8}$.

6. $\lim\limits_{h \to 0} \dfrac{\sqrt{3 + h} - \sqrt{3}}{h}$.

7. In Problem 5, let $f(x)$ represent the fraction. Graph the function f, showing a hole in the graph. Where is f discontinuous?

8. If $f(x) = 3$ when $x \leq 2$ and $f(x) = x + 2$ when $x > 2$, graph the function f thus defined for all real values of x. Where is f discontinuous? What can be said about $\lim_{x \to 2+} f(x)$; $\lim_{x \to 2-} f(x)$; $\lim_{x \to 2} f(x)$?

9. Let $f(x)$ be defined as the greatest integer less than or equal to x. Graph $y = f(x)$. Investigate the limits of the function f as $x \to 2-$, $x \to 2+$, and $x \to 2$. Where is f discontinuous? Why?

10. Let $f(x) = x/|x|$, and graph the function f. Where is f discontinuous? Why?

25. AVERAGE AND INSTANTANEOUS RATES OF CHANGE

The notion of the *derivative* of a function formalized the idea of "*the rate of change of the value of a function*," which was familiar earlier in physics and geometry. We shall study a few rates of change before a derivative is defined.

Note 1. For any function, f, unless otherwise stated, we assume that the domain consists of an interval, or intervals, of numbers. In any reference to $f(x)$, the number x is inferred to be in the domain of f.

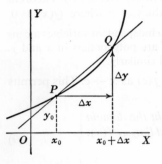

Fig. 61

Consider a function f, and let $y = f(x)$. If x_0 and $(x_0 + \Delta x)$ are neighboring values of x, we shall refer to the number Δx, read "*delta x*," as an *increment* added to the value $x = x_0$. Let

$$y_0 = f(x_0) \quad and \quad y_0 + \Delta y = f(x_0 + \Delta x). \quad (1)$$

Then, we shall call Δy the increment in the value of y, or $f(x)$, corresponding to the increment Δx added to $x = x_0$. From (1),

$$\Delta y = f(x_0 + \Delta x) - f(x_0) = \Delta f(x_0). \quad (2)$$

In Figure 61, $P{:}(x_0, y_0)$ and $Q{:}(x_0 + \Delta x, y_0 + \Delta y)$ are shown on the graph of $y = f(x)$.

ILLUSTRATION 1. Let $f(x) = x^2$, and use $y = x^2$. If the value $x_0 = 3$ is given the increment $\Delta x = .2$, then $x_0 + \Delta x = 3.2$ and, from (2),

$$\Delta y = f(3.2) - f(3) = 3.2^2 - 3^2 = 1.24.$$

Definition IV. *If $y = f(x)$, the* **average rate of change** *of y with respect to x, or the average rate of change of $f(x)$, from $x = x_0$ to $x = x_0 + \Delta x$ is the ratio of the change in $f(x)$ to the change in x:*

$$\left\{ \begin{array}{c} \textbf{average rate of change} \\ \textit{of } y \textit{ from } x_0 \textit{ to } (x_0 + \Delta x) \end{array} \right\} = \frac{\Delta y}{\Delta x} = \frac{f(x_0 + \Delta x) - f(x_0)}{\Delta x}. \quad (3)$$

ILLUSTRATION 2. With $y = f(x) = x^2$ in Illustration 1,

$$\left\{ \begin{array}{c} \textit{average rate of change} \\ \textit{of } y \textit{ from } x = 3 \textit{ to } x = 3.2 \end{array} \right\} = \frac{f(3.2) - f(3)}{.2} = \frac{1.24}{.2} = 6.2.$$

In Figure 61, $\Delta y/\Delta x$ is the slope of the secant through

$$P{:}(x_0, y_0) \quad and \quad Q{:}(x_0 + \Delta x, y_0 + \Delta y)$$

on the graph of $y = f(x)$. If this graph were a line, then $\Delta y/\Delta x$ in (3) would be a *constant* for all x_0 and Δx. The important situation occurs when the average rate in (3) is *not a constant*. This possibility leads to the following terminology.

Definition V. *If $y = f(x)$, the* **instantaneous rate** *of change of $f(x)$, or of y with respect to x, at $x = x_0$ is the limit of the average rate of change of $f(x)$ from x_0 to $(x_0 + \Delta x)$ as $\Delta x \to 0$, provided that the limit exists:*

$$\left\{ \begin{array}{c} \textbf{instantaneous rate of} \\ \textbf{change } \textit{of } y \textit{ at } x = x_0 \end{array} \right\} = \lim_{\Delta x \to 0} \frac{\Delta y}{\Delta x} = \lim_{\Delta x \to 0} \frac{f(x_0 + \Delta x) - f(x_0)}{\Delta x}. \quad (4)$$

EXAMPLE 1. At $x = 3$, find the instantaneous rate of change of y with respect to x if $y = x^2 - 4x + 7$.

Solution. 1. Let $f(x) = x^2 - 4x + 7$. Then, from $x = 3$ to $x = 3 + \Delta x$, by using $x_0 = 3$ in (3) we obtain

$$\left\{ \begin{array}{l} average\ rate\ of \\ \quad change\ of\ y \end{array} \right\} = \frac{\Delta y}{\Delta x} = \frac{f(3 + \Delta x) - f(3)}{\Delta x}. \tag{5}$$

Since $f(3) = 4$ and $f(3 + \Delta x) = (3 + \Delta x)^2 - 4(3 + \Delta x) + 7$,

$$\left\{ \begin{array}{l} average\ rate\ of \\ \quad change\ of\ y \end{array} \right\} = \frac{\Delta y}{\Delta x} = \frac{(\Delta x)^2 + 2\Delta x}{\Delta x} = \Delta x + 2. \tag{6}$$

2. By use of (6), we compute the following table of values.

$\Delta x =$	$-.5$	$-.1$	$-.01$	(As $\Delta x \to 0$)	$.01$	$.1$	$.5$
$\left\{ \begin{array}{l} \text{AVER. RATE} \\ \text{OF CHANGE} \end{array} \right\} = \dfrac{\Delta y}{\Delta x} =$	1.5	1.9	1.99	LIMIT *is* 2	2.01	2.1	2.5

3. The table checks the following result, from (4) and (6):

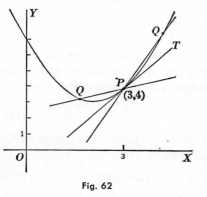

Fig. 62

$$\left\{ \begin{array}{l} instantaneous\ rate\ of \\ \quad change\ of\ y\ at\ x = 3 \end{array} \right\} = \lim_{\Delta x \to 0} \frac{\Delta y}{\Delta x}$$

$$= \lim_{\Delta x \to 0} (2 + \Delta x) = 2. \tag{7}$$

Comment. On the graph of $y = f(x)$ in Figure 62, or in Figure 61 on page 76,

$$m = (slope\ of\ secant\ PQ) = \frac{\Delta y}{\Delta x}. \tag{8}$$

From (7) and (8), $m \to 2$ as $\Delta x \to 0$, or as $Q \to P$ on the graph (that is, as distance $\overline{PQ} \to 0$). Then, if PT is the line through $P:(3, 4)$ with slope 2, we define PT as the *tangent* to the graph of $y = f(x)$ at $x = 3$. Hence, the equation of PT is $y - 4 = 2(x - 3)$.

As an application of average and instantaneous rates of change in physics, consider the motion of an object on a straight line, labeled as an *s*-axis in Figure 63, where the object is idealized as a point P. Motion of this nature is referred to as **rectilinear motion.** The object will be called a *particle.* Let s be the measure, in a given unit, of the directed distance of the particle from the origin of the *s*-axis. Let any instant be designated as t units of time from some fixed instant where $t = 0$, with $t > 0$ after $t = 0$ and $t < 0$ before $t = 0$. We assume that

Fig. 63

s is specified as a function of the time, that is, $s = f(t)$. Let Δt be a variable increment, not zero, with $s = s_0$ and $s = s_0 + \Delta s$ corresponding, respectively, to $t = t_0$ and

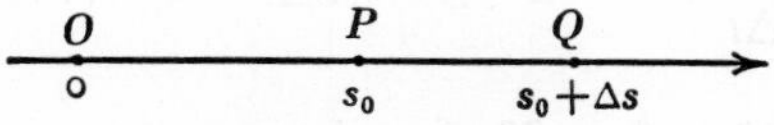

$t = t_0 + \Delta t$. Then, the **average velocity** of the particle from time t_0 to time $(t_0 + \Delta t)$ is defined as the *average rate of change of s with respect to t*, or

$$\text{(average velocity)} = \frac{\Delta s}{\Delta t} = \frac{f(t_0 + \Delta t) - f(t_0)}{\Delta t}. \tag{9}$$

In different notation than (9), if $s = s_1$ at $t = t_1$ and $s = s_2$ at $t = t_2$,

then $\Delta s = s_2 - s_1, \quad \Delta t = t_2 - t_1,$

and $(average\ velocity) = (s_2 - s_1)/(t_2 - t_1). \tag{10}$

If the average velocity is a constant for all time intervals, this means that equal distances, in the same direction, are passed over by the particle in equal intervals of time. Then, it is said that the object is moving with *uniform velocity*, and the motion is referred to as *uniform motion*. The *velocity* in this case is defined as the constant *average velocity*.

ILLUSTRATION 3. If the uniform velocity is 3′ per second, (9) gives $\Delta s = 3\Delta t$.

When the average velocity in (9) is *not a constant*, we define the **instantaneous velocity**, or simply the **velocity**, v, of the particle at t_0 as the *instantaneous rate of change of s with respect to t at $t = t_0$*, if the limit below exists.

$$v = \lim_{\Delta t \to 0} \frac{\Delta s}{\Delta t} = \lim_{\Delta t \to 0} \frac{f(t_0 + \Delta t) - f(t_0)}{\Delta t}, \tag{11}$$

EXAMPLE 2. Suppose that a projectile is shot vertically upward from the earth, with an initial velocity of v_0 feet per second. Then, if air resistance and other complications are neglected, the projectile's height s in feet above the ground t seconds later is given by

$$s = -\tfrac{1}{2}gt^2 + v_0 t, \tag{12}$$

where $g = 32$, approximately. If $v_0 = 96$, (a) find the projectile's average velocity from $t = 3$ to $t = 5$; (b) find the instantaneous velocity at $t = 2$.

Solution. 1. From (12) with $v_0 = 96$, $s = -16t^2 + 96t. \tag{13}$

2. From (13) at $t = 3$, $s = 144$; at $t = 5$, $s = 80$. Hence, from (10), over the time interval from $t = 3$ to $t = 5$,

$$(average\ velocity) = \frac{80 - 144}{5 - 3} = -32,\ ft.\ per\ sec.,$$

where the negative feature indicates that the projectile is falling.

3. Now use (9) with $f(t) = -16t^2 + 96t$ and $t_0 = 2$:

$$\Delta s = f(2 + \Delta t) - f(2) = -16(2 + \Delta t)^2 + 96(2 + \Delta t) - 128,\ or$$

$$\Delta s = 32\Delta t - 16(\Delta t)^2;$$

$$\left\{\begin{array}{l} average\ velocity\ from \\ t = 2\ to\ t = 2 + \Delta t \end{array}\right\} = \frac{\Delta s}{\Delta t} = \frac{32\Delta t - 16(\Delta t)^2}{\Delta t} = 32 - 16\Delta t. \tag{14}$$

$$v = \lim_{\Delta t \to 0} \frac{\Delta s}{\Delta t} = \lim_{\Delta t \to 0} (32 - 16\Delta t) = 32 - 0 = 32,\ ft.\ per\ sec.$$

EXERCISE 22

In Problems 1 and 2, use the fact that, if $y = f(x)$, the instantaneous rate of change of $f(x)$ at $x = x_0$ is the slope of the tangent line at the point on the graph of f where $x = x_0$.

1. If $y = x^2 - 6x + 4$, (a) find the average rates of change of y with respect to x from $x = 4$ to $x = 4 + \Delta x$ if $\Delta x = .5$, $\pm .1$, and $\pm .01$. (b) Obtain the instantaneous rate of change of y at $x = 4$. (c) Graph the given equation. (d) Write an equation for the tangent to the graph where $x = 4$, and draw this tangent.

2. Repeat Problem 1 if $y = 6 - x^2 - 4x$, for results at $x = -5$.

Find the instantaneous rate of change of y with respect to x.

3. $y = x^3$, at $x = 2$.   4. $y = 3x - 2x^2$, at $x = 3$.

   Hint. By the binomial expansion for $(a + b)^n$, page 673,

$$(2 + \Delta x)^3 = 2^3 + 3(2^2)\Delta x + 3(2)(\Delta x)^2 + (\Delta x)^3.$$

Note 1. Unless otherwise stated, in motion problems in this text, the units will be 1 foot for distance and 1 second for time.

5. For the projectile involved in (12) on page 78, let $v_0 = 128$. (a) Compute the average velocity by use of (10) on page 78, from $t = 0$ to $t = 2$; from $t = 1$ to $t = 2$; from $t = 2$ to $t = 4$. (b) By use of (9) on page 78, compute the average velocities over the intervals from $t = 2$ to $t = 2 + \Delta t$, if Δt has the values $\pm .2$, $\pm .1$, and $\pm .01$. (c) Find the instantaneous velocity at $t = 2$.

6. For an object moving in a vertical line, the height s above sea level at any time t is given by $s = -16t^2 + 96t + 48$. (a) Find the instantaneous velocity at $t = 4$. (c) Find the average velocity from $t = 4$ to $t = 4 + \Delta t$, if $\Delta t = 1$; $\Delta t = .1$; $\Delta t = .01$.

The equation specifies the position at any time t for an object on an s-axis. Find the instantaneous velocity at each value of t.

7. $s = 3t^2 + 5t - 6$; at $t = 3$; at $t = 2$.

8. $s = t^3 - 3t - 4$; at $t = 2$.   9. $s = 2t + t^3 - 7$; at $t = 2$.

26. DERIVATIVE OF A FUNCTION

Definition VI. *At any point c in the domain of a function f, if the average rate of change of $f(x)$ from $x = c$ to $x = (c + \Delta x)$ has a limit as $\Delta x \to 0$, this limit is called the* **derivative** *of the function f at $x = c$:*

$$\left\{ \begin{array}{l} \text{the derivative} \\ \text{of } f \text{ at } x = c \end{array} \right\} = \lim_{\Delta x \to 0} \frac{f(c + \Delta x) - f(c)}{\Delta x}. \tag{1}$$

In view of (4) on page 76, the *derivative* of f at $x = c$ in (1) has been defined as *the instantaneous rate of change of $f(x)$ at $x = c$.*

If f has a derivative at $x = c$, then f is said to be **differentiable** at $x = c$. To state merely that a function f is *differentiable* will mean that f has a derivative *at each point* in the domain of f. By Definition VI, at each point $x = c$ where the stipulated limit exists, there is specified a corresponding *number*, the limit in (1). The correspondence between values of x and values of the derivative defines a *new function*, called the **derivative of f.** This derivative function frequently is denoted by f', read "*f prime.*" The process of finding $f'(x)$ is spoken of either as

$$s = -\tfrac{1}{2}g t^2 + v_0 t$$

differentiating $f(x)$, or as *differentiating f*. If we let $y = f(x)$, then $f'(x)$ also is represented by $D_x y$, or by y', either of which may be read "*the derivative of y with respect to x*." Or, we may read y' simply as "*y prime*." The value of the derivative function at an assigned point $x = c$ is represented by $f'(c)$, or by $D_x y\,|_{x=c}$, which is read "*the derivative of y with respect to x at x = c*." From (1), at any point x where $f'(x)$ exists, with $y = f(x)$ and $y + \Delta y = f(x + \Delta x)$,

$$f'(x) = \lim_{\Delta x \to 0} \frac{f(x + \Delta x) - f(x)}{\Delta x}, \quad or \quad D_x y = \lim_{\Delta x \to 0} \frac{\Delta y}{\Delta x}. \tag{2}$$

In (2), we have replaced c of (1) by x, with the understanding that, in (2), x is considered as a *fixed number* with Δx as the variable corresponding to which the limits are specified, with $\Delta x \neq 0$. Sometimes we shall use the equation at the left in (2) with $\Delta x = h$, where $h \neq 0$:

$$f'(x) = \lim_{h \to 0} \frac{f(x + h) - f(x)}{h}. \tag{3}$$

EXAMPLE 1. Differentiate f if $f(x) = x^2 - 4x + 7$. Also find $f'(3)$.

Solution. 1. We shall use (3). With x as a fixed number,

$$f(x + h) = (x + h)^2 - 4(x + h) + 7, \; or \tag{4}$$

$$f(x + h) = x^2 - 4x + 7 + (2hx - 4h + h^2), \; and \tag{5}$$

$$f(x) = x^2 - 4x + 7. \tag{6}$$

From (3), (5), and (6),

$$f'(x) = \lim_{h \to 0} \frac{2hx - 4h + h^2}{h};$$

$$f'(x) = \lim_{h \to 0} (2x - 4 + h), \quad or \quad f'(x) = 2x - 4. \tag{7}$$

2. From (7), $f'(3) = 2$. Also, if we let $y = f(x)$, then

$$D_x y = 2x - 4 \quad and \quad D_x y\,|_{x=3} = 2.$$

Note 1. In using the equation at the right in (2), we recall that

$$y + \Delta y = f(x + \Delta x), \quad and \quad \Delta y = f(x + \Delta x) - f(x). \tag{8}$$

EXAMPLE 2. If $y = x^2$, find $D_x y$ and $D_x y\,|_{x=-1}$.

Solution. From (8), with $f(x) = x^2$, or

$$y = x^2, \quad we \; have \quad y + \Delta y = (x + \Delta x)^2 = x^2 + 2x\Delta x + (\Delta x)^2;$$

$$\Delta y = x^2 + 2x\Delta x + (\Delta x)^2 - x^2, \; or$$

$$\Delta y = 2x\Delta x + (\Delta x)^2.$$

Hence, from (2),

$$D_x y = \lim_{\Delta x \to 0} \frac{2x\Delta x + (\Delta x)^2}{\Delta x} = \lim_{\Delta x \to 0} (2x + \Delta x), \; or$$

$$D_x y = 2x; \quad D_x y\,|_{x=-1} = -2.$$

EXAMPLE 3. Differentiate f if
$$f(x) = \frac{3x}{2x + 5}. \tag{9}$$

Solution. In the notation of (3), with $x \neq -\frac{5}{2}$,

$$f(x + h) - f(x) = \frac{3(x + h)}{2(x + h) + 5} - \frac{3x}{2x + 5}$$

$$= \frac{(3x + 3h)(2x + 5) - 3x(2x + 5 + 2h)}{(2x + 5)(2x + 5 + 2h)} = \frac{15h + 6hx - 6hx}{(2x + 5)(2x + 5 + 2h)}.$$

Hence, from (3),
$$f'(x) = \lim_{h \to 0} \frac{15h}{h(2x + 5)(2x + 5 + 2h)};$$

$$f'(x) = \lim_{h \to 0} \frac{15}{(2x + 5)(2x + 5 + 2h)} \quad or \quad f'(x) = \frac{15}{(2x + 5)^2}.$$

If $f'(x)$ is obtained by direct use of Definition VI, as summarized in (2) or (3), we shall state that the **increment process** is being employed. Later, by means of it, we shall derive formulas which will make it unnecessary to use the process for large classes of functions.

EXAMPLE 4. Find the instantaneous rate of change of the area of a variable circle with respect to (*a*) its radius; (*b*) its diameter.

Solution. Let the measures of the radius, diameter, and area in appropriate units be r, x, and A, respectively.

(*a*) We have $A = \pi r^2$. The desired rate of change is the derivative of A with respect to r, or $D_r A$. By the increment process, we obtain $D_r A = 2\pi r$.

(*b*) We have $A = \frac{1}{4}\pi x^2$ and we desire $D_x A$; by the increment process, the student may verify that $D_x A = \frac{1}{2}\pi x \neq D_r A$.

Note 2. Hereafter, if we refer to the *derivative* of a function f, we shall mean the *derivative function f'*, except where our remarks are restricted to $f'(x)$ at some particular value of x.

Theorem XI. *If a function f has a derivative at a point x_0 in the domain of f, then f is continuous at x_0, or continuity is a necessary condition for differentiability.*

Proof. Let $y = f(x)$. Then, if $y_0 = f(x_0)$ and $y_0 + \Delta y = f(x_0 + \Delta x)$,

$$\lim_{\Delta x \to 0} \frac{\Delta y}{\Delta x} = f'(x_0). \tag{10}$$

Hence, $\lim_{\Delta x \to 0} \Delta y = \lim_{\Delta x \to 0} \frac{\Delta y}{\Delta x} \cdot \Delta x = \left(\lim_{\Delta x \to 0} \frac{\Delta y}{\Delta x} \right) \left(\lim_{\Delta x \to 0} \Delta x \right) = f'(x_0) \cdot 0 = 0.$

Therefore, by (7) on page 74, f is continuous at x_0.

The result of Problem 8 on page 87 will show that a function f may be *continuous* at a point x_0 and yet have *no derivative* at x_0.

Note 3. With $y = f(x)$, it follows from Theorem XI that $\Delta y/\Delta x$ tends to the meaningless form 0/0 as $\Delta x \to 0$ at any point x where $f'(x)$ exists. Hence, in applying (2) of page 80 to find $f'(x)$, it is necessary to alter the original form of $\Delta y/\Delta x$ before its limit is calculated.

EXERCISE 23

1. If $f(x) = 3x^2 + 4x - 5$, find the derivative of f; obtain $f'(-2)$.
2. Differentiate f if $f(x) = 3x - x^2$. Also obtain $f'(4)$.
3. Obtain $D_x y$ if $y = x^2 - x + 2$. Also compute $D_x y \vert_{x=-3}$.
4. Obtain y' if $y = 3x + 2x^2$.   5. If $f(z) = 3/z$, obtain f'.

Differentiate the function f, g, or h, or obtain $D_x y$.

6. $f(x) = x^3$.   7. $g(x) = 2x - x^3$.   8. $h(x) = x^4$.

9. $g(w) = \dfrac{2}{2w + 3}$.   10. $f(z) = \dfrac{2z - 1}{3z + 1}$.   11. $y = \dfrac{x}{2x + 1}$.

12. $y = \sqrt{2x}$.   13. $y = \sqrt{3x - 1}$.   14. $y = 1/\sqrt{3x}$.

Hint for Problem 12. In $\Delta y/\Delta x$, rationalize the numerator.

15. If $y = 3 - x^2$, calculate y'. Then obtain the instantaneous * rate of change of y with respect to x at $x = 4$.
16. Show that the rate of change of the area of a square with respect to the length of a side is equal to one-half of the perimeter of the square.
17. Show that the rate of change of the volume of a cube with respect to the length of an edge is equal to one-half of the surface area.
18. Show that the rate of change of the volume of a sphere with respect to its radius is equal to the surface area.

27. DERIVATIVE AS SLOPE OF A TANGENT

From an elementary viewpoint, the definition to be given for a *tangent* to a curve will yield tangents in various unexpected situations. However, usually, any tangent will appear to deserve the name intuitively. In any *xy*-plane, consider

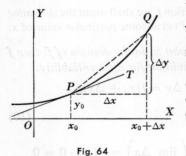

Fig. 64

the curve, C, which is the graph of an equation $y = f(x)$, where f is continuous at $x = x_0$. Let $Q:(x_0 + \Delta x, y_0 + \Delta y)$ be a point on C distinct from $P:(x_0, y_0)$, and consider secant PQ, as in Figure 64. We agree that the statement "$Q \to P$ on C" will mean that $\vert \overline{PQ} \vert \to 0$, and this is equivalent to stating that $\Delta x \to 0$, because f is continuous at x_0. We note that

$$(slope\ of\ PQ) = \frac{\Delta y}{\Delta x}. \qquad (1)$$

Then, to state that secant PQ has a **nonvertical limiting position** as $\overline{PQ} \to 0$ will mean that *there exists* $\lim_{\Delta x \to 0} (slope\ PQ)$, or that there exists $\lim_{\Delta x \to 0} (\Delta y/\Delta x)$, which means that $f'(x_0)$ exists. Then, we agree to call the line PT with slope $f'(x_0)$ the limiting position of secant PQ, and give PT a name as follows.†

---

* Frequently, the word *instantaneous* will be omitted and "*rate of change*" will mean "*instantaneous rate of change*," which is a derivative.
† This definition applies in any oblique or rectangular system of coordinates.

Definition VII. *To state that the graph of $y = f(x)$ has a* **nonvertical tangent** *PT at* $P:(x_0, y_0)$ *will mean that* $f'(x_0)$ *exists and PT is the line through P with slope* $f'(x_0)$. *That is,*

$$[\text{slope of tangent at } P:(x_0, y_0)] = f'(x_0) = D_x y \mid_{x=x_0}. \qquad (2)$$

Thus, by Definition VII, the tangent to the graph, C, of $y = f(x)$ at P is the line PT whose *slope* is *the limit of the slope of the secant PQ as* $Q \to P$ *along* C.

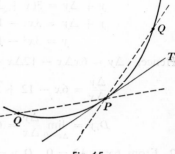

ILLUSTRATION 1. A typical situation is shown in Figure 65. As $Q \to P$ on the curve, from either side, the secant PQ revolves about P and the slope of PQ approaches the slope of PT. Thus, PT is the limiting position of PQ, and PT is the tangent at P.

ILLUSTRATION 2. If C is the curve QPQ in Figure 66, no limiting position exists for secant PQ as $Q \to P$ without restriction. Thus, there is no tangent to C at P. However, at P, so-called right-hand and left-hand tangents exist, which are distinct and are obtained as the limiting positions of PQ as $Q \to P$ from the right and from the left, respectively. In Figure 66, we call P a **corner point** of the curve.

Fig. 65

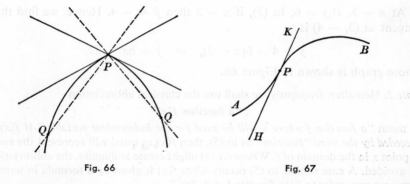

Fig. 66   Fig. 67

ILLUSTRATION 3. In Figure 67, PK satisfies Definition VII as the tangent to curve APB at the point P. The curve crosses its tangent at P. We call P an **inflection point** of curve APB. Inflection points are discussed in Chapter Six.

Note 1. The concept of a *vertical tangent PT* to the graph, C, of $y = f(x)$ at $P:(x_0, y_0)$ will be met on page 117. In such a case, $f'(x_0)$ will fail to exist and, in (1), usually $\mid \Delta y / \Delta x \mid$ will grow large without bound as $\Delta x \to 0$. At this point, we state informally that C has a vertical tangent at $P:(x_0, y_0)$ if secant PQ has a vertical limiting position as $PQ \to 0$.

If $f'(x_0)$ exists, so that the graph, C, of $y = f(x)$ has a nonvertical tangent PT at P, then the slope $f'(x_0)$ of PT also is called *the slope of C at P*. The slope of C is zero at $P:(x_0, y_0)$, or there is a horizontal tangent at P, if and only if $x = x_0$ is a solution of the equation $f'(x) = 0$, or $D_x y = 0$. If $f'(x_0)$ does not exist, then C

is said to have *no slope* at P. In such a case, if C has a vertical tangent PT at P, it may be said that C has *"infinite slope"* at P.

EXAMPLE 1. Obtain $D_x y$, graph the following equation (use any horizontal tangent), and find the tangent to the graph at $x = 3$, if

$$y = 3x^2 - 12x + 5. \tag{3}$$

Solution. 1. *To obtain* $D_x y$. We have

$$y + \Delta y = 3(x + \Delta x)^2 - 12(x + \Delta x) + 5;$$
$$y + \Delta y = 3x^2 - 12x + 5 + 6x\Delta x - 12\Delta x + 3(\Delta x)^2;$$
$$y = 3x^2 - 12x + 5.$$

Hence, $\Delta y = 6x\Delta x - 12\Delta x + 3(\Delta x)^2;$

$$\frac{\Delta y}{\Delta x} = 6x - 12 + 3\Delta x;$$

$$D_x y = \lim_{\Delta x \to 0} \frac{\Delta y}{\Delta x} = 6x - 12.$$

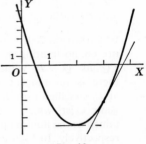

Fig. 68

2. From $6x - 12 = 0$, $D_x y = 0$ if $x = 2$, or the tangent to the graph of (3) at $(x = 2, y = -7)$ is horizontal. By use of this point and other solutions of (3) we obtain the graph of (3) in Figure 68.

3. At $x = 3$, $D_x y = 6$. In (3), if $x = 3$ then $y = -4$. Hence, we find that the tangent at $(3, -4)$ is

$$y + 4 = 6(x - 3), \quad or \quad y = 6x - 22, \tag{4}$$

whose graph is shown in Figure 68.

Note 2. Hereafter, frequently we shall use the classical abbreviation
$$\text{"a function } f(x)\text{"} \tag{5}$$
to mean *"a function f where x will be used for the independent variable."* If $f(x)$ is *not preceded by the word "function"* as in (5), then $f(x)$ as usual will represent the *value* of f at point x in the domain of f. Whenever (5) might create ambiguity, the abbreviation will be avoided. A case similar to (5) occurs when $f(x)$ is given by a formula in terms of x. Thus, we may refer to *"the function $(x^2 + 7x)$."*

To state that f is an **increasing function** on an interval, D, of the domain of f will mean that, with points x_1 and x_2 in D,

$$if\ x_1 < x_2 \quad then \quad f(x_1) < f(x_2). \tag{6}$$

To state that f is a **decreasing function** on D will mean that

$$if\ x_1 < x_2 \quad then \quad f(x_1) > f(x_2). \tag{7}$$

Theorem XII. *Assume that the domain of a function $f(x)$ includes $I = \{a \le x \le b\}$, and that $f'(x)$ exists if $a < x < b$. Then, if $f'(x) > 0$ when $a < x < b$, f is an increasing function on I; if $f'(x) < 0$ when $a < x < b$, then f is a decreasing function on I.*

At present, we shall accept Theorem XII intuitively,* since $f'(x)$ is the slope of the graph of f in an xy-plane at the point $(x, y = f(x))$. Thus, on an x-interval where $f'(x) > 0$, the slope of the graph of $y = f(x)$ is *positive* at all points, and the graph *rises* as x increases. On an x-interval where $f'(x) < 0$, the slope of the graph of $y = f(x)$ is *negative* at all points and the graph *falls* as x increases.

A function $f(x)$ is said to be **stationary** at $x = x_0$ if and only if $f'(x_0) = 0$. The corresponding point on the graph of $y = f(x)$ is called a **stationary point** of the graph; at such a point, the slope is *zero*, or the tangent is *horizontal*.

ILLUSTRATION 4. With $f(x) = 3x^2 - 12x + 5$, from the graph of $y = f(x)$ in Figure 68 on page 84, we see that f is an *increasing* function when $x \geq 2$; f is a *decreasing* function when $x \leq 2$; f is *stationary* at $x = 2$.

28. VELOCITY AS A DERIVATIVE

Consider a particle P, moving on an s-axis, with the coordinate s of P, in Figure 69, specified by $s = f(t)$ at any time, t, where f' is continuous. Let v be the velocity at the time t. Then, from page 78, and the definition of a derivative as an instantaneous rate of change, we find that

Fig. 69

$$v = D_t s, \quad or \quad v = f'(t), \tag{1}$$

at any time t. Thus, in rectilinear motion, *the velocity is the derivative of the distance with respect to the time.* Over any time interval where v, or $f'(t)$, is positive, s increases, or the particle moves in the positive direction on the s-axis. If $v < 0$ at any instant, the particle is instantaneously moving in the negative direction on the s-axis. At any instant when $v = 0$, it is said that the particle is instantaneously at rest.

Definition VIII. *With v representing the velocity of a particle in rectilinear motion, $|v|$ is called the* **speed** *of the particle.*

EXAMPLE 1. Let the motion of a projectile on a vertical s-axis, with the positive direction upward, be specified by $s = -\frac{1}{2}gt^2 + v_0 t$, where $g = 32$, approximately, with $v_0 = 96$. (a) Find the velocity at any instant t. (b) Compute the speed at $t = 5$. (c) Describe the motion of the projectile.

Solution. We have
$$s = -16t^2 + 96t. \tag{2}$$

(a) To obtain v, we find $D_t s$ by the increment process:

$$D_t s = \lim_{\Delta t \to 0} \frac{\Delta s}{\Delta t} = \lim_{\Delta t \to 0} (-32t + 96 - 16\Delta t) = -32t + 96; \ or \tag{3}$$
$$v = -32t + 96. \tag{4}$$

(b) If $t = 5$, then $v = -64$, and the projectile is falling with the speed $|-64|$, or 64, ft. per sec.

---

* Theorem XII will be proved on page 174.

(c) Consider the graph of (2) in Figure 70. For any value of t, at the corresponding point of the graph, the slope is $D_t s$, or v. At the stationary point of the graph, where s will have its maximum value, the slope is zero or

$$v = 0, \quad or \quad -32t + 96 = 0, \quad or \quad t = 3. \tag{5}$$

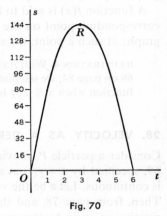

Fig. 70

If $t = 3$ in (2), then $s = 144$. The graph was drawn by use of the stationary point R:(3, 144), and other points. From the graph, we see that s *increases*, and the projectile *rises*, from $t = 0$ to $t = 3$, when the projectile comes to rest with $v = 0$ at the highest point in the motion. The projectile is at ground level at the two instants when $s = 0$, or

$$-16t^2 + 96t = 0, \quad or \quad t = 0 \quad and \quad t = 6.$$

Hence, if $t > 3$, the projectile is falling, and hits the ground at $t = 6$. These facts could be learned without a graph by considering $v = 32(3 - t)$ from (4). Thus,

$$v > 0 \; if \; t < 3; \quad v = 0 \; at \; t = 3; \quad v < 0 \; if \; t > 3.$$

EXERCISE 24

Any desired derivative should be obtained by the increment process.
(a) *Calculate* $D_x y$. (b) *Find each value of x where $D_x y = 0$ and use the corresponding stationary point in graphing the given equation.* (c) *Obtain the equations of the tangents as requested.* (d) *By inspection of the graph, specify the values of x where y increases, and where y decreases.*

1. $y = x^2 - 6x + 3$; find the tangents where $x = 2$ and $x = 4$.

2. $y = -x^2 - 4x + 5$; find the tangents where $x = -3$ and $x = 0$. Also, find the value of x where the slope of the graph is equal to 2.

3. $y = -2x^2 + 4x - 3$; find the tangents where $x = 1$ and $x = 4$. At what value of x is the slope of the graph equal to 5?

4. $y = 2x^2 - 8x + 3$; find the tangents where $x = 2$ and $x = 5$.

5. For the projectile discussed in Section 28, let $v_0 = 64$. (a) Find the velocity at any time t. (b) Compute v when $t = 3$. (c) Find the speed when $t = 3$. (d) Graph s as a function of t. (e) For what values of t is $v > 0$; $v = 0$; $v < 0$? (f) When is the speed 32' per second? (g) Describe the motion of the projectile from time $t = 0$ to the instant when the projectile hits the ground.

6. For a certain object moving in a vertical line, the height s above the earth at time t is given by $s = -16t^2 + 32t + 48$. (a) Find the velocity v at any instant t, and at some point where the object is rising; is falling. (b) Graph s as a function of t and describe the motion.

7. An object is sliding down an inclined plane. The distance s of the object from the top t seconds after starting is given by the equation $s = 8t^2 + 4t$. (a) Find v at any instant t and also when $t = 3$. (b) Find the initial velocity, that is, the velocity at $t = 0$.

★**8.** Let the function $f(x)$ be defined on the interval $0 \leqq x \leqq 2$ as follows:

$$f(x) = x \text{ if } x \leqq 2 \quad and \quad f(x) = 4 - x \text{ if } x > 2. \tag{1}$$

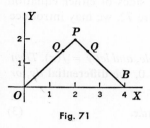

Fig. 71

The graph of $y = f(x)$ is the ridge OPB in Figure 71, where points on OP satisfy the equation $y = x$, and points on PB satisfy the equation $y = 4 - x$. If $x = 2$ then $y = 2$, which gives P:(2, 2) in Figure 71. We see that f is continuous. Let the point

$$Q:(2 + \Delta x, 2 + \Delta y)$$

be on the graph. If $\Delta x > 0$, then Q is on PB. If $\Delta x < 0$, then Q is on OP. Prove that

$$\lim_{\Delta x \to 0-} \frac{\Delta y}{\Delta x} = 1; \quad \lim_{\Delta x \to 0+} \frac{\Delta y}{\Delta x} = -1. \tag{2}$$

Comment. Since the left-hand and right-hand limits in (2) are *unequal*, $\Delta y/\Delta x$ *fails to have a limit as* $\Delta x \to 0$ without restriction, from either side. Thus, at $x = 2$, f is continuous but does not have a derivative. Hence, Problem 8 proves that **continuity at a point** $x = x_0$ **is not a sufficient condition to imply differentiability at** $x = x_0$. In Problem 8, because of (2), it is said that f has a *left-hand derivative*, $+ 1$, and a *right-hand derivative*, $- 1$, at $x = 2$. Also, at P, *the graph of* $y = f(x)$ is said to have a *left-hand tangent*, OP, and a *right-hand tangent*, PB, but the graph OPB has *no tangent* at the **corner point** P.

★**9.** Define a function f on some interval where f is continuous but where there is at least one point where f does not possess a derivative.

★**10.** Let f be a function with the domain $0 \leqq x \leqq 3$, where $f(x) = x^3$ if $0 \leqq x \leqq 1$, and $f(x) = \frac{1}{2}(3 - x)$ when $1 < x \leqq 3$. Graph f. Also, investigate the left-hand and right-hand derivatives of f at $x = 1$.

29. A QUOTIENT FORM FOR THE DERIVATIVE

Consider a differentiable function $f(x)$. Then, at any point P:(x, y) on the graph of $y = f(x)$, there is a nonvertical tangent PT with

$$(\text{slope of } PT) = f'(x). \tag{1}$$

For present purposes, we choose to use "dx" instead of "Δx" to represent an

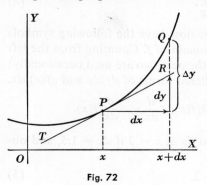

Fig. 72

increment in the value of x. Then, if an increment $dx \neq 0$ is given to the value of x, let dy, or $df(x)$, be the corresponding *increment of the ordinate of the tangent PT*, and let Δy be the increment of y, or $f(x)$, as in Figure 72. Q:$(x + dx, y + \Delta y)$ is on the graph of $y = f(x)$ and R:$(x + dx, y + dy)$ is on PT. The slope of PR is dy/dx. Hence, from (1),

$$\frac{dy}{dx} = f'(x) \quad or \quad \frac{df(x)}{dx} = f'(x). \tag{2}$$

From Figure 72, we notice that, in general, $\Delta y \neq dy$. We refer to dx, dy, and $df(x)$ as **differentials**. We may read "dx" as "*differential x*," or simply "*d, x*," and read "dy" and "$df(x)$" similarly. On multiplying both sides of either equation in (2) by dx, we observe that, without reference to Figure 72, we may introduce dy, or $df(x)$, as follows.

Definition IX. *Suppose that the function $f(x)$ is differentiable, and let $y = f(x)$. Then at any value of x, and at any value of the variable $dx \neq 0$, the* **differential** dy, *or $df(x)$, of the function is defined by the equation*

$$dy = f'(x)dx, \quad or \quad df(x) = f'(x)dx. \tag{3}$$

ILLUSTRATION 1. At P in Figure 72 on page 87, suppose that $f'(x) = \frac{1}{2}$. Then, at any value of dx, from (3) we obtain $dy = \frac{1}{2}dx$. Thus, if $dx = .6$ then $dy = .3$.

In (3), dy is specified as a function of *two* independent variables x and dx, where we never have $dx = 0$. From (2) and (3), we are led to use the left-hand sides of the equations in (2) as optional notations for $f'(x)$. Thus, $D_x y$ may be written as a **quotient of corresponding differentials**, dy divided by dx. We read "$\left(\dfrac{dy}{dx}\right)$" as "*the derivative of y with respect to x*," or simply "*dy over dx*." In place of $\dfrac{dy}{dx}$ or $\dfrac{df(x)}{dx}$, we sometimes write

$$\frac{d}{dx}y \quad and \quad \frac{d}{dx}f(x),$$

where $\dfrac{d}{dx}$ abbreviates "*the derivative with respect to x of*," and may be thought of as replacing "D_x" in the symbol $D_x y$. In using $\dfrac{dy}{dx}$ for a derivative, it is not necessary to think of any particular value of dx, because the fraction does not depend on the value of dx. We may treat $\dfrac{dy}{dx}$ *as a whole*, just as we have done with the symbol $D_x y$. Or, when desired, we may use dy/dx as a *fraction*, with $dx \neq 0$. From (2) on page 80,

$$\frac{dy}{dx} = \lim_{\Delta x \to 0} \frac{\Delta y}{\Delta x}. \tag{4}$$

If f represents any function, with $y = f(x)$, we now have the following symbols for the derivative of f at any point x in the domain of f. Counting from the left below, the first four are used very frequently; the next two are used occasionally; the last two at the right are merely slightly altered forms of dy/dx and $df(x)/dx$.

$$y', \quad f'(x), \quad \frac{dy}{dx}, \quad \frac{df(x)}{dx}, \quad D_x y, \quad D_x f(x), \quad \frac{d}{dx}y, \quad \frac{d}{dx}f(x).$$

EXAMPLE 1. Graph the following equation, find dy at $x = 2$ if $dx = 1.5$, and obtain the tangent to the graph at $x = 2$:

$$y = x^2 - 2x + 2. \tag{5}$$

Solution. 1. From $y + \Delta y = (x + \Delta x)^2 - 2(x + \Delta x) + 2,$

$$\Delta y = \Delta x(2x - 2) + (\Delta x)^2; \quad \frac{\Delta y}{\Delta x} = 2x - 2 + \Delta x;$$

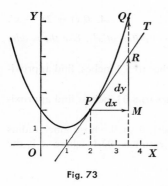

Fig. 73

$$\frac{dy}{dx} = \lim_{\Delta x \to 0} \frac{\Delta y}{\Delta x} = 2x - 2. \tag{6}$$

Hence, from (3), $dy = (2x - 2)dx$. Then, if $x = 2$ and $dx = 1.5$, we obtain $dy = 3$. With $\Delta x = dx = 1.5$, we find $\Delta y = 5.25$.

2. If $x = 2$ then $y = 2$; from (6), $y' = 2$. Hence, the tangent to the graph of (5) at $(x = 2, y = 2)$ has the equation $y - 2 = 2(x - 2)$. Figure 73 shows a graph of (5), with dx, dy, and Δy represented by directed line segments, where $x = 2$, $\Delta y = \overline{MQ}$, and $dx = 1.5$.

If $f(x) = x$, then $f'(x) = 1$ and (3) gives

$$df(x) = 1 \cdot dx, \quad \text{or} \quad d(x) = dx.$$

That is, at any value of x, *the differential of the function "x" is the same as dx.* Thus, although $d(x)$ and dx are distinct conceptually, they have the same value for any values of x and dx.

The following fact can be inferred from Figures 72 and 73.

Suppose that $y = f(x)$, and Δy is the increment in y due to an increment dx in the argument x. Then, if dx is small, dy may be a good approximation to Δy. That is,

$$\text{if} \quad \Delta y = f(x + dx) - f(x) \quad \text{then} \quad \Delta y \approx dy = f'(x)dx, \tag{7}$$

where we use $\approx$ for "approximately equal to."

In Chapter Seven, the statement above will be analyzed, and will become the basis for important applications. At this point, we intend to make only moderate use of (7).

EXAMPLE 2. A cylindrical shell (like a piece of pipe) is 10 inches long, and has inner radius 5 inches, and thickness .05 inch. Obtain an approximation to the volume of the wall of the shell by use of differentials.

Solution. 1. In cubic inches, the volume, V, of a solid cylinder of height 10 inches, with base-radius x inches, is $V = 10\pi x^2 = f(x)$. The volume of the wall of the shell is ΔV, due to a change from $x = 5$ to $x = 5 + dx$, where $dx = .05$. Then $\Delta V \approx dV$.

2. By the increment process, $f'(x) = 20\pi x$. Hence,

$$\Delta V \approx dV = f'(x)dx = f'(5)(.05) = 20\pi(5)(.05), \ or$$

ΔV is approximately 5π, in cubic inches.

Note 1. At present, our main interest in differentials is that they justify the quotient form dy/dx for a derivative. The notation dy/dx was introduced by LEIBNIZ.

EXERCISE 25

Calculate dy/dx, or df(x)/dx, by the increment process, using (4) *on page* 88. *Then, compute dy, or df(x), at x =* − 2 *when dx =* .4, *and when dx =* .01. *In any problem, k is a constant.*

1. $y = 2x + 5$.　　　　2. $y = kx^2$.　　　　3. $y = kx^3$.　　　　4. $f(x) = 2x - x^2$.

Find the requested increment in value approximately by use of differentials. Use the results from Problems 2 and 3.

5. If the length of a side of a square increases from 5 inches to 5.2 inches, find approximately the increase in the square's area.

6. If the length of a side of a cube increases from 8 inches to 8.03 inches, find approximately the increase in the volume of the cube.

7. Find approximately the volume of the wall of a spherical shell whose inner radius is 10 inches and thickness is .02 inch. Prove that the result is .02A, where A is the surface area of a sphere of radius 10 inches.

★*SUPPLEMENT FOR CHAPTER THREE*

8. Prove that $\lim_{x \to 0} \sin x^{-1}$ does not exist. Perhaps use an indirect proof referring to (7) on page 70.

9. If $f(x) = x \sin x^{-1}$, what value should be assigned to $f(0)$ in order that f shall be continuous at $x = 0$? Prove the fact analytically.

10. With $f(0)$ assigned as in Problem 9, prove that $f'(x)$ does not exist at $x = 0$.

11. Define a function g by specifying $g(0) = 0$ and $g(x) = x^2 \sin (1/x)$ when $x \neq 0$. Prove that $g'(x)$ exists at $x = 0$. Also, prove that the tangent line, as given by Definition VII on page 83, to the curve $y = g(x)$ at $(0, 0)$ intersects the curve at infinitely many points on any interval $|x| < d$.

Decide on the value of the limit, L, by use of Theorems I–IV on page 70. Then, prove the result analytically as illustrated in Example 1 of Note 5 of the Appendix, without use of Theorems I–IV.

12. $\lim_{x \to 4} (3x + 7)$.　　　　13. $\lim_{x \to -2} (6 - 5x)$.　　　　14. $\lim_{x \to 3} (x^2 + 5)$.

15. $\lim_{x \to 2} \dfrac{3}{2x + 5}$.　　　　16. $\lim_{x \to -3} \dfrac{6}{2x + 7}$.　　　　17. $\lim_{x \to 2} \dfrac{x}{2x + 1}$.

　　Hint for Problem 15. If $f(x) = 3/(2x + 5)$, obtain $|f(x) - \frac{1}{3}| < \frac{2}{21}|x - 2|$ if $x > 1$. With this nonessential limitation on x, prove that δ satisfies (7) on page 70 if δ is the minimum of 1 and $\frac{21}{2}\epsilon$.

18. Assume that the function $f(x)$ is defined at and near $x = c$. Write the definition of the statement "f *is continuous at x = c*" in an (ϵ, δ) form by use of Note 2 on page 70.

19. Prove analytically that the function $1/x$ is continuous at every value of $x \neq 0$, without use of Theorems I–IV on page 70.

20. If $\lim_{x \to c} f(x) = L > 0$, prove analytically that $f(x) > 0$ if x is sufficiently near c. That is, prove that there exists $\delta > 0$ so that, if $0 < |x - c| < \delta$, then $f(x) > 0$. We assume that $f(c)$ may not be defined.

CHAPTER FOUR

Differentiation of Algebraic Functions

30. DERIVATIVES OF POLYNOMIALS

From page 17, a monomial in two variables x and y is of the form Ax^hy^k where h and k are nonnegative integers and A is a nonzero constant. A polynomial is a sum of monomials. From page 28, a polynomial function $f(x, y)$ is a function whose values $f(x, y)$ are given by a polynomial in x and y. A **polynomial equation** in x and y is of the form $f(x, y) = g(x, y)$ where f and g are polynomial functions.

ILLUSTRATION 1. By the quadratic formula, the polynomial equation

$$xy^2 + y(x^4 - 3) - 5 = 0 \tag{1}$$

defines y as either one of two functions of x:

$$y = \frac{3 - x^4 \pm \sqrt{x^8 - 6x^4 + 20x + 9}}{2x}. \tag{2}$$

Definition I. *To say that a function $g(x)$ is an* **algebraic function** *means that g is continuous, and there exists a polynomial equation $f(x, y) = 0$ such that $y = g(x)$ is a solution of $f(x, y) = 0$, or $f(x, g(x)) = 0$ for all x in the domain of g.*

ILLUSTRATION 2. Equation (1) defines two algebraic functions whose values, y, are given by (2). In general, a polynomial equation $f(x, y) = 0$, of degree n in y alone, defines n values of y corresponding to each value of x. However, some or all of these n values of y may not be real numbers even though the constant coefficients in $f(x, y)$ are real numbers. If $n = 1$ or $n = 2$, formulas are obtainable by elementary means for the value or values of y when x has a given value. If $n = 3$ or $n = 4$, it is proved in advanced algebra that formulas exist which give y in terms of the value of x, but these formulas are so complicated as to be relatively useless for particular equations. If $n > 4$, in general no formulas exist which give the values of y in terms of the value of x.

ILLUSTRATION 3. Let f be a rational function, where $f(x) = P(x)/Q(x)$, with P and Q representing polynomial functions. If we let $y = P(x)/Q(x)$, then

$$yQ(x) - P(x) = 0,$$

which is a polynomial equation in x and y, such that $y = f(x)$. Hence, any rational function of x is an algebraic function of x.

Definition II. *An algebraic function g(x) which is not a rational function is called an* **irrational function.**

ILLUSTRATION 4. The values, y, of two irrational functions of x are given in (2). We shall call these functions *solution functions* of (1) for y in terms of x.

Note 1. The preceding terminology extends to functions of two or more independent variables. Thus, to state that g is an algebraic function of two variables means that g is continuous (in a sense to be defined on page 465), and there exists a polynomial equation $f(x, y, z) = 0$ having the solution $z = g(x, y)$, so that $f(x, y, g(x, y)) = 0$ for all (x, y) in the domain of g.

We shall prove formulas permitting us to differentiate any of the familiar functions of a single variable without direct use of the definition of a derivative. The following formulas constitute the first stage in our program. By means of these results, we shall be able to differentiate any algebraic function. In the formulas, c represents a constant; u, v, w, and y are differentiable functions of the independent variable x. We shall conclude that **any polynomial $f(x)$ can be differentiated by use of (I)–(IV).**

$$\frac{d}{dx}(c) = 0. \tag{I}$$

$(for\ all\ u)$
$$\frac{d}{dx}(cu) = c\frac{du}{dx}. \tag{II}$$

$(for\ all\ x)$
$$\frac{d}{dx}(cx) = c. \tag{II}_a$$

The power formula. *If n is any rational number,*

$(u \neq 0\ if\ n \leq 1)$
$$\frac{d}{dx}(u^n) = nu^{n-1}\frac{du}{dx}; \tag{III}$$

$(x \neq 0\ if\ n \leq 1)$
$$\frac{d}{dx}(x^n) = nx^{n-1}. \tag{III}_a$$

$$\frac{d}{dx}(u + v + w) = \frac{du}{dx} + \frac{dv}{dx} + \frac{dw}{dx}. \tag{IV}$$

$$\frac{d}{dx}(uv) = u\frac{dv}{dx} + v\frac{du}{dx}. \tag{V}$$

$(v \neq 0)$
$$\frac{d}{dx}\left(\frac{u}{v}\right) = \frac{v\dfrac{du}{dx} - u\dfrac{dv}{dx}}{v^2}. \tag{VI}$$

$(v \neq 0)$
$$\frac{d}{dx}\left(\frac{1}{v}\right) = -\frac{1}{v^2}\cdot\frac{dv}{dx}. \tag{VI}_a$$

If y is a differentiable function of u, where u is a differentiable function of x, then y is a differentiable function of x and

$$\frac{dy}{dx} = \frac{dy}{du}\cdot\frac{du}{dx}. \tag{VII}$$

If f and g are differentiable with $f'(x) \neq 0$ and $g'(y) \neq 0$, and if the equations $y = f(x)$ and $x = g(y)$ are equivalent, then

$$\frac{dy}{dx} = \frac{1}{\dfrac{dx}{dy}}. \tag{VIII}$$

In preceding formulas, u, v, and w are symbols for the values of corresponding differentiable functions f, g, and h, with x as the independent variable:

$$u = f(x); \quad v = g(x); \quad w = h(x). \tag{3}$$

If x is given an increment Δx, the corresponding increments Δu, Δv, and Δw are $\Delta u = f(x + \Delta x) - f(x)$; $\Delta v = g(x + \Delta x) - g(x)$; $\Delta w = h(x + \Delta x) - h(x)$.

Proof of (**I**). Let $F(x) = c$, at all values of x. Then

$$F'(x) = \lim_{\Delta x \to 0} \frac{F(x + \Delta x) - F(x)}{\Delta x} = \lim_{\Delta x \to 0} \frac{c - c}{\Delta x} = 0, \quad or \quad \frac{d(c)}{dx} = 0.$$

We may interpret (I) geometrically: the graph of the equation $y = c$ in an xy-plane is a line parallel to the x-axis and hence has slope 0 everywhere.

Proof of (**II**). Let $F(x) = cu$. Then $F(x + \Delta x) = c(u + \Delta u)$;

$$F'(x) = \lim_{\Delta x \to 0} \frac{F(x + \Delta x) - F(x)}{\Delta x} = \lim_{\Delta x \to 0} c\, \frac{\Delta u}{\Delta x} = c \left(\lim_{\Delta x \to 0} \frac{\Delta u}{\Delta x} \right). \tag{4}$$

Since $(\Delta u / \Delta x) \to du/dx$ as $\Delta x \to 0$, from (4) we obtain

$$F'(x) = c\, \frac{du}{dx}, \quad or \quad \frac{d}{dx}(cu) = c\, \frac{du}{dx}, \text{ as in (II).}$$

We notice that (II) becomes (II)$_a$ when $u = x$.

ILLUSTRATION 5. $\quad \dfrac{d}{dx}(6u) = 6\, \dfrac{du}{dx}. \quad \dfrac{d}{dx}(-v) = \dfrac{d}{dx}[(-1) \cdot v] = -\dfrac{dv}{dx}.$

Proof of (**III**)$_a$ *if $n \geq 1$, where n is an integer; $x \neq 0$ if $n = 1$.* Let $F(x) = x^n$. Then, $F(x + \Delta x) = (x + \Delta x)^n$. By the binomial expansion on page 673,

$$F(x + \Delta x) = x^n + nx^{n-1}(\Delta x) + \frac{n(n-1)}{2}\, x^{n-2}(\Delta x)^2 + \cdots + (\Delta x)^n.$$

$$F(x + \Delta x) - F(x) = nx^{n-1}(\Delta x) + \frac{n(n-1)}{2}\, x^{n-2}(\Delta x)^2 + \cdots + (\Delta x)^n. \tag{5}$$

We divide in (5) by Δx to obtain $\Delta F/\Delta x$; then

$$F'(x) = \lim_{\Delta x \to 0} \left[nx^{n-1} + \frac{n(n-1)}{2}\, x^{n-2}(\Delta x) + \cdots + (\Delta x)^{n-1} \right]. \tag{6}$$

In (6), with x as a fixed number, the first term on the right is a constant. Each other term has Δx as a factor and thus has the limit zero as $\Delta x \to 0$. Hence, by Theorem I on page 70, the limit on the right exists and is nx^{n-1}, or $F'(x) = nx^{n-1}$, which proves (III)$_a$ as desired.

ILLUSTRATION 6. From (III)$_a$, if $f(x) = x^5$ then $f'(x) = 5x^4$.

From (II) and (III)$_a$, $\dfrac{d}{dx}(7x^4) = 7\dfrac{d}{dx}(x^4) = 7 \cdot (4x^3) = 28x^3$.

Proof of (IV): *the derivative of a sum of differentiable functions is the sum of their derivatives.* From (3), with x fixed in value, u, v, and w take on increments Δu, Δv, and Δw when x is given an increment Δx. Hence, if we let

$$F(x) = u + v + w,\ then$$

$$F(x + \Delta x) = u + \Delta u + v + \Delta v + w + \Delta w;$$

$$\frac{F(x + \Delta x) - F(x)}{\Delta x} = \frac{\Delta u}{\Delta x} + \frac{\Delta v}{\Delta x} + \frac{\Delta w}{\Delta x}. \tag{7}$$

By Theorem I on page 70, since the limit as $\Delta x \to 0$ of each fraction on the right in (7) is a derivative, there exists

$$F'(x) = \lim_{\Delta x \to 0} \frac{F(x + \Delta x) - F(x)}{\Delta x} = \lim_{\Delta x \to 0} \frac{\Delta u}{\Delta x} + \lim_{\Delta x \to 0} \frac{\Delta v}{\Delta x} + \lim_{\Delta x \to 0} \frac{\Delta w}{\Delta x},\ or$$

$$F'(x) = \frac{du}{dx} + \frac{dv}{dx} + \frac{dw}{dx},\quad as\ in\ (IV).$$

If any term on the left in (IV) is given a minus sign, this is duplicated on the right. Thus, by use of Illustration 5,

$$\frac{d}{dx}(u - v) = \frac{d}{dx}[u + (-v)] = \frac{du}{dx} + \frac{d}{dx}(-v) = \frac{du}{dx} - \frac{dv}{dx}.$$

EXAMPLE 1. Graph $y = 2x^3 - 3x^2 - 12x + 4.$ \tag{8}

Solution. 1. $\dfrac{dy}{dx} = \dfrac{d}{dx}(2x^3) - \dfrac{d}{dx}(3x^2) - \dfrac{d}{dx}(12x) + 0,\ or$

$$y' = 6x^2 - 6x - 12,\quad or\quad y' = 6(x - 2)(x + 1).$$

2. *The stationary points of the graph, or the points where the tangent is horizontal.* We solve $y' = 0$, which gives $x = 2$ and $x = -1$. If $x = 2$ then $y = -16$; if $x = -1$ then $y = 11$. Hence, the tangents to the graph are horizontal at $(2, -16)$ and $(-1, 11)$. The graph of (8) in Figure 74 was constructed by use of the preceding points and others as given in the following table.

$x =$	-2	-1	0	1	2	3
$y =$	0	11	4	-9	-16	-5

3. At $x = 3$, $y' = 24$ and $y = -5$. Hence, the tangent at $(3, -5)$ in Figure 74 has the equation $y + 5 = 24(x - 3)$.

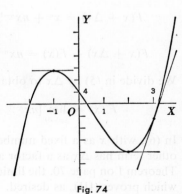

Fig. 74

Proof of (V): *the derivative of a product uv with respect to x is equal to u times the derivative of v plus v times the derivative of u.*

1. Let $F(x) = uv$ where u and v are given by (3). Then, when x is given the increment Δx,

$$F(x + \Delta x) = (u + \Delta u)(v + \Delta v) = uv + u\Delta v + v\Delta u + \Delta u\Delta v; \qquad (9)$$

$$F(x + \Delta x) - F(x) = u\Delta v + v\Delta u + \Delta u\Delta v.$$

$$F'(x) = \lim_{\Delta x \to 0} \frac{F(x + \Delta x) - F(x)}{\Delta x} = \lim_{\Delta x \to 0} \left(u\frac{\Delta v}{\Delta x} + v\frac{\Delta u}{\Delta x} + \Delta u\frac{\Delta v}{\Delta x} \right). \qquad (10)$$

2. From (3), $u = f(x)$ where f' exists, and thus f is continuous. Hence, $\Delta u \to 0$ when $\Delta x \to 0$. Each fraction on the right in (10) has a derivative as its limit. Therefore, from (10) and Theorem I on page 70, $F'(x)$ exists and

$$F'(x) = uD_x v + vD_x u + (0)(D_x v) = uD_x v + vD_x u,$$

which proves (V).

ILLUSTRATION 7. From (V), $\quad \dfrac{d}{dx}[(3x^2 + 7)(2x^3 - 3x)] =$

$$(3x^2 + 7)\frac{d}{dx}(2x^3 - 3x) + (2x^3 - 3x)\frac{d}{dx}(3x^2 + 7) =$$

$$(3x^2 + 7)(6x^2 - 3) + (2x^3 - 3x)(6x) = 30x^4 + 15x^2 - 21.$$

ILLUSTRATION 8. If $f(x) = (x^2 - 3)(2x + x^3)(x + x^4)$, by two applications of (V) we obtain

$$f'(x) = [(x^2 - 3)(2x + x^3)] \cdot \frac{d}{dx}(x + x^4) + (x + x^4)\frac{d}{dx}[(x^2 - 3)(2x + x^3)]$$

$$= (x^2 - 3)(2x + x^3)(1 + 4x^3) +$$
$$(x + x^4)[(x^2 - 3)(2 + 3x^2) + (2x + x^3)(2x)] = etc.$$

By use of (V) as in Illustration 8, we find that the derivative of a product of any number of factors is *the sum of all terms obtained by taking, in turn, the derivative of each factor and multiplying by all of the other factors.*

EXERCISE 26

Find dy/dx, or the derivative of the given function of x, t, or z. Early letters of the alphabet are constants. Use (I)–(V).

1. $3x^2 + 5x^3$.
2. $6t^3 - 4t^5$.
3. $3z + z^5 - z^8$.
4. $2 + 3x - 5x^2 - 11x^3$.
5. $6 - 3x - \frac{5}{2}x^2 + \frac{7}{6}x^3 - \frac{1}{8}x^4$.
6. $3x^4 - \frac{5}{6}x^3 - \frac{1}{4}x^2 + 17$.
7. $7z^4 - 3z^3 + \frac{1}{6}z^2 - 8$.
8. $3t^5 - 2t^2 - 5t + 16$.
9. $\frac{4}{3}t^3 - \frac{2}{3}t^2 + 6t - 3$.
10. $2z^6 - 3z^4 + \frac{5}{3}z^3 - \frac{9}{2}z^2$.
11. $21 - 5x - \frac{3}{8}x^2 + x^9$.
12. $y = (x + 2)(3x - 2)$.
13. $y = (x^2 + 3)(2x + 3)$.
14. $y = (x^2 + x)(x^4 - 3x^2)$.
15. $y = (x - 4x^2)(x^3 + 2x)$.
16. $f(x) = (3x + 1)(2x^2 + 7)$.
17. $f(z) = (z^3 - 3z)(1 - 4z)$.
18. $(x + 2)(x - 3)(x^2 + 5)$.
19. $(t^2 - 3t)(t - 1)(2t + 5)$.

Find where the graph of the equation has a horizontal tangent, and draw the graph. Also, find the equation of its tangent at the point where $x = 3$ and draw this tangent.

20. $y = \frac{1}{3}x^3 - \frac{1}{2}x^2 - 2x + 7$. **21.** $y = x^3 - 6x^2 + 12x - 3$.

22. The motion of a particle on an s-axis is specified by $s = 6 + 6t - t^2$, where t is the time. (*a*) Find the velocity at $t = 0$. (*b*) Find the speed at $t = 8$. (*c*) When is the velocity zero? (*d*) Graph s as a function of t and describe the motion for $t \geqq 0$; that is, specify where the particle starts; how long it moves to the right or the left; where it stops instantaneously, and where it moves thereafter.

23. Repeat (*d*) of Problem 22 with $s = t^3 - 9t^2 + 24t - 15$.

24. When an electric current flows through a resistance, the number of heat units developed is given by $h = .2389I^2Rt$, where h represents the number of gram-calories, I the current in amperes, R the resistance in ohms, and t the time in seconds for which the current flows. If $R = 500$ ohms and $t = 10$ seconds, find the rate of change of the developed heat units with respect to change in the current, when $I = 30$ amperes.

Note 1. Terminology from economics. Let x be the number of units of a certain commodity which can be sold when the price per unit is p units of money. Let the *total cost* of producing the x units be C; the *average cost* of production per unit be A, when x units are produced; the *revenue* obtained by their sale be R. Then p and C are considered as functions of x, say $p = f(x)$ and $C = g(x)$. Also, $R = px$ or $R = xf(x)$, and $A = C/x$ or $A = x^{-1}g(x)$. At any fixed value of x, the *marginal cost* is defined as the limit of the increment in cost, ΔC, divided by the increment in output, Δx, as $\Delta x \to 0$. That is,

$$\textbf{(marginal cost)} = \frac{dC}{dx} = C'. \tag{1}$$

Similarly, by definition $\qquad \textbf{(marginal revenue)} = \dfrac{dR}{dx} = R'. \tag{2}$

25. For a firm making steel drums, the demand function is $p = 300 - 9x - x^2$, where the units are \$1 for p and a certain trade unit for x. Find the marginal revenue when $x = 4$.

26. Let the total-cost function for a manufacturer be $C = 8500 + 6x - .0002x^2$. Find the marginal cost when $x = 12,000$.

31. DERIVATIVE OF A QUOTIENT

Proof of **(VI)**: *At any value of x where $v \neq 0$, the derivative with respect to x of u/v is equal to the denominator times the derivative of the numerator minus the numerator times the derivative of the denominator, divided by the square of the denominator:*

$$(v \neq 0) \qquad \frac{d}{dx}\left(\frac{u}{v}\right) = \frac{v\dfrac{du}{dx} - u\dfrac{dv}{dx}}{v^2}. \tag{VI}$$

In particular, $\qquad \dfrac{d}{dx}\left(\dfrac{1}{v}\right) = -\dfrac{1}{v^2}\dfrac{dv}{dx}. \tag{VI$_a$}$

1. With $u = f(x)$ and $v = g(x)$, let $y = u/v$, where x has a fixed value such that

$v = g(x) \neq 0$. Then, when the increment Δx is added to x, we have

$$y + \Delta y = \frac{u + \Delta u}{v + \Delta v}; \quad \Delta y = \frac{u + \Delta u}{v + \Delta v} - \frac{u}{v} = \frac{v\Delta u - u\Delta v}{v(v + \Delta v)};$$

$$\frac{\Delta y}{\Delta x} = \frac{v \dfrac{\Delta u}{\Delta x} - u \dfrac{\Delta v}{\Delta x}}{v(v + \Delta v)}. \tag{1}$$

2. Since g is differentiable, then g is continuous. Hence, $\lim_{\Delta x \to 0} \Delta v = 0$. Moreover, by hypothesis, $v \neq 0$ in (1). Therefore, if $|\Delta x|$ is sufficiently small, $(v + \Delta v) \neq 0$ and all calculation leading to (1) is justified. In the denominator in (1),

$$\lim_{\Delta x \to 0} v(v + \Delta v) = v^2 \neq 0.$$

Hence, we may apply Theorem IV on page 70 in (1) to obtain (VI):

$$\frac{dy}{dx} = \lim_{\Delta x \to 0} \frac{\Delta y}{\Delta x} = \frac{v \left(\lim_{\Delta x \to 0} \dfrac{\Delta u}{\Delta x} \right) - u \left(\lim_{\Delta x \to 0} \dfrac{\Delta v}{\Delta x} \right)}{\lim_{\Delta x \to 0} v(v + \Delta v)} = \frac{v \dfrac{du}{dx} - u \dfrac{dv}{dx}}{v^2}.$$

ILLUSTRATION 1. From (VI) with $u = 3x^2 + 2x$ and $v = 2x^3 - 7$,

$$\frac{d}{dx} \left(\frac{3x^2 + 2x}{2x^3 - 7} \right) = \frac{(2x^3 - 7) \dfrac{d}{dx} (3x^2 + 2x) - (3x^2 + 2x) \dfrac{d}{dx} (2x^3 - 7)}{(2x^3 - 7)^2}$$

$$= \frac{(2x^3 - 7)(6x + 2) - (3x^2 + 2x)(6x^2)}{(2x^3 - 7)^2} = - \frac{6x^4 + 8x^3 + 42x + 14}{(2x^3 - 7)^2}.$$

It would be clumsy to use (VI) in differentiating a fraction u/k, where k is a constant. Instead, we write u/k as $(1/k) \cdot u$, and use (II).

Proof of (VI)$_a$. From (VI) with $u = 1$, and hence $du/dx = 0$,

$$\frac{d}{dx} \left(\frac{1}{v} \right) = \frac{v \dfrac{d}{dx} (1) - 1 \cdot \dfrac{dv}{dx}}{v^2} = - \frac{1}{v^2} \cdot \frac{dv}{dx}.$$

ILLUSTRATION 2. By use of (VI)$_a$,

$$\frac{d}{dx} \left(\frac{10}{3x^2 + 5} \right) = 10 \frac{d}{dx} \left(\frac{1}{3x^2 + 5} \right) = - \frac{10 \cdot 6x}{(3x^2 + 5)^2}.$$

32. COMPOSITE FUNCTIONS

If $y = f(u)$ where $u = g(x)$, then $y = f(g(x))$. If we let $F(x) = f(g(x))$, we refer to F as the **composite function** of f by g.

ILLUSTRATION 1. With $f(u) = \sqrt{1 - u}$ and $g(x) = x^2 - 8$,
$$F(x) = f(g(x)) = \sqrt{9 - x^2}. \tag{1}$$

In considering a composite function, it is not always convenient or possible to eliminate the intermediate variable, such as u in Illustration 1. On this account, and for other reasons, the following result is of importance.

Theorem I. *If u, x, and y are variables where y is a differentiable function of u, and u is a differentiable function of x, then y is a differentiable function of x and*

$$\frac{dy}{dx} = \frac{dy}{du} \cdot \frac{du}{dx}. \tag{VII}$$

Proof. 1. The hypotheses mean that there exist differentiable functions f and g such that $y = f(u)$ and $u = g(x)$, where u is in the domain D_1 of f at all values of x in some set D. Then, $y = f(g(x))$, where the domain of x is D.

2. At any fixed point $x = x_0$ in D, and with $\Delta x \neq 0$ and such that $x = x_0 + \Delta x$ also is in D, let the corresponding values of (u, y) be

$$(u_0, y_0) \quad and \quad (u_0 + \Delta u, y_0 + \Delta y),$$

respectively. Assume * that $\Delta u \neq 0$ at all values of Δx which are sufficiently small, and restrict Δx to such values hereafter. Then

$$\frac{\Delta y}{\Delta x} = \frac{\Delta y}{\Delta u} \cdot \frac{\Delta u}{\Delta x}. \tag{2}$$

3. In (2), since $u = g(x)$ where $g'(x_0)$ exists, then g is continuous at x_0 so that $\Delta u \to 0$ as $\Delta x \to 0$. Also, by hypothesis, there exist

$$\lim_{\Delta x \to 0} \frac{\Delta y}{\Delta u} = f'(u_0); \quad \lim_{\Delta x \to 0} \frac{\Delta u}{\Delta x} = g'(x_0). \tag{3}$$

Hence, if $|\Delta x|$ is sufficiently small in (2), $\Delta u/\Delta x$ will be as close as we please to $g'(x_0)$, and $|\Delta u|$ will be so small that $\Delta y/\Delta u$ will be as close as we please to $f'(u_0)$. Thus, the product on the right in (2) will be as close as we please to $f'(u_0)g'(x_0)$ when $|\Delta x|$ is sufficiently small. Or, there exists

$$\lim_{\Delta x \to 0} \frac{\Delta y}{\Delta x} = f'(u_0)g'(x_0),$$

which is equivalent to

$$\left.\frac{dy}{dx}\right|_{x=x_0} = \left.\frac{dy}{du}\right|_{u=u_0} \cdot \left.\frac{du}{dx}\right|_{x=x_0}.$$

This proves (VII) at $x = x_0$.

Note 1. By use of $f(u)$, $g(x)$, and $F(x) = f(g(x))$, at each point x in the domain of F, formula (VII) becomes

$$F'(x) = f'(u)g'(x), \quad with \quad u = g(x), \tag{4}$$

which can be referred to as the formula for differentiating a composite function $f(g(x))$. Sometimes, (VII) is called the formula for dy/dx when y is *a function of a function of x*. Also, (VII) is spoken of as the **chain rule** for the case of three variables, (y, u, x), where, *first* (in dy/du), we treat u as an *independent variable* and, *second* (in du/dx), we take account of the fact that u is a function of the *primary independent variable x*.

ILLUSTRATION 2. If $y = (3x^2 + x)^9$, let $u = 3x^2 + x$. Then, $y = u^9$. From (III)$_a$ and (VII), without the binomial expansion for $(3x^2 + x)^9$,

$$\frac{dy}{dx} = \frac{d}{du}(u^9) \cdot \frac{du}{dx} = 9u^8(6x + 1) = 9(3x^2 + x)^8(6x + 1).$$

* For a proof without this assumption, see Note 6 in the Appendix.

By use of (VII), we shall prove that (III) and its special case (III)$_a$, below, are true if n is any rational number * and u is a differentiable function of x. Also, we observe immediately that (III) is true if $n = 0$ and $u \neq 0$, because then each side of (III) is equal to zero.

$(u \neq 0 \text{ if } n \leq 1)$

$$\frac{du^n}{dx} = nu^{n-1} \frac{du}{dx};$$

(III)

[with $u = x$ in (III)]

$$\frac{dx^n}{dx} = nx^{n-1}.$$

(III)$_a$

Proof of (III) if n is a positive integer. We proved (III)$_a$ for this case on page 93. Hence, from (III)$_a$ with x replaced by u,

$$\frac{du^n}{du} = nu^{n-1}.$$

Then, by use of (VII), we obtain (III) with n a positive integer:

$$\frac{du^n}{dx} = \frac{du^n}{du} \cdot \frac{du}{dx} = nu^{n-1} \frac{du}{dx}.$$

Proof of (III) if n is a negative integer. Let $n = -m$, where m is a positive integer, and recall $u^{-m} = 1/u^m$. Then, by use of (III) for the exponent m, and (VI)$_a$ of page 92, we obtain (III), as below, for the exponent $n = -m$:

$$\frac{du^n}{dx} = \frac{du^{-m}}{dx} = \frac{d}{dx}\left(\frac{1}{u^m}\right) = -\frac{1}{(u^m)^2} \cdot \frac{du^m}{dx} = \frac{(-m)u^{m-1}}{u^{2m}} \cdot \frac{du}{dx}$$

$$= (-m)u^{m-1-2m} \frac{du}{dx} = nu^{-m-1} \frac{du}{dx} = nu^{n-1} \frac{du}{dx}.$$

Hence, (III) is true if n is any integer.

ILLUSTRATION 3. By use of (III) with $u = 3x^2 + x$, we obtain

$$\frac{d}{dx}(3x^2 + x)^9 = 9(3x^2 + x)^8(6x + 1).$$

ILLUSTRATION 4.

$$\frac{d}{dx}\left(\frac{1}{3x^5}\right) = \frac{1}{3} \cdot \frac{dx^{-5}}{dx} = -\frac{5}{3} x^{-6} = -\frac{5}{3x^6}.$$

ILLUSTRATION 5. $\quad \dfrac{d}{dx}\left[\dfrac{7}{(3x+4)^4}\right] = 7(-4)(3x+4)^{-5}(3) = -84(3x+4)^{-5}.$

$$\frac{d}{dx}\left(\frac{5x^2+1}{2x-4}\right)^3 = 3\left(\frac{5x^2+1}{2x-4}\right)^2 \frac{d}{dx}\left(\frac{5x^2+1}{2x-4}\right) \qquad \left[u = \frac{5x^2+1}{2x-4} \text{ in (III)}\right]$$

$$= 3\left(\frac{5x^2+1}{2x-4}\right)^2 \cdot \frac{2(5x^2-20x-1)}{(2x-4)^2} = \frac{6(5x^2+1)^2(5x^2-20x-1)}{(2x-4)^4}.$$

Proof of (III) if $n = p/q$, p and q are integers, $q > 0$, and p/q is in lowest terms.
1. Let $y = u^{p/q}$. Then, since y is a qth root of u^p,

$$y^q = u^p.$$

(5)

2. In (5), by hypothesis, $u = f(x)$, where f is some differentiable function. Thus,

* See Note 7 in the Appendix for a review of rational exponents.

the two sides of (5) are merely different notations for the same function value, u^p or $[f(x)]^p$. Hence, by use of (VII), we may differentiate each side of (5) with respect to x, with (III) employed for integral exponents, and equate the results:

$$\frac{d}{dx}(y^q) = \frac{d}{dx}(u^p), \quad or \quad qy^{q-1}\frac{dy}{dx} = pu^{p-1}\frac{du}{dx}; \tag{6}$$

$$\frac{dy}{dx} = \frac{p}{q}\cdot\frac{u^{p-1}}{y^{q-1}}\cdot\frac{du}{dx} = \frac{p}{q}\cdot\frac{yu^{p-1}}{y^{q-1}y}\cdot\frac{du}{dx} = \frac{p}{q}\cdot u^{\frac{p}{q}-1}\frac{du}{dx}, \tag{7}$$

because

$$\frac{yu^{p-1}}{y^q} = yu^{p-1}y^{-q} = u^{\frac{p}{q}}u^{p-1}u^{-p} = u^{\frac{p}{q}-1}.$$

We note that (7) proves (III) for the case $n = p/q$.

To differentiate any radical, we first express it as a fractional power, and then use (III), or (III)$_a$.

ILLUSTRATION 6. By (III)$_a$, $\dfrac{d}{dx}\sqrt[5]{x^3} = \dfrac{d}{dx}x^{\frac{3}{5}} = \dfrac{3}{5}x^{-\frac{2}{5}}.$

$$\frac{d}{dx}\frac{1}{5\sqrt[3]{x}} = \frac{d}{dx}\frac{1}{5}x^{-\frac{1}{3}} = -\frac{1}{15}x^{-\frac{4}{3}}.$$

With $u = x^2 + 3x$ in (III), $\dfrac{d}{dx}\sqrt[4]{(x^2 + 3x)^3} = \dfrac{3}{4}(x^2 + 3x)^{-\frac{1}{4}}(2x + 3).$

$$\frac{d}{dx}\sqrt{\frac{2+x}{3-x}} = \frac{d}{dx}\left(\frac{2+x}{3-x}\right)^{\frac{1}{2}} = \frac{1}{2}\left(\frac{2+x}{3-x}\right)^{-\frac{1}{2}}\frac{d}{dx}\left(\frac{2+x}{3-x}\right) = \frac{5}{2}(3-x)^{-\frac{3}{2}}(2+x)^{-\frac{1}{2}}.$$

EXERCISE 27

Differentiate the function of s, t, x, y, or z whose values are defined, or find y' from the equation.

1. $y = \dfrac{3x + 3}{2x + 5}.$

2. $y = \dfrac{3x}{2x^2 + 4}.$

3. $y = \dfrac{2 - 3x^2}{5x - 7}.$

4. $g(z) = \dfrac{2z - 3z^2}{z^3 - 1}.$

5. $h(s) = \dfrac{3}{2s + 4}.$

6. $\dfrac{3x^2 - 5}{2x + 3x^2}.$

7. $4x^{-3}.$

8. $3x^{-5}.$

9. $2y^{\frac{4}{3}}.$

10. $5\sqrt[4]{z^3}.$

11. $7y^{-\frac{2}{3}}.$

12. $\dfrac{3}{x^2}.$

13. $\dfrac{8}{5x^3}.$

14. $\dfrac{a}{bx^6}.$

15. $\dfrac{5}{2\sqrt{x}}.$

16. $\dfrac{c}{a\sqrt{z^3}}.$

17. $y = (3x^2 + 2x)^{12}.$

18. $y = (4x - 5x^3)^7.$

19. $y = (3x - 2x^{-4})^5.$

20. $(2z^3 - z^{-2})^4.$

21. $(t^{-1} - 2t^4)^3.$

22. $(2y^{-2} - 3y^{-1})^6.$

23. $(2x^2 + 1)^{\frac{5}{4}}.$

24. $(3s + s^3)^{\frac{7}{2}}.$

25. $(y + 3y^2)^{\frac{3}{5}}.$

26. $y = \sqrt{16 - x^2}.$

27. $y = \sqrt{3s^2 + 5}.$

28. $y = \sqrt[3]{x^2 - 4x}.$

29. $\dfrac{3}{(2x + 5)^{\frac{3}{2}}}.$

30. $\dfrac{7}{\sqrt{x^2 + 1}}.$

31. $\dfrac{1}{\sqrt[3]{3t + 5}}.$

32. $(x^2 + 3x)^3(x - x^3)^4.$

33. $(2t^3 - t^4)^5(t^2 + 5t)^3.$

34. $y = \sqrt{\dfrac{2x}{x - 3}}.$

35. $y = \sqrt{\dfrac{3z + 1}{z - 1}}.$

36. $y = \dfrac{t + t^2}{\sqrt{2t + 5}}.$

37. $\left(\dfrac{x+3}{4x^2+5}\right)^4.$ **38.** $\left(\dfrac{2z-3}{z^2+z}\right)^3.$ **39.** $\dfrac{(2x-3x^2)^3}{5-4x}.$ **40.** $\dfrac{x^2}{\sqrt{a^2+2ax}}.$

41. $\sqrt{x^3-2x}\,\sqrt{4-x^2}.$ **42.** $\sqrt{2t^2+3t}\,\sqrt{3t+1}.$ **43.** $(s^{\frac{1}{2}}-a^{\frac{1}{2}})^{\frac{1}{3}}.$

44. The weight w, in pounds of steam per second which will flow through a hole whose cross-section area is A square inches, if the steam approaches the hole under a pressure of P pounds per square inch, is approximated by $w = .0165AP^{.97}$ (Grashof's formula). Find the rate of change of w with respect to P when $P = 80$, if $A = 8$.

33. IMPLICIT FUNCTIONS

Hereafter, to state that $y = f(x)$ is a *solution* of an equation

$$g(x, y) = h(x, y) \tag{1}$$

for y as a function of x will mean that the following facts are true:

$$\left\{\begin{array}{l}\textit{There is a solution } (x_0, y_0) \textit{ of } (1), \textit{ where } y_0 = f(x_0), \textit{ and an interval } D \\ \textit{of numbers } x, \textit{ where } D \textit{ includes } * \ x_0, \textit{ such that } f \textit{ is differentiable} \\ \textit{on the domain } D, \textit{ and } (x, y) \textit{ is a solution of } (1) \textit{ when } y = f(x).\end{array}\right\} \tag{2}$$

In (2), we may call f a *solution function* of (1) for y as a function of x. Geometrically, (2) implies that, through $P:(x_0, y_0)$ in an xy-plane, there passes an arc of the graph of (1) where the equation of this arc is $y = f(x)$. Suppose, now, that at least one solution $y = f(x)$ exists as just described. If (1) happens to be in the form $y = f(x)$, we say that (1) defines y *explicitly* as a function of x. Otherwise, we say that (1) defines y *implicitly* as a function of x (perhaps in several ways), or that (1) defines y as an **implicit function** of x. In general, it will be found either impossible or inconvenient to solve (1) for y in terms of x in an effort to obtain one or more explicit results of the form $y = f(x)$, even though solutions exist.

In (1), we may interchange the preceding roles of x and y, and earmark y as the independent variable. Then, we may speak of a solution $x = g(y)$ of (1) *for x as a function of y;* in such a case, an arc of the graph of (1) through a solution point $P:(x_0, y_0)$ would have the equation $x = g(y)$.

ILLUSTRATION 1. On solving $x^2 + y^2 = 25$ for y, we obtain the solutions

$$y = +\sqrt{25 - x^2} \quad and \quad y = -\sqrt{25 - x^2}. \tag{3}$$

Equations (3) and their graphs were met in Illustration 4 on page 25. Similarly, $x^2 + y^2 = 25$ defines x implicitly as a function of y, with the solutions

$$x = +\sqrt{25 - y^2} \quad and \quad x = -\sqrt{25 - y^2}.$$

ILLUSTRATION 2. With only real values allowed for x and y, (1) may have no solution, as in the case of $x^2 + y^2 = -4$, and thus would not have a solution for either x or y as a function of the other variable.

Let us assume that (1) has the solution $y = f(x)$. Then

$$g(x, f(x)) = h(x, f(x)). \tag{4}$$

* We allow for the possibility that $f'(x_0)$ may not exist, but f is continuous at $x = x_0$.

Thus, with $y = f(x)$, the two sides of (1) are identical at all points x, as in (4), and hence *the derivatives of the two sides of* (1) *are equal*, if the derivatives exist. These remarks justify the following method for obtaining dy/dx in terms of x and y, *without solving* (1) *for y in terms of x*. The result gives the slope y' at any corresponding point (x, y) on the graph of (1).

Summary. *To obtain dy/dx, or y', if the variables x and y are related by an equation* (1), *differentiate with respect to x on both sides of* (1), *and then solve for y'.*

ILLUSTRATION 3. Suppose that y is known to be a differentiable function of x. Then, by use of (III), without knowledge of the function,

$$\frac{d}{dx}(3x + y^2)^{\frac{1}{3}} = \tfrac{1}{3}(3x + y^2)^{-\frac{2}{3}} \cdot \frac{d}{dx}(3x + y^2) = \tfrac{1}{3}(3x + y^2)^{-\frac{2}{3}}(3 + 2yy').$$

If x is known to be a differentiable function of y, by use of (V),

$$\frac{d}{dy}(x^3y^2) = 3x^2y^2\frac{dx}{dy} + 2x^3y.$$

EXAMPLE 1. Obtain dy/dx at any point (x, y) satisfying

$$8x^2 + 4xy + 5y^2 + 28x = 2y - 20. \tag{5}$$

Also, obtain the slopes of the tangents to the graph of (5) where $x = -1$.

Solution. 1. Differentiate both sides of (5), with $y = f(x)$ where f is unknown, and equate the results:

$$16x + 4(y + xy') + 10yy' + 28 = 2y'; \text{ or,}$$

$$y'(4x + 10y - 2) = -16x - 4y - 28; \text{ or,}$$

$$y' = \frac{8x + 2y + 14}{1 - 2x - 5y}. \tag{6}$$

2. If $x = -1$ in (5), then $5y^2 - 6y = 0$, and $y = 0$ or $y = \frac{6}{5}$. The points on the graph of (5) are $P:(-1, 0)$ and $R:(-1, \frac{6}{5})$. From (6), we obtain the slopes of the tangents at P and R:

$$\frac{dy}{dx}\bigg|_{(x=-1,\, y=0)} = 2; \quad \frac{dy}{dx}\bigg|_{(x=-1,\, y=\frac{6}{5})} = -\frac{14}{5}. \tag{7}$$

Note 1. A request to obtain dy/dx from an equation (1) implies that (1) has a solution for y as a function of x, and then the Summary applies. A request for dx/dy specifies y as the independent variable and implies that (1) has a solution for x as a function of y. Then, the Summary applies with the roles of x and y interchanged. We refer to the Summary as the **implicit function method** for finding a derivative from an equation relating two variables x and y.

ILLUSTRATION 4. To obtain dx/dy for any solution $x = g(y)$ of (5), we differentiate with respect to y on both sides of (5) and solve for dx/dy:

$$16x\frac{dx}{dy} + 4x + 4y\frac{dx}{dy} + 10y + 28\frac{dx}{dy} = 2; \quad \frac{dx}{dy} = \frac{1 - 2x - 5y}{8x + 2y + 14}. \tag{8}$$

The fact that dy/dx in (6) and dx/dy in (8) are reciprocals is a general property, to be discussed on page 105.

EXERCISE 28

If $y = f(x)$, where f is unknown, find an expression for the derivative with respect to x of the function whose values are defined.

1. $x^3 y$. **2.** $2x^2 y$. **3.** xy^3. **4.** x/y. **5.** $1/(xy)$.
6. $(3x + 2y)^5$. **7.** $\sqrt{x - y^2}$. **8.** $x/(x^2 + y^2)$.

Find dy/dx in terms of x and y, without solving for y in terms of x.

9. $x^3 + y^3 = 1$. **10.** $x^2 + y^2 = 16$. **11.** $x + xy = 8$.
12. $xy = 10$. **13.** $4x^2 - 9y^2 = 36$. **14.** $x^2 + 5y^2 = 16$.
15. $x^2 + 2xy - y^2 = 5$. **16.** $x^3 - xy^2 - 7y = 4x - 2$.
17. $x^2 y + y^3 = 6$. **18.** $x^3 + y^3 - 6xy = 0$.
19. $x^2 y^2 = 4(x^2 + y^2)$. **20.** $(x + 3y)^2 = 2x - 3y + 5$.
21. $2\sqrt{x} + 3\sqrt{y} = 8$. **22.** $x + a\sqrt{xy} - y^2 = b$.
23. Find dr/dt if $r^2 + 3r^3 t^2 = 5t - 2$. **24.** Find ds/dy if $y^2 + 3sy - s^3 = 8$.

25–28. Find dx/dy in Problems 13–16, respectively, without use of dy/dx.

Find the equation of the tangent to the curve at each specified point.

29. $x^2 + y^2 = 34$; at $(3, -5)$. **30.** $3x^2 + 2y^2 = 14$; at $(-2, 1)$.
31. $2x^2 - 3xy + 5y^2 - 6x = 2y + 12$; where $x = -1$.
32. $2x^3 - y^2 + 3xy = x + 7$; where $x = 2$.
33. Find dy/dx if $2(x + 3y^2)^2 - (2x + 5y)^3 = 1$.
34. Find dy/dv if $\sqrt{v - y} + \sqrt{v + y} = 4$.

34. INVERSE FUNCTIONS

Suppose that $y = f(x)$, where the domain of f is a set, T, of numbers x and the range of f is a set, R, of numbers y. Then, by the definition of a function, to each x in T there corresponds a y in R so that $y = f(x)$. In general, it is *not* true that

$$\left\{ \begin{array}{l} \text{to each number } y \text{ in the range } R \text{ of } f \text{ there cor-} \\ \text{responds } \textbf{just one } \text{number } x \text{ in the domain } T \text{ of } f. \end{array} \right\} \tag{1}$$

However, (1) *is true* if f is an *increasing* function, or a *decreasing* function, as illustrated by the graphs of $y = f(x)$ in Figures 75 and 76, for f increasing and for f decreasing, respectively. When (1) is true, we say that there is a *one-to-one*

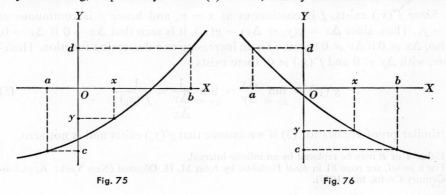

Fig. 75   Fig. 76

correspondence between the numbers x in the domain and y in the range of f. In such a case we meet the following terminology, where we restrict T and R to be *intervals* in this text.

Definition III. *Suppose that f is an increasing (or, a decreasing) function with the domain* * $T = \{a \leqq x \leqq b\}$ *and range* * $R = \{c \leqq y \leqq d\}$, *and let $g(y)$ represent the single number x in T which corresponds to the number y in R. Then, the function g, thus defined with domain R and range T, is called the* **inverse** *of f. Also, f is called the inverse of g, and the pair f and g jointly are called* **inverse functions.**

If f and g are inverse functions, then, as in Figures 75 and 76 on page 103,

$$(\text{with } a \leqq x \leqq b; c \leqq y \leqq d) \qquad y = f(x) \quad \text{is equivalent to} \quad x = g(y). \qquad (2)$$

On account of (2), the graphs of $y = f(x)$ and $x = g(y)$ on the same xy-plane are identical. In (2), if the equation $y = f(x)$ can be solved for x in terms of y, we thus obtain $x = g(y)$.

> ILLUSTRATION 1. If $f(x) = 3x + 7$, then $f'(x) = 3 > 0$, and hence f is an *increasing* function. On solving the equation $y = 3x + 7$ for x in terms of y, we obtain $x = \frac{1}{3}y - \frac{7}{3}$. Hence, the inverse of f is the function $g(y) = \frac{1}{3}y - \frac{7}{3}$.

Note 1. If $f'(x) > 0$ at all points x on $T = \{a \leqq x \leqq b\}$, or if $f'(x) < 0$ on T, then f is an increasing or a decreasing function on T, and hence Definition III applies.

We shall accept without proof † the fact that, in Definition III, *if f is continuous at x_0 in T then g is continuous at y_0 in R*, where $y_0 = f(x_0)$, because the graphs of the equations $y = f(x)$ and $x = g(y)$ are identical.

Theorem II. *Suppose that f and g are inverse functions and that $y_0 = f(x_0)$. Then, if one of $f'(x_0)$ and $g'(y_0)$ exists and is not zero, the other derivative also exists, and*

$$f'(x_0) = \frac{1}{g'(y_0)}. \qquad (3)$$

Proof. 1. Let (x_0, y_0) and $(x_0 + \Delta x, y_0 + \Delta y)$ be two solutions of the equivalent equations $y = f(x)$ and $x = g(y)$, and assume that $f'(x_0)$ exists. Then

$$\lim_{\Delta x \to 0} \frac{\Delta y}{\Delta x} = f'(x_0) \neq 0. \qquad (4)$$

2. Since $f'(x_0)$ exists, f is continuous at $x = x_0$ and hence g is continuous at $y = y_0$. Then, since $\Delta x = g(y_0 + \Delta y) - g(y_0)$, it is seen that $\Delta x \to 0$ if $\Delta y \to 0$. Also, $\Delta x \neq 0$ if $\Delta y \neq 0$ because f is an increasing or a decreasing function. Therefore, with $\Delta y \neq 0$ and $f'(x_0) \neq 0$, there exists

$$g'(y_0) = \lim_{\Delta y \to 0} \frac{\Delta x}{\Delta y} = \lim_{\Delta x \to 0} \frac{1}{\dfrac{\Delta y}{\Delta x}} = \frac{1}{f'(x_0)}. \qquad (5)$$

A similar proof applies for (3) if we assume that $g'(y_0)$ exists and is not zero.

---

* Either T or R may be replaced by an infinite interval.

† For a proof, see page 81 in *Real Variables* by John M. H. Olmsted (New York: Appleton-Century-Crofts, Inc., 1959).

Suppose that an equation $h(x, y) = 0$ has a solution $y = f(x)$ for *y as a function of x*, and assume that $f'(x) > 0$, or $f'(x) < 0$, at all values of x involved. Then, f has an inverse g so that

$$y = f(x) \quad \text{is equivalent to} \quad x = g(y). \tag{6}$$

Each solution (x, y) of $y = f(x)$ satisfies $h(x, y) = 0$. Hence, by (6), each solution (x, y) of $x = g(y)$ satisfies $h(x, y) = 0$, or $x = g(y)$ is a solution of $h(x, y) = 0$ for *x as a function of y*. With dy/dx meaning $f'(x)$, and dx/dy meaning $g'(y)$, from (3) we obtain

$$\frac{dy}{dx} = \frac{1}{\dfrac{dx}{dy}}. \tag{VIII}$$

Note 2. Hereafter, if we refer to both dy/dx and dx/dy, to be obtained from an equation $h(x, y) = 0$, we shall infer that this equation has inverse solution functions f and g so that an arc of the graph of $h(x, y) = 0$ has either equation in (6) at all points (x, y) involved. If (VIII) is used, we imply that $dy/dx \neq 0$ and $dx/dy \neq 0$.

ILLUSTRATION 2. The equation $y = x^3$ defines y explicitly as an increasing function of x [let $f(x) = x^3$], and hence also defines x implicitly as a function of y, with $x = y^{\frac{1}{3}} = g(y)$, where f and g are inverse functions. If $x \neq 0$, which is equivalent to $y \neq 0$, we obtain dy/dx from $y = x^3$ and dx/dy from $x = y^{\frac{1}{3}}$:

$$\frac{dy}{dx} = 3x^2; \quad \frac{dx}{dy} = \frac{1}{3} y^{-\frac{2}{3}} = \frac{1}{3y^{\frac{2}{3}}} = \frac{1}{3x^2} = \frac{1}{\dfrac{dy}{dx}}, \; \textit{checking} \text{ (VIII)}.$$

EXAMPLE 1. Obtain dy/dx and then dx/dy in case

$$2x^2 - 3xy + y^2 = 7. \tag{7}$$

Solution. First, we consider y as an implicit function of x and differentiate with respect to x on both sides in (7):

$$4x - 3y - 3x\frac{dy}{dx} + 2y\frac{dy}{dx} = 0; \quad \frac{dy}{dx} = \frac{4x - 3y}{3x - 2y}.$$

Then, by use of (VIII) and the result from the preceding differentiation,

$$\frac{dx}{dy} = \left(1 \div \frac{dy}{dx}\right) = \frac{3x - 2y}{4x - 3y},$$

provided that $\dfrac{dy}{dx} \neq 0$ at the solution (x, y) of (7).

Note 3. Suppose that the curve, C, in Figure 77 is the graph of $y = f(x)$ or $x = g(y)$, related as in (6), and satisfying (VIII). Then, at any point $P:(x, y)$ on the common graph C, with dx and dy as corresponding differentials associated with the tangent to C at P, we may recall (VIII) as a simple relation between a fraction and its reciprocal.

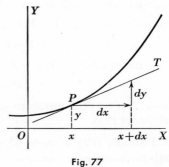

Fig. 77

35. DERIVATIVES OF HIGHER ORDERS

Let f be a differentiable function with values $f(\bullet)$. If the derivative f' has a derivative at $x = x_0$, this result is called the *second derivative* of f at x_0. At those values of x where f' has a derivative, we thus arrive at the second derivative function, f'', for f. If we let $y = f(x)$, the value of the second derivative of f at an arbitrary point x is denoted by any one of the following symbols:

$$f''(x); \quad \frac{d^2f(x)}{dx^2}; \quad y'', \quad \frac{d^2y}{dx^2}; \quad D_x^2 f(x); \quad D_x^2 y. \tag{1}$$

We read $f''(x)$ as "*f-second at x*," or "*the second derivative of $f(x)$*"; y'' is read "*y-second*"; either one of the last three symbols at the right in (1) is read "*the second derivative of y, or of $f(x)$, with respect to x.*" In (1), we favor use of the four symbols at the left. By definition,

$$f''(x) = \frac{d}{dx} f'(x), \quad or \quad \frac{d^2y}{dx^2} = \frac{d}{dx}\left(\frac{dy}{dx}\right). \tag{2}$$

Similarly, the derivative, if it exists, of the second derivative is called the *third derivative* (function) of f; etc. for the fourth, fifth, $\cdots$, nth derivatives, where n is any positive integer.

ILLUSTRATION 1. The 3d, 4th, $\cdots$, nth derivatives of a function f are represented by f''', $f^{(IV)}$, $\cdots$, $f^{(n)}$, read *f-third, f-fourth*, $\cdots$, *f-upper-n*. If we let $y = f(x)$, the values of the derivatives at an arbitrary value of x are represented by $f'''(x)$, $f^{(IV)}(x)$, $\cdots$, $f^{(n)}(x)$, or by

$$\frac{d^3y}{dx^3}, \frac{d^4y}{dx^4}, \cdots, \frac{d^ny}{dx^n}. \tag{3}$$

Or, we may use $D_x^n f(x)$, or $y^{(n)}(x)$ instead of $f^{(n)}(x)$. We read $f^{(n)}(x)$ as "*the nth derivative of f at x*," or simply "*f-upper-n at x*." We call $f^{(n)}$ a derivative of the nth *order*, or the nth *derived function for f*. To state that f is *differentiable twice* will mean that f'' exists, which implies that f' exists and is continuous. Similarly, to state that f is *differentiable n times*, where n is a positive integer, means that $f^{(n)}$ exists, and this implies that $f^{(k)}$ exists and is continuous for $k = 1, 2, \cdots, (n-1)$. By definition, for instance,

$$f'''(x) = \frac{d}{dx}(f''(x)); \quad \frac{d^4y}{dx^4} = \frac{d}{dx}\left(\frac{d^3y}{dx^3}\right); \quad \frac{d^ky}{dx^k} = \frac{d}{dx}\left(\frac{d^{k-1}y}{dx^{k-1}}\right).$$

ILLUSTRATION 2. If $f(x) = 5x^4 + 3x^3 + 2x - 9$, then

$$f'(x) = 20x^3 + 9x^2 + 2; \quad f''(x) = D_x f'(x) = 60x^2 + 18x;$$

$$f'''(x) = 120x + 18; \quad f^{(IV)}(x) = 120; \quad f^{(V)}(x) = 0.$$

ILLUSTRATION 3. If $y = x^{\frac{5}{3}} - 2x^7 - 7$, then

$$y' = \tfrac{5}{3}x^{\frac{2}{3}} - 14x^6; \quad y'' = D_x y' = \tfrac{2}{3}\cdot\tfrac{5}{3}x^{-\frac{1}{3}} - 84x^5.$$

Note 1. If we refer merely to *the derivative* of a function $f(x)$, we shall mean the *first derivative* $f'(x)$.

Formula (IV) of page 92 extends to derivatives of any order. That is, *the nth derivative of a sum of functions is the sum of their nth derivatives.*

ILLUSTRATION 4. $\quad \dfrac{d^2}{dx^2}(u + v) = \dfrac{d}{dx}D_x(u + v) = \dfrac{d}{dx}\left(\dfrac{du}{dx} + \dfrac{dv}{dx}\right) = \dfrac{d^2u}{dx^2} + \dfrac{d^2v}{dx^2}.$

Note 2. If $n \geqq 2$, we shall *not* consider $\dfrac{d^n y}{dx^n}$ as a quotient of separately defined quantities $d^n y$ and dx^n.* However,

$$\frac{d^2 y}{dx^2} = \frac{d}{dx}\left(\frac{dy}{dx}\right) = \frac{dy'}{dx},$$

which can be taken as an actual quotient, where dy' is the differential of the first derivative, y', and similarly for derivatives of higher orders.

EXERCISE 29

Define at least one solution $y = f(x)$ and a corresponding solution $x = g(y)$ so that f and g are inverse functions. State the domain and the range for f and for g. Then graph the given equation and calculate dy/dx and dx/dy at an arbitrary point (x, y).

1. $y = x^5.$ **2.** $x = y^2.$ **3.** $x = 4 - y^2.$ **4.** $4x^2 + 9y^2 = 36.$

Obtain just one of dy/dx and dx/dy by differentiation, and find the other derivative by use of the reciprocal relation.

5. $3x^2 - xy + y^3 = 3.$ **6.** $2x - 3xy + y^2 = 2y - 5.$

7. $9x^2 = 8y^3.$ **8.** $27x^3 = 4y^2.$ **9.** $x^2 + 4y^2 = 16.$

10. $b^2x^2 + a^2y^2 = a^2b^2.$ **11.** $x^{\frac{1}{2}} + y^{\frac{1}{2}} = a^{\frac{1}{2}}.$ **12.** $x^{\frac{2}{3}} + y^{\frac{2}{3}} = a^{\frac{2}{3}}.$

Find the 2d, 3d, and 4th derivatives of the function.

13. $3x^5 - 2x^3 + 7.$ **14.** $4x^3 - 2x^2 - 6.$ **15.** $x^6 - x^4 - x^3.$

Find the second derivative of the function, or y'' if y is involved.

16. $y = \dfrac{2x}{3 + x}.$ **17.** $y = \dfrac{2s^2 - 3s}{s - 1}.$ **18.** $f(x) = x^{-4} - \dfrac{3}{x}.$

19. $g(t) = 2t^{\frac{1}{2}} - 3t^{\frac{1}{3}}.$ **20.** $h(s) = 5s^4 - s^{-3}.$ **21.** $y = 4t^{-5} - 3t^{-2}.$

22. $f(x) = (3x + 7)^{14}.$ **23.** $g(t) = (2t - 3)^7.$ **24.** $h(x) = \sqrt{2x + 3}.$

25. $\sqrt[3]{2s^2 + 5}.$ **26.** $x\sqrt{2x - 3}.$ **27.** $t(6t - 3)^4.$

The equation defines y implicitly as a function of x. Symbols a, b, and p represent constants. Find y'' by implicit function differentiation, and simplify if convenient by use of the given equation, without solving it for y in terms of x.

28. $4x^2 - 9y^2 = 36.$ (1)

SOLUTION. 1. Differentiate both sides of (1) with respect to x:

$$8x - 18yy' = 0, \quad or \quad y' = \frac{4x}{9y}. \tag{2}$$

2. Differentiate y' in (2) with respect to x, using (2) again wherever $D_x y$ occurs:

$$y'' = \frac{d}{dx}\left(\frac{4x}{9y}\right) = \frac{4}{9} \cdot \frac{y - xy'}{y^2} = \frac{4}{9} \cdot \frac{y - x\frac{4x}{9y}}{y^2}. \tag{3}$$

From (1) and (3), $\quad y'' = \dfrac{4(9y^2 - 4x^2)}{81y^3} = \dfrac{4(-36)}{81y^3}, \quad or \quad y'' = -\dfrac{16}{9y^3}.$

* We could define $d^2 f(x)$ as $d^2 f(x) = f''(x)(dx)^2$. Then, we obtain $f''(x) = [d^2 f(x)] \div (dx)^2$. We shall not use $d^2 f(x)$.

29. $x^2 + y^2 = a^2$.   **30.** $y^2 = 8x^3$.   **31.** $x^2 - y^2 = a^2$.   **32.** $y^2 = 2px$.

33. $2x^2 + 5y^2 = 3$.   **34.** $x^3 + y^3 = 8$.   **35.** $b^2x^2 + a^2y^2 = a^2b^2$.

36. $b^2x^2 - a^2y^2 = a^2b^2$.   **37.** $x^{\frac{1}{2}} + y^{\frac{1}{2}} = a^{\frac{1}{2}}$.   **38.** $x^{\frac{2}{3}} + y^{\frac{2}{3}} = a^{\frac{2}{3}}$.

39. Find y' and y'' where $x = 2$ on the graph of $3x^2 - 2xy + 7y^2 = 15$.

40. Find y' and y'' where $y = 3$ on the graph of $2x^2 - 2xy + y^2 = 5$.

41–43. Find $D_y^2 x$ in Problems 29–31, respectively.

EXERCISE 30 (*Review of Chapters Three and Four*)

1. Graph the function f which is defined on the interval $-2 \leq x \leq 4$ by the equations
$$f(x) = 4 - x^2 \text{ when } -2 \leq x \leq 0, \quad and \quad f(x) = \tfrac{1}{4}(4 - x) \text{ when } 0 < x \leq 4.$$
What can be said about $\lim_{x \to 0} f(x)$; $\lim_{x \to 0-} f(x)$; $\lim_{x \to 0+} f(x)$? Where is f discontinuous? Why?

2. Evaluate $\lim_{x \to 9} (x - 9)/(2\sqrt{x} - 6)$.

3. If $f(x) = x^3 + 2x$, find the average rate of change of $f(x)$ from $x = 2$ to $x = 4$. Find the instantaneous rate of change of f at $x = 2$.

4. The position of a moving particle on an s-axis at time t is defined by
$$s = t^3 - 12t^2 + 5.$$
Find the average velocity of the particle from $t = 1$ to $t = 3$; the instantaneous velocity and the speed at $t = 2$.

By direct use of the increment process, calculate $f'(x)$, or y'.

5. $y = x^2 - 2x$.   **6.** $f(x) = (3x + 1)/(1 - 2x)$.   **7.** $y = \sqrt{1 - 2x}$.

8. Find the values of x where f is stationary, increasing, or decreasing if
$$f(x) = x^3 + 3x^2 - 9x + 5.$$
Also, obtain a graph of $y = f(x)$.

9. A particle is moving in a vertical line, with the height s above the earth at time t given by $s = -8t^2 + 64t - 56$. Find the velocity of the particle at any instant t. For what values of t is the particle rising; falling; stationary at its highest elevation?

10. Find the tangent to the graph of $y = f(x)$ in Problem 8 where $x = 2$.

By use of formulas for derivatives, differentiate the function of x, y, z, or t whose values are defined, or find dy/dx from the equation specifying y as a function of x.

11. $5/x^3$.   **12.** $4\sqrt[3]{z^5}$.   **13.** $y = (2x - 5x^3)^4$.   **14.** $y = \sqrt{x^3 - x}$.

15. $\sqrt[3]{2t + t^2}$.   **16.** $3/(2x + 5)$.   **17.** $(2y + y^2)^{\frac{3}{5}}$.   **18.** $1/(x^2 + 1)^3$.

19. $(x - 1)^2(2x + 3)^4$.   **20.** $\sqrt{1 + t}(t^2 + 1)^3$.

21. $\dfrac{1}{\sqrt{1 - z^2}}$.   **22.** $\sqrt{\dfrac{3x}{2 - x}}$.   **23.** $y = \left(\dfrac{x + 2}{1 - x^2}\right)^4$.

Calculate dy/dx and dx/dy without solving for y in terms of x, or for x in terms of y.

24. $x^2 + y^3 = 1$.   **25.** $2xy - y^2 = 3$.   **26.** $x^2y - 2xy^2 = 4$.

27. Find the tangent to the graph of $3x^2y - 4y - 2x = 4$ where $x = 2$.

28. Graph the equation $x^2 - 9 = y$. Define at least one solution $y = f(x)$ and a corresponding solution $x = g(y)$ so that f and g are inverse functions; state the domain and the range for f and for g. Also, calculate dy/dx and dx/dy.

29. Find $D_x^2 y$ if $4x^2 - 9y^2 = 64$.

30. Calculate y'' if $y = 3x/(2 - x)$.

31. If $y = f(u)$, where $f'(u)$ exists, and if $u = 3x^3 + x$, write an expression, as explicit as possible, for dy/dx.

32. If u and v are twice differentiable functions of x, calculate $D_x^2(uv)$ in terms of u, v, and their derivatives.

★SUPPLEMENT FOR CHAPTER FOUR

In Problems 33–35, use mathematical induction; u and v are functions of x possessing all desired derivatives; n is any positive integer.

33. Prove that $D_x^n x^n = n!$.

34. Prove that $D_x^n(uv) = uv^{(n)} + {}_nC_1 u^{(n-1)}v + \cdots + {}_nC_k u^{(n-k)}v^{(k)} + \cdots + {}_nC_n uv^{(n)}$, where ${}_nC_k = n!/k!(n-k)!$, the kth binomial coefficient, and $0! = 1$.

35. Obtain a formula for the derivative with respect to x of a product of n differentiable functions of x.

36. Obtain $f'(x)$ if $f(x) = (2a - 3bx)(a + bx)^{\frac{3}{2}}$.

37. Obtain $f'(x)$ if $f(x) = (3b^2x^2 - 4abx + 8a^2)\sqrt{a + bx}$.

38. If $y = f(g(x))$, where g and f are twice-differentiable functions, calculate $D_x^2 y$ in terms of derivatives of f and g.

39. If f and g are functions possessing derivatives, and $g(x) = f(y)$, calculate $D_x y$ and $D_x^2 y$ in terms of derivatives of g and f.

40. By use of a counter-example, prove that it is *not* always true that $D_x^2 y = 1/D_y^2 x$.

41. By reasoning with inequalities, prove that (1) on page 103 is true if f is an increasing function on the domain T.

CHAPTER FIVE

Role of Infinity in Limits

36. LIMITS INVOLVING INFINITY

Frequently, a limit of some sort is involved when the term *infinite*, or *infinity*, is used mathematically.

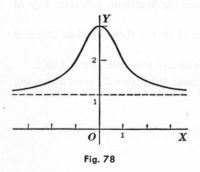

Fig. 78

ILLUSTRATION 1. Consider

$$f(x) = \frac{3 + x^2}{1 + x^2} = 1 + \frac{2}{1 + x^2}, \qquad (1)$$

and the graph of $y = f(x)$ in Figure 78. If x increases without bound, or decreases without bound, then $2/(1 + x^2)$ approaches zero, and $f(x) \to 1$. Hence, we say that *the limit of $f(x)$ is 1*, or $f(x) \to 1$, *as "x approaches plus infinity"* $(x \to +\infty)$, and also as "x approaches minus infinity" $(x \to -\infty)$; we write, respectively,

$$\lim_{x \to +\infty} f(x) = 1 \quad and \quad \lim_{x \to -\infty} f(x) = 1. \qquad (2)$$

The geometrical significance of (2) is that the line $y = 1$ is an asymptote of the graph of $y = f(x)$. Both results in (2) are included in the statement that $f(x) \to 1$ as $|x| \to \infty$, where plain "∞" has the force of "$+\infty$" because $|x|$ is never negative. Notations such as (2) are defined formally as follows.

Definition I. *Let f be a function, with values $f(x)$. Then, to say that the limit of $f(x)$ is L as x approaches plus infinity (or, as x becomes positively infinite) means that $|f(x) - L|$ is as small as we please at all values of x which are sufficiently large, and we write*

$$\lim_{x \to +\infty} f(x) = L, \quad or \quad f(x) \to L \ as \ x \to +\infty. \qquad (3)$$

Similarly, we introduce the symbolism "$f(x) \to L$ as $x \to -\infty$," whose definition, as above, would conclude with the phrase "*at all values of x where $-x$ is sufficiently large.*" In (3) we may also say that "*f has the limit L at $+\infty$.*"

110

ILLUSTRATION 2. Sin x varies from -1 to $+1$ at values of x on any interval of length 2π, if x increases. Hence, there is no number L so that $\lim_{x\to+\infty} \sin x = L$; that is, $\lim_{x\to+\infty} \sin x$ fails to exist.

In the following definition, f represents a function whose domain contains all numbers x except possibly $x = c$ on an interval including c.

Definition II. *To say that* **the limit of $f(x)$ is plus infinity ($+\infty$) as $x \to c$** *(or, $f(x)$ becomes positively infinite as $x \to c$) means that, when $x \neq c$, $f(x)$ is as large as we please at all values of x sufficiently near c, and we write*

$$\lim_{x\to c} f(x) = +\infty, \quad or \quad f(x) \to +\infty \text{ as } x \to c. \tag{4}$$

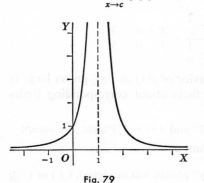

Fig. 79

Similarly, we define "$f(x) \to -\infty$ as $x \to c$," and "$|f(x)| \to \infty$ as $x \to c$." When (4) is true, we sometimes say that "f has the infinite limit $+\infty$ at $x = c$." For contrast, an ordinary limit then is called a *finite limit*. Hereafter, any limit is understood to be a *finite limit* unless otherwise stated.

ILLUSTRATION 3. Let f be defined by

$$f(x) = \frac{1}{(x-1)^2}. \tag{5}$$

A graph of $y = f(x)$ is given in Figure 79. In (5), $(x-1) \to 0$ as $x \to 1$; then $f(x) \to +\infty$ as $x \to 1$, which corresponds to the fact that the line $x = 1$ is an asymptote of the graph. We say that f has an *infinite discontinuity* at $x = 1$, where $f(x)$ is undefined. Also, in (5), $f(x) \to 0$ as $|x| \to \infty$; the graph of (5) has the line $y = 0$ as a corresponding asymptote.

ILLUSTRATION 4. Let $f(x) = 6/x$. In Figure 80, the hyperbola is the graph of $y = f(x)$, or $xy = 6$. If $x > 0$ then $f(x) > 0$, and hence $f(x) \to +\infty$ if $x \to 0+$ (from the right). Similarly,

$$f(x) \to -\infty \quad if \quad x \to 0-.$$

Since these *one-sided* infinite limits are *not identical*, $f(x)$ does not have an infinite limit as $x \to 0$ without restriction. However, $|f(x)| \to \infty$ as $x \to 0$. Thus, we have

Fig. 80

$$\lim_{x\to 0-} \frac{6}{x} = -\infty; \quad \lim_{x\to 0+} \frac{6}{x} = +\infty; \quad \lim_{x\to 0} \left|\frac{6}{x}\right| = \infty. \tag{6}$$

Because of (6), the graph in Figure 80 has the line $x = 0$ as an asymptote, approached downward ($y \to -\infty$) as $x \to 0-$, and upward as $x \to 0+$.

We may meet infinite limits as the absolute value of the independent variable becomes infinite. Thus, we may have $\lim_{x\to-\infty} f(x) = +\infty$.

ILLUSTRATION 5. $\lim_{x\to+\infty} \dfrac{5-3x}{2} = -\infty$, because $-3x \to -\infty$ as $x \to +\infty$.

The verbal forms of the theorems on limits in Note 3 on page 70 apply to finite limits such as (3), or similar limits involving $- \infty$. When infinite limits are involved, modifications of the theorems can be established. However, at this stage, any related expression involving infinite limits had best be treated as a special example, without use of general theorems about limits.

Let R be a rational function, with $R(x) = P(x)/Q(x)$, where $P(x)$ and $Q(x)$ are polynomials. Then, to obtain $\lim_{|x| \to \infty} R(x)$, first divide the numerator and denominator of $R(x)$ by the *highest power of x found in* $Q(x)$.

ILLUSTRATION 6. In evaluating the following limit, we divide by x^2, and use Theorems I and IV, page 70 (in revised forms):

$$\lim_{|x| \to \infty} \frac{3x^2 + 2}{5x^2 - x} = \lim_{|x| \to \infty} \frac{3 + \dfrac{2}{x^2}}{5 - \dfrac{1}{x}} = \frac{3 + 0}{5 - 0} = \frac{3}{5}.$$

In dealing with a function f, where the behavior of $f(x)$ as $| x |$ grows large is well appreciated, we agree to accept simple facts about corresponding limits without formal proof.

ILLUSTRATION 7. After thinking of cases like 3^{50} and $3^{-50} = 1/3^{50}$, etc., we accept

$$\lim_{x \to +\infty} 3^x = + \infty; \qquad \lim_{x \to -\infty} 3^x = 0.$$

★*Note 1.* In this text, the symbol "∞" for "infinity" always will be signed, $(+)$ or $(-)$, with plain ∞ meaning "$+ \infty$." At some places in mathematics it proves convenient to introduce not only $+ \infty$ and $- \infty$ but also ∞ without any implied sign. Then, "$v \to \infty$" means "$| v | \to + \infty$" in the sense of this text.

EXERCISE 31

For the function f as defined, calculate the value of each specified limit, or decide that it does not exist. Then, graph f by use of corresponding asymptotes and very few computed points.

1. $f(x) = 1/x^2$; limits as $| x | \to \infty$ and as $x \to 0$.

2. $f(x) = 1/x^3$; limits as $| x | \to \infty$, $x \to 0+$, and $x \to 0$.

3. $f(x) = 3/(x - 2)$; limits as $| x | \to \infty$, $x \to 2+$, and $x \to 2-$.

4. $f(x) = 3/(x - 2)^2$; limits as $| x | \to \infty$, $x \to 2+$, $x \to 2-$, and $x \to 2$.

Evaluate each limit, or reach a conclusion that it does not exist.

5. $\displaystyle \lim_{|x| \to \infty} \frac{4x^3 + 2x^2}{5x^3 - 3}.$ **6.** $\displaystyle \lim_{|x| \to \infty} \frac{2 - 4x}{3 + 5x}.$ **7.** $\displaystyle \lim_{|x| \to \infty} \frac{5x - 2x^4}{3x + 4x^4}.$

8. $\displaystyle \lim_{|x| \to \infty} \frac{2x^3 - 3x^2 - 5}{5x^3 + x - 4}.$ **9.** $\displaystyle \lim_{x \to +\infty} \frac{3x - 2x^2 - x^3}{5x^2 + 3x}.$

10. $\displaystyle \lim_{x \to -\infty} \frac{2x^4 - 3x^2 - 5}{5x^3 - x + 2}.$ **11.** $\displaystyle \lim_{x \to -\infty} \frac{2x^2 + 3x}{5x^3 + 2x - 4}.$

Inspect the graphs of $y = \sin x$, $y = \cos x$, and $y = \tan x$ on page 709. Then state conclusions about the following limits.

12. $\displaystyle \lim_{x \to 0} \frac{1}{\sin^2 x}.$ **13.** $\displaystyle \lim_{x \to 0+} \frac{1}{\sin x}.$ **14.** $\displaystyle \lim_{x \to 0-} \frac{1}{\sin x}.$

15. (a) $\lim\limits_{x \to \frac{1}{2}\pi+} \tan x$;   (b) $\lim\limits_{x \to \frac{1}{2}\pi-} \tan x$;   (c) $\lim\limits_{x \to \frac{1}{2}\pi} \tan x$;   (d) $\lim\limits_{x \to +\infty} \cos x$.

16. If $\lim_{x \to c} f(x) = 0$, what is true about $\lim_{x \to c} \dfrac{1}{|f(x)|}$?

17. If $\lim_{x \to c} |f(x)| = \infty$, what is true about $\lim_{x \to c} \dfrac{1}{f(x)}$?

★*Evaluate the limit, with the aid of appropriate verbal statements.*

18. $\lim\limits_{x \to \infty} \dfrac{\sin x}{x}$.   **19.** $\lim\limits_{x \to 0-} \dfrac{\sqrt{5 + x^2}}{x}$.   **20.** $\lim\limits_{x \to 0+} \dfrac{\sqrt{5 + x^2}}{x}$.

★**21.** Definition I, page 110, translates into the following analytic form: *The limit of $f(x)$ is L as $x \to +\infty$ if and only if, for every $\epsilon > 0$, there exists a corresponding number K, sufficiently large, so that*

$$|f(x) - L| < \epsilon \quad if \quad x > K. \tag{1}$$

Interpret (1) with respect to the graph of $y = f(x)$.

★**22.** Write the analytic forms, like that in Problem 21, for the definitions of

$$\lim_{x \to -\infty} f(x) = L, \quad \lim_{x \to c} f(x) = +\infty, \quad and \quad \lim_{x \to c} f(x) = -\infty.$$

37. LIMITS OF SEQUENCES

A **sequence**, S, is a *function* whose domain, D, is a set of positive integers. Unless otherwise stated, we shall infer that D consists of either (a) *all positive integers $n \leq k$*, where k is a fixed integer, or (b) *all positive integers*. In case (a), S is called a **finite sequence**; its values are $S(1)$, $S(2)$, $\cdots$, $S(k)$. In case (b), S is called an **infinite sequence**; the set of values of S, or its *range*, consists of the numbers

$$S(1), S(2), S(3), \cdots, S(n), \cdots, \tag{1}$$

where $S(n)$ is listed to fix the notation, and the final dots $\cdots$, read "*and so forth*," indicate that unwritten values of S extend endlessly to the right. Instead of (1), we usually write the range of S as follows:

$$S_1, S_2, S_3, \cdots, S_n, \cdots, \tag{2}$$

where we employ subscripts, instead of customary functional notation, to indicate that the domain of the independent variable, n, consists of *integers*. We shall think of the values of S arranged, as in (2), with the subscripts in increasing order. Then, we call S_1 the 1st term, S_2 the 2d term, $\cdots$, S_n the nth term or the **general term** of the sequence. A sequence S is defined if a formula in terms of n is given for S_n.

Note 1. Unless otherwise stated, any sequence to which we refer will be an *infinite sequence*. We may describe (2) as "*the sequence S,*" or as "*the sequence $\{S_n\}$.*"

ILLUSTRATION 1. If $S_n = 3n + 5$, then the sequence $\{S_n\}$ has the values, called *terms*, $S_1 = 8$, $S_2 = 11$, $S_3 = 14$, $\cdots$.

ILLUSTRATION 2. An **arithmetic progression** of k terms with first term a and common difference d is a sequence, S, where $S_n = a + (n - 1)d$, and n has the domain $1, 2, \cdots, k$.

ILLUSTRATION 3. A geometric progression of k terms with first term a and common ratio r is the sequence $a, ar, ar^2, \cdots, ar^{k-1}$, where the nth term is $S_n = ar^{n-1}$.

Note 2. Recall that the symbol $n!$, where n is a positive integer, is read "*n factorial,*" and $n! = 1 \cdot 2 \cdot 3 \cdots n$. Separately, we define $0! = 1$.

ILLUSTRATION 4. In the sequence $S = \left\{ + \frac{2}{1!}, - \frac{4}{3!}, + \frac{6}{5!}, \cdots \right\}$, we infer that

$$S_n = \frac{(-1)^{n+1}(2n)}{(2n-1)!}.$$

As a check, we place $n = 1, 2,$ and 3 in S_n to obtain the given terms.

Essentially, we obtain the following definition by rewriting Definition I of page 110 with n replacing x.

Definition III. *To say that* **the limit of S_n as n approaches plus infinity is L** *(or,* **S_n approaches L as a limit when n becomes infinite)** *means that* $| S_n - L |$ *is as small as we please at all values of n which are sufficiently large. Then, we write*

$$\lim_{n \to \infty} S_n = L, \quad or \quad S_n \to L \text{ as } n \to \infty. \tag{3}$$

When (3) is true, we say that the sequence $\{S_n\}$ has a limit, or **converges,** or **converges to L.** We also may say that S_n has the limit L as $n \to \infty$.

For sequences, we introduce infinite limits and may have $S_n \to +\infty$ or $S_n \to -\infty$ as $n \to \infty$, with meanings like those for $x \to \infty$ on page 111. If a sequence $\{S_n\}$ has no *finite* limit, it is said that the sequence is **divergent,** or the sequence **diverges.**

ILLUSTRATION 5. Consider the sequence $\{S_n\}$ defined by

$$S_n = 2 + \frac{(-1)^n}{2^n}.$$

Observe that $2^n \to +\infty$ as $n \to \infty$, and hence

$$\lim_{n \to \infty} S_n = 2 + 0 = 2.$$

We verify that $S_1 = \frac{3}{2}, S_2 = \frac{9}{4}, S_3 = \frac{15}{8}, S_4 = \frac{33}{16}, \cdots$. In Figure 81, the values of S_n are represented by points on the scale. As $n \to \infty$, the point S_n approaches 2 on the scale in a geometrical sense, or $| S_n - 2 | \to 0$.

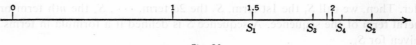

Fig. 81

ILLUSTRATION 6. Let $S_n = (-1)^n$. Then, $S_1 = -1, S_2 = 1, \cdots$, with -1 and $+1$ occurring alternately. Hence, there is no number L such that S_n will be as close to L as we please for all values of n which are sufficiently large. That is, the sequence $\{S_n\}$ does not have a limit, or is divergent.

Theorems I, II, III, and IV about finite limits on page 70 apply when interpreted for sequences, that is, for functions of n as $n \to \infty$.

ILLUSTRATION 7. If $S_n = \dfrac{3n^2 + 2n - 3}{7n^2 + 5n - 4}$, to obtain $\lim\limits_{n \to \infty} S_n$ we first divide the numerator and denominator in S_n by *the highest power of n in the denominator*:

$$\lim_{n \to \infty} S_n = \lim_{n \to \infty} \frac{3 + \dfrac{2}{n} - \dfrac{3}{n^2}}{7 + \dfrac{5}{n} - \dfrac{4}{n^2}} = \frac{3 + 0 + 0}{7 + 0 - 0} = \frac{3}{7}.$$

ILLUSTRATION 8. If $S_n = \dfrac{(2n)!}{(4n + 5)[(2n - 1)!]}$, then

$$\lim_{n \to \infty} S_n = \lim_{n \to \infty} \frac{1 \cdot 2 \cdots (2n - 1)(2n)}{1 \cdot 2 \cdots (2n - 1)(4n + 5)} = \lim_{n \to \infty} \frac{2n}{4n + 5} = \frac{1}{2}.$$

★*Note 3.* Definition III may be restated in the following analytic form: $S_n \to L$ as $n \to \infty$ *if and only if, for every positive number ϵ, however small, there exists a corresponding integer N such that*

$$|S_n - L| < \epsilon \quad when \quad n > N.$$

That is, if n is sufficiently large ($n > N$), then S_n will fall between $(L - \epsilon)$ and $(L + \epsilon)$ on the scale in Figure 82.

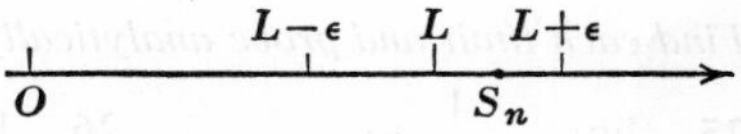

Fig. 82

★*Note 4.* Intimate connections can be established between the two concepts of a limit as defined for a sequence $\{S_n\}$, and for a function, f, of a continuous variable. Thus, it can be proved that, if $\lim_{x \to c} f(x) = L$, and if $\{x_n\}$ is any sequence (with $x_n \neq c$) such that $x_n \to c$ as $n \to \infty$, then the sequence $\{f(x_n)\}$ converges to L. Also, conversely, if $f(x_n) \to L$ for *every* sequence $\{x_n\}$ as just described, then $\lim_{x \to c} f(x) = L$.

EXERCISE 32

Write a formula for the nth term of the given arithmetic or geometric progression, and also find the 4th and 5th terms.

1. 2, 6, 10, $\cdots$. **2.** 17, 15, 13, $\cdots$.

3. 3, $- 6$, 12, $\cdots$. **4.** 4, $- .4$, .04, $\cdots$.

Write the first four terms of the sequence $\{S_n\}$, $\{T_n\}$, or $\{W_n\}$.

5. $S_n = 3n + 2$. **6.** $T_n = (- 1)^n(n!)$. **7.** $W_n = (- 1)^{n-1}(2n + 1)3^n$.

Write a formula for the nth term of the sequence, consistent with the given terms.

8. 3, 5, 7, $\cdots$. **9.** 2!, 4!, 6!, $\cdots$.

10. 2, $- 4$, 6, $\cdots$. **11.** $\frac{2}{1}$, $- \frac{4}{3}$, $\frac{8}{5}$, $\cdots$.

Evaluate the limit, if it exists.

12. $\lim\limits_{n \to \infty} \dfrac{3n + 2}{5 - 4n}$.

13. $\lim\limits_{n \to \infty} \dfrac{2n + n^2}{n + 3n^2}$.

14. $\lim\limits_{n \to \infty} \dfrac{n + 5n^2}{6 + 2n^3}$.

15. $\lim\limits_{n \to \infty} \dfrac{6 - 3n + 4n^3}{2n + n^2 - 6n^3}$.

16. $\lim\limits_{n \to \infty} \dfrac{2 + 5n - n^2}{3 + 4n}$.

17. $\lim\limits_{n \to \infty} \dfrac{3 - 4n + 2n^2}{2 + 3n}$.

18. $\lim\limits_{n \to \infty} \dfrac{(2n + 1)(n!)}{(n + 1)!}$.

19. $\lim\limits_{n \to \infty} \dfrac{(3n + 2)(2n - 1)!}{(2n)!}$.

20. $\lim\limits_{n \to \infty} [3 + (- 1)^n]$.

★SUPPLEMENT FOR CHAPTER FIVE

21. Write both a verbal and an analytic definition (as in Problem 21 on page 113) for the following symbolisms; L is finite:

$$\lim_{x \to +\infty} f(x) = +\infty; \quad \lim_{x \to -\infty} f(x) = +\infty; \quad \lim_{|x| \to \infty} f(x) = L.$$

In each problem, an analytic proof should be given, by use of Problems 21 and 22 on page 113, the preceding Problem 21, or similar definitions.

22. Let $f(x) = x^{-1}$. Find K so that $|f(x)| < \epsilon$ if $|x| > K$. Thus, proceed to prove that $f(x) \to 0$ if $|x| \to \infty$.

23. Let $f(x) = (x - 2)/(2x + 3)$. Prove that $|f(x) - \frac{1}{2}| < \epsilon$ if $x > K$, where $K = 7/4\epsilon$, and thus obtain a proof that $f(x) \to \frac{1}{2}$ if $x \to +\infty$. Also, give an independent proof that $f(x) \to \frac{1}{2}$ if $x \to -\infty$. Then, try to give a single proof that $f(x) \to \frac{1}{2}$ if $|x| \to \infty$.

24. If $f(x) = 1/(x + 2)$, prove that $f(x) \to 0$ if $x \to -\infty$. [Notice that, if $x < -2$, we have $|x + 2| = -(x + 2)$. Then proceed with $x < -2$.]

Find each limit and prove analytically that this limit is correct.

25. $\lim_{x \to +\infty} \dfrac{1}{2x + 5}$.   **26.** $\lim_{x \to -\infty} \dfrac{1}{x - 4}$.   **27.** $\lim_{x \to 2+} \dfrac{x}{x - 2}$.

28. If $\lim_{x \to +\infty} f(x) = L$ and $\lim_{x \to +\infty} g(x) = M$, where L and M are finite, prove that (a) $[f(x) + g(x)] \to (L + M)$ if $x \to +\infty$; (b) if h is a constant, then $hf(x) \to hL$ when $x \to +\infty$.

29. Prove the theorems corresponding to those in Problem 28 for the case where L and M are both $+\infty$.

30. If $f(x) \to +\infty$ and $g(x) \to +\infty$ when $x \to c$, prove analytically that $f(x)g(x) \to +\infty$ and $[f(x) + g(x)] \to +\infty$ when $x \to c$.

31. Give explicit examples where $f(x) \to +\infty$ and $g(x) \to -\infty$ when $x \to c$, to show that it is possible for $[f(x) + g(x)]$ to have a *finite limit*, the limit $+\infty$, the limit $-\infty$, or *no limit*, finite or infinite, as $x \to c$. For this reason, sometimes it is said that the "*form*" $(\infty - \infty)$ is **indeterminate.**

32. If $f(x) < g(x)$ and $\lim_{x \to c} f(x) = +\infty$, prove that $\lim_{x \to c} g(x) = +\infty$.

33. If $\lim_{x \to c} f(x) = L$, and if $\{x_n\}$ is a sequence of numbers in the domain of f such that $x_n \neq c$ for any n and $\lim_{n \to \infty} x_n = c$, prove analytically that $\lim_{n \to \infty} f(x_n) = L$.

34. If the function $f(x)$ is continuous at $x = c$, state a property of f based on Problem 33.

CHAPTER SIX

First Applications of Derivatives

38. TANGENTS AND NORMALS

On the graph of an equation

$$h(x, y) = 0,$$ (1)

let C be an arc through $P{:}(x_0, y_0)$, where C is the graph of a solution $y = f(x)$ of (1) for y as a function of x. From page 83, C has a nonvertical tangent at P if and only if $f'(x_0)$ exists. Then, with $dy/dx = f'(x)$,

$$\left\{ \begin{matrix} tangent\ nonvertical \\ at\ P{:}(x_0, y_0){:} \end{matrix} \right\} \qquad \left\{ \begin{matrix} \textbf{slope of} \\ \textbf{tangent} \end{matrix} \right\} = \left. \frac{dy}{dx} \right|_{(x_0,\, y_0)};$$ (2)

$$\left\{ \begin{matrix} tangent\ horizontal\ at \\ P{:}(x_0, y_0)\ means\ that \end{matrix} \right\} \qquad \left. \frac{dy}{dx} \right|_{(x_0,\, y_0)} = \mathbf{0.}$$ (3)

Second, suppose that C is the graph of a solution $x = g(y)$ of (1) for x as a function of y. On interchanging the roles of x and y in (3), we decide to *define* * the tangent at $P{:}(x_0, y_0)$ to be the *vertical line through P if and only if $g'(y_0)$ exists and is zero.* Thus, with $dx/dy = g'(y)$,

$$\left\{ \begin{matrix} tangent\ vertical\ at \\ P{:}(x_0, y_0)\ means\ that \end{matrix} \right\} \qquad \left. \frac{dx}{dy} \right|_{(x_0,\, y_0)} = \mathbf{0.}$$ (4)

If the arc C through P has an equation $y = f(x)$ and also an equation $x = g(y)$, where f and g are *inverse functions*, then

$$y = f(x) \quad is\ equivalent\ to \quad x = g(y).$$ (5)

In such a case, if $f'(x)$ and $g'(y)$ exist, with neither equal to zero at a solution (x, y) of (1), then from page 105 we obtain

$$g'(y) = \frac{1}{f'(x)}, \quad or \quad \frac{dx}{dy} = \left(1 \div \frac{dy}{dx} \right).$$ (6)

Relation (6) would apply in (2) if the tangent is nonhorizontal. However, (6) would not apply in (3) or (4).

* Vertical tangents were discussed without a formal definition in Note 1 on page 83.

ILLUSTRATION 1. In Figure 83, C represents an arc with equations as in (5); there is a tangent PT at P as described in (2). In Figure 84, C would have equations as in (5), with $dx/dy = 0$ at P, where dy/dx fails to exist, and PT is vertical. In Figure 85, C is the graph of an equation $x = g(y)$, with $dx/dy = 0$ at $P:(x_0, y_0)$, where the tangent is vertical, but C has no equation $y = f(x)$. This is true because, if x_1 is near x_0 with $x_1 < x_0$, there exist two points (x_1, y_1) and (x_1, y_2) on C. No equation $y = f(x)$, where f is single-valued as usual, can have two solutions (x_1, y_1) and (x_1, y_2) with the same value for x.

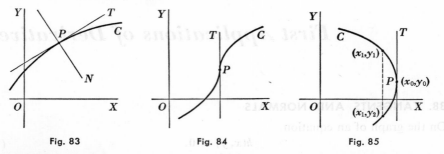

Fig. 83   Fig. 84   Fig. 85

The discussion for (1) in this section applies in particular if (1) is of the form $y - f(x) = 0$ or $x - g(y) = 0$. In any case, dy/dx and dx/dy are obtained by implicit differentiation in (1), without any necessity for finding solution functions, such as f or g in (5).

Note 1. Hereafter in this section, and in corresponding applications, we shall assume that the scale units on the coordinate axes are *equal* in the xy-plane, because we shall discuss facts about angles between lines.

On an arc, C, of the graph of (1), let $P:(x_0, y_0)$ be a point where a tangent PT exists. Then, we define the **normal line** to C at P to be the line PN which is *perpendicular to the tangent PT*. In case (3) applies, PN is vertical. In case (4) applies, PN is horizontal. Suppose, now, that arc C has either equation in (5), with the tangent PT nonvertical and nonhorizontal. Then, the slope of PN is the negative reciprocal of the slope of PT as given in (2). Or, from (6), when the normal PN is nonhorizontal and nonvertical, as in Figure 83,

$$\left\{ \begin{array}{l} \textbf{slope of normal} \\ \quad \textbf{at } P:(x_0, y_0) \end{array} \right\} is \quad - \frac{1}{\dfrac{dy}{dx}}\bigg|_{(x_0, y_0)}, \quad or \quad - \frac{dx}{dy}\bigg|_{(x_0, y_0)}. \tag{7}$$

Note 2. For the typical equation (1) which we shall consider, with an arc C of its graph having equations as in (5), it will be found that,

when (3) *is true,* $\lim\limits_{x \to x_0} \left| \dfrac{dx}{dy} \right|_{(x, y)} = \infty \, ;$ \hfill (8)

when (4) *is true,* $\lim\limits_{y \to y_0} \left| \dfrac{dy}{dx} \right|_{(x, y)} = \infty \, .$ \hfill (9)

EXAMPLE 1. Find the equations of the tangent and normal where $x = 2$ on the parabola $y = 3x^2 - 2x + 5$.

Solution. 1. $y' = 6x - 2$; at $x = 2$, we find $y' = 10$, the slope of the tangent. If $x = 2$, then $y = 13$. Hence, the equation of the tangent at (2, 13) is found to be $y - 13 = 10(x - 2)$, or $10x - y = 7$.

2. Since the tangent has slope 10, the slope of the normal is $-\frac{1}{10}$. The equation of the normal at (2, 13) is $\quad y - 13 = -\frac{1}{10}(x - 2)$, *or* $\quad x + 10y = 132$.

EXAMPLE 2. Find the points on the graph of

$$x^2 - 4x + 4y^2 + 8y = 8 \tag{10}$$

at which the tangent is horizontal or vertical.

Solution. 1. On differentiating with respect to x on both sides of (10), with y considered as a function of x, we obtain

$$2x - 4 + 8y \frac{dy}{dx} + 8 \frac{dy}{dx} = 0; \quad \frac{dy}{dx} = \frac{2 - x}{4y + 4}. \tag{11}$$

Then, from (6), $\qquad\qquad\qquad \dfrac{dx}{dy} = \dfrac{4y + 4}{2 - x}. \tag{12}$

2. *Horizontal tangents.* We use (3). From (11), $dy/dx = 0$ where $x = 2$, if $y \neq -1$. From (10) with $x = 2$, we obtain $y^2 + 2y - 3 = 0$, whose solutions are $y = -3$ and $y = 1$. Hence, the tangent is horizontal at the points (2, -3) and (2, 1).

3. *Vertical tangents.* We use (4). From (12), $dx/dy = 0$ when $y = -1$, if $x \neq 2$. From (10) with $y = -1$, we find the solutions $x = 6$ and $x = -2$. Hence, the tangent is vertical at the points (6, -1) and (-2, -1).

4. From page 62, we recognize (10) as the equation of an ellipse. The end points of the axes of the ellipse are given in parts (2) and (3) of the solution. The student may draw the ellipse.

The points of intersection of two curves $g(x, y) = 0$ and $h(x, y) = 0$, in the xy-plane, are the real solutions of the system of equations

$$g(x, y) = 0 \quad and \quad h(x, y) = 0. \tag{13}$$

To obtain the intersections, we solve (13) for x and y.

Suppose that the curves in (13) intersect at $P{:}(x_0, y_0)$. Then, we define *the angle of intersection* of the curves at P as *the smallest nonnegative angle θ formed by their tangents at P.* The value of dy/dx at P for each curve gives the slope of its tangent, if it is not vertical. Formula (1), page 30, gives $\tan \theta$ if $\theta \neq 90°$:

$$\tan \theta = \left| \frac{m_2 - m_1}{1 + m_1 m_2} \right|, \tag{14}$$

where m_1 and m_2 are the values at P of y', from (3), on the two curves. If $\theta = 90°$, we say that the curves **intersect orthogonally** at P. This fact can be recognized by recalling that, in such a case, $m_1 m_2 = -1$.

EXAMPLE 3. Find the angles at which the curves intersect:

$$y = \tfrac{1}{2}x + 3 \quad and \quad y = 2x^2 - 4. \tag{15}$$

Solution. 1. *Intersections.* From (15),

$$2x^2 - 4 = \tfrac{1}{2}x + 3 \quad or \quad 4x^2 - x - 14 = 0, \quad or \quad (x - 2)(4x + 7) = 0.$$

Hence, $x = 2$ or $x = -\tfrac{7}{4}$; then $y = 4$ and $y = \tfrac{17}{8}$, respectively.

2. *The slopes at* (2, 4). From (15), $y' = \tfrac{1}{2}$ and $y' = 4x$. Hence, the slopes are, respectively, $m_1 = \tfrac{1}{2}$ and $m_2 = 8$. Then, from (14),

$$\tan \theta = 1.500; \quad \theta = 56.3°. \quad \text{(Table VI)}$$

Similarly, at $(-\tfrac{7}{4}, \tfrac{17}{8})$, we find $\theta = 71.6°$.

EXERCISE 33

Find dy/dx and dx/dy, perhaps obtaining dx/dy first. Graph the equation, by use of each point where the tangent is horizontal or vertical. Also, obtain the equations of the tangent and normal where x or y has the specified value, and show these lines in the graph. Check some graphs by results in Chapter 2.

1. $y = x^2 - 4x + 6$; where $x = 3$.   **2.** $y = 6x - x^2 - 5$; where $x = 0$.

3. $x = y^2 + 6y - 4$; where $y = -1$.   **4.** $x = 3y^2 - 6y + 10$; where $y = -2$.

5. $x^2 + 4y^2 = 8$; where $x = 2$.   **6.** $x^2 - 9y^2 = 27$; where $x = -6$.

7. $y = \tfrac{1}{8}x^3$.   **8.** $y = 9 - x^2$.   **9.** $x = y^4$.

10. $x^2 + y^2 - 4x + 6y = 3$.   **11.** $x^2 + 6x + 4y^2 = 16y - 9$.

Find each angle of intersection for the curves. Draw a figure.

12. $y = x^2$ and $y = \sqrt{x}$, where they intersect.

13. $y = x^2 + 2x - 5$ and $x = 2y - 4$, where $x = 2$.

14. $y = x^2 - 4x + 1$ and $x = 7 - y^2$, where $x = 3$.

Prove that the curves intersect orthogonally.

15. $3x^2 - 3xy + y^3 = 17$ and $x^2 - 2xy + x = 10y - y^2 - 12$, at $(-1, 2)$.

16. $y^2 = 4x + 4$ and $y^2 = 4 - 4x$, where they intersect.

Find the equation of the tangent at any point (x_1, y_1) on the curve.

17. $b^2x^2 + a^2y^2 = a^2b^2$.   **18.** $b^2x^2 - a^2y^2 = a^2b^2$.   **19.** $y^2 = 2px$.

★20. $Ax^2 + 2Bxy + Cy^2 + 2Dx + 2Ey + F = 0$.

★21. Prove that the tangent at an end point of the focal chord of a parabola meets its axis at the directrix.

★22. At any point P on a parabola with focus F and axis l, as in Figure 86, let SPT be the tangent. Construct PR parallel to l and draw PF. Prove that SPT makes equal angles with PF and PR.

Note 1. Suppose that the parabola in Figure 86 is revolved about l to create a surface for a parabolic mirror. Then, if a source of light is at F, each ray of light to the mirror is reflected parallel to the axis, l, because of Example 22. Hence, the mirror would send out a beam of light parallel to l.

★23. Prove that the tangent at the point (x_1, y_1) on the ellipse with the equation $b^2x^2 + a^2y^2 = a^2b^2$ makes equal angles with the focal radii of (x_1, y_1).

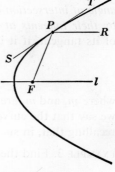

Fig. 86

39. BOUNDS, MAXIMA, AND MINIMA

Let T be a set of real numbers t, $T = \{t\}$. To state that T is *bounded above* means that there exists a number B, called *an upper bound* for T, such that all $t \leq B$. Then, also, any number $B_1 > B$ is an upper bound for T because all $t \leq B < B_1$. To state that T is *bounded below* means that there exists a number b, called *a lower bound* for T, such that $b \leq t$ for all t in T. Then, also, any number $b_1 < b$ is a lower bound for T. To state merely that T is a *bounded set* of numbers means that T is bounded *below and above*.

Theorem I. *If a set $T = \{t\}$ is bounded above, then T has a **least upper bound**, U. If T is bounded below, then T has a **greatest lower bound**, l.*

This theorem will be accepted by us without proof * as intuitively evident. If U of Theorem I is in T, we call this *largest number of T* the **maximum** of T. If l of Theorem I is in T, we call this *smallest number of T* the **minimum** of T.

ILLUSTRATION 1. Consider the sequence $S = \{S_n\}$ where $S_n = 2 - 2^{-n}$, and $n = 0, 1, 2, \cdots$. The first few terms of S are plotted in Figure 87. The greatest lower bound for S is $l = 1$; thus, S has a *minimum*, or *least term*, 1, because $S_0 = 1$. The least upper bound for S is $U = 2$, because $S_n \to 2$ as $n \to \infty$ and $S_n < 2$ for all values of n. But, $S_n \neq 2$ for any value of n and hence S has *no maximum*.

Fig. 87

Let f be a function with domain D; the range of f is the set of numbers $T = \{f(x)\}$, for all x in D. To state that f is *bounded, bounded below,* or *bounded above* means that T has the specified property. If T has a *maximum M*, that is, if f has a largest value M, we call M the **absolute maximum** of f on D. Then $f(x) \leq M$ at all x in D and, also, *there exists at least one point x_1 in D such that $f(x_1) = M$*. If T has a *minimum, m*, that is, if f has a smallest value m, we call m the **absolute minimum** of f on D. Then $m \leq f(x)$ at all x in D and *there exists at least one point x_2 in D such that $f(x_2) = m$.*

ILLUSTRATION 2. Let $f(x) = 4x + 5 - x^2$. A graph of $y = f(x)$ is in Figure 88. With the domain, D, for x as all real numbers, f has the absolute maximum 9 in D, attained at $x = 2$; $f(2) = 9$ and the point $(2, 9)$ is the highest point of the graph of f. However, f is not bounded below and thus has no absolute minimum for x in D. If, now, the domain for x is taken as the interval $D_1 = \{-1 \leq x \leq 5\}$, then f has 0 as the absolute minimum in D_1 because

$$f(-1) = f(5) = 0 \leq f(x)$$

at all x in D_1.

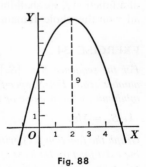

Fig. 88

We shall accept the following theorem without proof.*

* For a proof, see any text giving a foundation for the theory of functions of a real variable.

Theorem II. *If a function f is continuous on a* **closed interval** $D = \{a \leqq x \leqq b\}$, *then f is bounded, and has an* **absolute maximum,** M, *and* **absolute minimum,** m, *on D. Also, if γ is any number such that $m \leqq \gamma \leqq M$, then there exists at least one point x_1 on D where $f(x_1) = \gamma$.*

ILLUSTRATION 3. In Illustration 2, with the continuous function f considered only on the domain $D_1 = \{-1 \leqq x \leqq 5\}$, f has the absolute minimum $m = 0$ and absolute maximum $M = 9$, with $f(-1) = f(5) = 0$ and $f(2) = 9$.

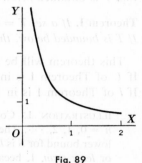

Fig. 89

ILLUSTRATION 4. Let $f(x) = 1/x$, with x on the half-open interval $D = \{0 < x \leqq 2\}$. From the graph of f in Figure 89, f is bounded below, with the absolute minimum, or greatest lower bound, $f(2) = \frac{1}{2}$. However, f is *not* bounded above because $f(x) \to +\infty$ when $x \to 0+$. Thus, f has no absolute maximum on D. This discussion of f shows that, if the word *closed* were omitted in Theorem II, the conclusion of the theorem might not be true. If f now is given the domain $0 < x < +\infty$, then f is bounded below, with 0 as the greatest lower bound because $f(x) \to 0$ as $x \to +\infty$. However, $f(x) \neq 0$ at any value of x and hence f has *no absolute minimum on* $0 < x < +\infty$.

ILLUSTRATION 5. Let f have the values

$$\left.\begin{array}{l} f(x) = 1 \quad if \quad 0 \leqq x \leqq 2, and \\ f(x) = 3 \quad if \quad 2 < x \leqq 4. \end{array}\right\} \tag{1}$$

Then, on the domain $D = \{0 \leqq x \leqq 4\}$, f is bounded, with maximum $M = 3$ and minimum $m = 1$. If $\gamma = 2$, we have $m \leqq \gamma \leqq M$, but there is no point x on D where $f(x) = \gamma$. Thus, the statement about γ in Theorem II does not apply to f as defined in (1). This fact could be expected because f is *discontinuous* at $x = 2$, and hence does not satisfy the continuity hypothesis of Theorem II on D. The student should graph f.

Note 1. Unless otherwise stated, in any reference to an *absolute maximum* or *minimum* of a function f, we shall infer that the set of numbers $T = \{f(x)\}$ is being considered for all x on the whole domain of f.

EXERCISE 34

For the sequence $S = \{S_n\}$, with $n = 1, 2, \cdots$, as defined, plot a few terms of S on a number scale. For S, specify its least upper or greatest lower bound, its maximum, and its minimum, wherever one or more of them exist. Is S bounded?

1. $S_n = 1/n$.   **2.** $S_n = n$.   **3.** $S_n = (-1)^n$.

Graph the function $f(x)$, with D as the domain of f. For each D, specify which of the following exist for f on D: least upper bound; greatest lower bound; absolute maximum; absolute minimum. Is f bounded on D?

4. $f(x) = x^2$; $D = \{all\ x\}$; $D = \{0 \leqq x \leqq 2\}$.

5. $f(x) = \dfrac{1}{x-1}$; $D = \{all\ x > 1\}$; $D = \{2 \leqq x < \infty\}$.

6. $f(x) = [x]$, the greatest integer at most equal to x; $D = \{-3 \leqq x < 5\}$.

7. $f(x) = |x|$; $D = \{all\ x\}$; $D = \{all\ |x| < 4\}$; $D = \{all\ |x| \leqq 4\}$.

8. $f(x) = \sin x$; $D = \{all\ x\}$.

★9. $f(x) = \sin (1/x)$; $D = \{all\ positive\ x\}$.

★10. In Problem 6, select a number γ such that $3 < \gamma < 4$, and consider f on the domain $D_1 = \{2 \leqq x \leqq 4\}$. Is there a number x in D_1 such that $f(x) = \gamma$? Does this fact contradict Theorem II? Why?

40. FIRST TESTS FOR RELATIVE MAXIMA AND MINIMA

To state that a function $f(x)$ has a **relative maximum**, $f(x_0)$, at a point x_0 in the domain, D, of f will mean that

$$\left\{\begin{array}{c} relative \\ maximum\ at\ x_0: \end{array}\right\} \quad \left\{\begin{array}{c} at\ all\ x\ in\ D \\ sufficiently\ near\ x_0, \end{array}\right\} \quad f(x) \leqq f(x_0). \qquad (1)$$

To state that f has a **relative minimum**, $f(x_0)$, at x_0 will mean that

$$\left\{\begin{array}{c} relative \\ minimum\ at\ x_0: \end{array}\right\} \quad \left\{\begin{array}{c} at\ all\ x\ in\ D \\ sufficiently\ near\ x_0, \end{array}\right\} \quad f(x_0) \leqq f(x). \qquad (2)$$

From (1), f attains a relative maximum at x_0 if and only if the point $P{:}(x_0, y_0)$ on the graph of $y = f(x)$ is *at least as high* as any neighboring point on the graph. From (2), f attains a relative minimum at x_0 if and only if P is *at least as low* as any neighboring point on the graph.

ILLUSTRATION 1. Let $f(x) = x^3 - 3x^2 - 9x + 5$; a graph of $y = f(x)$ is in Figure 90. Note that f has a relative maximum 10, with $f(-1) = 10$; f has a relative minimum -22, with $f(3) = -22$.

Hereafter, the word *extremum* * (plural, *extrema*) will refer to either a *maximum* or a *minimum* when there is no necessity to be more explicit. Also, unless otherwise specified, the unqualified word *maximum* (or, *minimum*) will mean a *relative maximum* (or, *minimum*). If a function f attains a maximum (or, minimum) at $x = x_0$, the point (x_0, y_0) on the graph of $y = f(x)$ sometimes is called a *maximum* (or, *minimum*) *point* of the graph.

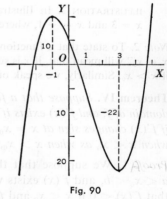

Fig. 90

Note 1. An extremum at x_0, as in (1) or (2), can be called a *two-sided* relative extremum when x_0 is an *interior point* of an interval in the domain D of f, because neighboring values of x on both sides of x_0 are referred to in (1) and (2). Any *absolute extremum* for f also is a *relative extremum* for f. Thus, with an absolute maximum at x_0, the condition $f(x) \leqq f(x_0)$ holds at *all* values of x, and hence at *all x sufficiently near* x_0, as required by (1).

* Sometimes written *extreme* (plural, *extremes*).

Theorem III. *If a function f attains a relative extremum at an* **interior** * *point* x_0 *in the domain of f, and if* $f'(x_0)$ *exists, then* $f'(x_0) = 0$.

Proof. 1. Let $y = f(x)$. Then, with

$$y_0 = f(x_0), \quad y_0 + \Delta y = f(x_0 + \Delta x), \quad and \quad \Delta y = f(x_0 + \Delta x) - f(x_0),$$

$$f'(x_0) = \lim_{\Delta x \to 0} \frac{\Delta y}{\Delta x}. \tag{3}$$

2. Suppose that f attains a relative maximum at x_0. Then,

$$if \mid \Delta x \mid is \ sufficiently \ small, \quad f(x_0 + \Delta x) \leqq f(x_0). \tag{4}$$

3. Either $f'(x_0) > 0$, or $f'(x_0) < 0$, or $f'(x_0) = 0$. We shall rule out $f'(x_0) > 0$ and $f'(x_0) < 0$ by an indirect proof. Assume, first, that $f'(x_0) > 0$. Then, by (3), for all Δx where $\mid \Delta x \mid$ is sufficiently small, $\Delta y/\Delta x$ will be so near $f'(x_0)$ that $\Delta y/\Delta x$ as well as $f'(x_0)$ will be *positive*, and hence Δy and Δx will be *both positive* or *both negative*. Thus, in particular,

$$if \ \Delta x > 0 \ then \ \Delta y > 0, \quad or \ f(x_0 + \Delta x) - f(x_0) > 0, \quad or \ f(x_0 + \Delta x) > f(x_0). \tag{5}$$

But, (5) contradicts (4). Hence, *we cannot have* $f'(x_0) > 0$. Similarly, if we assume that $f'(x_0) < 0$, we conclude that, for all Δx where $\mid \Delta x \mid$ is sufficiently small, Δy and Δx have *opposite* signs. Hence,

$$if \ \Delta x < 0 \quad then \quad \Delta y > 0, \quad or \quad f(x_0 + \Delta x) > f(x_0). \tag{6}$$

Since (6) contradicts (4), we *cannot have* $f'(x_0) < 0$. Therefore, $f'(x_0) = 0$. Similarly, $f'(x_0) = 0$ if f has a relative minimum at x_0. Thus, *a necessary condition for an extremum at x_0 is that* $f'(x_0) = 0$.

ILLUSTRATION 2. In Illustration 1, $y' = 3(x^2 - 2x - 3)$. We find that $y' = 0$ at $x = 3$ and $x = -1$, where Figure 90 on page 123 shows relative extrema.

Note 2. To state that a function value $g(x)$ "**changes sign,** *from negative to positive, at* $x = x_0$" will mean that, if x is sufficiently near x_0, then $g(x) < 0$ if $x < x_0$ and $g(x) > 0$ if $x > x_0$. Similarly, we speak of $g(x)$ changing sign *from positive to negative.*

Theorem IV. *Suppose that a function f is continuous at an* **interior point** x_0 *of the domain of f, and* $f'(x)$ *exists if x is near* x_0, *except that* $f'(x_0)$ **might not exist.** *Then, if* $f'(x)$ *changes sign at* $x = x_0$, *f has an extremum at* x_0. *If* $f'(x)$ *has the same sign when* $x < x_0$ *as when* $x > x_0$, *sufficiently near* x_0, *then f has no extremum at* x_0.

Proof. 1. We suppose that the domain of f includes $I = \{a \leqq x \leqq b\}$, where $a < x_0 < b$, and $f'(x)$ exists when x is on I, except possibly at $x = x_0$. Assume that $f'(x) < 0$ if $x < x_0$ and $f'(x) > 0$ if $x > x_0$, when x is on I.

2. By Theorem XII, page 84, f is a *decreasing* function if x satisfies $a \leqq x \leqq x_0$, and is an *increasing* function if $x_0 \leqq x \leqq b$. Hence, with x on I,

$$f(x) > f(x_0) \ when \ x < x_0, \quad and \ also \ when \ x > x_0,$$

as in (β) of Figure 91 on page 125, where $y = f(x)$, so that f has a relative minimum at $x = x_0$.

* Not an end point of an interval of the domain of f.

3. Similarly, if $f'(x)$ changes from *positive* to *negative* at $x = x_0$, we find that f has a relative maximum at $x = x_0$, as in (α) of Figure 91.

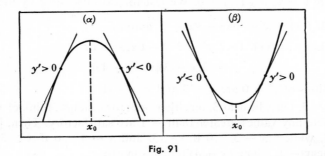

Fig. 91

4. Suppose, now, that $f'(x)$ has the *same sign*, say $f'(x) > 0$, when $x < x_0$ and when $x > x_0$. Then, by Theorem XII, page 84, f is an *increasing function* on both sides of x_0. Hence, with x on I,

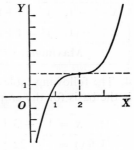

$$f(x) < f(x_0) \text{ when } x < x_0, \text{ and}$$

$$f(x_0) < f(x) \text{ when } x > x_0.$$

Therefore, the f has neither a maximum nor a minimum at $x = x_0$, as illustrated at $x = 2$ for the graph of a function f in Figure 92. This completes proof of Theorem IV.

Fig. 92

Hereafter, unless otherwise stated, any extremum which we mention for a function f will be attained at an *interior point* of an interval of the domain of f. Then, from the results in Theorems III and IV, we obtain the following **sufficient conditions for extrema** of a differentiable function f.

$$\left\{ \begin{array}{c} \textbf{Relative maximum,} \\ \textit{at interior point } x_0 \textit{ of domain:} \end{array} \right\} \quad \left\{ \begin{array}{c} f'(x_0) = 0 \text{ and } f'(x) \text{ changes} \\ \text{from } (+) \text{ to } (-) \text{ at } x_0. \end{array} \right\} \quad (7)$$

$$\left\{ \begin{array}{c} \textbf{Relative minimum} \\ \textit{at interior point } x_0 \textit{ of domain:} \end{array} \right\} \quad \left\{ \begin{array}{c} f'(x_0) = 0 \text{ and } f'(x) \text{ changes} \\ \text{from } (-) \text{ to } (+) \text{ at } x_0. \end{array} \right\} \quad (8)$$

Summary. *To find extrema for a function $f(x)$ where $f'(x)$ exists.*

1. *Obtain critical values of x by solving $f'(x) = 0$.*

2. *Test each critical value x_0 by finding the sign of $f'(x)$ when $x < x_0$ and when $x > x_0$, for x near x_0, and using (7) and (8).*

3. *Reject any critical value x_0 where $f'(x)$ does not change sign.*

Before testing a critical value x_0, try to exhibit a linear factor $(x - x_0)$ of $f'(x)$ corresponding to each value $x = x_0$ where $f'(x) = 0$. To graph an equation $y = f(x)$ where $f'(x)$ exists, first solve $f'(x) = 0$ when possible. The graph has a horizontal tangent at x_0 if $f'(x_0) = 0$. Then, test for extrema by use of the Summary. It applies with the roles of x and y *interchanged* in graphing an equation $x = g(y)$. By (4) on page 117, the graph has a *vertical tangent* where $y = y_0$ if $g'(y_0) = 0$. We test for extrema for g by the Summary.

EXAMPLE 1. If $f(x) = x^3 - 3x^2 - 9x + 5$, graph f.

Solution. 1. Let $y = f(x)$. Then $y' = 3x^2 - 6x - 9$, or

$$y' = 3(x - 3)[x - (-1)]. \tag{9}$$

2. The solutions of $y' = 0$ are $x = 3$ and $x = -1$.

3. *Test of $x = 3$.* Let x be near 3, on either side; for instance, think of $x = 3.1$ and $x = 2.9$, where any values greater than -1 are satisfactory. Then, $[x - (-1)]$ is near $+4$, while * $x - 3 < 0$ if $x < 3$, and $x - 3 > 0$ if $x > 3$. Similarly, consider x near -1, where $(x - 3)$ remains negative.

NEAR $x = -1$	NEAR $x = 3$
$x < -1$, $y' = (+)(-)(-) = (+)$	$x < 3$, $y' = (+)(-)(+) = (-)$
$x > -1$, $y' = (+)(-)(+) = (-)$	$x > 3$, $y' = (+)(+)(+) = (+)$
Maximum, *with* $y = 10$	**Minimum,** *with* $y = -22$

4. The following table of values, with the preceding information about extrema, is the basis for the graph of f, in Figure 90, page 123.

$x =$	-3	-2	-1	0	1	2	3	4	5
$f(x) =$	-22	3	10	5	-6	-17	-22	-15	10

If $y = f(x)$, then *"an extremum for y,"* or for the set of numbers $\{f(x)\}$, is understood to mean an extremum for the function f.

EXAMPLE 2. Graph the equation $\qquad y = (x - 2)^3(x + 1)^2.$ $\hfill(10)$

Solution. 1. From (10), $\qquad y' = 5(x + 1)(x - \frac{1}{5})(x - 2)^2.$

2. The critical values of x for extrema for y are -1, $\frac{1}{5}$, and 2. On testing, we find that y has a relative maximum at $x = -1$, and a relative minimum at $x = \frac{1}{5}$. Since $(x - 2)^2 > 0$ if $x \neq 2$, then y' does *not* change sign at $x = 2$, and $y' > 0$ near $x = 2$ when $x \neq 2$. Hence, by Theorem IV, f does *not* have an extremum at $x = 2$; $f(x)$ increases as x increases near 2, and f is stationary at $x = 2$.

3. At $x = -1$, the relative maximum is $y = 0$; at $x = \frac{1}{5}$, the relative minimum is $y = -8.4$. The graph has a horizontal tangent at $x = 2$. A graph of (10) is in Figure 93.

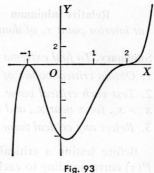

Fig. 93

* It is useful to notice that, if $x < a$, then $x - a < 0$; if $x > a$, then $x - a > 0$.

Comment. The absence of an extremum at $x = 2$ for (10) shows that the *necessary condition* $f'(x_0) = 0$, of Theorem III on page 124, for an extremum is *not a sufficient condition.*

A continuous function f may have an extremum at a point x_0 in the domain of f where the derivative $f'(x_0)$ does not exist.

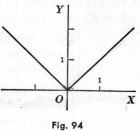

ILLUSTRATION 3. Let $f(x) = |x|$. A graph of $y = f(x)$ is in Figure 94. We note that f attains a *relative* minimum, which also is the *absolute* minimum of f, at $x = 0$ where $f(0) = 0$. But, $f'(0)$ does not exist, and the graph has a corner point at $(0, 0)$.

Fig. 94

Suppose that a function $f(x)$ is **continuously differentiable** (that is, f' *exists and is continuous*) if x is on an interval D, and that $f'(x) = 0$ at just a finite number of points on D. Then, as x increases, if $f'(x)$ changes from $(-)$ to $(+)$ at $x = x_0$, the next change of sign will be from $(+)$ to $(-)$, if a change occurs. Thus, from (7) and (8), if f has at least two extrema at interior points of D, maxima and minima alternate.

EXERCISE 35

Find all relative extrema of the function, and draw its graph by use of extrema and any other points where the tangent is horizontal.

1. x^2.
2. $-x^4$.
3. x^3.
4. $(x + 2)^5$.

5. $4x - 2 - x^2$.
6. $2x^3 - 9x^2 + 12x + 12$.

7. $-2x^3 - 3x^2 + 12x + 5$.
8. $x^3 + 6x^2 + 12x - 4$.

Without graphing, find all extrema of the function $f(x)$, or $g(y)$. Then graph the equation $y = f(x)$, or $x = g(y)$. Use all horizontal and vertical tangents of the graph, and a horizontal x-axis.

9. $g(y) = 2y^3 - 3y^2 - 12y - 4$.
10. $g(y) = 2y^3 + 6y^2 + 6y - 1$.

11. $f(x) = x^2(x - 1)^3$.
12. $f(x) = (x + 1)^2(x - 2)^2$.
13. $g(y) = y(y - 4)^3$.

Note 1. If the domain of f is a closed interval D where f' exists, then f is continuous, and hence has an absolute maximum, M, and absolute minimum, m, on D. If f is an increasing or a decreasing function near an end point x_0 of D, then $f(x_0)$ is a *one-sided* relative extremum of f. Suppose that this is true at each end point of D. Then, to find M and m for f, *first* obtain all relative extrema of f at *interior points* of D; *second*, compute f at each *end point* of D. Finally, M is the maximum and m is the minimum of all relative extrema just found.

Find the absolute extrema of f on D.

14. $f(x) = x^2 - 6x + 3$; $D = \{-1 \leq x \leq 4\}$.

15. $f(x) = 6 - 4x - x^2$; $D = \{-3 \leq x \leq 1\}$.

16. $f(x) = \frac{1}{3}x^3 - x^2 - 8x + 5$; $D = \{-3 \leq x \leq 5\}$.

17. $f(x) = x^3 - \frac{3}{2}x^2 - 18x + 4$; $D = \{-2 \leq x \leq 7\}$.

18. Find the absolute maximum or minimum of the slope of the graph of the equation
$y = 6x^2 - 6x - x^3 + 7$.

41. CONCAVITY AND RELATED TESTS FOR EXTREMA

Consider the graph, C, of $y = f(x)$ for x on an open interval $T = \{a < x < b\}$ where f'' exists and is always positive, or always negative. Then, to say that

$$\left\{ \begin{array}{l} \textit{"C is \textbf{concave upward} on T" will mean that f' is an in-} \\ \textit{creasing function on T, or the tangent to C at P:(x, y) re-} \\ \textit{volves counterclockwise as x increases on T (see Figure 95);} \end{array} \right\} \quad (1)$$

$$\left\{ \begin{array}{l} \textit{"C is \textbf{concave downward} on T" will mean that f' is a de-} \\ \textit{creasing function on T, or the tangent to C at P:(x, y)} \\ \textit{revolves clockwise as x increases on T (see Figure 96).} \end{array} \right\} \quad (2)$$

We define "*convex downward* (or, *upward*)" to be equivalent to "*concave upward* (or, *downward*)." Observe that the tangent at any point P on C is below or above C according as C is concave upward or downward (proved on page 175).

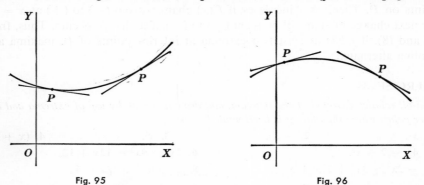

Fig. 95   Fig. 96

Theorem V. *On any open interval $T = \{a < x < b\}$ of the domain of a function, f, where f'' exists, the graph, C, of $y = f(x)$ is concave upward if $f''(x) > 0$ on T, and concave downward if $f''(x) < 0$. Also, if f'' is continuous at $x = x_0$ on T, then*

$$C \text{ is \textbf{concave upward} near } P:(x_0, y_0) \text{ if } f''(x_0) > 0; \quad (3)$$

$$C \text{ is \textbf{concave downward} near } P:(x_0, y_0) \text{ if } f''(x_0) < 0. \quad (4)$$

Proof. The first sentence of Theorem V is true because $f'(x)$ increases where its derivative $f''(x) > 0$, and decreases if $f''(x) < 0$. To prove (3), assume that $f''(x_0) > 0$. Since f'' is continuous at $x = x_0$, then $f''(x) \to f''(x_0)$ when $x \to x_0$. Hence, $f''(x) > 0$ if x is sufficiently near x_0, and thus C is concave upward there. Similarly, (4) is true.

Note 1. Sometimes, we may say that a graph is concave upward (or, downward) "**at $x = x_0$**" with the meaning that the statement is true on some open interval including the number x_0.

ILLUSTRATION 1. If $f(x) = x^3 - 6x^2 + 9x + 15$, then

$$f'(x) = 3x^2 - 12x + 9; \quad f''(x) = 6(x - 2); \quad f''(3) = 6. \quad (5)$$

The unbroken curve in Figure 97 on page 129 is a graph of $y = f(x)$ and is concave upward at $x = 3$, where $f''(3) > 0$. The broken curve is a graph of $y' = f'(x)$.

Note 2. In this text, the following definition applies only to a function $f(x)$ which is continuous on an interval $T = \{a < x < b\}$, where f' exists and is continuous except possibly at a particular point x_0, and is continuous also at x_0 in case $f'(x_0)$ exists. If $f'(x_0)$ does not exist, we assume that $|f'(x)| \to \infty$ when $x \to x_0$ and the graph of $y = f(x)$ has a vertical tangent at $x = x_0$. Thus, this graph has a tangent for every x on T. In particular, the conditions are satisfied if $f''(x)$ exists at all x on T, because then f' is continuous on T.

Definition I. *To state that the graph, C, of $y = f(x)$ has an* **inflection point** *at $P:(x_0, y_0)$ will mean that, if x is sufficiently near x_0, C is concave in one sense (upward or downward) if $x < x_0$, and in the opposite sense if $x > x_0$.*

ILLUSTRATION 2. In Figure 97, for Illustration 1, P is an inflection point of the graph. In Figure 98, P and R are inflection points, with the tangent vertical at R.

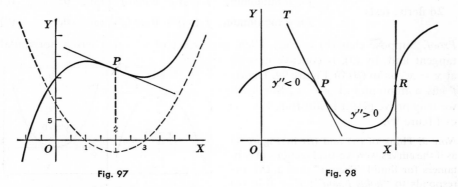

Fig. 97   Fig. 98

Theorem VI. *If the graph, C, of $y = f(x)$ has an inflection point at $P:(x_0, y_0)$, and if $f''(x_0)$ exists, then $f''(x_0) = 0$.*

Proof. Since $f''(x_0)$ exists, then $f'(x)$ exists and is continuous at $x = x_0$. Suppose that C changes from concave downward to concave upward at P. Then, by (1) and (2), $f'(x)$ decreases when $x < x_0$ and increases when $x > x_0$, as at $x = 2$ on the broken graph of $y' = f'(x)$ for Illustration 1 in Figure 97. Therefore f' has a relative minimum at $x = x_0$. Since $D_x f'(x) = f''(x)$, by Theorem III on page 124 it is *necessary* that $f''(x_0) = 0$. Similarly, f' has a maximum at $x = x_0$ if C changes from concave upward to concave downward, and again $f''(x_0) = 0$.

Suppose now that $f''(x)$ exists except possibly at $x = x_0$. Then, if $f''(x)$ changes sign at $x = x_0$, the graph of $y = f(x)$ is concave in one sense if $x < x_0$ and in the opposite sense if $x > x_0$. If $f''(x)$ maintains the same sign when $x < x_0$ as when $x > x_0$, the sense of concavity does not change at $x = x_0$. These remarks, and Definition I, justify the following conclusions.

$$\left\{ \begin{array}{l} \text{If } f''(x) \text{ changes sign at } x = x_0, \text{ then the graph} \\ \text{of } y = f(x) \text{ has an inflection point at } x = x_0. \end{array} \right\} \qquad (6)$$

$$\left\{ \begin{array}{l} \text{If } f''(x) \text{ has the same sign when } x < x_0 \text{ as when} \\ x > x_0, \text{ for } x \text{ sufficiently near } x_0, \text{ then the graph of} \\ y = f(x) \text{ does not have an inflection point at } x = x_0. \end{array} \right\} \qquad (7)$$

ILLUSTRATION 3. In Illustration 1, $f''(x) = 6(x - 2)$ and $f''(2) = 0$. If $x < 2$ then $f''(x) < 0$; if $x > 2$ then $f''(x) > 0$. Hence, the graph of $y = f(x)$ has an inflection point at P in Figure 97 on page 129, where $x = 2$, and changes from concave downward to concave upward as x increases through $x = 2$.

We agree that, if $f'(x)$ or $f''(x)$ is used at $x = x_0$ in graphing an equation $y = f(x)$, it is implied that the derivative employed exists and is continuous at $x = x_0$.

Theorem VII. *Suppose that x_0 is an interior point of an interval, T, of the domain of a function $f(x)$ where f'' is continuous. Then, sufficient conditions for a relative extremum at $x = x_0$ are as follows:*

2d deriv. test: $\begin{cases} \textit{for a } \textbf{minimum,} \quad f'(x_0) = 0 \textit{ and } f''(x_0) > 0; & (8) \\ \textit{for a } \textbf{maximum,} \quad f'(x_0) = 0 \textit{ and } f''(x_0) < 0. & (9) \end{cases}$

Proof. Suppose that (8) is true. Then, the graph of $y = f(x)$ has a horizontal tangent and, by (3), is concave upward at $x = x_0$, as in (β) of Figure 99. Hence, f has a minimum at $x = x_0$. Similarly, we may prove (9); it is illustrated in (α) of Figure 99.

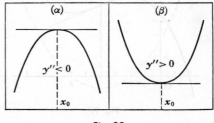

Note 3. Think of (α) and (β) in Figure 99 as if the curves were vertical sections of containers for liquid. Then, $y'' > 0$ in (β) corresponds to "*holds liquid*"; $y'' < 0$ in (α) corresponds to "*spills liquid.*"

Fig. 99

Recall that, in Theorem IV on page 124, the tests for extrema at $x = x_0$ are valid even when $f'(x_0)$ does not exist. Similarly, the discussion about inflection points leading to (6) and (7) is valid even when $f''(x_0)$ does not exist. These facts are recognized in paragraphs (1) and (2) of the following Summary, which applies under the conditions of Note 2.

Summary. *Concerning graphing an equation $y = f(x)$, where f is continuous.*

1. *The critical values of x for extrema of f consist of the solutions of $f'(x) = 0$, and the values of x where $f'(x)$ does not exist. Test each critical value by use of (8) or (9), if applicable; otherwise use the test based on Theorem IV, page 124, or (7) and (8) on page 125.*

2. *The critical values of x for inflection points consist of the solutions of $f''(x) = 0$, and the values of x where $f''(x)$ does not exist. Test each critical value by use of (6) and (7).*

3. *Locate any vertical tangent by investigating $\dfrac{dx}{dy} = 0$.*

EXAMPLE 1. Graph $y = x^3 - 6x^2 + 9x + 15.$ (10)

Solution. 1. The graph of (10) is the unbroken curve in Figure 97 on page 129, which we obtain as follows.

2. From (10), $y' = 3(x - 3)(x - 1); \quad y'' = 6(x - 2).$

Critical values for extrema: $\quad y' = 0 \quad$ yields $\quad x = 3 \quad$ and $\quad x = 1.$

Critical value for an inflection point: $\qquad y'' = 0 \quad$ yields $\quad x = 2.$

In the following table, $x = 3$ and $x = 1$ are tested by use of (8) and (9); $x = 2$ is tested by use of (6).

3. From (6) on page 117, $dx/dy = 1/[3(x - 3)(x - 1)]$, and is never equal to zero. Hence, the graph has no vertical tangent. [This conclusion is a *certainty* whenever we consider the graph of $y = f(x)$ where $f(x)$ is a polynomial.] We summarize as follows before graphing.

x	1	3	2	$x < 2$	$x > 2$
y	19	15	17		
y'	0	0	-3		
y''	-6	$+6$	0	< 0	> 0
CONCLUSION	MAX.	MIN.	INFL. PT.		

ILLUSTRATION 4. To graph $y = (x - 2)^3 + 2$, we calculate $y' = 3(x - 2)^2$ and $y'' = 6(x - 2)$. Then, $y' = 0$ at $x = 2$ and, also, $y'' = 0$ at $x = 2$. Hence, (8) and (9) do not apply. We use Theorem IV, page 124: y' does not change sign at $x = 2$; therefore there is no extremum at $x = 2$. We verify by use of (6) that there is an inflection point at $x = 2$, where the tangent is horizontal because $y' = 0$. The graph is in Figure 92 on page 125.

Note 4. In many applications, we shall be searching for extrema of functions, *with no interest in graphing*. Then, only paragraph (1) of the Summary will be used.

Note 5. The Summary, with the roles of x and y *interchanged*, applies in graphing $x = g(y)$. To graph an equation $h(x, y) = 0$ which is not equivalent to a *single* equation $x = g(y)$ or $y = f(x)$, generally we shall be content to locate only the points on the graph where the tangent is *horizontal* or *vertical*, as in Section 38 on page 117. However, the Summary on page 130 is available in graphing any arc $y = f(x)$, or $x = g(y)$ of the graph of $h(x, y) = 0$.

EXERCISE 36

Test for extrema for y, or x, and inflection points of the graph of the equation. Obtain the graph, with the tangent drawn accurately at each extreme point and each inflection point.

1. $y = (x + 1)^3$.   2. $y = (x - 2)^4$.   3. $x = (y - 1)^3$.
4. $y = \frac{1}{3}x^3 - \frac{1}{2}x^2 - 6x + 2$.   5. $y - 7 = -x^3 + 3x^2 + 24x$.
6. $x + 6 = y^3 - 12y$.   7. $x = -y^3 - 3y^2 + 9y$.
8. $y = 4 - 5x + 3x^2 - x^3$.   9. $y = x^3 - 6x^2 + 15x - 12$.
10. $y = x^4 - 2x^3$.   11. $y = 2x^4 + 4x^3$.
12. $y = x^4 - 6x^2 - 8x - 6$.   13. $y + 5 = 3x^4 - 8x^3 + 6x^2$.
14. $y = (x - 1)(x + 2)^3$.   15. $y = x^2(x - 1)^2$.   16. $x - 3y = y^3$.

17. If $a \neq 0$, prove the facts stated in (20) on page 63 about concavity, and the location of the vertex for $y = ax^2 + bx + c$, by use of y' and y''.

Test for relative extrema of f without graphing.

18. $f(v) = (v - 1)^2(v + 2)^3$.   **19.** $f(u) = (u - a)^4(u - b)^3$, with $b < a$.

20. $f(x) = (x - a)^n$ where n is a positive integer which is (*i*) even; (*ii*) odd.

42. CRITICAL POINTS WHERE A DERIVATIVE FAILS TO EXIST

In the Summary on page 130 concerning the graph of $y = f(x)$, critical points are mentioned for extrema where $f'(x)$ fails to exist, and for inflection points where $f''(x)$ fails to exist. We proceed to consider related examples.

EXAMPLE 1. Graph the equation $y = 2(x - 3)^{\frac{2}{3}}$.   (1)

Solution. 1. From (1), with $D_x y = y'$ and $D_x^2 y = y''$,

$$y' = \frac{4}{3}(x - 3)^{-\frac{1}{3}} = \frac{4}{3\sqrt[3]{x - 3}}; \quad \frac{dx}{dy} = \frac{3}{4}\sqrt[3]{x - 3}; \quad y'' = -\frac{4}{9(x - 3)^{\frac{4}{3}}}. \quad (2)$$

2. *Extrema of y.* $D_x y \neq 0$ at any value of x. Hence, the graph, C, of (1) has no extreme point where the tangent is horizontal. $D_x y$ fails to exist where $x = 3$; therefore it is a critical value for investigation. We use Theorem IV on page 124:

$$\text{If } x < 3, \text{ then } x - 3 < 0, \quad \sqrt[3]{x - 3} < 0, \quad \text{and} \quad \frac{dy}{dx} < 0.$$

$$\text{If } x > 3, \text{ then } x - 3 > 0, \quad \sqrt[3]{x - 3} > 0, \quad \text{and} \quad \frac{dy}{dx} > 0.$$

Hence, y has a *minimum value*, $y = 0$, which is attained where $x = 3$.

3. At $x = 3$, $\frac{dx}{dy} = 0$; hence, C has a *vertical tangent* at $(3, 0)$.

4. *Inflection points.* From (2), y'' is never zero, and fails to exist just at $x = 3$, which becomes a critical value for investigation. We have already found that $(3, 0)$ is a minimum point of the graph, and hence cannot be an inflection point. Since $y'' < 0$ if $x \neq 3$, C is concave downward whenever $x \neq 3$. The graph is in Figure 100. $P{:}(3, 0)$ is a corner point of C where two arcs of C which meet at P have a *common tangent*. A point such as P is called a **cusp**.

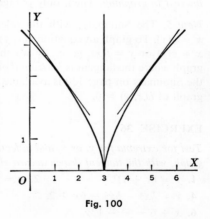

Fig. 100

EXERCISE 37

With y defined as a function of x, test for extrema of the function, and inflection points of its graph. Graph the equation.

1. $y = x^{\frac{2}{3}}$.   **2.** $y = (x - 2)^{\frac{1}{3}}$.   **3.** $y = (x + 2)^{\frac{2}{3}}$.   **4.** $y = (x - 1)^{\frac{1}{2}}$.

With x defined as a function of y, test for extrema of the function and inflection points of its graph. (Interchange the roles of x and y on page 130.) *Graph the equation.*

5. $x = (y - 1)^{\frac{1}{3}}$.   **6.** $x = (y + 3)^{\frac{1}{2}}$.   **7.** $x = (y - 2)^{\frac{2}{3}}$.

Graph by use of just dy/dx and dx/dy, and horizontal and vertical tangents.

8. $y = x(x - 2)^{\frac{1}{3}}$.   **9.** $y = (x - 2)^{\frac{2}{3}}(x + 1)^{\frac{1}{3}}$.   **10.** $x^2 = y^3$.

11. $8y^3 = x^2$.   **12.** $8y^2 = 27x^3$.   **13.** $x^{\frac{1}{2}} + y^{\frac{1}{2}} = 2$.

Note 1. In Problems 10–12, each curve is a **semicubical parabola** (Figure 5, page 709).

★14. Test the function f for extrema, if it is defined as follows for all x:

$$f(x) = -x \quad if \quad x \leqq 0 \quad and \quad f(x) = \sqrt{x} \quad if \quad x > 0.$$

★15. Graph the equation $x^{\frac{2}{3}} + y^{\frac{2}{3}} = a^{\frac{2}{3}}$ where $a > 0$. The curve is called the **hypocycloid** with four cusps. See page 712.

43. GRAPHING OF RATIONAL FUNCTIONS

From page 74, if f is a rational function, then $f(x) = P(x)/Q(x)$, where $P(x)$ and $Q(x)$ are polynomials, which we shall assume have no common polynomial factor which is not a mere constant. Hence, $P(x)$ and $Q(x)$ are not equal to zero simultaneously. If $x = c$ is a real solution of $Q(x) = 0$, then f is not defined at $x = c$. Thus, the domain, T, of f consists of all x where $Q(x) \neq 0$, and f is differentiable in T, by use of (VI) on page 92. As a characteristic feature, the graph, H, of $y = P(x)/Q(x)$ has a line $x = c$ as a vertical asymptote corresponding to each solution c of $Q(x) = 0$, because $\lim_{x \to c} |y| = \infty$. We then say that f has a **pole** at $x = c$. Also, $f(x) = 0$ if and only if $P(x) = 0$. We shall observe later that H may have a horizontal asymptote.

Note 1. For any function $F(x)$, a **zero** of F is defined as a number k such that $F(k) = 0$. If $f(x) = P(x)/Q(x)$ as above, the *poles* of f are the *zeros* of Q; the *zeros* of f are the *zeros* of P.

If a rational function $f(x)$ is merely a polynomial function, we graph f as previously. Otherwise, we refer to the following routine.

Summary.* *To graph a function $f(x) = P(x)/Q(x)$, let $y = P(x)/Q(x)$ and check for the following features of the graph, H.*

1. **Horizontal asymptote.** *Evaluate* $\lim_{|x| \to \infty} P(x)/Q(x)$. *If this limit is finite, L, then the line $y = L$ is a horizontal asymptote.*

2. **Poles.** *Solve $Q(x) = 0$; if $x = c$ is any real root, then the line $x = c$ is a vertical asymptote.*

3. **Zeros.** *Solve $P(x) = 0$ to obtain the x-intercepts.*

4. **Extrema.** *Calculate y'; solve $y' = 0$ to find critical values of x for extrema. Usually test these values by use of Theorem IV, page* 124.

5. *Draw H by use of asymptotes, zeros of f (x-intercepts of H), extrema, and a few other computed points.*

* *Useful frequently when $P(x)$ and $Q(x)$ are not polynomials.*

Note 2. Investigation of inflection points and testing for extrema by use of y'' could be added to the Summary. Frequently, however, y'' would be too complicated for use.

EXAMPLE 1. Graph

$$y = \frac{2(x^2 - 4x)}{x^2 - 4x - 5}.$$ (1)

Solution. 1. $\displaystyle\lim_{|x|\to\infty} y = \lim_{|x|\to\infty} \frac{2(x^2 - 4x)}{x^2 - 4x - 5} = \lim_{|x|\to\infty} \frac{2\left(1 - \dfrac{4}{x}\right)}{1 - \dfrac{4}{x} - \dfrac{5}{x^2}} = 2.$ (2)

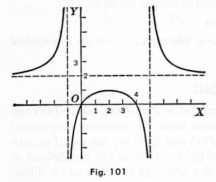

Fig. 101

Hence, the line $y = 2$ is an asymptote.

2. *Poles.* $x^2 - 4x - 5 = 0$ if $x = 5$ or $x = -1$. Then $|y| \to \infty$ as $x \to 5$ and as $x \to -1$, or the lines $x = 5$ and $x = -1$ are asymptotes of the graph. There is no value of y when $x = 5$ and when $x = -1$.

3. *Zeros.* From $x^2 - 4x = 0$, the x-intercepts are $x = 0$ and $x = 4$.

4. From (1),

$$y' = \frac{20(2 - x)}{(x^2 - 4x - 5)^2}.$$ (3)

5. *Extrema.* The only solution of $y' = 0$ is $x = 2$. If x is near 2 and $x < 2$, then $y' > 0$; if $x > 2$, then $y' < 0$. Hence, there is a maximum at $x = 2$; from (1), the maximum value of y is $y = \frac{8}{9}$. The graph is in Figure 101.

ILLUSTRATION 1. To graph the equation $xy^2 - 3y = 3xy + 2,$ (4)

we notice that (4) is linear in x. Hence, we solve for x:

$$xy^2 - 3xy = 3y + 2, \quad or \quad x = \frac{3y + 2}{y^2 - 3y}.$$ (5)

In (5), the Summary applies with the roles of x and y interchanged, and *horizontal* and *vertical* interchanged. Thus, from (5), the graph would have the lines $y = 0$ and $y = 3$ as *horizontal* asymptotes. Since $x \to 0$ as $|y| \to \infty$, the graph would have the *vertical* line $x = 0$ as an asymptote. We would investigate vertical tangents by solving $D_y x = 0$ for values of y.

EXERCISE 38

Graph by use of asymptotes and points where the tangent is horizontal or vertical.

1. $y = \dfrac{1}{(x + 3)^2}.$ **2.** $y = \dfrac{1}{(x - 1)^3}.$ **3.** $x = \dfrac{1}{y - 4}.$ **4.** $x = \dfrac{1}{(2 + y)^2}.$

5. $y = \dfrac{1}{x(x + 1)}.$ **6.** $y = \dfrac{8 - 4x}{x + 2}.$ **7.** $y = \dfrac{3}{x^2 + 4}.$

8. $x = \dfrac{6y}{y^2 + 4}.$ **9.** $y = \dfrac{2x + 2}{x - 3}.$ **10.** $x = \dfrac{4}{y^2 + 3y - 4}.$

11. $y = \dfrac{2(x^2 - 4)}{x^2 - 9}.$ **12.** $y = \dfrac{x^3}{x + 2}.$ **13.** $x = \dfrac{3y^2 + 6y}{y^2 + 2y - 8}.$

14. $y = \dfrac{3x^2 + x - 2}{x^2 + x - 6}.$ **15.** $x = \dfrac{2y^2 - 2}{y^2 - 4}.$ **16.** $x = \dfrac{2}{y^2 + 5}.$

17. $2xy + 2 = x + 5y.$ **18.** $xy^2 - 2x = 2y^2 - xy.$

19. The **serpentine:** $y = k^2x/(x^2 + a^2)$, with k a constant, not zero.

44. RELATED RATES OF CHANGE *

Suppose that two or more variables are related by a given equation, and that each variable is a differentiable function of a certain independent variable, t. On differentiating both sides of the equation with respect to t, we obtain a relation between the derivatives of the dependent variables with respect to t. If t is the time, we thus obtain a relation between time-rates of change.

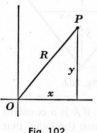

Fig. 102

EXAMPLE 1. A particle P is moving in an xy-plane. At any instant, the abscissa of P is increasing at the rate of .2 unit per second and the ordinate is decreasing at the rate of .3 unit per second. At what time-rate is the distance from the origin to P changing when P is at $(5, 12)$?

Solution. 1. In Figure 102, let $R = OP$. Let t be the time in seconds measured from any zero time. Then, at any value of t,

$$R^2 = x^2 + y^2, \tag{1}$$

where R, x, and y are functions of t, with $dx/dt = .2$ and $dy/dt = -.3$. Let $x' = D_t x$ and $y' = D_t y$.

2. Since (1) is an identity in the variable t, the derivatives with respect to t of the two sides are equal at all values of t. Hence, we differentiate with respect to t on each side of (1) and equate the results:

$$2R\frac{dR}{dt} = 2x\frac{dx}{dt} + 2y\frac{dy}{dt}, \quad or \quad \frac{dR}{dt} = \frac{xx' + yy'}{R}. \tag{2}$$

From (1), when $x = 5$ and $y = 12$ we find $R = 13$. Then, with $x' = .2, y' = -.3$, $x = 5, y = 12$, and $R = 13$, from (2) we obtain $dR/dt = -.2$. Or, R is decreasing at the rate of .2 unit per second. We avoided radicals by *not solving* (1) *for R*.

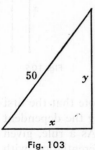

Fig. 103

EXAMPLE 2. A ladder is 50′ long and reaches from horizontal ground to a vertical wall. The lower end of the ladder is pulled from the wall at the rate of 5′ per second. How fast is the upper end of the ladder descending when the upper end is 48′ from the ground?

Solution. 1. At t seconds, measured from some instant, let the distance in feet of the ladder's lower end from the wall, and of the upper end from the ground, be x and y, respectively. **At an arbitrary time t,** from Figure 103,

$$x^2 + y^2 = 2500. \tag{3}$$

---

* In any coordinate plane in the remainder of the chapter, we assume that the unit for distance in the plane is used as the scale unit on each axis.

2. Since x and y are functions of t, and (3) is an identity in t, we would continue by differentiating with respect to t on both sides of (3) and equating the results. On substituting $y = 48$ in (3) to obtain $x = 14$, then substituting $dx/dt = 5$, $x = 14$, and $y = 48$ in the equation involving derivatives, we would obtain $dy/dt = -\frac{35}{24}$. Thus, y is *decreasing* at the rate of $\frac{35}{24}$ feet per second. The student should check this result.

EXAMPLE 3. A reservoir is in the shape of an inverted cone, with altitude 24' and base-radius 18'. Water is flowing into the reservoir at the rate of 60π cubic feet per minute. How fast is the surface of the water rising when it is 12' above the vertex of the cone?

Partial solution. Let t be the number of minutes after the flow starts. At *an arbitrary value of t*, in Figure 104, let x feet be the radius, y feet be the altitude, and V cubic feet be the volume of the inverted cone formed by the water. From similar triangles, $x = \frac{3}{4}y$, and hence $V = \frac{1}{3}\pi x^2 y$, or $V = \frac{3}{16}\pi y^3$, where we are given $D_t V = 60\pi$. Then, $D_t V = 3(\frac{3}{16})\pi y^2 D_t y$, etc. We obtain $D_t y = \frac{20}{27}$.

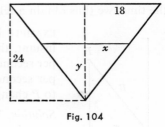

Fig. 104

Note 1. Suppose that s is a function of t, where $s = 0$ at $t = 0$. Then, if k is a constant and $D_t s = k$ for all values of t, at this point in the text we shall assume the fact * that $s = kt$. If we interpret s as the measure of *distance* traveled in a path, and t as the measure of the *time* in a given unit, then $s = kt$ is merely the elementary result "*distance is equal to the rate times the time*" for uniform rectilinear motion.

EXAMPLE 4. A ship S_1 is sailing north at the rate of 20 miles per hour, and a ship S_2 is sailing west at the rate of 10 miles per hour. At noon, S_1 is 220 miles due south of S_2. When will S_1 be closest to S_2?

Solution. 1. Let t represent the time in hours after noon; let x and y be the distances in miles traveled by S_1 and S_2, respectively, in t hours, and let W be the distance between S_1 and S_2 at time t. Then, if S_1 is not north of S_2 at time t (as is essential for minimum distance), from Figure 105 we find that

$$x = 20t, \quad y = 10t, \quad W^2 = (220 - x)^2 + y^2; \; or$$
$$W^2 = 500t^2 - 8800t + (220)^2.$$

2. To avoid radicals, let $U = W^2$. The student may verify that $D_t U = 0$ at $t = 8\frac{4}{5}$. The minimum occurs at 8:48 P.M.

Fig. 105

In a typical problem about related rates as just considered, note that the first stage of the solution consists of obtaining an equation involving the dependent variables at an **arbitrary value** of the independent variable, t. As a rule, given values of the dependent variables are inserted only after differentiation with respect to t.

* This result will be proved in Problem 9 on page 176.

EXERCISE 39

1. If $u = xy^2$, where x and y are functions of t with $\dfrac{dx}{dt} = 3$ and $\dfrac{dy}{dt} = -2$, find du/dt at $(x = 4, y = 8)$.

2. If $u = x^2 + y^3$, where x and y are functions of t with $\dfrac{dx}{dt} = -3$ and $\dfrac{dy}{dt} = 4$, find du/dt at $(x = 1, y = 2)$.

When possible in the following problems, avoid introducing radicals.

3. A metal cylinder is shrinking in cooling, with the radius decreasing .001″, and the altitude decreasing .01″, per minute. At the instant when the altitude is 100″ and the radius is 5″, find the rate of decrease of (*a*) the curved surface area; (*b*) the volume.

4. A boat is being pulled to a wharf by a rope attached to the deck. If the rope is hauled in at the rate of 12′ per minute from a point 10′ above the deck, how fast is the boat approaching the wharf when it is 24′ away?

5. A man, who is 6′ tall, is walking horizontally at the rate of 75′ per minute, directly toward a light which is 20′ above the ground. At what rate is the length of his shadow changing?

6. The time T in seconds for one oscillation of a simple pendulum whose length is l centimeters is given by $T = \pi\sqrt{l/g}$, where $g = 980$ and $\pi = 3.1416$. If l is increasing at the rate of .2 centimeter per second, find the rate of change of T, at an instant when $l = 81$.

7. A vat is in the form of a rectangular parallelepiped, with a horizontal base $4' \times 6'$. Water is flowing in at the rate of 30 cubic feet per second. How fast is the water level rising in the vat?

8. An airplane is flying horizontally at a speed of 500′ per second, at an elevation of 8000′, toward a ground observer. When the line-of-sight distance from the observer to the airplane is 10,000′, at what rate is the distance decreasing?

9. At 9 P.M., a ship S_1 is 80 miles north of a ship S_2. If S_1 is traveling south at 20 miles per hour and S_2 is traveling east at 10 miles per hour, (*a*) at what rate will the distance between S_1 and S_2 be changing 3 hours later; (*b*) when will S_1 and S_2 be closest?

10. A horizontal *V*-shaped oil reservoir is 100′ long, and its cross section is an isosceles right triangle with the hypotenuse horizontal, and each perpendicular side 30′ long. Oil flows in at the rate of 750 cubic feet per minute. How fast is the surface of the oil rising when it is 10 feet deep?

11. The dimensions of a rectangular parallelepiped are decreasing by .2′, .3′, and .1′ per minute. When the corresponding dimensions are 6′, 9′, and 2′, find the rate of change of (*a*) the volume; (*b*) the length of a diagonal.

12. A conical reservoir, with a horizontal top 60′ in diameter, is 25′ deep and is filled with water to a level of 20′. (*a*) At this instant, how fast is the level falling if water is leaking out at the rate of 80 cubic feet per minute? (*b*) If the level is falling .4′ per minute, how fast is water leaking from the reservoir?

13. The electromotive force E in volts which is necessary to produce a current of I amperes in a certain circuit with wire of diameter d inches is given by $E = .1137I/d^2$. At an instant when $E = 300$, it is found that E is decreasing at the rate of 5 volts per second. Find the corresponding rate of change in I, if $d = .05$.

14. The pressure, p, and volume, v, of a given quantity of a gas at a constant temperature satisfy the relation $pv = c$, where c is a constant. At an instant when the pressure is 5 pounds per square inch and the volume is 100 cubic feet, the volume is decreasing by 2 cubic feet per minute. Find the rate of change of p at this instant.

15. Wheat is being poured on the ground in such a way that the wheat on the ground continually forms a cone, with its altitude twice the radius of the base. If the wheat is being poured at the rate of 12 cubic feet per second, find the rate at which the altitude of the pile is increasing when the altitude is 8'.

16. In manufacturing a certain article, a corporation finds that the proper selling price, H, in dollars per article to assure a required margin of profit is given by

$$H = 3x^2 + 2x + 7,$$

where x is a cost index number associated with the business. Find the rate of change of H at an instant when $x = 4$, and x is increasing at the rate of .15 per month.

17. A balloon is maintaining spherical shape as gas is inserted. When the radius of the balloon is 15', the rate of increase of the volume is 100 cubic feet per second. Find the rate of change of the radius then.

18. A reservoir is 85' long and its cross section is a trapezoid with the parallel sides horizontal, and sides of lengths 17', 10', 5', and 10', as shown in Figure 106. At an instant when the water is 5' deep in the reservoir, find the rate at which water is leaking out if the water level is falling by .2' per hour.

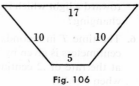

Fig. 106

19. In a triangle, a first side, a, is increasing by .2'' per minute, a second side, b, is decreasing by .4'' per minute, and their included angle is 150°. At what rate is the triangle's area changing when $a = 15''$ and $b = 20''$?

20. An automobile is traveling east at 60 miles per hour, and an airplane is flying south at an elevation of 1 mile, at 300 miles per hour. At a certain instant, the airplane is directly above the automobile. At what rate are they separating 10 minutes later?

21. The combined electrical resistance R resulting from two resistances R_1 and R_2, in ohms, connected in parallel, satisfies

$$\frac{1}{R} = \frac{1}{R_1} + \frac{1}{R_2}.$$

If R_1 and R_2 are increasing at the rates of .5 and .4 per second, respectively, at what rate is R changing when $R_1 = 100$ and $R_2 = 200$?

22. For a perfect gas, the volume v, pressure p, and absolute temperature T, are connected by the relation $pv = RT$, where R is a constant. It is found that $p = 20$ pounds per square inch and $v = 200$ cubic inches when $T = 400°$. Find T and its time-rate of change at an instant when $p = 15$ pounds per square inch and $v = 300$ cubic inches, if the pressure is decreasing at the rate of .4 pound per second, while the volume is increasing at the rate of .3 cubic inch per second.

Find du/dt without eliminating x, y, or z.

23. $u^2 = x^2 + y^2 + z^2$, when $x = \sqrt{t}$, $y = t^2 + 3$, and $z = 2t + 5$.

24. $u = x^2 + 5xy - y^4$, when $x = t^3 + 2$ and $y = t + t^2$.

25. $u = (2x^2 - 4y)^7$, when $\dfrac{dx}{dt} = 3$ and $\dfrac{dy}{dt} = 2$; evaluate at $(x = 2, y = 1)$.

45. ACCELERATION IN RECTILINEAR MOTION SKIP

Consider the motion of a particle on a straight line, labeled as an s-axis. Let the motion be defined by specifying s as a function of t, say $s = f(t)$, where s is the coordinate of the particle at the instant of time t. Hereafter, in such a setting, we shall suppose that f has a continuous second derivative, f''. On page 85, we defined the velocity, v, of the particle at any instant t as follows.

$$v = \frac{ds}{dt}, \quad or \quad v = f'(t). \tag{1}$$

Now, we introduce the following terminology.

Definition II. *In the* **rectilinear motion** *of a particle on an s-axis, the* **acceleration,** *a, of the particle at any instant of time, t, is defined as the corresponding* **instantaneous rate of change of the velocity,** *v, with respect to the time. That is,*

$$a = \frac{dv}{dt}, \quad or \quad a = \frac{d^2s}{dt^2}. \tag{2}$$

EXAMPLE 1. For $t \geqq 0$, study the motion of a particle on an s-axis as governed by the equation

$$s = t^3 - 9t^2 + 24t + 6. \tag{3}$$

Solution. 1. From (1) and (2),

$$v = 3t^2 - 18t + 24 = 3(t - 4)(t - 2);$$

$$a = \frac{d^2s}{dt^2} = 6(t - 3). \tag{4}$$

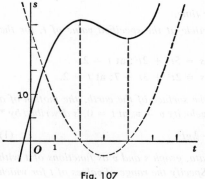

Fig. 107

2. The graph of (3) is the unbroken curve in Figure 107. The graph has extrema at $t = 2$ and $t = 4$, where $ds/dt = v = 0$. The broken parabola in Figure 107 is the graph of $v = 3t^2 - 18t + 24$.

3. Let the s-axis be horizontal, as in Figure 108. From Figure 107 and (3), the particle starts at $s = 6$ where $t = 0$ and moves to the right ($v > 0$) until $s = 26$ at $t = 2$, where the particle instantaneously is at rest. Meanwhile, with $a < 0$ at $t = 0$, the velocity decreases until $t = 3$, where $a = 0$; then v increases for all $t > 3$. If $2 < t < 4$, $v < 0$ and the particle moves to the left, reaching $s = 22$ at $t = 4$. For $t > 4$, since $v > 0$, the particle moves continually to the right. Thus, as $t \to \infty$, we find $v \to \infty$, $s \to \infty$, and $a \to \infty$. The arrows in Figure 108 show how the particle moves.

4. Let $\sigma = |v|$, where σ is the speed. At any value of t, σ is the *length of the ordinate* of the graph of v. From Figure 107, if t increases, σ decreases when $t < 2$; increases when $2 < t < 3$; decreases when $3 < t < 4$; increases when $t > 4$.

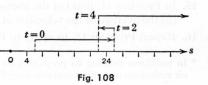

Fig. 108

Comment. Since $\sigma = |v|$, it follows that σ is increasing if $v < 0$ and $a < 0$, or if $v > 0$ and $a > 0$; that is, *the speed is increasing when v and a have the same sign.* Similarly, *the speed is decreasing when v and a have opposite signs.* These facts check with Step 4 above.

EXAMPLE 2. An object is shot vertically upward from the ground with an initial velocity of 128 feet per second at $t = 0$. Find the acceleration.

Solution. Let s be the distance in feet, measured positive upward, with $s = 0$ at ground level. By (12) on page 78, the motion is defined by

$$s = 128t - 16t^2. \tag{5}$$

Then, $v = 128 - 32t$, and $a = -32$. Thus, the acceleration is a constant, -32 feet per second per second, in the terminology of physics.

Comment. In physics, we learn that *"force equals mass times acceleration,"* or $F = ma$, where the force F acts on an object with mass m, and imparts the acceleration a. In Example 2, the result $a = -32$, a constant, is due to the fact that the object is acted on only by the constant force of gravity.

EXERCISE 40

The units are 1 foot for distance and 1 second for time.

Find the velocity and the acceleration of the particle at the specified value of t, for the motion defined by the equation.

1. $s = 5t^3 + 3t - 2$; at $t = 3$.   **2.** $s = 5t^3 + 2t^2$; at $t = 2$.

3. $s = 3t^3 - 2t^2 - 5$; at $t = 0$; at $t = 3$.   **4.** $s = 2t^3 + 3t - 7$; at $t = 2$.

With s measured positive upward, and $s = 0$ at the surface of the earth, the motion of a particle shot vertically from the point $s = s_0$, with velocity $v = v_0$ at $t = 0$, is described by *

$$s = s_0 + v_0 t - \tfrac{1}{2}gt^2, \tag{1}$$

where $g = 32$ approximately. For the specified data, graph s and v as functions of t with $t \geqq 0$. (α) Find when s attains its maximum. (β) Specify the range of values of t for which $v > 0$; v is decreasing; the speed is increasing.

5. $s_0 = 0$; $v_0 = 256$.   **6.** $s_0 = 0$; $v_0 = 144$.   **7.** $s_0 = 1600$; $v_0 = 0$.

8. $s_0 = 240$; $v_0 = 160$.   **9.** $s_0 = 153$; $v_0 = 192$.   **10.** $s_0 = 272$; $v_0 = -4$.

A particle has its motion on an s-axis defined by the given equation. Graph s and v as functions of t, with $t \geqq 0$. Then, describe how the particle moves on the s-axis, with remarks about the variation of the velocity and the acceleration. Also, by use of inequalities, specify the values of t for which the velocity is increasing; for which the speed is increasing.

11. $s = t^3 - 3t + 5$.   **12.** $s = 2t^3 - 3t^2 - 12t + 5$.

13. $s = t^3 - 6t^2 + 9t + 12$.   **14.** $s = t^3 - 3t^2 + 3t - 9$.

15. In Problem 11, find (α) the average velocity over the interval from $t = 1$ to $t = 4$; (β) the average of the velocities at $t = 1$ and $t = 4$.

16. Repeat Problem 15, to apply to Problem 12.

---

* In problems relating to projectiles or falling bodies in the earth's atmosphere, we neglect air resistance and other complicating features.

46. APPLICATIONS OF MAXIMA AND MINIMA

In determining an extremum for a function which arises in an application, the following procedure frequently is convenient.

    I. *Introduce auxiliary variables and express the fundamental dependent variable, W, as a function of the auxiliary variables.*

    II. *If two * auxiliary variables were used, search for an equation relating them. Then, use this relation to eliminate one variable. Thus, W is expressed as a function of just one independent variable.*

    III. *Apply tests to determine each extremum of W.*

The typical problem which we shall meet demands location of an *absolute* maximum or minimum. Frequently, the existence of the absolute extremum will be a consequence of Theorem II on page 122. Note 1 on page 123 is useful in our present discussion. In this section, *extremum* will mean *absolute extremum*.

EXAMPLE 1. Find the altitude of the right circular cone † of maximum volume which can be inscribed in a sphere of radius r.

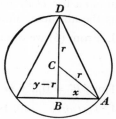

Solution. 1. Figure 109 shows a cross section of the sphere through its center, with the cross section of an inscribed cone. Let the measures of the base-radius, the altitude, and the volume in corresponding units be x, y, and V, respectively. Then, $V = \frac{1}{3}\pi x^2 y$. We desire to find the value of x, or y, which maximizes V.

Fig. 109

2. From Figure 109, $\overline{AB}^2 + \overline{BC}^2 = r^2$ and $\overline{BD} = y$. Hence, ‡

$$x^2 + (y - r)^2 = r^2, \quad or \quad x^2 = 2ry - y^2. \tag{1}$$

Thus, $$V = \frac{1}{3}\pi y(2ry - y^2). \tag{2}$$

Let $W = 3V/\pi$. Then, $$W = y(2ry - y^2). \tag{3}$$

Since V and W attain any maximum at the same value of y, we choose to investigate extrema for the simpler function W. We note that W is a continuous function of y with nonnegative values on the *closed* interval $T = \{0 \le y \le 2r\}$; also, $W = 0$ at $y = 0$ and $y = 2r$. Hence, by Theorem II on page 122, W has a *positive absolute maximum at some point interior* to D.

3. From (3), $$\frac{dW}{dy} = 4ry - 3y^2 = y(4r - 3y). \tag{4}$$

Thus, $W' = 0$ at $y = 0$ and $y = \frac{4}{3}r$. V has an absolute maximum at some point y where $0 < y < 2r$, and $y = \frac{4}{3}r$ is *the only possible value for y* at this maximum. Hence, V attains its maximum at $y = \frac{4}{3}r$.

---

* If k variables are used, search for $(k - 1)$ relations between them.

† Hereafter, in this chapter, "*cone*" and "*cylinder*" will mean "*right circular cone*" and "*right circular cylinder*," respectively.

‡ A new figure shows that (1) holds if $y < r$.

EXAMPLE 2. A rectangular field along a river with a straight bank is to have an area of 800 square yards, and is to be fenced along the sides not on the bank. Find the dimensions to minimize the fencing.

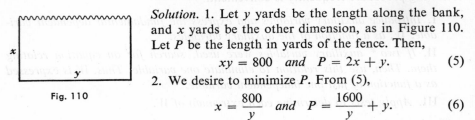

Fig. 110

Solution. 1. Let y yards be the length along the bank, and x yards be the other dimension, as in Figure 110. Let P be the length in yards of the fence. Then,

$$xy = 800 \quad and \quad P = 2x + y. \tag{5}$$

2. We desire to minimize P. From (5),

$$x = \frac{800}{y} \quad and \quad P = \frac{1600}{y} + y. \tag{6}$$

In (6), the domain for y is $D = \{all\ y > 0\}$, and $P > 0$. Also, $P \to \infty$ as $y \to 0$ and as $y \to \infty$. Hence, on visualizing a graph of (6), we infer that P has a *positive absolute minimum*, which also is a *relative minimum at an interior point* of D (all of its points are interior points). Therefore, we shall obtain all relative minima for D by use of Theorem III on page 124 and select the *smallest result* as the absolute minimum.

3. From (6) we obtain

$$\frac{dP}{dy} = 1 - \frac{1600}{y^2} = \frac{y^2 - 1600}{y^2}. \tag{7}$$

Thus, $P' = 0$ if $y = \pm 40$, where only $y = 40$ is pertinent.

4. *Test of $y = 40$.* From (7), $P'' = 3200/y^3$, which is *positive* at $y = 40$. Hence, P has a relative minimum at $y = 40$. Since we have found *just one relative minimum* on D, this extremum must be the *absolute minimum* of P, which thus occurs at $y = 40$. Then $x = \frac{800}{y} = 20$. The desired dimensions are 20 by 40, in yards.

EXAMPLE 3. In an isosceles triangle, the base is 10' and the altitude is 20'. A rectangle has its base on the base of the triangle, and two vertices on its equal sides. Find the dimensions of the rectangle to give it maximum area.

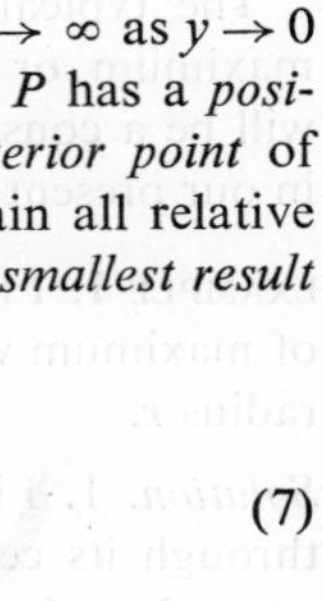

Solution outline. 1. For the rectangle, let the length of the base be $2x$ feet, the altitude be y feet, and the area be W square feet; $W = 2xy$.

2. In Figure 111, $\triangle$'s ABC and DBE are similar, with $AB = 5 - x$. Hence, from ratios of corresponding sides,

$$\frac{5 - x}{y} = \frac{5}{20}, \quad or \quad y = 20 - 4x.$$

Fig. 111

Therefore, $W = 2x(20 - 4x)$. Then, we desire to maximize the function W.

EXERCISE 41

1. A rectangular field is to be surrounded by a fence, and also will have a similar fence, parallel to one side, dividing the field into two equal parts. Find the dimensions of the field to minimize the cost of fencing, if the area is to be 3750 square yards.

$2 \times y = 3750$
$4 \times + 3y = P$

2. A piece of wire 40″ long is bent to form a rectangle. Find its dimensions, to give maximum area.

3. A box with open top will be made by cutting equal squares from the corners of a 10″ × 20″ piece of copper, and folding up the sides. Find the size of the square to give maximum capacity for the box.

4. Find the dimensions of a rectangular parallelepiped with square base, open top, volume of 256 cubic inches, and minimum surface area.

5. A wooden beam of rectangular cross section, given length, and specified material, will be supported at both ends. Then, the permissible load for the beam varies directly as its breadth and the square of its depth. Find the dimensions of the strongest beam which can be cut from a log whose diameter is 2′.

6. Find the dimensions of the rectangular parallelepiped with a square base and volume of 64,000 cubic inches, where the length of a diagonal is a minimum. Avoid use of a radical.

7. Find the dimensions of the rectangle of maximum area which can be inscribed in a circle whose radius is 8′.

8. Find the dimensions of a rectangle with assigned perimeter, h, and minimum length for the diagonal.

9. Find the dimensions of the rectangular box with square base and open top, of maximum capacity, to be made with 48 square feet of material.

10. Find the altitude of the cone of maximum volume which can be obtained by rotating a right triangle about one leg, if the hypotenuse is 3′ long.

11. A fence, 16′ high, is 2′ from a high wall. Find the length of the shortest ladder which will reach over the fence to the wall.

12. Let p be the unknown probability of success for a certain event at any trial. In n trials, suppose that h successes have been observed. Then, in mathematical statistics, the *maximum likelihood estimator* for p is defined as that value $p = \hat{p}$ which maximizes the likelihood function $L(p) = p^h(1 - p)^{n-h}$. Find $\hat{p}$.

13. A closed rectangular parallelepiped will have a square base, and a volume of 16,000 cubic inches. The base and top will be made of material twice as expensive as that for the sides. Find the dimensions to minimize the cost of the material.

14. A rectangle is placed inside a triangle with two vertices of the rectangle on the base of the triangle, and one vertex on each of the other sides of the triangle. If the lengths of the base and corresponding altitude of the triangle are 20′ and 8′, respectively, find the dimensions of the rectangle to maximize its area.

15. A gutter will have a horizontal plane bottom and equally inclined sides, where the bottom and the sides are each 5″ wide. Find the width of the gutter across the top, to create maximum capacity.

16. Find the base and altitude of the isosceles triangle of maximum area which can be inscribed in a circle of radius 8″.

17. Find the point on the curve $y^2 = 4x$ which is nearest to (2, 1).

18. Find an equation for the line through the point (3, 2) making with the coordinate axes a triangle of minimum area, in the first quadrant.

19. Find the dimensions of the cylinder of maximum curved surface area which can be inscribed in a sphere of radius r.

20. An experimenter obtains $x_1, x_2, \cdots, x_n$ as n measurements of the value of a quantity whose true value Z is unknown. As an approximation to Z, he decides to take that number Z for which

$$(x_1 - Z)^2 + (x_2 - Z)^2 + \cdots + (x_n - Z)^2$$

is a minimum. Prove that $Z = (x_1 + x_2 + \cdots + x_n)/n$, which is called the **arithmetic mean** of the x's.

21. Find the dimensions of the cone of minimum volume which can be circumscribed about a sphere of radius r.

22. Find the dimensions of the rectangular parallelepiped with a square base and maximum volume which can be inscribed in a given sphere.

23. In dollars, the average annual cost, A, of operating a certain machine, whose cost is C, which will be used x years is $A = rC + Cx^{-1} + bx$, where the annual cost for interest and taxes is rC, for depreciation is Cx^{-1}, and for repairs is bx. Find x to minimize A.

In the remaining problems, refer to Note 1 *on page* 96.

With the given total-cost function, find the production, x, for which the average cost, A, is a minimum. Also, draw graphs of A and the marginal cost C' on the same coordinate system, to verify that the curves intersect where A has its minimum.

24. $C = x^3 - 6x^2 + 15x$.   **25.** $C = 2x^3 - 9x^2 + 10x$.

26. Let the total cost and demand curves be

$$C = x^3 - 15x^2 + 76x + 25 \quad and \quad p = 55 - 3x.$$

Find the number of units of production for which the total profit obtained will be a maximum.

27. Prove that, if the profit assumes a maximum value at an output $x = x_0$ inside the possible domain for x, then the marginal cost is equal to the marginal revenue at $x = x_0$. Verify this fact in Problem 26.

47. EXTREMUM WITH SIDE CONDITION

Suppose that just two auxiliary variables, say x and y, are introduced in a problem of the type met in Section 46. We search for absolute extrema. Then, the analytical basis for the solution is as follows:

$$\left\{ \begin{array}{l} relation \ between \ x \ and \ y, \\ based \ on \ problem \ constants \end{array} \right\} \qquad g(x, y) = 0; \qquad (1)$$

$$\left\{ \begin{array}{l} function, \ U, \ to \ be \\ given \ an \ extremum \end{array} \right\} \qquad U = f(x, y). \qquad (2)$$

In [(1), (2)], we may refer to (1) as a "*constraint*" or "*side condition*," a relation between the auxiliary variables.

Instead of using (1) to eliminate one variable, say y, as in Section 46, sometimes it is convenient to consider (1) as defining y implicitly as a function of x, and *to retain both x and y until a final stage*. Then, the resulting procedure may be called an *implicit function method* for obtaining extrema. The routine we shall employ is as follows.

I. *Select one variable, say x, to be the independent variable. Then, differentiate in (1) and (2) with respect to x; y′ will arise from (1) and (2).*

II. *Solve for y′ as given by differentiation in (1), and substitute the result in dU/dx as obtained from (2). Then, use dU/dx = 0 to obtain a necessary condition on x and y for an extremum of U.*

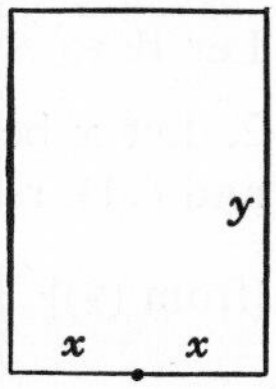

EXAMPLE 1. Find the shape of a solid cylinder of given volume with minimum surface area.

Solution. 1. Let x, y, V, and S be the measures of the base-radius, altitude, volume, and surface area, respectively, for the cylinder, whose cross section is seen in Figure 112. Then,

Fig. 112

$$\left\{ \begin{array}{l} relation\ between \\ auxiliary\ variables \end{array} \right\} \qquad V = \pi x^2 y, \quad or \quad x^2 y = \frac{V}{\pi}; \tag{3}$$

$$(function\ to\ minimize) \qquad S = 2\pi xy + 2\pi x^2. \tag{4}$$

2. Let x be the independent variable with domain $D = \{all\ x > 0\}$. Then, (3) defines y as a function of x, and hence (4) expresses S as a function of x. If $x \to \infty$, from (4) we have $S \to \infty$. From $V = \pi x(xy)$, if $x \to 0$ then $xy \to \infty$ and again $S \to \infty$. Thus, there is no absolute maximum for S. Since $S > 0$, S must have a positive absolute minimum at some point x interior to D (all of its points are interior points). Hence, when (below) we find that S has *just one relative extremum*, we shall conclude that it is the absolute minimum of S.

3. Let $W = S/2\pi$. We shall investigate relative minima on D for

$$W = xy + x^2. \tag{5}$$

Differentiate with respect to x in (3) and (5), with V as a constant:

[from (3)] $\qquad\qquad 2xy + x^2 y' = 0, \quad or \quad y' = -\frac{2y}{x}; \tag{6}$

[from (5) and (6)] $\qquad\qquad \dfrac{dW}{dx} = y + xy' + 2x = 2x - y. \tag{7}$

Thus, if W has a relative extremum, $\qquad 2x - y = 0. \tag{8}$

If $y = 2x$, then (3) would yield just *one* value for x (which we do not desire to obtain). Hence, from Step (2) of the solution, the minimum surface area is attained if $y = 2x$, or when *the diameter is equal to the altitude.*

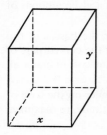

Fig. 113

EXAMPLE 2. A closed box will be a rectangular parallelepiped with a square base, as in Figure 113. The material for the sides will cost twice as much per square foot as the material for the top and bottom. Find the relative dimensions of the box, to minimize the expense of the material, for given capacity. (Disregard the thickness of the material in such a problem.)

Solution. 1. Let x, y, V, k, and E represent the measures of a side of the base, the altitude, the constant volume, the cost per square unit of the sides, and the cost of the material, respectively. Then,

(*relation between variables*) $V = x^2 y$;   (9)

(*function to minimize*) $E = 4kxy + kx^2$.   (10)

Let $W = E/k$; we shall minimize W: $W = 4xy + x^2$.   (11)

2. Let x be the independent variable, and differentiate with respect to x in (9)
and (11), recalling that V is a constant and y is a function of x:

[from (9)] $2xy + x^2 y' = 0$,   *or* $y' = -\dfrac{2y}{x}$;   (12)

[from (11) and (12)] $\dfrac{dW}{dx} = 4y + 4xy' + 2x = 2x - 4y$.   (13)

If W has a relative extremum, then $2x - 4y = 0$ or $x = 2y$.   (14)

3. In the problem, $0 < x < \infty$. If $x \to 0$ or if $x \to \infty$, the surface area of the
box becomes infinite and thus E becomes infinite. Hence, E has an absolute
minimum. Since (14) leads to *just one extremum*, it must be the absolute minimum.
That is, for minimum cost, the length of a side of the base must be twice the altitude.

EXERCISE 42

*It is recommended that each problem be solved by the method involving use of an implicit
function, except perhaps near the end of the exercise.*

1. Find the dimensions of the rectangle of maximum area situated with two vertices
   on the diameter of a semicircle of radius r, and the other two vertices on the semicircle.

2. Find the dimensions of the rectangle of maximum perimeter which can be inscribed
   in a circle of radius r.

3. Find the relative dimensions * of a closed rectangular parallelepiped with a square
   base, a specified volume, and minimum surface area.

4. Find the relative dimensions of a solid cylinder with given volume and minimum
   surface area.

5. Find the shape of a rectangle with an assigned area and (*a*) minimum perimeter;
   (*b*) minimum length for a diagonal.

6. Find the relative dimensions of the cylinder of maximum curved surface area which
   can be inscribed in a given sphere.

7. A closed rectangular box with a square base is to be made from a given amount of
   material. Find the relative dimensions for maximum volume.

8. To construct a cylindrical container, we shall use material for the base and top
   which is twice as expensive, per square foot, as the material for the curved part of
   the surface. Find the ratio of the radius to the altitude, for minimum cost of material,
   with a given volume.

9. A cylinder is inscribed in a given cone, with the base of the cylinder on the base of
   the cone. Find the ratio of the base-radius of the cylinder to its altitude, to maximize
   the cylinder's volume.

* That is, find a simple relation between the dimensions.

10. Find the relative dimensions of a solid cylinder with given surface area and maximum volume.

11. Find the relative dimensions of the cone of maximum volume which can be inscribed in a given sphere.

12. To reduce friction for water flowing in a channel with rectangular cross section, it is desired to minimize the surface area in contact with the water. Find the ratio of the depth to the breadth, to obtain the desired result, for a channel with specified capacity, that is, with specified cross-section area.

13. Find the ratio of the radius of the base to the altitude, for a conical tent of given capacity which will require the least material.

14. A vat with open top is to form a cylinder. Find the ratio of its base-radius to the altitude, to yield a given volume with minimum surface.

15. Find the relative dimensions of a rectangular parallelepiped with a square base (*a*) if the length of a diagonal is assigned, and the volume is a maximum; (*b*) if the volume is assigned, and the length of a diagonal is a minimum.

16. Find the shape of the right triangle of maximum area, with a given hypotenuse.

17. Find the maximum area for an isosceles triangle whose perimeter is 24″.

18. At what point on the ellipse $b^2x^2 + a^2y^2 = a^2b^2$, in the first quadrant, should a tangent be drawn in order that the triangle formed with the coordinate axes will have minimum area?

19. A trapezoidal gutter is to be made from a strip of tin 15″ wide by bending up equal sides at an angle of 60°. Find the width of the base of the gutter for maximum capacity.

20. A pyramid with a square base and maximum volume is inscribed in a sphere of radius *r*. Find the ratio of a side of the base to the altitude, for the pyramid.

48. GENERAL CURVE TRACING

In graphing an equation $h(x, y) = 0$, we consider those parts of the following routine which are applicable conveniently.

I. *Solve for one variable (or, for each variable) in terms of the other variable. Use the result to find the domains for x and y to give real solutions.*

II. *Find the x-intercepts and y-intercepts.*

III. *Test for asymptotes. (Does either variable become infinite as the other variable approaches some value? What is the limit of y, or x, as the other variable becomes infinite?)*

IV. *Notice any symmetry, with tests of page 41 applied.*

V. *Calculate dy/dx and dx/dy; locate horizontal or vertical tangents.*

VI. *When second derivatives are convenient, locate inflection points.*

In graphing an equation $y^n = R(x)$, where *n* is an *even* integer, it may be useful to draw an auxiliary graph of the new equation $y_1 = R(x)$ in finding the domain for *x* to make *y* real valued. Similar remarks apply in graphing an equation $x^n = R(y)$.

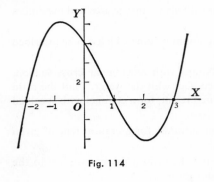

Fig. 114

EXAMPLE 1. Graph:

$$y^2 = (x + 2)(x - 1)(x - 3). \qquad (1)$$

Solution. 1. Solve for y:

$$y = \pm \sqrt{(x + 2)(x - 1)(x - 3)}; \qquad (2)$$

y will have real values if and only if

$$(x + 2)(x - 1)(x - 3) \geqq 0. \qquad (3)$$

Let $y_1 = (x + 2)(x - 1)(x - 3)$. A graph of this equation is in Figure 114, where $y_1 \geqq 0$ if $-2 \leqq x \leqq 1$ and if $3 \leqq x$. These values are the domain for x in (1).

2. With $y = 0$ in (1), the x-intercepts are $x = -2$, 1, and 3. With $x = 0$, the y-intercepts are $y = \pm \sqrt{6} = \pm 2.45$, from Table I.

3. The graph is symmetric to OX. (Why?)

4. From (1), by implicit function differentiation,

$$2y \frac{dy}{dx} = 3x^2 - 4x - 5, \quad or \quad \frac{dy}{dx} = \frac{3x^2 - 4x - 5}{2y}; \quad \frac{dx}{dy} = \frac{2y}{3x^2 - 4x - 5}. \qquad (4)$$

5. The tangent to the graph is *vertical* when $dx/dy = 0$, or when $y = 0$, that is, at each point where the graph meets the x-axis.

6. We have $y' = 0$ when $3x^2 - 4x - 5 = 0$, or, by the quadratic formula from page 673, when $x = 2.1$ and $x = -.8$. Since 2.1 is an excluded value of x, only $x = -.8$ applies, to give two points with the tangent horizontal. The graph of (1) consists of the loop and separate branch in Figure 115. The graph is called a **bipartite cubic** curve. The following table of values and preceding information were used in obtaining the graph.

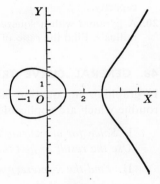

Fig. 115

$x =$	-2	$-.8$	1	3	4	5
$y =$	0	± 2.9	0	0	± 4.2	± 7.5

EXAMPLE 2. If $a > 0$, graph $\qquad x^3 + xy^2 = 2ay^2. \qquad (5)$

Solution. 1. Solve for y: $\qquad y^2 = \frac{x^3}{2a - x}; \quad y = \pm \sqrt{\frac{x^3}{2a - x}}. \qquad (6)$

The fraction in (6) is negative if $x < 0$, or $x > 2a$. Hence, since $y^2 \geqq 0$, x must have the domain $0 \leqq x < 2a$, to give real values for y.

2. y is not defined at $x = 2a$, and $|y| \to \infty$ as $x \to 2a-$ (from the left). Hence, the line $x = 2a$ is a vertical asymptote. Substitution of $-y$ for y leaves (4) unaltered. Hence, the graph is symmetric to the x-axis.

3. Calculate dy/dx by differentiation in (5):

$$2yy' = \frac{3x^2(2a - x) + x^3}{(2a - x)^2}, \quad or \quad y' = \frac{x^2(3a - x)}{y(2a - x)^2}.$$

By use of (6),
$$y' = \pm \frac{(3a - x)\sqrt{x}}{\sqrt{(2a - x)^3}}. \tag{7}$$

In (7), the fraction is equal to zero at $x = 3a$ and $x = 0$. Since $x = 3a$ is outside the domain for x (found above), the only horizontal tangent occurs when $x = 0$; then $y = 0$. The graph is on page 712, and has a cusp at the origin. The curve is called the **cissoid** of DIOCLES.

EXERCISE 43

Graph the equation. Any constant a, b, or k is considered positive. Wherever a, b, or k occurs, carry out the discussion without using a particular value for the constant.

1. $y^2 = (x - 2)(x - 4)$.
2. $x^2 = (y + 3)(y - 1)$.
3. $y^2 = x(x - 1)(x - 4)$.
4. $y^2 = (x + 2)(x - 2)(x - 4)$.
5. $y^2 = x^2(x - 2)$.
6. $x^2 = y^2(y + 3)$.
7. The **semicubical parabola**: $y^2 = kx^3$.
8. $y^2 = \dfrac{x + 3}{x - 4}$.
9. The **witch** of AGNESI: $y = \dfrac{a^3}{x^2 + a^2}$.
10. The **bipartite cubic**: $y^2 = x(x - a)(x - b)$, where $0 < a < b$.
11. The **cruciform curve**: $x^2 y^2 = k^2(x^2 + y^2)$.
12. The **serpentine**: $y = \dfrac{k^2 x}{a^2 + x^2}$.
13. The **strophoid**: $y^2 = x^2 \left(\dfrac{k + x}{k - x}\right)$.

★SUPPLEMENT FOR CHAPTER SIX

Find all relative maxima and minima, and any absolute maximum or minimum of the function f(x) for x on the domain, D. Also, graph f.

14. $f(x) = |x - 2|^3$; D is all x.
15. $f(x) = x - 3|x - 2|$; D is all x.
16. $f(x) = |2x + 3| - x^2$; D is all x.

17. With $f(x) = 10^{1/(x-2)}$, and the domain of x as all $x \neq 2$, does f have an upper bound; a greatest lower bound; a least upper bound; an absolute maximum; an absolute minimum? Answer the same questions if the domain for x is all $x < 2$.

18. Find the point on the curve $x^2 = y^3$ which is closest to the point $(\frac{5}{3}, 0)$. Apply a calculus test to prove the result.

19. A man is standing on the top of a north-south wall, with his eyes 64′ above a level plane. A boy is running north at the rate of 10′ per second on a path which is 96′ east of the wall. At what rate is the line of sight distance from the man to the boy changing when he is 72′ south of the man's position?

20. A particle has its motion on an s-axis defined by $s = t^3 - 6t^2 + 9t + 18$, where t is the time in seconds measured from some fixed instant and s is measured in feet. Find the values of t on the interval $0 \leq t \leq 5$ at which the *speed* of the particle has a relative or absolute minimum, and a relative or absolute maximum, and specify the speed in each case.

21. Let a function f with the domain $0 \leq x \leq 1$ be defined by specifying that $f(x) = 0$ if x is a rational number and $f(x) = 1$ if x is an irrational number. Draw a graph of f as it would appear visually. At what values of x is f continuous; discontinuous? At what values of x does f have a relative maximum; a relative minimum? Give a discussion to justify your remarks.

22. Obtain the graph of $x^3 + y^3 = 3axy$, where $a > 0$, with some calculus employed. Incidentally, find a value of m so that the line $y = mx + b$, for any value of b, intersects the graph in two points (x_1, y_1) and (x_2, y_2) with $x_1 = y_2$ and $y_1 = x_2$, where possibly $x_1 = 0$, or in no real points. For this value of m, show that there is a number b_0 such that, if $b \to b_0+$, then $|x_1| \to \infty$ and $|x_2| \to \infty$, and thus the line $y = mx + b_0$ is an asymptote of the graph.

23. Graph the **cocked hat**: $(x^2 + 2ay - a^2)^2 = y^2(a^2 - x^2)$, $a > 0$.

24. Graph the **bifolium**: $(x^2 + y^2)^2 = ax^2y$, $a > 0$.

25. Find the radius of the circle for which a circular sector of given perimeter, P, has maximum area. See page 224.

26. Find the radius of the circle for which a circular sector of given area, A, has maximum or minimum perimeter, whichever is the case. See page 224.

27. The functions f and g have a common* domain, involving an interval of numbers including c. Given that f and g attain a relative maximum at c. Prove or disprove the statement that "the function $f(x)g(x)$ attains a relative maximum at $x = c$."

28. Let $(x_1, x_2, \cdots, x_n)$ and $(y_1, y_2, \cdots, y_n)$ be any numbers, where $\Sigma y_i^2 \neq 0$. By applying reasoning about extrema to the function $f(\lambda) = \Sigma(x_i + \lambda y_i)^2$, prove that

$$(\Sigma x_i y_i)^2 \leq (\Sigma x_i^2)(\Sigma y_i^2), \tag{1}$$

where the sums are for $i = 1$ to $i = n$, inclusive. Show that (1) holds if and only if there exists a constant k such that, for all values of i, we have $x_i = ky_i$. Inequality (1) is called the *Schwarz inequality*, which is used in many fields of mathematics.

29. With x_1, x_2, and x_3 such that $x_1 < x_2 < x_3$, prove that the unique value of x for which the function

$$f(x) = |x - x_1| + |x - x_2| + |x - x_3| \tag{2}$$

attains its absolute minimum is $x = x_2$, the **median** of (x_1, x_2, x_3). With

$$x_1 < x_2 < x_3 < x_4,$$

prove that the function $g(x) = f(x) + |x - x_4|$ attains its absolute minimum at

$$x = \tfrac{1}{2}(x_2 + x_3),$$

but that there are other values of x with the same property. [In this case, $\tfrac{1}{2}(x_2 + x_3)$ sometimes is defined as the median for (x_1, x_2, x_3, x_4)]. Generalize and prove these results for any odd number, and for any even number of values of x. These facts are useful in statistics. In the data, "$<$" could be replaced by "$\leq$" without serious complication in the proofs.

30. A cone is inscribed in a given cone having the same axis, and the vertex of the inscribed cone is at the center of the base of the given cone. Find the altitude of the inscribed cone, to maximize its volume.

31. Let C be the graph of $y = f(x)$ in an xy-plane where the scale units are equal on the axes, and the domain of f consists of all x on some interval I. Assume that $f'(x)$ exists on I, and let H represent the distance between a fixed point $Q:(\alpha, \beta)$ and $P:(x, y)$ on C. Assume that H takes on a relative minimum at an interior point $x = x_0$ of I. Prove that Q lies on the normal line for C at P.

CHAPTER SEVEN

Differentials and Parametric Form

49. CALCULATION OF DIFFERENTIALS BY FORMULAS

Consider a differentiable function f and let $y = f(x)$. Let dx (instead of Δx) represent an arbitrary increment, not zero, to be assigned to any value of x, and let Δy be the corresponding increment for y. Then,

$$\Delta y = f(x + dx) - f(x) = \Delta f(x). \tag{1}$$

On page 88, we defined the differential dy, or $df(x)$, by the equation

$$dy = f'(x)dx, \quad or \quad df(x) = f'(x)dx. \tag{2}$$

EXAMPLE 1. If $f(x) = x^2 + 2x$, graph $y = f(x)$; exhibit dx, dy, and Δy at the point where $x = 1$, if $dx = 1.5$.

Solution. 1. $y' = 2x + 2$; $dy = (2x + 2)dx$. If $x = 1$ and $dx = 1.5$, then $y' = 4$ and

$$dy = 4\,dx = 6.$$

2. If (x, y) and $(x + dx, y + \Delta y)$ are pairs of corresponding values of x and y, then

$$y = x^2 + 2x \quad and$$

$$y + \Delta y = (x + dx)^2 + 2(x + dx).$$

Hence, we obtain $\quad \Delta y = (2x + 2)dx + (dx)^2$.

3. If $x = 1$ and $dx = 1.5$, then $\Delta y = 8.25$. Figure 116 exhibits a graph of $y = x^2 + 2x$ with dx, dy, and Δy represented by directed line segments at $x = 1$ when $dx = 1.5$.

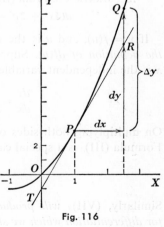

Fig. 116

Let $P:(x, y)$ be any point on the graph of $y = f(x)$, with PT tangent to the graph at P. Notice that, for any value of dx, the point $R:(x + dx, y + dy)$ is on PT, whereas $Q:(x + dx, y + \Delta y)$ is on the graph of $y = f(x)$, as illustrated in Figure 116.

151

We obtain standard forms for differentials on multiplying by dx on both sides of (I)–(VII) on page 92. Thus, if u and v are differentiable functions of x, we obtain the following formulas, where du and dv are functions of x and dx:

$$d(k) = 0. \qquad \text{(I)}_d \qquad\qquad d(ku) = k\ du. \qquad \text{(II)}_d$$

$$du^n = nu^{n-1}\ du. \qquad \text{(III)}_d \qquad d(u + v) = du + dv. \qquad \text{(IV)}_d$$

$$d(uv) = v\ du + u\ dv. \qquad \text{(V)}_d \qquad d\left(\frac{u}{v}\right) = \frac{v\ du - u\ dv}{v^2}. \qquad \text{(VI)}_d$$

If $y = f(u)$, where f' exists, then dy is given by the formula

$$dy = f'(u)du, \qquad\qquad \text{(VII)}_d$$

not only when u is the independent variable, but also when u is a differentiable function of the independent variable x, so that du is a function of x and dx.

ILLUSTRATION 1. From (III) on page 92,

$$\frac{du^n}{dx} = nu^{n-1}\frac{du}{dx}. \qquad (3)$$

On multiplying by dx on both sides in (3), we obtain (III)$_d$.

ILLUSTRATION 2. From (VI)$_d$,

$$d\left(\frac{3x + 2}{5x^2 + 7}\right) = \frac{(5x^2 + 7)d(3x + 2) - (3x + 2)d(5x^2 + 7)}{(5x^2 + 7)^2}$$

$$= \frac{3(5x^2 + 7) - 10x(3x + 2)}{(5x^2 + 7)^2}\ dx = \frac{21 - 20x - 15x^2}{(5x^2 + 7)^2}\ dx,$$

because $d(3x + 2) = 3\ dx$ and $d(5x^2 + 7) = 10x\ dx$.

ILLUSTRATION 3. From (III)$_d$, with $u = 4x^2 + 2$,

$$d(4x^2 + 2)^8 = 8(4x^2 + 2)^7 d(4x^2 + 2) = 64x(4x^2 + 2)^7\ dx.$$

If $y = f(u)$, and u is the *independent variable*, then (VII)$_d$ is true simply *by the definition of $df(u)$*. Suppose, now, that $y = f(u)$ where $u = \phi(x)$, and that x is the independent variable. Then, from (VII) on page 92,

$$\frac{dy}{dx} = \frac{dy}{du}\cdot\frac{du}{dx}, \quad \text{or} \quad \frac{dy}{dx} = f'(u)\frac{du}{dx}. \qquad (4)$$

On multiplying both sides of (4) by dx, we obtain (VII)$_d$, where $du = \phi'(x)dx$. Formula (III)$_d$ is a special case of VII$_d$. Thus, if $y = u^n$,

$$dy = \frac{dy}{du}\ du = nu^{n-1}\ du.$$

Similarly, (VII)$_d$ *will produce a differential formula from each standard form for differentiation which we shall present in a later chapter*.

ILLUSTRATION 4. $d(4x + 5)^{\frac{1}{3}} = \frac{1}{3}(4x + 5)^{-\frac{2}{3}}d(4x + 5) = \frac{4}{3}(4x + 5)^{-\frac{2}{3}}\ dx.$

EXAMPLE 2. Find dy in terms of x, y, and dx, and then find dy/dx, if

$$x^2 + 2xy - 3y^2 = 5x - 7. \qquad (5)$$

Solution. Consider (5) as defining y implicitly as a function of x. Then, each side of (5) represents the value, at x, of a differentiable function of x. Hence, we may take the differential of each side of (5) and equate the results (this method corresponds to implicit function differentiation on page 102):

$$2x\,dx + 2(y\,dx + x\,dy) - 6y\,dy = 5\,dx;$$

$$(2x - 6y)dy = (5 - 2x - 2y)dx, \quad or \quad dy = \frac{5 - 2x - 2y}{2x - 6y}\,dx. \qquad (6)$$

Then, from (6),
$$\frac{dy}{dx} = \frac{5 - 2x - 2y}{2x - 6y}.$$

Usually, there is no particular merit in obtaining dy/dx as above, in comparison with the method of page 102.

Note 1. From the nature of differentials, if one term in an equation involves a differential as a factor, then each term involves a differential factor.

ILLUSTRATION 5. By use of (III)$_d$ with $n = -1$ and $u = 3 + x^3$,

$$d\left(\frac{5}{3 + x^3}\right) = d[5(3 + x^3)^{-1}] = -5(3 + x^3)^{-2}(3x^2\,dx) = -15(3 + x^3)^{-2}x^2\,dx.$$

EXERCISE 44

1. Let $f(x) = \frac{1}{2}x^2$ and let $y = f(x)$. Compute dy and Δy at $x = 2$ with $dx = .5$, by use of (1) and (2) on page 151. Graph $y = f(x)$; find the slope of the graph and draw the tangent at $x = 2$. Exhibit line segments representing dx, dy, and Δy.

2. If $y = 5x^2 + 3x$, compute dy if $x = 3$, when $dx = 2$; when $dx = -.3$.

Find the differential of the function of x, without expanding unnecessarily.

3. $2x^3 + 5x^2$. **4.** $(2x^2 + x)^5$. **5.** $(3 - 5x)^4$.

6. $\sqrt{2x + 3}$. **7.** $\sqrt{x^2 + x}$. **8.** $\sqrt[3]{2x + 3}$.

9. $(3x + 2)^2(5x - 3)$. **10.** $(2x - 1)^3(4x + x^2)^4$.

11. $\sqrt{3x}$. **12.** x^{-2}. **13.** $5(2x + 3)^{-1}$. **14.** $\sqrt[3]{x - x^2}$.

15. $\dfrac{\sqrt[3]{2x + 4}}{7}$. **16.** $\dfrac{2x - 5}{3x + 1}$. **17.** $\dfrac{(2x - 1)^2}{4x + 3}$.

18. $\dfrac{6}{\sqrt[3]{2x + 5}}$. **19.** $\dfrac{(1 + 2x)^2}{3x}$. **20.** $\dfrac{\sqrt{2x - 1}}{x}$.

Find dy in terms of x, y, and dx from the given equation, and then obtain dy/dx by use of the preceding result.

21. $2x^3 + 3xy - y = x^2$. **22.** $2x^{\frac{3}{2}} + y^2 + xy = 3x$.

23. $x^2 + 2y^2 + y = 3x$. **24.** $(3x + 2y)^4 + y^3 = x^2$.

50. DIFFERENTIALS AS APPROXIMATIONS

From Figure 116 on page 151, we infer geometrically, as on page 89, that dy will be a close approximation to Δy if dx is small. The sense in which this inference is correct is stated in the following theorem.

Theorem I. *Let $y = f(x)$, where f is differentiable. Then, at any point (x, y),*

$$\lim_{dx \to 0} \frac{\Delta y - dy}{dx} = 0, \quad or \quad \lim_{dx \to 0} \frac{\Delta f(x) - df(x)}{dx} = 0. \tag{1}$$

Proof. Let dx be replaced by Δx, for contact with earlier notations. At any point $x = a$ in the domain of f, we have $dy = f'(a)\Delta x$ and

$$\lim_{\Delta x \to 0} \frac{\Delta y - dy}{\Delta x} = \lim_{\Delta x \to 0} \left[\frac{\Delta y}{\Delta x} - f'(a) \right] = 0, \tag{2}$$

by the definition of $f'(a)$. Hence, (1) is true.

Note 1. If A is the *true value* of a quantity, and B is an *approximation to A*, hereafter we shall allow ourselves the latitude of referring to either $(A - B)$, or $(B - A)$, or $|A - B|$ as the *error of B*. Any reference to a *maximum* or a *minimum error* will imply use of the *nonnegative error formula* $|A - B|$.

In (1), let $\qquad \dfrac{\Delta y - dy}{dx} = \epsilon, \quad or \quad \Delta y - dy = \epsilon\, dx. \tag{3}$

Then, from (2) with $\Delta x = dx$, we have $\epsilon \to 0$ as $dx \to 0$. In (3), $|\Delta y - dy|$ is the *error of dy as an approximation to* Δy. Thus, (3) shows that, as $dx \to 0$, the error $|\Delta y - dy|$ is *so small* that, even after it is divided by $|dx|$, *the quotient approaches zero*. Or, if the fraction, ϵ, in (1) or (3) is thought of in percent form, the error $|\Delta y - dy|$ will be as small a percentage * of $|dx|$ as we please if dx is sufficiently small.

From Figure 116 on page 151, it is seen that, when we take dy as an approximation to Δy, we act as if the graph of $y = f(x)$ is identical with the tangent at (x, y) on the interval from x to $(x + dx)$. Hereafter, if it is requested that Δy be computed approximately by use of differentials, it is implied that we take

dy as an approximation to Δy. $\tag{4}$

From (4), with $df(x) = dy$ and $\Delta y = f(x + dx) - f(x)$, we obtain

$$df(x) \approx f(x + dx) - f(x), \; or$$
$$f(x + dx) \approx f(x) + df(x), \tag{5}$$

where we use "$\approx$" for "*is approximately equal to*."

EXAMPLE 1. The interior of a closed box is a cube, with a $10''$ edge, and the walls of the box are $\frac{1}{8}''$ thick. Find the volume of the walls approximately.

Solution. 1. Let x be the length in inches of an edge of a variable cube, with volume V. Then, $V = x^3$ and hence $dV = 3x^2\, dx$.

2. The volume of the walls is the increment ΔV due to a change from $x = 10$ to $x = 10\frac{1}{4}$, and is *approximately dV*, with $x = 10$ and $dx = \frac{1}{4}$:

$$\Delta V \approx dV = 3(10^2)(\tfrac{1}{4}) = 75, \text{ cu. in.}$$

---

* To give a measure of the size of one number M as compared to another number N, we may describe the ratio M/N in percent form. Thus, 6 is 3% of 200 because $\frac{6}{200} = .03$.

EXAMPLE 2. Compute $\sqrt{38}$ approximately by use of differentials.

Solution. Let $f(x) = \sqrt{x}$, whose value is known at $x = 36$. Then, $df(x) = \frac{1}{2}x^{-\frac{1}{2}} dx$. Hence, from (5) with $f(x) = \sqrt{x}$, $x = 36$, and $dx = 2$,

$$\sqrt{38} = \sqrt{36 + 2} \approx \sqrt{36} + df(x) = 6 + \frac{1}{2}(36^{-\frac{1}{2}})(2) = 6\frac{1}{6}.$$

Suppose that $y = f(x)$, where x is a variable whose value will be determined experimentally as a basis for computing y. Let (x_0, y_0) be the true values of the variables, with $x = x_0 + dx$ as the measured value of x, for which $f(x_0 + dx) = y_0 + \Delta y$. Then, we define the **relative error** in y as the error Δy divided by the true value y_0. Or,

$$\left\{ \begin{array}{l} \text{relative error } in \ y \\ \text{due to error } dx \ in \ x \end{array} \right\} = \frac{\Delta y}{y_0} \approx \frac{dy}{y}, \tag{6}$$

where we take y as y_0 and $dy = f'(x_0)dx$ when (x_0, y_0) are *known,* and we take $dy = f'(x)dx$ and $y = f(x)$, with x as the *observed value,* when (x_0, y_0) are *unknown.* In (6), when $(dy)/y$ is expressed in percent form, we refer to it as the **percent of error.**

EXAMPLE 3. For a cone of altitude $24''$, the radius of the base was measured as $4''$, with at most a 2% error. For the computed volume, find approximately the maximum possible error and percent of error.

Solution. 1. With a *variable* cone of altitude $24''$ and base radius r, the volume is $V = 8\pi r^2$. Then, $dV = 16\pi r \, dr$.

2. *Maximum error.* With $r = 4$ and an error dr,

$$(error \ in \ V \ due \ to \ error \ dr) = \Delta V \approx dV = 16\pi(4)dr = 64\pi \, dr.$$

Since $|\, dr \,| \leqq 4(.02) = .08$,

$$|\, dV \,| \leqq 64\pi(.08) = 16.1, \ cu. \ in.$$

Or, the error in the volume will not exceed 16.1 cu. in., approximately.

3. *Percent of error.* From (6), for any error dr,

$$\left\{ \begin{array}{l} \text{relative error in } V \\ \text{due to error } dr \text{ in } r \end{array} \right\} \approx \frac{dV}{V} = \frac{16\pi r \, dr}{8\pi r^2} = \frac{2 \, dr}{r}. \tag{7}$$

Since the approximate relative error in r is dr/r, from the data we have

$$\left| \frac{dr}{r} \right| \leqq .02, \quad and \ thus \quad \left| \frac{dV}{V} \right| = 2 \left| \frac{dr}{r} \right| \leqq 2(.02) = .04. \tag{8}$$

Hence, the maximum percent of error in V is 4%, approximately.

★*Note 2.* From (3) and (1), at any point $x = a$ in the domain of f,

$$\Delta f(a) - df(a) = \epsilon \, dx, \quad or \quad \Delta f(a) = f'(a)dx + \epsilon \, dx. \tag{9}$$

In (9), $\Delta f(a)$, $f'(a)dx$, and $\epsilon \, dx$ all have the limit zero as $dx \to 0$. However, when $dx \to 0$, $(\epsilon \, dx/dx) \to 0$ whereas $(f'(a)dx/dx) \to f'(a)$, generally not zero. Colloquially, then, we may say that $|\, \epsilon \, dx \,|$ becomes *very small* compared to $|\, f'(a)dx \,|$ when $|\, dx \,|$ is *sufficiently small.* Hence, we call $f'(a)dx$ the **principal part** of $\Delta f(a)$, when $|\, dx \,|$ is sufficiently small.

★*Note 3.* If g is a function such that $g(v) \to 0$ when $v \to 0$, it is sometimes said that $g(v)$ is an **infinitesimal** relative to v as the **independent infinitesimal.** If $[g(v)/v] \to L$ as $v \to 0$, we say that $g(v)$ is an infinitesimal of **higher order** than v if $L = 0$, and of the **same order** if $L \neq 0$. When $dx \to 0$ in (9), then $df(a)$, or $f'(a)dx$, is an infinitesimal of the same order as dx if $f'(a) \neq 0$. Also, $\mid \epsilon \, dx \mid$ or the error, $\mid \Delta f(a) - df(a) \mid$, of $df(a)$ as an approximation to $\Delta f(a)$, is an infinitesimal of higher order than dx, because $\epsilon \to 0$ when $dx \to 0$.

EXERCISE 45

Solve by use of differentials.

1. An ivory ball is $3''$ in diameter, and will be turned down to a diameter of $2.8''$. Find approximately the volume of ivory which is taken off.

2. A cylindrical wooden rod is 3 feet long and $4.4''$ in diameter. The rod will be turned down to a diameter of $4''$. (*a*) Find approximately the volume of wood taken off. (*b*) Compute the exact volume taken off.

   Hint. With x as the measure of the radius, the problem would permit computation of a differential corresponding to either $x = 2$ with $dx = .2$, or $x = 2.2$ with $dx = -2$. In such a case, use the most convenient values, at present $x = 2$ with $dx = .2$.

3. Find approximately the volume of a cylindrical shell, with altitude $20''$, outer radius $5''$, and shell thickness $.3''$.

4. A particle moves with the equation of motion $s = 25t^2 - 20t + 5$, where s is in feet and the time t is in seconds. If t is measured as 20.4, with known accuracy to one decimal place, find approximately the maximum error in the computed position coordinate, s, and the computed velocity, v.

5. The side of a square is measured as $10''$, with an error of at most $.3''$, and then the area, A, is computed. Find approximately the maximum possible error, and percent of error in A. Draw a sketch showing the exact error ΔA and dA.

6. A uniform cylindrical steel bearing, $30''$ long, has worn down symmetrically by 2% from a diameter of $3''$. Find approximately the percent of change in the weight of the bearing.

7. Assume that the time t in seconds for one oscillation of a simple pendulum of length l feet is $t = \pi \sqrt{\dfrac{l}{32}}$. If l is measured with an error of at most 4%, find approximately the maximum possible percent of error in the computed value of t.

8. With what largest percent of error, approximately, is it satisfactory to measure the radius of a sphere in order to compute its surface area with at most 4% error?

9. A cone has the altitude $30''$. The radius of the base is measured as $5''$. Find approximately the maximum allowable error in the radius if the computed volume is desired with an error of at most 5 cubic inches.

10. A cylinder is known to have the altitude $75''$, and the radius of the base is known to be less than $5''$. The radius will be measured and then the volume will be computed. To obtain the volume accurate to the nearest cubic inch, what accuracy in the measured radius would be satisfactory?

Compute the specified number approximately by use of differentials.

11. $\sqrt{50}$.   12. $\sqrt{66}$.   13. $\sqrt[3]{130}$.   14. $\sqrt[3]{68}$.

15. Find an approximate formula for the area of a circular ring, with outer radius r, and a small width dr.

16. The horsepower which a rotating shaft can transmit safely varies as the cube of its diameter and the angular speed of rotation of the shaft. With a given speed of rotation, find approximately the percent of change in the possible horsepower due to an increase of 2% in the diameter.

17. The lifting force exerted by the atmosphere on the wings of an airplane in flight is proportional to the square of the plane's airspeed. Find approximately the percent of change in the lifting force due to an increase of 5% in the airspeed.

18. The electrical resistance of a wire is proportional to its length and inversely proportional to the square of its diameter. For a wire of given length, the diameter is measured with an error of at most 3% and the resistance is computed. Find approximately the maximum possible percent of error in the resistance.

19. Find an approximate expression for the volume of the walls in a spherical shell of outer radius r, and thickness dr. Show that the result is the product of dr and the surface area of the shell.

If $|y|$ is small, find an approximate expression for the function value.

20. $\sqrt{1+y}$.   **21.** $\sqrt[3]{1+y}$.   **22.** $(1+y)^{-1}$.   **23.** $1/\sqrt{1+y}$.

Hint for Problem 20. Consider the function $\sqrt{x}$, and use $y = dx$.

51. PARAMETRIC EQUATIONS FOR A CURVE

Let the domain, D, of a variable t be a finite or an infinite interval. Suppose that ϕ and ψ are continuous functions with the common domain D. Then, at each point t in D, the equations

$$x = \phi(t) \quad and \quad y = \psi(t) \tag{1}$$

give a point $P:(x, y)$ in the xy-plane. The locus, C, of all points $P:(x, y)$ thus obtained is called a *continuous curve*, and we refer to (1) as *parametric equations* for C in terms of the *parameter t*. If the domain for t consists of two or more disconnected intervals, then C may consist of corresponding disconnected arcs, but for convenience may be referred to simply as one curve. Sometimes, it may be possible to eliminate t between equations as in (1), and thus obtain a single equation in x and y defining the locus of (1). Frequently, the parametric form (1) is more convenient than the xy-equation.

ILLUSTRATION 1. On page 33, we found that a set of parametric equations for the line through $P_1:(x_1,y_1)$ and $P_2:(x_2,y_2)$ is

$$x = x_1 + t(x_2 - x_1) \quad and \quad y = y_1 + t(y_2 - y_1). \tag{2}$$

Note 1. If a curve C can be defined by one set of parametric equations (1), then C can be represented parametrically by infinitely many distinct pairs of equations. With two different representations (1), the domains for the two corresponding parameters in general would be different. Thus, if we replace t by $2t$ in (2), a new parametric form is obtained for the line. A study of consequences of a change in the parameter is beyond the scope of this text.

EXAMPLE 1. Obtain the xy-equation of the curve defined by

$$x = 2 \cos t° \quad and \quad y = 3 \sin t°. \tag{3}$$

Solution. From (3), $\cos t° = \frac{1}{2}x$ and $\sin t° = \frac{1}{3}y$; hence,

$$\tfrac{1}{4}x^2 + \tfrac{1}{9}y^2 = \sin^2 t° + \cos^2 t° = 1, \; or$$

$$9x^2 + 4y^2 = 36. \tag{4}$$

Therefore, curve (3) is the ellipse whose xy-equation is (4). Equations (3) are convenient for computing points on the ellipse. Thus, if $t = 10$, from (3) we obtain $x = 2 \cos 10° = 1.97$; $y = 3 \sin 10° = .52$.

EXAMPLE 2. Find the xy-equation of the curve, C, defined parametrically by $x = \frac{27}{4}t^2$ and $y = \frac{27}{4}t^3$.

Solution. 1. If $t \neq 0$, then $y/x = t$ and, from $x = \frac{27}{4}t^2$, we obtain

$$(x \neq 0, y \neq 0) \qquad\qquad x = \frac{27y^2}{4x^2}, \quad or \quad 4x^3 = 27y^2. \tag{5}$$

2. Hence, the xy-equation of C, except possibly for the point $P:(x = 0, y = 0)$, is $4x^3 = 27y^2$. However, we verify by substitution that P satisfies $4x^3 = 27y^2$. Thus, this is the xy-equation of the *whole of C*.

Note 2. Let C be the curve defined by $x = \sqrt{t}$ and $y = 3\sqrt{t}$, where "$\sqrt{t}$" as usual means the *nonnegative* square root of t. The xy-equation obtained on eliminating t is $y = 3x$; this line l extends into quadrant III, whereas x and y are nonnegative on C. Thus, C consists only of *part of l*. This illustration shows that the elimination of t from (1) should be inspected carefully to justify any claim that the xy-equation is equivalent to (1). Equivalence except for a few points usually is satisfactory in applications.

Theorem II. *Suppose that ϕ and ψ are continuously differentiable, with a common domain, and that t, x, and y are related by*

$$x = \phi(t) \quad and \quad y = \psi(t). \tag{6}$$

Then, if $\phi'(t_0) \neq 0$, there exists an interval of numbers T such that t_0 is on T and, if t is on T, (6) defines y as a differentiable function of x, with

$$\frac{dy}{dx} = \frac{\dfrac{dy}{dt}}{\dfrac{dx}{dt}}, \quad or \quad \frac{dy}{dx} = \frac{\psi'(t)}{\phi'(t)}. \tag{7}$$

If $\psi'(t_0) \neq 0$, similarly there exists an interval T as above such that, if t is on T, (6) defines x as a differentiable function of y, with

$$\frac{dx}{dy} = \frac{\dfrac{dx}{dt}}{\dfrac{dy}{dt}}, \quad or \quad \frac{dx}{dy} = \frac{\phi'(t)}{\psi'(t)}. \tag{8}$$

Proof. 1. At $t = t_0$, assume that $\phi'(t_0) \neq 0$. Then, since ϕ' *is* continuous, there exists an interval T of numbers t, including t_0, such that $\phi'(t)$ is always positive, or always negative if t is on T. Hence, by Note 1 on page 104, if t is on T, the equation $x = \phi(t)$ has the solution $t = g(x)$, where ϕ and g are *inverse functions*. Moreover, from (3) on page 104, the function $g(x)$ is differentiable, with

$$\frac{dt}{dx} = g'(x) = \frac{1}{\phi'(t)}. \tag{9}$$

2. On placing $t = g(x)$ in $y = \psi(t)$, we obtain $y = f(x)$ where $f(x) = \phi(g(x))$. From formula (VII) on page 92, with $y = \psi(t)$ and $t = g(x)$, dy/dx exists and

$$\frac{dy}{dx} = \frac{dy}{dt} \cdot \frac{dt}{dx} = \psi'(t) \cdot \frac{1}{\phi'(t)} = \frac{\psi'(t)}{\phi'(t)}, \tag{10}$$

which proves (7). Similarly, (8) can be proved.

It is also possible to prove (7) by reasoning, which we shall omit, based on use of $dx = \phi'(t)dt$ and $dy = \psi'(t)dt$, and computation of the quotient

$$\frac{dy}{dx} = \frac{\psi'(t)dt}{\phi'(t)dt} = \frac{\psi'(t)}{\phi'(t)}. \tag{11}$$

Without justifying the procedure (11), we accept it as a device for recalling (7). Similar remarks apply to (8).

Note 3. If $\phi'(t) = \psi'(t) = 0$, neither (7) nor (8) is available. However, dy/dx or dx/dy may exist under such circumstances. At any value of t where both $\phi'(t) \neq 0$ and $\psi'(t) \neq 0$, we have the usual reciprocal relation $(dy/dx) = 1/(dx/dy)$.

ILLUSTRATION 2. From the equations

$$x = 3t^2 + 2t \quad and \quad y = 2t^2 - 5, \tag{12}$$

we obtain $$dx = (6t + 2)dt \quad and \quad dy = 4t\,dt;$$

$$\frac{dy}{dx} = \frac{4t\,dt}{(6t + 2)dt} = \frac{2t}{3t + 1}; \quad \frac{dx}{dy} = \frac{3t + 1}{2t}. \tag{13}$$

At $t = 1$, in (12) and (13) we find $x = 5$, $y = -3$, and $dy/dx = \frac{1}{2}$.

Let $y' = dy/dx$, where y' is given as a function of t in (7). Then, we apply Theorem II to the variables x and y' to obtain

$$y'' = \frac{d^2y}{dx^2} = \frac{dy'}{dx}. \tag{14}$$

EXAMPLE 3. Find $D_x^2 y$, or y'', in case x, y, and t satisfy (12).

Solution. 1. From (13), $y' = dy/dx$ or $y' = 2t/(3t + 1)$. We now have

$$x = 3t^2 + 2t \quad and \quad y' = \frac{2t}{3t + 1}.$$

2. From (14), $y'' = dy'/dx$, where

$$dy' = d\left(\frac{2t}{3t + 1}\right) = \frac{2\,dt}{(3t + 1)^2} \quad and \quad dx = (6t + 2)dt.$$

Hence, $$y'' = \frac{dy'}{dx} = \left[\frac{2\,dt}{(3t + 1)^2} \div (6t + 2)dt\right] = \frac{1}{(3t + 1)^3}.$$

EXERCISE 46

Write parametric equations for the line through the points; from these equations, compute coordinates for a third point and plot the line.

1. $(2, 5)$; $(-1, 3)$. **2.** $(-2, 4)$; $(-3, 5)$. **3.** $(-2, -4)$; $(1, 5)$.

Obtain the xy-equation of the curve with the given parametric equations. Obtain points on the curve by use of the parametric equations. Draw the curve.

4. $x = 3 + 2t$; $y = -2 + 5t$. **5.** $x = 2 - 3t$; $y = 1 + 2t$.
6. $x = 3 \cos t$; $y = 3 \sin t$. **7.** $x = 2 \cos t$; $y = 5 \sin t$.
8. $x = 2 - 3 \cos t$; $y = 1 - 3 \sin t$. **9.** $x = -1 + 2 \sin t$; $y = 3 + 4 \cos t$.

Obtain the xy-equation of the curve with the given equations.

10. $x = at^2$; $y = 9at^3$. **11.** $x = 5 - t^2$; $y = 5t - t^3$.

Find the intersections of the line l with the given curve. Show the results in a figure.

12. l:$[x = 7 + 2t, y = -1 - t]$; $x^2 + y^2 = 25$.
13. l:$[x = -4 + 4t, y = 6 - 3t]$; $9x^2 + 16y^2 = 144$.

Without eliminating t, find $D_x y$ and $D_x^2 y$.

14. $x = 2t - 3$, $y = 4 - 5t^2$. **15.** $x = 3 - 4t$, $y = t^2 + 3t$.
16. $x = 3t + 2$, $y = t^3 + 3t^2 - 5t + 6$. **17.** $x = 2t - t^2$, $y = 3 - t^2$.
18. $x = t^2 + 4$, $y = t - t^2$. **19.** $x = \frac{1}{4}t^2$, $y = \frac{1}{3}t^3$.
20. $x = t + 3t^3$, $y = t^2 + t$. **21.** $x = 4t + \frac{1}{2}t^3$, $y = \frac{1}{2}t^2 + 4$.

Find dy/dx and the equation of the tangent to the curve at the given value of t.

22. In Problem 17 at $t = 2$. **23.** In Problem 18 at $t = -3$.
24. $x = t^2(3 + 2t)$, $y = t^3(3 + 2t)$; where $t = 2$.

25. Suppose that a projectile is shot from the earth at an angle of elevation α, with initial speed v_0 feet per second, and that the time t, in seconds, is measured from the instant of firing. Then, under idealized conditions, parametric equations for the projectile's trajectory in a vertical plane, with the x-axis horizontal, are

$$x = v_0 t \cos \alpha \quad and \quad y = -\tfrac{1}{2}gt^2 + v_0 t \sin \alpha.$$

(*a*) Find the trajectory's slope at any t. (*b*) Find the maximum elevation.

52. GRAPHING IN PARAMETRIC FORM

Let a curve C in the xy-plane be defined by

$$x = \phi(t) \quad and \quad y = \psi(t), \tag{1}$$

where ϕ and ψ have continuous derivatives of the first and second orders, except perhaps at isolated values of t. From (1), and page 158,

$$\frac{dx}{dt} = \phi'(t); \quad \frac{dy}{dt} = \psi'(t); \quad \frac{dy}{dx} = \frac{\psi'(t)}{\phi'(t)}; \quad \frac{dx}{dy} = \frac{\phi'(t)}{\psi'(t)}; \quad \frac{d^2y}{dx^2} = \frac{dy'}{dx}. \tag{2}$$

As a basis for the graph of a curve of type (1), frequently it is convenient to compute a table of corresponding values of t, x, and y, where the values of t for important points (x, y) on C are found by the following routine.

I. *Find x- and y-intercepts by solving $\phi(t) = 0$ and $\psi(t) = 0$.*

II. *Find where x has an extremum by testing the values of t where $\phi'(t) = 0$, and similarly with respect to y, by solving $\psi'(t) = 0$.*

III. *Horizontal and vertical tangents. Solve $\psi'(t) = 0$ to find the critical values of t for horizontal tangents. If $\psi'(t) = 0$ at $t = t_0$ and $\phi'(t_0) \neq 0$, from (2) we find $dy/dx = 0$ at $t = t_0$, so that C has a horizontal tangent at $t = t_0$. Solve $\phi'(t) = 0$ to find the critical values of t for vertical tangents; the tangent is vertical at $t = t_0$ if $\phi'(t_0) = 0$ and $\psi'(t_0) \neq 0$.*

IV. *If both $\phi'(t) = 0$ and $\psi'(t) = 0$ at $t = t_0$, investigate dy/dx or dx/dy as $t \to t_0$, to decide about a possible tangent at $t = t_0$.*

V. *Investigate for inflection points if $D_x^2 y$ is convenient (rarely the case).*

EXAMPLE 1. Graph the curve C defined parametrically by

$$x = 6t - \tfrac{1}{2}t^3 \quad and \quad y = \tfrac{1}{2}t^2 - 6. \tag{3}$$

Solution. 1.

$$\frac{dx}{dt} = (6 - \tfrac{3}{2}t^2); \quad \frac{dy}{dt} = t. \tag{4}$$

Hence,

$$\frac{dy}{dx} = \frac{2t}{3(4 - t^2)}; \quad \frac{dx}{dy} = \frac{3(4 - t^2)}{2t}. \tag{5}$$

2. Since $D_t y = 0$ at $t = 0$, and $D_t^2 y = 1 > 0$, hence y has a minimum at $t = 0$. Since $D_t x \neq 0$ at $t = 0$, in (5) we find $dy/dx = 0$ at $t = 0$, and thus C has a horizontal tangent when $t = 0$.

3. The solutions of $D_t x = 0$ are $t = \pm 2$. Since $D_t^2 x = -3t$, we have $D_t^2 x > 0$ at $t = -2$ and $D_t^2 x < 0$ at $t = 2$. Hence, x has a minimum at $t = -2$ and a maximum at $t = 2$. When $t = \pm 2$, we find $D_t y \neq 0$, and hence, in (5), $dx/dy = 0$, so that C has a vertical tangent.

4. *Intercepts.* From (3), $x = 0$ when $t = 0$ and $t = \pm 2\sqrt{3}$, and $y = 0$ when $t = \pm 2\sqrt{3}$. Thus, C goes through the origin when $t = \pm 2\sqrt{3}$. From (5), the slopes of C at $(0, 0)$ are $y' = \pm .3$.

5. Coordinates were computed from (3) for all values of t met in preceding details, and for other values, as a basis for the graph of C in Figure 117. Arc $ABOH$ on C is traced as t ranges from 0 to $+\infty$, and arc $ADOE$ as t ranges from 0 to $-\infty$.

t	0	± 2	$\pm 2\sqrt{3}$	± 4
x	0	± 8	0	∓ 8
y	-6	-4	0	2

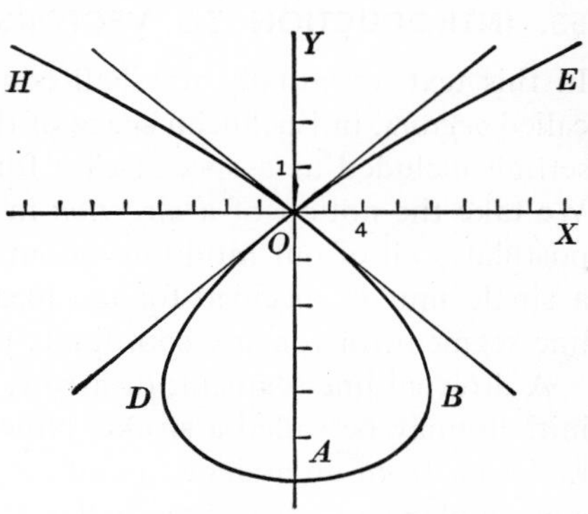

Fig. 117

Note 1. From (3), $x = -ty$ or $t = -x/y$.
With $t = -x/y$ in $y = \tfrac{1}{2}t^2 - 6$, we obtain $x^2 = 2y^2(y + 6)$ as the xy-equation for (3).

EXERCISE 47

Without eliminating t, plot the curve given in parametric form. Locate all points where the tangent is horizontal or vertical. Do not investigate inflection points except where directed by the instructor. Describe how the curve is traced as t varies over its domain.

1. $x = 2t^{-\frac{1}{2}}$, $y = 2\sqrt{t}$. Also, find the xy-equation. Is the whole locus of the xy-equation included in the given locus?

2. $x = 2t^{-1}$, $y = 2t$. Compare with Problem 1.

3. $x = \frac{8}{9}t^3$, $y = \frac{8}{9}t^2$. Also, find the xy-equation.

4. $x = \dfrac{2}{1 + t^2}$, $y = \dfrac{2t}{1 + t^2}$. Also, find the xy-equation.

   Hint. When x and y have finite limits x_0 and y_0 as $|t| \to \infty$, include the point (x_0, y_0) if this gives an unbroken curve.

5. $x = 4t^2 + 4$, $y = 4t^3 + 4t$. Also, find the xy-equation.

6. $x = 12 - t^2$, $y = 12t - t^3$. Also, find the xy-equation.

7. $x = 16t - t^3$, $y = 16 - t^2$. Also, find the tangents at $(0, 0)$.

8. $x = \dfrac{2at^2}{1 + t^2}$, $y = \dfrac{2at^3}{1 + t^2}$; $a > 0$. (The **cissoid** of DIOCLES; see page 712.)

9. $x = \dfrac{a(3 - t^2)}{1 + t^2}$, $y = \dfrac{at(3 - t^2)}{1 + t^2}$; $a > 0$. (The **trisectrix** of MACLAURIN.)

   Hint. If $|t| \to \infty$, $x \to -a$ and $|y| \to \infty$; $x = -a$ is an asymptote.

10. $x = \dfrac{a(t^2 - 1)}{t^2 + 1}$, $y = \dfrac{a(t^3 - t)}{t^2 + 1}$; $a > 0$. (The **strophoid**.)

11. $x = \dfrac{at}{1 + t^3}$, $y = \dfrac{at^2}{1 + t^3}$. (The **folium** of DESCARTES.)

12. Obtain an xy-equation for the strophoid in Problem 10.

13. Introduce a parameter t by use of $y = tx$, and obtain parametric equations for the curve $ay^2 + xy^2 = 3ax^2 - x^3$. Check with preceding problems.

14. Repeat Problem 13 for the curve $2ay^2 - xy^2 = x^3$.

53. INTRODUCTION TO VECTORS

In this text, eventually we shall consider in detail certain geometric * entities, called *vectors*, in Euclidean space of three dimensions (*three-space*), with a similar setting included as a special case for *two-space* (a plane) or *one-space* (a line). We take the notion of a *direction* in space as an undefined term, and accept as postulates all of our intuitions about directions. We assume that a single unit is specified for the measure of the length of any line segment, or for any coordinate to which we shall refer.

A directed line segment, or arrow, such as OR in Figure 118, initially may be called a **stroke.** Now conceive of all strokes (*a*) radiating from an assigned point, or (*b*) in a given line, or (*c*) in a given plane, or (*d*) in three-space. For the set of strokes in any

Fig. 118

* An abstract introduction for vectors, without a geometric setting, is described briefly in Note 2 on page 413.

of these cases, we shall define certain terminology and operations (some of which will remind us of the algebra of numbers). Then, we shall call each stroke a **vector,** and shall say that we have introduced an *algebra of vectors.*

Note 1. In Case (*a*) above, we refer to the vectors as **bound vectors.** Otherwise, the vectors are said to be **free vectors.** At present, we shall deal with the set of free vectors in a plane, Case (*c*) above. In this chapter, we shall limit vector algebra to that minimum which is sufficient for our present objective, the elementary * study of curvilinear motion in a plane in Section 54.

To indicate that a directed line segment OR, as in Figure 118, is considered as a vector, we insert an arrow over OR, giving "$\overrightarrow{OR}$," read "*the vector OR.*" Or, we may represent a vector by a capital Roman letter, say † **A,** in boldface type. The measure of the length of $\overrightarrow{OR}$ is called its **magnitude,** represented by "$| \overrightarrow{OR} |$" and read "*the magnitude of* $\overrightarrow{OR}$." Thus, $\overrightarrow{OR}$ has a direction, a magnitude, an initial point, O, and a terminal point, R, sometimes called the **tip** of $\overrightarrow{OR}$. We could write $| \overrightarrow{OR} | = | \overline{OR} |$.

Definition I. *Two vectors* **A** *and* **B** *are said to be* **equal** *if they have the same direction and magnitude.*

Thus, if **A** is moved without altering its magnitude and direction, the vector is considered unaltered, and **A** may be thought of as a representative of the set of all vectors, with arbitrary initial points, which are equal to **A.**

Definition II. *The* **zero vector, O,** *is defined as that vector whose magnitude is* 0 *and whose direction is taken as we please.*

By Definition II, **O** appears geometrically as just a point.

Definition III. *To state that two vectors* **A** *and* **B** *are* **collinear** *means that their directions are the same or are opposites.*

ILLUSTRATION 1. In Figure 119, vectors **A** and **B** are collinear. If **A** and **B** are collinear and are drawn from the same initial point, then **A** and **B** lie on a line.

Fig. 119

Definition IV. *The* **sum** (*or,* **resultant**) *of two vectors* **A** *and* **B** *is the vector* **C** *obtained as follows: Place the initial point of* **B** *on the tip of* **A**; *then* **C** *is the vector drawn from the initial point of* **A** *to the new location of the tip of* **B**. *We write,*

$$C = A + B, \tag{1}$$

and refer to the operation of finding **C** *as* **vector addition.**

The sum **C** in (1) is illustrated in Figure 120 on page 164. We sometimes construct **C** as follows, when **A** and **B** are not collinear:

* A more advanced study of such motion will be met on page 431.

† In writing, the student might use "$\overrightarrow{A}$" as a vector symbol.

$$\left\{ \begin{array}{l} \textit{Draw } \mathbf{A} \textit{ and } \mathbf{B} \textit{ with a common initial point, } O\textit{; com-} \\ \textit{plete the parallelogram with } \mathbf{A} \textit{ and } \mathbf{B} \textit{ as adjacent sides;} \\ \textit{then } \mathbf{C} \textit{ is the vector obtained by drawing the diagonal} \\ \textit{of the parallelogram from } O \textit{ to the opposite vertex.} \end{array} \right\} \quad (2)$$

Construction (2) is referred to as the **parallelogram law** for the addition of vectors, and is illustrated in Figure 120. It can be verified that, if **A** and **B** have the same magnitude and opposite directions, then $\mathbf{A} + \mathbf{B} = \mathbf{O}$.

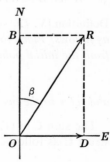

The *order* in which we refer to **A** and **B** in Definition IV, or in which we write $(\mathbf{A} + \mathbf{B})$, is immaterial. That is, the same parallelogram and diagonal, as in Figure 120, is obtained with either order of reference to **A** and **B**. Thus, we have proved the following result:

Fig. 120

Proposition I. *The addition of two vectors is* **commutative,** *that is,*

$$\mathbf{A} + \mathbf{B} = \mathbf{B} + \mathbf{A}.$$

When $\mathbf{C} = \mathbf{A} + \mathbf{B}$, we call **A** and **B** the *components* of **C** along the corresponding lines on which **A** and **B** lie.

ILLUSTRATION 2. Any force, velocity, or acceleration, as defined in physics, possesses a direction and a magnitude, and hence can be represented geometrically by a properly directed stroke, with the measure of its length in some linear unit equal to the measure of the physical quantity in some physical unit. In Figure 120 above, let **A** and **B** represent two forces pulling (or *acting*) simultaneously on an object at O. Then, in physics it is found that the combined effect of the forces is the same as the effect of *the single resultant force* which is represented in magnitude and direction by the resultant vector $\mathbf{C} = \mathbf{A} + \mathbf{B}$. This fact is referred to as the *parallelogram law for composition of forces*. If **A** and **B** in Figure 120 represent velocities simultaneously imposed on an object at O, the resultant velocity is correctly represented by the sum $\mathbf{C} = \mathbf{A} + \mathbf{B}$. Thus, velocities and, similarly, accelerations also obey the parallelogram law in composition. Hence, it is convenient to represent forces, velocities, and accelerations as vectors.

Any physical quantity with the property just mentioned for forces, velocities, and accelerations is referred to as a **vector quantity.** In contrast to vectors or vector quantities, we sometimes refer to *numbers* as **scalars.**

The vector components of a vector $\overrightarrow{OR}$ along two perpendicular lines ON and OE are the vectors obtained by projecting $\overrightarrow{OR}$ on ON and OE. In Figure 121, the magnitudes of the components are

$$|\overline{OB}| = |\overline{OR}| \cos \beta; \quad |\overline{OD}| = |\overline{OR}| \sin \beta.$$

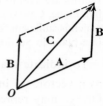

The vector $\overrightarrow{OR}$ is the resultant of its components $\overrightarrow{OB}$ and $\overrightarrow{OD}$. In finding them, we say that we have *resolved* the given vector into *components*.

Fig. 121

ILLUSTRATION 3. In Figure 121, let $\overrightarrow{OR}$ represent a force of 150 pounds acting in the direction $N\,31°\,E$; the acute bearing angle is $\beta = 31°$.

$$|\,\overline{OB}\,| = 150 \cos 31° = 129; \quad |\,\overline{OD}\,| = 150 \sin 31° = 77.$$

The north component is 129 pounds; the east component is 77 pounds.

54. INTRODUCTION TO CURVILINEAR MOTION

In discussing *rectilinear* motion for a particle, we conceived of the motion occurring on a number scale, and then defined *velocity* and *acceleration* as *signed numbers*. It was mentioned that our setting made the velocity, or acceleration, a *directed* quantity, with its sign showing the direction. This use of signs avoided the introduction of vectors in the study of rectilinear motion. In the discussion of curvilinear motion, we find it essential to define velocity and acceleration as *vectors*.

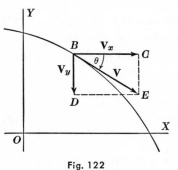

Fig. 122

Let the motion of a particle P in an *xy*-plane be defined by specifying the coordinates of P at any instant as functions of the time, t,

$$x = \phi(t) \quad and \quad y = \psi(t), \tag{1}$$

where $\phi(t)$ and $\psi(t)$ have continuous first and second derivatives. Then, (1) gives parametric equations for the path of P. At any instant in the motion, let

$$v_x = \frac{dx}{dt} \quad and \quad v_y = \frac{dy}{dt}, \tag{2}$$

and call v_x and v_y the *x-rate of change* and *y-rate of change*, respectively. At any instant t, when the particle is at B, in Figure 122, define a *vector* $\mathbf{V}_x$ whose magnitude is $|\,v_x\,|$, with $\mathbf{V}_x$ directed to the right or the left according as $v_x > 0$ or $v_x < 0$. Similarly, define a vector $\mathbf{V}_y$, whose magnitude is $|\,v_y\,|$, with $\mathbf{V}_y$ directed upward or downward according as $v_y > 0$ or $v_y < 0$. We call $\mathbf{V}_x$ the **x-velocity,** and $\mathbf{V}_y$ the **y-velocity** for P. Then, at any instant, the **velocity** of P is defined as the **vector** $\mathbf{V}$ which is the resultant of $\mathbf{V}_x$ and $\mathbf{V}_y$. We call $\mathbf{V}_x$ and $\mathbf{V}_y$ the *vector components*, and v_x and v_y the *scalar components* of $\mathbf{V}$ in the directions of the axes.

The velocity vector $\mathbf{V}$ in Figure 122 shows the path which P would cover in the next unit of time if the instantaneous velocities $\mathbf{V}_x$ and $\mathbf{V}_y$ at B should continue unchanged. We refer to the direction of $\mathbf{V}$ at any instant as the *instantaneous direction* of the motion of P.

In Figure 122, the length of BC is $|\,v_x\,|$, and of BD is $|\,v_y\,|$. Hence,

$$\overline{BE}^2 = \overline{BC}^2 + \overline{BD}^2 = v_x^2 + v_y^2. \tag{3}$$

At any instant t, we define the **instantaneous speed,** v, of P, or simply its *speed*, as *the magnitude of the velocity vector* $\mathbf{V}$, or the length of BE in Figure 122. Hence, $v = |\,\mathbf{V}\,|$ and, from (3),

$$|\mathbf{V}| = \text{speed} = v = \sqrt{v_x^2 + v_y^2}, \text{ or} \qquad (4)$$

$$\text{speed} = v = \sqrt{\left(\frac{dx}{dt}\right)^2 + \left(\frac{dy}{dt}\right)^2}. \qquad (5)$$

Let θ be an angle from the positive x-direction to the direction of $\mathbf{V}$, in Figure 122. Then, with reference to B as an origin, rectangular coordinates for E are v_x and v_y. Hence, by the definitions of the trigonometric functions,

$$\tan \theta = \frac{v_y}{v_x} = \frac{\dfrac{dy}{dt}}{\dfrac{dx}{dt}} = \frac{dy}{dx}. \qquad (6)$$

Thus, the slope of $\mathbf{V}$ is the slope of the tangent to the path at B, and we have the following result.

$$\left\{\begin{array}{l}\textit{If the particle P is at point B, and if the velocity } \mathbf{V} \textit{ is drawn} \\ \textit{from B, then } \mathbf{V} \textit{ lies along the tangent to the path at B. Or, the} \\ \textit{instantaneous direction of motion at B is along the tangent.}\end{array}\right\} \qquad (7)$$

In a later chapter, we shall prove that *the speed v is the time-rate of change of distance for the particle P, measured along the path of P.*

EXAMPLE 1. A particle P has the equations of motion

$$x = 3t^3 - 2t^2 \quad and \quad y = 2t - t^3. \qquad (8)$$

Investigate the velocity and speed at $t = 2$.

Solution. 1. At $t = 2$, we have $x = 16$ and $y = -4$. From (8),

$$\frac{dx}{dt} = v_x = 9t^2 - 4t \Big|_{t=2} = 28; \quad \frac{dy}{dt} = v_y = 2 - 3t^2 \Big|_{t=2} = -10.$$

2. At $B:(16, -4)$, as in Figure 123, construct the vectors $\mathbf{V}_x$ and $\mathbf{V}_y$, and the velocity $\mathbf{V}$. From (6), a direction angle θ for $\mathbf{V}$ satisfies

$$\tan \theta = \frac{-10}{28} = -.357, \ \theta \text{ in quadrant IV.}$$

From Table VI, $\tan 19.6° = .357$. Hence,

$$\theta = 360° - 19.6° = 340.4°.$$

3. The speed is $v = \sqrt{28^2 + 10^2} = 29.7$, feet per second.

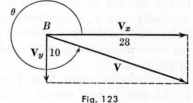

Fig. 123

To introduce the notion of vector acceleration for the motion of P defined by (1), denote the time-rates of change of v_x and v_y by a_x and a_y, respectively:

$$a_x = \frac{dv_x}{dt} = \frac{d}{dt}\left(\frac{dx}{dt}\right) = \frac{d^2x}{dt^2}, \text{ or}$$

$$a_x = \frac{d^2x}{dt^2}; \quad a_y = \frac{d^2y}{dt^2}. \qquad (9)$$

Then, at any instant, define a *vector* $\mathbf{A}_x$, where the magnitude of $\mathbf{A}_x$ is $|a_x|$ and $\mathbf{A}_x$ is directed to the right or the left according as $a_x > 0$ or $a_x < 0$. Similarly, define $\mathbf{A}_y$ in association with a_y. Finally, at any point B in the path, define the

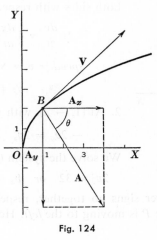

Fig. 124

acceleration of P as the **vector** $\mathbf{A}$ *which is the resultant of* $\mathbf{A}_x$ *and* $\mathbf{A}_y$, as in Figure 124. The magnitude of $\mathbf{A}$ will be represented by a, that is, $a = |\mathbf{A}|$. Then, as in the discussion of speed,

$$|\mathbf{A}| = a = \sqrt{a_x^2 + a_y^2}. \tag{10}$$

If θ is a direction angle of $\mathbf{A}$, from the positive x-direction as in Figure 124,

$$\tan \theta = \frac{a_y}{a_x}. \tag{11}$$

In general, $\tan \theta$ *will not equal* dy/dx, or *the acceleration is not directed along the tangent to the path.* We describe $|\mathbf{A}|$ in *linear units, per second per second*, in the terminology of physics.

EXAMPLE 2. Investigate the acceleration at $t = 2$ if the motion of P is defined by

$$x = t^3 - t^2 \quad and \quad y = 2t^2 - t^3. \tag{12}$$

Solution. By differentiation in (12), we obtain

$$v_x = 3t^2 - 2t; \quad v_y = 4t - 3t^2;$$
$$a_x = 6t - 2; \quad a_y = 4 - 6t;$$
$$a = |\mathbf{A}| = \sqrt{(6t - 2)^2 + (4 - 6t)^2}.$$

If $t = 2$, then $x = 4$, $y = 0$, $a_x = 10$, $a_y = -8$, and $a = \sqrt{164} = 12.8$, feet per second per second.

If a particle P moves in an xy-plane along a path C which is described by its xy-equation, we may meet problems involving v_x, v_y, a_x, and a_y, which will be related time-rates of change obtained by differentiation in the given equation.

EXAMPLE 3. A particle P travels *upward* on the parabola $y^2 = 4x$ with the constant speed $4\sqrt{2}$ feet per second. Find v_x and v_y at $(1, -2)$.

Solution. 1. In $y^2 = 4x$, x and y are functions of the time t. On differentiating both sides with respect to t, we obtain

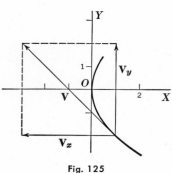

Fig. 125

$$2y\,\frac{dy}{dt} = 4\,\frac{dx}{dt}, \quad or \quad yv_y = 2v_x; \qquad (13)$$

$$speed = v = \sqrt{v_x^2 + v_y^2} = 4\sqrt{2}, \ or$$

$$v_x^2 + v_y^2 = 32. \qquad (14)$$

2. At $(1, -2)$, with $y = -2$ in (13) and (14),

$$-2v_y = 2v_x \quad and \quad v_x^2 + v_y^2 = 32. \qquad (15)$$

We solve the system (15) for v_x and v_y:

$$2v_x^2 = 32 \quad or \quad v_x = \pm 4, \quad and \quad v_y = \mp 4,$$

where the upper and lower signs go together, respectively. From Figure 125, $v_x < 0$ at $(1, -2)$ because P is moving to the *left*. Hence, $v_x = -4$ and $v_y = 4$, in feet per second.

EXAMPLE 4. A particle P moves along the hyperbola $x^2 - y^2 = 3$. When P is at the point $(-2, 1)$, the x-rate of change is $-3'$ per second. Find the y-rate of change, and the speed at $(-2, 1)$.

Solution. 1. Differentiate with respect to t in $x^2 - y^2 = 3$:

$$2x\,\frac{dx}{dt} - 2y\,\frac{dy}{dt} = 0, \quad or \quad xv_x - yv_y = 0. \qquad (16)$$

2. Substitute $x = -2$, $y = 1$, and $v_x = -3$ in (16):

$$6 - v_y = 0, \quad or \quad v_y = 6.$$

Hence, $$speed = v = \sqrt{v_x^2 + v_y^2} = \sqrt{9 + 36} = 3\sqrt{5}.$$

The y-rate of change is 6, feet per second; the speed is $3\sqrt{5}$, feet per second.

EXAMPLE 5. A particle P moves on the curve $y^2 = 4x$. When P is at $B:(1, 2)$, $v_x = 4$ and $a_x = 3$. Find v_y and a_y at B.

Solution. 1. In $y^2 = 4x$, differentiate twice in succession with respect to t:

$$2y\,\frac{dy}{dt} = 4\,\frac{dx}{dt}, \quad or \quad y\,\frac{dy}{dt} = 2\,\frac{dx}{dt};$$

$$\left(\frac{dy}{dt}\right)^2 + y\,\frac{d^2y}{dt^2} = 2\,\frac{d^2x}{dt^2}.$$

Thus, we obtain $$yv_y = 2v_x \quad and \quad v_y^2 + ya_y = 2a_x. \qquad (17)$$

2. At $(x = 1, y = 2)$ with $v_x = 4$ and $a_x = 3$, from (17) we obtain $v_y = 4$ and then $a_y = -5$. The velocity **V**, and the accelerations $\mathbf{A}_x$, $\mathbf{A}_y$, and **A** are shown at B in Figure 124 on page 167.

$\tan \theta = \dfrac{v_y}{v_x}$ or $\dfrac{a_y}{a_x}$

$a^2 = a x^2 + a y^2$

$v^2 = v x^2 + v y^2$

EXERCISE 48

*In an xy-plane, draw vectors **A** and **B**, respectively, to the given points from the origin, and construct $(\mathbf{A} + \mathbf{B})$. Also, find the magnitude of **A**, **B**, and $(\mathbf{A} + \mathbf{B})$.*

1. $(3, 4); (-7, 12).$ 2. $(-4, 1); (-4, -3).$
3. $(2, 3); (1, 6)$ 4. $(12, -7); (4, 3).$

The equations define the motion of a particle P in an xy-plane. At the indicated value of the time t, find the values of x, y, v_x, v_y, v, a_x, a_y, and a. Then, plot the velocity and acceleration vectors at the instantaneous location (x, y).

5. $x = 3t + t^3, y = t - t^2; t = 2.$ 6. $x = 4t^2 + 4, y = \frac{1}{6}t^3 + 4t; t = 3.$
7. $x = 12 - t^2, y = 12t - t^3; t = 1.$ Also, plot the path for $0 \leq t \leq 2$ by use of points obtained for five values of t.
8. $x = \frac{8}{9}t^3, y = \frac{8}{9}t^2; t = 2.$ Also, plot the path from its xy-equation.
9. $x = t^2 + 4, y = t - t^2; t = 0.$ Also, find the minimum speed.
10. $x = \dfrac{3}{2 - t}, y = \dfrac{2}{3 - t}; t = 4.$

11. In an xy-plane, the x-axis is horizontal and the y-axis is vertical, directed upward. Under idealized conditions, the motion of a certain projectile is defined by $x = 60t$ and $y = 80t - 16t^2$. (a) Carry out the directions preceding Problem 5, at $t = 3$. (b) Find the speed of the projectile at $t = 0$. (c) Find when the speed is a minimum.

12. Find when the magnitude of the acceleration of a particle P is a minimum if its equations of motion are $x = \frac{1}{3}t^3 + \frac{1}{2}t^2$ and $y = 3t^2 - \frac{1}{6}t^3$.

*Use the instantaneous location of the particle P as the initial point for the vectors. Graph the path and any vectors **V** or **A** which are found.*

13. A particle P moves to the right on the curve $x^2 = 8y$, with a constant speed of $10\sqrt{2}$ feet per second. Find the velocity at (a) $(-4, 2)$; (b) $(4, 2)$.

14. A particle P moves clockwise with a constant speed of $15'$ per second on the ellipse $2x^2 + 3y^2 = 21$. Find the velocity at $(-3, -1)$.

15. A particle P moves upward on the curve $x^3 = 2y^2$, with a constant speed of $6\sqrt{13}$ feet per second. (a) Find the velocity when P is at $(2, -2)$. (b) How fast is P approaching the origin at $(2, -2)$?

16. A particle P moves on the upper branch of the hyperbola $xy = 4$, with $v_x = 4$. (a) Find v_y and the speed, and plot the velocity at $(4, 1)$. (b) How fast is P receding from the origin at $(4, 1)$?

17. A particle P moves clockwise on the curve $y^2 = (x - 2)(4 - x)$, with a speed of $8'$ per second. Find the velocity at (a) $(3, 1)$; (b) $(4, 0)$.

18. A particle P moves on the lower branch of the curve $xy = -6$, with $v_y = 4$ at all points. Find v_x, a_x, a_y, v, and $|\mathbf{A}|$ when P is at $(3, -2)$.

19. A particle P moves on the curve $9y^3 = 8x^2$. When P is at $(-3, 2)$, $v_y = 4$ and $a_y = 12$. Find v_x, a_x, v, and $|\mathbf{A}|$ when P is at $(-3, 2)$.

20. A particle P moves downward on the curve $y^2 = 16x$ with a speed of $15\sqrt{2}$ feet per second. When P is at $(4, -8)$ find v_x, v_y, a_x, a_y, and $|\mathbf{A}|$.

21. A ladder $40'$ long rests against a wall. A man has his feet halfway up the ladder. Its top slides down the wall at a speed of $.5'$ per second. Find the speed of his feet when the foot of the ladder is $32'$ from the wall.

EXERCISE 49   (*Review of Chapters Six and Seven*)

Find the equations of the tangent and normal to the curve.

1. $y = 4x^3 + 6x^2 - 9x + 5$, (a) at $x = -2$; (b) at the inflection point.

2. $x^2 + 3xy - y^2 + 3 = 0$, at the points where $x = 2$.

3. Find the angle of intersection of $x^2 + y^2 = 2$ and $y = x^2$.

4. Prove that every cubic curve $y = ax^3 + bx^2 + cx + d$, where $a \neq 0$, has just one inflection point, and either one maximum and one minimum or no extremum.

5. Find the absolute maximum and absolute minimum of the function $y = 3x - 5$, where x is restricted to the interval $-2 \leq x \leq 3$.

6. Graph $y = 4x^3 + 6x^2 - 9x + 5$ and $x = y^3 + 2y^2 - 4y + 5$.

Test for extrema and inflection points of the curve.

7. $y = (x + 3)^6$.   **8.** $y = x^3(x - 1)^2$.   **9.** $y = (x - 5)^{\frac{2}{3}}$.

Graph by use of asymptotes, intercepts, and vertical or horizontal tangents.

10. $y = \dfrac{1}{(x - 2)(x + 1)}$.   **11.** $y = \dfrac{x - 2}{3x + 4}$.   **12.** $x^2 = \dfrac{y^3}{4 - y}$.

13. The perpendicular sides of a right triangle are $7''$ and $24''$ long. The shorter side is increasing at the rate of $.2''$ per second and the longer side is decreasing at the rate of $.3''$ per second. Find the rate of change of (a) the length of the hypotenuse; (b) the area.

14. A fire department ladder $75'$ long extends from the ground against a factory building. The bottom of the ladder is being shoved toward the factory at the rate of $1.5'$ per second. How fast is the top of the ladder rising when the bottom is $21'$ from the structure?

15. A curve is defined by the equations $x = 6t^2 - 2t^3$ and $y = t^2 - 3t$, where t is a parameter. Without eliminating t, (a) find equations for the tangent and normal to the curve where $t = 3$; (b) find $D_x^2 y$.

Find the differential of the function.

16. $\sqrt[3]{4x^2 - 5}$.   **17.** $(2 + 3t)\sqrt{3t + 2}$.   **18.** $(x^2 + 5x)/(x - 2x)^4$.

Solve Problems 19–22 by use of differentials.

19. A building consists of a cylinder of height $30'$ and base radius $10'$, with a hemisphere as the roof. The side walls and the roof are $1''$ thick. Find the volume of the material in the wall and roof, approximately.

20. If a body has fallen a distance s feet from rest in a vacuum near the earth's surface, the body's velocity, v, in feet per second is given by $v = 8\sqrt{s}$, approximately. If we measure $s = s_0$ with an error ds, and compute v, find approximately the error in v.

21. A monument $40'$ high is a pyramid with a square base. A side of the base is measured as $8.7'$, with accuracy to one decimal place. Find approximately the maximum possible error and percent of error in the volume of the monument, as computed from these data.

22. The force of attraction between two spheres of masses m and M is given by $F = k/r^2$, where k is a constant depending on the physical units employed, and r is the distance between the centers of the spheres. If r is increased by 3%, find approximately the percent of change in F.

23. Write parametric equations for the line through (2, 3) and (− 4, 2).

The equations define the motion of a particle P in an xy-plane. At t = 3, find the magnitudes of the velocity and acceleration and plot them.

24. $x = 3t^2 - 2t$; $y = 4t - t^2$.   **25.** $x = (t + 3)^2$; $y = t^3 - t^2$.

26. Graph the equation $y^2 = x(x + 1)(x - 2)$.

27. Graph the curve having the parametric equations $x = t^3 - 2t$ and $y = t^2 - 2$, with t as the parameter.

28. If a, b, c, and d are constants, where $ab \neq 0$, and t is a parameter, prove that the locus of $[x = at + c, y = bt + d]$ is a line.

29. A closed box is to be a rectangular parallelepiped with a square base and a capacity of 1125 cubic feet. The cost of the material for the box per square foot is 5¢ for the base and top, and 15¢ for the sides. Find the dimensions of the box to minimize the cost of the material.

30. A U-shaped gutter will have a cross section consisting of a semicircle at the bottom, with vertical sides of equal length. Find the radius of the semicircle and the length of a side, to give maximum capacity, if the perimeter of a cross section is 10″.

31. An observatory will be a cylinder capped by a hemisphere. Find a relation between the base-radius and the altitude of the cylinder to give a specified volume for the building, with minimum area for the floor and exterior surface, combined.

★SUPPLEMENT FOR CHAPTER SEVEN

32. Graph the trisectrix of Maclaurin: $y^2(a + x) = x^2(3a - x)$, $a > 0$.

33. A particle P moves to the left with a speed of $2\sqrt{73}$ feet per second on a branch of the curve $4y^2 - x^2 = 7$. Plot the path. Find v_x and v_y when P is at $(3, -2)$, and plot the velocity at this point.

34. Give an example to show that, if $x = \phi(t)$ and $y = \psi(t)$, where $\phi''(t)$ and $\psi''(t)$ exist, it is not always true that $D_x^2 y = \psi''(t)/\phi''(t)$.

35. With $x = \phi(t)$ and $y = \psi(t)$ as in Problem 31, obtain an expression for $D_x^2 y$ in terms of ϕ', ψ', ϕ'', and ψ''.

36. A particle moves on the curve $y^2 = 2px$ in such a way that v_y is a constant. Prove that a_x is a constant.

37. In the notation of pages 165–166, let v be the speed. Calculate dv/dt in terms of v_x, v_y, a_x, and a_y.

38. Suppose that the functions $f(x)$ and $g(y)$ have first and second derivatives. If $y = h(x)$ is a solution of $f(x) = g(y)$ for y as a function of x, obtain dy. If $z = f(x)$ and $x = g(y)$, obtain $D_y^2 z$ in terms of derivatives of f and g.

39. The position of a moving particle at time t on an s-axis is determined by $s = \sqrt{h^2 t^2 + k^2}$, where h and k are constants. Prove that, at any time t, the acceleration of the particle is inversely proportional to s^3.

40. Prove that each of the following pairs of equations, where t is a parameter, form parametric equations of the same curve in an xy-plane. Solve without finding an xy-equation for the curve.

$$(x = 3 \cos t \quad and \quad y = 2 \sin t, \quad 0 \leq t \leq \pi).$$
$$(x = 6t^2 - 3 \quad and \quad y = 4t\sqrt{1 - t^2}, \quad 0 \leq t \leq 1).$$

CHAPTER EIGHT

Mean Value Theorem

55. LAW OF THE MEAN

Theorem I. (*Rolle's theorem.*) *Suppose that the function $f(x)$ is continuous on $T = \{a \leqq x \leqq b\}$, and has a derivative if $a < x < b$. Then, if $f(a) = 0$ and $f(b) = 0$, there is at least one point ξ between a and b such that $f'(\xi) = 0$.*

Geometrical interpretation. In Figure 126, let the curve be the graph of $y = f(x)$. Theorem I states that, if the graph meets the x-axis at $x = a$ and $x = b$, and has a *nonvertical tangent* at all points *between* $x = a$ and $x = b$, then there is at least one point $x = \xi$ between a and b where the tangent is horizontal.

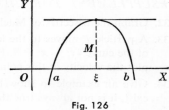

Fig. 126

Proof of Theorem I. 1. If $f(x) = 0$ at *all points* on T, then $f'(x) = 0$ on T; hence Theorem I is true with ξ taken as any point between a and b.

2. Suppose, now, that $f(x) \neq 0$ at some point x_1 on T. Since f is continuous, it has an absolute maximum M and an absolute minimum m, where at least one of m and M is *not zero*, because $f(x_1) \neq 0$.

3. Consider the case $M \neq 0$, and let ξ be a value of x where $f(x) = M$. Certainly, $a < \xi < b$, because $f(a) = f(b) = 0$. Thus, f assumes its maximum M at the *interior* point $x = \xi$ of T. Hence, by Theorem III on page 124, $f'(\xi) = 0$. A similar proof applies if $m \neq 0$.

ILLUSTRATION 1. If $f(x) = x^3 - 12x$, then $f'(x) = 3x^2 - 12$, and $f'(x) = 0$ at $x = \pm 2$. The solutions of $f(x) = 0$ are 0 and $\pm 2\sqrt{3}$. We have $f(\pm 2\sqrt{3}) = 0$. Then, Theorem I states that $f'(x) = 0$ *at least once* between $x = -2\sqrt{3}$ and $x = 2\sqrt{3}$. However, in this case, we have *two points*, $\xi = 2$ and $\xi = -2$, where $f'(\xi) = 0$, as seen on the graph of f in Figure 127.

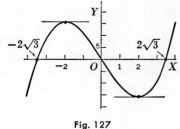

Fig. 127

172

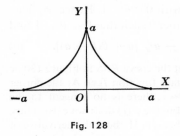

Fig. 128

ILLUSTRATION 2. Figure 128 shows a graph of

$$y = \sqrt{(a^{\frac{2}{3}} - x^{\frac{2}{3}})^3},$$ (1)

where $y = 0$ at $x = a$ and at $x = -a$. There is no value $x = \xi$ between $x = -a$ and $x = a$ where the slope of the graph is zero. This does not contradict Theorem I, because its hypothesis about the derivative is *not satisfied* in (1). That is, y' does not exist at $x = 0$, where we observe that there is a vertical cusp.

Theorem II. (*Mean value theorem for a function, or law of the mean.*) *Suppose that the function $f(x)$ is continuous when $a \leq x \leq b$, and has a derivative if x is* **between** *a and b. Then, there exists at least one point ξ* **between** *a and b such that*

$$f(b) - f(a) = (b - a)f'(\xi). \qquad (a < \xi < b).$$ (2)

Geometrical interpretation. From (2), $\dfrac{f(b) - f(a)}{b - a} = f'(\xi).$ (3)

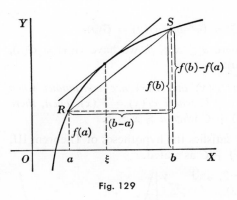

Fig. 129

Consider the graph of $y = f(x)$, in Figure 129. The fraction in (3) is the slope of the chord RS through the points $[a, f(a)]$ and $[b, f(b)]$ on the graph. Then, geometrically, Theorem II is as follows:

If a function $f(x)$ is continuous on $a \leq x \leq b$, and if the graph, C, of $y = f(x)$ has a nonvertical tangent at each point x between a and b, then there exists at least one point ξ between a and b where the corresponding tangent to the graph is parallel to the chord of C through the points where $x = a$ and $x = b$.

Thus, with any *secant* playing the role occupied by the x-axis in Theorem I, the geometrical significance of Theorem II is the same as in Theorem I.

Proof of Theorem II. Consider the function

$$\phi(x) = \frac{f(b) - f(a)}{b - a} (x - a) + f(a) - f(x).$$ (4)

In (4), $\phi(a) = 0$ and $\phi(b) = 0$. Also, $\phi'(x) = \dfrac{f(b) - f(a)}{b - a} - f'(x),$ (5)

which exists if $a < x < b$. Thus, ϕ satisfies the hypotheses of Theorem I. Hence, there exists a point $x = \xi$ between a and b such that

$$\phi'(\xi) = 0, \quad or \quad \frac{f(b) - f(a)}{b - a} - f'(\xi) = 0, \; which \; gives \; (3).$$

★*Note 1.* The student may write the equation of RS in Figure 129, and verify that $\phi(x)$ in (4) is the directed vertical distance *from $(x, f(x))$* on the graph of $y = f(x)$ *to RS.*

If ξ is between a and b, then $\xi = a + \theta(b - a)$, with $0 < \theta < 1$. Hence, by The-orem II, there is a number θ such that $0 < \theta < 1$ and

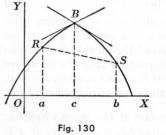

$$f(b) - f(a) = (b - a)f'[a + \theta(b - a)]. \qquad (6)$$

ILLUSTRATION 3. Let the curve RBS in Figure 130 be the graph of a certain function $f(x)$. At the corner point B, where $x = c$, there is no tangent to the curve $y = f(x)$, and hence $f'(c)$ does not exist. Thus, the hypothesis in Theorem II about the derivative of f is not satisfied. Hence, we have no reason to expect a point $x = \xi$ between a and b where the tangent is parallel to the secant RS.

Fig. 130

Theorem III. *Assume that the function $G(x)$ is continuous on $a \leqq x \leqq b$, and $G'(x)$ exists if $a < x < b$, where $G'(x) = 0$ for all x. Then, $G(x)$ is a constant; that is, there exists a constant C such that $G(x) = C$ when $a \leqq x \leqq b$.*

Proof. By the law of the mean, if $a < x \leqq b$, there exists ξ such that $a < \xi < x \leqq b$ and, from (2) with $b = x$,

$$G(x) - G(a) = (x - a)G'(\xi) = 0, \quad or \quad G(x) = G(a),$$

because $G'(\xi) = 0$. Hence, for all x where $a \leqq x \leqq b$, we have $G(x) = G(a)$, which proves Theorem III with $C = G(a)$.

Theorem IV. *Assume that the functions $\phi(x)$ and $F(x)$ are continuous when $a \leqq x \leqq b$, and have derivatives if $a < x < b$, where $\phi'(x) = F'(x)$. Then, there exists a constant C such that $\phi(x) = F(x) + C$ when $a \leqq x \leqq b$.*

Proof. Let $G(x) = \phi(x) - F(x)$. Then, G satisfies the hypotheses of Theorem III, so that $\phi(x) - F(x) = C$, or $\phi(x) = F(x) + C$ as stated.

EXAMPLE 1. If $f(x) = x^2 - 6x + 7$, $a = 2$, and $b = 5$, obtain all values of ξ satisfying (3).

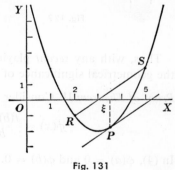

Solution. $\qquad \dfrac{f(5) - f(2)}{3} = \dfrac{2 + 1}{3} = 1.$

Since $f'(x) = 2x - 6$, equation (3) becomes

$$2\xi - 6 = 1 \quad or \quad \xi = \tfrac{7}{2}.$$

We verify that $f'(\tfrac{7}{2}) = 1$, which is the slope of the graph of $y = f(x)$ at P where $x = \tfrac{7}{2}$, in Figure 131, and is equal to the slope of RS.

Fig. 131

The results which we proceed to prove by use of Theorem II were accepted intuitively in earlier chapters.

Proof of Theorem XII, * *page* 84. 1. Let f be a function whose domain includes an interval $I = \{a \leqq x \leqq b\}$ where f' exists except possibly at $x = a$ and $x = b$, and $f'(x) > 0$ if $a < x < b$. We wish to prove that f is an increasing function on the interval I.

* The student should read this theorem again.

2. Suppose that x_1 and x_2 are numbers on I such that $a \leq x_1 < x_2 \leq b$. Then, by Theorem II on page 173, there exists a number ξ such that $x_1 < \xi < x_2$ and

$$f(x_2) - f(x_1) = (x_2 - x_1)f'(\xi). \tag{7}$$

Since $f'(\xi) > 0$ and $x_2 - x_1 > 0$, from (7) we obtain

$$f(x_2) - f(x_1) > 0 \quad or \quad f(x_1) < f(x_2),$$

which proves that f is an *increasing* function on I. Similarly, if we assume that $f'(x) < 0$ when $a < x < b$, it follows that f is a *decreasing* function on I. This completes the proof of Theorem XII on page 84.

In discussing concavity for a curve on page 128, we accepted the following fact without proof, on an intuitional basis.

$$\left\{ \begin{array}{l} \text{Suppose that the graph, } C, \text{ of } y = f(x) \text{ is concave downward (upward),} \\ \text{as met in Theorem V on page 128, on an interval } I = \{a < x < b\}. \\ \text{Then, if } L \text{ is the tangent to } C \text{ at any point } Q{:}(x_0, y_0), \text{ where } x_0 \text{ is on } I, \\ \text{all points } P{:}(x, y) \text{ of } C \text{ except } Q \text{ lie below (above) } L \text{ when } x \text{ is on } I. \end{array} \right\} \tag{8}$$

Proof of (8). 1. Suppose that $f''(x) < 0$, so that C is concave downward, and let all values of x which we mention lie on I. The equation of L, in Figure 132, is

$$y = f(x_0) + f'(x_0)(x - x_0). \tag{9}$$

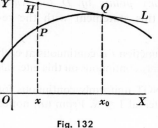

Fig. 132

2. Let $P{:}(x, y = f(x))$ be any point on C with $x \neq x_0$. Let $\overline{PH}$ be the directed vertical distance from P to L, as in Figure 132, and let $g(x) = \overline{PH}$. Then, $\overline{PH}$ is equal to y, from (9), minus $f(x)$, or

$$g(x) = f(x_0) - f(x) + f'(x_0)(x - x_0). \tag{10}$$

3. Suppose that $x < x_0$. Then, by Theorem II on page 173, there exists a number ξ such that $a < x < \xi < x_0$, with

$$f(x_0) - f(x) = f'(\xi)(x_0 - x). \tag{11}$$

By use of (11) in (10),

$$g(x) = (x_0 - x)[f'(\xi) - f'(x_0)]. \tag{12}$$

In (12), $x_0 - x > 0$. Since $f''(x) < 0$ on I, $f'(x)$ *decreases* as x *increases*, so that $f'(\xi) > f'(x_0)$ or $[f'(\xi) - f'(x_0)] > 0$. Hence, in (12), $g(x) > 0$, or PH is directed *upward*, and thus P is *below* L. A similar proof would apply if $x > x_0$. We omit the details for the case where C is concave upward.

EXERCISE 50

Find explicitly all values of ξ satisfying statement (2) of page 173 for the mean value theorem (including Rolle's theorem as a special case). Exhibit the secant corresponding to a and b, and the tangent at $x = \xi$ with a graph of f.

1. $f(x) = 15 - 8x + x^2$; $a = 3$ and $b = 5$.

2. $f(x) = 3x - x^3$; $a = -\sqrt{3}$ and $b = \sqrt{3}$.

3. $y = x^2 - 4x + 7$; $a = 0$ and $b = 2$.　　　4. $y = 6x - x^2 + 4$; $a = 3$ and $b = 5$.

Graph the function $f(x)$ defined by the formula, or formulas. State which hypothesis, or hypotheses, of the mean value theorem are not satisfied on the interval (a, b).

5. $f(x) = |x|$; $a = -3$ and $b = 2$.

6. $f(x) = 1$ if $0 \leq x \leq 2$ and $f(x) = 2$ if $2 < x \leq 4$; $a = 0$ and $b = 3$.

7. $f(x) = -x$ when $x \leq 0$ and $f(x) = 3x$ when $x > 0$; $a = -2$ and $b = 1$.

8. $f(x) = (x - 2)^{\frac{2}{3}}$; $a = 1$ and $b = 4$.

9. Assume that $f(0) = 0$ and $f'(t) = k$ at all values of t. Prove that $f(t) = kt$ at all values of t. This result was used in connection with the statement that *"distance is equal to (rate)·(time)"* in Note 1 on page 136. Also, the result will be useful otherwise.

★SUPPLEMENT FOR CHAPTER EIGHT

Prove the results in Problems 10–12 by use of the mean value theorem.

10. Prove that, if $k > 0$ and $h > 1$, then $(1 + k)^h > 1 + hk$. Assume that (III) of page 92 is available for all real numbers n.

11. If $0 < x$ or if $-1 < x < 0$, prove that

$$1 + \frac{x}{2\sqrt{1 + x}} < \sqrt{1 + x} < 1 + \tfrac{1}{2}x.$$

12. Obtain inequalities similar to those in Problem 10 for $\sqrt[3]{1 + x}$.

Definition I. *Let f be a function whose domain, D, consists of real numbers x. Then, it is said that f is **uniformly continuous** on D in case it is true that, for every $\epsilon > 0$, there exists $\delta > 0$ such that, if x_1 and x_2 are any points of D for which $|x_1 - x_2| < \delta$, then $|f(x_1) - f(x_2)| < \epsilon$.* Compare this statement with the result of Problem 18 on page 90.

Note 1. At a more advanced level it is proved that, if a function f is continuous at each point of a CLOSED interval $a \leq x \leq b$, then f is uniformly continuous on this interval.

13. Prove analytically that, if $f(x) = x^{-1}$, then (a) f is NOT uniformly continuous for $0 < x \leq 1$; (b) f IS uniformly continuous on the interval $1 \leq x$. From (a), notice that the word CLOSED is essential in Note 1.

14. Suppose that a function f has the domain D, $a \leq x \leq b$, and that f has a derivative at each point of D. Then, if there exists k such that $|f'(x)| < k$ when x is on D, prove that f is uniformly continuous on D.

15. If $f(x) = x^n$, where n is a positive integer, prove that f is uniformly continuous on any interval $a \leq x \leq b$.

CHAPTER NINE

Introduction to Definite Integrals

56. THE DEFINITE INTEGRAL

Calculus deals primarily with two fundamental concepts, the notion of a *derivative*, which was defined in Chapter Three, and the notion of a *definite integral*, which we proceed to introduce. It is important to notice that the definite integral will be defined *independently of the notion of a derivative*.

Note 1. We shall make frequent use of summation notation. Thus, to abbreviate

$$(u_1 + u_2 + \cdots + u_n),$$

we write $\sum_{i=1}^{n} u_i$, or $\sum_{i=1}^{n} u_i$, which is read "*the sum of u_i for $i = 1$ to $i = n$.*" We refer to capital Greek sigma, $\sum$, as the *sign of summation* and call i the *index of summation;* the letter used for the index is immaterial. For example,

$$\sum_{i=1}^{5} a_i = a_1 + a_2 + a_3 + a_4 + a_5 = \sum_{k=1}^{5} a_k.$$

$$\sum_{i=1}^{4} kf(\xi_i) = kf(\xi_1) + kf(\xi_2) + kf(\xi_3) + kf(\xi_4) = k \sum_{i=1}^{4} f(\xi_i).$$

On a number scale, consider a closed interval $I = \{a \leq x \leq b\}$, to which we may refer as the "*interval (a, b).*" If n is any positive integer, let I be divided into n subintervals $\{T_i\}$, not necessarily of equal lengths, by the points $x_0, x_1, x_2, \cdots, x_{n-1}, x_n$, where

$$a = x_0 < x_1 < x_2 < \cdots < x_{i-1} < x_i < \cdots < x_{n-1} < x_n = b, \tag{1}$$

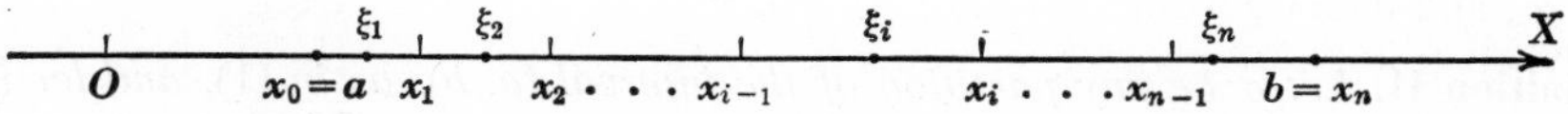

Fig. 133

as in Figure 133. We shall call this subdivision a **partition,** σ, of I. The ith sub-interval T_i consists of those numbers x such that

$$x_{i-1} \leq x \leq x_i; \quad length \ of \ T_i \ is \quad \Delta_i x = x_i - x_{i-1}. \tag{2}$$

177

Let d_σ be the maximum of the lengths $\Delta_i x$, and call d_σ the **norm** of σ. We read "d_σ" as "*d sub σ*," and "$\Delta_i x$" as "*delta i of x.*"

ILLUSTRATION 1. If the interval $2 \leqq x \leqq 8$ is divided into 18 equal parts by a partition σ, as in (1), then $n = 18$ and $d_\sigma = \frac{6}{18} = \frac{1}{3}$.

Let f be a function whose domain includes I. Let σ be any partition (1) of I, and select arbitrarily a point ξ_i on the ith subinterval T_i of σ, for $i = 1, 2, 3, \cdots, n$, as in Figure 133. For each value of i, form the product $f(\xi_i)\Delta_i x$, and denote the sum of these products by S_σ:

$$S_\sigma = f(\xi_1)\Delta_1 x + f(\xi_2)\Delta_2 x + \cdots + f(\xi_n)\Delta_n x = \sum_{i=1}^{n} f(\xi_i)\Delta_i x. \tag{3}$$

ILLUSTRATION 2. Let $f(x) = 1 + x^2$, and restrict x to satisfy $0 \leqq x \leqq 2$. Subdivide this interval by the points

(*Partition σ*) $\qquad\qquad\qquad 0 < \frac{1}{2} < 1 < \frac{3}{2} < 2,$ $\qquad\qquad$ (4)

as in Figure 134. On the ith subinterval in (4), let ξ_i be the mid-point, to give $\xi_1 = \frac{1}{4}$, $\xi_2 = \frac{3}{4}$, $\xi_3 = \frac{5}{4}$, and $\xi_4 = \frac{7}{4}$. Then, $\Delta_i x = \frac{1}{2}$ and

Fig. 134

$$f(\xi_i)\Delta_i x = f(\xi_i) \cdot \frac{1}{2}; \tag{5}$$

$$f(\xi_1) = 1 + (\tfrac{1}{4})^2; \quad f(\xi_2) = 1 + (\tfrac{3}{4})^2; \quad f(\xi_3) = 1 + (\tfrac{5}{4})^2; \quad f(\xi_4) = 1 + (\tfrac{7}{4})^2;$$

$$f(\xi_1)\Delta_1 x = \tfrac{17}{16} \cdot \tfrac{1}{2}; \qquad f(\xi_2)\Delta_2 x = \tfrac{25}{16} \cdot \tfrac{1}{2}; \qquad f(\xi_3)\Delta_3 x = \tfrac{41}{16} \cdot \tfrac{1}{2}; \; etc.$$

$$S_\sigma = \tfrac{17}{32} + \tfrac{25}{32} + \tfrac{41}{32} + \tfrac{65}{32} = \tfrac{37}{8} = 4.625. \tag{6}$$

In place of (4), let σ be the partition of the interval $(0, 2)$ into 8 equal parts:

(*Partition σ*) $\qquad\quad 0 < \frac{1}{4} < \frac{1}{2} < \frac{3}{4} < 1 < \frac{5}{4} < \frac{3}{2} < \frac{7}{4} < 2.$ $\qquad\qquad$ (7)

Then, with each ξ_i as the mid-point of its subinterval, we obtain $S_\sigma = 4.656$.

Sometimes, S_σ of (3) *has a limit as $d_\sigma \to 0$*, where this limit requires a special definition as follows.

Definition I. *To state that* **the limit of S_σ is L as $d_\sigma \to 0$** *means that $| S_\sigma - L |$ will be as small as we please for all σ where d_σ is sufficiently small. Then, we write*

$$S_\sigma \to L \text{ as } d_\sigma \to 0, \quad or \quad \lim_{d_\sigma \to 0} S_\sigma = L. \tag{8}$$

Note 2. Instead of saying "*as $d_\sigma \to 0$*" in (8), we could say "*as the lengths of all subintervals of σ approach zero*," because d_σ is the maximum of these lengths. Also, if $d_\sigma \to 0$, the number of subintervals in σ becomes infinite. However, a statement merely that $n \to \infty$ in (1) would *not* imply that all $\Delta_i x \to 0$. For instance, x_1 might remain fixed in (1) while $n \to \infty$, and then we would not have $d_\sigma \to 0$.

Definition II. *Let σ be any partition of the interval (a, b), as in (1), and let ξ_i be selected arbitrarily on the ith subinterval, T_i, of σ. Let $S_\sigma = \sum_{i=1}^n f(\xi_i)\Delta_i x$, where $\Delta_i x$ is the length of T_i. Then, if S_σ approaches a limit as $d_\sigma \to 0$, we call this limit* "*the* **integral** *of $f(x)$ from $x = a$ to $x = b$,*" *denoted by $\int_a^b f(x)dx$:*

$$\int_a^b f(x)dx = \lim_{d_\sigma \to 0} S_\sigma, \quad or \quad \int_a^b f(x)dx = \lim_{(\text{as all } \Delta_i x \to 0)} \sum_{i=1}^{n} f(\xi_i)\Delta_i x. \tag{9}$$

Note 3. In place of $\int_a^b f(x)dx$ in (9), we could write simply $\int_a^b f$, read *"the integral of f from a to b."* However, the symbol $\int_a^b f(x)dx$ has many advantages in applications.

ILLUSTRATION 3. If $f(x) \geqq 0$ when x is on I, then $f(\xi_i) \geqq 0$ and $S_\sigma \geqq 0$ for every σ. Hence, with $a < b$, if $\int_a^b f(x)dx$ exists, we have $\int_a^b f(x)dx \geqq 0$. Similarly, if $f(x) \leqq 0$ we would obtain $\int_a^b f(x)dx \leqq 0$.

Note 4. In honor of the great German mathematician GEORG FRIEDRICH BERNHARD RIEMANN (1826–1866), who clarified the notion of an integral, S_σ of (3) sometimes is called a **Riemann sum.** Any integral which exists, as in (9), is called a **Riemann integral.** At more advanced levels, other types of integrals are defined.

In (9), we call a and b the **limits of integration,** the function $f(x)$ the **integrand,** and x the **variable of integration.** We refer to S_σ in (3) as an **approximating sum** for the integral in (9). A term like $f(\xi_i)\Delta_i x$ is called an **element** of such a sum. Observe that $\int_a^b f(x)dx$ does not depend on x, but represents the limit of S_σ as $d_\sigma \to 0$. Thus, *the letter used for the variable of integration is immaterial:*

$$\int_a^b f(x)dx = \int_a^b f(t)dt = \int_a^b f(z)dz = etc.$$

For this reason, sometimes the variable of integration is called a *dummy variable.*

If the limit in (9) exists, we say that f is *integrable* over (a, b). The following theorem, stating a condition for integrability, harmonizes with our intuitions. This theorem is proved in Note 8 of the Appendix.

Theorem I. *If a function f is continuous on the interval (a, b), then f is integrable on (a, b), or $\int_a^b f(x)dx$ exists.*

The operation of computing an integral is referred to as **integration.** Later, we shall call $\int_a^b f(x)dx$ a **definite integral,** instead of simply an *integral,* whenever there is danger of confusing it with another type of expression which will be called an *indefinite integral.* Then, the computation of a definite integral may be called **definite integration.**

Let $\{\sigma_k\}$, $k = 1, 2, \cdots$, be any infinite sequence of partitions where σ_k has the norm d_k, and $d_k \to 0$ as $k \to \infty$. Let τ_k represent S_σ when σ is σ_k. Then, from Definition I and (9), τ_k will be as near $\int_a^b f(x)dx$ as we please if k is *so large* that d_k is *sufficiently small,* or

$$\lim_{k \to \infty} \tau_k = \int_a^b f(x)dx. \tag{10}$$

Thus, the integral is equal to *the limit of any sequence of approximating sums,* $\{\tau_k\}$, *for which the norm $d_k \to 0$ as $k \to \infty$.*

ILLUSTRATION 4. Consider $\int_0^2 (1 + x^2)dx$, and refer to Illustration 2. Let σ_k be the partition of $(0, 2)$ into 2^k equal parts. Then σ_2 is (4) on page 178, σ_3 is (7) on page 178, $\tau_2 = 4.625$, $\tau_3 = 4.656$, and (10) shows that

$$\tau_k \to \int_0^2 (1 + x^2)dx \quad as \quad k \to \infty. \tag{11}$$

By later methods, the exact value of the integral in (11) is found to be $4\frac{2}{3}$.

57. AREAS OF SIMPLE REGIONS

Consider a Euclidean plane, with an assigned unit for measuring distance in any direction. If an *xy*-system of rectangular co-ordinates is introduced, hereafter in this text we shall assume that the unit for distance in the plane will be used as the scale unit on *each axis*, unless otherwise specified. However, for convenience, any associated figure may employ unequal units on the axes.

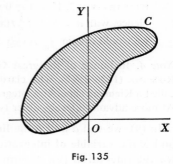

Fig. 135

In the plane, let *C* be a closed curve which does not cross itself, as in Figure 135. Then, the set of points of the plane *inside or on C* will be referred to as a **plane region,** with *C* as its boundary. If *C* is a familiar curve, such as a circle or a rectangle, sometimes we shall use its name to refer also to the region for which the curve is the boundary, when the context prevents ambiguity. Thus, a reference to the *area of a rectangle* will mean the area of the *region* bounded by the rectangle.

The notion of *area* for an arbitrary region requires definition. The following introduction to areas will cover present cases, but a more general definition of area will be met in a later chapter. We commence *by defining the area of any rectangle*, with dimensions *h* and *k* linear units, *to be hk "square units"*; we call *hk* the *measure of this area*. Then, for any region *R*, we agree that the area of *R* will be defined as the limit (if it exists) of the sum of the areas of a finite number of associated rectangles, which do not overlap except at boundaries, as the number of rectangles becomes infinite in some fashion. Also, if a set of points *S* in a plane consists of a finite number of regions which overlap at most in boundary points, we define the area of *S* as the sum of the areas of the specified regions.

Consider the region *R* with the boundary *KLMNK* in Figure 136, bounded by the *x*-axis, the lines $x = a$ and $x = b$, and a curve $y = f(x)$, where *f* is continuous and $f(x) \geq 0$ when *x* is on the interval $I = \{a \leq x \leq b\}$. Let σ be any

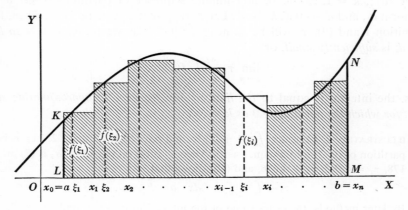

Fig. 136

partition of I as in Figure 136, with ξ_i as an arbitrary point on subinterval $T_i = \{x_{i-1} \leq x \leq x_i\}$. Then $f(\xi_i)\Delta_i x$ is the area of the rectangle with altitude $f(\xi_i)$ and base of length $\Delta_i x$. Hence, S_σ of (9) on page 178 becomes the sum of the areas * of n rectangles, as in Figure 136. Then, we define the area, A, of R as *the limit of S_σ as all lengths*, $\Delta_i x$, *of the bases of the rectangles approach zero, if the limit exists*. This means that A is defined as an integral as follows.

Definition III. *If $f(x) \geq 0$, the area, A, of the region R bounded by the ordinates $x = a$ and $x = b$, the x-axis, and the curve $y = f(x)$, is the integral of f from $x = a$ to $x = b$, if the integral exists. Or,*

$(a \leq b)$
$$A = \int_a^b f(x)dx. \tag{1}$$

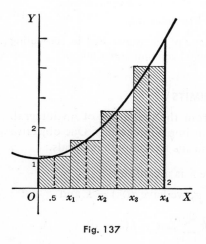

Fig. 137

ILLUSTRATION 1. In Figure 137, R is bounded by the x-axis, the curve $y = 1 + x^2$, and the lines $x = 0$ and $x = 2$. From (1),

$$(area\ of\ R) = A = \int_0^2 (1 + x^2)dx. \tag{2}$$

We approximated A in Illustration 4 on page 179. When σ is the partition with division points $0, \frac{1}{2}, 1, \frac{3}{2},$ and 2, and each ξ_i is chosen as the mid-point of the corresponding subinterval, then S_σ of (9) on page 178 is the sum of the areas of the ruled rectangles in Figure 137. From (6) on page 178, $S_\sigma = 4.625$. The figure was drawn with a reduced vertical unit.

Note 1. From Theorem I on page 179, it is seen that the area described in Definition III exists when f is continuous on the interval (a, b).

In this text, we agree that the area, A, of any region R will be defined as *positive* or *zero*. Hence, if $f(x) \leq 0$ when $a \leq x \leq b$, we *define* the area, A, of the region R of Definition III by the equation

$[f(x) \leq 0]$
$$A = -\int_a^b f(x)dx. \tag{3}$$

EXERCISE 51

For the integral, compute S_σ of (9) on page 178, accurately to three significant digits, if ξ_i is the indicated point on the ith subinterval of σ. With $f(x)$ representing the integrand, graph $y = f(x)$, showing rectangles corresponding to S_σ, and the region whose area is the given integral. In each partition, take the subintervals of equal lengths.

1. $\int_0^2 (1 + \frac{1}{2}x^2)dx$; σ has 4 subintervals; ξ_i as the mid-point.

2. $\int_0^2 (1 + \frac{1}{2}x^2)dx$; σ has 8 subintervals; (a) ξ_i as the mid-point; (b) ξ_i as the left-hand end point; (c) ξ_i as the right-hand end point.

* Hereafter, the single word *area* will abbreviate "*measure of the area.*"

3. $\int_{-1}^{1} (4 - x^2)dx$; σ has 6 subintervals; ξ_i as the mid-point.

4. $\int_{0}^{3} \dfrac{dx}{1 + x}$; σ has 9 subintervals; ξ_i as the mid-point.

5. $\int_{1}^{6} \dfrac{dx}{x}$; σ has 10 subintervals; ξ_i as the mid-point.

By use of (9) *on page* 178, *find an approximation to the area of the region bounded by the graph of* $y = f(x)$ *and the x-axis between ordinates at the given values of x. Use a partition* σ *with the assigned number of equal subintervals, and the arbitrary* ξ_i *chosen as the mid-point of its subinterval. Draw a figure showing corresponding rectangles.*

6. $f(x) = 2x - x^2$, between $x = 0$ and $x = 2$; (*a*) σ has 4 subintervals; (*b*) σ has 8 subintervals.

7. $f(x) = (x + 1)(x - 3)$, between $x = -1$ and $x = 3$; σ has 8 subintervals.

8. $f(x) = x^3$, between $x = -1$ and $x = 2$; σ has 9 subintervals.

Note 1. The method of the requested solutions is one of the means used in computing approximations to integrals by use of electronic digital computing machines.

58. COMPUTATION OF INTEGRALS AS LIMITS

Certain integrals can be evaluated directly from the definition of an integral. However, the details are complicated even with simple integrands. One objective at present is to emphasize the need for other means to compute integrals.

EXAMPLE 1. With $a < b$, obtain $\int_{a}^{b} k \, dx$, where k is a constant.

Solution. In (3) on page 178, for any partition σ, we have $f(\xi_i) = k$ and

$$S_\sigma = \sum_{i=1}^{n} f(\xi_i)\Delta_i x = \sum_{i=1}^{n} k\Delta_i x = k \sum_{i=1}^{n} \Delta_i x = k(b - a),$$

because $\Delta_1 x + \Delta_2 x + \cdots + \Delta_n x = b - a$. Hence,

$$\int_{a}^{b} k \, dx = \lim_{d_\sigma \to 0} S_\sigma = \lim_{d_\sigma \to 0} k(b - a) = k(b - a).$$

EXAMPLE 2. With $a < b$, obtain $\int_{a}^{b} x \, dx$.

Solution. Let σ_n be the partition of (a, b) into n equal parts. On the ith subinterval of σ_n, let ξ_i be the right-hand end point. Let $h = (b - a)/n$. Then, in σ_n, $\Delta_i x = h$ for every i. In (3) of page 178 with $f(x) = x$, let τ_n represent S_σ when σ is σ_n, and let d_n be the norm of σ_n. Then,

$$\xi_1 = a + h, \quad \xi_2 = a + 2h, \cdots, \quad \xi_n = a + nh = b; \tag{1}$$

$$\tau_n = (a + h)h + (a + 2h)h + \cdots + (a + nh)h$$

$$= nah + h^2(1 + 2 + \cdots + n); \tag{2}$$

$$\left(\text{using } h = \frac{b - a}{n}\right) \qquad \tau_n = ab - a^2 + \frac{(b - a)^2}{n^2} \cdot \frac{n(n + 1)}{2}, \tag{3}$$

where we used formula (4) of page 544 for an arithmetic progression. With

$f(x) = x$, the function f is continuous, and thus the desired integral exists. Hence, from (10) on page 179, since $\lim_{n \to \infty} d_n = 0$,

$$\int_a^b x\, dx = \lim_{n \to \infty} \tau_n = ab - a^2 + \frac{(b-a)^2}{2} \left[\lim_{n \to \infty} \frac{n(n+1)}{n^2} \right]$$

$$= ab - a^2 + \frac{(b-a)^2}{2} \cdot 1 = \tfrac{1}{2}(b^2 - a^2).$$

Note 1. The following auxiliary results, needed in Exercise 52, can be proved by mathematical induction.

$$1^2 + 2^2 + \cdots + n^2 = \tfrac{1}{6}n(n+1)(2n+1); \quad 1^3 + 2^3 + \cdots + n^3 = \tfrac{1}{4}n^2(n+1)^2.$$

EXERCISE 52

Obtain the exact value of each integral by evaluating a limit such as (10) *on page* 179.

1. $\int_0^5 hx\, dx$, where h is a constant.   **2.** $\int_0^3 (2 + 3x)dx$.

3. $\int_0^b 3x^2\, dx$.   **4.** $\int_0^x t^3\, dt$.   **5.** $\int_a^b x^2\, dx$.   **6.** $\int_1^3 (x^2 - 3x)dx$.

59. PROPERTIES OF INTEGRALS

In the definition of $\int_a^b f(x)dx$, we assumed that $a < b$. If $b < a$, or if $b = a$, we employ the following definitions.

If $b < a$: $$\int_a^b f(x)dx = -\int_b^a f(x)dx. \tag{1}$$

Equal limits of integration: $$\int_a^a f(x)dx = 0. \tag{2}$$

ILLUSTRATION 1. $$\int_3^1 f(x)dx = -\int_1^3 f(x)dx.$$

Hereafter, in any integral, suppose that the integrand is a continuous function, unless otherwise stated or observed in particular cases. Then, by Theorem I, the integral will exist. Also, we assume that the theorems on limits, from page 70, can be restated for limits of the type "$S_\sigma \to L$ as $d_\sigma \to 0$." In the proofs of the following properties, for convenience we shall assume usually that the lower limit of integration is less than the upper limit in any integral. The properties are true for other limits of integration because of (1) and (2).

Theorem II. *If k is any constant, and if $\int_a^b f(x)dx$ exists, then*

$$\int_a^b kf(x)dx = k\int_a^b f(x)dx.$$

Proof. With usual notation, from (9) on page 178,

$$\int_a^b kf(x)dx = \lim_{d_\sigma \to 0} \sum_{i=1}^n kf(\xi_i)\Delta_i x = \lim_{d_\sigma \to 0} k \sum_{i=1}^n f(\xi_i)\Delta_i x = k\int_a^b f(x)dx.$$

Theorem III. *For any numbers a, b, and c on an interval where a function $f(x)$ is continuous,*

$$\int_a^b f(x)dx + \int_b^c f(x)dx = \int_a^c f(x)dx. \tag{3}$$

Comment 1. A formal proof of (3) would involve consideration of corresponding partitions of the intervals (a, b), (b, c), and (a, c). We shall omit the details. With $a < b < c$ and $f(x) \geqq 0$, if each integral in (3) is interpreted as an *area*, then (3) becomes evident as a statement that the sum of the areas from a to b, and from b to c, is equal to the area from a to c. Suppose that (3) has been proved if $a < b < c$. Then, to prove (3) when $a < c < b$, we first apply (3) with (a, c, b) replacing (a, b, c), and use (1):

$$\int_a^b f(x)dx = \int_a^c f(x)dx + \int_c^b f(x)dx = \int_a^c f(x)dx - \int_b^c f(x)dx.$$

On transposing the last term above to the left, we obtain (3). Similarly, (3) could be proved for any order of a, b, and c on the number scale.

Theorem IV. *If $\int_a^b f(x)dx$ and $\int_a^b g(x)dx$ exist, then*

$$\int_a^b [f(x) + g(x)]dx = \int_a^b f(x)dx + \int_a^b g(x)dx. \tag{4}$$

Proof. From page 178, $\displaystyle \int_a^b [f(x) + g(x)]dx = \lim_{d_\sigma \to 0} \sum_{i=1}^n [f(\xi_i) + g(\xi_i)]\Delta_i x$

$$= \lim_{d_\sigma \to 0} \sum_{i=1}^n f(\xi_i)\Delta_i x + \lim_{d_\sigma \to 0} \sum_{i=1}^n g(\xi_i)\Delta_i x = \int_a^b f(x)dx + \int_a^b g(x)dx.$$

Theorem V. *Suppose that a function $f(x)$ is continuous when x is on the interval $I = \{a \leqq x \leqq b\}$. Let M be the absolute maximum and m be the absolute minimum of f on I. Then*

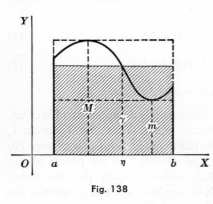

$$m(b - a) \leqq \int_b^a f(x)dx \leqq M(b - a). \tag{5}$$

Comment 2. Let $\int_a^b f(x)dx$ be interpreted as an area in Figure 138, for the case where $f(x) \geqq 0$. Then, (5) is equivalent to the geometric fact that the area of the region bounded by the lines $x = a$, and $x = b$, the x-axis, and the curve $y = f(x)$ lies between the area of the small rectangle with height m and the large rectangle with height M, in Figure 138. A formal proof of (5) is suggested in a later exercise.

Fig. 138

Theorem VI. (*A mean value theorem for an integral.*) *If a function $f(x)$ is continuous on the interval $I = \{a \leqq x \leqq b\}$, there exists a number η on I such that*

$$\int_a^b f(x)dx = (b - a)f(\eta). \tag{6}$$

Proof. From (5), there exists a number γ such that $m \leqq \gamma \leqq M$ and

$$\int_a^b f(x)dx = (b - a)\gamma, \tag{7}$$

where m is the absolute minimum and M is the absolute maximum of $f(x)$ on I. Then, from Theorem II on page 122, there exists at least one number η on I such that $f(\eta) = \gamma$, and thus (7) gives (6). By use of (1), it is easily seen that (6) is true when $b < a$ as well as when $a < b$.

Comment 3. For Figure 138 on page 184, (6) states that the area of the region bounded by $x = a$, $x = b$, the x-axis, and the curve $y = f(x)$ is equal to the area of the ruled rectangle with altitude $f(\eta)$, represented by γ.

Theorem VII. *Suppose that a function $f(t)$ is continuous on the domain $I = \{a \leqq t \leqq b\}$, which also is the domain of a variable x. Let*

$$\phi(x) = \int_a^x f(t)dt. \tag{8}$$

Then, ϕ has a derivative ϕ' where $\phi'(x) = f(x)$ when x is on I.

Proof. 1. In Figure 139 below, which shows a graph of $y = f(t)$ where $f(t) > 0$, we notice that $\phi(x)$ is the measure of the area of the region marked by horizontal rulings. The condition $f(t) > 0$ will not be assumed. To obtain $\phi'(x)$, we shall use the increment process.

2. Let x be fixed temporarily. Then, for any Δx,

$$\Delta\phi = \phi(x + \Delta x) - \phi(x) = \int_a^{x+\Delta x} f(t)dt - \int_a^x f(t)dt. \tag{9}$$

From Theorem III, page 183, with "a, b, c," as "$a, x, (x + \Delta x)$,"

$$\int_a^{x+\Delta x} f(t)dt = \int_a^x f(t)dt + \int_x^{x+\Delta x} f(t)dt. \tag{10}$$

Hence, from (9) and (10),

$$\Delta\phi = \int_x^{x+\Delta x} f(t)dt. \tag{11}$$

In Figure 139, $\Delta\phi$ is the area of the region ruled obliquely.

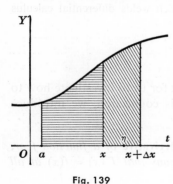

Fig. 139

3. In (11), by Theorem VI, there exists a number η on the interval from x to $(x + \Delta x)$, inclusive, as in Figure 139, such that

$$\Delta\phi = f(\eta)(x + \Delta x - x) = f(\eta)\Delta x. \tag{12}$$

If $\Delta x \to 0$ then $\eta \to x$, and hence $f(\eta) \to f(x)$, because the function $f(t)$ is continuous at $t = x$. Thus, from (12),

$$\lim_{\Delta x \to 0} \frac{\Delta\phi}{\Delta x} = \lim_{\Delta x \to 0} f(\eta) = f(x).$$

That is, ϕ has a derivative, and $\phi'(x) = f(x)$.

ILLUSTRATION 2. $\dfrac{d}{dx} \displaystyle\int_a^x (3t + \cos^3 t)dt = 3x + \cos^3 x.$

Note 1. Interval I in Theorem VII may be replaced by $b \leqq x \leqq a$, with no change in the proof, because (9), (10), and (12) remain unaltered if $b < a$. That is, in (8), we may have $x < a$.

Note 2. Recall Theorem IV on page 174: *If ϕ and F are such that $F'(x) = \phi'(x)$, when x is on an interval (a, b), then there exists a constant C such that $\phi(x) = F(x) + C$ when x is on (a, b).*

Theorem VIII. (*Fundamental theorem of integral calculus.*) *If F and f are functions whose domains include the interval $I = \{a \leqq x \leqq b\}$, where f is continuous and $F'(x) = f(x)$, then*

$$\int_a^b f(x)dx = F(b) - F(a). \tag{13}$$

Proof. 1. Let $\phi(x) = \int_a^x f(t)dt$. Then, $\phi'(x) = f(x)$. Since $F'(x) = f(x)$, we have $F'(x) = \phi'(x)$. Hence, by Note 2, there exists a constant C such that, when x is on I,

$$\phi(x) = F(x) + C, \text{ or} \tag{14}$$

$$\int_a^x f(t)dt = F(x) + C. \tag{15}$$

2. If $x = a$ in (15), we obtain $\qquad 0 = F(a) + C; \quad C = -F(a).$

Then, from (15),
$$\int_a^x f(t)dt = F(x) - F(a). \tag{16}$$

When $x = b$ in (16), we obtain (13).

Note 3. We shall use the symbol

$$F(x) \Big]_a^b \qquad to\ abbreviate \qquad [F(b) - F(a)]. \tag{17}$$

ILLUSTRATION 3. To obtain $\int_3^5 2x\,dx$, notice that, if $F(x) = x^2$, then $F'(x) = 2x$. Hence, from (13),

$$\int_3^5 2x\,dx = x^2 \Big]_3^5 = 25 - 9 = 16.$$

Note 4. The importance of Theorem VIII cannot be overemphasized. It establishes a connection between differentiation and integration which welds differential calculus and integral calculus into a single discipline.

60. ANTIDERIVATIVES

In order to use Theorem VIII, it becomes important for us to investigate how to find a function whose derivative is known. In this connection, we introduce the following terminology.

Definition IV. *To say that a function F is an* **antiderivative** *of a function f or, briefly, that "$F(x)$ is an antiderivative of $f(x)$," means that $F'(x) = f(x)$ at all numbers x in the domain of f.*

The process of finding an antiderivative is called **antidifferentiation,** and is referred to as the *inverse of differentiation.* To verify that a function $F(x)$ is an antiderivative of a given function $f(x)$, calculate $F'(x)$ to verify that $F'(x) = f(x)$. Thus, if n is a rational number, we verify that

(if $n \neq -1$) $\qquad$ *an antiderivative of x^n is* $\dfrac{x^{n+1}}{n+1}$, $\qquad$ (1)

because $\qquad \dfrac{d}{dx}\left(\dfrac{x^{n+1}}{n+1}\right) = \dfrac{n+1}{n+1}x^n = x^n.$ $\qquad$ (2)

ILLUSTRATION 1. From (1) with $n = 3$, an antiderivative of x^3 is $\frac{1}{4}x^4$; also, if C is any constant, then $(\frac{1}{4}x^4 + C)$ is an antiderivative of x^3 because the derivative of C is zero. From (1) with $n = \frac{2}{3}$, an antiderivative of $\sqrt[3]{x^2}$, or $x^{\frac{2}{3}}$, is $\frac{3}{5}x^{\frac{5}{3}}$. **If k is a constant, an antiderivative of k is kx because $D_x(kx) = k$.**

At present, we shall determine antiderivatives by use of (1) and the following easily appreciated facts, which will be discussed later.

$$\left\{\begin{array}{l} \textit{An antiderivative of a sum of functions is} \\ \textit{the sum of antiderivatives of the functions.} \end{array}\right\} \tag{3}$$

$$\left\{\begin{array}{l} \textit{An antiderivative of } kf(x), \textit{ where } k \textit{ is a constant,} \\ \textit{is equal to } k \textit{ times an antiderivative of } f(x). \end{array}\right\} \tag{4}$$

In the terminology of Definition IV, Theorem VIII yields the following procedure for computing $\int_a^b f(x)dx$:

$$\left\{\begin{array}{l} \textit{Obtain an antiderivative } F(x) \textit{ of } f(x), \textit{ if} \\ \textit{possible, and compute } [F(b) - F(a)]. \end{array}\right\} \tag{5}$$

EXAMPLE 1. Integrate: $\int_{-1}^{2} (x^2 - 3x + 5)dx$.

Solution. 1. An antiderivative of x^2 is $\frac{1}{3}x^3$; of $3x$, is $3 \cdot \frac{1}{2}x^2$; of 5, is $5x$. Hence, an antiderivative of $(x^2 - 3x + 5)$ is $F(x) = (\frac{1}{3}x^3 - \frac{3}{2}x^2 + 5x)$.

2. By use of the fundamental theorem of integral calculus,

$$\int_{-1}^{2} (x^2 - 3x + 5)dx = \frac{1}{3}x^3 - \frac{3}{2}x^2 + 5x \Big]_{-1}^{2} = 6\frac{2}{3} - (-6\frac{5}{6}) = 13\frac{1}{2}.$$

ILLUSTRATION 2. $\int_{1}^{3} (2x^4 + 2x - 1)dx = (\frac{2}{5}x^5 + x^2 - x)\Big]_{1}^{3} = \frac{514}{5}.$

because $\dfrac{d}{dx}(\frac{2}{5}x^5 + x^2 - x) = 2x^4 + 2x - 1.$

EXAMPLE 2. Find the area of the finite region above the x-axis, and of the finite * region below the x-axis, bounded by the x-axis and the curve $y = x^3 - x^2 - 2x$.

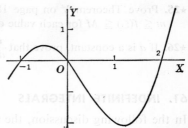

Fig. 140

Solution. 1. Since $y = x(x^2 - x - 2)$,   or $y = x(x - 2)(x + 1)$, the graph of this equation has the x-intercepts 0, -1, and 2, as observed in Figure 140.

2. From (1) and (3) in Section 57,

$$(area,\ above\ x\text{-}axis) = \int_{-1}^{0} (x^3 - x^2 - 2x)dx = (\frac{1}{4}x^4 - \frac{1}{3}x^3 - x^2)\Big]_{-1}^{0} = \frac{5}{12};$$

$$(area,\ below\ x\text{-}axis) = -\int_{0}^{2} (x^3 - x^2 - 2x)dx = (-\frac{1}{4}x^4 + \frac{1}{3}x^3 + x^2)\Big]_{0}^{2} = \frac{8}{3}.$$

* Hereafter, the word "*finite*" will be omitted in descriptions of regions. Unless otherwise specified, any region will be a *finite*, or *bounded region*.

EXERCISE 53

Obtain an antiderivative of the function by use of (1) *on page* 186.

1. $2x^4$. 2. $3x^{\frac{1}{2}}$. 3. $5x^{-3}$. 4. $2\sqrt[3]{x}$.
5. $3x^5 - 2x^2 - 2\sqrt{x} + 6$.   6. $2x^{-3} - 3x^4 - 5\sqrt[3]{x} + 3$.

Integrate by use of the fundamental theorem of integral calculus.

7. $\int_2^4 3x^2\, dx$.   8. $\int_{-2}^1 4y^3\, dy$.   9. $\int_6^2 5x\, dx$.
10. $\int_{-1}^1 (3x^2 - x + 4)dx$.   11. $\int_{-3}^0 (x^3 + 2x^2 - x + 2)dx$.
12. $\int_2^5 y^{-3}\, dy$.   13. $\int_1^9 3y^{\frac{1}{2}}\, dy$.   14. $\int_{-8}^1 2\sqrt[3]{x}\, dx$.

Find the area of the region bounded by the x-axis and the given curve.

15. $y = 3x - x^2$; between $x = 0$ and $x = 3$.
16. $y = 9 - x^2$; between $x = -3$ and $x = 3$.
17. $y = x^2 - 4x$; between $x = 0$ and $x = 4$.
18. $y = x^2 - 6x + 8$; between (a) $x = 2$ and $x = 4$; (b) $x = 0$ and $x = 3$.
19. $y = x^3 - 4x$; between (a) $x = -2$ and $x = 0$; (b) $x = -2$ and $x = 1$.
20. $y = (x^2 - 4)(x - 5)$; between (a) $x = -2$ and $x = 0$; (b) $x = 4$ and $x = 6$.
21. $y = 1/x^2$; between $x = 1$ and $x = 3$.

22. Calculate $\dfrac{d}{dx}\int_2^x \sqrt{2 + t^3}\, dt$.

★23. If f and g are continuous, and $f(x) \leq g(x)$ when x is on the interval (a, b), prove that $\int_a^b f(x)dx \leq \int_a^b g(x)dx$. Use (3) on page 178.

★24. Let $\phi(x) = \int_a^x f(t)dt$, where the function $f(x)$ is continuous. Apply the mean value theorem from page 173 to show that

$$\phi(b) - \phi(a) = \int_a^b f(t)dt = f(\eta)(b - a),$$

with $a < \eta < b$. (In Theorem VI, page 184, we concluded merely that $a \leq \eta \leq b$, where $\eta = a$ and $\eta = b$ would be possibilities.)

★25. Prove Theorem V on page 184. Make use of the fact that, in (9) on page 178, $m \leq f(\xi_i) \leq M$ for each value of i.

★26. If a is a constant, prove that $\dfrac{d}{dx}\int_x^a f(t)dt = -f(x)$.

61. INDEFINITE INTEGRALS

In the following discussion, the domain for x will be an interval of numbers.

Theorem IX. *If a function F is any particular antiderivative of a function f, so that $F'(x) = f(x)$, then the set of all antiderivatives of F is the set of functions $[F(x) + C]$, where C is any number.*

Proof. 1. For any C, $[F(x) + C]$ is an antiderivative of $f(x)$, since

$$\frac{d[F(x) + C]}{dx} = F'(x) + \frac{dC}{dx} = f(x). \tag{1}$$

2. Now, let $G(x)$ be any antiderivative of $f(x)$. Then $G'(x) = f(x)$, or $G'(x) = F'(x)$. Hence, by Theorem IV on page 174, there exists a constant C so that $G(x) = F(x) + C$, which proves Theorem IX.

ILLUSTRATION 1. An antiderivative of $3x^2$ is x^3. Hence, the set of all antiderivatives of $3x^2$ is the family of functions $(x^3 + C)$.

Theorem X. *If the function $f(x)$ is continuous on $I = \{h \leq x \leq k\}$, then f has antiderivatives, consisting of all functions G such that*

$$G(x) = \int_a^x f(t)dt + C, \tag{2}$$

where a is any number on I and C is any number.

Proof. By Theorem VII on page 185, if we let $\qquad \phi(x) = \int_a^x f(t)dt,$

then $\phi'(x) = f(x)$ at all x on I. Hence, by Theorem IX with ϕ in place of F, all antiderivatives of f are given by (2).

Suppose that f in (2) is integrable (not necessarily continuous). Then, an **indefinite integral** of f is defined as any function G given by (2). In particular, *if f is continuous*, Theorem X states that *the set of indefinite integrals,* given by (2), also is *the set of antiderivatives of f.* Hereafter in this text, in any reference to an indefinite integral of a function f, it will be assumed that f is continuous. With this understanding, *"antiderivative of f"* and *"indefinite integral of f"* have the same meaning.* Except on rare occasions, we shall discard the name *anti-derivative* in favor of *indefinite integral*, described as follows for future reference:

$$\left\{\begin{array}{l} An \text{ \textbf{indefinite integral}} \text{ of a continuous function} \\ f(x) \text{ is any function } F(x) \text{ such that } F'(x) = f(x) \\ or, \text{ equally well, such that } dF(x) = f(x)dx. \end{array}\right\} \tag{3}$$

If the functions F and f are related as in (3), sometimes we may state briefly that "$F(x)$ *is an indefinite integral (or, antiderivative) of $f(x)$,*" when $F'(x) = f(x)$. In our new terminology, by Theorem IX, if $F(x)$ is any particular indefinite integral of $f(x)$, then the set of *all* indefinite integrals of $f(x)$ is the family of functions $[F(x) + C]$, where C is an arbitrary constant. We introduce the symbol $\int f(x)dx$ to represent any one of the indefinite integrals, or

$$\int f(x)dx = F(x) + C, \quad where \quad F'(x) = f(x), \tag{4}$$

and C is called a **constant of integration.** Sometimes we shall use "$\int f(x)dx$" to represent *just a particular function*, and then "$\int f(x)dx$" should be read "**AN** *indefinite integral of $f(x)$.*" We read "$\int f(x)dx$" as "**THE** *indefinite integral of $f(x)$*" when the integral represents *any function* $[F(x) + C]$ from (4), and this meaning should be inferred when no contrary information is at hand.

---

* If $f(x)$ is *not* assumed to be continuous, the notions of an indefinite integral and an antiderivative (or *primitive*) of $f(x)$ are not identical. See page 90 of *The Theory of Functions of Real Variables, Second Edition,* by L. M. Graves (New York: McGraw-Hill Book Company, Inc., 1956).

In $\int f(x)dx$, we call x the *variable of integration* and $f(x)$ the **integrand.** To calculate $\int f(x)dx$, we search for a function $F(x)$ such that $F'(x) = f(x)$, and then add an arbitrary constant to $F(x)$. The process of finding indefinite integrals is called **indefinite integration,**[*] or simply *integration*, when there is no danger of confusion with *definite integration*. We refer to *indefinite integration* and *differentiation* as *inverse operations* because $\int f(x)dx$ is a function of x such that

$$\frac{d}{dx} \int f(x)dx = f(x), \quad or \quad d\left[\int f(x)dx\right] = f(x)dx. \tag{5}$$

In contrast, for fixed a and b, the definite integral $\int_a^b f(x)dx$ is some particular number, and is not a function of the dummy variable x. In any formula for indefinite integration, C will represent an arbitrary constant.

Theorem XI. *If u is a continuously differentiable function of a variable x, then*

$$\int du = u + C, \tag{6}$$

where du is expressed in terms of x and dx, and x is the variable of integration.

Proof. Suppose that $u = F(x)$. Then, F' is continuous, so that F' is integrable. Then, in (6), by use of (4) we obtain

$$\int du = \int F'(x)dx = F(x) + C = u + C.$$

Note 1. Theorem XI states that, in $\int du$, the symbol du can be treated as if it actually is a differential, even though "dx" was introduced in the definition of the Leibniz symbols $\int_a^b f(x)dx$ and $\int f(x)dx$ as a mere convenience, reminding us of "$\Delta_i x$" in Definition II on page 178. We shall meet other similar justification for the traditional use of "dx" in integrals with respect to x.

ILLUSTRATION 2. $\int 3x^2\, dx = x^3 + C$. *AN* indefinite integral of x^3 is $\frac{1}{4}x^4$; *THE* indefinite integral of x^3 is $(\frac{1}{4}x^4 + C)$, or $\int x^3\, dx = \frac{1}{4}x^4 + C$.

If a variable u is a continuously differentiable function of x, and n is a rational number where $n \neq -1$, from (III)$_d$ on page 152 we obtain

$$du^{n+1} = (n+1)u^n\, du, \quad or \quad d\left(\frac{u^{n+1}}{n+1}\right) = u^n\, du. \tag{7}$$

Then, from (6) with u replaced by $u^{n+1}/(n+1)$, we obtain

$$\int u^n\, du = \int d\left(\frac{u^{n+1}}{n+1}\right) = \frac{u^{n+1}}{n+1} + C, \quad or$$

(the power formula, $n \neq -1$) $\qquad\qquad \int u^n\, du = \frac{u^{n+1}}{n+1} + C. \tag{8}$

We refer to (8) as a *fundamental form* for indefinite integration.

After an indefinite integration, we may verify the result by differentiating it, to show that thus we obtain the given integrand. We use this method in proving some of the properties of indefinite integration.

[*] Previously called antidifferentiation.

I. *If k is any constant, then* $\qquad\qquad \int kf(x)dx = k\int f(x)dx.$ $\qquad$ (9)

Proof. $\qquad\qquad \dfrac{d}{dx}\left[k\int f(x)dx\right] = k\dfrac{d}{dx}\left[\int f(x)dx\right] = kf(x),$ $\qquad$ (10)

which is the integrand on the left in (9). Hence, (9) is true.

ILLUSTRATION 3. By use of (9), and the power formula with $n = -\frac{2}{5}$,

$$\int \frac{3x}{\sqrt[5]{x^7}}\,dx = 3\int x^{1-\frac{7}{5}}\,dx = 3\int x^{-\frac{2}{5}}\,dx = 3\cdot\frac{1}{\frac{3}{5}}x^{\frac{3}{5}} + C = 5x^{\frac{3}{5}} + C.$$

II. *The indefinite integral of a sum of functions is the sum of their indefinite integrals:*

$$\int [f(x) + g(x) + h(x)]dx = \int f(x)dx + \int g(x)dx + \int h(x)dx. \qquad (11)$$

Proof. $\qquad\qquad \dfrac{d}{dx}\left[\int f(x)dx + \int g(x)dx + \int h(x)dx\right] =$

$$\frac{d}{dx}\int f(x)dx + \frac{d}{dx}\int g(x)dx + \frac{d}{dx}\int h(x)dx = f(x) + g(x) + h(x), \qquad (12)$$

where we used (5) of page 190. On the right in (12), we obtained the integrand on the left in (11), which proves (11). In using (11), all arbitrary constants on the right can be added to give a single arbitrary constant.

ILLUSTRATION 4. By use of (8), (9), and (11),

$$\int (3x^2 - 5x - x^3 + 3)dx = \int 3x^2\,dx - 5\int x\,dx - \int x^3\,dx + \int 3\,dx$$
$$= x^3 - \tfrac{5}{2}x^2 - \tfrac{1}{4}x^4 + 3x + C.$$

III. *If the variables u and v are continuously differentiable functions of an independent variable x, then*

$$\int (du + dv) = u + v + C. \qquad (13)$$

where du and dv are understood to be expressed in terms of x and dx, x is the variable of integration, and C is an arbitrary constant.

Proof. Let $u = F(x)$ and $v = G(x)$, where F' and G' are continuous. By (11),

$$\int (du + dv) = \int [F'(x) + G'(x)]dx = \int F'(x)dx + \int G'(x)dx \qquad (14)$$

$$= F(x) + C_1 + G(x) + C_2 = F(x) + G(x) + C, \qquad (15)$$

where C_1 and C_2 are arbitrary constants, and we let $C_1 + C_2 = C$, which thus is an arbitrary constant. We note that (13) extends to the case of any number of continuously differentiable dependent variables. For instance,

$$\int (du + dv + dw) = u + v + w + C.$$

ILLUSTRATION 5. $\qquad\qquad \displaystyle\int \frac{2x^3 - x}{x^5}\,dx = \int \frac{2}{x^2}\,dx - \int \frac{dx}{x^4}$

$$= 2\int x^{-2}\,dx - \int x^{-4}\,dx = -2x^{-1} + \tfrac{1}{3}x^{-3} + C.$$

The fundamental theorem of integral calculus yields the following routine, in terminology involving the notion of an indefinite integral.

Summary. *Computation of* $\int_a^b f(x)dx$. *If possible, find an indefinite integral of* $f(x)$, *that is, a function* $F(x)$ *such that* $F'(x) = f(x)$. *Then*

$$\int_a^b f(x)dx = F(b) - F(a). \tag{16}$$

62. USE OF A FUNDAMENTAL FORM FOR INDEFINITE INTEGRATION

In obtaining an indefinite integral, $\int f(x)dx$, by use of a fundamental form for integration, such as (8) on page 190, first decide on the function whose values are to be represented by u. Then, adjust constant multipliers before and after the integral sign, in order to exhibit du. When possible, avoid expanding powers.

EXAMPLE 1. Calculate $\qquad\qquad \int t(2t^2 + 1)^{15}\, dt. \qquad\qquad (1)$

Solution. Work toward $\int u^{15}\, du$ with $u = 2t^2 + 1$. Since $du = 4t\, dt$, multiply by 4 in the integrand, and divide by 4 before the integral:

$$\int t(2t^2 + 1)^{15}\, dt = \tfrac{1}{4} \int (2t^2 + 1)^{15}(4t\, dt) = \tfrac{1}{4} \int u^{15}\, du$$

$$= \tfrac{1}{4} \cdot \tfrac{1}{16} u^{16} + C = \tfrac{1}{64} (2t^2 + 1)^{16} + C.$$

For brevity, we could omit $\tfrac{1}{4} \int u^{15}\, du$ and $(\tfrac{1}{64} u^{16} + C)$ above.

ILLUSTRATION 1. In $\int \dfrac{dx}{\sqrt[3]{4x + 1}}$, if $u = 4x + 1$ then $du = 4\, dx$ and

$$\int \frac{dx}{\sqrt[3]{4x + 1}} = \frac{1}{4} \int (4x + 1)^{-\frac{1}{3}}(4\, dx)$$

$$= \frac{1}{4} \int u^{-\frac{1}{3}}\, du = \frac{1}{4} \frac{u^{\frac{2}{3}}}{\frac{2}{3}} + C = \frac{3}{8} (4x + 1)^{\frac{2}{3}} + C.$$

ILLUSTRATION 2. In the following case, we work toward $\int u^{-3}\, du$ with

$$u = 2x^3 + 4 \quad and \quad du = 6x^2\, dx:$$

$$\int \frac{x^2\, dx}{(2x^3 + 4)^3} = \frac{1}{6} \int (2x^3 + 4)^{-3}(6x^2\, dx) = -\frac{1}{12} (2x^3 + 4)^{-2} + C.$$

EXERCISE 54

1. Verify by differentiation that $\int (3x + 5)^{-2}\, dx = -\tfrac{1}{3}(3x + 5)^{-1} + C.$

2. Without integrating, find $D_x \left[\int_3^x \sqrt{u^5 + 3}\, du \right]$; $d\left[\int (x^3 + \sin x)dx \right]$.

Integrate. Avoid expanding before integrating, if possible.

3. $\int x^5\, dx.$ **4.** $\int \sqrt[3]{x^4}\, dx.$ **5.** $\int (x + 2)^9\, dx.$ **6.** $\int (y - 3)^7\, dy.$

7. $\int \dfrac{1}{2x^3}\, dx.$ **8.** $\int \dfrac{x^2}{x^{\frac{1}{3}}}\, dx.$ **9.** $\int \dfrac{\sqrt[4]{x^3}}{3x^2}\, dx.$ **10.** $\int \dfrac{2x^3}{\sqrt{x}}\, dx.$

11. $\int (3 + t)^{-4}\, dt.$ **12.** $\int (2x + 3)^4(2\, dx).$ **13.** $\int (3 - 4x)^3\, dx.$

14. $\int \sqrt{6 - 5x}\, dx.$

15. $\int \sqrt[3]{3y - 2}\, dy.$

16. $\int_1^4 (2 - x)^4\, dx.$

17. $\int_1^2 \sqrt{3y - 2}\, dy.$

18. $\int (2x^2 + 3)^5 x\, dx.$

19. $\int (y^3 - 3)^7 y^2\, dy.$

20. $\int \dfrac{2 + 3z}{z^3}\, dz.$

21. $\int_1^4 \dfrac{(2 - t)^2}{\sqrt{t}}\, dt.$

22. $\int_4^9 \dfrac{x - 1}{\sqrt{x}}\, dx.$

23. $\int \dfrac{du}{(3u + 2)^5}.$

24. $\int \dfrac{w\, dw}{(2w^2 - 7)^2}.$

25. $\int \dfrac{dz}{\sqrt{3 - 5z}}.$

26. $\int (x^2 + 2x - 3)^7 (x + 1)\, dx.$

27. $\int_2^1 (6 - 2z)^{\frac{1}{2}}\, dz.$

28. $\int \dfrac{t^2\, dt}{\sqrt[3]{t^3 + 1}}.$

29. $\int_{-1}^2 \dfrac{x}{\sqrt{5 + x^2}}\, dx.$

30. $\int_{\sqrt{6}}^3 \dfrac{2u\, du}{\sqrt{u^2 - 5}}.$

Find the area to three decimal places for the region with the given boundaries.

31. The x-axis and the curve $y = x(x + 1)(x - 4)$.

32. The x-axis, the lines $x = \frac{3}{2}$ and $x = 4$, and the curve $y = \sqrt{2x + 1}$.

33. The x-axis, the curve $y^3 = x + 8$, and the line $x = 19$.

63. AREA OF THE REGION BETWEEN TWO CURVES

Let R represent the region in Figure 141 bounded by the ordinates $x = a$ and $x = b$, and the curves $y_1 = g(x)$ and $y_2 = f(x)$, with $y_1 \le y_2$, where g and f are continuous when $a \le x \le b$. We shall define the area of R in a fashion consistent with the definition of area on page 180.

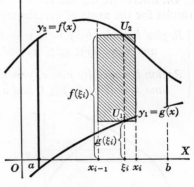

Fig. 141

Form a partition σ of the interval (a, b), as in (1) on page 177, with the subintervals $\{T_i\}$ where T_i is the interval $x_{i-1} \le x \le x_i$. On each interval T_i, select a point ξ_i arbitrarily. The line $x = \xi_i$, as in Figure 141, intersects the given curves in points U_1 and U_2 with ordinates $g(\xi_i)$ and $f(\xi_i)$, respectively. Construct the rectangle with

$$altitude = \overline{U_1 U_2} = f(\xi_i) - g(\xi_i);$$

$$base = \Delta_i x = x_i - x_{i-1};$$

$$area = \Delta_i A = [f(\xi_i) - g(\xi_i)]\Delta_i x. \qquad (1)$$

Then, we define the *area*, A, of the region R to be *the limit of the sum of all elements of area*, $\Delta_i A$, for the partition σ, as all $\Delta_i x \to 0$. By comparison with (9) on page 178, we recognize (1) as the typical element in an approximating sum for the integral of $[f(x) - g(x)]$ from $x = a$ to $x = b$. Thus, we have defined A as follows:

$$\left\{ \begin{array}{l} Region\ bounded\ by\ x = a,\ x = b,\ y_1 = g(x), \\ and\ y_2 = f(x);\ y_1 \le y_2\ and\ a < b. \end{array} \right\} \qquad A = \int_a^b (y_2 - y_1)\, dx. \qquad (2)$$

We obtain (1) of page 181 from (2) with $y_1 = 0$ and $y_2 = y = f(x) \geqq 0$:

$$\left\{ \begin{array}{l} \textit{Region bounded by } x = a,\ x = b,\ y = 0, \\ \quad \textit{and } y = f(x); f(x) \geqq 0 \textit{ and } a < b. \end{array} \right\} \qquad A = \int_a^b y\ dx. \qquad (3)$$

EXAMPLE 1. Find the area of the region bounded by

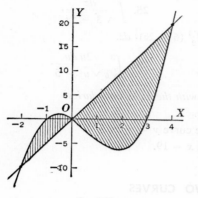

Fig. 142

$$y = x(x + 1)(x - 3) \quad and \quad y = 5x. \qquad (4)$$

Solution. 1. *Intersections.* Solve the system (4):

$$5x = x(x + 1)(x - 3); \textit{ hence,}$$

$$x = 0 \quad or \quad 5 = x^2 - 2x - 3.$$

We obtain $x = 0, -2$, and 4; then, from (4), $y = 0, -10$, and 20, respectively, as shown on the graphs of (4) in Figure 142.

2. To find the area of the region with inclined rulings, use (2) with $y_2 = 5x$ and $y_1 = x(x + 1)(x - 3)$, so that $y_1 \leqq y_2$; reverse these roles for the region with vertical rulings. The area A, in square units, is

$$A = \int_{-2}^0 [x(x + 1)(x - 3) - 5x]dx + \int_0^4 [5x - x(x + 1)(x - 3)]dx = \tfrac{148}{3}.$$

On interchanging the roles of x and y in (2) and (3), we obtain the following results for the areas of certain regions:

$$\left\{ \begin{array}{l} \textit{Region bounded by } y = c,\ y = d,\ x_1 = g(y), \\ \quad \textit{and } x_2 = f(y);\ x_1 \leqq x_2 \textit{ and } c < d. \end{array} \right\} \qquad A = \int_c^d (x_2 - x_1)dy. \qquad (5)$$

$$\left\{ \begin{array}{l} \textit{Region bounded by } y = c,\ y = d,\ x = 0, \\ \quad \textit{and } x = f(y);\ f(y) \geqq 0 \textit{ and } c < d. \end{array} \right\} \qquad A = \int_c^d x\ dy. \qquad (6)$$

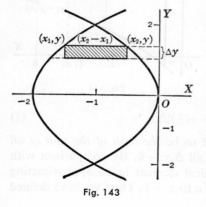

Fig. 143

EXAMPLE 2. Find the area, A, of the region bounded by the parabolas

$$x = -\tfrac{1}{4}y^2 \quad and \quad x = \tfrac{1}{4}(y^2 - 8). \qquad (7)$$

Solution. 1. The curves intersect at $(-1, \pm 2)$, in Figure 143. Let Δy be the length of a typical subinterval of a partition of the interval $-2 \leqq y \leqq 2$. Let ΔA be the area of the corresponding rectangle in the background of an approximating sum for the integral in (5) related to (7). Let $x_2 = -\tfrac{1}{4}y^2$ and $x_1 = \tfrac{1}{4}(y^2 - 8)$, so that $x_1 \leqq x_2$. Then, in Figure 143,

$$\Delta A = (x_2 - x_1)\Delta y = [-\tfrac{1}{4}y^2 - \tfrac{1}{4}(y^2 - 8)]\Delta y. \qquad (8)$$

2. Hence, from (5), $\qquad A = \int_{-2}^2 [-\tfrac{1}{4}y^2 - \tfrac{1}{4}(y^2 - 8)]dy = \tfrac{16}{3}$, *sq. units.* $\qquad (9)$

Comment 1. The element ΔA in (8) and the ruled rectangle in Figure 143 were not essential for writing (9). However, ΔA in (8) leads naturally to (9), and the student is advised to give a similar background for at least several of the problems in the next exercise.

Comment 2. To graph $x = \frac{1}{4}(y^2 - 8)$, we obtain $dx/dy = \frac{1}{2}y = 0$ at $y = 0$. Hence, the vertex is at $(x = -2, y = 0)$, where the tangent is vertical. The y-intercepts are

$$y = \pm 2\sqrt{2}.$$

Formula (2) applies only when there is an upper boundary and a lower boundary where each is given as *the graph of a single function over the whole domain for x.* Similarly, (5) can be employed only for a region with a left-hand boundary and a right-hand boundary, where each is given as the graph of a single function. Sometimes, both (2) and (5) apply conveniently.

EXERCISE 55

Draw graphs in an xy-plane exhibiting the region R bounded by the given curves. Find the area of R. Use whichever variable is best for integration, except when a particular variable is specified.

1. The parabola $y = 4x^2$ and $y = 9$.   **2.** $y = (x - 3)^2$ and $y = 4$.

3. The y-axis and $x = y^2 - 3y$.   **4.** $y = x^2 + 5$ and $y = 2x^2 - 4$.

5. $y = 6x$ and $y = 2x^2$. Integrate with respect to (a) x; (b) y.

6. $y = x^3$ and $x = y^3$. Integrate with respect to (a) x; (b) y.

7. $x = (y - 1)^2$ and $2 - x = (y - 1)^2$.

8. $y = x(x + 1)(x - 5)$ and $y = 7x$.   **9.** $x = (y + 2)^2$ and $x = 9$.

10. $x = y(y - 3)(y + 2)$ and $x = 0$.   **11.** $y + 2x + 6 = 0$ and $y = 9 - x^2$.

12. $4y^3 = x^2$ and $y = 1$.   **13.** $8y^2 = 9x^3$ and $x = 2$.

14. The region bounded by segments of the axes and an arc of $x^{\frac{1}{2}} + y^{\frac{1}{2}} = 2$.

15. The curves $y = \frac{1}{4}x^{-2}$ and $y = (2x - 3)^{-2}$, and the line $x = \frac{1}{4}$.

Note 1. Let the function $f(x)$ be continuous when $a \leq x \leq b$. Let σ be a partition of the interval (a, b) into n equal subintervals, each of length Δx, so that $n\Delta x = b - a$. Then, with $\{x_i\}$, $i = 0, 1, 2, \cdots, n$, as the division points of σ, let

$$\mu_n = \frac{f(x_1) + f(x_2) + \cdots + f(x_n)}{n}, \text{ or} \tag{1}$$

$$\mu_n = \frac{f(x_1)\Delta x + f(x_2)\Delta x + \cdots + f(x_n)\Delta x}{n\Delta x} = \frac{\sum_{i=1}^{n} f(x_i)\Delta x}{b - a}. \tag{2}$$

In (1), μ_n is the *arithmetic mean* of $f(x_1), f(x_2), \cdots, f(x_n)$. The numerator in (2) is a particular value of S_σ of (3) on page 178, and hence has the limit $\int_a^b f(x)dx$ when $n \to \infty$. Let $\gamma = \lim_{n \to \infty} \mu_n$. Then,

$$\gamma = \frac{\int_a^b f(x)dx}{b - a}. \tag{3}$$

On account of the arithmetic mean μ_n in the background, sometimes γ is called the **mean value** of $f(x)$ over interval (a, b). In (3), γ has the same value as γ in the proof of the mean value theorem for $\int_a^b f(x)dx$, in (7) on page 184.

Find the mean value of f(x) over the given interval.

16. $f(x) = x^2 + 4x; 0 \leqq x \leqq 6.$ **17.** $f(x) = \sqrt{x}; \ 0 \leqq x \leqq 9$

18. $f(x) = (2x - 1)^3; \ -1 \leqq x \leqq 2.$ **19.** $f(x) = (2 - x)^3; \ -2 \leqq x \leqq 2.$

64. VOLUME OF A SOLID OF REVOLUTION

Let W be the set of points, to be called a *region*, inside or on a closed surface S in three-dimensional space. The notion of the *volume* of W is intuitively apparent. However, it is essential to define the *"measure of the volume,"* hereafter abbreviated simply as the *"volume."* Any definition of volume which will be met in later sections will be based on a limiting process, leading to a definite integral. In each case, the element in any approximating sum for the integral will be computed directly or indirectly on the following basis, where (II) clearly includes (I) as a special case.

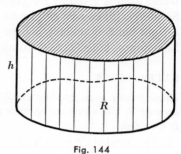

Fig. 144

I. *If W is the region bounded by a rectangular parallelepiped, with dimensions a, b, and c, we define the volume of W as abc volume units (cubic units).*

II. *Let W be a region, as in Figure 144, swept out if a plane region R, with area A, is moved h linear units perpendicular to the plane of R. Then, we define the volume of W as Ah volume units.* We refer to W as a slab.*

> ILLUSTRATION 1. Consider a solid circular cylinder with altitude h and r as the radius of the base. From (II), the volume of the cylinder is $h(\pi r^2)$, or $\pi r^2 h$.

In an xy-plane, let R be the region bounded by the x-axis, the lines $x = a$ and $x = b$, and a curve $y = f(x)$, where f is continuous on the interval $I = \{a \leqq x \leqq b\}$. In Figure 145 on page 197, the boundary of R is $MUWNM$. If R is revolved about the x-axis, the curve $y = f(x)$ sweeps out a so-called *surface of revolution*, as in Figure 146 on page 197; the ordinates MN and UW sweep out circular discs. Thus, R sweeps out a region to be called a *solid of revolution*, H, bounded by a surface of revolution, and two circular plane regions.

To arrive at a definition for the *volume* of H, first form any partition σ of I into n subintervals $\{T_i\}$, as in (1) on page 177, where $T_i = \{x_{i-1} \leqq x \leqq x_i\}$ with length $\Delta_i x$. In Figure 145, construct a perpendicular to OX at each division point x_i of σ, and thus divide R into n vertical strips corresponding to the n subintervals $\{T_i\}$ of σ. When R is revolved about OX, the section corresponding to T_i generates a *slab* of thickness $\Delta_i x$, as in Figure 146, with vertical circular faces having the radii

$$|y_{i-1}| = |f(x_{i-1})| \quad and \quad |y_i| = |f(x_i)|, \tag{1}$$

---

* In Chapter 20, this formula will be proved by use of (I), instead of being taken as a definition, as at present.

where absolute value signs are necessary because $f(x)$ may have negative values. Now, in Figure 145, with each subinterval T_i as a base, construct a rectangle with its vertical side as the ordinate y_i, or $f(x_i)$.* Revolution about OX of the region bounded by this rectangle generates a cylindrical slab C_i, as in Figure 146, with base-radius $|y_i|$, thickness $\Delta_i x$, and volume $\Delta_i V$, where

$$\Delta_i V = \pi y_i^2 \Delta_i x, \quad or \quad \Delta_i V = \pi[f(x_i)]^2 \Delta_i x. \tag{2}$$

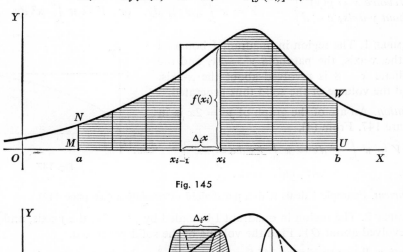

Fig. 145

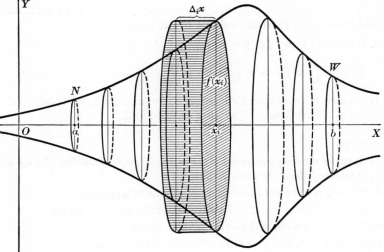

Fig. 146

Then, *we define the volume, V, of the solid H as the limit of the sum of all of the volumes $\Delta_i V$ of the cylindrical slabs C_i corresponding to a partition σ, as the norm of σ approaches zero. That is, by definition,*

$$V = \lim_{(as\ all\ \Delta_i x \to 0)} \sum_{i=1}^{n} \Delta_i V = \lim_{(as\ all\ \Delta_i x \to 0)} \sum_{i=1}^{n} \pi[f(x_i)]^2 \Delta_i x. \tag{3}$$

* Instead of $f(x_i)$, we could take any point ξ_i on T_i and use $f(\xi_i)$, with the same final result.

Expression (2) is recognized as the typical element in an approximating sum for an integral of $\pi [f(x)]^2$. Thus, in (3) *we defined V as a definite integral:*

$$\left\{ \begin{array}{l} revolve\ y = f(x) \\ about\ x\text{-}axis;\ a < b \end{array} \right\} \quad V = \pi \int_a^b [f(x)]^2\ dx, \quad or \quad V = \pi \int_a^b y^2\ dx. \quad (4)$$

On interchanging the roles of x and y, from (4) we obtain

$$\left\{ \begin{array}{l} revolve\ x = g(y) \\ about\ y\text{-}axis;\ c < d \end{array} \right\} \quad V = \pi \int_c^d [g(y)]^2\ dy, \quad or \quad V = \pi \int_c^d x^2\ dy. \quad (5)$$

EXAMPLE 1. The region in quadrant I bounded by the x-axis, the parabola $y^2 = 2x$, and the ordinate $x = 8$ is revolved about the x-axis. Find the volume of the solid thus generated.

Solution. An arc of the graph of $y^2 = 2x$ is in Figure 147. From (4),

$$V = \pi \int_0^8 y^2\ dx = \pi \int_0^8 2x\ dx = \pi x^2 \Big]_0^8$$

$$= 64\pi,\ \textit{cubic units}.$$

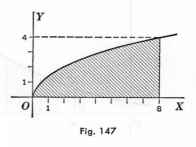

Fig. 147

Comment. Example 1 deals with a **paraboloid of revolution** (see page 449).

EXAMPLE 2. The region in quadrant I bounded by $y^2 = 2x$, the y-axis, and $y = 4$ is revolved about OY. Find the volume of the solid generated.

Solution. Refer to Figure 147 for a graph of $y^2 = 2x$. From (5),

$$V = \pi \int_0^4 x^2\ dy = \pi \int_0^4 \frac{y^4}{4}\ dy = \frac{\pi}{20} y^5 \Big]_0^4 = \frac{256\pi}{5},\ \textit{cubic units}.$$

Note 1. If a region W is enclosed by a surface S, for brevity we may refer to "*the volume of S*" instead of "*the volume of W which is enclosed by S.*"

EXERCISE 56

Find the volume of the solid generated if the region in an xy-plane bounded by the curve, or curves, is revolved about the specified axis.

1. $x^2 + y^2 = r^2$; revolve about either axis (volume of a sphere).

2. $2y = x$, $x = 4$, and the x-axis. Revolve about the x-axis (a cone).

3. $2y = 3 + x$, the x-axis, and $x = 2$. Revolve about the x-axis.

4. $y = 4x^2$, the y-axis, and $y = 4$. Revolve about the y-axis.

5. $x = 4y - y^2$ and the y-axis. Revolve about the y-axis.

6. $4x^2 + y^2 = 36$. Revolve about (*a*) the x-axis; (*b*) the y-axis.

Note 1. If an ellipse is rotated about one of its axes, the surface thus generated is called an **ellipsoid** of revolution. Moreover, the surface is called a *prolate* or an *oblate spheroid* according as the major axis or the minor axis is the axis of revolution.

7. $y = x^2 - 3x$ and the x-axis. Revolve about the x-axis.

8. $9y^2 - x^2 = 36$, $x = 3$, and $x = 0$. Revolve about the x-axis.

9. $x = y^3$, the y-axis, and $y = 2$. Revolve about the y-axis.

10. $x^2 = 6y$, and $3y = 2x + 6$. Revolve about the x-axis.

   Hint. Express the result as a sum or a difference of volumes.

11. $y^2 = 4x$ and $y^2 = 16 - 4x$. Revolve about the x-axis; the y-axis.

12. $y^2 = 3x$ and $y^2 = x + 4$. Revolve about the x-axis.

13. The smaller region bounded by $x^2 - 2x + y^2 = 0$ and $y = x$. Revolve about the x-axis.

14. $x^{\frac{1}{2}} + y^{\frac{1}{2}} = 3$ and the coordinate axes. Revolve about the y-axis.

15. $x^{\frac{2}{3}} + y^{\frac{2}{3}} = a^{\frac{2}{3}}$, where $a > 0$. Revolve about the x-axis.

16. A spheroid is generated by revolving the ellipse $b^2x^2 + a^2y^2 = a^2b^2$ about the x-axis. Find the volume of the spheroid.

17. By use of calculus, find the volume of a right circular cone with altitude h and with b as the radius of the base.

65. WORK AS AN INTEGRAL

Suppose that a particle T is moving along a line, which we shall label as an x-axis. In physics, the notion of a *force* is defined as a *vector*. However, for rectilinear motion, we shall avoid vector language by the following agreement. We shall represent any force **V** by a *number* whose absolute value is the magnitude of **V**, where the *number* is positive or negative according as the direction of **V** is the positive or the negative direction, respectively, on the x-axis. With this understanding, hereafter we shall refer to a *force F*, meaning that $|F|$ is the magnitude of the force, and that the nature, positive or negative, of F specifies the direction of the force on the x-axis, the line of motion.

Note 1. To state that an object *weighs w pounds*, means that gravitational attraction acts vertically downward on the object with a force of w pounds. That is, *weight is measured in force units.* We assume that a standard force of *one pound* has been defined, and we shall measure all forces in pounds. Another physical unit for force is a *dyne* (which we shall not use, as a rule).

   ILLUSTRATION 1. To state that, when the particle T is at the point x on the x-axis, the force acting on T is -3 pounds, means that a force with magnitude 3 pounds acts on T in the *negative* direction on the x-axis.

Suppose, now, that T is acted on by a *constant force F* during the motion of T from x_1 to x_2 on the x-axis. Then, we *define* the work, W, done by F as follows:

$$W = (x_2 - x_1)F. \tag{1}$$

Equation (1) conveniently translates the following description.

$$\left\{ \begin{array}{l} \textit{The work, W, done by a constant force F acting through} \\ \textit{a distance s (undirected) on a line is equal to } s|F| \textit{ if F} \\ \textit{has the same direction as the motion, and is equal to} \\ -s|F| \textit{ if F and the motion have opposite directions.} \end{array} \right\} \tag{2}$$

   ILLUSTRATION 2. In the notation of (1) and (2), $s = |x_2 - x_1|$. If $x_2 < x_1$, then $(x_2 - x_1) = -s$; if $F < 0$, then, from (1), $W = -Fs = s|F|$, in agreement with (2). The student may check other cases of (1) with (2).

In (1), or (2), the *unit for work* is named by joining the name of the distance unit to the name of the force unit by a hyphen: *foot-pound, inch-pound, centimeter-dyne*, etc. We say, colloquially, that *work is equal to force times distance*.

ILLUSTRATION 3. Suppose that a 20-pound weight is raised 50′ vertically. To raise the object, a force of 20 pounds must be applied upward at the object to counteract gravity. Thus, the applied force does (20)(50) or 1000 foot-pounds of work. Simultaneously, gravity does − 1000 foot-pounds of work, where the result is negative because gravity acts in the direction opposite to that of the motion.

If a moving particle T on an x-axis is acted on by a *variable* force, then (1) does not apply, and we shall define work as an integral, introduced as follows.

Suppose that T moves from $x = a$ to $x = b$ on the x-axis. When T is at point x on the axis, as in Figure 148, let $f(x)$ be the force acting on T, where we assume that f is continuous. Let σ be a partition of interval (a, b):

Fig. 148

Partition σ: $x_0 = a < x_1 < \cdots < x_{i-1} < x_i < \cdots < x_n = b,$ (3)

where we let $\Delta_i x = x_i - x_{i-1}$. Let d_σ be the maximum of the lengths of $\Delta_i x$ in σ. Select ξ_i arbitrarily on the ith subinterval of σ, as in Figure 149. From (1), if a constant force $f(\xi_i)$ were to act from x_{i-1} to x_i, the element of work would be

$$\Delta_i W = f(\xi_i)(x_i - x_{i-1}) = f(\xi_i)\Delta_i x.$$

Fig. 149

Let $S_\sigma = \sum_{i=1}^{n} \Delta_i W = \sum_{i=1}^{n} f(\xi_i)\Delta_i x.$ (4)

Then, we define the work, W, done by $f(x)$ in acting from $x = a$ to $x = b$ as *the limit of S_σ as $d_\sigma \to 0$*, if the limit exists. That is, we obtain

$$W = \lim_{d_\sigma \to 0} \sum_{i=1}^{n} f(\xi_i)\Delta_i x, \text{ or}$$ (5)

$$\begin{Bmatrix} \text{work done by force} \\ f(x) \text{ acting from } a \text{ to } b \end{Bmatrix} \quad W = \int_a^b f(x)dx, \text{ units of work.}$$ (6)

In case $b < a$, we also accept (6) as the definition of W.

EXAMPLE 1. A cask of wine weighs 1200 pounds. When the cask is raised vertically, wine leaks from it so that, after being raised x feet, the cask weighs $(1200 - 5x)$ pounds. Find the work done by a force applied at the base of the cask to raise it 20′.

Solution. With the x-axis directed upward from the initial position of the cask, the force $f(x)$, in pounds, which acts on the cask at any point x is $f(x) = 1200 - 5x$, as in Figure 150. From (6),

$$work = \int_0^{20} (1200 - 5x)dx = \left(1200x - \frac{5}{2}x^2\right)\Big]_0^{20} = 23,000, \text{ ft.-lbs.}$$

Fig. 150

Work done in deforming elastic material. Consider an elastic object such as a steel spring, a wire, a rod, etc. For discussion, we shall call the object a *spring*. Then, it has a certain natural length, L, when undisturbed. Now, think of one end of the spring as being attached to a fixed point M, and let the other end be pulled, to stretch the length by x linear units, $x \geqq 0$, as in Figure 151, where a force * $\tau(x) \geqq 0$ maintains the length. Likewise, the spring pulls with a force $T(x)$, of the same magnitude as $\tau(x)$, and opposite direction. We call $T(x)$ the **tension** in the spring due to the elongation x. Also, if the spring is *compressed* to shorten the length by x units, a tension $T(x)$ again exists, where the compression force $\tau(x)$ and $T(x)$ have the same magnitude and opposite directions. Then, HOOKE's *law* in physics states that, with a certain so-called *elastic upper limit* on the value of x, there exists a constant $k > 0$ such that, with $x \geqq 0$ and $\tau(x) = |T(x)|$,

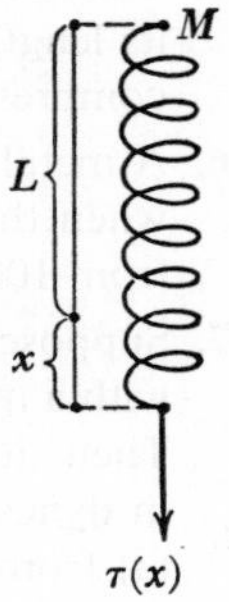

Fig. 151

(*magnitude of tension*) $\tau(x) = kx.$ (7)

Thus, in Figure 151, when the spring has the length $(L + x)$, the applied force is $\tau(x)$. Hence, the work, W, done in stretching the spring from length $(L + a)$ to $(L + b)$, where $0 \leqq a < b$, is found from (6) with $f(x)$ replaced by $\tau(x)$:

$$W = \int_a^b \tau(x)dx.$$ (8)

Similarly, with $\tau(x)$ as the deforming force in compression, (8) gives the work done in compressing the spring from length $(L - a)$ to length $(L - b)$.

EXAMPLE 2. A wire has the natural length 4′. When the wire is vertical, with one end held fast, and a weight of 10 pounds is attached to the other end, the length of the wire is 4′ 3″. Find the work done if this wire is stretched from 4′ 1″ to 4′ 5″ in length.

Solution. In (7), to find the constant of proportionality, k, substitute $x = \frac{1}{4}$ and $\tau(x) = 10$. Then, $10 = \frac{1}{4}k$ or $k = 40$, and thus $\tau(x) = 40x$. From (8), the specified

work is given by $W = \int_{1/12}^{5/12} 40x \, dx = 20x^2 \Big]_{1/12}^{5/12} = \frac{10}{3}, \, ft.\text{-}lbs.$

EXERCISE 57

1. To push a car from $x = 0$ to $x = 25$ along an x-axis, where the unit is one foot, the applied force is $(250 + 10x)$ pounds from $x = 0$ to $x = 10$, and remains constant while $10 \leqq x \leqq 25$. Find the work done.

2. A basket of sand is raised from the ground by a pulley. At ground level, the basket weighs 300 pounds, but sand spills out so that, after the basket has been raised x feet, the weight is $(300 - 2x)$ pounds. Find the work done in raising the basket 50′.

3. A tank contains 1000 cubic feet of water. Find the work done in raising the tank 40′ vertically if water leaks out at the constant rate of 5 cubic feet per foot of rise. Use 62 pounds as the weight of a cubic foot of water.

* We have designated the deforming force $\tau(x)$ as nonnegative in both elongation and depression, with the change of length $x \geqq 0$ in both cases. Hence, in (8), $W \geqq 0$ in both cases.

4. The natural length of a spring is 15″. If a force of 60 pounds stretches the spring 3″, find the work done in stretching the length from 16″ to 20″.

5. The natural length of a spring is 6′, and the tension in the spring is 30 pounds when its length is 8′. Find the work done (a) in stretching the length from 6′ to 9′; (b) in compressing the spring from 6′ to 5.5′ in length.

6. A metal rod has the natural length 100″, and the tension in the rod is 1000 pounds when the rod is stretched by .5″. Find the work done when the length is increased from 100″ to 100.5″.

7. Suppose that a particle P_1 with a mass of m_1 grams is at the origin, and a particle P_2 with a mass of m_2 grams is at the point x on an x-axis, where the unit is 1 centimeter. Then, it is known that P_1 attracts P_2 with a force whose magnitude is km_1m_2/x^2, in dynes, where k is a constant. Find the work done by this force when P_2 moves (a) from $x = 1$ to $x = 3$; (b) from $x = 4$ to $x = 2$.

8. Suppose that the particles P_1 and P_2 are r units apart on a line, and have the charges e_1, of positive electricity, and e_2, of negative electricity, respectively. Then, e_1 attracts e_2 with a force ke_1e_2/r^2, where k is a constant of proportionality depending on the units of measurement. How much work is done by this force when P_2 moves on the line from the distance $r = a$ to the distance $r = b$ from P_1, where $a < b$?

9. An earth satellite weighs 30 pounds (or, is attracted by the earth with a force of 30 pounds) at the earth's surface. Find the work in foot-pounds done in moving the satellite (considered as a mass point) against the force of gravity vertically from the earth's surface to a point 400 miles above it. Assume that the earth is a sphere with radius 4000 miles, and that the force of gravity at a distance r from the center is inversely proportional to r^2.

66. SIMPLE DIFFERENTIAL EQUATIONS

Suppose that f is an unknown function, and let $y = f(x)$. Sometimes, it may happen that f is defined only through an equation relating x, y, and derivatives of y. Such a relation is called a **differential equation** for y as a function of x. The situation just described occurs frequently in pure and applied mathematics. The *order* of the derivative of *highest order* in a differential equation is called its **order.**

ILLUSTRATION 1. The equation $y'' + 3y' = 7xy^3$ is a differential equation of the second order for y as a function of x because y'' occurs.

EXAMPLE 1. Obtain $f(x)$ if the graph of $y = f(x)$ passes through the point $(3, 3)$, and has the slope $(2x - 4)$ at each point $P:(x, y)$.

Solution. 1. We are given
$$\frac{dy}{dx} = 2x - 4, \tag{1}$$

$$with \quad y = 3 \quad when \quad x = 3. \tag{2}$$

2. By the definition of an indefinite integral, (1) is equivalent to

$$y = \int (2x - 4)dx, \quad or \quad y = x^2 - 4x + C, \tag{3}$$

where C is an arbitrary constant. We substitute (2) in (3) and obtain $3 = 9 - 12 + C$, or $C = 6$. Hence, $y = x^2 - 4x + 6$ is the desired result.

Comment. Figure 152 shows several curves of the family (3), with C as a parameter. We call (1) the differential equation of the family of parabolas (3). Equation (1) thus determines a *family of functions,* defined in (3). The conditions (2) then pick out a particular function from (3).

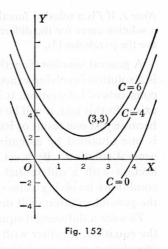

Fig. 152

Definition V. *To state that a function $f(x)$ is a solution function of a differential equation for y as a function of x means that the equation is satisfied when $y = f(x)$, or becomes an identity in x when we place $y = f(x)$ and express the derivatives of y in terms of x.*

On the basis of Definition V, we may state, briefly, that "$y = f(x)$ is a solution." For any differential equation, we shall consider only those solution functions possessing continuous derivatives of all orders involved in the equation.

EXAMPLE 2. Verify that $y = x^2 + x^{-3}$ is a solution of

$$xy' + 3y = 5x^2. \tag{4}$$

Solution. If $y = x^2 + x^{-3}$, then $y' = 2x - 3x^{-4}$. On substituting for y and y' in (4), we find that it becomes an identity in x, and hence $y = x^2 + x^{-3}$ is a solution of (4):

$$x(2x - 3x^{-4}) + 3(x^2 + x^{-3}) = 5x^2, \quad or \quad 5x^2 = 5x^2.$$

It is convenient to employ the word *solution* in the following context, as well as in the setting of Definition V.

$$\left\{ \begin{array}{l} \textit{To state that an equation } F(x, y) = 0 \textit{ is a } \textbf{solution (equation)} \textit{ of a dif-} \\ \textit{ferential equation for } y \textit{ as a function of } x \textit{ will mean that, if } y = f(x) \\ \textit{satisfies * } F(x, y) = 0, \textit{ then } y = f(x) \textit{ satisfies the differential equation.} \end{array} \right\} \tag{5}$$

Briefly, a solution *equation,* as in (5), defines solution *functions* (usually implicitly) as in Definition V. Hereafter, in considering a differential equation, the unqualified word *solution* will refer to a *solution equation* as in (5), except where we imply that a *solution function* as in Definition V is involved.

ILLUSTRATION 2. The equation † $x + yy' = 0$ has the solution $x^2 + y^2 = C$ for every $C > 0$, because differentiation in $x^2 + y^2 = C$ yields $x + yy' = 0$. From $x^2 + y^2 = C$, we obtain two families of solution curves,

$$y = \sqrt{C - x^2} \quad and \quad y = -\sqrt{C - x^2}, \tag{6}$$

which represent semicircles, each on a circle with $(0, 0)$ as center. If $f(x) = \sqrt{C - x^2}$ and $g(x) = -\sqrt{C - x^2}$, then f and g are solution functions of $x + yy' = 0$, with x on the interval $|x| < \sqrt{C}$.

---

* We assume that $F(x, y) = 0$ has at least one solution $y = f(x)$.
† Where $y \neq 0$. We shall not discuss such an exception at this point.

Note 1. If f is a solution function as in Definition V, the graph of $y = f(x)$ will be called a **solution curve** for the differential equation. In Example 1, the solution curves for (1) are the parabolas (3).

A **general solution** (function, or equation) of a differential equation of order n is a solution involving exactly n arbitrary constants,* which can be thought of as constants of integration. It is a characteristic feature that such a solution usually exists. In this text, it will be safe to refer to **"THE"** instead of **"A"** general solution because just one result or its equivalent will arise in any case. A **particular solution** is one obtained by assigning a special value to each arbitrary constant in the general solution.† By a set of **initial conditions,** or **boundary conditions** in connection with a differential equation for y as a function of x, we shall mean conditions involving values of x, y, and its derivatives which, when applied to the general solution, will determine a particular solution.

To solve a differential equation will mean to obtain its *general solution*. To solve the equation, together with given initial conditions, will mean to find the corresponding *particular solution*.

ILLUSTRATION 3. In Example 1, (3) is the general solution of (1); the initial conditions (2) determined the particular solution $y = x^2 - 4x + 6$.

If a function $f(x)$ is continuous, the following statement is true because of the definition of an indefinite integral:

$$y' = f(x) \quad \textit{is equivalent to} \quad y = \int f(x)dx + C, \tag{7}$$

where $\int f(x)dx$ is any particular indefinite integral of $f(x)$, and C is an arbitrary constant. That is, the *general solution* of the simple differential equation $y' = f(x)$ is given at the right in (7). Similarly, if n is any positive integer, a differential equation

$$y^{(n)} = f(x) \tag{8}$$

has as its general solution the equation resulting from n successive indefinite integrations on the right in (8), as in the following example.

EXAMPLE 3. Solve

$$\frac{d^2y}{dx^2} = 12x - 4, \tag{9}$$

with the initial conditions

$$y = 4 \quad \textit{and} \quad y' = 3 \quad \textit{at} \quad x = 2. \tag{10}$$

Solution. 1. Since $y'' = dy'/dx$, equation (9) becomes

$$\frac{dy'}{dx} = 12x - 4; \quad \textit{hence,} \quad y' = \int (12x - 4)dx = 6x^2 - 4x + C_1. \tag{11}$$

2. On using $(y' = 3 \textit{ at } x = 2)$ in (11), we find $3 = 24 - 8 + C_1$, or $C_1 = -13$.

Then, from (11),

$$\frac{dy}{dx} = 6x^2 - 4x - 13.$$

---

* We assume that the constants are *independent;* we accept this phraseology informally to mean that we could not replace them by fewer than n parameters.

† There are peculiar solutions not obtainable in this way, in the case of certain differential equations. See Comment for Example 1 on page 295.

Hence, $\qquad y = \int (6x^2 - 4x - 13)dx = 2x^3 - 2x^2 - 13x + C_2.$

By use of ($y = 4$ *at* $x = 2$) from (10), we find $4 = C_2 - 18$, or $C_2 = 22$. Thus, the desired *particular solution* is $y = 2x^3 - 2x^2 - 13x + 22$.

Comment. Without initial conditions, and thus with C_1 remaining arbitrary, from (11) we obtain a solution involving two arbitrary constants:

$$y = \int (6x^2 - 4x + C_1)dx, \quad \text{or} \quad y = 2x^3 - 2x^2 + C_1 x + C_2, \qquad (12)$$

which is the *general solution* of (9). With given initial conditions, it was more desirable to determine C_1 from (11) before proceeding to the next stage.

EXERCISE 58

Verify the given solution of the differential equation.

1. $y'' - 3xy' + 3y = 2 - 3x^2$; solution, $y = x^2 + 3x$.

2. $xy'' - xy' = 12x^2 - 6x^3$; solution, $y = 2x^3 + 5$.

Find the solution of the differential equation satisfying the initial conditions.

3. $y' = 4x + 7$; $y = 3$ at $x = 2$.   **4.** $y' = -x^2 - 3$; $y = 4$ at $x = -1$.

5. $\dfrac{ds}{dt} = 3t - 5$; $s = -3$ at $t = 2$.   **6.** $\dfrac{dv}{dt} = -2t + 3$; $v = 4$ at $t = 3$.

7. $\dfrac{d^2y}{dx^2} = 3x - 2$; $y = 4$ and $\dfrac{dy}{dx} = -2$ at $x = 4$.

8. $\dfrac{d^2y}{dx^2} = -5$; $y = -1$ and $\dfrac{dy}{dx} = 3$ at $x = -2$.

9. $\dfrac{d^2u}{dt^2} = -2t^2 + 5$; $u = 4$ and $\dfrac{du}{dt} = -2$ at $t = -1$.

Find the general solution of the equation.

10. $\dfrac{d^2y}{dx^2} = 3x + 2$.   **11.** $\dfrac{d^3s}{dt^3} = 6t + 5$.

Obtain $f(x)$ so that the graph of $y = f(x)$ passes through the given point and has the specified slope at any point (x, y). In Problems 12 and 13, graph the solution $y = f(x)$ and one other curve of the family determined by the differential equation which is used.

12. Slope $= 4x + 4$; through the point $(2, -12)$.

13. Slope $= -6x - 12$; through the point $(1, -22)$.

14. Slope $= 9x^2 - 10x - 2$; through the point $(1, 3)$.

15. Slope $= -4/x^2$; through the point $(-2, -2)$.

16. Slope $= -2/\sqrt{x+1}$; through the point $(0, 2)$.

17. Find $f(x)$ so that $f''(x) = 3$ at all values of x, and the tangent to the graph of $y = f(x)$ at $(2, 1)$ is $y = 5x - 9$.

18. Find $f(x)$ so that $f''(x) = -2$ at all values of x, and the tangent to the graph of $y = f(x)$ at $(-1, 2)$ is parallel to $4x - 2y = 5$.

19. Find the equation of the family of curves in an xy-plane whose slope at any point (x, y) is $3x^2 - 5x$. Also, find the equation of that curve of the family passing through the point $(2, 5)$.

67. DIFFERENTIAL EQUATIONS OF MOTION

Suppose that a particle is moving on an s-axis. If s represents the coordinate of the particle at the time t, then s is a function of t. We recall that the velocity v and the acceleration a at time t are given by

$$v = \frac{ds}{dt}; \quad a = \frac{d^2s}{dt^2}, \quad or \quad a = \frac{dv}{dt}. \tag{1}$$

EXAMPLE 1. A particle moves on an s-axis with the acceleration

$$\frac{d^2s}{dt^2} = 6t - 4. \tag{2}$$

At $t = 1$, $s = 4$ and the velocity is $v = 3$. Find the coordinate s at any time t.

Solution. 1. We refer to (2) as *the differential equation of the motion.* From (1) and (2),

$$\frac{dv}{dt} = 6t - 4; \quad v = \int (6t - 4)dt, \quad or \quad v = 3t^2 - 4t + C_1, \tag{3}$$

where C_1 is an arbitrary constant. From the initial conditions $v = 3$ at $t = 1$, we obtain $3 = 3 - 4 + C_1$ or $C_1 = 4$.

2. From (3), at any time t, $\qquad \frac{ds}{dt} = 3t^2 - 4t + 4;$

$$s = \int (3t^2 - 4t + 4)dt, \quad or \quad s = t^3 - 2t^2 + 4t + C_2, \tag{4}$$

where C_2 is an arbitrary constant. From the initial conditions, $s = 4$ at $t = 1$; hence, from (4), $C_2 = 1$ and $s = t^3 - 2t^2 + 4t + 1$.

Unless otherwise stated, in any problem relating to a falling body in the earth's atmosphere, we shall take account only of the effect of gravity, and thus shall neglect air resistance and other disturbing features. Then, the acceleration of the body will be a constant, g, approximately 32, feet per second per second, directed downward. Thus, if distance is measured in feet with the positive direction upward, and if time t is measured in seconds, the differential equation for the motion of a falling body is

$$\frac{d^2s}{dt^2} = -g. \tag{5}$$

EXAMPLE 2. A balloon is rising at the rate of 64' per second. A stone is dropped from the balloon when it is 3072' above the ground. With what speed, and how many seconds later will the stone hit the ground?

Solution. 1. Measure time in seconds from the instant when the stone is dropped. Measure distance in feet, positive downward, from the point where the stone is dropped, as in Figure 153 on page 207. Then,

$$\frac{d^2s}{dt^2} = 32, \tag{6}$$

with $s = 0$ and $v = -64$ at $t = 0$.

$s = 0$

2. From (6), $\dfrac{dv}{dt} = 32;$ $v = \int 32\,dt = 32t + C_1.$ (7)

Since $v = -64$ at $t = 0$, from (7) we obtain $C_1 = -64.$

3. Hence, $v = \dfrac{ds}{dt} = 32t - 64;$ (8)

$$s = \int (32t - 64)dt = 16t^2 - 64t + C_2.$$

Since $s = 0$ at $t = 0$, we obtain $C_2 = 0.$ Thus, at any time t, $s = 16t^2 - 64t.$

4. The stone hits the ground when

$$16t^2 - 64t = 3072; \quad or \quad t^2 - 4t - 192 = 0;$$
$$(t - 16)(t + 12) = 0; \quad t = 16, \ seconds.$$

Fig. 153

Then, from (8), $v = 448$, ft. per sec. The speed is $|v| = 448$, ft. per sec.

EXERCISE 59

A particle moves on an s-axis, with the velocity v and the acceleration a at any time t. Find s as a function of t, to satisfy the conditions.

1. $v = 3t + 4; s = 2$ at $t = 0.$ 2. $v = -2t + 3; s = -3$ at $t = 1.$
3. $a = -t; s = 2$ and $v = 3$ at $t = 0.$ 4. $a = 3; s = 3$ and $v = 4$ at $t = 2.$
5. $a = 3t + 1; s = 0$ and $v = 3$ at $t = 1.$
6. $a = -2t + 4; s = -2$ and $v = 1$ at $t = -3.$
7. $a = 3t^2 + 6t; s = 3$ and $v = -2$ at $t = 2.$
8. $a = \sqrt{t} + 3; s = 1.3$ and $v = 0$ at $t = 9.$
9. $a = 6t + 3; s = 18$ at $t = 2,$ and $s = -2$ at $t = 0.$
10. $a = 24t - 4; s = -13$ at $t = -1,$ and $s = 95$ at $t = 3.$

Solve by use of a differential equation. Be explicit in your choice of the origin and the positive direction for measuring distance.

11. A soldier is descending with a parachute at 80′ per second. He drops his 60-pound knapsack when he is 2400′ above the ground. How many seconds later, and with what speed, will his knapsack hit the ground?

12. A projectile is shot vertically upward from the ground with an initial speed of 160′ per second. (*a*) When will the projectile reach its greatest height above the ground? (*b*) How many seconds after the shot is fired, and with what speed, will the projectile hit the ground?

13. A balloon is rising at the rate of 20′ per second. A projectile is shot vertically upward from the balloon with a speed of 108′ per second relative to the balloon, when it is 3840′ above the ground. When will the projectile hit the ground?

14. A soldier is descending with a parachute at the rate of 20′ per second. He drops his revolver and it hits the ground 8 seconds later. How high was he above the ground when the revolver was dropped?

15. A particle is projected upward on an inclined plane, with an initial speed of 24′ per second along the plane. Friction and other forces cause the particle to be affected by an acceleration of 4′ per second per second downward along the plane. When will the particle start downward, and how far will it travel upward along the plane?

★**16.** A projectile is shot with an initial velocity of v_0 feet per second in a direction elevated at an angle α from the horizontal. Disregard all forces except that of gravity. (a) Find parametric equations for the path (*trajectory*) of the projectile in terms of the time t in seconds as a parameter, with t measured from the instant of firing. (b) Eliminate t to find an equation for the trajectory in rectangular coordinates.

Hint. Set up xy-coordinates, with the x-axis horizontal and the projectile shot from the origin into quadrant I in the xy-plane. The motion is determined by the system of differential equations $a_x = 0$ and $a_y = -g$. See page 166.

68. DISTRIBUTION OF MASS ON A LINE

We accept the physical concept of the **mass** of an object as a basic undefined notion. Mass is measured in grams, pounds, and other units. If a mass of μ units (referred to hereafter simply as "*a mass μ*") is concentrated at a point Q, we shall call Q a "*mass particle.*" Now conceive of mass spread on an x-axis from $x = a$ to $x = b$. For concreteness, this distribution can be thought of as the mass of a wire of negligible diameter. Suppose that there is a positive constant δ such that the mass Δm on any interval of length Δx is given by $\Delta m = \delta \Delta x$. Then, it is said that mass is distributed *uniformly* on the line with the density δ.

In a uniform distribution of mass, with δ as the density, the mass Δm on an interval $x_1 \leq x \leq x_2$, where $x_2 - x_1 = \Delta x$, is given by

$$\Delta m = \delta \Delta x = (x_2 - x_1)\delta = \int_{x_1}^{x_2} \delta \, dx. \tag{1}$$

The form of (1) suggests the notion of a variable density as follows:

Definition VI. *To state that a function δ, with domain $I = \{a \leq x \leq b\}$ on an x-axis, is the* **density function** *for a distribution of mass on I means that δ is continuous, $\delta(x) \geq 0$, and the mass on any subinterval $x_1 \leq x \leq x_2$ of I is the integral of $\delta(x)$ from $x = x_1$ to $x = x_2$.*

When Definition VI applies, it is said that there is a *continuous distribution of mass* on I. Then, the total mass, m, of I is

$$m = \int_a^b \delta(x)dx. \tag{2}$$

On any subinterval $x_1 \leq x \leq x_2$ of I, the mass, Δm, is given by

$$\Delta m = \int_{x_1}^{x_2} \delta(x)dx, \tag{3}$$

which is consistent with (1) when $\delta(x)$ is a constant. By the mean value theorem for an integral, on page 184, from (3) there exists a point ξ on the interval (x_1, x_2) such that $\Delta m = \delta(\xi)(x_2 - x_1)$ or, with $\Delta x = x_2 - x_1$,

$$\Delta m = \delta(\xi)\Delta x; \qquad \frac{\Delta m}{\Delta x} = \delta(\xi). \tag{4}$$

Thus, on any interval of length Δx, there exists a point ξ such that $\Delta m = \delta(\xi)\Delta x$; we call $\delta(\xi)$ the *average density* over the interval.

If x_1 is held fast in the details leading to (4), and $x_2 \to x_1$, then $\xi \to x_1$ and, from (4) for the interval $x_1 \leqq x \leqq x_2$,

$$\lim_{x_2 \to x_1} (average\ density) = \lim_{\Delta x \to 0} \frac{\Delta m}{\Delta x} = \lim_{\xi \to x_1} \delta(\xi) = \delta(x_1), \tag{5}$$

because δ is continuous at x_1 on I. On account of (5), sometimes we refer to $\delta(x)$ as the density *at the point* x, or as the instantaneous density at x.

EXAMPLE 1. In a distribution of mass on an x-axis, the density at an arbitrary point x is $\delta(x) = 2x + 5$, grams per unit length. Find the mass, m, where $3 \leqq x \leqq 6$, and the average density on this interval.

Solution. From (2), $\qquad m = \int_3^6 (2x + 5)dx = 42,\ grams.$

From (4), the average density is $\qquad \delta(\xi) = \dfrac{42}{6-3} = 14,\ grams\ per\ unit\ length.$

If the word *mass* in Definition VI is changed to "*electric charge,*" then $\delta(x)$ is the density of electric charge. In statistics, with "*density of mass*" changed to "*probability density,*" (2) gives a "*probability.*"

69. CENTER OF MASS, DISCRETE CASE ON A LINE OR IN A PLANE

Consider a system of mass particles $\{m_i\}$, $i = 1, 2, \cdots, n$, on a line labeled as an x-axis, with m_i at the point $x = x_i$, as in Figure 154. Let m be the mass of the system, $m = \sum_{i=1}^{n} m_i$. We define the **moment** of any mass m_i about an arbitrary point $x = c$ to be $m_i(x_i - c)$. The corresponding moment for the system is defined as the sum of the moments for all of the masses m_i. Thus, the moment of m_i about the origin, where $x = 0$, is $m_i x_i$ and the moment, M, of the system about the origin is

$$M = m_1 x_1 + m_2 x_2 + \cdots + m_n x_n,\ or$$

Fig. 154

$$M = \sum_{i=1}^{n} m_i x_i. \tag{1}$$

Now, let us search for a point $x = \bar{x}$ such that, *if all of the mass m were concentrated at $\bar{x}$, the moment of m about an arbitrary point $x = c$ would be equal to the moment of the given system about $x = c$.* Then $\bar{x}$ should satisfy

$$m_1(x_1 - c) + m_2(x_2 - c) + \cdots + m_n(x_n - c) = m(\bar{x} - c),\ or \tag{2}$$

$$\sum_{i=1}^{n} m_i x_i - c \sum_{i=1}^{n} m_i = m\bar{x} - mc, \tag{3}$$

where $mc = c \sum_{i=1}^{n} m_i$. Hence, (3) gives $m\bar{x} = M$, or

$$\bar{x} = \frac{\sum_{i=1}^{n} m_i x_i}{m}, \quad where \quad m = \sum_{i=1}^{n} m_i. \tag{4}$$

In each case where we shall consider mass distributions, on a *line*, in a *plane*, or in *three-dimensional space*, one or more varieties of moments, such as M in (1), will be introduced. Then, the following terminology will apply.

Definition VII. *The* **center of mass** *for a mass distribution is that point where the total mass would have to be concentrated in order for it to have the same moment, of each variety, as the given distribution.*

As a special case of Definition VII, $\bar{x}$ of (4) is called the *center of mass* of the system $\{m_i\}$. The equation $m\bar{x} = M$, preceding (4), states that $\bar{x}$ is a point such that, *if all of mass m were at* $\bar{x}$, as in Figure 155, *the moment of m about the origin would be the same as the moment, M, of the system about the origin*. In other words, this condition on $\bar{x}$ is equivalent to (2), where moments were taken about the *arbitrary point* $x = c$.

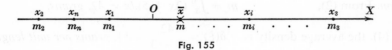

Fig. 155

ILLUSTRATION 1. If masses of magnitudes 2, 5, and 7 are at $x = 3$, $x = 5$, and $x = -4$, respectively, from (4) we obtain $\bar{x} = \frac{1}{14}(6 + 25 - 28) = \frac{3}{14}$.

Note 1. Suppose that OX is idealized as a weightless rod, with the attached masses m_i subject to the attraction of gravity. Then, if OX is horizontal instantaneously, directed to our right, and is supported just at a point $x = c$, from physics we learn that m_i tends to produce rotation of OX about $x = c$ in the *clockwise* sense if the moment

$$m_i(x_i - c) > 0,$$

and *counterclockwise* if $m_i(x_i - c) < 0$, with the tendency to rotation proportional to the absolute value of $m_i(x_i - c)$. In (2), if we place $c = \bar{x}$, the right-hand side is zero, or *the sum of the moments of all masses m_i about $\bar{x}$ is zero*. Thus, the forces which would produce clockwise rotation are exactly counteracted by the forces which would produce counterclockwise rotation. In other words, *if OX were supported at $\bar{x}$, the system of masses would remain in equilibrium with OX horizontal*. For this reason, in physics, $\bar{x}$ is called the **center of gravity** of the system of masses. We shall continue to call $\bar{x}$ the center of mass, to emphasize that $\bar{x}$ depends solely on the *mass distribution*, and is independent of the nature of the *forces* to which the mass may be exposed.

Note 2. The property of $\bar{x}$ as the center of gravity, or actual transformation of coordinates in (2), shows that the location of the point $x = \bar{x}$ on OX is not affected by a translation of the origin to an arbitrary point on the line.

Note 3. Recall that, in any given plane, we are assuming that the scale units on the axes are equal in any xy-system of coordinates.

Now, suppose that a mass particle μ is located at a point (x, y) in an xy-system of rectangular coordinates in a *plane*. Then, *the moment of μ about either coordinate axis* is defined as *the product of μ and its directed distance from that axis*, as indicated in Figure 156. Thus, the moments of μ about the x-axis and y-axis are μy and μx, respectively.

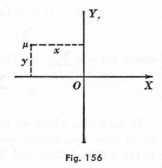

Fig. 156

If n mass particles $\{m_i\}$ are at points (x_i, y_i) in the xy-plane, the moments M_x and M_y about the x-axis and y-axis, respectively, for the system are defined as the sums of the corresponding moments for all masses $\{m_i\}$, or

$$M_y = \sum_{i=1}^{n} m_i x_i \quad and \quad M_x = \sum_{i=1}^{n} m_i y_i. \tag{5}$$

By Definition VII, the coordinates of the center of mass, $(\bar{x}, \bar{y})$, of the system are defined by the equations

$$m\bar{x} = M_y, \quad m\bar{y} = M_x, \quad where \quad m = \sum_{i=1}^{n} m_i, \quad or \tag{6}$$

$$\bar{x} = \frac{\sum_{i=1}^{n} m_i x_i}{m} \quad and \quad \bar{y} = \frac{\sum_{i=1}^{n} m_i y_i}{m}. \tag{7}$$

It can be proved that the location of $(\bar{x}, \bar{y})$ in the plane of the masses is independent of the choice of coordinate axes in the plane.

Note 4. Idealize the xy-plane as a rigid sheet without mass, where the masses m_i at the points (x_i, y_i) are subject to the attraction of gravity. Then, if the plane is horizontal instantaneously, and is supported just at the point $(\bar{x}, \bar{y})$, in physics we learn that the plane will remain in equilibrium. Then, $(\bar{x}, \bar{y})$ of (7) is called the **center of gravity** of the system of masses.

Note 5. Let (h, k) be an arbitrary point in the xy-plane. Define the moments of a mass μ at (x, y) about the lines $x = h$ and $y = k$ to be $\mu(x - h)$ and $\mu(y - k)$, respectively. Just as in (2), (3), and (4), it can be shown that (7) is obtained if Definition VII is employed with moments taken about the *arbitrary lines* $x = h$ and $y = k$, instead of about $x = 0$ and $y = 0$, as used in (5) and (6). Then, from (2) with $c = \bar{x}$, and from the similar equation involving the coordinates y_i, we could prove that *the sum of the moments of all of the masses m_i about the line $x = \bar{x}$ is zero*, and similarly for *moments about the line $y = \bar{y}$.*

ILLUSTRATION 2. Suppose that masses with measures 2, 4, and 6 are located at $(-1, 2)$, $(3, -4)$, and $(2, 6)$, respectively. Then, in (7),
$$\bar{x} = \tfrac{1}{12}(-2 + 12 + 12) = \tfrac{11}{6}; \quad \bar{y} = \tfrac{1}{12}(4 - 16 + 36) = 2.$$

The mass distributions leading to (4) and (7) are called **discrete distributions of mass** because only mass particles are involved.

70. CENTER OF MASS ON A LINE, CONTINUOUS CASE

Suppose that there is a continuous distribution of mass over the interval $I = \{a \le x \le b\}$ of the x-axis, with $\delta(x)$ as the density of mass at point x on I. To generalize (4) of Section 69, first form a partition, σ, of I with the representative subinterval $T_i = (x_{i-1} \le x \le x_i)$, where $x_i - x_{i-1} = \Delta_i x$, as in Figure 157 on page 212. Let $\Delta_i m$ be the mass of T_i. Then, from (3) and (4) on page 208, there exists a point ξ_i on T_i such that

$$\Delta_i m = \int_{x_{i-1}}^{x_i} \delta(x)dx = \delta(\xi_i)(x_i - x_{i-1}), \quad or \quad \Delta_i m = \delta(\xi_i)\Delta_i x. \tag{1}$$

Now, let $\Delta_i m$ be thought of as concentrated at an arbitrary point η_i on T_i, as in Figure 157, and let $\Delta_i M$ be the corresponding moment of $\Delta_i m$ about the x-origin. Then,

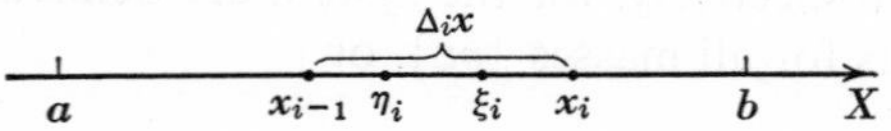

$$\Delta_i M = \eta_i \Delta_i m = \eta_i \delta(\xi_i) \Delta_i x. \quad (2)$$

Fig. 157

Finally, we define the moment, M, of the continuous distribution of mass over T as the following limit, where d_σ is the norm of σ:

$$M = \lim_{d_\sigma \to 0} \sum_{i=1}^{n} \Delta_i M = \lim_{d_\sigma \to 0} \sum_{i=1}^{n} \eta_i \delta(\xi_i) \Delta_i x. \quad (3)$$

The distance between ξ_i and η_i, as in Figure 157, approaches zero as $d_\sigma \to 0$. Hence, since δ is continuous, we accept the fact that the limit in (3), if this limit exists, would not be changed if we should replace * η_i by ξ_i, or

$$M = \lim_{d_\sigma \to 0} \sum_{i=1}^{n} \xi_i \delta(\xi_i) \Delta_i x. \quad (4)$$

By comparison with (9) on page 178, the sum in (4) is recognized as an approximating sum S_σ for an integral of the function "$x\delta(x)$." Thus,

$$M = \int_a^b x\delta(x)dx. \quad (5)$$

Let $\bar{x}$ be the center of mass for I. If the total mass m of I were at $\bar{x}$, the moment about the origin would be $m\bar{x}$. Hence, by Definition VII of page 210, $m\bar{x} = M$:

$$m\bar{x} = \int_a^b x\delta(x)dx, \quad where \quad m = \int_a^b \delta(x)dx, \quad or \quad (6)$$

$$\bar{x} = \frac{\int_a^b x\delta(x)dx}{m}, \quad or \quad \bar{x} = \frac{\int_a^b x\delta(x)dx}{\int_a^b \delta(x)dx}. \quad (7)$$

EXAMPLE 1. On a wire of length 30 units, and negligible diameter, mass is distributed with the density of mass at any point proportional to its distance from one end, B. Find the distance of the center of mass from B.

Solution. Choose B as the origin on the wire for an x-scale, with $x \geq 0$ on the wire, as in Figure 158. We have $\delta(x) = kx$, where k is a constant of proportionality. From (5), (6), and (7),

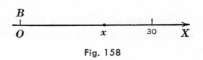

Fig. 158

$$m = k\int_0^{30} x\, dx = 450k; \quad M = k\int_0^{30} x^2\, dx = 9000k; \quad \bar{x} = 20.$$

Note 1. It can be proved that the location of $x = \bar{x}$ on OX is independent of the selection of the origin on OX. From physics we learn that the mass on OX would remain horizontal under the attraction of gravity if supported just at the point $x = \bar{x}$. For this reason, the point $\bar{x}$ would be called the *center of gravity* of the mass distribution.

* By use of the advanced notion of "*uniform continuity*" for the function of *two variables* $y\delta(x)$, it can be proved that $\sum_{i=1}^{n} \eta_i \delta(\xi_i) \Delta_i x$ is equal to $\sum_{i=1}^{n} \xi_i \delta(\xi_i) \Delta_i x + (b-a)\epsilon$, where $\epsilon \to 0$ as $d_\sigma \to 0$. This fact justifies the replacement of η_i by ξ_i above.

★*Note 2.* The type of reasoning involved in passing from (3) to (4) occurs frequently. A general expression like the sum in (3) is

$$\tau_\sigma = \sum_{i=1}^{n} g(\eta_i)f(\xi_i)\Delta_i x, \tag{8}$$

where the two arbitrary points ξ_i and η_i are on the subinterval T_i of the partition σ, while the functions $g(x)$ and $f(x)$ are continuous when $a \leqq x \leqq b$. By continuity reasoning, as suggested in the footnote about (3), it can be proved that the *two indeterminates* ξ_i and η_i in (8) may be replaced by the *single point* ξ_i, to give

$$\lim_{d_\sigma \to 0} \tau_\sigma = \lim_{d_\sigma \to 0} \sum_{i=1}^{n} g(\xi_i)f(\xi_i)\Delta_i x = \int_a^b g(x)f(x)dx. \tag{9}$$

The final equality in (9) is a consequence of the definition of an integral on page 178. Result (9) was recommended by the American mathematician GILBERT AMES BLISS (1876–1950) as a partial substitute for a more complicated theorem usually referred to as *Duhamel's principle.* Hereafter, in cases like (3), we shall justify passage to a simplified form like (4) by recalling the continuity argument illustrated in the footnote on page 212. Such reasoning covers many cases to which (9) would not apply.

EXERCISE 60

If the specified masses are located at the corresponding points on an x-axis, or in an xy-plane, find the center of mass.

1. Masses 1, 3, 2, and 7 at $x = -3$, $x = 2$, $x = 4$, and $x = 8$.

2. Masses 5, 1, 3, and 9 at $x = -4$, $x = -2$, $x = 3$, and $x = 5$.

3. Masses 2, 4, 3, and 5 at $(2, -3)$, $(1, 5)$, $(-3, 2)$, and $(4, 6)$.

4. Masses 3, 2, 4, and 10 at $(-3, 2)$, $(-4, 3)$, $(2, -3)$, and $(0, 4)$.

Mass is distributed on the given interval of an x-axis with the specified density $\delta(x)$ at any point x. Find the total mass, the average density over the interval, and the center of mass.

5. $2 \leqq x \leqq 7$; $\delta(x) = 4(x - 1)$. **6.** $-3 \leqq x \leqq 2$; $\delta(x) = 2x^2$.

7. $1 \leqq x \leqq 9$; $\delta(x) = 2\sqrt{x}$. **8.** $-3 \leqq x \leqq 3$; $\delta(x) = 2x^4$.

9. $0 \leqq x \leqq 4$; $\delta(x) = 3x + 1$. **10.** $-2 \leqq x \leqq 1$; $\delta(x) = x^2 + 1$.

★**11.** If $\delta(x)$ is the density of mass at point x on an interval $a \leqq x \leqq b$, obtain an expression for the average density on the interval. Notice that the result is the mean value of $\delta(x)$ as described by (3) on page 195.

★**12.** Suppose that a mass of magnitude m is located at each vertex of a triangle whose vertices have the coordinates (x_i, y_i), $i = 1, 2$, and 3. By use of (7) on page 211, find the center of mass, Q, for the system. Then, from Problem 40 on page 38, notice that Q is the intersection of the medians of the triangle.

71. CENTROID OF A REGION IN A PLANE *

Consider a region R in an xy-plane, and visualize mass spread like paint over R, where the mass is idealized as having no thickness. Then, we refer to R as a

---

* A later treatment by use of double integrals is completely independent. If the instructor desires, Sections 71–72 can be omitted without handicap. No review of these sections will be given in the chapter review.

lamina. Suppose that there exists a constant $\delta > 0$ such that, if T is any subregion of R with area ΔA, the mass Δm of T is given by $\Delta m = \delta \Delta A$. Then, we say that mass is distributed *uniformly* over R with the *constant density* δ, or that R is a *homogeneous lamina.**

We proceed under the assumption that R has a *center of mass* $(\bar{x}, \bar{y})$, which is the same as the *center of gravity* for R, and can be visualized as a point of support for horizontal equilibrium under the attraction of gravity. This assumption implies that the location of $(\bar{x}, \bar{y})$ in R is independent of the choice of axes of coordinates in the plane. Thus, if R has an axis of symmetry, $(\bar{x}, \bar{y})$ is on this axis. If R has two distinct axes of symmetry, $(\bar{x}, \bar{y})$ is their intersection.

ILLUSTRATION 1. By symmetry, the center of mass of a homogeneous rectangular lamina is the intersection of its diagonals.

We shall prove the following result for R as in Figure 159 below, where R has the density δ, area A, and mass m:

$$\left\{ \begin{array}{c} \textit{boundaries of R:} \\ y = 0,\ x = a,\ x = b, \\ \textit{with } a < b;\ y = f(x) \geqq 0 \end{array} \right\} \qquad \bar{x} = \frac{\int_a^b xy\,dx}{A}; \qquad \bar{y} = \frac{\frac{1}{2}\int_a^b y^2\,dx}{A}. \qquad (1)$$

In the integrals, $y = f(x)$ and $A = \int_a^b f(x)\,dx$. We assume that f is continuous.

Proof. 1. Let σ be any partition of the interval $a \leqq x \leqq b$, as on page 177, with the representative subinterval T_i of length $\Delta_i x$.

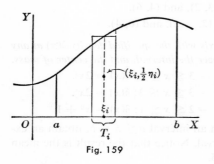

Fig. 159

2. By Definition VII on page 210,

$$m = \delta A,\ M_x = m\bar{y},\ \textit{and}\ M_y = m\bar{x}. \qquad (2)$$

3. Let ξ_i be the mid-point of T_i, and let W_i be the rectangular region with base T_i and altitude $\eta_i = f(\xi_i)$, approximating the strip of R over T_i. Now, act as if mass with density δ is spread over all of W_i, even where W_i extends outside R. Then, W_i has the area $\Delta_i A = f(\xi_i)\Delta_i x$ and mass $\Delta_i m = \delta \Delta_i A$. By Illustration 1, the center of mass of W_i is $(\xi_i, \frac{1}{2}\eta_i)$, or $[\xi_i, \frac{1}{2}f(\xi_i)]$. Let $\Delta_i M_x$ and $\Delta_i M_y$ be the moments of W_i about OX and OY. By Definition VII, $\Delta_i M_x = \frac{1}{2}\eta_i \Delta_i m$ and $\Delta_i M_y = \xi_i \Delta_i m$. Since

$$\eta_i = f(\xi_i) \quad \textit{and} \quad \Delta_i m = \delta \Delta_i A = \delta \eta_i \Delta_i x,\ \textit{we have}$$

$$\Delta_i M_x = \tfrac{1}{2}\delta[f(\xi_i)]^2 \Delta_i x; \quad \Delta_i M_y = \delta \xi_i f(\xi_i)\Delta_i x. \qquad (3)$$

4. We define M_x and M_y for R to be the limits, respectively, of the expressions $\sum_{(\text{all } i)} \Delta_i M_x$ and $\sum_{(\text{all } i)} \Delta_i M_y$, for the partition σ, as all $\Delta_i x \to 0$. In (3), the

---

* The general case where the density is *not a constant* will be treated on a logical basis in Chapter 22 by use of *double integrals;* this case cannot be treated by use of *one-fold integrals,* with which we are concerned now. In the present chapter, all necessary concepts will be introduced intuitively, and acceptable assumptions will be employed to obtain results.

right-hand sides are the typical elements in approximating sums for integrals of $\frac{1}{2}\delta[f(x)]^2$ and $\delta x f(x)$. Hence,

$$M_x = \tfrac{1}{2}\delta \int_a^b [f(x)]^2 \, dx; \quad M_y = \int_a^b x f(x) dx. \tag{4}$$

From (2), $\bar{x} = M_y/m$ and $\bar{y} = M_x/m$, with $m = \delta A$. Hence,

$$\bar{x} = \frac{\delta \int_a^b xy \, dx}{\delta A}, \quad \bar{y} = \frac{\tfrac{1}{2}\delta \int_a^b y^2 \, dx}{\delta A}, \tag{5}$$

where $y = f(x)$, and δ divides out; thus, (1) is obtained.

Notice that δ is not met in (1). This feature illustrates the fact that the center of mass of a homogeneous lamina R *does not depend on its density of mass*, and hence is *a purely geometric characteristic* of the region involved. From the geometric viewpoint, the center of mass for a *homogeneous lamina* also is called the **centroid** of the region R of the lamina. Whenever the centroid $(\bar{x}, \bar{y})$ of a region R is requested, as an aid to intuition we shall choose to think of mass spread over R with an arbitrary constant density.

ILLUSTRATION 2. Let R be the region bounded by the x-axis, the parabola $y^2 = 4x$, and the line $x = 4$, where $y \geq 0$. The student should make a sketch showing R. From (1), with $A = 2\int_0^4 x^{\frac{1}{2}} \, dx = \frac{32}{3}$, the centroid of R is given by

$$\bar{x} = \frac{\int_0^4 2x^{\frac{3}{2}} \, dx}{\frac{32}{3}} = \frac{12}{5}; \quad \bar{y} = \frac{\tfrac{1}{2}\int_0^4 4x \, dx}{\frac{32}{3}} = \frac{3}{2}.$$

To emphasize increment reasoning, the student may treat special cases without (1), as in the following solution where, moreover, (1) would not apply.

EXAMPLE 1. A region R is bounded above by $x^2 + y^2 = 4$ and below by $x^2 + 4y^2 = 4$, as in Figure 160. Find the centroid for R.

Solution. 1. Consider R as a homogeneous lamina. Since R is symmetric to OY, we have $\bar{x} = 0$. Let δ be the density of mass.

2. *To obtain the mass m of R.* In standard form, the ellipse is $\frac{1}{4}x^2 + y^2 = 1$, where $a = 2$ and $b = 1$. Hence, the area of the semi-ellipse * where $y \geq 0$ is $\frac{1}{2}\pi ab$, or π. The area of the semicircle, where $y \geq 0$,

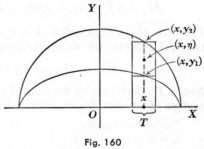

Fig. 160

is 2π. Hence, the area of R is $(2\pi - \pi)$, or $A = \pi$. Then $m = \pi\delta$.

3. *To obtain M_x.* Figure 160 shows a typical subinterval T with length Δx and mid-point x, in a partition σ of the interval $-2 \leq x \leq 2$. For any value of x, let the ordinate of the semi-ellipse be y_1, and of the semicircle be y_2. An approximating rectangular region W for the strip of R over T has

---

* At present, we accept without proof the fact that the area of an ellipse with semi-axes a and b is πab. This result will be proved later in the text.

$$area = \Delta A = (y_2 - y_1)\Delta x \quad and \quad mass = \Delta m = \delta(y_2 - y_1)\Delta x, \qquad (6)$$

where we act as if mass is spread over all of W with density δ. The center of mass of W is (x, η) where $\eta = \frac{1}{2}(y_1 + y_2)$. Hence, the moment ΔM_x of W is

$$\Delta M_x = \eta\Delta m = \frac{1}{2}\delta(y_2 + y_1)(y_2 - y_1)\Delta x = \frac{1}{2}\delta(y_2^2 - y_1^2)\Delta x; \qquad (7)$$

$$M_x = \lim_{\substack{(all\ \Delta x \to 0)}} \sum_{\substack{(all,\ for\ \sigma)}} \Delta M_x = \frac{1}{2}\delta \int_{-2}^{2} (y_2^2 - y_1^2)dx = 4\delta, \qquad (8)$$

where $y_2^2 = 4 - x^2$ and $y_1^2 = \frac{1}{4}(4 - x^2)$. From Definition VII, $\bar{y} = M_x/m$, or $\bar{y} = 4\delta/\pi\delta$; the centroid is $(0, 4/\pi)$.

EXAMPLE 2. A triangle has the vertices $(0, 0)$, $(3, 2)$, and $(6, 0)$. Find the centroid of the region R bounded by the triangle.

Solution. 1. In Figure 161, the equation of OL is $x = \frac{3}{2}y$ and of LN is

$$x = \frac{1}{2}(12 - 3y).$$

Consider R as a lamina with density δ.

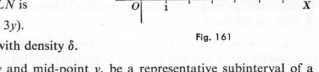

Fig. 161

2. Let T, with length Δy and mid-point y, be a representative subinterval of a partition of $0 \leqq y \leqq 2$. The corresponding elementary rectangular region W, thought of as a lamina with density δ, has area $\Delta A = (x_2 - x_1)\Delta y$, and mass

$$\Delta m = \delta(x_2 - x_1)\Delta y, \quad where \quad x_2 = \frac{1}{2}(12 - 3y)\ and\ x_1 = \frac{3}{2}y. \qquad (9)$$

The center of mass of W is (h, k), where $k = y$ and $h = \frac{1}{2}(x_2 + x_1)$. The moments for W are $h\Delta m$ and $k\Delta m$, or

$$\Delta M_x = \delta y(x_2 - x_1)\Delta y \quad and \quad \Delta M_y = \frac{1}{2}\delta(x_2^2 - x_1^2)\Delta y; \qquad (10)$$

$$M_x = \delta \int_0^2 y(x_2 - x_1)dy = 4\delta; \quad M_y = \frac{1}{2}\delta \int_0^2 (x_2^2 - x_1^2)dy = 18\delta. \qquad (11)$$

The area of the region R is $A = 6$ and the mass is $m = 6\delta$. Hence, from Definition VII and (11) we obtain the centroid $(3, \frac{2}{3})$, where "3" is obvious (why?):

$$6\delta\bar{x} = M_y \quad or \quad \bar{x} = 3; \quad 6\delta\bar{y} = M_x \quad or \quad \bar{y} = \frac{2}{3}.$$

Note 1. By interchanging the roles of x and y in (1) on page 214, we obtain the center of mass of a region R with uniform density δ and area A, as follows:

$$\left\{\begin{array}{c} boundaries\ of\ R: \\ x = 0,\ y = a,\ y = b, \\ with\ a < b;\ x = g(y) \geqq 0. \end{array}\right\} \qquad \bar{x} = \frac{\frac{1}{2}\int_a^b x^2\,dy}{A}; \quad \bar{y} = \frac{\int_a^b xy\,dy}{A}. \qquad (12)$$

EXERCISE 61

Find the centroid of the specified region. Use known areas.

1. Bounded by the lines $y = 0$, $x = 2y$, and $x = 4$.

2. Bounded by the lines $x = 0$, $y = 0$, and $x + 3y = 6$.

3. Bounded by $y = 0$ and $y = 2x - x^2$, where $y \geqq 0$.

4. Bounded by $x = 0$ and $x = 3y - y^2$, where $x \geqq 0$. Use (12) above.

5. Bounded by $y^2 = 2x$ and the lines $y = 0$ and $x = 8$, with $y \geq 0$.
6. Bounded by $x^2 = 9y$ and the line $y = 1$, with $x \geq 0$.
7. Bounded by $x^2 + y^2 = 4$ and $y = 0$, above OX.
8. Bounded by $4x^2 + y^2 = 4$, in quadrant I.
9. Bounded by the ellipse $b^2x^2 + a^2y^2 = a^2b^2$, with $y \geq 0$.
10. Bounded by $y = 6x$ and $y = 2x^2$.
11. Bounded by a diameter and semicircle in a circle of radius a.
12. Bounded by $y^3 = 8x^2$ and $y = 2$.
13. Bounded by the triangle with the vertices $(0, 0)$, $(3, 0)$, and $(1, 2)$.
14. Bounded by $y = 4 - x^2$ and $y = 2 - x$.
15. Bounded by the triangle with vertices $(0, 0)$, $(a, 0)$, and (b, c), where $a > 0$ and $c > 0$. Show that the centroid is the intersection of the medians of the triangle. From this result, without integration obtain the centroid when the triangle's vertices are (x_1, y_1), (x_2, y_2), and (x_3, y_3).

Comment. Problem 15, and Problem 12 in Exercise 60, lead to the same point $(\bar{x}, \bar{y})$. Hence, the center of mass of a homogeneous triangular lamina is the same as the center of mass for a system of three equal masses located at the triangle's vertices.

72. CENTROID OF A SOLID OF REVOLUTION

Let R be a region in an xy-plane bounded by the lines $x = a$, $x = b$, and $y = 0$, and the curve $y = f(x)$ as in Figure 145 on page 197.* Let H be the region swept out by revolving R about OX, as in Figure 146 on page 197. Now, suppose that mass is spread uniformly over H; that is, there exists a constant $\delta > 0$, called the *density of mass*, so that any subregion of H with volume ΔV has the mass $\Delta m = \delta \Delta V$. Since H has the x-axis as an axis of symmetry, the center of mass (center of gravity) of H is at some point $x = \bar{x}$ on OX. Let N be the plane perpendicular to the xy-plane along OY. The moment of any point mass μ with respect to N is defined as the product of μ by its distance from N. Hence, if the whole mass m of H were concentrated at $x = \bar{x}$ on OX, the moment, M, of m with respect to N would be $M = m\bar{x}$. By Definition VII on page 210, M also is the moment of H with respect to N. We shall express M as an integral, and thus obtain $\bar{x}$.

Let $T_i:(x_{i-1} \leq x \leq x_i)$ be a representative subinterval of a partition σ of $a \leq x \leq b$, with $\Delta_i x = x_i - x_{i-1}$. Figure 145 on page 197 shows an approximating rectangular region for the strip of R corresponding to T_i; a cylindrical slab C_i, in Figure 146, is obtained by revolving the rectangular region about OX. We proceed as if mass with density δ were spread over all of C_i.

For the cylinder C_i, let the volume, mass, and moment with respect to plane N be $\Delta_i V$, $\Delta_i m$, and $\Delta_i M$, respectively. From (2) on page 197,

$$\Delta_i V = \pi [f(x_i)]^2 \Delta_i x; \quad \text{hence,} \quad \Delta_i m = \delta \pi [f(x_i)]^2 \Delta_i x. \tag{1}$$

---

* The student should stop at this point and briefly review details leading to (4) on page 198. That discussion is a background here.

The center of mass of cylinder C_i is its geometric center, which is at the point $x = x_i' = \frac{1}{2}(x_i + x_{i-1})$ on OX, where $x_{i-1} \leqq x_i' \leqq x_i$. Hence

$$\Delta_i M = x_i' \Delta_i m, \quad or \quad \Delta_i M = \delta \pi x_i' [f(x_i)]^2 \Delta_i x. \tag{2}$$

Let
$$S_\sigma = \sum_{(all, \, for \, \sigma)} \Delta_i M, \tag{3}$$

and let d_σ, the norm of partition σ, as usual represent the largest of the lengths $\Delta_i x$ in σ. Then, we define the *moment* M of H to be the limit of S_σ as $d_\sigma \to 0$. By continuity reasoning, as in the footnote on page 212, the limit of S_σ will not be changed if we replace x_i' by x_i in (2). Then, $\Delta_i M$ becomes the typical increment element for an integral of $\delta \pi x [f(x)]^2$. Hence,

$$M = \lim_{d_\sigma \to 0} S_\sigma = \delta \pi \int_a^b x [f(x)]^2 \, dx. \tag{4}$$

Let V be the volume of H, as obtained on page 198. Then $M = m\bar{x}$, where $m = \delta V$. Hence, $\bar{x} = M/m$ and (4) gives

$$[with \; y = f(x)] \qquad \bar{x} = \frac{\pi \int_a^b xy^2 \, dx}{V}, \quad where \quad V = \pi \int_a^b y^2 \, dx. \tag{5}$$

If K represents a region in three-dimensional space, with mass spread uniformly over K to form a solid H, the center of mass of H also is called the **centroid** of the region K. In (5), we illustrate the fact that the location of the centroid does not depend on δ, the constant density of mass. Hence, the centroid can be considered as a purely geometric characteristic of K.

EXAMPLE 1. A region R in quadrant I is bounded by the x-axis, the parabola $y^2 = 2x$, and the line $x = 8$. Find the x-coordinate of the centroid of the solid H obtained on revolving R about the x-axis.

Solution. Refer to Example 1 on page 198. With V from page 198, by use of (5),

$$\bar{x} = \frac{\pi \int_0^8 2x^2 \, dx}{64\pi} = 5\frac{1}{3}.$$

Note 1. In (5), V may be known from geometry. The roles of x and y may be interchanged in (5), to give $\bar{y}$ for a solid obtained by revolving about the y-axis a region bounded by a curve $x = f(y)$, the y-axis, and the lines $y = a$ and $y = b$.

EXERCISE 62

Find the centroids of the solids which are described.

1–7. The solids in Problems 2, 3, 4, 5, 7, 8, and 9, respectively, of Exercise 56, page 198. Use the volume found previously.

8. A hemisphere of radius r.

9. The solid obtained on revolving the region bounded by the triangle in an xy-plane with vertices $(0, 0)$, $(4, 3)$, and $(6, 0)$ about OX. ($\int_a^b xy^2 \, dx$ should be expressed as a sum of two integrals.)

10. The solid obtained by revolution about OX in Problem 11 on page 199.

11. The solid obtained by revolving about OX the region bounded by the lines $y = 4x$, $y = 2x$, and $x = 3$.

   HINT. Obtain V as a *difference* of two volumes, and M as the *difference* of two moments. Then use $m = \delta V$ and $m\bar{x} = M$.

12. The solid in Problem 12 on page 199. Use the volume obtained there.

★13. By an example, prove that the centroid of a region R in a plane is *not necessarily a point of R*.

★14. A region R is bounded by $y_2 = f(x)$ and $y_1 = g(x)$, $0 \leq g(x) \leq f(x)$, and the lines $x = a$ and $x = b$, with $a < b$. A solid H is generated by revolving R about OX. Derive expressions for the volume V of H, and the abscissa of the centroid of H. Use increment reasoning, but do not use previous formulas.

EXERCISE 63 (*Review of Chapters Eight and Nine*)

1. Find ξ to satisfy (2) on page 173 when $f(x) = x^2 - 4x + 5$, $a = 1$, and $b = 4$.

2. Let f be defined on the domain $0 \leq x \leq 5$ by specifying that $f(x) = x$ when $0 \leq x \leq 3$ and $f(x) = 6 - x$ when $3 \leq x \leq 5$. Graph f. Is (2) on page 173 true for f when $a = 0$ and $b = 5$? Why should your conclusion be expected, from inspection of Theorem II on page 173?

3. By use of a sum S_σ as on page 178, compute $\int_0^2 \sqrt{1 + x^3}\, dx$ approximately by use of a partition of the interval of integration into four equal subintervals, with the arbitrary point on each of them chosen as the right-hand end point. Use Table I.

4. Calculate $g'(x)$ if $g(x) = \int_3^x \sqrt{t^5 + 1}\, dt$.

5. Calculate the area of the region in an xy-plane bounded by the x-axis and the curve $y = (x + 1)(2 - x)(x - 3)$.

Integrate. Avoid expanding before integrating if possible.

6. $\int \sqrt[3]{x^5}\, dx$.   7. $\int (2 - x)^8\, dx$.   8. $\int x(3x^2 - 5)^4\, dx$.   9. $\int \sqrt{4x + 7}\, dx$.

10. $\int_3^1 \sqrt{5z - 1}\, dz$.   11. $\int t^2(4t^3 + 1)^5\, dt$.   12. $\int \sqrt[3]{2x + 5}\, dx$.

13. $\int \dfrac{x\, dx}{\sqrt{4 - x^2}}$.   14. $\int_{\sqrt{3}}^{\sqrt{10}} \dfrac{u\, du}{\sqrt{6 + u^2}}$.   15. $\int \dfrac{(3t^2 + 1)^2}{t^2}\, dt$.

Find the area of the region bounded by the curves. Use whichever variable, x or y, is best in integration, except where a particular choice is specified.

16. $y = x(x + 1)(x - 2)$ and $y = 4x$.

17. $y^3 = 8x^2$ and $4x = y^2$. Integrate with respect to (a) x; (b) y.

Find the volume of the solid generated if the region in an xy-plane bounded by the curve, or curves, is revolved about the specified axis.

18. $y = x^3$, the x-axis, and $x = 2$. Revolve about the x-axis.

19. $x = 3y$, $y = 2$, and the y-axis. Revolve about the y-axis.

20. $x^2 - 4y^2 = 16$, $y = 2$, and $y = 0$. Revolve about the y-axis.

21. $x^2 = 6y$ and $3y = 2x + 6$. Revolve about the x-axis.

22. The natural length of a spring is $10'$ and the tension in the spring is 50 pounds when it is stretched by $2'$. Find the work done in stretching the spring from length $11'$ to length $13'$.

23. Obtain $f(x)$ so that the graph of $y = f(x)$ passes through the point $(2, -1)$ and has the slope $(4x - 2)$ at any point (x, y).

A particle moves on an x-axis with the velocity v and acceleration a at any time t. Find s as a function of t to satisfy the conditions.

24. $v = 2t - 3$; $s = 3$ at $t = 1$.   **25.** $a = 6t + 2$; $s = -1$ and $v = 2$ at $t = 2$.

26. If masses of magnitudes 2, 5, and 8 are located, respectively, at the points $(-1, 2)$, $(3, -1)$, and $(2, 5)$ in an xy-plane, find the center of mass for this system of masses.

27. Mass is distributed over $-1 \leq x \leq 3$, with the density $\delta(x) = (2x + 1)$. Find the total mass, center of mass, and average density of mass over the interval.

★SUPPLEMENT FOR CHAPTER NINE

28. Suppose that $0 < a < b$ and assume the fact that $\lim_{n \to \infty} \sqrt[n]{b/a} = 1$. Then, with the aid of just the definition of an integral, obtain the value of $\int_a^b x^4 \, dx$ by use of a sequence of partitions σ_n, where σ_n has the division points $a, ah_n, ah_n^2, \cdots, ah_n^n = b$, and $h_n = \sqrt[n]{b/a}$.

29. The following theorem is due to the Greek mathematician PAPPUS: If a plane region R is revolved about an axis in its plane, and *not crossing* * R, the volume swept out is equal to the product of the area of R and the length of the path described by its centroid. Prove the theorem if R can be placed as in (3) on page 194, with the x-axis as the axis of rotation.

Prove that the expression, whose limit is involved, may be considered as a special case of S_σ in (9) on page 178. Then evaluate the limit as an integral.

30. $\lim_{n \to \infty} \dfrac{\sqrt[3]{1} + \sqrt[3]{2} + \cdots + \sqrt[3]{n}}{n^{\frac{4}{3}}}$.   **31.** $\lim_{n \to \infty} \dfrac{(n + 1)^4 + (n + 2)^4 + \cdots + (2n)^4}{n^5}$.

32. $\lim_{n \to \infty} n \left\{ \dfrac{1}{(2n + 1)^2} + \dfrac{1}{(2n + 2)^2} + \cdots + \dfrac{1}{(2n + 2n)^2} \right\}$.

33. Suppose that a function f is continuous, with the domain $I = \{a \leq x \leq b\}$, and $f(x) \geq 0$ on I. Then, if there exists a number c on I such that $f(c) > 0$, prove analytically that $\int_a^b f(x)dx > 0$.

34. Let $P_i : (x_i, y_i)$, with $i = 1, 2, 3$, and 4, be any four points, where no three of them are collinear. Let lines l, m, and n be drawn joining the mid-points of the line segments of each pair (P_1P_2, P_3P_4), (P_1P_3, P_2P_4), and (P_1P_4, P_2P_3). Prove analytically that l, m, and n are concurrent (meet in a point) and find their point of intersection. Note that this point would be the center of mass for a system of four equal masses located at P_1, P_2, P_3, and P_4, respectively.

35. A spherical segment is that part of the region bounded by a sphere which is included between two parallel planes, called the *faces* of the segment. If one of these planes is tangent to the sphere, the segment has just one face. Find the volume of a spherical segment of altitude h, with just one face, in a sphere of radius a.

36. If the function $f(x)$ is integrable, the constant which gives the best approximation to the values of f in the *least square sense* over the interval $a \leq x \leq b$ is defined as that number k for which $\int_a^b |f(x) - k|^2 \, dx$ attains its absolute minimum. Obtain this best approximation. What other name has been given to this result?

37. If $\phi(t) = \int_t^3 (\cos^3 x + 5) dx$, calculate $\phi'(t)$ and $d\phi$.

* No interior point of R is on the axis of rotation.

CHAPTER TEN

Differentiation of Transcendental Functions

73. THE ELEMENTARY TRANSCENDENTAL FUNCTIONS

On page 91, we defined the algebraic functions. Any function which is *not* an algebraic function is called a **transcendental function.** In particular, trigonometric,* inverse trigonometric, exponential, and logarithmic functions are transcendental functions. These functions and the algebraic functions then are referred to as the *elementary functions* of mathematical analysis. The present chapter will consider differential calculus for the elementary transcendental functions. The following forms for derivatives will be met. Those which will be emphasized are given in boldface type. In the formulas, the variables u and v are differentiable functions of x. We use "ln" for "$\log_e u$," as discussed later. Derivative formulas (I)–(VIII), not listed here, were met on pages 92–93.

$$\frac{d}{dx}(\sin u) = \cos u \frac{du}{dx}. \tag{IX}$$

$$\frac{d}{dx}(\cos u) = -\sin u \frac{du}{dx}. \tag{X}$$

$$\frac{d}{dx}(\tan u) = \sec^2 u \frac{du}{dx}. \tag{XI}$$

$$\frac{d}{dx}(\cot u) = -\csc^2 u \frac{du}{dx}. \tag{XII}$$

$$\frac{d}{dx}(\sec u) = \sec u \tan u \frac{du}{dx}. \tag{XIII}$$

$$\frac{d}{dx}(\csc u) = -\csc u \cot u \frac{du}{dx}. \tag{XIV}$$

$$\frac{d}{dx}(\text{Arcsin } u) = \frac{1}{\sqrt{1-u^2}} \frac{du}{dx}. \tag{XV}$$

* The student should review trigonometry and radian measure for angles in Note 4 of the Appendix.

221

$$\frac{d}{dx} (\text{Arctan } u) = \frac{1}{1 + u^2} \frac{du}{dx}. \tag{XVI}$$

$$\frac{d}{dx} (\ln u) = \frac{1}{u} \frac{du}{dx}. \tag{XVII}$$

$(a > 0)$
$$\frac{d}{dx} (\log_a u) = \frac{\log_a e}{u} \frac{du}{dx}. \tag{XVIII}$$

$$\frac{d}{dx} (e^u) = e^u \frac{du}{dx}. \tag{XIX}$$

$(a > 0)$
$$\frac{d}{dx} (a^u) = a^u (\ln a) \frac{du}{dx}. \tag{XX}$$

$(u > 0)$
$$\frac{d}{dx} (u^v) = vu^{v-1} \frac{du}{dx} + (\ln u) u^v \frac{dv}{dx}. \tag{XXI}$$

$$\frac{d}{dx} (\text{Arccos } u) = - \frac{1}{\sqrt{1 - u^2}} \frac{du}{dx}. \tag{XXII}$$

$$\frac{d}{dx} (\text{Arccot } u) = - \frac{1}{1 + u^2} \frac{du}{dx}. \tag{XXIII}$$

$$\frac{d}{dx} (\text{Arcsec } u) = \frac{1}{u\sqrt{u^2 - 1}} \frac{du}{dx}. \tag{XXIV}$$

Derivative formulas (I)–(XXIV) will be referred to by their Roman numerals throughout the text.

74. THE STANDARD TRIGONOMETRIC FUNCTIONS OF NUMBERS

When we plot ordered pairs (x, y) in an xy-plane, or define the graph of an equation $G(x, y) = 0$, or discuss the derivative and integral of a function f where $y = f(x)$, it is implied that the domains for both of the variables x and y consist of *numbers*.

ILLUSTRATION 1. If $f(\theta) = \sin \theta$, where the domain of θ consists of geometric entities called *angles, not numbers*, we cannot speak of "*the graph of $y = f(\theta)$ in a θy-plane.*" To obtain a related function of *numbers*, we could use "$x°$" as a symbol for "*the angle x degrees*" and let $g(x) = \sin x°$. Then we could call g a *sine function of numbers*, based on a one-to-one correspondence between angles and their degree measures. A graph of $y = g(x)$ would be the familiar graph of the sine function, with angles in degree measure, as met in elementary trigonometry.

For the purposes of calculus we introduce trigonometric functions of numbers by means of the *one-to-one correspondence between angles and their measures in* **radians.** Thus, for every number x, there is a corresponding number sin x, originally met geometrically as the sine of the *angle x radians.* Let $S(x) = sin \ x$. Then, we call S the **standard sine function of numbers.** We think of "sin x" as a special case of functional notation, which might have been written sin (x). The customary symbol "sin x" of elementary trigonometry for $S(x)$ is convenient because, whenever desirable, we may give sin x a double meaning by again interpreting it as the *geometrical sine* of the *angle x radians*. Then, the results and intuitions based on the trigonometry of angles become available.

Similarly, we introduce the other standard trigonometric functions of numbers, cos x, tan x, cot x, sec x, and csc x; each function value is the value of the same-named geometrical function of the angle x radians. Hence, we may use Table IV, or other trigonometric tables for functions of angles, to find values of the standard functions of numbers.

For our future purposes, each of the identities (I)–(XIX) on page 679 now may be interpreted in two ways. First, the identities are true for trigonometric function of *angles*, with each independent variable considered as a symbol whose domain consists of angles; the symbol may be such as 45°, or simply x, meaning "*x radians*." Second, the identities are true for the standard trigonometric functions of numbers, with the domain of each independent variable consisting of *numbers*.

> ILLUSTRATION 2. On page 679, identity (XVI) states that each of the standard trigonometric functions has the period 2π; (XVII) states that each of the functions tan x and cot x also has the smaller period π.

Hereafter, unless otherwise implied, a *trigonometric function* will mean *one of the standard trigonometric functions of numbers*. Sometimes we shall refer to these functions as the *direct trigonometric functions*, for contrast with their inverses, which we shall introduce later.

> ILLUSTRATION 3. From (XIX) on page 679, sin $(\frac{3}{2}\pi + x) = \pm$ cos x. To determine the sign, $\pm$, which is independent of x, we choose to think of the functions as functions of *angles* described in radian measure. Then, if x radians is an acute angle, $(\frac{3}{2}\pi + x)$ radians is an angle in quadrant IV where the sine is negative, and cos $x > 0$. Hence, the minus sign applies, to give
>
> $$\sin (\tfrac{3}{2}\pi + x) = - \cos x.$$

Graphs of the standard functions sin x, cos x, tan x, and sec x are found on page 709; in each figure, the scale units on the axes are equal. The periodicity mentioned previously is exhibited in the graphs.

> ILLUSTRATION 4. To obtain sin 3.76, interpret it as *the sine of* 3.76 *radians*, an angle in quadrant III. Since $\pi = 3.14$ and $3.76 = 3.14 + .62$, the reference angle (see page 677) for 3.76 radians is .62 radian. Hence,
>
> $$\sin 3.76 = - \sin .62 = - .58104. \qquad \text{(Table IV)}$$

Note 1. An alternative introduction of the standard trigonometric functions of numbers, without dependence on previous acquaintance with the trigonometric functions of *angles* (in radian measure) is given in Note 9 of the Appendix by use of the so-called *winding process.*

Note 2. If a number x is the argument of a standard trigonometric function, we shall say that x is a *quadrantal number* if x radians is a *quadrantal angle*, and that x is *on a specified quadrant-interval* if x radians is an angle in that quadrant. Thus, in Illustration 4, 3.76 is on a IIId quadrant-interval.

75. AREA OF A SECTOR OF A CIRCLE

Suppose that θ is a number and $0 < \theta < 2\pi$. Let A represent the area of a sector in a circle of radius r, as in Figure 162, bounded by the sides of a central angle of θ radians and the arc intercepted on the circle by this angle.

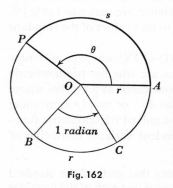

Fig. 162

Then, since the radian measure of a complete revolution about a point is 2π, and the area of a circle is πr^2, we have

$$\frac{A}{\pi r^2} = \frac{\theta}{2\pi}, \quad or \quad A = \tfrac{1}{2}r^2\theta. \tag{1}$$

Note 1. Throughout calculus, except where otherwise implied, if the measure of an angle is indicated, it should be understood that this measure is in *radians*. The importance of this agreement will be explained on page 225. As a rule, any symbol, such as x, for an *angle* should be interpreted as an abbreviation for "*x* radians," where x is a *number*.

REVIEW EXERCISE 64

1. Specify the radian measure of the angle whose measure in degrees is $30°$; $135°$; $270°$; $450°$; $120°$; $210°$; $-135°$; $-60°$.

2. Specify the degree measure of the angle whose measure is the given number of radians: $\tfrac{1}{4}\pi$; $\tfrac{1}{3}\pi$; $-\pi$; $-\tfrac{1}{12}\pi$; $\tfrac{11}{6}\pi$; 4; $\tfrac{5}{4}\pi$; $\tfrac{5}{6}\pi$.

Find the function value by use of Table IV; use $\pi = 3.14$.

3. $\sin 1.40$.   4. $\sin 3.39$.   5. $\cos 1.98$.   6. $\cos 5.64$.

7. Let $g(x) = \sin x°$; the domain for x is the set $I = \{all\ real\ numbers\ x\}$. Let S be the standard sine function, $S(x) = \sin x$, whose domain also is I. Find $g(1)$ and $S(1)$ from tables. Are S and g the same function?

8. Compute $(\sin x)/x$ if $x = 1.4$. Compute $(\sin x°)/x$ if $x = 1.4$. Use Table VI.

76. BEHAVIOR OF $(\sin x)/x$ AS $x \to 0$

The fundamental formulas of calculus for the trigonometric functions will be based on the following result.

Theorem I. $\lim\limits_{x \to 0} \dfrac{\sin x}{x} = 1.$ (1)

ILLUSTRATION 1. By use of Table IV, we obtain the following table, which suggests the truth of (1). Since $\sin .1 = .09983$, and $\sin(-x) = -\sin x$ [see (XV) on page 679], we obtain $\sin(-.1) = -.09983$. Hence,

$$\frac{\sin .1}{.1} = \frac{.09983}{.1} = .9983; \quad \frac{\sin(-.1)}{-.1} = \frac{-.09983}{-.1} = .9983.$$

$(\sin x)/x$	.9589	.9851	.9934	.9983	No value
x	$\pm .5$	$\pm .3$	$\pm .2$	$\pm .1$	0

Proof of Theorem I. 1. We shall interpret sin x for any number x as *the sine of the angle x radians*. Suppose that $x > 0$, as in Figure 163, where a quadrant of a circle of radius 1 is shown. Since $\overline{OR} = \overline{OM} = 1$, we have

$$\sin x = \overline{NR}; \quad \cos x = \overline{ON}; \quad \tan x = \overline{MP}. \tag{2}$$

Also, $\qquad (area \triangle ONR) < (area\ sector\ OMR) < (area \triangle OMP).$ (3)

From (2), $\qquad (area \triangle ONR) = \tfrac{1}{2}(\overline{ON})(\overline{NR}) = \tfrac{1}{2} \sin x \cos x;$ (4)

$$(area \triangle OMP) = \tfrac{1}{2}(\overline{OM})(\overline{MP}) = \tfrac{1}{2} \tan x. \tag{5}$$

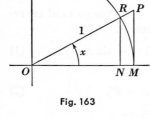

From (1) on page 224, $(area\ of\ sector\ OMR) = \tfrac{1}{2}x$. Hence, from (3),

$$\tfrac{1}{2} \sin x \cos x < \tfrac{1}{2}x < \tfrac{1}{2} \tan x. \tag{6}$$

2. On dividing by $\tfrac{1}{2} \sin x$ in (6), we find

$$\cos x < \frac{x}{\sin x} < \frac{1}{\cos x}, \tag{7}$$

Fig. 163

since $\tan x = (\sin x)/\cos x$. On taking reciprocals in (7), we obtain

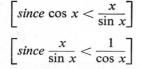

$\left[since\ \cos x < \dfrac{x}{\sin x} \right]$ $\qquad \dfrac{\sin x}{x} < \dfrac{1}{\cos x};$ (8)

$\left[since\ \dfrac{x}{\sin x} < \dfrac{1}{\cos x} \right]$ $\qquad \cos x < \dfrac{\sin x}{x}.$ (9)

From (8) and (9), $\qquad \cos x < \dfrac{\sin x}{x} < \dfrac{1}{\cos x}.$ (10)

3. If $x \to 0+$, then $\cos x \to 1$ and $(1/\cos x) \to 1$. Hence, the central expression in (10) has the limit 1 as $x \to 0+$. Since $(\sin x)/x$ is unchanged in value when x is replaced by $-x$, it follows that (1) also is true when $x \to 0-$. Thus, (1) is true as $x \to 0$.

ILLUSTRATION 2. By (1), $\qquad \lim\limits_{x \to 0} \dfrac{\sin 3x}{x} = \lim\limits_{x \to 0} 3 \cdot \dfrac{\sin 3x}{3x} = 3 \cdot 1 = 3;$

ILLUSTRATION 3. Let $g(x) = \sin x°$, as in Illustration 1 on page 222. Let $S(y) = \sin y$, where $\sin y$ is the sine of the angle y radians. For any angle $x°$, the corresponding measure, y, in radians is given by $y = x \cdot (\pi/180)$. Hence,

$$g(x) = S(\pi x/180), \quad or \quad \sin x° = \sin (\pi x/180).$$

Then, $\qquad \lim\limits_{x \to 0} \dfrac{g(x)}{x} = \lim\limits_{x \to 0} \dfrac{\sin x°}{x} = \lim\limits_{x \to 0} \dfrac{\sin (\pi x/180)}{x}$

$$= \lim\limits_{x \to 0} \frac{\pi}{180} \cdot \frac{\sin (\pi x/180)}{(\pi x/180)} = \frac{\pi}{180} \cdot 1 = \frac{\pi}{180}, \tag{11}$$

where we used (1) with x replaced by $\pi x/180$. Notice the simplicity of the limit 1 in (1) as compared to $\pi/180$ in (11). This feature is responsible for our use of $S(x)$, and the other *standard* trigonometric functions of numbers, in place of those like $g(x) = \sin x°$, related to degree measure.

77. DERIVATIVES OF DIRECT TRIGONOMETRIC FUNCTIONS

To prove (IX)–(XIV) on page 221, first we shall prove their following special cases, where we place $u = x$ in (IX)–(XIV).

$$\frac{d \sin x}{dx} = \cos x. \qquad \text{(IX)}' \qquad \qquad \frac{d \cot x}{dx} = -\csc^2 x. \qquad \text{(XII)}'$$

$$\frac{d \cos x}{dx} = -\sin x. \qquad \text{(X)}' \qquad \qquad \frac{d \sec x}{dx} = \sec x \tan x. \qquad \text{(XIII)}'$$

$$\frac{d \tan x}{dx} = \sec^2 x. \qquad \text{(XI)}' \qquad \qquad \frac{d \csc x}{dx} = -\csc x \cot x. \qquad \text{(XIV)}'$$

Proof of (IX)′. Let $y = \sin x$. With (x, y) and $(x + \Delta x, y + \Delta y)$ as pairs of corresponding values of x and y, and x held fixed for the moment,

$$y + \Delta y = \sin (x + \Delta x); \quad \Delta y = \sin (x + \Delta x) - \sin x. \tag{1}$$

From (XIV) on page 679,

$$\sin A - \sin B = 2 \cos \tfrac{1}{2}(A + B) \sin \tfrac{1}{2}(A - B). \tag{2}$$

Hence, by use of (2) with $A = x + \Delta x$ and $B = x$, (1) gives

$$\Delta y = 2 \cos (x + \tfrac{1}{2}\Delta x) \sin \tfrac{1}{2}\Delta x;$$

$$\frac{\Delta y}{\Delta x} = \cos (x + \tfrac{1}{2}\Delta x) \frac{\sin \tfrac{1}{2}\Delta x}{\tfrac{1}{2}\Delta x}. \tag{3}$$

If $\Delta x \to 0$, then $\tfrac{1}{2}\Delta x \to 0$, and $\cos (x + \tfrac{1}{2}\Delta x) \to \cos x$. Hence, from Theorem I on page 224 with $x = \tfrac{1}{2}\Delta x$, by use of (3) we obtain (IX)′:

$$\frac{d \sin x}{dx} = \lim_{\Delta x \to 0} \frac{\Delta y}{\Delta x} = (\cos x) \left(\lim_{\Delta x \to 0} \frac{\sin \tfrac{1}{2}\Delta x}{\tfrac{1}{2}\Delta x} \right) = (\cos x) \cdot 1 = \cos x.$$

Proof of (IX). Let u be a differentiable function of x, and let $y = \sin u$. Then, by use of (IX)′ and the formula for the derivative of a composite function on page 98, we obtain (IX):

$$\frac{dy}{dx} = \frac{dy}{du} \cdot \frac{du}{dx} = \frac{d \sin u}{du} \cdot \frac{du}{dx} = \cos u \frac{du}{dx}. \tag{4}$$

ILLUSTRATION 1. $\qquad \dfrac{d \sin 3x}{dx} = (\cos 3x) \dfrac{d(3x)}{dx} = 3 \cos 3x.$

$$\frac{d \sin (3 - 5x)}{dx} = \cos (3 - 5x) \frac{d(3 - 5x)}{dx} = -5 \cos (3 - 5x).$$

Proof of (X)′. 1. Let $y = \cos x$. Then, by use of the cofunction identity (XVIII) on page 679, $\cos x = \sin (\tfrac{1}{2}\pi - x)$. Hence, by use of (IX),

$$\frac{d \cos x}{dx} = \frac{d \sin (\tfrac{1}{2}\pi - x)}{dx} = \cos (\tfrac{1}{2}\pi - x) \frac{d(\tfrac{1}{2}\pi - x)}{dx}$$

$$= -\cos (\tfrac{1}{2}\pi - x) = -\sin x.$$

Then, by the method of (4), from (X)′ we obtain (X).

Proof of **(XI)′**. From (IX)′, (X)′, and the derivative of a quotient,

$$\frac{d \tan x}{dx} = \frac{d}{dx}\left(\frac{\sin x}{\cos x}\right) = \frac{\cos x \dfrac{d \sin x}{dx} - \sin x \dfrac{d \cos x}{dx}}{\cos^2 x}$$

$$= \frac{\cos x \cos x + \sin x \sin x}{\cos^2 x} = \frac{\cos^2 x + \sin^2 x}{\cos^2 x} = \frac{1}{\cos^2 x} = \sec^2 x,$$

which proves (XI)′. Then, as in (4), we obtain (XI) from (XI)′.

Note 1. In the next exercise, the student will prove (XII)′, (XIII)′ by use of sec $x = 1/\cos x$, and (XIV)′, and then (XII)–(XIV).

ILLUSTRATION 2. By use of (X) with $u = (3x^2 + 2)$,

$$\frac{d}{dx} \cos (3x^2 + 2) = - \sin (3x^2 + 2) \frac{d}{dx} (3x^2 + 2) = - 6x \sin (3x^2 + 2).$$

To indicate powers of values of a trigonometric function, we shall place the exponent, n, of the power with the name of the function, except when $n = -1$. The reason for this exception will appear later.

ILLUSTRATION 3. $(\sin x)^3$ is written $\sin^3 x$.

$$\frac{1}{\tan^4 x} \quad \textit{may be written} \quad \tan^{-4} x.$$

However, the reciprocal of sin x, or its (-1)th power, is written

$$\frac{1}{\sin x} = (\sin x)^{-1} \quad \textit{and is not written} \quad \sin^{-1} x.$$

ILLUSTRATION 4. By use of the power formula (III) of page 92 first,

$$\frac{d}{dx} \tan^3 (2x + 3) = 3 \tan^2 (2x + 3) \frac{d}{dx} \tan (2x + 3)$$

$$= 3 \cdot 2 \tan^2 (2x + 3) \sec^2 (2x + 3). \qquad [(XI), \text{ with } u = 2x + 3]$$

$$\frac{d}{dz}\left(\frac{5}{\sqrt{\csc 3z}}\right) = \frac{d}{dz} 5(\csc 3z)^{-\frac{1}{2}} = 5 \cdot (-\tfrac{1}{2})(\csc 3z)^{-\frac{3}{2}} \frac{d \csc 3z}{dz} \qquad [\text{use (III)}]$$

$$= -\tfrac{5}{2} (\csc 3z)^{-\frac{3}{2}}(- \csc 3z \cot 3z)\frac{d(3z)}{dz} \qquad [\text{using (XIV)}]$$

$$= \tfrac{15}{2} (\csc 3z)^{-\frac{1}{2}} \cot 3z.$$

EXAMPLE 1. Obtain dy/dx if y is a function of x defined implicitly by

$$\sin (2x + 3y) + \cos (x - 2y) = 2. \tag{5}$$

Solution. Differentiate with respect to x on each side in (5):

$$\cos (2x + 3y) \frac{d(2x + 3y)}{dx} - \sin (x - 2y) \frac{d(x - 2y)}{dx} = 0, \textit{ or}$$

$$(2 + 3y')\cos (2x + 3y) - (1 - 2y')\sin (x - 2y) = 0, \textit{ or}$$

$$y'[3 \cos (2x + 3y) + 2 \sin (x - 2y)] = \sin (x - 2y) - 2 \cos (2x + 3y);$$

$$y' = \frac{\sin (x - 2y) - 2 \cos (2x + 3y)}{3 \cos (2x + 3y) + 2 \sin (x - 2y)}.$$

ILLUSTRATION 5. By use of the product formula (V) of page 92,

$$\frac{d}{dt} (\cot^2 4t \tan \sqrt{1 - 2t}) =$$

$$(\tan \sqrt{1 - 2t}) \left[2(\cot 4t) \frac{d \cot 4t}{dt} \right] + (\cot^2 4t)(\sec^2 \sqrt{1 - 2t}) \left(\frac{d\sqrt{1 - 2t}}{dt} \right)$$

$$= -8(\csc^2 4t \cot 4t)\tan \sqrt{1 - 2t} - (\cot^2 4t)(\sec^2 \sqrt{1 - 2t})(1 - 2t)^{-\frac{1}{2}}.$$

EXERCISE 65

Find the derivative of the function whose values are defined.

1. $\sin 5x$.　　　　**2.** $\cos \frac{3}{2}x$.　　　　**3.** $\tan 4t$.　　　　**4.** $\sec 5t$.

5. $\csc \frac{3}{2}t$.　　　　**6.** $\sin^4 x$.　　　　**7.** $\cot^5 z$.　　　　**8.** $\sec^3 4t^2$.

9. $\sqrt{\sin x}$.　　　　**10.** $\sqrt[3]{\tan x}$.　　　　**11.** $\sqrt[4]{\cos 2x}$.　　　　**12.** $\sqrt{\sec 3x}$.

13. $\dfrac{1}{\sin^3 4x}$.　　　**14.** $\dfrac{3}{\tan^2 6z}$.　　　**15.** $\dfrac{1}{\cos \sqrt{x}}$.　　　**16.** $-\dfrac{5}{\sec^2 x}$.

Note 1. In Problem 13, we could write $\sin^{-3} 4x$ and use the power formula with exponent -3. Or, first we could use $\csc 4x = 1/\sin 4x$, to obtain $\csc^3 4x$, and then apply the power formula with exponent 3.

17. $\sin (2x^2 + x)$.　　　**18.** $\cot (3 - 5x)$.　　　**19.** $\csc^2 (2 + 7x)$.

20. $a \csc k\theta$.　　　**21.** $\sqrt{\cos (2x - 3)^2}$.　　　**22.** $\sec^2 (4x + 3)^2$.

23. $x^3 \sin x$.　　　**24.** $\sin 3x \cos 2x$.　　　**25.** $\cos^2 x \sin 4x$.

26. $(\tan 2x)\sqrt{\cos 3x}$.　　**27.** $(\sec^2 x)(3 + 4x)^2$.　　**28.** $\cos 3x \sin \sqrt{x}$.

29. $\dfrac{1 - \cos x}{1 + \cos x}$.　　**30.** $\dfrac{1 - \tan x}{1 + \tan x}$.　　**31.** $\dfrac{\sin^2 3x}{4x^2 - x}$.

32. $\dfrac{\sin (3t - 1)}{t + \cos t}$.　　**33.** $\dfrac{t^3 \tan t}{2 + \cos^2 t}$.　　**34.** $\dfrac{1}{3 \sin 2x - 1}$.

35. $x \cos \dfrac{1}{x}$.　　　**36.** $\tan \dfrac{2x}{x - 1}$.　　　**37.** $\sin \dfrac{x + 1}{2 - x}$.

Find dy/dx at the given value of x.

38. $y = 2x + \cos 2x$; $x = \frac{3}{4}\pi$.　　　**39.** $y = x \sin^2 x$; $x = \frac{5}{6}\pi$.

40. $y = x(\cos x - \sin x)$; $x = \frac{1}{4}\pi$.　　**41.** $y = \tan 2x + \cot 4x$; $x = \frac{1}{3}\pi$.

Find the second derivative of the function.

42. $f(x) = \cos 3x$.　　　**43.** $f(t) = x \sin x$.　　　**44.** $g(x) = x^2 \tan x$.

Find dy/dx if x and y are related by the equation.

45. $\sin x - \cos y = 3y - 1$.　　　**46.** $\tan x + \sin y = 2y^3$.

47. $x = \sin (x + 3y)$.　　　**48.** $\cos (2x + 3y) = x$.

49. $\tan (x^2 - y) + \cot y = 5$.　　　**50.** $x \tan (x + 2y) = 3 + x^2$.

51. Prove formulas (XII), (XIII), and (XIV).

★52. Prove that　$\dfrac{d^n \sin x}{dx^n} = \sin \left(x + \dfrac{n\pi}{2} \right);\quad \dfrac{d^n \cos x}{dx^n} = \cos \left(x + \dfrac{n\pi}{2} \right).$

Hint. Use $\cos \theta = \sin (\theta + \frac{1}{2}\pi)$ or $\sin \theta = -\cos (\theta + \frac{1}{2}\pi)$, after each differentiation. Use mathematical induction.

78. GRAPHS INVOLVING TRIGONOMETRIC FUNCTIONS

EXAMPLE 1. Use derivatives to study the graph of $y = \sin x$.

Solution. 1. Since the sine function is periodic with the period 2π, we restrict details to the domain $0 \leq x < 2\pi$. We have

$$y' = \cos x; \quad y'' = -\sin x. \tag{1}$$

2. *Extrema.* Critical values of x satisfy $\cos x = 0$, whose solutions are $x = \frac{1}{2}\pi$ and $x = \frac{3}{2}\pi$. Since $y'' < 0$ at $x = \frac{1}{2}\pi$ and $y'' > 0$ at $x = \frac{3}{2}\pi$, there is a maximum at $x = \frac{1}{2}\pi$ and a minimum at $x = \frac{3}{2}\pi$, as in Figure 164.

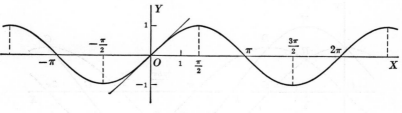

Fig. 164

3. *Inflection points.* $y'' = 0$ leads to $\sin x = 0$, whose solutions are $x = 0$ and $x = \pi$. Since $\sin x$ changes sign at $x = 0$ and at $x = \pi$, hence y'' changes sign, and there are inflection points at $x = 0$ and $x = \pi$. At $x = 0$, $y' = 1$ and the inflection tangent has slope 1. The tangent at $x = \pi$ has slope -1. The preceding details check the graph in Figure 164.

EXAMPLE 2. If $0 \leq x < 2\pi$, test for extrema and inflection points:

$$y = \sin x + \cos x. \tag{2}$$

Solution. 1. $\qquad \dfrac{dy}{dx} = \cos x - \sin x \quad and \quad \dfrac{d^2y}{dx^2} = -\sin x - \cos x. \tag{3}$

2. Critical values for extrema satisfy the equation

$$\cos x - \sin x = 0, \ or$$

$$1 = \frac{\sin x}{\cos x}, \quad or \quad \tan x = 1,$$

whose solutions are $x = \frac{1}{4}\pi$ and $x = \frac{5}{4}\pi$. From (3),

$$at \ x = \tfrac{1}{4}\pi, \ \ y'' = -\sqrt{2}; \quad at \ x = \tfrac{5}{4}\pi, \ \ y'' = \sqrt{2}.$$

Thus, there is a maximum at $x = \frac{1}{4}\pi$ and a minimum at $x = \frac{5}{4}\pi$, as in Figure 165 on page 230.

3. Critical values for inflection points satisfy $y'' = 0$, or

$$-\sin x - \cos x = 0, \quad or \quad \tan x = -1,$$

whose solutions are $x = \frac{3}{4}\pi$ and $x = \frac{7}{4}\pi$. To test these values, write

$$y'' = -\cos x \left(1 + \frac{\sin x}{\cos x}\right) = -\cos x \,(\tan x + 1).$$

If x is near $\frac{3}{4}\pi$, or $\frac{7}{4}\pi$, then cos x remains of constant sign. At each of these values of x, tan x increases, or decreases, through the value -1; hence, (tan $x + 1$) and y'' change sign. Therefore, there are inflection points at $x = \frac{3}{4}\pi$ and $x = \frac{7}{4}\pi$, or at F and G in Figure 165. The graph was checked by *composition* (addition) *of ordinates* of the curves $y = \sin x$ and $y = \cos x$. Thus, the graph of (2) crosses the graph of $y = \cos x$ at those points where sin $x = 0$, and crosses the graph of $y = \sin x$ where cos $x = 0$.

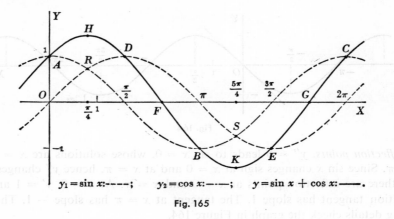

$y_1 = \sin x$:----; $y_2 = \cos x$:--·--; $y = \sin x + \cos x$:——.

Fig. 165

EXERCISE 66

Graph the equation on an interval including $0 \leqq x \leqq 2\pi$. *Locate horizontal tangents and test for extrema, by use of* y'' *if possible.*

1. $y = \cos x$. 2. $y = \tan x$. 3. $y = \cot x$. 4. $y = \csc x$.
5. $y = \sin x - \cos x$. 6. $y = x - \sin x$. 7. $y = \tan^2 x$.
8. $y = \sin x + \sqrt{3} \cos x$. 9. $y = 4 \sin x + \cos 2x$. 10. $y = \cos^3 x$.

Graph the equation over the specified interval by use of both $\dfrac{dy}{dx}$ *and* $\dfrac{dx}{dy}$, *showing each horizontal or vertical tangent.*

11. $y^2 = \sin x$; $-2\pi \leqq x \leqq 2\pi$. 12. $y^2 = \tan x$; $-\frac{1}{2}\pi \leqq x \leqq \frac{1}{2}\pi$.

Find each angle of intersection of the curves if $0 \leqq x \leqq 2\pi$, *when the equations are graphed in an xy-plane with equal scale units on the axes.*

13. $y = \sin x$ and $y = \cos x$. 14. $y = \tan x$ and $y = \cot x$.

Find all relative extrema of f, and its absolute maximum and absolute minimum, on the domain $0 \leqq x \leqq 2\pi$.

15. $f(x) = 2 \sin x + \sin 2x$. 16. $f(x) = 4 \cos x + \cos 2x$.
17. $f(x) = 3 \sin x + 4 \cos x$. 18. $f(x) = \sin x \cos^3 x$.

19. For Problem 15, find the absolute maximum and absolute minimum of the slope of the graph where $-\frac{1}{4}\pi \leqq x \leqq \pi$.

79. APPLICATIONS INVOLVING TRIGONOMETRIC FUNCTIONS

EXAMPLE 1. In a triangle, two sides have the lengths 20″ and 30″, and the included angle is increasing at the rate of 2° per hour. At what rate is the area of the triangle changing when the included angle is 50°?

Solution. 1. In a variable $\triangle ABC$, as in Figure 166, let α be the measure in radians of the angle at A. The area, K, of $\triangle ABC$ in square inches is

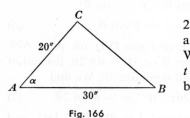

Fig. 166

$$K = \tfrac{1}{2}(20)(30) \sin \alpha, \quad or \quad K = 300 \sin \alpha. \quad (1)$$

2. To apply calculus, we now consider $\sin \alpha$ as a value of the *standard sine function of numbers.* With K and α considered as functions of the time t in hours, we differentiate with respect to t on both sides of (1):

$$\frac{dK}{dt} = 300 \cos \alpha \, \frac{d\alpha}{dt}. \quad (2)$$

3. Since $2° = 2(\pi/180)$ radians, in (2) we have $d\alpha/dt = \pi/90$ and (α radians) $= 50°$, so that $\cos \alpha = \cos 50°$. Hence, from (2),

$$\frac{dK}{dt} = 300(\cos 50°) \frac{\pi}{90} = 6.731, \, sq. \, in. \, per \, hr. \quad (3)$$

EXAMPLE 2. An airplane is flying horizontally at an elevation of 8000′ directly toward an observer, at a speed of 500′ per second. Find the rate of change of the angle of elevation of the airplane at the observer's position when the angle is 60°.

Solution. 1. In Figure 167, P represents the airplane, A the observer, and B the vertical projection of P onto the horizontal plane through A. Let θ be the measure in radians of the angle of elevation of P at any instant and let $x = AB$, measured in feet. Then,

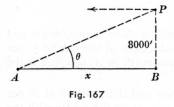

Fig. 167

$$\frac{x}{8000} = \cot \theta, \quad or \quad x = 8000 \cot \theta. \quad (4)$$

2. In (4), x and θ are functions of the time t in seconds. On differentiating both sides of (4) with respect to t, we find

$$\frac{dx}{dt} = -8000 \csc^2 \theta \, \frac{d\theta}{dt}. \quad (5)$$

3. In (5), substitute $dx/dt = -500$ with θ as the measure in radians of 60°, so that $\csc^2 \theta = \csc^2 60°$. This gives

$$\frac{d\theta}{dt} = \frac{500}{8000 \csc^2 \theta} = \frac{500}{8000} \sin^2 60° = \frac{1}{16} \cdot \frac{3}{4} = \frac{3}{64}.$$

Thus, the angle θ is increasing at the rate of $\frac{3}{64}$ radians, or 2.7° per second.

EXAMPLE 3. Find the relative dimensions of the cylinder of maximum curved surface area which can be inscribed in a sphere of radius r.

Solution. 1. Figure 168 shows a cross section through the center of a sphere with an inscribed cylinder. Let θ be the measure in radians of the angle subtended at the center of the circle by the radius of the base of the cylinder. Let the measure,

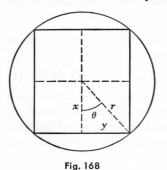

in some unit, of the base-radius be y, and of one-half of the altitude of the cylinder be x. Let the area in square units of the curved surface of the cylinder be S. Then,

$$x = r \cos \theta; \quad y = r \sin \theta;$$

$$S = 4\pi r^2 \sin \theta \cos \theta. \tag{6}$$

2. Let $W = S/(2\pi r^2)$, and use (VI) on page 679. Then $W = 2 \sin \theta \cos \theta$ or $W = \sin 2\theta$. Instead of minimizing S, we shall minimize W. We find

Fig. 168

$$W' = 2 \cos 2\theta; \quad W'' = -4 \sin 2\theta. \tag{7}$$

3. From Figure 168, the domain for θ is the interval $I = \{0 \leq \theta \leq \frac{1}{2}\pi\}$, and $W = 0$ at the end points, $\theta = 0$ and $\theta = \frac{1}{2}\pi$. Hence, the absolute maximum of W occurs at an *interior point* of I. The critical values of θ interior to I for an extremum satisfy $W' = 0$, or $\cos 2\theta = 0$, whose only solution on I is $\theta = \frac{1}{4}\pi$. At $\theta = \frac{1}{4}\pi$, $W'' = -4 \sin \frac{1}{2}\pi = -4$; hence W has a *relative maximum*, which is the desired *absolute maximum*, when $\theta = \frac{1}{4}\pi$. In Figure 168, this gives $x = y$, or the area of the curved surface is a maximum when the diameter of the base is equal to the cylinder's altitude.

EXERCISE 67

1. Given that x and θ are functions of t, with $dx/dt = 3$ and $d\theta/dt = .2$, and that $y = x \sin \theta$. Find dy/dt when $x = 5$ and $\theta = \frac{2}{3}\pi$.

2. Given that x and y are functions of t with $dx/dt = 2$ and $dy/dt = -3$, and that $\tan \theta = x/y^2$. Find $d\theta/dt$ when $x = 3$ and $y = 2$.

Solve by first introducing a variable angle.

3. In a lighthouse 6000 yards west of point A on a straight shore running north and south, a horizontal searchlight is revolving counterclockwise at the rate of $3°$ per second. When the light beam hits a point 5000 yards north of A, how fast is the beam moving north on the shore?

4. A ladder 25' long leans against a wall, with the upper end sliding down at .5' per second. Find the rate of change of the acute angle made by the ladder with the ground, when the upper end is 20' above ground.

5. Find the maximum volume of a cylinder inscribed in a given sphere.

6. A horizontal reservoir has a cross section which is an inverted isosceles triangle, where the length of a leg is 60'. Find the angle between the equal legs to give maximum capacity. (Use one-half of the angle.)

7. In a right triangle, the horizontal and vertical sides of the right angle are increasing at the rates of 2" and 3" per second, respectively. Find the rate at which the smaller acute angle is changing when the horizontal and vertical sides are 25" and 15", respectively.

8. Find the shape of a cylinder with maximum curved surface area inscribed in a given hemisphere, where the cylinder's base is on the plane face.

9. A wall rises from a horizontal plane, and a fence 16′ high is 2′ from the wall. A beam to brace the wall will extend from the ground over the fence to the wall. Find the minimum length for the beam.

10. A boat is being drawn to a dock by a mooring rope, which passes through a retaining hole on the dock, and is attached to the boat at a point 20′ lower than the hole. If the rope is pulled in at 1.5′ per second, find the rate of change of the acute angle made by the rope with the horizontal, when there are 60′ of rope out; when the angle is 45°.

11. A reservoir has a horizontal plane bottom and a cross section as shown in Figure 169. Find the angle of inclination of the sides from the horizontal, to give maximum capacity.

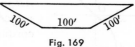

Fig. 169

12. In a triangle, one side is 10″ long and the opposite angle is 30°. A second angle is 45° and is increasing .3° per second. Find the rate of change of the side opposite the second angle. Use (10) on page 679.

13. When light from a point source strikes a plane surface, the intensity of the illumination is proportional to the cosine of the angle of incidence and inversely proportional to the square of the distance from the source. How high should a light be located above the center of a circle of radius 25′ to give the best illumination along the circumference? (The angle of incidence is measured from the perpendicular to the plane.)

14. A sector is cut from a circle of radius r, and is bent to form the lateral surface of a cone of maximum volume. Find the sector's angle.

15. The minute hand of a clock is 3″ long and the hour hand is 2″ long. At what rate are the ends of the hands approaching each other at 4 P.M.?

16. In a 120° sector of a circle, an inscribed rectangle has one side as a chord perpendicular to the radius which bisects the sector, and the opposite side has its end points on the boundary radii of the sector. Find the angle subtended by the chord at the center of the circle, and the area of the rectangle, when its area is a maximum.

17. A helicopter leaves the ground 1000′ from an observer and rises vertically 20′ per second. At what rate is the observer's angle of elevation of the helicopter changing, when the helicopter is 800′ above the ground?

18. An airplane is flying south at an elevation of 3000′, with a speed of 600′ per second, in a vertical plane with a searchlight on the ground. To keep the light on the airplane, what is the rate of revolution of the searchlight when the airplane is due south, at an airline distance of 5000′?

19. A boat is sailing at the rate of 6 miles per hour in the direction of a tower whose top is 300′ above the base of a vertical cliff on the shore. Find the rate of change, per minute, of the angle of elevation of the top of the tower from the boat when it is 1800′ from shore.

20. An airplane is flying south at an elevation of 12,000′ toward an antiaircraft gun on the ground. An automatic sighting mechanism at the gun keeps a direction indicator pointed at the airplane. The airline distance from the airplane to the gun is decreasing at 500′ per second. Find the rate of revolution of the indicator when the airline distance is 13,000′.

80. INVERSE SINE FUNCTION *

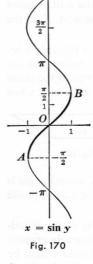

$x = \sin y$

Fig. 170

Consider the graph in Figure 170 showing the sine curve $x = \sin y$ along the y-axis. For each eligible number x, the equation $x = \sin y$ is satisfied by infinitely many values of y. Thus, if $x = \frac{1}{2}$, we obtain

$$\sin y = \tfrac{1}{2}, \quad \text{whose solutions are}$$
$$y = \tfrac{1}{6}\pi + 2n\pi \quad \text{and} \quad y = \tfrac{5}{6}\pi + 2n\pi, \tag{1}$$

where n may be any integer. Now, restrict attention to arc AB in Figure 170. If $P:(x, y)$ moves on AB from A to B, then y increases as x increases, as in Figure 75 on page 103. Accordingly, we consider the restricted relation

$$\left\{ \begin{array}{l} x \text{ on } I: \quad -1 \leq x \leq 1; \\ y \text{ on } R: \quad -\tfrac{1}{2}\pi \leq y \leq \tfrac{1}{2}\pi. \end{array} \right\} \quad x = \sin y, \tag{2}$$

whose graph is AB, transferred also to Figure 171. For each x on I, there exists just one y on R. Hence, (2) defines y as a function of x, to be called the **Arcsine function,** with the value Arcsin x for any x on I. That is,

$$\left\{ \begin{array}{l} \text{with } -1 \leq x \leq 1, \\ -\tfrac{1}{2}\pi \leq y \leq \tfrac{1}{2}\pi: \end{array} \right. \qquad x = \sin y \quad \text{is equivalent to} \quad y = \text{Arcsin } x; \tag{3}$$

(*for all x*)

$$-\tfrac{1}{2}\pi \leq \text{Arcsin } x \leq \tfrac{1}{2}\pi. \tag{4}$$

Thus, the sine function and the Arcsine function are *inverse* functions, for the restricted domains of x and y in (3), so that

$$x = \sin (\text{Arcsin } x); \quad y = \text{Arcsin } (\sin y). \tag{5}$$

Because of (3), the graph of $y = \text{Arcsin } x$ is the graph of $x = \sin y$ with $-\tfrac{1}{2}\pi \leq y \leq \tfrac{1}{2}\pi$, as in Figure 171.

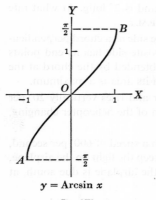

$y = \text{Arcsin } x$

Fig. 171

ILLUSTRATION 1. To find any particular value of Arcsin x, we use (3). Thus, to obtain Arcsin $(-\frac{1}{2})$, let $y = \text{Arcsin } (-\frac{1}{2})$; then $\sin y = -\frac{1}{2}$ with $-\tfrac{1}{2}\pi \leq y \leq \tfrac{1}{2}\pi$. Hence, $y = -\tfrac{1}{6}\pi$.

ILLUSTRATION 2. To form a table for graphing $y = \text{Arcsin } x$, as in Figure 171, write $x = \sin y$ and assign values to y on the interval in (3).

$x = \sin y$	-1	$-.87$	$-.5$	0	.5	.87	1
$y = \text{Arcsin } x$	$-\tfrac{1}{2}\pi$	$-\tfrac{1}{3}\pi$	$-\tfrac{1}{6}\pi$	0	$\tfrac{1}{6}\pi$	$\tfrac{1}{3}\pi$	$\tfrac{1}{2}\pi$
y, dec. form	$.-1.57$	-1.05	$-.52$	0	.52	1.05	1.57

* It is essential to review inverse functions on page 103.

ILLUSTRATION 3. For the moment, interpret the *number* Arcsin x as the radian measure of an angle. Then, sometimes, "Arcsin x" is referred to as "*an angle whose sine is x*," which is equivalent to sin (Arcsin x) = x.

EXAMPLE 1. Find sin [Arcsin $\frac{1}{2}$ + Arcsin $(-\frac{3}{5})$].

Solution. 1. Let α = Arcsin $\frac{1}{2}$; then $\sin \alpha = \frac{1}{2}$ and $0 < \alpha < \frac{1}{2}\pi$. Let β = Arcsin $(-\frac{3}{5})$; $\sin \beta = -\frac{3}{5}$ and $-\frac{1}{2}\pi < \beta < 0$. We desire sin $(\alpha + \beta)$.

2. From the identity $\cos^2 \theta + \sin^2 \theta = 1$, we find $\cos \alpha = \frac{1}{2}\sqrt{3}$; $\cos^2 \beta = \frac{16}{25}$ or $\cos \beta = \pm \frac{4}{5}$, where we use $\cos \beta = \frac{4}{5}$ because the number β is on a IVth-quadrant interval. From (III) on page 679,

$$\sin (\alpha + \beta) = \tfrac{1}{2}(\tfrac{4}{5}) + \tfrac{1}{2}\sqrt{3}(-\tfrac{3}{5}) = \tfrac{1}{10}(4 - 3\sqrt{3}).$$

★*Note 1.* In certain books, instead of "**Arcsin** x" we find "$\sin^{-1} x$," which then is read "*inverse sine x.*" We prefer not to use $\sin^{-1}$ because of possible confusion with exponents applied to the sine function.

EXAMPLE 2. Find all trigonometric functions of Arcsin $(-\frac{2}{3})$.

Solution. 1. Let y = Arcsin $(-\frac{2}{3})$. Then, $\sin y = -\frac{2}{3}$, and $-\frac{1}{2}\pi < y < 0$ because $\sin y < 0$. For the moment, interpret $\sin y$ as the sine of the angle with measure y radians. Let the reference angle for y have the measure z radians. Then, $0 < z < \frac{1}{2}\pi$ and $\sin z = \frac{2}{3}$.

2. From the reference triangle for z in Figure 172, and knowledge of the signs of the trigonometric functions in quadrant IV,

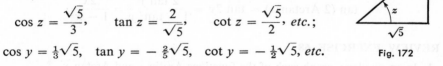

$$\cos z = \frac{\sqrt{5}}{3}, \quad \tan z = \frac{2}{\sqrt{5}}, \quad \cot z = \frac{\sqrt{5}}{2}, \text{ etc.};$$

$$\cos y = \tfrac{1}{3}\sqrt{5}, \quad \tan y = -\tfrac{2}{5}\sqrt{5}, \quad \cot y = -\tfrac{1}{2}\sqrt{5}, \text{ etc.}$$

Fig. 172

81. INVERSE TANGENT FUNCTION

The graph of $x = \tan y$ consists of the branch in Figure 173, on page 236, and its endless repetitions above and below. To define an *inverse* for the tangent function, we consider the restricted relation

$$\left\{ \begin{array}{l} x \text{ on } T: \quad -\infty < x < \infty; \\ y \text{ on } R: \quad -\frac{1}{2}\pi < y < \frac{1}{2}\pi: \end{array} \right\} \qquad x = \tan y, \qquad (1)$$

whose graph is in Figure 173. We notice that, in (1), y increases if x increases. Hence, (1) defines y as a function of x, to be called the **Arctangent** function, with the value Arctan x, read "*Arctangent x, at any point in T.*" That is,

$$\left\{ \begin{array}{l} with -\infty < x < \infty, \\ -\frac{1}{2}\pi < y < \frac{1}{2}\pi: \end{array} \right\} \qquad x = \tan y \quad is\ equivalent\ to \quad y = \textbf{Arctan } x; \qquad (2)$$

(*for all x*) $\qquad\qquad -\frac{1}{2}\pi < \text{Arctan } x < \frac{1}{2}\pi.$ $\qquad\qquad$ (3)

Thus, the *tangent* and *Arctangent* functions are *inverses*. From (3),

$$x = \tan(\text{Arctan } x); \quad y = \text{Arctan}(\tan y). \tag{4}$$

Because of (2), the graph of $y = \text{Arctan } x$ is the graph of $x = \tan y$, with $-\frac{1}{2}\pi < y < \frac{1}{2}\pi$, as in Figure 173. Since $|\tan y| \to \infty$ when $y \to \frac{1}{2}\pi -$ and also when $y \to -\frac{1}{2}\pi +$, the graph of $y = \text{Arctan } x$ has the lines $y = \pm\frac{1}{2}\pi$ as asymptotes.

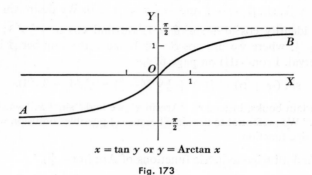

$x = \tan y$ or $y = \text{Arctan } x$

Fig. 173

ILLUSTRATION 1. To find Arctan (-1), let $y = \text{Arctan}(-1)$. Then, from (2), $\tan y = -1$ and $-\frac{1}{2}\pi < y < 0$. Hence, $y = -\frac{1}{4}\pi = \text{Arctan}(-1)$.

EXAMPLE 1. Find $\tan(2 \text{ Arctan } x)$.

Solution. Let $y = \text{Arctan } x$; then $x = \tan y$. From (V) on page 679 with $x = y$,

$$\tan(2 \text{ Arctan } x) = \tan 2y = \frac{2 \tan y}{1 - \tan^2 y} = \frac{2x}{1 - x^2}.$$

REVIEW EXERCISE 68

1. In an xy-plane, graph each of the functions Arcsin x and Arctan x.

Find each function value either from memory of function values for convenient angles, or by use of Table IV.

2. Arcsin $\frac{1}{2}$.   **3.** Arctan 1.   **4.** Arctan 0.   **5.** Arcsin 0.

6. Arcsin $\frac{1}{2}\sqrt{3}$.   **7.** Arcsin $\frac{1}{2}\sqrt{2}$.   **8.** Arctan $\sqrt{3}$.   **9.** Arctan $\frac{1}{3}\sqrt{3}$.

10. Arcsin .64422.   **11.** Arctan .25534.   **12.** Arctan .49545.

13. Arcsin $(-\frac{1}{2})$.   **14.** Arctan (-1).   **15.** Arctan $(-\sqrt{3})$.

16. Arcsin $(-\frac{1}{2}\sqrt{3})$.   **17.** Arctan $(-\frac{1}{3}\sqrt{3})$.   **18.** Arcsin $(-\frac{1}{2}\sqrt{2})$.

19. Arcsin (-1).   **20.** Arcsin $(-.40776)$.   **21.** Arctan (-1.7844).

Find the value of the expression without using a table.

22. sin Arcsin $\frac{1}{3}$.   **23.** tan Arctan (-2).   **24.** tan Arctan $2z$.

25. sin Arcsin $(-\frac{2}{5})$.   **26.** tan Arcsin $(-\frac{1}{2})$.   **27.** sin Arctan $\sqrt{3}$.

28. cos Arcsin $\frac{1}{4}$.   **29.** cot Arcsin $(-\frac{3}{5})$.   **30.** cos Arctan (-2).

31. sin Arcsin $\frac{4}{7}$.   **32.** tan Arctan (-4).   **33.** cos Arcsin $\frac{1}{5}$.

34. Find all trigonometric functions of Arcsin $(-\frac{12}{13})$.

35. Find all trigonometric functions of Arctan $(-\frac{3}{4})$.

Find sin $(y + z)$, cos $(y + z)$, sin $2y$, cos $2y$, *and* tan $2y$ *for the data.*

36. $y = $ Arcsin (-1); $z = $ Arcsin $(-\frac{1}{2})$.

37. $y = $ Arcsin $\frac{3}{5}$; $z = $ Arctan $(-\sqrt{3})$.

Find the function value by interpolation in Table IV.

38. Arcsin .80357.   **39.** Arctan 3.2754.   **40.** Arctan (-1.2149).

41. Prove the identity Arctan $(-x) = -$ Arctan x.

42. Prove the identity Arcsin $(-x) = -$ Arcsin x.

★**43.** The functions *Arccosine, Arctangent, Arcsecant,* and *Arccosecant* are defined as the inverses of corresponding direct trigonometric functions, on restricted domains, by the following equivalence statements. Graph $y = $ Arccos x, $y = $ Arccot x, $y = $ Arcsec x, and $y = $ Arccsc x.

$$\left\{ \begin{array}{c} \textit{With } -1 \leq x \leq 1 \textit{ and } 0 \leq y \leq \pi, \, x = \cos y \textit{ is equivalent to} \\ \boldsymbol{y = } \textbf{Arccos } \boldsymbol{x;} \quad \textit{hence} \quad \boldsymbol{0 \leq} \textbf{Arccos } \boldsymbol{x \leq \pi.} \end{array} \right\} \quad (1)$$

$$\left\{ \begin{array}{c} \textit{With } -\infty < x < \infty \textit{ and } 0 < y < \pi, \, x = \cot y \textit{ is equivalent to} \\ \boldsymbol{y = } \textbf{Arccot } \boldsymbol{x;} \quad \textit{hence} \quad \boldsymbol{0 <} \textbf{Arccot } \boldsymbol{x < \pi.} \end{array} \right\} \quad (2)$$

$$\left\{ \begin{array}{c} \textit{If } 0 \leq y < \frac{1}{2}\pi \textit{ when } 1 \leq x, \textit{ and } -\pi \leq y < -\frac{1}{2}\pi \textit{ when } x \leq -1, \\ \boldsymbol{x = \sec y} \textit{ is equivalent to } \boldsymbol{y = } \textbf{Arcsec } \boldsymbol{x.} \end{array} \right\} \quad (3)$$

$$\left\{ \begin{array}{c} \textit{If } 0 < y \leq \frac{1}{2}\pi \textit{ when } 1 \leq x, \textit{ and } -\pi < y \leq -\frac{1}{2}\pi \textit{ when } x \leq -1, \\ \boldsymbol{x = \csc y} \textit{ is equivalent to } \boldsymbol{y = } \textbf{Arccsc } \boldsymbol{x.} \end{array} \right\} \quad (4)$$

Note 1. Arcsin x and Arctan x are of great importance, and Arcsec x is occasionally useful in integration. Arccos x, Arccot x, and Arccsc x can be avoided without inconvenience in calculus.

82. DERIVATIVES OF INVERSE TRIGONOMETRIC FUNCTIONS

Proof of (**XV**), *page* 221. 1. Let $y = $ Arcsin u, where the variable u is a differentiable function of x. Then, by (3) and (4) on page 234,

$$u = \sin y \quad \textit{and} \quad -\tfrac{1}{2}\pi \leq y \leq \tfrac{1}{2}\pi. \quad (1)$$

2. Differentiate with respect to x on both sides of $u = \sin y$, where u and y are differentiable functions of x, and use (IX) on page 221:

$$\frac{du}{dx} = (\cos y)\frac{dy}{dx}, \quad \textit{or} \quad \frac{dy}{dx} = \frac{1}{\cos y}\frac{du}{dx}. \quad (2)$$

3. In dividing by cos y in (2), we rule out $y = \pm \frac{1}{2}\pi$, where cos $y = 0$ and $u = \sin y = \pm 1$. Otherwise, from (1) we notice that

$$\cos y = \pm \sqrt{1 - \sin^2 y} = \pm \sqrt{1 - u^2}. \quad (3)$$

Since $-\frac{1}{2}\pi < y < \frac{1}{2}\pi$, then cos $y > 0$. Hence, in (3), cos $y = +\sqrt{1 - u^2}$. Then, from (2) and (3) with $y = $ Arcsin u,

$$\frac{d}{dx}\textbf{Arcsin } \boldsymbol{u} = \frac{1}{\sqrt{1 - u^2}}\frac{du}{dx}. \quad (\textbf{XV})$$

Proof of (**XVI**), *page* 222. 1. Let $y = $ Arctan u, where the variable u is a differentiable function of x. Then, from (2) and (3) on page 235,

$$u = \tan y \quad and \quad -\tfrac{1}{2}\pi < y < \tfrac{1}{2}\pi. \tag{4}$$

By use of (XI), page 221, $\dfrac{du}{dx} = (\sec^2 y)\,\dfrac{dy}{dx}, \quad or \quad \dfrac{dy}{dx} = \dfrac{1}{\sec^2 y}\,\dfrac{du}{dx}.$ (5)

2. From $\sec^2 y = 1 + \tan^2 y = 1 + u^2$ and (5) with $y = $ Arctan u,

$$\frac{d}{dx}(\text{Arctan } u) = \frac{1}{1 + u^2}\,\frac{du}{dx}. \tag{XVI}$$

As special cases of (XV) and (XVI) with $u = x$,

$$\frac{d\,\text{Arcsin } x}{dx} = \frac{1}{\sqrt{1 - x^2}}; \qquad \frac{d\,\text{Arctan } x}{dx} = \frac{1}{1 + x^2}. \tag{6}$$

ILLUSTRATION 1. To check the graph of $y = $ Arcsin x on page 234, consider

$$\frac{dy}{dx} = \frac{1}{\sqrt{1 - x^2}}; \qquad \frac{d^2y}{dx^2} = \frac{x}{(1 - x^2)^{\frac{3}{2}}}. \tag{7}$$

Since $y' \neq 0$ at any value of x, note that there is no extremum with $|x| \neq 1$. From (7), $y'' = 0$ at $x = 0$, and y'' changes sign from "$-$" to "$+$" at $x = 0$. Hence, there is an inflection point at $x = 0$ where the graph changes from concave downward to concave upward. From (7), y' does not exist at $x = \pm 1$, and $y' \to \infty$ as $x \to -1+$ and as $x \to +1-$. From $y = $ Arcsin x, we have

$$x = \sin y \quad and \ hence \quad \frac{dx}{dy} = \cos y = \sqrt{1 - \sin^2 y} = \sqrt{1 - x^2}.$$

Thus, $dx/dy = 0$ at $x = \pm 1$, and the graph has a vertical tangent at $x = \pm 1$.

ILLUSTRATION 2. From (XV), $\dfrac{d\,\text{Arcsin } x^2}{dx} = \dfrac{1}{\sqrt{1 - x^4}}\,\dfrac{dx^2}{dx} = \dfrac{2x}{\sqrt{1 - x^4}}.$

With $u = \sin x$ in (XVI), $\dfrac{d\,\text{Arctan (sin } x)}{dx} = \dfrac{1}{1 + \sin^2 x}\cdot\cos x.$

EXAMPLE 1. A statue 8′ high stands on a pedestal 4′ above the eye level of an observer. How far from the pedestal should he stand to obtain the best view of the statue? (We assume that the view is best where the statue subtends the greatest angle.)

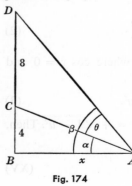

Fig. 174

Solution. 1. In Figure 174, A represents the eye of the observer, and θ is the measure in radians of the angle subtended by the statue, CD, when A is at a distance of x feet, where the domain of x is all $x > 0$. Let $\alpha = \angle BAC$ and $\beta = \angle BAD$. Then,

$$\theta = \beta - \alpha, \quad or \quad \theta = \text{Arctan}\,\frac{12}{x} - \text{Arctan}\,\frac{4}{x}; \tag{8}$$

$$\frac{d\theta}{dx} = \left[\frac{12}{1 + (144/x^2)} - \frac{4}{1 + (16/x^2)}\right]\cdot\left(-\frac{1}{x^2}\right), \ or$$

$$\frac{d\theta}{dx} = \frac{8(48 - x^2)}{(144 + x^2)(16 + x^2)}. \tag{9}$$

2. From (9), $d\theta/dx = 0$ at $x = 4\sqrt{3}$, and $d\theta/dx$ changes sign from "$+$" to "$-$" as x increases through $x = 4\sqrt{3}$. Hence, θ is a maximum when the observer stands $4\sqrt{3}$ feet from the pedestal.

EXAMPLE 2. A searchlight S is situated 4000 yards west of point A on a north-south road. The beam of light is following a fugitive F who is running north at the rate of 5 yards per second. Find the rate at which the searchlight is revolving when F is 2000 yards north of A.

Solution. 1. Figure 175 shows a position of F, at any instant. From Figure 175, where $dx/dt = 5$,

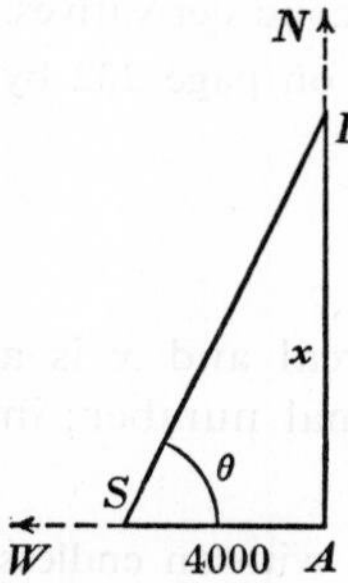

$$\tan \theta = \frac{x}{4000}, \quad or \quad \theta = \text{Arctan } \frac{x}{4000}. \qquad (10)$$

The rate of revolution is $d\theta/dt$. From (10),

$$\frac{d\theta}{dt} = \frac{d}{dt}\left(\text{Arctan } \frac{x}{4000}\right) = \frac{1}{1 + \dfrac{x^2}{(4000)^2}} \cdot \frac{1}{4000} \cdot \frac{dx}{dt}.$$

2. With $x = 2000$ and $dx/dt = 5$,

$$\frac{d\theta}{dt} = \frac{4000}{(4000)^2 + (2000)^2} \cdot 5 = \frac{1}{1000}.$$

That is, the searchlight revolves .001 radian per second.

Fig. 175

Comment. Example 2 could be solved without an inverse function by use of $\tan \theta = x/4000$ in (10), as in Section 79 on page 231. *No particular merit can be claimed for use of* Arctan $(x/4000)$.

EXERCISE 69

Find the derivative of the function whose values are defined. Early letters of the alphabet represent positive constants.

1. Arcsin $4x$.

2. Arctan $2x$.

3. Arctan $(3x + 2)$.

4. Arcsin $(x^2 + 1)$.

5. Arcsin $(\tan^2 x)$.

6. Arctan $(\cos x)$.

7. Arctan $(\tan x^3)$.

8. Arcsin $(\sin \sqrt[3]{x})$.

9. Arctan (x^{-2}).

10. Arctan $\dfrac{2t}{t^2 - 1}$.

11. Arcsin $\dfrac{x}{a}$.

12. Arcsin $\dfrac{3z}{2 - z}$.

13. $\dfrac{1}{a}$ Arctan $\dfrac{x}{a}$.

14. v Arctan $\dfrac{2}{v}$.

15. $\dfrac{1}{t^2}$ Arcsin t.

16. x^2 Arcsin $3x$.

17. $\sin 3x$ Arcsin $\sqrt{x}$.

18. $\tan^3 x$ Arctan x^2.

19. $\dfrac{a^2}{2}$ Arcsin $\dfrac{x}{a} + \dfrac{x}{2}\sqrt{a^2 - x^2}$.

20. $\dfrac{x}{\sqrt{a^2 - x^2}}$ $-$ Arcsin $\dfrac{x}{a}$.

Obtain dy/dx if x and y are related by the equation.

21. Arctan y + Arcsin $x = x^3$.

22. Arcsin $2x$ + Arctan $3y = 1$.

23. Arctan $(x + 2y) + \sin x = \cos y - 1$.

Find the second derivative of the function.

24. Arcsin $2x$.

25. Arctan $4x$.

26. x Arcsin x.

27. Graph $y = \text{Arctan } x$ by use of y' and y'', using equal scale units on the axes.

28. A picture with a rectangular frame 5′ high hangs on a wall, and the lower edge of the frame is 10′ above eye level of an observer. How far from the wall should he stand to obtain the best view?

29. A set of enemy trenches starts 900 yards from the base and extends 100 yards upward on a hill which rises to the north at an angle of 30° from a horizontal plane. To maximize the vertical angle subtended by the trenches at a machine gun emplacement south of the hill, how far from its base should the emplacement be located by the attacking force?

★30. Prove each of formulas (XXII), (XXIII), and (XXIV). Then graph each of the functions Arccos x, Arccot x, and Arcsec x by use of first and second derivatives.

★31–37. Solve Problems 4, 7, 10, 17–20, respectively, of Exercise 67 on page 232 by use of an inverse trigonometric function.

83. THE EXPONENTIAL FUNCTION

In Note 7 of the Appendix, a^x is defined for cases where a is real and x is a rational number. We proceed to define a^x when x is an irrational number; in this case **it will be necessary to assume that $a > 0$.**

Note 1. We accept the fact that any real number x can be identified with an endless decimal, which is a repeating decimal (possibly terminating in an unbroken sequence of zeros *) if and only if x is a rational number.

ILLUSTRATION 1. To assign a meaning to $10^{\sqrt{2}}$, we recall

$$\sqrt{2} = 1.414 \cdots, \quad or \quad \sqrt{2} = \lim_{n \to \infty} r_n, \tag{1}$$

where r_n is the terminating decimal obtained from the non-repeating endless decimal in (1) by replacing each of its digits by zero beyond the nth decimal place. Then, we define $10^{\sqrt{2}}$ as follows:

$$10^{\sqrt{2}} = \lim_{n \to \infty} 10^{r_n}. \tag{2}$$

In (1), r_n is a rational number; thus, $r_2 = 1.41 = \frac{141}{100}$. Hence, 10^{r_n} is a special case of $10^{p/q}$ as defined on page 683. Without proof, we accept the fact that the limit in (2) exists. Thus, we conclude that $10^{\sqrt{2}}$ has meaning, and can be approximated as closely as we desire by use of 10^{r_n} with n sufficiently large.

Let x be any real number, and let $\{r_n\}$ be the sequence of terminating decimals obtained as in Illustration 1 from the expression for x as an endless decimal, so that $\lim_{n \to \infty} r_n = x$. Then, we define a^x as follows, if $a > 0$:

$$a^x = \lim_{n \to \infty} a^{r_n}. \tag{3}$$

An advanced discussion, which is beyond the scope of this text, would prove that the limit in (3) exists, and gives the same value for a^x as on page 683 when x is a rational number. Then, it can be proved that the familiar laws of exponents apply if the base of each power is positive and the exponent is *any real number*.

Let $E(x) = a^x$, with $a > 0$. We call E the **exponential function** with **base** a. Since $a^x > 0$ when x is rational, hence $a^{r_n} > 0$ in (3), and we conclude that $a^x > 0$ for

---

* Then x is called a *terminating decimal*.

all values of x. We shall assume that E is continuous. On the basis of special cases such as $y = 2^x$ and $y = 2^{-x}$, we accept the following facts.

> *If $a > 1$, then a^x increases as x increases.* (4)

> *If $0 < a < 1$, then a^x decreases as x increases.* (5)

ILLUSTRATION 2. A graph of $y = a^x$ with $a > 1$ ($y = 2^x$ was used) is given in Figure 176. We note that

$$(a > 1) \qquad a^0 = 1; \quad \lim_{x \to -\infty} a^x = 0; \quad \lim_{x \to \infty} a^x = \infty. \qquad (6)$$

ILLUSTRATION 3. In (3), a^x is not defined if $a \leq 0$. If $x = -p/q$ where p and q are positive integers, 0^x is *not defined* on page 683 because $0^{-p/q}$ would lead to $1/0^{p/q}$, where the denominator is zero. Hence, if we desire a^x to be defined as a real number for *all real numbers x*, we must *eliminate $a = 0$ even when x is rational*. If $a < 0$, then a^x represents an imaginary number if $x = p/q$, where p and q are positive integers, p is odd, and q is even. This of itself would account for *the exclusion of $a < 0$* in (3). However, a related reason is that, if $a < 0$, we have no assurance that a^{r_n} in (3) represents a real number. Thus, if $a = -10$ and $x = \sqrt{2}$, we have $a^{r_2} = (-10)^{1.41}$ or $a^{r_2} = \sqrt[100]{(-10)^{141}}$, which is imaginary.

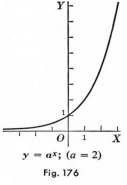

$y = a^x;\ (a = 2)$

Fig. 176

84. THE LOGARITHM AND EXPONENTIAL FUNCTIONS AS INVERSES

Let $E(x) = a^x$ with $a > 0$ and $a \neq 1$. From Figure 176 for the important case **$a > 1$**, notice that, for each value of $y > 0$, there exists *just one value of x* such that $y = E(x)$. The same statement is true if **$0 < a < 1$**.* Hence, the equation $y = E(x)$ defines x as a function, G, of y where G is the inverse of the exponential function E. We call G the **logarithm function** to the **base a** and write **$G(y) = \log_a y$**, where we read "$\log_a y$" as "*logarithm to the base a of y*." Since E and G are inverse functions,

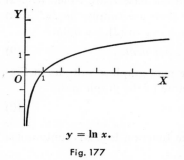

$y = \ln x.$

Fig. 177

> $y = a^x$ *is equivalent to* $x = \log_a y.$ (1)

For a case $a > 1$, the graph of each of equations (1) is in Figure 176. On interchanging x and y in (1), so that the independent variable will be x with the logarithm function, we obtain

> $y = \log_a x$ *is equivalent to* $x = a^y.$ (2)

A graph of (2) for the case $a = 2.71828\cdots$, and then $\log_a x$ replaced by $\ln x$ (to be read later as *the natural logarithm* of x), is in Figure 177. The equivalence (2) justifies the following statement, which usually is adopted as a definition of "$\log_a x$" in elementary mathematics.

---

* The student may check this fact by graphing $y = 2^{-x}$. The most important case is $a > 1$.

$$\left\{ \begin{array}{l} \textit{The } \textbf{logarithm} \textit{ of a number } x > 0 \textit{ to a base } \boldsymbol{a} > \boldsymbol{0}, \textit{ where } \boldsymbol{a} \neq \boldsymbol{1}, \textit{ is the} \\ \textit{exponent of the power to which the base must be raised to obtain } x. \end{array} \right\} \quad (3)$$

ILLUSTRATION 1. If the exponential form, $y = a^x$, in (1) is given for particular numbers a, x, and y, we can write the logarithmic form, $x = \log_a y$, and vice versa. Thus, if $N = 4^5$, then $\log_4 N = 5$. Since $64 = 2^6$, then $\log_2 64 = 6$. If $\log_a 625 = 2$, then $a^2 = 625$, or $a = \sqrt{625} = 25$. If $\log_a 2 = -\frac{1}{3}$, then

$$2 = a^{-\frac{1}{3}} = \frac{1}{\sqrt[3]{a}}, \quad \sqrt[3]{a} = \frac{1}{2}, \quad or \quad a = \frac{1}{8}.$$

If $\log_4 N = -\frac{5}{2}$, then $\qquad\qquad N = 4^{-\frac{5}{2}} = \frac{1}{4^{\frac{5}{2}}} = \frac{1}{2^5} = \frac{1}{32}.$

ILLUSTRATION 2. For any base a, since $a^0 = 1$ and $a^1 = a$, then

$$\log_a 1 = 0 \quad and \quad \log_a a = 1. \tag{4}$$

From (3), $\qquad\qquad\qquad\qquad\qquad x = a^{\log_a x}. \tag{5}$

Note 1. If $G(x) = \log_a x$, we emphasize that the domain of G consists of **all** $x > 0$. That is, **we do not define $\log_a x$ if x is negative or zero.**

We recall the following properties of logarithms, where M and N are any positive numbers, k is any real number, and no denominator is zero. The proofs of these properties would involve the same details as were met when the student studied logarithms at an elementary level.

$$\log_a MN = \log_a M + \log_a N. \tag{6}$$

$$\log_a \frac{M}{N} = \log_a M - \log_a N. \tag{7}$$

$$\log_a M^k = k \log_a M. \tag{8}$$

Logarithms to the base 10 are called **common logarithms** and are the most useful variety in computation. We shall find that, in calculus, the most convenient base for logarithms is a certain irrational number $e = 2.71828\cdots$, which will be introduced in the next section. Logarithms to the base e are called **natural logarithms.** Hereafter, instead of using $\log_e N$, we shall use simply **"ln N,"** read *"natural logarithm of N."* Then, with $x > 0$ and $a = e$ in (2), we obtain

$$y = \ln x \quad and \quad x = e^y \quad are \; equivalent. \tag{9}$$

Hence, to graph $y = \ln x$, more conveniently we may graph $x = e^y$, as in Figure 177 on page 241. The line $x = 0$ is an asymptote of the graph and

$$\lim_{x \to 0+} \ln x = -\infty; \quad \lim_{x \to \infty} \ln x = \infty. \tag{10}$$

We are accepting without proof the fact that the function $\log_a x$ is continuous. Hence, at every point $x = c > 0$,

$$\lim_{x \to c} \ln x = \ln c. \tag{11}$$

As a special case of (5) above, if $x > 0$ then

$$x = e^{\ln x}. \tag{12}$$

Theorem II. *If* $a > 0$, $a \neq 1$, $b > 0$, $b \neq 1$, *and* $N > 0$, *then*

$$\log_a N = (\log_a b)(\log_b N). \tag{13}$$

Proof. Let $y = \log_b N$; then $N = b^y$. Hence, we obtain (13):

$$\log_a N = \log_a b^y = y \log_a b = (\log_a b)(\log_b N).$$

In (13), if $N = a$ then $\log_a a = 1$ and $1 = (\log_a b)(\log_b a)$, or

$$\log_a b = \frac{1}{\log_b a}. \tag{14}$$

We refer to (13) as *the formula for change of base*. In (13), we call $\log_a b$ the **modulus** of the system of logarithms of base a with respect to the system of base b. Given a table of logarithms to the base b, we could form a table for the base a by multiplying each entry of the given table by $\log_a b$. In particular, from (13) with $a = 10$ and $b = e$,

$$\log_{10} N = (\log_{10} e) \ln N, \quad or \quad \ln N = \frac{\log_{10} N}{\log_{10} e}. \tag{15}$$

From (14) with $b = e$,

$$\log_a e = \frac{1}{\ln a}. \tag{16}$$

85. BASE FOR NATURAL LOGARITHMS

With the aid of an advanced discussion of the real number system, it can be proved that the following limit exists, and is equal to the irrational number $e = 2.71828 \cdots$. Thus, e is defined as follows:

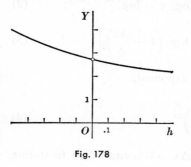

Fig. 178

$$\lim_{h \to 0} (1 + h)^{\frac{1}{h}} = e. \tag{1}$$

Let $f(h) = (1 + h)^{\frac{1}{h}}$. Then, intuitional appreciation of (1) is gained by inspection of the following table and the graph of $y = f(h)$ in Figure 178. The graph has a hole where $h = 0$ because $f(0)$ is undefined.

h	$-.5$	$-.1$	$-.01$	$-.001$	$\cdots$	$.001$	$.01$	$.1$	$.5$	5
$f(h)$	4.000	2.868	2.732	2.718	$\cdots$	2.717	2.705	2.594	2.250	1.431

ILLUSTRATION 1. From (1),

$$\lim_{k \to 0} (1 + 2k)^{\frac{1}{k}} = \lim_{2k \to 0} \left[(1 + 2k)^{\frac{1}{2k}} \right]^2 = e^2.$$

Note 1. We could define e as follows, by using $h = \frac{1}{k}$ in (1):

$$e = \lim_{k \to \infty} \left(1 + \frac{1}{k} \right)^k. \tag{2}$$

REVIEW EXERCISE 70

Write an equivalent logarithmic form:

1. $x = 3^5$.   **2.** $x = 5^{\frac{1}{2}}$.   **3.** $z = 10^{-2}$.   **4.** $.001 = 10^{-3}$.   **5.** $x = 2^y$.

Find the number whose logarithm is given.

6. $\log_4 y = 2$.   **7.** $\log_{125} y = \frac{1}{3}$.   **8.** $\log_8 x = \frac{5}{3}$.

9. Find $\log_9 81$; $\log_3 81$; $\log_{10} 1000$; $\log_7 \frac{1}{7}$; $\log_{10} 1$.

10. Find the base a if $\log_a 64 = 3$; $\log_a 10,000 = -2$; $\log_a 4 = \frac{1}{3}$.

Obtain the limit by use of the definition of e.

11. $\lim\limits_{h \to 0} (1 + h)^{\frac{3}{h}}$.   **12.** $\lim\limits_{k \to 0} (1 + k)^{\frac{1}{2k}}$.   **13.** $\lim\limits_{x \to 0} (1 + \sin x)^{\csc x}$.

86. DIFFERENTIATION OF LOGARITHMIC FUNCTIONS

If the domain of the variable x is all numbers $x > 0$, and if $a > 0$ and $a \neq 1$, we shall prove that

$$\frac{d}{dx} \log_a x = \frac{\log_a e}{x}. \tag{1}$$

Proof. 1. Let $y = \log_a x$. For a fixed number x, suppose that Δx is such that $x + \Delta x > 0$. Then $y = \log_a x$ *and* $y + \Delta y = \log_a (x + \Delta x)$;

from (7), page 242, $\Delta y = \log_a (x + \Delta x) - \log_a x = \log_a \dfrac{x + \Delta x}{x}$;   (2)

$$\frac{\Delta y}{\Delta x} = \frac{1}{\Delta x} \log_a \left(1 + \frac{\Delta x}{x}\right) = \frac{1}{x}\left[\frac{x}{\Delta x} \log_a \left(1 + \frac{\Delta x}{x}\right)\right]. \tag{3}$$

2. From (3), and (8) on page 242 with $\dfrac{x}{\Delta x}$ as the exponent,

$$\frac{\Delta y}{\Delta x} = \frac{1}{x} \log_a \left(1 + \frac{\Delta x}{x}\right)^{\frac{x}{\Delta x}}. \tag{4}$$

In (4), let $h = \dfrac{\Delta x}{x}$; then $\dfrac{x}{\Delta x} = \dfrac{1}{h}$. To say that $\Delta x \to 0$ is equivalent to stating that $h \to 0$. Hence, by use of Section 85, and the fact that the function $\log_a x$ is continuous at $x = e$, we obtain (1):

$$\frac{dy}{dx} = \lim\limits_{\Delta x \to 0} \frac{\Delta y}{\Delta x} = \frac{1}{x} \lim\limits_{h \to 0} \log_a (1 + h)^{\frac{1}{h}} = \frac{1}{x} \log_a \left[\lim\limits_{h \to 0} (1 + h)^{\frac{1}{h}}\right] = \frac{1}{x} \log_a e.$$

If $a = e$ in (1), then $\log_a e = \log_e e = 1$, and (1) becomes

$$\frac{d \ln x}{dx} = \frac{1}{x}. \tag{XVII$'$}$$

Hence, a very simple formula (XVII)′ is obtained for $D_x \log_a x$, **if** $a = e$. For this reason, we decide that, hereafter in calculus, *we shall use logarithms to the base e wherever possible.*

Proof of **(XVII)** *on page* 222. Let u be a differentiable function of x. Then, by use of (XVII)′ and the derivative of a composite function,

$$\frac{d}{dx}\ln u = \frac{d\ln u}{du}\cdot\frac{du}{dx} = \frac{1}{u}\frac{du}{dx}.$$

Similarly, we could prove **(XVIII)** by use of (1).

ILLUSTRATION 1. $\dfrac{d}{dx}\ln(1+4x) = \dfrac{1}{1+4x}\dfrac{d(1+4x)}{dx} = \dfrac{4}{1+4x}.$

$\dfrac{d}{dx}\ln[\ln(3x-2)] = \dfrac{1}{\ln(3x-2)}\dfrac{d\ln(3x-2)}{dx} = \dfrac{3}{(3x-2)\ln(3x-2)}.$

EXAMPLE 1. Differentiate $\ln[(3+5x)\sqrt[3]{2x+7}]$.

Solution. Let $y = \ln[(3+5x)\sqrt[3]{2x+7}]$. By use of the properties of logarithms in (6) and (8) on page 242, with $\sqrt[3]{2x+7}$ rewritten as $(2x+7)^{\frac{1}{3}}$,

$$y = \ln(3+5x) + \tfrac{1}{3}\ln(2x+7);$$

$$\frac{dy}{dx} = \frac{5}{3+5x} + \frac{1}{3}\cdot\frac{2}{2x+7} = \frac{40x+111}{3(3+5x)(2x+7)}.$$

Notice the simplification due to using properties of logarithms before differentiation.

EXAMPLE 2. Find dy/dx if y is defined implicitly as a function of x by the equation

$$\ln x + \ln(3y+2) = 16x^2. \tag{5}$$

Solution. Differentiate with respect to x on both sides of (5):

$$\frac{1}{x} + \frac{1}{3y+2}\frac{d(3y+2)}{dx} = 32x, \quad or \quad \frac{1}{x} + \frac{1}{3y+2}(3y') = 32x, \; or$$

$$y' = \frac{96x^2y + 64x^2 - 3y - 2}{3x}.$$

To obtain the derivative of a function $f(x)$ which is a complicated product or quotient, it may be convenient to start by finding $\ln f(x)$. This method will be referred to as *logarithmic differentiation.*

EXAMPLE 3. Find dy/dx: $\qquad y = (3+2x)^3(5-x)^2\sqrt[3]{2-4x}. \tag{6}$

Solution. 1. From (6), and properties of logarithms,

$$\ln y = 3\ln(3+2x) + 2\ln(5-x) + \tfrac{1}{3}\ln(2-4x). \tag{7}$$

2. Differentiate with respect to x on both sides of (7):

$$\frac{1}{y}\frac{dy}{dx} = \frac{6}{3+2x} - \frac{2}{5-x} - \frac{4}{3(2-4x)}, \; or$$

$$\frac{1}{y}\frac{dy}{dx} = \frac{84 - 376x + 128x^2}{3(3+2x)(5-x)(2-4x)}. \tag{8}$$

Multiply both sides of (8) by y, and use (6):

$$y' = \tfrac{1}{3}(84 - 376x + 128x^2)(3+2x)^2(5-x)(2-4x)^{-\frac{2}{3}}.$$

EXERCISE 71

Differentiate the function whose values are defined. Where convenient, first use properties of logarithms.

1. $\ln (3 + 5x)$. **2.** $\ln (4 - 3x)$. **3.** $\ln (z^2 + 2z)$. **4.** $\ln (z^2 - 4)$.

5. $\log_a (\cot x)$. **6.** $\ln \cos \frac{1}{2}x$. **7.** $\ln \sec 3x$. **8.** $\ln \tan \frac{1}{3}x$.

9. $\log_a (\ln x)$. **10.** $\ln (\ln \csc x)$. **11.** $\ln x^3$. **12.** $(\ln x)^4$.

13. $\ln (2 + 4x)^2$. **14.** $\ln \sin^3 x$. **15.** $\log_{10} \tan^2 x$. **16.** $\ln \sqrt{\sec x}$.

17. $[\ln (1 - 4x)]^3$. **18.** $(\ln \cot x)^2$. **19.** $\sqrt{\ln (3x - 1)}$.

20. $(\ln \sin x)^{-2}$. **21.** $\ln \sqrt[4]{1 - x^3}$. **22.** $\ln \sqrt[3]{4 + 5x}$.

23. $(5 \ln x)^{-2}$. **24.** $(\ln x)\ln (3x - 2)$. **25.** $(\ln 2x)\ln \sin x$.

26. $\ln (2 + 3x)(5 + 7x)$. **27.** $\ln (1 + x^2)(2 - 5x)$.

28. $\ln (1 - x)^2(2 - 5x)^3$. **29.** $\ln (3 + z^3)^2(2 - 4z)^5$.

30. $\ln (\sin^3 x)(2 + \cos x)^2$. **31.** $\ln \tan^3 x \sin^2 2x \cos 3x$.

32. $\ln \sqrt{4 + 7x}\sqrt[3]{2 + 5x}$. **33.** $\ln \sqrt{\sin x}\sqrt[3]{1 - \cos x}$.

34. $\dfrac{5}{\ln x}$. **35.** $\dfrac{3}{(\ln x)^2}$. **36.** $\dfrac{2}{\ln \cos x}$. **37.** $\dfrac{\sin x}{\ln \cos x}$.

38. $\ln \dfrac{2 + 3x}{5 - x}$. **39.** $\dfrac{\ln \sin x}{\ln \cos x}$. **40.** $\ln \dfrac{1 - \sin x}{1 + \cos x}$.

41. $\ln \sqrt{\dfrac{2 - x}{3 + x}}$. **42.** $\ln \sqrt[3]{\dfrac{1 - \cos x}{1 + \cos x}}$. **43.** $\dfrac{\ln (3x - 1)^3}{(3x - 1)^2}$.

Evaluate y' at the specified point, perhaps by use of Table III.

44. $y = x^2 \ln x$; at $x = 3$. **45.** $y = x \ln \sqrt{3 - x}$; at $x = 1$.

46. Find f'' if $f(x) = x^2 \ln (x + 1)$; $f(x) = x \ln \sin 3x$.

Find y', with y defined as an implicit function of x by the equation.

47. $\ln x + \ln y = 5$. **48.** $\ln (x + 2y) + \sin x = y^2$.

49. $\ln \sqrt{2x + 3y} - x^2 = \ln x^2$. **50.** $\sin \ln y + \cos x = 5$.

Obtain dy/dx by differentiating $\ln y$.

51. $y = (2 + x)^3(2x - 3)^8$. **52.** $y = (3 + 4x)^7(1 - 2x)^9$.

53. $y = \dfrac{(x + 2)^3}{(3x - 1)^4}$. **54.** $y = \dfrac{(2x + 3)^5}{(4x - 3)^4}$. **55.** $y = \sqrt{\dfrac{2x - 1}{3x + 2}}$.

56. $y = \dfrac{(5x + 1)^{\frac{3}{2}}}{(1 - 2x)^{\frac{2}{3}}}$. **57.** $y = \dfrac{\sqrt[5]{1 - 3x}}{\sqrt[3]{2 + 4x}}$. **58.** $y = \dfrac{\sqrt[3]{1 + \sin 2x}}{(3 + \cos x)^2}$.

Obtain the nth derivative of the function, and prove the result by induction.

59. $\ln x$. **60.** $\ln (1 - x)$. **61.** $\ln (1 + x)$.

87. DIFFERENTIATION OF EXPONENTIAL FUNCTIONS

Proof of (XIX) *on page* 222. Let u be a differentiable function of x, and let $y = e^u$. Then, we have

$$u = \ln y, \tag{1}$$

where u and y are functions of x. On differentiating with respect to x on both sides in (1), and using (XVII), we obtain (XIX):

$$\frac{du}{dx} = \frac{1}{y}\frac{dy}{dx}, \quad or \quad \frac{dy}{dx} = y\frac{du}{dx} = e^u\frac{du}{dx}. \tag{2}$$

Proof of (XX). If $y = a^u$ then $u = \log_a y$. On differentiating both sides of this equation with respect to x, by use of (XVIII) we obtain

$$\frac{du}{dx} = \frac{\log_a e}{y}\frac{dy}{dx} = \frac{1}{y\ln a}\frac{dy}{dx}, \tag{3}$$

where (16) on page 243 was used. Hence, from (3) we obtain (XX):

$$\frac{dy}{dx} = y(\ln a)\frac{du}{dx} = a^u(\ln a)\frac{du}{dx}.$$

ILLUSTRATION 1. From (XIX) with $u = 3x$, $\quad \dfrac{de^{3x}}{dx} = e^{3x}\dfrac{d(3x)}{dx} = 3e^{3x}.$

$$\frac{de^{\sin^2 4x}}{dx} = e^{\sin^2 4x}\frac{d\sin^2 4x}{dx} = 8e^{\sin^2 4x}\sin 4x \cos 4x.$$

$$\frac{de^{e^{\tan x}}}{dx} = e^{e^{\tan x}}\frac{de^{\tan x}}{dx} = e^{\tan x}\, e^{e^{\tan x}}\sec^2 x.$$

From (12) on page 242, $\quad \dfrac{de^{\ln(2x+3)}}{dx} = \dfrac{d(2x+3)}{dx} = 2.$

We have proved that $\qquad \dfrac{d}{dx}u^n = nu^{n-1}\dfrac{du}{dx}$ (III)

only when n is a rational number. Now we are prepared to prove (III) for any real number n, provided that $u > 0$.

Proof of (III). Let $y = u^n$, where u is a differentiable function of x, with $u > 0$ at all values of x. Then, $u = e^{\ln u}$ and

$$y = (e^{\ln u})^n = e^{n\ln u}. \tag{4}$$

Hence, from (4) and (XIX) we obtain (III):

$$\frac{dy}{dx} = e^{n\ln u}\left[\frac{d(n\ln u)}{dx}\right] = \frac{n}{u}(e^{n\ln u})\frac{du}{dx} = \frac{nu^n}{u}\cdot\frac{du}{dx} = nu^{n-1}\frac{du}{dx}.$$

EXAMPLE 1. Find y' if $y = x^{\sin x}$.

Solution. Use logarithmic differentiation: $\qquad \ln y = (\sin x)\ln x. \tag{5}$

Differentiate with respect to x on both sides of (5) and finally use $y = x^{\sin x}$:

$$\frac{1}{y}\frac{dy}{dx} = \frac{\sin x}{x} + (\ln x)\cos x; \quad \frac{dy}{dx} = x^{\sin x}\left[\frac{\sin x}{x} + (\cos x)\ln x\right].$$

By the method of the preceding solution, in the next exercise the student will derive the general exponential formula (XXI) on page 222. Any particular case may be solved as in Example 1. On the right in (XXI), the first term is what we would obtain if v were a constant; the second term is what we would obtain from (XX) if u were a constant.

88. GRAPHING OF LOGARITHMIC AND EXPONENTIAL FUNCTIONS

EXAMPLE 1. Graph the function xe^{-x}, given that

$$\lim_{x \to \infty} xe^{-x} = 0. \tag{1}$$

Solution. 1. The domain for x is $-\infty < x < \infty$. Let $y = xe^{-x}$. We find

$$y' = e^{-x}(1 - x); \quad y'' = e^{-x}(x - 2). \tag{2}$$

2. *Extrema.* $y' = 0$ just at $x = 1$, because e^{-x} is never zero. Then, at $x = 1$, we find $y'' < 0$. Hence, there is a maximum $y = e^{-1} = .37$ at $x = 1$.

3. *Inflection points.* $y'' = 0$ just when $x = 2$. Also, y'' changes sign from "$-$" to "$+$" as x increases through 2. Hence, there is an inflection point at $x = 2$, where the graph changes from concave downward to concave upward as x increases through $x = 2$.

4. From (1), whose proof will be given later in this chapter, the graph has the line $y = 0$ as an asymptote, approached as $x \to \infty$. If $x \to -\infty$, then $y \to -\infty$. Values of y were computed with the aid of Table V. The graph is given in Figure 179.

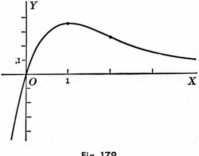

In graphing exponential or logarithmic functions, investigation of extrema and inflection points may involve the solution of logarithmic or exponential equations.

Fig. 179

ILLUSTRATION 1. To solve $e^{2x} = \frac{1}{2}$, take logarithms and use Table III:

$$\ln e^{2x} = \ln \tfrac{1}{2}, \quad or \quad 2x = -\ln 2; \quad x = -\tfrac{1}{2}\ln 2 = -.34658.$$

EXAMPLE 2. Graph the function $y = \ln \cos x$.

Solution. 1. Since the function $\ln \cos x$ is periodic with the period 2π, consider just the graph on the interval $-\frac{1}{2}\pi < x < \frac{3}{2}\pi$. Since $\ln N$ is defined only when $N > 0$, the domain for x in $y = \ln \cos x$ is $-\frac{1}{2}\pi < x < \frac{1}{2}\pi$, where $\cos x > 0$. Since $\cos x \to 0$ as $x \to \frac{1}{2}\pi$ and as $x \to -\frac{1}{2}\pi$, hence we obtain

$$\lim_{x \to \frac{1}{2}\pi-} \ln \cos x = -\infty, \; and$$

$$\lim_{x \to -\frac{1}{2}\pi+} \ln \cos x = -\infty.$$

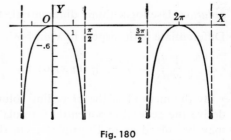

Thus, the lines $x = \pm\frac{1}{2}\pi$ are asymptotes of the curve.

2. By investigating y' and y'', the student may verify that the graph, as in Figure 180, has a maximum at $x = 0$ and no inflection point, because

Fig. 180

$$y' = -\tan x, \quad y'' = -\sec^2 x, \quad and \quad y'' \neq 0 \; at \; any \; x.$$

EXERCISE 72

Differentiate the function.

1. e^{4x}. **2.** e^{2x+3}. **3.** $e^{\cot x}$. **4.** $e^{\ln t^2}$. **5.** e^{-2x}.

6. $e^{-\sqrt{z}}$. **7.** a^{4t}. **8.** $10^{\cos x}$. **9.** $e^{(\ln x)^2}$. **10.** $10^x e^x$.

11. e^{3x-x^2}. **12.** $e^{x \ln x}$. **13.** $x^3 e^{-x^3}$. **14.** $\ln e^{4z}$.

15. $\sin e^x$. **16.** $\cos a^t$. **17.** $\text{Arcsin } e^{2t}$. **18.** $\text{Arctan } e^x$.

19. $\dfrac{\ln x}{e^{3x}}$. **20.** $\dfrac{a^x e^x}{\ln x}$. **21.** $\dfrac{\sin x}{e^{\sqrt{2x}}}$. **22.** $\dfrac{\ln z^3}{e^{z^3}}$.

23. $\text{Arctan } (xe^{2x})$. **24.** $\text{Arcsin } (e^{x^2} \ln x)$. **25.** $e^{-2t} \cos 5t$.

26. $\dfrac{\tan x + \sec x}{e^{-2x}}$. **27.** $\dfrac{e^x + e^{-2x}}{e^x - e^{-2x}}$. **28.** $\dfrac{e^{3x} - 1}{e^{3x} + 1}$.

29. $(3x + e^{-2x})^5$. **30.** $\sqrt{5 - 2e^{-3t}}$. **31.** $e^x\sqrt{1 + \ln x}$.

Find y' if x and y are related by the equation.

32. $e^{x+2y} - \ln x = 3$. **33.** $xy - \ln y = e^{-y}$.

34. Find the tangent at the point where $x = -2$ on the graph of $y = (2x - 1)e^{-\frac{1}{4}x}$.

Find y' by differentiating $\ln y$. Check by use of (XXI).

35. $y = x^{x^2}$. **36.** $y = \sqrt{x^x}$. **37.** $y = x^{\cos x}$. **38.** $y = (\sin x)^{\cos x}$.

39. Find the nth derivative of f if $f(x) = e^x$; $f(x) = xe^x$.

40. Specify the value of each limit: $\lim\limits_{x \to \frac{1}{2}\pi -} e^{\tan x}$; $\lim\limits_{x \to 0+} \ln \sin x$.

Apply tests for extrema and inflection points and graph the equation.

41. $y = \ln (x - 3)$. **42.** $y = e^x$. **43.** $y = e^{-x}$. **44.** $x = e^{2y}$.

45. $x = \ln (4 + x^2)$. **46.** $y = \ln x^2$. **47.** $y = x - \ln x$.

48. $y = xe^x$, given that $y \to 0$ as $x \to -\infty$.

49. The **hyperbolic sine** of x: $y = \frac{1}{2}(e^x - e^{-x})$.

50. The **hyperbolic cosine** of x: $y = \frac{1}{2}(e^x + e^{-x})$.

51. $y = \dfrac{1}{\sqrt{2\pi}} e^{-\frac{1}{2}x^2}$, the **normal probability density function** of statistics.

52. $y = \ln \sin x$. **53.** $y = \ln \sec x$. **54.** $y = \ln \tan x$.

89. APPLICATIONS TO RECTILINEAR MOTION

Let the position of a particle at time t in motion on an s-axis be given by

$$s = k \sin (\omega t - \alpha), \tag{1}$$

where k, ω, and α are constants, with $k > 0$ and $\omega > 0$. Then, the motion is called **simple harmonic motion.** Since the function $\sin x$ is periodic with the period 2π, the function $\sin (\omega t - \alpha)$ is a periodic function of t with the period $2\pi/\omega$, because

$$\sin [\omega(t + 2\pi/\omega) - \alpha] = \sin (\omega t - \alpha + 2\pi) = \sin (\omega t - \alpha).$$

EXAMPLE 1. For $t \geqq 0$, study the motion defined by

$$s = 5 \sin (3t - \tfrac{1}{4}\pi) = 5 \sin 3(t - \tfrac{1}{12}\pi). \tag{2}$$

Solution. 1. In (2), s is a periodic function of t with the period $\frac{2}{3}\pi$.

2. In (2), if we translated the st-axes to $(0, \frac{1}{12}\pi)$, the new equation, with co-ordinates labeled $(\hat{s}, \hat{t})$, would be $\hat{s} = 5 \sin 3\hat{t}$, which is a sine curve with amplitude 5. We shall not introduce $(\hat{s}, \hat{t})$ below. The domain for s is $-5 \leqq s \leqq 5$. With n taking on all integral values $n \geqq 0$, we find that

$$s = 5 \quad at \quad 3t - \tfrac{1}{4}\pi = \tfrac{1}{2}\pi + 2n\pi, \; or \qquad t = \tfrac{1}{4}\pi + n(\tfrac{2}{3}\pi); \tag{3}$$

$$s = -5 \quad at \quad 3t - \tfrac{1}{4}\pi = \tfrac{3}{2}\pi + 2n\pi, \; or \qquad t = \tfrac{7}{12}\pi + n(\tfrac{2}{3}\pi); \tag{4}$$

$$s = 0 \quad at \quad 3t - \tfrac{1}{4}\pi = n\pi, \; or \qquad t = \tfrac{1}{12}\pi + n(\tfrac{1}{3}\pi). \tag{5}$$

The graph of (2) is in Figure 181.

3. $\quad v = \dfrac{ds}{dt} = 15 \cos (3t - \tfrac{1}{4}\pi); \quad a = \dfrac{d^2s}{dt^2} = -45 \sin (3t - \tfrac{1}{4}\pi) = -9s. \tag{6}$

Hence, $v = 0$ when $3t - \tfrac{1}{4}\pi = \tfrac{1}{2}\pi + n\pi$, where we found $s = \pm 5$ in (3) and (4). Also, the speed $|v|$ has its maximum, 15, when $3t - \tfrac{1}{4}\pi = n\pi$, where $s = 0$. Since $a = -9s$, a and s have *opposite signs* when not equal to zero. The acceleration attains its minimum -45 whenever $s = 5$, and maximum 45 whenever $s = -5$. The particle P starts at the point $s = -\tfrac{5}{2}\sqrt{2} = -3.5$ on the s-axis, as seen in Figure 182, and thereafter oscillates between $s = -5$ and $s = 5$. The speed $|v|$ of P attains its maximum 15 whenever $s = 0$.

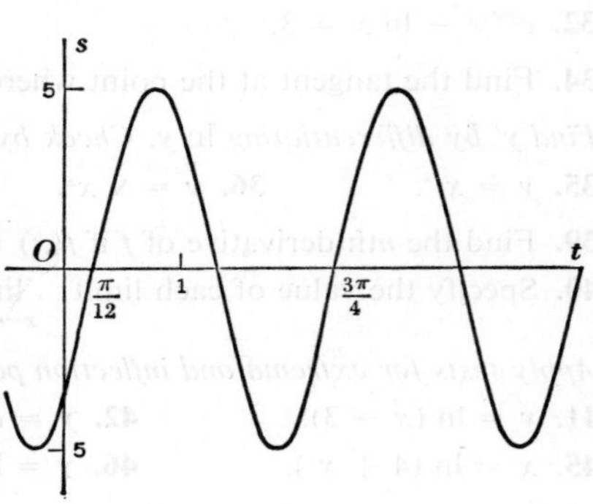

Fig. 181

Comment. In Example 1, if P has mass m, then the force, F, acting on P at the instant t is $F = ma = -9ms$. Thus, in simple harmonic motion about the origin $s = 0$, $|F|$ is proportional to the distance of P from the origin $s = 0$, and F is always directed at the origin when $s \neq 0$, since $F > 0$ when $s < 0$, and $F < 0$ when $s > 0$.

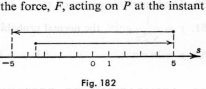

Fig. 182

Similarly, as in Example 1, the motion determined by (1) is periodic with the period $2\pi/\omega$, and the particle oscillates between $s = k$ and $s = -k$. In (1), we call k the **amplitude** and α the **phase constant** of the motion. The graph of s as a function of t is a sine curve shifted a distance α/ω along the t-axis. In (1), $\cos (\omega t - \alpha)$ could be used instead of $\sin (\omega t - \alpha)$ with similar conclusions.

Note 1. If $s = A \cos \omega t + B \sin \omega t$, where A and B are not both zero and $\omega > 0$, we can find constants α and $k > 0$, with $-\pi < \alpha \leqq \pi$, so that $s = k \sin (\omega t - \alpha)$. For this purpose, we write

$$A \cos \omega t + B \sin \omega t = k (\sin \omega t \cos \alpha - \cos \omega t \sin \alpha), \tag{7}$$

where $\qquad\qquad k \cos \alpha = B \quad and \quad k \sin \alpha = -A. \tag{8}$

Then, $k^2 = A^2 + B^2,$ *and we select* $k = \sqrt{A^2 + B^2}.$ (9)

From (8), $\sin \alpha = -\dfrac{A}{k}$ *and* $\cos \alpha = \dfrac{B}{k}.$ (10)

With $k > 0$ from (9), we can find α and its quadrant from (10). Thus,

$$s = A \cos \omega t + B \sin \omega t \quad becomes \quad s = k \sin (\omega t - \alpha).$$ (11)

Hence, the standard form (1) is equivalent to the form at the left in (11).

ILLUSTRATION 1. To change $s = 5 \sin 2t + 12 \cos 2t$ (12)

to the form (1), we use (9) to obtain $k = 13$; (10) gives $\sin \alpha = -\frac{12}{13}$ and $\cos \alpha > 0$. Hence, α is on an interval in quadrant IV. From Table IV, $\frac{12}{13} = \sin 1.176$; thus, $\alpha = -1.176$ and (11) gives $s = 13 \sin (2t + 1.176)$.

ILLUSTRATION 2. If the motion of a particle P on an s-axis is determined by

$$s = e^{-at} \sin (\omega t - \alpha),$$ (13)

where $a > 0$, the motion is referred to as a **damped vibration.** In (13), $s = 0$ periodically with the period $2\pi/\omega$ as t increases, and P oscillates through $s = 0$, with the amplitude of oscillation approaching zero as $t \to \infty$, because then $e^{-at} \to 0$. A graph of (13) with $a = .5$, $\alpha = 0$, and $\omega = 2$ is the continuous curve in Figure 183, tangent to the broken-line curves $s = e^{-at}$ and $s = -e^{-at}$ at common points.

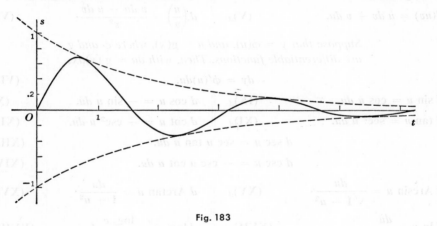

Fig. 183

EXERCISE 73

Find the velocity, v, and acceleration, a, of a particle P at the indicated values of the time t, if P has the given equation for motion on an s-axis. Also, graph s as a function of t without using calculus and describe the motion when $t \geqq 0$. State the period of the motion. Use Note 1 on page 250 where appropriate.

1. $s = 3 \sin 2t$; find v and a at $t = 0, \frac{1}{4}\pi, \frac{1}{2}\pi, \frac{3}{4}\pi, \pi$.
2. $s = 5 \sin (t - \frac{1}{4}\pi)$; find v and a at $t = 0, \frac{1}{4}\pi, \frac{1}{2}\pi, \frac{3}{4}\pi, \pi$.
3. $s = 4 \cos (2t - \frac{1}{3}\pi)$; find v and a at $t = 0, \frac{1}{3}\pi, \frac{2}{3}\pi, \pi, \frac{5}{3}\pi$.
4. $s = \cos t - \sqrt{3} \sin t$; find v and a at $t = 0, \frac{1}{6}\pi, \frac{1}{3}\pi, \frac{5}{6}\pi$.
5. $s = 3 \sin 2t - 3 \cos 2t$; find v and a at $t = 0, \frac{1}{4}\pi, \frac{1}{2}\pi, \frac{3}{4}\pi$.
6. $s = 3 \sin t + 4 \cos t$; find v and a at $t = 0, \frac{1}{2}\pi, \pi$.

★7. The equation of motion for a particle P is $s = e^{-t}\sin t$. (a) Locate all extrema and graph s as a function of t; also graph $s = e^{-t}$ and $s = -e^{-t}$ on the same coordinate system. (b) Prove that the curve $s = e^{-t}\sin t$ is tangent to each of the exponential curves at any common point. (c) Describe the motion of P on the s-axis.

★8. Repeat Problem 7 for the equation of motion $s = e^{-.5t}\cos .5t$.

90. DIFFERENTIALS OF TRANSCENDENTAL FUNCTIONS

Corresponding to each of the derivative formulas (I)–(XXI), except (VIII), on pages 92, 221, and 222, we obtain a differential formula, labeled with the subscript d below, on multiplying both sides of the derivative formula by dx. From page 152, recall that (VII)$_d$ includes each of the later differential formulas as a special case. In the following results, u and v represent differentiable functions of x, and k is a constant; (I)$_d$–(VII)$_d$ were met on page 152.

SUMMARY OF FUNDAMENTAL DIFFERENTIALS

$d(k) = 0.$ (I)$_d$ $\qquad$ $d(ku) = k\,du.$ (II)$_d$

$d(u^n) = nu^{n-1}\,du.$ (III)$_d$ $\qquad$ $d(u + v) = du + dv.$ (IV)$_d$

$d(uv) = u\,dv + v\,du.$ (V)$_d$ $\qquad$ $d\left(\dfrac{u}{v}\right) = \dfrac{v\,du - u\,dv}{v^2}.$ (VI)$_d$

*Suppose that $y = \phi(u)$, and $u = g(x)$, where ϕ and g
are differentiable functions. Then, with $du = g'(x)dx$,*

$$dy = \phi'(u)du. \tag{VII$_d$}$$

$d\sin u = \cos u\,du.$ (IX)$_d$ $\qquad$ $d\cos u = -\sin u\,du.$ (X)$_d$

$d\tan u = \sec^2 u\,du.$ (XI)$_d$ $\qquad$ $d\cot u = -\csc^2 u\,du.$ (XII)$_d$

$d\sec u = \sec u \tan u\,du.$ (XIII)$_d$

$d\csc u = -\csc u \cot u\,du.$ (XIV)$_d$

$d\,\text{Arcsin}\,u = \dfrac{du}{\sqrt{1 - u^2}}.$ (XV)$_d$ $\qquad$ $d\,\text{Arctan}\,u = \dfrac{du}{1 + u^2}.$ (XVI)$_d$

$d\ln u = \dfrac{du}{u}.$ (XVII)$_d$ $\qquad$ $d\log_a u = \dfrac{\log_a e}{u}\,du.$ (XVIII)$_d$

$d(e^u) = e^u\,du.$ (XIX)$_d$ $\qquad$ $d(a^u) = a^u \ln a\,du.$ (XX)$_d$

$d(u^v) = vu^{v-1}\,du + (\ln u)u^v\,dv.$ (XXI)$_d$

ILLUSTRATION 1. By (IX)$_d$ with $u = x^2 + e^x$, and $du = (2x + e^x)dx$,
$$d\sin(x^2 + e^x) = [\cos(x^2 + e^x)](2x + e^x)dx.$$

From (XVII)$_d$, $d\ln\csc x = \dfrac{1}{\csc x}\,d\csc x = -\dfrac{\csc x \cot x}{\csc x}\,dx = -\cot x\,dx.$

From (XIX)$_d$, $de^{\text{Arcsin}\,x} = e^{\text{Arcsin}\,x}\,d\,\text{Arcsin}\,x = e^{\text{Arcsin}\,x}\left(\dfrac{dx}{\sqrt{1 - x^2}}\right).$

From (V)$_d$, $d(e^{-3x}\ln x) = (\ln x)de^{-3x} + e^{-3x}d\ln x = -3(\ln x)e^{-3x} + \dfrac{e^{-3x}}{x}.$

EXAMPLE 1. For the triangle in Figure 184, the base AC has length 7.4′. The angle at A is measured as 35.3°, with an error not larger than .5°. Find approximately the maximum possible error in the triangle's area as computed from the data.

Solution. 1. Let α be the measure in radians of the angle at A in a *variable* right triangle ABC, and let W be its area. Then,

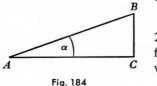

Fig. 184

$$\overline{BC} = 7.4 \tan \alpha; \quad W = \tfrac{1}{2}(7.4)^2 \tan \alpha. \qquad (1)$$

2. In (1), interpret $\tan \alpha$ as a standard trigonometric function. An error $d\alpha$ in α causes an error ΔW in W, where

$$\Delta W \approx dW = \tfrac{1}{2}(7.4)^2 \sec^2 \alpha \, d\alpha. \qquad (2)$$

3. We use (2) with (α *radians*) = 35.3°, so that $\sec^2 \alpha = \sec^2 35.3°$; $|d\alpha|$ is at most the number of radians in .5°, or $|d\alpha| \leq \tfrac{1}{2}(\pi/180)$. Hence,

$$|\Delta W| \approx \tfrac{1}{2}(7.4)^2(\sec^2 \alpha) |d\alpha| \leq \tfrac{1}{2}(7.4)^2(\sec^2 35.3°) \cdot \frac{\pi}{360} = .36,$$

by logarithms. Or, approximately, the error is at most .36 square foot.

EXAMPLE 2. Compute $\sin 32°$ approximately by differentials.

Solution. 1. Let $y = \sin x$, which we shall interpret as the standard $\sin x$ in differentiation, with $\sin x$ being the sine of the angle x radians. We shall obtain $\sin 32°$ by adding to $\sin 30°$ (known) the increment Δy, approximated as dy, due to an increase of 2° in the angle. First, we change the data to radian measure:

$$30° = \frac{\pi}{6} \, radians; \quad 2° = \frac{2\pi}{180} \, radians = \frac{\pi}{90} \, radians.$$

2. We desire dy corresponding to $x = \pi/6$ and $dx = \pi/90$:

$$dy = \cos x \, dx; \quad \Delta y \approx dy = \left(\cos \frac{1}{6}\pi\right)\frac{\pi}{90} = \left(\frac{1}{2}\sqrt{3}\right)\left(\frac{\pi}{90}\right) = .0302.$$

Hence, $\qquad \sin 32° = \sin 30° + \Delta y \approx .5000 + .0302 = .5302.$

Suppose that $y = f(x)$, where f is a differentiable function. Consider a problem where we measure the value of x in some type of experiment, and then compute the corresponding value of y from $y = f(x)$. On page 155, we used dy/y as an approximation to the relative error, $\Delta y/y$, in the computed value of y due to an error dx in x. We notice that $d \ln y = dy/y$. Hence,

$$\left\{ \begin{array}{l} \textbf{relative error in } y \\ \textbf{due to error } dx \textbf{ in } x \end{array} \right\} \approx \frac{dy}{y} = d \ln y. \qquad (3)$$

Use of (3) is convenient if $d \ln y$ is expressible simply in terms of dx/x.

EXAMPLE 3. A cone has the altitude h units. The radius of the base of the cone is measured as r units, with an error of at most 3%. Find approximately the maximum possible percent of error in the computed volume, V.

Solution. 1. For a variable cone, and with V and r as related variables,

$$V = \tfrac{1}{3}\pi r^2 h; \quad \ln V = \ln \tfrac{1}{3}\pi + \ln h + 2 \ln r. \tag{4}$$

With r given by measurement, h a constant, and V then computed,

$$\left\{ \begin{array}{c} relative \\ error\ in\ V \end{array} \right\} \approx d \ln V = 0 + 0 + 2\,\frac{dr}{r}. \tag{5}$$

2. The percent of error in r is the relative error expressed as a percent, and thus is the value of dr/r. Hence, from (5),

$$| d \ln V | \leq 2\left|\frac{dr}{r}\right| \leq 2(.03) = .06, \tag{6}$$

or the error in V does not exceed 6%, approximately.

Comment. Focus on the necessity for *absolute value signs* in (6). The data give us an *upper bound* for the relative error.

EXERCISE 74

Calculate the differential of the function, where t, x, y, or z is the independent variable.

1. e^{4x}.
2. $\cos 5x$.
3. $\tan 2x$.
4. $\sin \tfrac{1}{3}x$.
5. $e^{\sin z}$.
6. $\ln 8y$.
7. $\ln (\ln x)$.
8. $\ln (x + 3)^5$.
9. $\ln \cos y$.
10. $\text{Arcsin } \tfrac{1}{2}z$.
11. $\text{Arctan } 3y$.
12. $\ln 2z$.
13. $e^x \sin 3x$.
14. $\cos (e^{2z} + x)$.
15. $e^{-2x} \ln x$.
16. $(\tan x) \ln x$.
17. $\ln \text{Arctan } x$.
18. $10^{4z} \sin 2z$.
19. $a^t \ln \sin t$.
20. $\dfrac{e^x - 1}{e^x + 1}$.
21. $\dfrac{\sin t + \cos t}{\sin t - \cos t}$.
22. $\dfrac{\ln x}{x^2 + 1}$.

Solve Problems 23–27 by use of differentials. Recall (3) of Section 90.

23. From a point on a shore of a lake, the angle of elevation of the top of a wall 75' high on the opposite shore is measured as 30°, with an error not larger than 6'. Find approximately the maximum possible error in the distance across the lake as computed from these data.

24. The angle at the vertex in a cross section through the vertex of a cone perpendicular to its base is measured as 40°, with an error not larger than .2°. The radius of the base is 10'. Find approximately the maximum possible error in (a) the volume and (b) the lateral area of the cone as computed from the data. Use logarithms.

25. If a certain metal sphere of radius r is heated to a specified temperature, the radius will increase by .3%. Find approximately the percent of increase in (a) the surface area and (b) the volume of the sphere.

26. Suppose that the time T, in seconds, for one oscillation of a pendulum l feet long is given by $T = \pi\sqrt{l/g}$ where $g = 32$. If l is measured with an error not larger than 2.5%, find approximately the maximum possible percent of error in the value computed for T.

27. Find approximately the maximum percent of error permissible in measuring the radius of a circle if the computed area is to be in error by not more than 3%.

Find the function value approximately, by use of differentials. Check by a table.

28. $\tan 47°$.
29. $\cos 61°$.
30. $\sin 148°$.
31. $e^{.03}$.
32. $\ln 1.02$.
33. $\ln .99$.
34. $e^{1.03}$.
35. $e^{.98}$.

91. PARAMETRIC FORM WITH TRANSCENDENTAL FUNCTIONS

Sometimes, a geometric definition of a locus in an xy-plane may lead easily to parametric equations, and only with difficulty to an xy-equation.

ILLUSTRATION 1. If a circle rolls on a straight line in a plane, any point on the circumference traces out a curve called a **cycloid**. To obtain parametric equations for it, let the line be the x-axis, let the length of the radius of the circle be r, and suppose that, at some fixed instant, the moving point P is at the origin. At a later instant when the circle is tangent to OX at K, let H be the center of the circle, and let $P:(x, y)$ be the position of the moving point, in Figure 185. Let θ be the measure, in radians, of angle PHK, considered positive in the direction indicated by the arrow. Let all vertical and horizontal line segments be *directed*, with the usual directions specified as positive. Then, since the circle has rolled from O to K, we have *arc* $KSP = \overline{OK}$;

$$\overline{MK} = \overline{PN} = r \sin \theta \quad and \quad \overline{OK} = arc\ KSP = r\theta;$$

$$x = \overline{OM} = \overline{OK} - \overline{MK} = r\theta - r \sin \theta; \tag{1}$$

$$y = \overline{MP} = \overline{KH} - \overline{NH} = r - r \cos \theta. \tag{2}$$

Therefore,
$$\begin{cases} x = r(\theta - \sin \theta)\ and & (3) \\ y = r(1 - \cos \theta) & (4) \end{cases}$$

are parametric equations for the cycloid. It consists of an endless sequence of arches to the left and right of the y-axis; those on the left are obtained when $\theta < 0$.

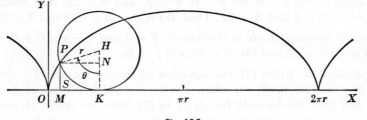

Fig. 185

EXAMPLE 1. Obtain an xy-equation for the curve

$$x = a \cos t \quad and \quad y = b \sin t, \tag{5}$$

where $a > 0$, $b > 0$, and t is a variable. By use of (5), locate the points where the tangent is horizontal or vertical.

Solution. 1. $\qquad\qquad dx = - a \sin t\, dt; \qquad dy = b \cos t\, dt.$

$$y' = \frac{dy}{dx} = - \frac{b}{a} \cdot \frac{\cos t}{\sin t}; \quad \frac{dx}{dy} = - \frac{a}{b} \cdot \frac{\sin t}{\cos t}.$$

2. To eliminate t in (5), square in both equations, and add:

$$\cos^2 t + \sin^2 t = \frac{x^2}{a^2} + \frac{y^2}{b^2}, \quad or \quad \frac{x^2}{a^2} + \frac{y^2}{b^2} = 1.$$

Thus, (5) gives parametric equations for the ellipse with semi-axes a and b along the coordinate axes, and center at the origin.

3. *Horizontal and vertical tangents.* Since x and y are periodic functions of t, with the period 2π, we get all points of the ellipse by use of $0 \leq t < 2\pi$.

$$\frac{dy}{dx} = 0 \quad gives \quad \cos t = 0; \quad t = \frac{1}{2}\pi \quad and \quad t = \frac{3}{2}\pi;$$

$$\frac{dx}{dy} = 0 \quad gives \quad \sin t = 0; \quad t = 0 \quad and \quad t = \pi.$$

If $t = \frac{1}{2}\pi$, then (5) gives $(x = 0, y = b)$; etc. The tangent to (5) is horizontal at $(0, \pm b)$, and vertical at $(\pm a, 0)$, which verifies known features of (5), as recalled from its xy-form.

EXAMPLE 2. With $0 \leq \theta \leq 2\pi$, obtain the points on the cycloid [(3), (4)] where the tangent is horizontal or vertical, and test for concavity.

Solution. 1. From [(3), (4)],

$$dx = r(1 - \cos \theta)d\theta; \quad dy = r \sin \theta \, d\theta; \tag{6}$$

$$\frac{dy}{dx} = \frac{\sin \theta}{1 - \cos \theta}; \quad \frac{dx}{dy} = \frac{1 - \cos \theta}{\sin \theta}. \tag{7}$$

From (7), the cycloid has a tangent at all values of θ except possibly where

$$both \quad \sin \theta = 0 \quad and \quad 1 - \cos \theta = 0. \tag{8}$$

The solutions of $\sin \theta = 0$ are $\theta = 0$, $\theta = \pi$, and $\theta = 2\pi$. The solutions of $1 = \cos \theta$ are $\theta = 0$ and $\theta = 2\pi$. Thus, (8) is true at $\theta = 0$ and $\theta = 2\pi$.

2. *Horizontal tangents.* $dy/dx = 0$ when $\sin \theta = 0$ and $1 - \cos \theta \neq 0$, or when $\theta = \pi$. Then, from (3) and (4), $x = \pi r$ and $y = 2r$.

3. *Vertical tangents.* From (7), the equation $dx/dy = 0$ requires $1 - \cos \theta = 0$ and $\sin \theta \neq 0$. But, $\sin \theta = 0$ when $\cos \theta = 1$, which occurs at $\theta = 0$ and $\theta = 2\pi$, and thus the formula for dx/dy in (7) does not apply. Hence, $\theta = 0$ and $\theta = 2\pi$ must be investigated otherwise. By use of half-angle formulas,

$$\lim_{\theta \to 0} \frac{dx}{dy} = \lim_{\theta \to 0} \frac{1 - \cos \theta}{\sin \theta} = \lim_{\theta \to 0} \frac{2 \sin^2 \frac{1}{2}\theta}{2 \sin \frac{1}{2}\theta \cos \frac{1}{2}\theta} = \lim_{\theta \to 0} \tan \frac{1}{2}\theta = 0.$$

Hence, we conclude * that $dx/dy = 0$ at $\theta = 0$, or the curve has a vertical tangent at $\theta = 0$, and similarly at $\theta = 2\pi$. Thus, there is a cusp with a vertical tangent at $\theta = 2k\pi$, for all integral values of k.

4. *Concavity.* Let $y' = dy/dx$. Then, from (7),

$$y'' = \frac{dy'}{dx} = -\frac{1}{r(1 - \cos \theta)^2}.$$

If $0 < \theta < 2\pi$, then $(1 - \cos \theta)^2 > 0$, $y'' < 0$, and hence the cycloid is concave downward at all points except the cusps.

---

* Our reasoning is not complete here. Essentially, we assume that dx/dy exists at $\theta = 0$ because $dx/dy \to 0$ as $\theta \to 0$. This is true in the case involved but is not a general result.

EXERCISE 75

Find $D_x y$ and $D_x^2 y$ in terms of the other variable in the equations.

1. $x = 3 \sin \theta$, $y = 2 \cos \theta$.

2. $x = 2 \cos^3 t$, $y = 2 \sin^3 t$.

3. $x = 2 \sin t$, $y = 2(1 - \cos t)$.

4. $x = t^3$, $y = 2 \ln t$.

Find equations for the tangent and normal to the curve with the given parametric equations.

5. $x = 1 - \cos t$, $y = t + \sin t$; where $t = \frac{3}{2}\pi$.

6. $x = a \cos^3 t$, $y = a \sin^3 t$, with the constant $a > 0$; where $t = \frac{3}{4}\pi$.

Plot the curve given in parametric form if the constant $a > 0$. In Problems 7–10, also find the xy-equation. What part of its graph gives the curve defined parametrically?

7. $x = 2 + 5 \sin t$; $y = 3 \cos t - 1$.

8. $x = 2 \sin^2 t$; $y = 2 \cos^2 t$.

9. $x = 3 \cos^3 t$; $y = 3 \sin^3 t$.

10. $x = a \cos^4 t$; $y = a \sin^4 t$.

11. $x = 4(\theta + \sin \theta)$; $y = 4(1 - \cos \theta)$.

12. $x = 2(\cos \theta + \theta \sin \theta)$; $y = 2(\sin \theta - \theta \cos \theta)$.

The equations define the motion of a particle P in an xy-plane. At the specified instant t, find the values of x, y, v_x, v_y, the speed v, a_x, a_y, and the magnitude of the acceleration, a. Then, plot the velocity and acceleration vectors at the location found for P.

13. $x = 3 \sin t$, $y = 3 \cos t$; at $t = \frac{2}{3}\pi$.

14. $x = 4 \sin t$, $y = \cos t$; at $t = \frac{5}{4}\pi$.

15. $x = 2(t - \sin t)$, $y = 2(1 - \cos t)$; at $t = \frac{3}{2}\pi$.

16. $x = e^{-t} \sin 2t$, $y = e^{-t} \cos 2t$; at $t = \frac{1}{4}\pi$.

17. A particle P moves in an xy-plane, according to the equations $x = k \cos ht$ and $y = k \sin ht$, where t is the time, $h > 0$, and $k > 0$. (a) Find the xy-equation of the path. (b) Find the magnitude and direction of the acceleration at any instant t.

92. L'HOSPITAL'S RULE

In a fraction $F(t) = \psi(t)/\phi(t)$, suppose that $\phi(t) \to L$ and $\psi(t) \to M$ as $t \to a$, where we allow L, M, and a to be finite or $\pm \infty$. When a is finite, we do not demand that $\phi(t)$ and $\psi(t)$ be defined at $t = a$. However, in such a case, if ϕ and ψ are continuous at $t = a$ then $L = \phi(a)$ and $M = \psi(a)$. Suppose that we do *not* have $L = M = 0$, or $L = \pm \infty$ and $M = \pm \infty$. Then, the fundamental theorem on the limit of a quotient (*L and M finite, and $L \neq 0$*) or simple direct reasoning immediately specifies a limit, finite or infinite, for $F(t)$ or for $|F(t)|$.

ILLUSTRATION 1. Consider $\qquad \lim\limits_{x \to 0+} \dfrac{\ln x}{\sin x}$.

Recall that $\sin x \to 0+$ when $x \to 0+$. Since $\ln x \to -\infty$ when $x \to 0+$, hence the fraction has the limit $-\infty$ as $x \to 0+$.

If $L = M = 0$, we say that $\psi(t)/\phi(t)$ tends to the **(indeterminate) form 0/0**, where this symbol has *no meaning except as an abbreviation for the facts that* $\phi(t) \to 0$ and $\psi(t) \to 0$. Similarly, if $L = \pm \infty$ and $M = \pm \infty$, we say that $\psi(t)/\phi(t)$ tends to the **(indeterminate) form ∞/∞**.* For either of these cases, we shall find that $\psi(t)/\phi(t)$ may have a limit, finite or infinite, as $t \to a$.

* In our notations for indeterminate forms, we shall not use any sign, $\pm$, with the symbol ∞. We take care of signs in the details of calculation.

Note 1. If the functions $\phi(t)$ and $\psi(t)$ are defined and continuous at $t = a$, and $\psi(t)/\phi(t)$ tends to the form 0/0 as $t \to a$, then $\phi(a) = \psi(a) = 0$. In this case, $\psi(t)/\phi(t)$ assumes the meaningless form 0/0 at $t = a$.

The following result is due to the French mathematician GUILLAUME FRANÇOIS ANTOINE DE L'HOSPITAL, 1661–1704.

Theorem III (*L'Hospital's rule*). *Suppose that the functions $\phi(t)$ and $\psi(t)$ are differentiable on some interval T:($c < t < a$), or T:($a < t < c$), where a is finite. Assume that $\phi(t) \neq 0$ and $\phi'(t) \neq 0$ on T, and that* *

$$\phi(t) \to 0 \quad and \quad \psi(t) \to 0 \quad as \quad t \to a, \tag{1}$$

or that
$$\phi(t) \to \pm \infty \quad as \quad t \to a. \tag{2}$$

Then, as $t \to a$, if $\psi'(t)/\phi'(t)$ approaches a limit, finite or infinite, the fraction $\psi(t)/\phi(t)$ also approaches a limit and

$$\lim_{t \to a} \frac{\psi(t)}{\phi(t)} = \lim_{t \to a} \frac{\psi'(t)}{\phi'(t)}. \tag{3}$$

EXAMPLE 1. Evaluate: $$\lim_{t \to 2} \frac{\ln (t - 1)}{t - 2}. \tag{4}$$

Solution. As $t \to 2$, $\qquad \ln (t - 1) \to \ln 1 = 0; \quad (t - 2) \to 0.$
Hence, the fraction in (4) tends to the form 0/0 and (3) applies:

$$\lim_{t \to 2} \frac{\ln (t - 1)}{t - 2} = \lim_{t \to 2} \frac{\frac{1}{t - 1}}{1} = 1.$$

Note 2. Geometrical interpretation of a special case of L'Hospital's rule under assumption (1). Let T be the interval $a < t < c$. Extend the domain for ϕ and ψ of Theorem III to include $t = a$, by defining $\phi(a) = \psi(a) = 0$. Then, the functions $\phi(t)$ and $\psi(t)$ are continuous when $a \leqq t < c$. In an xy-plane, let W be the curve defined parametrically by

$$x = \phi(t) \quad and \quad y = \psi(t), \tag{5}$$

with $a \leqq t < c$. Since $\phi(a) = \psi(a) = 0$, W goes
through the origin when $t = a$, as in Figure 186.
From (5), if $t > a$, at the corresponding point
P:(x, y) on W there is a tangent PT where

$$(\textit{slope of tangent } PT) = \frac{dy}{dx} = \frac{\psi'(t)}{\phi'(t)}.$$

In Figure 186, $\qquad (\textit{slope of } OP) = \frac{\psi(t)}{\phi(t)}.$

Then, (3) states that, if the slope of the tangent PT
has a limit λ, the slope of the chord OP has the
same limit, which would be the slope of the tangent
OM to the curve (5) in Figure 186.

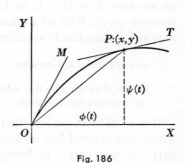

Fig. 186

* We interpret "$t \to a$" as $t \to a+$ or $t \to a-$ according as $t = a$ is at the left-hand or right-hand end of the interval T. If the hypotheses hold on both sides of a, then in (3) we imply the usual meaning for "$t \to a$."

In Note 10 of the Appendix, Theorem III is discussed not only for the case where $t = a$ is a finite value, but also when "a" is replaced by $+\infty$ or $-\infty$. When (2) is true, frequently $\lim_{t \to a} \psi(t)/\phi(t)$ can be found without (3), unless $\psi(t) \to \pm \infty$ as $t \to a$. That is, (3) *is needed for investigation of indeterminate forms of the type* ∞/∞. In applying (3), if it is found that $\psi'(t)/\phi'(t)$ tends to a form $0/0$ or ∞/∞ as $t \to a$, then we reapply L'Hospital's rule to $\psi'(t)/\phi'(t)$, and investigate $\psi''(t)/\phi''(t)$, provided that the derivatives satisfy proper hypotheses. Thus, we may be led to any number of successive applications of (3); it is possible to meet an endless sequence of indeterminate forms, and thus reach no conclusion about the limit. We may summarize (3) as follows:

To evaluate $\lim_{t \to a} [\psi(t)/\phi(t)]$, *if it tends to the form* $0/0$ *or* ∞/∞, *differentiate the numerator for a new numerator, and the denominator for a new denominator, and obtain the limit of the new fraction as* $t \to a$.

After any application of (3), before evaluating the limit, *we are at liberty to simplify the new fraction*, and *to perform any legitimate transformations*.

EXAMPLE 2. Evaluate:
$$\lim_{x \to +\infty} \frac{x^3}{e^{2x}}.$$

Solution. The fraction tends to the form ∞/∞, because
$$\lim_{x \to +\infty} x^3 = +\infty; \qquad \lim_{x \to +\infty} e^{2x} = +\infty.$$

Hence, by (3),
$$\lim_{x \to +\infty} \frac{x^3}{e^{2x}} = \lim_{x \to +\infty} \frac{3x^2}{2e^{2x}}; \qquad \text{(form, } \infty/\infty)$$

[applying (3) twice]
$$= \lim_{x \to +\infty} \frac{6x}{4e^{2x}} = \lim_{x \to +\infty} \frac{6}{8e^{2x}} = 0.$$

ILLUSTRATION 2. After one application of (3) to the following case where the form ∞/∞ arises, we obtain
$$\lim_{x \to 0+} \frac{\ln x}{x^{-\frac{1}{2}}} = \lim_{x \to 0+} \frac{\dfrac{1}{x}}{-\frac{1}{2}x^{-\frac{3}{2}}} = \lim_{x \to 0+} (-2x^{\frac{1}{2}}) = 0. \tag{6}$$

EXAMPLE 3. Evaluate:
$$\lim_{\theta \to \frac{1}{2}\pi} \frac{\tan 3\theta}{\tan \theta}.$$

Solution. The fraction tends to the form ∞/∞. We apply (3).
$$\lim_{\theta \to \frac{1}{2}\pi} \frac{\tan 3\theta}{\tan \theta} = \lim_{\theta \to \frac{1}{2}\pi} \frac{3 \sec^2 3\theta}{\sec^2 \theta} = \lim_{\theta \to \frac{1}{2}\pi} \frac{3 \cos^2 \theta}{\cos^2 3\theta}; \qquad \text{(form, } 0/0)$$

$$= \lim_{\theta \to \frac{1}{2}\pi} \frac{6 \sin \theta \cos \theta}{6 \sin 3\theta \cos 3\theta} = \lim_{\theta \to \frac{1}{2}\pi} \frac{\sin 2\theta}{\sin 6\theta}; \tag{7}$$

where we used the identity $\sin 2\alpha = 2 \sin \alpha \cos \alpha$ in both numerator and denominator. In (7), we arrive at the form $0/0$. From (7),
$$\lim_{\theta \to \frac{1}{2}\pi} \frac{\tan 3\theta}{\tan \theta} = \lim_{\theta \to \frac{1}{2}\pi} \frac{2 \cos 2\theta}{6 \cos 6\theta} = \frac{\cos \pi}{3 \cos 3\pi} = \frac{1}{3}.$$

EXERCISE 76

Evaluate the limit by inspection, if it exists. L'Hospital's rule is not involved.

1. $\lim\limits_{\theta \to \frac{1}{2}\pi} \dfrac{\sin 2\theta}{\sin \theta}$.

2. $\lim\limits_{x \to 0-} \dfrac{\sec x}{x}$.

3. $\lim\limits_{x \to 0+} \dfrac{\sec x}{x}$.

4. $\lim\limits_{x \to \infty} \dfrac{e^{-(1/x)}}{x}$.

5. $\lim\limits_{x \to \infty} \dfrac{\sin x}{x}$.

6. $\lim\limits_{x \to 0+} \dfrac{\ln x}{x}$.

*Evaluate the limit. Use L'Hospital's rule **if it applies**. Verify the form, $0/0$ or ∞/∞, before each application of the rule.*

7. $\lim\limits_{t \to 0} \dfrac{1 - \cos 2t}{t - 1}$.

8. $\lim\limits_{x \to -3} \dfrac{x^2 - 9}{x - 3}$.

9. $\lim\limits_{x \to 0} \dfrac{\tan x}{x}$.

10. $\lim\limits_{x \to 1} \dfrac{\ln x}{x - 1}$.

11. $\lim\limits_{x \to \frac{1}{2}\pi} \dfrac{1 - \sin x}{x - \frac{1}{2}\pi}$.

12. $\lim\limits_{\theta \to \frac{1}{4}\pi} \dfrac{\tan \theta - 1}{\theta - \frac{1}{4}\pi}$.

13. $\lim\limits_{x \to 1} \dfrac{\ln (2x - 1)}{1 - x^2}$.

14. $\lim\limits_{x \to 0} \dfrac{\sin x}{e^x - e^{-x}}$.

15. $\lim\limits_{x \to 0-} \dfrac{x^2}{\sin x - x}$.

16. $\lim\limits_{x \to 0+} \dfrac{x}{\sin^2 x}$.

17. $\lim\limits_{x \to 0-} \dfrac{x}{\sin^2 x}$.

18. $\lim\limits_{x \to 0+} \dfrac{x^2}{\sin x - x}$.

19. $\lim\limits_{x \to \infty} \dfrac{x - 2x^3}{x^2}$.

20. $\lim\limits_{x \to \infty} \dfrac{x^2}{e^x}$.

21. $\lim\limits_{x \to \infty} \dfrac{x}{\ln x}$.

22. $\lim\limits_{x \to \infty} \dfrac{e^x}{x^3}$.

23. $\lim\limits_{x \to \infty} \dfrac{\ln x}{x^3}$.

24. $\lim\limits_{x \to \infty} \dfrac{e^x}{\ln x}$.

25. $\lim\limits_{x \to 0} \dfrac{e^x + e^{-x} - 2}{\cos x - 1}$.

26. $\lim\limits_{x \to 0} \dfrac{2^x - 3^x}{x}$.

27. $\lim\limits_{|x| \to \infty} \dfrac{x^4 + 3}{2x^4 - 5x}$.

28. $\lim\limits_{x \to \frac{1}{2}\pi+} \dfrac{\sin 2x}{\sin x - 1}$.

29. $\lim\limits_{x \to 0} \dfrac{1 + \csc x}{\cot x}$.

30. $\lim\limits_{x \to \infty} \dfrac{e^{-x}}{x^8}$.

31. $\lim\limits_{x \to 0} \dfrac{x - \sin x}{2x^3}$.

32. $\lim\limits_{x \to \infty} \dfrac{(\ln x)^2}{x}$.

33. $\lim\limits_{x \to 0+} \dfrac{\cot x}{\ln x}$.

34. $\lim\limits_{x \to 0} \dfrac{\sin 3x}{\sin 2x}$.

35. $\lim\limits_{x \to 0} \dfrac{\tan x}{\tan 2x}$.

36. $\lim\limits_{x \to \infty} \dfrac{\tan x}{x}$.

37. $\lim\limits_{x \to 0} \dfrac{\csc^2 2x}{\csc^2 x}$.

38. $\lim\limits_{x \to 0} \dfrac{\cot 3x}{\cot x}$.

39. $\lim\limits_{x \to 0+} \dfrac{\ln \sin x}{\ln \sin 2x}$.

Hint for Problem 37. Sines are more convenient than cosecants.

40. $\lim\limits_{x \to \frac{1}{2}\pi+} \dfrac{\cot^2 (x^2 - \frac{1}{2}\pi)}{x - \frac{1}{2}\pi}$.

41. $\lim\limits_{\theta \to \frac{1}{2}\pi-} \dfrac{\ln \tan \theta}{e^{\sec^2 \theta}}$.

42. $\lim\limits_{x \to 0} \dfrac{x \sin x}{1 - \cos x}$.

43. $\lim\limits_{x \to 0} \dfrac{\sin 3x}{\ln (1 - x)}$.

44. $\lim\limits_{\theta \to 0} \dfrac{\sin^2 \theta}{\sin \theta^2}$.

45. $\lim\limits_{x \to 0} \dfrac{e^x \tan x}{x}$.

46. $\lim\limits_{x \to 0} \dfrac{\tan 2x}{x \sec x}$.

47. $\lim\limits_{x \to 0} \dfrac{\ln \cos x}{\sin^2 x}$.

48. $\lim\limits_{x \to 1} \dfrac{\tan \pi x}{x - 1}$.

49. $\lim\limits_{x \to 0} \dfrac{\text{Arcsin } 2x}{\text{Arcsin } 3x}$.

50. $\lim\limits_{x \to 0} \dfrac{\ln (1 + x)}{\cot x}$.

51. $\lim\limits_{x \to 0+} \dfrac{\ln x}{10^x}$.

52. $\lim\limits_{x \to +\infty} \dfrac{\sin (1/x)}{\ln x}$.

53. $\lim\limits_{x \to \frac{1}{2}\pi} \dfrac{\tan 5\theta}{\tan \theta}$.

54. $\lim\limits_{x \to 0} \dfrac{\sin x - x}{x^3}$.

55. $\lim\limits_{x \to \infty} \dfrac{(\ln x)^2}{e^x}$.

56. $\lim\limits_{x \to 0-} \dfrac{\tan x}{\sec x - 1}$.

57. $\lim\limits_{x \to -\infty} \dfrac{\text{Arctan } x + \frac{1}{2}\pi}{\sin (1/x)}.$ 　　　　　**58.** $\lim\limits_{x \to \infty} \dfrac{\sin e^{-x}}{\sin (1/x)}.$

59. Prove that $\lim_{x \to \infty} \dfrac{x^n}{e^x} = 0$, if n is any real number. That is, prove that e^x grows large faster than any power of x, as $x \to \infty$.

60. Evaluate $\lim_{x \to \infty} \dfrac{\ln x}{x^n}$, for any real number n.

93. LIMITS OF PRODUCTS AND SUMS

If $\phi(t) \to + \infty$ and $\psi(t) \to - \infty$ as $t \to a$, we say that $[\phi(t) + \psi(t)]$ tends to the * **(indeterminate) form** $(\infty - \infty)$ as $t \to a$. If $\phi(t) \to 0$ and $\psi(t) \to \pm \infty$ as $t \to a$, we say that $\phi(t)\psi(t)$ tends to the **(indeterminate) form** $0 \cdot \infty$ as $t \to a$.

In order to evaluate the limit of a product or sum which tends to the form $0 \cdot \infty$ or $(\infty - \infty)$, we try to rewrite the given expression as a fraction, which may tend to the form $0/0$ or ∞/∞. Then, we apply L'Hospital's rule.

EXAMPLE 1. Evaluate: 　　　　　　　　　　$\lim\limits_{x \to 0+} (\csc x - \cot x).$

Solution. Test of form: as $x \to 0+$, $\csc x \to + \infty$ and $\cot x \to + \infty$. Hence, $(\csc x - \cot x)$ tends to the form $(\infty - \infty)$. We obtain

$$\lim_{x \to 0+} (\csc x - \cot x) = \lim_{x \to 0+} \left(\frac{1}{\sin x} - \frac{\cos x}{\sin x} \right)$$

$$= \lim_{x \to 0+} \frac{1 - \cos x}{\sin x}; \qquad\qquad (form,\ 0/0)$$

$$= \lim_{x \to 0+} \frac{\sin x}{\cos x} = \frac{0}{1} = 0. \qquad (apply\ L'Hospital's\ rule)$$

Comment. Similarly, the limit as $x \to 0-$ also is found to be 0. Hence,

$$\lim_{x \to 0} (\csc x - \cot x) = 0,$$

with "$x \to 0$" indicating the *unrestricted, two-sided limit* as usual.

EXAMPLE 2. Evaluate: 　　　　　　　　　　$\lim\limits_{x \to \infty} x \tan \frac{1}{x}.$

Solution. The expression tends to the form $\infty \cdot 0$. Then,

$$\lim_{x \to \infty} x \tan \frac{1}{x} = \lim_{x \to \infty} \frac{\tan \dfrac{1}{x}}{\dfrac{1}{x}} \qquad\qquad (form,\ 0/0)$$

(because sec 0 = 1) 　　　$= \lim\limits_{x \to \infty} \dfrac{-\left(\sec^2 \dfrac{1}{x}\right) \dfrac{1}{x^2}}{-\dfrac{1}{x^2}} = \lim\limits_{x \to \infty} \sec^2 \dfrac{1}{x} = 1.$

* See Problem 31 on page 116.

94. LIMITS OF EXPONENTIAL FORMS

If $b > 0$, recall that $$b = e^{\ln b}.$$ (1)

Then, if h is any real number, $(e^{\ln b})^h = e^{h \ln b}$, or

$$b^h = e^{h \ln b}.$$ (2)

If $b \neq 0$, then $b^0 = 1$, by definition. However, in Illustration 3 on page 241, we mentioned that 0^0 is not defined, and hence has *no meaning as a number*. Also, if h is an irrational number, we do not define the symbol b^h when $b < 0$.

Now, consider functions $\phi(t)$ and $\psi(t)$, where $\phi(t) > 0$, and let

$$W(t) = \phi(t)^{\psi(t)}; \quad then \quad \ln W(t) = \psi(t) \ln \phi(t).$$ (3)

If $\phi(t) \to 0+$ and $\psi(t) \to 0$ as $t \to a$, then $W(t)$ tends to the form 0^0, and $\ln W(t)$ tends to the form $0 \cdot \infty$, because $\ln \phi(t) \to -\infty$ when $\phi(t) \to 0+$. If $\phi(t) \to 1$ and $\psi(t) \to \pm \infty$, then $W(t)$ tends to the form 1^∞ as $t \to a$, and then $\ln W(t)$ tends to the form $\infty \cdot 0$. If $\phi(t) \to +\infty$ and $\psi(t) \to 0$, then $W(t)$ tends to the form ∞^0, and then $\ln W(t)$ tends to the form $0 \cdot \infty$. Thus, we refer to 0^0, 1^∞, and ∞^0 as *indeterminate forms* because the corresponding logarithms tend to the form $0 \cdot \infty$, and special investigation is demanded in evaluating any particular case of $\lim_{t \to a} W(t)$.

Note 1. From (1), $W(t) = e^{\ln W(t)}$. Suppose that $\ln W(t) \to L$ as $t \to a$, where L is finite. Then, since e^x is continuous at $x = L$,

$$\lim_{t \to a} e^{\ln W(t)} = e^{\lim_{t \to a} \ln W(t)} = e^L,$$ (4)

or, there exists $$\lim_{t \to a} W(t) = e^L.$$ (5)

From (3) and (5), we are led to the following procedure.

To evaluate $\lim_{t \to a} W(t)$ where $W(t) = \phi(t)^{\psi(t)}$ and $W(t)$ tends to one of the forms 0^0, 1^∞, and ∞^0 as $t \to a$, first calculate $\ln W(t)$. Then, evaluate $\lim_{t \to a} \ln W(t) = L$, and use (5).

EXAMPLE 1. Evaluate: $$\lim_{x \to \frac{1}{2}\pi} (\sin x)^{\tan x}.$$

Solution. 1. The expression tends to the form 1^∞.

2. Let $W(x) = (\sin x)^{\tan x}$. Then, $\ln W(x) = \tan x \ln \sin x$.

As $x \to \frac{1}{2}\pi$, $\ln W(x)$ tends to the form $\infty \cdot 0$, because $\sin x \to 1$ and $\ln 1 = 0$.

3. By L'Hospital's rule, $$\lim_{x \to \frac{1}{2}\pi} \ln W(x) = \lim_{x \to \frac{1}{2}\pi} \frac{\ln \sin x}{\cot x} \qquad (form, 0/0)$$

$$= \lim_{x \to \frac{1}{2}\pi} -\frac{\dfrac{\cos x}{\sin x}}{\csc^2 x} = \lim_{x \to \frac{1}{2}\pi} -\cos x \sin x = 0. \qquad (by \ L'Hospital's \ rule)$$

Hence, $$\lim_{x \to \frac{1}{2}\pi} W(x) = e^{\lim_{x \to \frac{1}{2}\pi} \ln W(x)} = e^0 = 1.$$

Note 2. In (5), let us understand that, if $L = +\infty$ then e^L is replaced by $+\infty$; if $L = -\infty$ then e^L is replaced by 0.

EXAMPLE 2. Evaluate: $\lim\limits_{x \to 0+} (\sin x)^x$.

Solution. 1. The form involved is 0^0. Let $W(x) = (\sin x)^x$. Then,

$$\ln W(x) = x \ln \sin x,$$

which tends to the form $0 \cdot \infty$ as $x \to 0+$.

2. By L'Hospital's rule, $\lim\limits_{x \to 0+} \ln W(x) = \lim\limits_{x \to 0+} \dfrac{\ln \sin x}{\dfrac{1}{x}}$ (*form*, ∞/∞)

$$= \lim_{x \to 0+} \frac{\dfrac{\cos x}{\sin x}}{-x^{-2}} = \lim_{x \to 0+} - \frac{x^2 \cos x}{\sin x} \qquad (\textit{form}, \, 0/0)$$

$$= - \lim_{x \to 0+} \frac{2x \cos x - x^2 \sin x}{\cos x} = \frac{0}{1} = 0.$$

Hence, $\lim\limits_{x \to 0+} W(x) = e^{\lim_{x \to 0} \ln W(x)} = e^0 = 1.$

EXAMPLE 3. Evaluate: $\lim\limits_{t \to 0} (1 + 3t)^{\frac{1}{t}}$.

Solution. 1. The form involved is 1^∞. Let $W(t) = (1 + 3t)^{\frac{1}{t}}$. Then,

$$\ln W(t) = \frac{\ln (1 + 3t)}{t},$$

which tends to the form $0/0$ as $t \to 0$.

2. By L'Hospital's rule, $\lim\limits_{t \to 0} \ln W(t) = \lim\limits_{t \to 0} \dfrac{\dfrac{3}{1 + 3t}}{1} = 3; \quad \lim\limits_{t \to 0} W(t) = e^3.$

EXERCISE 77

Evaluate the limit, by use of L'Hospital's rule when desirable.

1. $\lim\limits_{x \to \infty} xe^{-x}$.   2. $\lim\limits_{x \to 0+} x \ln x$.   3. $\lim\limits_{x \to 0+} x^3 \ln x$.   4. $\lim\limits_{x \to -\infty} x^2 e^x$.

5. $\lim\limits_{x \to \frac{1}{2}\pi} (\pi - 2x)\sec x$.   6. $\lim\limits_{x \to 0+} (\sin x)\ln \sin x$.

7. $\lim\limits_{x \to 0} (\csc x)\ln (1 + \sin x)$.   8. $\lim\limits_{x \to \infty} x \sin 2x^{-1}$.

9. $\lim\limits_{x \to \frac{1}{2}\pi} (\sec x - \tan x)$.   10. $\lim\limits_{x \to 1} \left(\dfrac{1}{\ln x} - \dfrac{x}{x - 1} \right)$.

11. $\lim\limits_{x \to 1} \left(\dfrac{x}{\ln x} - \dfrac{1}{x - 1} \right)$.   12. $\lim\limits_{x \to 0} \left(\dfrac{1}{x \tan x} - \dfrac{1}{x^2} \right)$.

13. $\lim\limits_{x \to 0+} \left(\dfrac{1}{e^x - 1} - \dfrac{2}{x} \right)$.   14. $\lim\limits_{h \to \infty} \left(1 + \dfrac{1}{2h} \right)^{3h}$.

15. $\lim\limits_{x \to \frac{1}{2}\pi -} (\cos x)^{\cos x}$.   16. $\lim\limits_{x \to 0} (\sec x)^{\frac{1}{x}}$.   17. $\lim\limits_{x \to \frac{1}{2}\pi} (\sin^2 x)^{\tan x}$.

18. $\lim\limits_{x \to \infty} (1 + x)^{\frac{4}{x}}$.   19. $\lim\limits_{x \to 0} (x + e^{2x})^{-\frac{2}{x}}$.   20. $\lim\limits_{x \to 0+} x^x$.

21. $\lim\limits_{x\to\infty} e^{-x} \tan \dfrac{1}{x}$.

22. $\lim\limits_{x\to\infty} x \tan \dfrac{a}{x}$.

23. $\lim\limits_{x\to\infty} \left(\cos \dfrac{1}{x}\right)^x$.

24. $\lim\limits_{x\to\frac{1}{2}\pi-} (\cos x)^{\tan x}$.

25. $\lim\limits_{x\to 1} x^{\tan \frac{1}{2}\pi x}$.

26. $\lim\limits_{x\to\frac{1}{2}\pi} (\sin x)^{4 \tan^2 x}$.

27. $\lim\limits_{x\to 0} (\csc 2x)\text{Arcsin } x$.

28. $\lim\limits_{x\to\frac{1}{2}\pi} (1 + 2 \cot x)^{\tan x}$.

29. $\lim\limits_{x\to 0} x(\sin x^{-1})$.

30. $\lim\limits_{x\to\frac{1}{2}\pi} (\csc^2 x)^{-\tan^2 x}$.

31. $\lim\limits_{x\to\frac{1}{2}\pi} (x - \frac{1}{2}\pi)\tan x$.

32. $\lim\limits_{t\to\frac{1}{4}\pi} (1 - \cot t)\tan 2t$.

33. $\lim\limits_{x\to 0} (\csc x)\ln (1 + 2x)$.

34. $\lim\limits_{x\to 0+} (\text{Arctan } x^{-1} - \frac{1}{2}\pi)\csc 2x$.

35. $\lim\limits_{x\to 0} (\sin x + \cos x)^{\frac{3}{x}}$.

36. $\lim\limits_{\theta\to\frac{1}{2}\pi} \left(\dfrac{1}{1 - \sin \theta} - \dfrac{2}{\cos^2 \theta}\right)$.

37. $\lim\limits_{\theta\to\alpha} \dfrac{\tan \theta - \tan \alpha}{\theta - \alpha}$.

38. $\lim\limits_{x\to 0} \dfrac{\cos x - 1 + \frac{1}{2}x^2}{\sin^2 x}$.

39. $\lim\limits_{x\to 0-} \dfrac{\ln (1 + x)}{e^x - 1 - x}$.

40. $\lim\limits_{x\to 0} \left(\dfrac{1}{x^2} - \dfrac{1}{x \sin x}\right)$.

41. $\lim\limits_{x\to 0+} \left(\ln x - \dfrac{1}{x}\right)$.

42. $\lim\limits_{x\to 0} \left(\dfrac{1}{\text{Arctan } x} - \dfrac{1}{x}\right)$.

43. $\lim\limits_{x\to\infty} \dfrac{\sin e^{-x}}{\sin x^{-1}}$.

Graph the equation. Investigate asymptotes of the form $y = k$, where k is a constant, by evaluating $\lim_{x\to\infty} y$ and $\lim_{x\to-\infty} y$. Obtain extrema, and inflection points wherever the derivatives are convenient.

44. $y = x^2 e^x$.

45. $y = xe^{-x^2}$.

46. $y = e^{-\frac{1}{x}}$.

47. $y = xe^{-\frac{1}{x}}$.

Hint for Problems 46–47. Define y at $x = 0$ as $\lim_{x\to 0+} y$, and also investigate $\lim_{x\to 0-} y$.

★95. NEWTON–RAPHSON METHOD FOR SOLVING EQUATIONS

Let f be a function possessing first and second derivatives, f' and f'', where f'' is continuous on the domain $T = \{a \leqq x \leqq b\}$. Assume that $f'(x) \neq 0$ and $f''(x) \neq 0$ on T. We desire to solve the equation $f(x) = 0$. Since $f'(x) \neq 0$ and f' is continuous on T (because f'' exists), then $f'(x)$ is always positive or always negative on T. Hence, f is either an *increasing* function, $f'(x) > 0$, or a *decreasing* function, $f'(x) < 0$, on T. Therefore, there exists just one solution, r, or no solution of $f(x) = 0$ on T. We shall discuss the so-called **Newton-Raphson** *method of successive approximations* for obtaining r to any specified degree of accuracy.

Since $f''(x) \neq 0$, then $f'(x)$ increases when x is on T, or decreases when x is on T. Let the curve in Figure 187 on page 265 be a graph of $y = f(x)$, for a case where $f'(x) > 0$ so that f increases on T. Suppose that $f(a)$ and $f(b)$ have opposite signs, so that just one solution, r, of $f(x) = 0$ is known to exist between a and b. Let x_1 be a number which we believe is near the unknown solution r, and suppose that x_1 is on that side of r, as in Figure 187, where $|f'(x)|$ has its largest values for x on T. Let $P_1:(x_1, y_1)$ be the corresponding point on the curve $y = f(x)$. At P_1, construct the tangent P_1T_1, intersecting the x-axis at $x = x_2$. Then, from Figure 187, it is evident geometrically that x_2 is closer than

x_1 to the unknown solution r. To obtain x_2 in terms of x_1, first we write the equation of P_1T_1:

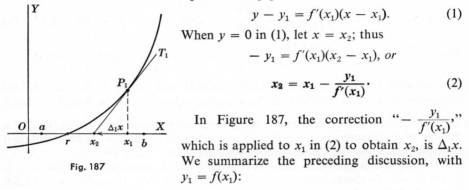

Fig. 187

$$y - y_1 = f'(x_1)(x - x_1). \qquad (1)$$

When $y = 0$ in (1), let $x = x_2$; thus

$$-y_1 = f'(x_1)(x_2 - x_1), \; or$$

$$x_2 = x_1 - \frac{y_1}{f'(x_1)}. \qquad (2)$$

In Figure 187, the correction "$-\dfrac{y_1}{f'(x_1)},$" which is applied to x_1 in (2) to obtain x_2, is $\Delta_1 x$. We summarize the preceding discussion, with $y_1 = f(x_1)$:

$$\left\{ \begin{array}{l} \textit{First approximation to solution, } x_1; \textit{ correction, } \Delta_1 x = -\dfrac{f(x_1)}{f'(x_1)}. \\ \textit{Second approximation to solution, } x_2 = x_1 + \Delta_1 x. \end{array} \right\} \qquad (3)$$

We accept the fact that x_2 is nearer than x_1 to r. Then, we would obtain a correction $\Delta_2 x$, and a third approximation x_3 to r:

$$\Delta_2 x = -\frac{f(x_2)}{f'(x_2)} \quad and \quad x_3 = x_2 + \Delta_2 x; \; etc.$$

$$\Delta_n x = -\frac{f(x_n)}{f'(x_n)} \quad and \quad x_{n+1} = x_n + \Delta_n x. \qquad (4)$$

Thus, we define a sequence $\{x_n\}$. It can be proved that, with the hypotheses stated at the beginning of our discussion, $x_n \to r$ as $n \to \infty$. We accept this fact without proof. For a case as in Figure 187, it is clear geometrically that

$$x_1 > x_2 > x_3 \cdots > x_n \cdots > r.$$

That is, the sequence $\{x_n\}$ is a decreasing sequence, with each term $x_n > r$.

EXAMPLE 1. Solve

$$f(x) = x^3 - 3x^2 - 2x + 5 = 0. \qquad (5)$$

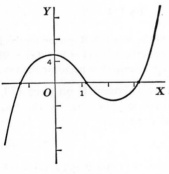

Fig. 188

Solution. 1. Let $y = f(x)$. We have

$$f'(x) = 3x^2 - 6x - 2. \qquad (6)$$

2. First, we obtain a reasonably approximate graph of $y = f(x)$, in Figure 188. From it, we read the approximate solutions -1.3, 1.2, and 3.2 for (5).

3. *To obtain more accurately the solution r which is near 3.2.* In Figure 188, the slope of the graph, or $f'(x)$, *increases* to the right of r. Hence, as a first approximation to r, we take $x_1 = 3.5$. From (3),

$$\Delta_1 x = -\frac{f(3.5)}{f'(3.5)} = -\frac{4.125}{13.75} = -.30; \quad x_2 = 3.5 - .30 = 3.20. \tag{7}$$

From (5), $\Delta_2 x = -\dfrac{f(3.2)}{f'(3.2)} = -\dfrac{.648}{9.52} = -.07; \quad x_3 = 3.20 - .07 = 3.13.$ (8)

Similarly, $\Delta_3 x = -\dfrac{f(3.13)}{f'(3.13)} = -.0016; \quad x_4 = 3.13 - .0016 = 3.1284.$

We consider the final digit in 3.1284 doubtful and accept 3.128 as our final approximation to the solution of (5). Its other solutions can be found similarly.

Comment. To check the accuracy of the approximate solution, $x_4 = 3.1284$, let ξ be a number in the direction of the unknown root r from x_4, where $|x_4 - \xi| < .001$, and compute $f(\xi)$. From the figure, without computation we know that $f(x_4) > 0$. If $f(\xi)$ and $f(x_4)$ have opposite signs, then r is between ξ and x_4, and hence the error of x_4 is less than .001. To check, we use $\xi = 3.128; f(3.128) = -.004$. Hence, $\xi < r < 3.1284$, and evidently r is close to 3.128, which we accept as our result, certainly accurate to three decimal places, with an error of at most .0004.

Under preceding assumptions, suppose that the first approximation x_1 to a solution of $f(x) = 0$ is selected on that side of r where the values of $|f'(x)|$ are *smallest*, as in Figure 189 below. Then, if the construction of Figure 187 is applied in the new situation, the second approximation x_2 is on the side of r opposite to x_1. From this point on, the successive approximations remain on the same side of r, as in the discussion leading to (3) and (4). Hence, with $f'(x) \neq 0$ and $f''(x) \neq 0$, a first approximation x_1 may be chosen somewhat recklessly,* if desirable, with assurance that the method will yield a sequence $\{x_n\}$ having r as the limit when $n \to \infty$.

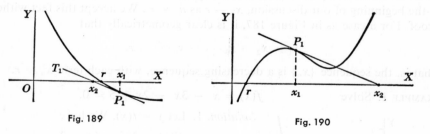

Fig. 189   Fig. 190

ILLUSTRATION 1. Figure 190 shows the construction of the Newton-Raphson method with an approximation x_1 on a domain where the condition $[f'(x) \neq 0, f''(x) \neq 0]$ is violated. In Figure 190, the second approximation x_2 is much less accurate than x_1.

The Newton-Raphson method can be motivated by Theorem II on page 173. Let x_1 be an approximation to a root r of the equation $f(x) = 0$. By the law of the mean, there exists a number ξ between x and x_1 so that

$$f(x) = f(x_1) + f'(\xi)(x - x_1). \tag{9}$$

---

* Provided that, with x_1 as in Figure 189, the domain of x where $f'(x) \neq 0$ and $f''(x) = 0$ is large enough so that x_2 is on this domain.

As an approximation, let $\xi = x_1$; then, instead of considering $f(x) = 0$, we may solve the linear equation

$$f(x_1) + f'(x_1)(x - x_1) = 0; \quad we\ obtain \quad x = x_1 - \frac{f(x_1)}{f'(x_1)}. \tag{10}$$

We recognize x in (10) as the approximation x_2 obtained in (2).

It is emphasized that the Newton-Raphson method applies to *any* equation $f(x) = 0$, not necessarily a polynomial equation, where we have means for calculating $f(x)$ and $f'(x)$. If $f(x)$ is a polynomial in x, methods of the theory of polynomial equations may apply for obtaining irrational solutions of $f(x) = 0$. However, even in such cases, the Newton-Raphson method may be superior in convenience. This method can be used with high-speed digital computers.

★EXERCISE 78

By use of the Newton-Raphson method, find the specified solutions, correct to two decimal places except where otherwise specified.

1. The two roots of $x^2 - 6x + 6 = 0$, without using the quadratic formula.

2. The root of $x^3 - 7x^2 + 15x + 89 = 0$ between -2 and -3.

3. The root of $x^3 + 3x - 5 = 0$ between 1 and 2.

4. All roots of $x^3 + 2x^2 - 7x + 1 = 0$.   **5.** All roots of $x^3 - 2x^2 = 5x - 4$.

Find the indicated root by use of the Newton-Raphson method.

6. $\sqrt[4]{10}$.   **7.** $\sqrt[3]{185}$.   **8.** $\sqrt[3]{-62}$.   **9.** $\sqrt[5]{-148}$.

Hint for Problem 6. If x is the root, then $x^4 = 10$.

10. The relation $M = x - \eta \sin x$, called **Kepler's equation,** holds between the mean anomaly M and the eccentric anomaly x of a planet at any point in its path around the sun; η is the eccentricity of the ellipse which forms the path. If $\eta = .4$ and $M = 4$, find x. To obtain an initial approximate solution, perhaps graph
$$y = x - .4 \sin x$$
roughly and find the intersection of this graph and the line $y = 4$.

11. The thermal conductivity, k, of air at an absolute temperature of $t°$ (Fahrenheit) is given by

$$k = .0129 \frac{717}{t + 225} \left(\frac{t}{492}\right)^{\frac{3}{2}}.$$

Find t to the nearest degree if $k = .0158$.

12. Obtain that root of $10 \ln x = x^2 - 3$ where $x > 1$. A first approximation can be obtained from preliminary graphs of $y_1 = 10 \ln x$ and $y_2 = x^2 - 3$ on the same coordinate system.

EXERCISE 79 (*Review of Chapter Ten*)

Differentiate the function, or find dy/dx from the given equation.

1. $\sin^2 (3x^3 - x)$.   **2.** $\sqrt{\tan 5x}$.   **3.** Arctan $(\sin 2x)$.

4. $\cos (\ln x)$.   **5.** $\sec e^{3x}$.   **6.** $\cot (\frac{1}{2}x^3 + 4x)$.

7. Arcsin e^{2t}.   **8.** $\csc^2 (x + 3)^3$.   **9.** $e^{3x} \sin 4x$.

10. $\ln \sin^4 3z$.   **11.** $e^{3 \cos 4x}$.   **12.** $\sqrt{\sin^2 x + \cos x}$.

13. $x \sin \dfrac{3}{x}$.

14. $\dfrac{5}{\cos 4x}$.

15. $\dfrac{\ln t}{\sin t - 1}$.

16. $\log_{10} \dfrac{1}{\csc x}$.

17. $\ln \dfrac{\cos^3 x}{\sin^2 x}$.

18. $\ln \dfrac{8}{(3x^2 - 5)^7}$.

19. $\sqrt{\ln (2z - 3)^2}$.

20. $a^{5 \sin z}$.

21. Arcsin $(\ln x^2)$.

22. $\sin y + \ln xy = 5$.

23. $e^y + \ln x = y^2 - 5$.

24. $\ln [\ln (3 \sin x)]^2$.

25. $\tan (x + 2y) - \sin (x + y) = 4$.

26. $(\sin x)^{\tan x}$.

27. $(\ln x)^{\cos x}$.

28. $(e^x)^{e^x}$.

29. $e^{\ln 6x}$.

30. $(x^2 - 1)^6 \sqrt[3]{3x - 5}$.

31. $\ln [(2x^2 + 5)^3 (\sin 2x - 1)^5]$.

Find the second derivative of the function whose values are defined.

32. x Arctan $2x$.

33. $[\ln (\ln x)]^2$.

34. $e^{2x} \ln x$.

Find all extrema of the function f. If trigonometric functions are involved, restrict x to the domain $0 < x < 2\pi$.

35. $f(x) = 4 \cos x - \cos 2x$.

36. $f(x) = x \ln x$.

37. $f(x) = 5 \sin x - 12 \cos x$.

38. $f(x) = x^3 \ln x$.

39. $f(x) = \ln \sin 2x$.

40. $f(x) = e^x + 4e^{-x}$.

41. A bomber is flying south at an elevation of 5000 yards, with a speed of 200 yards per second. The automatic bombsight is focused on an enemy bridge south of the plane, and continuously measures the angle of depression, θ, of the bridge as seen from the bomber. Find the time-rate of change of θ when $\theta = \frac{1}{4}\pi$. Express the result in degree measure.

42. Find the minimum value of $y = 3e^{4x} + 5e^{-4x}$.

Find the differential of the function.

43. $e^{-2x} \ln (\ln x)$.

44. Arctan $(\ln \sin x)$.

45. $10^{2x} \cot 3x$.

46. A pyramid has a square base, whose side is measured as 90′, with essentially no error. The inclination of a side of the pyramid from the horizontal is measured as 60°, with an error not larger than 10′. By differentials, find approximately the maximum possible error in the volume of the pyramid as computed from the given measurements.

Evaluate the limit.

47. $\displaystyle\lim_{x \to 0} \csc 2x$.

48. $\displaystyle\lim_{x \to 0} x \cot x$.

49. $\displaystyle\lim_{\theta \to \frac{1}{2}\pi +} e^{-\tan \theta} \sec \theta$.

50. $\displaystyle\lim_{x \to 0} \dfrac{\tan x - x}{x^3}$.

51. $\displaystyle\lim_{x \to 0-} \dfrac{\sin x - 1}{\tan^3 x}$.

52. $\displaystyle\lim_{x \to 0} (1 + 4x)^{\frac{3}{x}}$.

53. $\displaystyle\lim_{t \to \frac{1}{2}\pi -} (\sec^3 t - \tan^3 t)$.

54. The electromotive force E, in volts, which is necessary to produce a current of I amperes in a certain circuit with wire of diameter d inches is given by $E = .1137I/d^2$. For a given value of I, if d is measured with an error of at most 2%, and if E then is computed, find the maximum possible percent of error in E, approximately, by use of differentials.

55. Find equations for the tangent and normal where $t = \frac{1}{4}\pi$ on the curve C defined by $x = 2 \sin t - 2t \cos t$ and $y = 2 \cos t + 2t \sin t$. Also, find the sense of concavity of C where $t = \frac{1}{4}\pi$.

56. A curve C is defined by $x = 4 \cos^2 \theta$ and $y = 4 \cos \theta \sin \theta$, where θ is a parameter. Without eliminating θ, obtain the points on C where the tangent is horizontal or vertical, and plot C. Also, eliminate θ, to obtain an xy-equation for C.

57. A given radioactive substance decomposes at such a rate that, if h is the initial number of atoms of the substance and x is the number remaining at the end of t hours, then $x = he^{-.15t}$. Find the time-rate of change of x when $t = 5$. By use of differentials, find approximately the decrease in x when t increases from $t = 5$ to $t = 5.2$.

★SUPPLEMENT FOR CHAPTER TEN

58. A wire of negligible diameter and mass M forms a circle of radius r in a horizontal plane. A particle, P, of mass m is above the center of the circle. In physics, it is shown that P is attracted vertically by the wire with a force inversely proportional to the square of the distance from P to a point on the circle, and directly proportional to the cosine of the acute angle between the vertical and a line from P to a point on the circle. Find the height of P above the circle to maximize the attraction.

59. In a hotel, a straight hall is 3′ wide. A rectangular dining room, 80′ long and 24′ wide, has a 24′ side open on the hall. Find the length of the longest banquet table top which can be carried horizontally on edge into the room. The hall extends 40′ on each side.

60. An iron girder 64′ long must be carried horizontally along a straight hall 8′ wide into a second hall meeting it at right angles. Find the minimum possible width of the second hall.

61. Find the altitude of a conical goblet of minimum capacity, to permit a ball of radius r to be submerged in the goblet when it is filled.

62. Let P be the moving point, thought of as a particle, which traces the cycloid of Illustration 1 on page 255. Assume that the generating circle rolls with constant angular velocity about its center, that is, $d\theta/dt = h$, a positive constant, where t is the time. For the moving particle P: (a) Find v_x, v_y, v, a_x, a_y, and a, at any instant t. (b) With θ on $0 \leq \theta \leq 2\pi$, find the location of P when its speed is a minimum, and a maximum. (c) Prove that the magnitude of the acceleration is a constant.

63. Without eliminating x, y, or z, find du/dt if $u = $ Arcsin xyz, with $x = \sin 2t$, $y = \cos 2t$, and $z = \sec t$.

Calculate dy in terms of x, y, and dx without solving for y in terms of x.

64. $\sin x + \cos y = 1.4$.

65. $\ln (x + y) + \sin x = 2$.

66. $e^{3x-2y} + \sin x = \cos y$.

67. $\ln (x^2 + 2y) + e^{3x} = 5$.

68. Recall Illustration 2, page 251. Prove the properties mentioned for the graph of (13) on page 251 with respect to maxima, minima, and tangency to the exponential curves $y = e^{-at}$ and $y = -e^{-at}$.

69. Prove that $\dfrac{x}{1 + x} < \ln (1 + x) < x$ if $x > 0$ and also if $-1 < x < 0$.

70. By use of a derivative, obtain an upper and a lower bound for Arctan x in terms of the fixed number x if $x > 0$.

71. Evaluate $\lim_{x \to \infty} \dfrac{x + \sin x}{2x + 1}$; $\lim_{x \to 0} \dfrac{x^2 \sin x^{-1}}{\tan x}$.

Note 1. In a plane, if a curve T rolls (without slipping) on a fixed curve C, the curve traced by a fixed point P on T is called a **roulette**. If a circle T of radius b rolls on the *inside* of a fixed circle C of radius a, where $b < a$, the roulette traced by P is called a **hypocycloid**. If a circle of radius b rolls on the *outside* of a circle of radius a, the roulette is called an **epicycloid**. In the following problems on roulettes, we assume that the scale units are equal on the axes in any xy-plane.

72. A circle of radius a rolls on a straight line, taken as the x-axis, in an xy-coordinate plane. The path traced by a fixed point on a radius at the distance b from the center is called a **trochoid**, also named a *cycloid* if $b = a$, and a *prolate* or *curtate cycloid* according as $b > a$ or $b < a$. Prove that, with proper location for the y-axis, parametric equations for the trochoid can be taken as

$$[x = a\theta - b \sin \theta, \quad y = a - b \cos \theta].$$

73. In Note 1 for a hypocycloid H, let the fixed circle C be $x^2 + y^2 = a^2$, and let a point of contact of C and the rolling circle T be $A:(a, 0)$. At any instant, let the point of contact be $P:(x, y)$ and let $a\theta$ be the length of arc AP traced on C as the point of contact moves from A to P, with $\theta > 0$ for rolling counterclockwise and $\theta < 0$ for rolling clockwise. Prove that parametric equations for H are

$$\left[x = (a - b)\cos \theta + b \cos \frac{a - b}{b} \theta, \quad x = (a - b)\sin \theta - b \sin \frac{a - b}{b} \theta \right]. \quad (1)$$

If $a/b = k$, an integer, prove that H is a closed curve, and that H has k cusps, at each of which the tangent is a radius of C, extended. Show that the hypocycloid of 4 cusps is obtained if $a = 4b$ in (1).

74. Prove that parametric equations for an epicycloid as described in Note 1 can be written in the form

$$\left[x = (a + b)\cos t - b \cos \frac{a + b}{b} t, \quad y = (a + b)\sin t - b \sin \frac{a + b}{b} t \right].$$

75. Plot the following epicycloid with the aid of calculus. Draw the associated circle.

$$[x = 4 \cos t - \cos 4t, \quad y = 4 \sin t - \sin 4t].$$

76. A conical goblet has altitude h and generating angle α (half-angle at vertex), and is full of water. A sphere of radius r is lowered into the goblet. Find r, to cause the maximum overflow of water. [Recall that, in a sphere of radius r, the volume of a segment of one base with altitude y is $\frac{1}{3}\pi(3ry^2 - y^3)$.]

77. Graph the equation $y = x \sin x^{-1}$, with the value of y at $x = 0$ defined by

$$y = \lim_{x \to 0} x \sin x^{-1}.$$

Show that there is a horizontal asymptote. Instead of finding all extrema, prove that the graph is tangent to the lines $y = x$ and $y = -x$, and there is no extremum if $|x| > 2/\pi$.

CHAPTER ELEVEN

Fundamentals of Integration

96. EMPHASIS ON DIFFERENTIALS IN INDEFINITE INTEGRALS

On page 189, we observed that an indefinite integral of a continuous function f can be defined as a function F such that $F'(x) = f(x)$ or, equally well, such that $dF(x) = f(x)dx$, for all numbers x in the domain of f. Also, if F is any particular indefinite integral of f, then the set of all of its indefinite integrals is the family of functions $[F(x) + C]$, where C is an arbitrary constant. That is,

$$\int f(x)dx = F(x) + C, \quad where \quad F'(x) = f(x). \tag{1}$$

ILLUSTRATION 1. A particular indefinite integral of $\cos x$ is $\sin x$ because

$$D_x \sin x = \cos x; \quad hence, \quad \int \cos x \, dx = \sin x + C.$$

We recall Theorem XI on page 190, which states that, if a variable v is a continuously differentiable function of a variable x, then

$$\int dv = v + C. \tag{2}$$

We shall obtain standard forms for integration by use of (2) and formulas for differentials on page 252, where we shall assume that the variables u and v, which are involved, are continuously differentiable functions of a variable x. In particular, u or v could be x itself.

ILLUSTRATION 2. From $(X)_d$ on page 252, we obtain $d(-\cos u) = \sin u \, du$. Hence, from (2) with $v = -\cos u$,

$$\int \sin u \, du = \int d(-\cos u) = -\cos u + C.$$

Since $d(\tan u) = \sec^2 u \, du$, from (2) with $v = \tan u$,

$$\int \sec^2 u \, du = \int d(\tan u) = \tan u + C.$$

Since $d(\cot u) = -\csc^2 u \, du$, or $d(-\cot u) = \csc^2 u \, du$, from (2) with $v = -\cot u$,

$$\int \csc^2 u \, du = \int d(-\cot u) = -\cot u + C.$$

Similarly,
$$\int \cos u \, du = \int d(\sin u) = \sin u + C.$$

271

97. STANDARD INDEFINITE INTEGRALS

$$\int u^n \, du = \frac{u^{n+1}}{n+1} + C. \qquad (n \neq -1) \tag{I}$$

$$\int \frac{du}{u} = \ln|u| + C. \qquad (u \ never \ 0) \tag{II}$$

$$\int a^u \, du = \frac{a^u}{\ln a} + C. \qquad (a > 0, \ a \neq 1) \tag{III}$$

$$\int e^u \, du = e^u + C. \tag{III}'$$

$$\int \sin u \, du = -\cos u + C. \tag{IV}$$

$$\int \cos u \, du = \sin u + C. \tag{V}$$

$$\int \tan u \, du = -\ln|\cos u| = \ln|\sec u| + C. \tag{VI}$$

$$\int \cot u \, du = \ln|\sin u| = -\ln|\csc u| + C. \tag{VII}$$

$$\int \sec^2 u \, du = \tan u + C. \tag{VIII}$$

$$\int \csc^2 u \, du = -\cot u + C. \tag{IX}$$

$$\int \sec u \, du = \ln|\sec u + \tan u| + C. \tag{X}$$

$$\int \csc u \, du = \ln|\csc u - \cot u| + C. \tag{XI}$$

$$\int \sec u \tan u \, du = \sec u + C. \tag{XII}$$

$$\int \csc u \cot u \, du = -\csc u + C. \tag{XIII}$$

$$\int \frac{du}{a^2 + u^2} = \frac{1}{a} \text{Arctan} \frac{u}{a} + C. \tag{XIV}$$

$$\int \frac{du}{\sqrt{a^2 - u^2}} = \text{Arcsin} \frac{u}{a} + C. \tag{XV}$$

$$\int \frac{du}{u^2 - a^2} = \frac{1}{2a} \ln\left|\frac{u - a}{u + a}\right| + C. \tag{XVI}$$

$$\int \frac{du}{a^2 - u^2} = \frac{1}{2a} \ln\left|\frac{a + u}{a - u}\right| + C. \tag{XVI}'$$

$$\int \frac{du}{\sqrt{u^2 \pm a^2}} = \ln|u + \sqrt{u^2 \pm a^2}| + C. \tag{XVII}$$

$$\int \frac{du}{u\sqrt{u^2 - a^2}} = \frac{1}{a} \text{Arcsec} \frac{u}{a} + C. \tag{XVIII}$$

We obtained (I) on page 190, and (IV), (V), (VIII), and (IX) in the preceding Section. Problems to be considered at present will involve only (I), (IV), (V), (VIII), and (IX).

Note 1. In any formula where a *positive constant* is denoted by a^2, we agree to let a represent a *positive number.* In (XVII), "$+ a^2$" and "$- a^2$" on the left correspond to "$+ a^2$" and "$- a^2$" on the right, respectively.

ILLUSTRATION 1. By use of general properties of indefinite integrals (see page 191), (I), (IV), and (VIII),

$$\int (5x^2 - 2 \sin x + 7 \sec^2 x)dx = 5\int x^2 \, dx - 2\int \sin x \, dx + 7\int \sec^2 x \, dx$$
$$= \tfrac{5}{3}x^3 + 2 \cos x + 7 \tan x + C.$$

To compute a definite integral, $\int_a^b f(x)dx$, by use of the fundamental theorem of integral calculus, as summarized in (16) on page 192, recall that we first search for any indefinite integral of f, that is, for any function F such that $F'(x) = f(x)$. Then,

$$\int_a^b f(x)dx = F(b) - F(a). \tag{1}$$

ILLUSTRATION 2. $\qquad \int_{\pi/4}^{3\pi/2} \cos x \, dx = \sin x \big]_{\pi/4}^{3\pi/2} = -1 - \tfrac{1}{2}\sqrt{2}.$

With a function f assigned, to obtain $\int f(x)dx$ by use of a standard form for integration from page 272, we first decide on the function whose values will be represented by u. Then, we adjust constant factors before and after the integral sign in $\int f(x)dx$ to exhibit u and du.

ILLUSTRATION 3. To calculate the following indefinite integral, we decide to let $u = 5x^3 + 1$. Then, $du = 15x^2 \, dx$; we finally use (I):

$$\int x^2(5x^3 + 1)^4 \, dx = \tfrac{1}{15}\int (5x^3 + 1)^4(15x^2 \, dx)$$

$(u = 5x^3 + 1; \int u^4 \, du) \qquad\qquad = \tfrac{1}{75}(5x^3 + 1)^5 + C.$

ILLUSTRATION 4. $\quad \int (3 \tan x + 2)^3 \sec^2 x \, dx = \tfrac{1}{3}\int (3 \tan x + 2)^3(3 \sec^2 x \, dx)$

$(u = 3 \tan x + 2; \int u^3 \, du) \qquad = \tfrac{1}{12}(3 \tan x + 2)^4 + C.$

ILLUSTRATION 5. $\qquad\qquad\qquad \int \sin 2x \, dx = \tfrac{1}{2}\int (\sin 2x)(2 \, dx)$

(with $u = 2x$) $\qquad = \tfrac{1}{2}\int \sin u \, du = -\tfrac{1}{2} \cos u + C = -\tfrac{1}{2} \cos 2x + C.$

For rapid work, we prefer the following details:

$$\int \sin 2x \, dx = \tfrac{1}{2}\int (\sin 2x)d(2x) = -\tfrac{1}{2} \cos 2x + C.$$

EXAMPLE 1. Calculate: $\qquad\qquad\qquad \int \sin^4 x \cos x \, dx.$

Solution. Work toward $\int u^4 \, du$, with $u = \sin x$; $du = \cos x \, dx$:

$$\int \sin^4 x \cos x \, dx = \int u^4 \, du = \tfrac{1}{5}u^5 + C = \tfrac{1}{5} \sin^5 x + C, \textit{ or}$$
$$\int (\sin x)^4 d(\sin x) = \tfrac{1}{5} \sin^5 x + C.$$

EXAMPLE 2. Calculate: $\displaystyle\int \frac{\sin x\, dx}{(1 + 2\cos x)^3}$.

Solution. We use $\int u^{-3}\, du$ with $u = 1 + 2\cos x$, and obtain

$$\int \frac{\sin x\, dx}{(1 + 2\cos x)^3} = -\frac{1}{2}\int u^{-3}\, du = \frac{1}{4}(1 + 2\cos x)^{-2} + C.$$

ILLUSTRATION 6. With $u = \tan 2x$ and $\cot 2x = 1/\tan 2x$,

$$\int \cot^3 2x \sec^2 2x\, dx = \int (\tan 2x)^{-3} \sec^2 2x\, dx$$

$$= \tfrac{1}{2}\int (\tan^{-3} 2x)(2\sec^2 2x\, dx) = \tfrac{1}{2}\int u^{-3}\, du = -\tfrac{1}{4}\tan^{-2} 2x + C.$$

ILLUSTRATION 7. With $u = \ln x$ and $du = dx/x$,

$$\int \frac{1}{(\ln x)^3} \cdot \frac{dx}{x} = \int u^{-3}\, du = -\frac{1}{2u^2} + C = -\frac{1}{2(\ln x)^2} + C.$$

EXERCISE 80

Integrate. Radicals should be changed to fractional powers. Avoid expanding if possible. Any letter other than t, x, y, z, and u represents a constant. Beyond Problem 15, perhaps use abbreviated solutions, as suggested in Illustration 5 on page 273.

1. $\displaystyle\int \frac{dx}{5x^4}$.   **2.** $\displaystyle\int \frac{x^3}{\sqrt[4]{x}}\, dx$.   **3.** $\displaystyle\int \frac{3 + 5t}{6t^3}\, dt$.   **4.** $\displaystyle\int \frac{3\, dx}{\sqrt{3x + 4}}$.

5. $\displaystyle\int (x^2 + 2x - 3)^7 (x + 1)\, dx$.   **6.** $\displaystyle\int (5 - 3x - x^3)^4 (1 + x^2)\, dx$.

7. $\displaystyle\int \sin 5x\, dx$.   **8.** $\displaystyle\int \cos 4x\, dx$.   **9.** $\displaystyle\int \cos \tfrac{1}{3}x\, dx$.

10. $\displaystyle\int_{-3\pi/4}^{2\pi/3} \sin t\, dt$.   **11.** $\displaystyle\int_{-5\pi/4}^{7\pi/8} \cos 2x\, dx$.   **12.** $\displaystyle\int \sec^2 3x\, dx$.

13. $\displaystyle\int \csc^2 au\, du$.   **14.** $\displaystyle\int \csc^2 \tfrac{1}{4}t\, dt$.   **15.** $\displaystyle\int \sec^2 \tfrac{1}{2}x\, dx$.

16. $\displaystyle\int v\sqrt{3v^2 + 2}\, dv$.   **17.** $\displaystyle\int \sin^6 x \cos x\, dx$.   **18.** $\displaystyle\int \cos^3 x \sin x\, dx$.

19. $\displaystyle\int \tan^3 x \sec^2 x\, dx$.   **20.** $\displaystyle\int \cot^4 x \csc^2 x\, dx$.   **21.** $\displaystyle\int \cos^4 2x \sin 2x\, dx$.

22. $\displaystyle\int (2 + 5\cos x)^3 \sin x\, dx$.   **23.** $\displaystyle\int (3 + 2\tan y)^6 \sec^2 y\, dy$.

24. $\displaystyle\int (3 + 5e^t)^6 e^t\, dt$.   **25.** $\displaystyle\int x^2 \cos x^3\, dx$.   **26.** $\displaystyle\int e^{2z} \sin e^{2z}\, dx$.

27. $\displaystyle\int \frac{4\, dy}{\cos^2 2y}$.   **28.** $\displaystyle\int \frac{3\, dx}{\sin^2 x}$.   **29.** $\displaystyle\int \frac{\sin x\, dx}{\cos^5 x}$.

30. $\displaystyle\int \frac{\cos 2x\, dx}{\sin^4 2x}$.   **31.** $\displaystyle\int \frac{(t - 1)dt}{\sqrt{2t^2 - 4t}}$.   **32.** $\displaystyle\int \frac{\sec^2 2t\, dt}{\tan^4 2t}$.

33. $\displaystyle\int_1^3 (\ln x)^4 \frac{dx}{x}$.   **34.** $\displaystyle\int \frac{\sin t\, dt}{\sqrt{2 - 3\cos t}}$.   **35.** $\displaystyle\int \frac{\sec^2 t\, dt}{\sqrt[3]{2 + \tan t}}$.

36. $\displaystyle\int \frac{(\text{Arctan } x)^2\, dx}{1 + x^2}$.   **37.** $\displaystyle\int \frac{\text{Arcsin } x}{\sqrt{1 - x^2}}\, dx$.

38. $\displaystyle\int \cos t \sqrt[3]{\sin t}\, dt$.   **39.** $\displaystyle\int_{-5}^{-6/5} \sqrt[3]{2 - 5x}\, dx$.

40. $\displaystyle\int \frac{du}{\tan^5 u \cos^2 u}$.   **41.** $\displaystyle\int \frac{e^{-z}\, dx}{(3 + e^{-z})^4}$.   **42.** $\displaystyle\int \frac{e^x - e^{-x}}{(e^x + e^{-x})^2}\, dx$.

Find the area of the region in the xy-plane described in the problem.

43. Bounded by the x-axis and one arch of $y = \sin x$.

44. Bounded by the y-axis, and the curves $y = \sin x$ and $y = \cos x$ from $x = 0$ to the first intersection of the curves where $x > 0$.

45. Bounded by $y = x + \sin 2x$ and the line $y = x$, from $x = 0$ to $x = \pi$.

46. Bounded by the x-axis, the lines $x = \frac{3}{2}$ and $x = 4$, and the curve $y = \sqrt{2x + 1}$. Obtain the result correct to three decimal places.

47. Find the volume of the solid of revolution obtained if the region in an xy-plane bounded by the axes, $y = \sec x$, and the line $x = \frac{1}{4}\pi$ is revolved about the x-axis.

98. EXPONENTIAL FORMS

If the variable u is a continuously differentiable function of some independent variable x, if a > 0, and if a ≠ 1, then

$$\int a^u \, du = \frac{a^u}{\ln a} + C. \tag{III}$$

Proof. From $(XX)_d$ on page 252, $da^u = a^u (\ln a) du$. Hence,

$$\int a^u \, du = \int d\left(\frac{a^u}{\ln a}\right) = \frac{a^u}{\ln a} + C.$$

If $a = e$ then $\ln a = 1$ and (III) gives

$$\int e^u \, du = e^u + C. \tag{III$'$}$$

ILLUSTRATION 1. From (III), $\qquad \int 2^x \, dx = \frac{2^x}{\ln 2} + C.$

ILLUSTRATION 2. With $u = 3 - 4x$, then $du = -4 \, dx$ and

$$\int e^{3-4x} \, dx = -\frac{1}{4} \int e^{3-4x} (-4 \, dx) = -\frac{1}{4} \int e^u \, du$$
$$= -\frac{1}{4} e^u + C = -\frac{1}{4} e^{3-4x} + C.$$

ILLUSTRATION 3. With $u = \tan 3x$ in (III)$'$,

$$(du = 3 \sec^2 3x \, dx) \qquad \int e^{\tan 3x} \sec^2 3x \, dx = \frac{1}{3} \int e^{\tan 3x} (3 \sec^2 3x \, dx)$$
$$= \frac{1}{3} \int e^u \, du = \frac{1}{3} e^u + C = \frac{1}{3} e^{\tan 3x} + C.$$

ILLUSTRATION 4. $\qquad \int \frac{dx}{\sqrt[3]{e^{3x}}} = \int e^{-\frac{3}{4}x} \, dx$

$$= -\frac{4}{3} \int e^{-\frac{3}{4}x} \cdot (-\frac{3}{4} \, dx) = -\frac{4}{3} e^{-\frac{3}{4}x} + C,$$

where we used (III)$'$ with $u = -\frac{3}{4}x$.

EXERCISE 81

Integrate. Any letter other than t, x, y, z, and u represents a constant.

1. $\int e^{3x} \, dx.$ **2.** $\int 3^x \, dx.$ **3.** $\int 10^x \, dx.$ **4.** $\int e^{-x} \, dx.$

5. $\int e^{2+5x} \, dx.$ **6.** $\int 2^x e^x \, dx.$ **7.** $\int a^x e^x \, dx.$ **8.** $\int e^{-4x} \, dx.$

9. $\int e^{3-4t}\, dt.$ 10. $\int x^3 e^{x^4}\, dx.$ 11. $\int x^2 e^{-x^3}\, dx.$ 12. $\int \sqrt{e^t}\, dt.$

13. $\int \dfrac{4\, dx}{e^{\frac{1}{2}x}}.$ 14. $\int \dfrac{e^{\sqrt{x}}}{\sqrt{x}}\, dx.$ 15. $\int \dfrac{dt}{\sqrt[3]{e^t}}.$ 16. $\int \dfrac{x\, dx}{e^{x^2}}.$

17. $\int e^{3\ln x}\, dx.$ 18. $\int_{-2}^{0} 3xe^{-x^2}\, dx.$ 19. $\int x^{-2} e^{\frac{1}{x}}\, dx.$

20. $\int e^{e^x} e^x\, dx.$ 21. $\int \sqrt{x}\, e^{x\sqrt{x}}\, dx.$ 22. $\int e^{\sin u}\cos u\, du.$

23. $\int e^{\sin 2y}\cos 2y\, dy.$ 24. $\int e^{\cot z}\csc^2 z\, dz.$ 25. $\int_{\pi}^{3\pi/4} e^{\tan z}\sec^2 z\, dz.$

26. $\int e^{\sec y}\sec y \tan y\, dy.$ 27. $\int (e^{ax} + e^{-ax})^2\, dx.$

28. $\int e^{-y^2 + \ln y}\, dy.$ 29. $\int e^z\sqrt{3 + 4e^z}\, dz.$ 30. $\int_{0}^{3\pi/2} e^{\cos 2t}\sin 2t\, dt.$

31. $\int \dfrac{e^u\, du}{(2 - 3e^u)^3}.$ 32. $\int \dfrac{e^{\operatorname{Arctan} y}}{2 + 2y^2}\, dy.$ 33. $\int \dfrac{e^{\cos^2 y}}{\csc 2y}\, dy.$

Find the area of the region of the xy-plane which is described.

34. The region bounded by the x-axis, the curve $y = e^x$, and the lines $x = -1$ and $x = 2$.

35. The region bounded by the coordinate axes, the curve $y = e^{-x}$, and the line $x = 3$.

36. The region between $y = \frac{1}{2}(e^x + e^{-x})$ and $y = \frac{1}{2}e^x$, from $x = 0$ to $x = 1$.

37. The region bounded by the catenary $y = \frac{1}{2}a(e^{\frac{x}{a}} + e^{-\frac{x}{a}})$, the lines $x = \pm \frac{1}{2}a$, and the x-axis.

38–39. Find the volumes of the solids of revolution obtained if the regions of Problems 34 and 35, respectively, are revolved about the x-axis.

40. Find the mean value of $e^{\frac{1}{2}x}$ over the interval $1 \leqq x \leqq 3$.

99. THE LOGARITHMIC FORM

If the variable u is a continuously differentiable function of some independent variable x, where $u \neq 0$ at any value of x in its domain, then

$$\int \frac{du}{u} = \ln |u| + C. \tag{II}$$

Proof. 1. If $u > 0$ at all points on the domain of x, then $\ln u$ is well defined and $d(\ln u) = du/u$. Hence, by (2) on page 271, with $v = \ln u$,

$$(if\ u > 0) \qquad \int \frac{du}{u} = \int d(\ln u) = \ln u + C. \tag{1}$$

2. Assume, now, that $u < 0$ at all points in the domain of x. Then, since

$$d(-u) = -du,$$

by use of (1) with u replaced by $-u$, we obtain

$$(if\ u < 0) \qquad \int \frac{du}{u} = \int \frac{-du}{-u} = \int \frac{d(-u)}{(-u)} = \ln(-u) + C. \tag{2}$$

3. If $u > 0$ then $|u| = u$. If $u < 0$ then $|u| = -u$. Hence, in both (1) and (2), the right-hand side can be written $\ln |u| + C$, which proves (II).

Note 1. An integral such as $\int_{-5}^{1} du/u$ cannot be considered at present because $1/u$ is not defined at $u = 0$, which is on the interval of integration.

ILLUSTRATION 1. $\qquad \int_{1}^{e^2} \dfrac{dx}{x} = \ln|x|\Big]_{1}^{e^2} = \ln e^2 - \ln 1 = 2.$

ILLUSTRATION 2. $\qquad \int_{-5}^{-2} \dfrac{dx}{x} = \ln|x|\Big]_{-5}^{-2} = \ln|-2| - \ln|-5|$

(Table III) $\qquad\qquad\qquad = \ln 2 - \ln 5 = -.91629.$

ILLUSTRATION 3. $\qquad \int \dfrac{(2x+1)dx}{2x^2+2x+3} = \dfrac{1}{2}\int \dfrac{(4x+2)dx}{2x^2+2x+3}$

$[u = 2x^2 + 2x + 3;\ du = (4x+2)dx] \qquad = \dfrac{1}{2}\int \dfrac{du}{u} = \dfrac{1}{2}\ln|u| + C$

$$= \tfrac{1}{2}\ln|2x^2 + 2x + 3| + C.$$

ILLUSTRATION 4. With $u = 1 + 3\sec 2x$,

$$\int \frac{\sec 2x \tan 2x\ dx}{1 + 3\sec 2x} = \frac{1}{6}\int \frac{du}{u} = \frac{1}{6}\ln|1 + 3\sec 2x| + C.$$

EXAMPLE 1. Obtain $\displaystyle\int \frac{6x^2 + 5}{2x - 2}\,dx.$

Solution. In the integrand, first carry out long division until the remainder is of lower degree than the denominator:

$$\int \frac{6x^2 + 5}{2x - 2}\,dx = \int \left(3x + 3 + \frac{11}{2x - 2}\right) dx$$
$$= \tfrac{3}{2}x^2 + 3x + \tfrac{11}{2}\ln|2x - 2| + C.$$

ILLUSTRATION 5. $\qquad \int_{.235}^{1} \dfrac{dx}{x} = \ln x\Big]_{.235}^{1} = \ln 1 - \ln .235 = 1.44817.$

To obtain ln .235 from Table III, we wrote .235 = 2.35/10:

$$\ln .235 = \ln 2.35 - \ln 10 = .85442 - 2.30259 = -1.44817.$$

(Similar details would give ln .0235 = ln 2.35 − 2 ln 10.)

EXERCISE 82

1. Compute by use of Table III if possible: $\displaystyle\int_{2}^{7} \frac{du}{u};\quad \int_{-4}^{2} \frac{du}{u}.$

Integrate. Any letter other than t, x, y, z, and u represents a constant.

2. $\displaystyle\int \frac{du}{1 - 3u}.$

3. $\displaystyle\int \frac{2x\ dx}{1 + x^2}.$

4. $\displaystyle\int \frac{x^2\ dx}{2 - 5x^3}.$

5. $\displaystyle\int_{-5}^{-2} \frac{dt}{2t + 1}.$

6. $\displaystyle\int_{0}^{\pi/2} \frac{\cos x\ dx}{1 + \sin x}.$

7. $\displaystyle\int \frac{\sec^2 x\ dx}{1 - 2\tan x}.$

8. $\displaystyle\int \frac{\sin kt}{\cos kt}\,dt.$

9. $\displaystyle\int \frac{\sec t \tan t\ dt}{1 + 4\sec t}.$

10. $\displaystyle\int_{-1}^{1} \frac{e^x\ dx}{1 + 2e^x}.$

11. $\displaystyle\int \frac{4x^2 + 2}{2x + 1}\,dx.$

12. $\displaystyle\int \frac{t^3 + 4t^2}{t + 3}\,dt.$

13. $\displaystyle\int_{1}^{3} \frac{(2x + 4)dx}{x^2 + 4x}.$

14. $\int \dfrac{e^x + e^{-x}}{e^x - e^{-x}} dx.$ **15.** $\int \dfrac{\csc^2 y \, dy}{1 + 2 \cot y}.$ **16.** $\int \dfrac{(2 + \sin z)dz}{2z - \cos z}.$

17. $\int \dfrac{dy}{y(2 + \ln y)}.$ **18.** $\int \dfrac{(1 + \ln y)dy}{1 + y \ln y}.$ **19.** $\int \dfrac{\cos u \sin u \, du}{1 + \cos^2 u}.$

20. $\int \dfrac{e^{2x} \, dx}{2e^x + 1}.$ **21.** $\int \dfrac{e^{-3x} \, dx}{1 + e^{-x}}.$ **22.** $\int \dfrac{\sin 2x \, dx}{5 + \sin^2 x}.$

23. $\int \dfrac{du}{\sqrt{1 - 4u^2} \, \text{Arcsin} \, 2u}.$ **24.** $\int \dfrac{\csc ay \cot ay \, dy}{1 + 3 \csc ay}.$

Find the area of the region of the xy-plane which is described.

25. The region bounded by the hyperbola $xy = 4$, the x-axis, and the lines $x = 1$ and $x = 5$. Compute accurately to 3 decimal places.

26. The region bounded by the curve $y = 1/(x - 1)$, the x-axis, and the lines $x = 1.463$ and $x = 4$.

27. The region between the curves $xy = 1$ and $x^2 y = 1$, from the line $x = 1$ to the line $x = 3$.

28. Find the mean value of the function $2/(x - 3)$ over the interval $4 \le x \le 9$.

100. MISCELLANEOUS TRIGONOMETRIC INTEGRANDS

Proof of **(VI)** *on page* 272. We obtain

$$\int \tan u \, du = \int \frac{\sin u \, du}{\cos u} = -\int \frac{- \sin u \, du}{\cos u}.$$

With $v = \cos u$ and $dv = - \sin u \, du,$

$$\int \tan u \, du = - \int \frac{dv}{v} = - \ln | \cos u | + C. \tag{1}$$

Since $\sec u = \dfrac{1}{\cos u},$ *and* $\ln 1 = 0,$

$$\ln | \sec u | = \ln 1 - \ln | \cos u | = - \ln | \cos u |.$$

Hence, from (1), $\int \tan u \, du = \ln | \sec u | + C. \tag{VI}$

The student will prove (VII) of page 272 similarly as an exercise. We obtain (XII) and (XIII) of page 272 immediately from

$$d \sec u = \sec u \tan u \, du \quad and \quad d(- \csc u) = \csc u \cot u \, du.$$

Proof of **(X)** *on page* 272. In sec $u \, du$, multiply and also divide by (sec u + tan u):

$$\int \sec u \, du = \int \frac{\sec u \, (\sec u + \tan u)du}{\sec u + \tan u}.$$

If we let $v = \sec u + \tan u, \quad then \quad dv = (\sec u \tan u + \sec^2 u)du.$

Hence, $\int \sec u \, du = \int \dfrac{dv}{v} = \ln | v | + C,$ *or*

$$\int \sec u \, du = \ln | \sec u + \tan u | + C. \tag{X}$$

Similarly, the student will prove (XI) later.

ILLUSTRATION 1. From (XII), $\int \sec 2x \tan 2x \, dx = \frac{1}{2} \sec 2x + C.$

ILLUSTRATION 2. By use of (VII) of page 272, we obtain

$$\int \cot \tfrac{1}{2}x \, dx = 2 \int (\cot \tfrac{1}{2}x)(\tfrac{1}{2} \, dx) = -2 \ln |\csc \tfrac{1}{2}x| + C.$$

ILLUSTRATION 3. $\quad \displaystyle\int \frac{3 + \sin 2x}{\cos 2x} \, dx = 3 \int \sec 2x \, dx + \int \tan 2x \, dx$

$$= \tfrac{3}{2} \int (\sec 2x)(2 \, dx) + \tfrac{1}{2} \int (\tan 2x)(2 \, dx)$$

$$= \tfrac{3}{2} \ln |\sec 2x + \tan 2x| + \tfrac{1}{2} \ln |\sec 2x| + C.$$

ILLUSTRATION 4. $\quad \displaystyle\int_{\pi/3}^{3\pi/8} \tan 2x \, dx = \tfrac{1}{2} \int_{\pi/3}^{3\pi/8} (\tan 2x)(2 \, dx)$

$$= \tfrac{1}{2} \ln |\sec 2x| \,]_{\pi/3}^{3\pi/8} = \tfrac{1}{2}(\ln |\sec \tfrac{3}{4}\pi| - \ln |\sec \tfrac{2}{3}\pi|)$$

$$= \tfrac{1}{2}(\ln \sqrt{2} - \ln 2) = -\tfrac{1}{4} \ln 2 = -.17329 \qquad \text{(Table III)}$$

Note 1. From (II) and (VIII) on page 679, we have the following identities for the standard direct trigonometric functions of numbers.

$$2 \sin^2 \alpha = 1 - \cos 2\alpha; \quad 2 \cos^2 \alpha = 1 + \cos 2\alpha; \qquad (2)$$

$$\sin^2 \alpha + \cos^2 \alpha = 1; \quad 1 + \tan^2 \alpha = \sec^2 \alpha; \quad 1 + \cot^2 \alpha = \csc^2 \alpha. \qquad (3)$$

To evaluate integrals of the form $\int \sin^2 u \, du$ or $\int \cos^2 u \, du$, we use (2) to introduce the cosine function with the argument $2u$.

ILLUSTRATION 5. By use of (2) with $\alpha = 2x$,

$$\int \cos^2 2x \, dx = \tfrac{1}{2} \int (1 + \cos 4x) dx = \tfrac{1}{2} \int dx + \tfrac{1}{2} \int \cos 4x \, dx$$

$$= \tfrac{1}{2}x + \tfrac{1}{8} \int (\cos 4x)(4 \, dx) = \tfrac{1}{2}x + \tfrac{1}{8} \sin 4x + C.$$

ILLUSTRATION 6. From (3), $\tan^2 3x = \sec^2 3x - 1$. Hence,

$$\int \tan^2 3x \, dx = \int (\sec^2 3x - 1) dx = \int \sec^2 3x \, dx - \int dx$$

$$= \tfrac{1}{3} \int (\sec^2 3x)(3 \, dx) - x = \tfrac{1}{3} \tan 3x - x + C.$$

EXERCISE 83

Integrate. Letters a, b, and k represent constants.

1. $\int \tan 2x \, dx.$ **2.** $\int \csc 3x \, dx.$ **3.** $\int \cot \tfrac{1}{4}x \, dx.$

4. $\int \sec 5x \, dx.$ **5.** $\int \csc^2 4t \, dt.$ **6.** $\int \tan ku \, du.$

7. $\int \dfrac{dv}{\sin v}.$ **8.** $\int \dfrac{dy}{\cos 2y}.$ **9.** $\int \dfrac{dv}{\sec 3v}.$ **10.** $\int \dfrac{dx}{\cot 5x}.$

11. $\int \sec \tfrac{1}{2}x \tan \tfrac{1}{2}x \, dx.$ **12.** $\int \csc 4x \cot 4x \, dx.$

13. $\int \sec ax \, dx.$ **14.** $\int \csc bx \, dx.$ **15.** $\int \cos^2 x \, dx.$

16. $\int \sin^2 x \, dx.$ **17.** $\int \cos^2 3x \, dx.$ **18.** $\int \tan^2 x \, dx.$

19. $\int \cot^2 u \, du.$ **20.** $\int_{-\pi/3}^{3\pi/4} \sin^2 3x \, dx.$ **21.** $\int_{\pi/3}^{3\pi/2} \cos^2 \tfrac{1}{2}x \, dx.$

22. $\int \cos^2 ax \, dx.$ **23.** $\int \tan^2 4u \, du.$ **24.** $\int \cot^2 \tfrac{1}{2}u \, du.$

25. $\int (\sec y - \tan y)^2 \, dy.$ **26.** $\int (\tan x + \cot x)^2 \, dx.$

27. $\int \dfrac{\sec^2 t \, dt}{4 + 3 \tan t}.$ **28.** $\int \dfrac{2 + \cos 3x}{\sin 3x} \, dx.$ **29.** $\int \dfrac{(3 + 2x)dx}{\csc (3x + x^2)}.$

30. $\int_{-\pi/3}^{\pi/4} \tan y \, dy.$ **31.** $\int_{3\pi/4}^{5\pi/4} \sec u \, du.$ **32.** $\int (\sin x - 3)^2 \, dx.$

33. $\int \dfrac{e^x}{\cot e^x} \, dx.$ **34.** $\int \dfrac{\sec 2e^{-x}}{e^x} \, dx.$ **35.** $\int \dfrac{x^2}{\tan x^3} \, dx.$

36. $\int \dfrac{\cot (\ln x)}{x} \, dx.$ **37.** $\int \dfrac{\sin e^{-x}}{e^x} \, dx.$ **38.** $\int \dfrac{e^{2x} \, dx}{\cot e^{2x}}.$

Find the area of the region of the xy-plane which is described.

39. The region bounded by the x-axis, $y = \tan x$, and lines $x = -\frac{1}{4}\pi$ and $x = \frac{1}{3}\pi$.

40. The region bounded below by the curve $y = \sec x$ and above by the line $y = \sqrt{2}$, between $x = -\frac{1}{4}\pi$ and $x = \frac{1}{4}\pi$.

Find the volume of the solid of revolution obtained by revolving the specified region of the xy-plane about the x-axis.

41. Bounded by the x-axis and one arch of $y = \sin x$.

42. Bounded by $y = \sec x$, the coordinate axes, and the line $x = \frac{1}{4}\pi$.

43. Bounded by $y = \tan x$, the x-axis, and the line $x = \frac{1}{3}\pi$.

44. Find the mean value of the function $\sin x$ over the interval $0 \leqq x \leqq 2\pi$; $0 \leqq x \leqq \frac{3}{2}\pi$.

45. Prove (VII) and (XI) of page 272.

101. INVERSE TRIGONOMETRIC FORMS

If u is a continuously differentiable function of some independent variable x, then

$$\int \frac{du}{a^2 + u^2} = \frac{1}{a} \operatorname{Arctan} \frac{u}{a} + C. \tag{XIV}$$

In particular,
$$\int \frac{du}{1 + u^2} = \operatorname{Arctan} u + C.$$

Proof. From (XVI)$_d$ on page 252,

$$d \operatorname{Arctan} \frac{u}{a} = \frac{1}{1 + \dfrac{u^2}{a^2}} \cdot d\left(\frac{u}{a}\right) = \frac{a \, du}{a^2 + u^2}, \quad or \quad \frac{du}{a^2 + u^2} = d\left(\frac{1}{a} \operatorname{Arctan} \frac{u}{a}\right).$$

Hence, from (2) on page 271,

$$\int \frac{du}{a^2 + u^2} = \int d\left(\frac{1}{a} \operatorname{Arctan} \frac{u}{a}\right) = \frac{1}{a} \operatorname{Arctan} \frac{u}{a} + C.$$

Similarly, we obtain (XV), page 272, and the special case where $a = 1$,

$$\int \frac{du}{\sqrt{a^2 - u^2}} = \operatorname{Arcsin} \frac{u}{a} + C, \quad and \quad \int \frac{du}{\sqrt{1 - u^2}} = \operatorname{Arcsin} u + C, \quad \text{(XV)}$$

by first verifying that $d\left(\operatorname{Arcsin} \dfrac{u}{a}\right) = \dfrac{du}{\sqrt{a^2 - u^2}}.$

ILLUSTRATION 1. By use of (XIV) with $a = \sqrt{5}$ and $u = 2x$,

$$\int \frac{dx}{5 + 4x^2} = \frac{1}{2} \int \frac{2\,dx}{5 + (2x)^2} = \frac{1}{2\sqrt{5}} \text{ Arctan } \frac{2x}{\sqrt{5}} + C.$$

ILLUSTRATION 2. By use of $a = 2$ and $u = 3x$ in (XV),

$$\int_{-\sqrt{3}/3}^{\sqrt{2}/3} \frac{dx}{\sqrt{4 - 9x^2}} = \frac{1}{3} \int_{-\sqrt{3}/3}^{\sqrt{2}/3} \frac{3\,dx}{\sqrt{2^2 - (3x)^2}} = \frac{1}{3} \text{ Arcsin } \frac{3x}{2}\Big]_{-\sqrt{3}/3}^{\sqrt{2}/3}$$

$$= \frac{1}{3}\left[\text{Arcsin } \frac{\sqrt{2}}{2} - \text{Arcsin}\left(-\frac{\sqrt{3}}{2}\right)\right] = \frac{1}{3}\left[\frac{\pi}{4} - \left(-\frac{\pi}{3}\right)\right] = \frac{7\pi}{36}. \qquad (1)$$

To verify (1), let $y = \text{Arcsin } \frac{1}{2}\sqrt{2}$; then $0 \leqq y \leqq \frac{1}{2}\pi$ and $\sin y = \frac{1}{2}\sqrt{2}$; hence $y = \frac{1}{4}\pi$. Let $y = \text{Arcsin }(-\frac{1}{2}\sqrt{3})$; then $\sin y = -\frac{1}{2}\sqrt{3}$ and, from Figure 171 on page 234, $-\frac{1}{2}\pi \leqq y \leqq 0$; hence $y = -\frac{1}{3}\pi$.

ILLUSTRATION 3. $\int \frac{x^2\,dx}{4 + x^6} = \frac{1}{3} \int \frac{3x^2\,dx}{4 + (x^3)^2} = \frac{1}{6} \text{ Arctan } \frac{x^3}{2} + C.$

Note 1. In (XV), we cannot permit $|u| = a$ because then the denominator in the integrand is equal to zero. Later, definite integrals involving (XV) will be introduced where $|u| = a$ at a limit of integration, and will be called *improper integrals*.

EXAMPLE 1. A region R is bounded by the curve $y = 4/\sqrt{16 - x^2}$, the lines $x = \pm 2\sqrt{2}$, and the x-axis. Find the area, A, of R.

Solution. The graph of $y = 4/\sqrt{16 - x^2}$, in Figure 191, has the lines $x = \pm 4$ as asymptotes, and y is not defined if $|x| = 4$. From symmetry, A is twice the area of the region between $x = 0$ and $x = 2\sqrt{2}$:

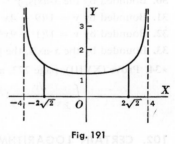

Fig. 191

$$A = 2\int_0^{2\sqrt{2}} y\,dx = 2\int_0^{2\sqrt{2}} \frac{4\,dx}{\sqrt{16 - x^2}} = 8 \text{ Arcsin } \frac{x}{4}\Big]_0^{2\sqrt{2}} = 8\left(\frac{\pi}{4}\right) = 2\pi.$$

Note 2. We could express $\int -\frac{du}{a^2 + u^2}$ *and* $\int -\frac{du}{\sqrt{a^2 - u^2}}$

in terms of the Arccotangent and Arccosine functions, respectively. However, *such formulas are not needed.* Instead, we multiply by -1 on each side in (XIV) and (XV).

EXERCISE 84

Integrate. Use Table **IV** *where desirable.*

1. $\int \dfrac{dx}{x^2 + 4}.$

2. $\int \dfrac{dx}{\sqrt{9 - x^2}}.$

3. $\int \dfrac{dx}{\sqrt{9 - 25x^2}}.$

4. $\int \dfrac{-\,dx}{4 + 25x^2}.$

5. $\int \dfrac{-\,dy}{\sqrt{16 - 9y^2}}.$

6. $\int \dfrac{dt}{\sqrt{121 - 9t^2}}.$

7. $\int_{-1/2}^{1/2} \dfrac{dt}{\sqrt{1 - t^2}}.$

8. $\int_1^{\sqrt{3}} \dfrac{du}{1 + u^2}.$

9. $\int_{-1}^{\sqrt{2}} \dfrac{dx}{\sqrt{4 - x^2}}.$

10. $\int_{-1}^{3} \dfrac{dz}{3 + z^2}$.

11. $\int_{0}^{-1} \dfrac{dv}{\sqrt{2 - v^2}}$.

12. $\int_{-2/3}^{.5068} \dfrac{dz}{4 + 9z^2}$.

13. $\int_{0}^{.1237} \dfrac{dx}{\sqrt{1 - 4x^2}}$.

14. $\int_{-1/2}^{\sqrt{3}/6} \dfrac{dx}{\sqrt{3 - 9x^2}}$.

15. $\int \dfrac{\cos\theta \, d\theta}{49 + 4\sin^2\theta}$.

16. $\int \dfrac{\sec^2 t \, dt}{1 + 9\tan^2 t}$.

17. $\int \dfrac{x^2 \, dx}{9 + x^6}$.

18. $\int \dfrac{\csc^2 x \, dx}{\sqrt{5 - \cot^2 x}}$.

19. $\int \dfrac{x \, dx}{4 + x^4}$.

20. $\int \dfrac{e^{\frac{1}{3}u} \, du}{9 + \sqrt[3]{e^{2u}}}$.

21. $\int \dfrac{(8x^2 + 4)dx}{25 + 4x^2}$.

22. $\int \dfrac{\sec u \tan u \, du}{\sqrt{4 - \sec^2 u}}$.

23. $\int \dfrac{du}{u\sqrt{1 - (\ln u)^2}}$.

24. $\int \dfrac{e^z \, dx}{\sqrt{16 - 9e^{2z}}}$.

25. $\int \dfrac{dx}{\sqrt{4 - (2 + x)^2}}$.

26. $\int \dfrac{dz}{121 + (2z + 1)^2}$.

27. $\int \dfrac{dx}{9 + 25(2x + 3)^2}$.

28. $\int \dfrac{dx}{\sqrt{9 - 4(2 - 3x)^2}}$.

Find the area of the region of the xy-plane which is described.

29. Bounded by the x-axis, $y = 1/\sqrt{4 - x^2}$, and the lines $x = \pm 1$.

30. Bounded by the x-axis, $y = 1/\sqrt{9 - 25x^2}$, and the lines $x = \pm \frac{3}{10}\sqrt{3}$.

31. Bounded by $y = 1/(9 + 4x^2)$, and the lines $x = -\frac{3}{2}\sqrt{3}$, $x = \frac{3}{2}$, and $y = 0$.

32. Bounded by $y = 1/(1 + 9x^2)$, and the lines $x = -\frac{1}{3}\sqrt{3}$, $x = .43$, and $y = 0$.

33. Bounded by the x-axis, the y-axis, $y = 1/\sqrt{3 - x^2}$, and the line $x = \frac{1}{2}\sqrt{6}$.

★34. Prove (XVIII), page 272, and use it to obtain

$$\int \frac{dy}{y\sqrt{4y^2 - 9}}; \qquad \int \frac{dx}{x\sqrt{9x^2 - 25}}; \qquad \int \frac{dx}{x\sqrt{x^2 - 4}}.$$

102. CERTAIN LOGARITHMIC FORMULAS

If u is a continuously differentiable function of some independent variable x, then

$$\int \frac{du}{u^2 - a^2} = \frac{1}{2a}\ln\left|\frac{u - a}{u + a}\right| + C; \qquad \textbf{(XVI)}$$

$$\int \frac{du}{a^2 - u^2} = \frac{1}{2a}\ln\left|\frac{a + u}{a - u}\right| + C. \qquad \textbf{(XVI)}'$$

Proof of **(XVI).** We verify $\qquad \dfrac{1}{u^2 - a^2} = \dfrac{1}{2a}\left(\dfrac{1}{u - a} - \dfrac{1}{u + a}\right).$

Hence, $\qquad \displaystyle\int \frac{du}{u^2 - a^2} = \frac{1}{2a}\left[\int \frac{du}{u - a} - \int \frac{du}{u + a}\right]$

$$= \frac{1}{2a}(\ln|u - a| - \ln|u + a|) + C = \frac{1}{2a}\ln\left|\frac{u - a}{u + a}\right| + C.$$

Proof of **(XVI)′.** From (XVI),

$$\int \frac{du}{a^2 - u^2} = -\int \frac{du}{u^2 - a^2} = -\frac{1}{2a}\ln\left|\frac{u - a}{u + a}\right| + C. \qquad (1)$$

We recall that
$$\ln \frac{1}{N} = \ln 1 - \ln N = -\ln N.$$

Hence,
$$-\ln \left|\frac{u-a}{u+a}\right| = \ln \left|\frac{u+a}{u-a}\right| = \ln \left|\frac{a+u}{a-u}\right|.$$

Thus, the right-hand sides of (1) and (XVI)' are identical.

ILLUSTRATION 1. From (XVI) with $u = 3x$, $\displaystyle\int \frac{dx}{9x^2 - 4} = \frac{1}{3}\int \frac{3\,dx}{(3x)^2 - 2^2}$

$$= \frac{1}{3}\int \frac{du}{u^2 - 2^2} = \frac{1}{12}\ln \left|\frac{u-2}{u+2}\right| + C = \frac{1}{12}\ln \left|\frac{3x-2}{3x+2}\right| + C.$$

ILLUSTRATION 2. $\displaystyle\int_{-3}^{2} \frac{dt}{t^2 - 36} = \frac{1}{12}\ln \left|\frac{t-6}{t+6}\right|\Big]_{-3}^{2}$

$$= \tfrac{1}{12}(\ln \tfrac{1}{2} - \ln 3) = -\tfrac{1}{12}\ln 6 = -.14931. \qquad \text{(Table III)}$$

EXERCISE 85

Integrate.

1. $\displaystyle\int \frac{du}{u^2 - 4}.$ 2. $\displaystyle\int \frac{dt}{9 - t^2}.$ 3. $\displaystyle\int \frac{dz}{16z^2 - 9}.$

4. $\displaystyle\int \frac{dx}{25 - 9x^2}.$ 5. $\displaystyle\int_{-2}^{1} \frac{du}{u^2 - 16}.$ 6. $\displaystyle\int_{3}^{6} \frac{dy}{9 - 4y^2}.$

7. $\displaystyle\int_{-5}^{-10} \frac{dz}{25 - 4z^2}.$ 8. $\displaystyle\int_{-1}^{0} \frac{dt}{9t^2 - 25}.$ 9. $\displaystyle\int \frac{e^x\,dx}{9e^{2x} - 5}.$

10. $\displaystyle\int \frac{y\,dy}{7 - 4y^4}.$ 11. $\displaystyle\int \frac{x^2\,dx}{x^6 - 9}.$ 12. $\displaystyle\int \frac{y^{\frac{1}{2}}\,dy}{9 - 4y^3}.$

13. $\displaystyle\int \frac{dx}{4 - (3x-1)^2}.$ 14. $\displaystyle\int \frac{dx}{4(2x+3)^2 - 25}.$ 15. $\displaystyle\int \frac{\sec^2 x\,dx}{\tan^2 x - 9}.$

16. Find the area of the region of the xy-plane which is bounded by the x-axis, the curve $y = 1/(x^2 - 9)$, and the lines $x = -4$ and $x = -9$.

103. CHANGE OF VARIABLE IN AN INTEGRAL

In the following theorem, we shall deal with functions $g(u)$ whose domain is $R = \{c \leqq u \leqq d\}$,* $f(x)$ whose domain is $T = \{a \leqq x \leqq b\}$,* and $\psi(x)$ whose domain is T and range is R. Thus, if $u = \psi(x)$ then $c \leqq u \leqq d$.

Theorem I. *Suppose that g is continuous, ψ is continuously differentiable, and $g(u)du = f(x)dx$ when $u = \psi(x)$. Then, if $\int g(u)du = G(u) + C$, where C is an arbitrary constant, it follows that*

$$\int f(x)dx = G(\psi(x)) + C. \qquad (1)$$

Also, if u_1 and u_2 are on R, and if $u_1 = \psi(x_1)$ and $u_2 = \psi(x_2)$, then

$$\int_{u_1}^{u_2} g(u)du = \int_{x_1}^{x_2} f(x)dx.$$

* R, and also T, may be an open or a half-open interval without altering Theorem I.

Proof. 1. If $u = \psi(x)$, then $du = \psi'(x)dx$ and

$$f(x)dx = g(u)du = g(\psi(x))\psi'(x)dx, \quad or \quad f(x) = g(\psi(x))\psi'(x). \tag{3}$$

The function $g(\psi(x))$ is a continuous function of x because g and ψ are continuous. Since ψ' also is continuous, hence f, as given by (3), is continuous. Therefore, both $\int f(x)dx$ and $\int g(u)du$ exist, when x is on T and u is on R.

2. Let $\int g(u)du = G(u) + C$. Then, $dG(u)/du = g(u)$.

3. From (VII) on page 92, for the derivative of a function of a function, and (3),

$$[with \ u = \psi(x)] \qquad \frac{dG(u)}{dx} = \frac{dG(u)}{du} \cdot \frac{du}{dx} = g(u)\psi'(x) = f(x). \tag{4}$$

Hence, if we let $F(x) = G(\psi(x))$, then $F'(x) = f(x)$, or $F(x)$ is an indefinite integral of $f(x)$. Thus, (1) is obtained:

$$\int f(x)dx = F(x) + C = G(\psi(x)) + C. \tag{5}$$

4. From the fundamental theorem of integral calculus, with x_1, x_2, u_1, and u_2 as described in Theorem I, we obtain (2):

$$\int_{u_1}^{u_2} g(u)du = G(u_2) - G(u_1) = G(\psi(x_2)) - G(\psi(x_1))$$

$$[from \ (5)] \qquad\qquad = F(x_2) - F(x_1) = \int_{x_1}^{x_2} f(x)dx.$$

From (1), we formulate a routine for calculating an indefinite integral, $\int f(x)dx$, by a change of variable.

$$\left\{ \begin{array}{l} \textit{If the substitution } u = \psi(x) \textit{ changes } f(x)dx \textit{ into } g(u)du, \\ \textit{then } \int f(x)dx \textit{ can be determined by calculating} \\ \int g(u)du \textit{ and, in the result, substituting } u = \psi(x), \textit{ or} \end{array} \right\} \tag{6}$$

$$\int f(x)dx = \int g(u)du \quad with \quad u = \psi(x). \tag{7}$$

ILLUSTRATION 1. To calculate $\int 2\sin^4 2x \cos 2x \, dx$, substitute $u = \sin 2x$. Then $du = \cos 2x \, dx$ and

$$\int 2\sin^4 2x \cos 2x \, dx = \int u^4 \, du = \tfrac{1}{5}u^5 + C = \tfrac{1}{5}\sin^5 2x + C. \tag{8}$$

In (8), the method based on (6) is seen to be equivalent to our previous method of substitution in using formulas on page 272. However, (6) is not restricted to use with those formulas.

We shall frequently employ (2) as follows in computing definite integrals.

$$\left\{ \begin{array}{l} \textit{To evaluate } \int_{u_1}^{u_2} g(u)du \textit{ by substituting } u = \psi(x), \textit{ transform } g(u)du \textit{ into} \\ f(x)dx, \textit{ and simultaneously change the limits } u_1 \textit{ and } u_2 \textit{ into } x_1 \textit{ and } x_2, \\ \textit{respectively, where } u_1 = \psi(x_1) \textit{ and } u_2 = \psi(x_2), \textit{ to obtain } \int_{x_1}^{x_2} f(x)dx. \end{array} \right\} \tag{9}$$

Suppose that the equation $u = \psi(x)$ of (9) defines an inverse function ϕ for ψ so that $x = \phi(u)$ is equivalent to $u = \psi(x)$. Then, from (9) and (2), we may state that, with the substitution $u = \psi(x)$ or $x = \phi(u)$, *either integral in (2) can be computed by calculating the other integral.*

ILLUSTRATION 2. Consider $\int_0^{1/2} u^4\, du$. Let $u = \sin 2x$, as in Illustration 1. Then, $u = 0$ if $x = 0$; $u = \frac{1}{2}$ if $x = \frac{1}{12}\pi$ because $\sin \frac{1}{6}\pi = \frac{1}{2}$. Also, $u = \frac{1}{2}$ if $x = \frac{5}{12}\pi$. Then, from (2), we obtain

$$\int_0^{1/2} u^4\, du = \int_0^{\pi/12} 2\sin^4 2x \cos 2x\, dx = \frac{1}{5}\sin^5 2x\Big]_0^{\pi/12} = \frac{1}{5}(\tfrac{1}{2})^5 = \tfrac{1}{160}.$$

Also, $$\int_0^{1/2} u^4\, du = \int_0^{5\pi/12} 2\sin^4 2x \cos 2x\, dx = \frac{1}{5}\sin^5 \tfrac{5}{6}\pi = \tfrac{1}{160}.$$

Note 1. In Illustration 2, the substitution $u = \sin 2x$ does *not* define an inverse substitution $x = \phi(u)$ (single-valued) where $u = \sin 2x$ is equivalent to $x = \phi(u)$. This serves to emphasize that Theorem I does *not* involve a hypothesis that ψ has an inverse ϕ. If the inverse exists, then $x_1 = \phi(u_1)$ and $x_2 = \phi(u_2)$ in (2).

Note 2. In our original introduction of $\int_a^b f(x)dx$, our only justification for the use of dx was that it served as a reminder of $\Delta_i x$ in Definition II for $\int_a^b f(x)dx$ on page 178. In the hypotheses of Theorem I, and in applications of (1) and (2), the symbols dx and du, with great convenience, are actually *treated as differentials*. Thus, we have added justification for the traditional use of dx in integral symbols.

104. ELEMENTARY RATIONALIZING SUBSTITUTIONS

Suppose that, in $\int f(x)dx$, f is an algebraic function, and that $f(x)$ involves just one radical $\sqrt[n]{ax + b}$, with a **linear radicand**, as the only irrational feature. Then, by substituting $u = \sqrt[n]{ax + b}$, we change to a new integral where the integrand is a rational function of u. In such a case, we refer to the change of variable as a *rationalizing substitution*.

EXAMPLE 1. Calculate the following integral J by a rationalizing substitution:

$$J = \int \frac{x\, dx}{\sqrt{3x + 1}}.$$

Solution. Let $u = \sqrt{3x + 1}$. Then, by use of (6) on page 284, we carry out the following sequence of details:

$$u^2 = 3x + 1; \quad x = \tfrac{1}{3}(u^2 - 1); \quad dx = \tfrac{2}{3}u\, du;$$

$$J = \frac{1}{3}\cdot\frac{2}{3} \int \frac{(u^2 - 1)u\, du}{u} = \frac{2}{9} \int (u^2 - 1)du \tag{1}$$

$$= \tfrac{2}{27}u^3 - \tfrac{2}{9}u + C = \tfrac{2}{27}(3x + 1)^{\frac{3}{2}} - \tfrac{2}{9}(3x + 1)^{\frac{1}{2}} + C. \tag{2}$$

EXAMPLE 2. Integrate: $$J = \int x^2(2x + 1)^{\frac{2}{3}}dx.$$

Solution. Note that $(2x + 1)^{\frac{2}{3}} = (\sqrt[3]{2x + 1})^2$. Thus, substitute $u = \sqrt[3]{2x + 1}$. Then, by use of (6) on page 284,

$$u^3 = 2x + 1; \quad x = \tfrac{1}{2}(u^3 - 1); \quad dx = \tfrac{3}{2}u^2\, du;$$

$$J = \tfrac{1}{4}\cdot\tfrac{3}{2} \int (u^3 - 1)^2 u^2(u^2\, du) = \tfrac{3}{88}u^{11} - \tfrac{3}{32}u^8 + \tfrac{3}{40}u^5 + C$$

$$= \tfrac{3}{88}(2x + 1)^{\frac{11}{3}} - \tfrac{3}{32}(2x + 1)^{\frac{8}{3}} + \tfrac{3}{40}(2x + 1)^{\frac{5}{3}} + C.$$

EXAMPLE 3. Calculate:
$$\int_5^8 \frac{u \, du}{\sqrt{3u + 1}}. \tag{3}$$

Solution. 1. Let $x = \sqrt{3u + 1}$. Then, $x^2 = 3u + 1$, or
$$u = \tfrac{1}{3}(x^2 - 1); \quad du = \tfrac{2}{3}x \, dx. \tag{4}$$

We find that $x = 4$ when $u = 5$; $x = 5$ when $u = 8$.

2. From (9) on page 284, with u and du from (4),
$$\int_5^8 \frac{u \, du}{\sqrt{3u + 1}} = \frac{2}{9} \int_4^5 (x^2 - 1) dx = \frac{2}{27} x^3 - \frac{2}{9} x \Big]_4^5 = \frac{116}{27}. \tag{5}$$

Comment. The preceding solution shows that, to arrive at a substitution $u = \psi(x)$ for use in (9) on page 284, it may be best to start with the inverse substitution $x = \phi(u)$, when it exists.

ILLUSTRATION 1. To calculate $I = \int_1^{14} x\sqrt[3]{2x - 1} \, dx$, we would apply (9) on page 284 with x playing the role of u. A rationalizing substitution is
$$v = \sqrt[3]{2x - 1}, \quad or \quad x = \tfrac{1}{2}(v^3 + 1).$$

Then, $I = \int_1^3 f(v)dv$, where the student may complete the details.

EXERCISE 86

Integrate. Use a substitution if necessary.

1. $\int x\sqrt{2 + x} \, dx.$ **2.** $\int v\sqrt{3 + 4v} \, dv.$ **3.** $\int x\sqrt[3]{1 + 2x} \, dx.$

4. $\int \dfrac{(2x + 1)dx}{\sqrt{2x + 3}}.$ **5.** $\int \dfrac{(6x - 1)dx}{\sqrt{1 - 3x}}.$ **6.** $\int \dfrac{(x + 2)dx}{(\sqrt{x + 1})^3}.$

7. $\int \dfrac{u \, du}{\sqrt{3 + 4u}}.$ **8.** $\int \dfrac{(3 + 5w)dw}{\sqrt[3]{2 - w}}.$ **9.** $\int \dfrac{x \, dx}{\sqrt[3]{5 + 2x}}.$

10. $\int x(2x + 5)^{\frac{3}{2}} \, dx.$ **11.** $\int x(3 - x)^{\frac{2}{3}} \, dx.$

12. $\int \dfrac{(x^{\frac{3}{4}} - x^{\frac{5}{2}})dx}{3x^{\frac{1}{4}}}.$ **13.** $\int \dfrac{(4x + 3)dx}{(1 + 4x)^{\frac{3}{2}}}.$

Compute by use of a substitution and a change in limits of integration.

14. $\int_2^7 x\sqrt{2 + x} \, dx.$ **15.** $\int_{-8}^{-1} x\sqrt{1 - 3x} \, dx.$

16. $\int_{-4}^{-1} \dfrac{z \, dz}{\sqrt{2 - 4z}}.$ **17.** $\int_{-1}^{11} \dfrac{x^2 \, dx}{\sqrt{2x + 3}}.$ **18.** $\int_{-11}^{-4} \dfrac{t^2 \, dt}{\sqrt[3]{t + 3}}.$

19. $\int_2^7 (6x + 5)\sqrt{3x - 1} \, dx.$ **20.** $\int_{-7}^0 x\sqrt{4 - 3x} \, dx.$

105. CERTAIN RADICAL FORMS

If u is a continuously differentiable function of some independent variable x, then
$$\int \frac{du}{\sqrt{u^2 \pm a^2}} = \ln |u + \sqrt{u^2 \pm a^2}| + C. \tag{XVII}$$

Proof of (XVII) *for* $\sqrt{u^2 + a^2}$. Let $u = a \tan \theta$, with the agreement that $a > 0$, and that we choose θ on the interval

$$-\tfrac{1}{2}\pi < \theta < \tfrac{1}{2}\pi, \quad \text{where} \quad \sec \theta > 0. \tag{1}$$

With (1) assumed, $u = a \tan \theta$ defines the inverse transformation $\theta = \text{Arctan} (u/a)$, where the two equations are equivalent. We apply (6) of page 284 with the roles of x and u played here by u and θ, respectively. Then,

$$du = a \sec^2 \theta \, d\theta; \quad \sqrt{u^2 + a^2} = a\sqrt{\tan^2 \theta + 1} = a \sec \theta; \tag{2}$$

$$\int \frac{du}{\sqrt{u^2 + a^2}} = \int \frac{\sec^2 \theta \, d\theta}{\sec \theta} = \int \sec \theta \, d\theta$$

$$= \ln | \sec \theta + \tan \theta | + C', \tag{3}$$

where C' is an arbitrary constant. From $u = a \tan \theta$, (1), and (2),

$$\tan \theta = \frac{u}{a}; \quad \sec \theta = \sqrt{1 + \tan^2 \theta} = \frac{\sqrt{u^2 + a^2}}{a}.$$

Hence, from (3), $\qquad\qquad \int \frac{du}{\sqrt{u^2 + a^2}} = \ln \left| \frac{\sqrt{u^2 + a^2} + u}{a} \right| + C'$

$$= \ln (u + \sqrt{u^2 + a^2}) + (C' - \ln a). \tag{4}$$

On letting $C = C' - \ln a$, from (4) we obtain (XVII), for the case where "+" is used on both sides in the radical. We omitted absolute value signs with

$$(u + \sqrt{u^2 + a^2})$$

in (4) because

$$\sqrt{u^2 + a^2} > | u | \quad \text{and hence} \quad \sqrt{u^2 + a^2} + u > 0.$$

Proof of (XVII) *for* $\sqrt{u^2 - a^2}$. 1. We must have $u^2 - a^2 > 0$ or $u^2 > a^2$, or $| u | > a$. Hence, the domain for u is one of the infinite intervals

$$u < - a \quad \text{and} \quad u > a. \tag{5}$$

2. Substitute $u = a \sec \theta$ with the agreement that $0 < \theta < \tfrac{1}{2}\pi$ if $u > a$, and $\pi < \theta < \tfrac{3}{2}\pi$ if $u < - a$. In either case, $\tan \theta > 0$ and hence

$$\tan \theta = + \sqrt{\sec^2 \theta - 1}.$$

Then, $\qquad du = a \sec \theta \tan \theta \, d\theta; \quad \sqrt{u^2 - a^2} = a\sqrt{\sec^2 \theta - 1} = a \tan \theta;$

$$\int \frac{du}{\sqrt{u^2 - a^2}} = \int \sec \theta \, d\theta = \ln | \sec \theta + \tan \theta | + C',$$

from which we obtain (XVII), for $\sqrt{u^2 - a^2}$, as in (3) and (4).

ILLUSTRATION 1. $\qquad\qquad \int \frac{dt}{\sqrt{4t^2 - 25}} = \frac{1}{2} \int \frac{2 \, dt}{\sqrt{4t^2 - 25}}$

[(XVII) *with* $u = 2t$] $\qquad\qquad = \frac{1}{2} \ln | 2t + \sqrt{4t^2 - 25} | + C.$

ILLUSTRATION 2. $\qquad\qquad \int_{-5}^{-4} \frac{dx}{\sqrt{x^2 - 9}} = \ln | x + \sqrt{x^2 - 9} | \Big]_{-5}^{-4}$

$$= \ln | - 4 + \sqrt{7} | - \ln | - 5 + 4 | = \ln 1.354 - \ln 1 = .3028.$$

EXERCISE 87

Integrate.

1. $\int \dfrac{dx}{\sqrt{x^2 + 4}}.$ **2.** $\int \dfrac{du}{\sqrt{u^2 - 25}}.$ **3.** $\int \dfrac{dz}{\sqrt{z^2 + 16}}.$

4. $\int \dfrac{dx}{\sqrt{4x^2 + 9}}.$ **5.** $\int \dfrac{dt}{\sqrt{9t^2 + 25}}.$ **6.** $\int \dfrac{dw}{\sqrt{4w^2 + 1}}.$

7. $\int \dfrac{dt}{\sqrt{9t^2 - 121}}.$ **8.** $\int \dfrac{dx}{\sqrt{25x^2 - 1}}.$ **9.** $\int \dfrac{dy}{\sqrt{1 + 36y^2}}.$

10. $\int \dfrac{\sin x \, dx}{\sqrt{\cos^2 x + 4}}.$ **11.** $\int \dfrac{\sec^2 t \, dt}{\sqrt{\tan^2 t + 9}}.$ **12.** $\int \dfrac{e^t \, dt}{\sqrt{4e^{2t} + 49}}.$

13. $\int \dfrac{\cos 2x \, dx}{\sqrt{16 + \sin^2 2x}}.$ **14.** $\int \dfrac{dx}{x\sqrt{(\ln x)^2 + 25}}.$

15. $\int_5^{10} \dfrac{du}{\sqrt{u^2 - 16}}.$ **16.** $\int_0^4 \dfrac{dx}{\sqrt{x^2 + 9}}.$ **17.** $\int_5^6 \dfrac{dt}{\sqrt{t^2 - 9}}.$

18. $\int_{-6}^{-5} \dfrac{du}{\sqrt{u^2 - 16}}.$ **19.** $\int_{-5}^{-4} \dfrac{dx}{\sqrt{x^2 - 9}}.$ **20.** $\int_{-5/2}^{5/2} \dfrac{dw}{\sqrt{4w^2 + 25}}.$

21. A region R is bounded by the curve $y = 1/\sqrt{x^2 + 16}$, the x-axis, and the lines $x = 3$ and $x = 4$. (*a*) Find the area of R. (*b*) Find the volume of the solid generated if R is revolved about the x-axis.

106. INTEGRANDS INVOLVING QUADRATIC FUNCTIONS

By completing a square based on the terms in x, we can write any quadratic function $Ax^2 + Bx + C$ in one of the forms $(a^2 + u^2)$, $(a^2 - u^2)$, $(u^2 - a^2)$, or $(-a^2 - u^2)$, perhaps multiplied by a constant, where u is some linear function of x. Then, (XIV)–(XVII) enable us to calculate integrals of the types

$$\int \frac{dx}{Ax^2 + Bx + C} \quad and \quad \int \frac{dx}{\sqrt{Ax^2 + Bx + C}}. \tag{1}$$

ILLUSTRATION 1. $\displaystyle\int \frac{dx}{7 - 4x^2 + 12x} = \int \frac{dx}{7 + 9 - (4x^2 - 12x + 9)}$

$[(\text{XVI})', u = 2x - 3]$ $\displaystyle= \frac{1}{2} \int \frac{2 \, dx}{16 - (2x - 3)^2} = \frac{1}{2} \int \frac{du}{16 - u^2}$

$$= \frac{1}{2} \cdot \frac{1}{8} \ln \left| \frac{4 + 2x - 3}{4 - (2x - 3)} \right| + C = \frac{1}{16} \ln \left| \frac{1 + 2x}{7 - 2x} \right| + C.$$

Note 1. If $A > 0$, we complete a square with $(Ax^2 + Bx)$ by adding the square of $B/2\sqrt{A}$. If A is not a perfect square, we may prefer to remove A as a factor before completing a square. When $A < 0$, group the terms involving x within parentheses preceded by a minus sign, before completing a square.

ILLUSTRATION 2. $\displaystyle\int \frac{dx}{\sqrt{16 - x^2 - 6x}} = \int \frac{dx}{\sqrt{16 + 9 - (x^2 + 6x + 9)}}$

$$= \int \frac{dx}{\sqrt{25 - (x + 3)^2}} = \text{Arcsin} \, \frac{x + 3}{5} + C.$$

ILLUSTRATION 3.
$$\int \frac{dx}{\sqrt{10x - x^2 - 29}} = \int \frac{dx}{\sqrt{-4 - (x - 5)^2}}.$$

We stop, because the radicand is *negative*, and hence the integrand is *imaginary*, at all values of x. Thus, *the integral has no meaning.*

If $A < 0$, the graph of $y = Ax^2 + Bx + C$ is a parabola which is concave *downward*. If, besides, the discriminant ($B^2 - 4AC$) is *negative*, the equation $Ax^2 + Bx + C = 0$ has *imaginary roots*. Then, the parabola lies entirely below the x-axis, as in Figure 192. Or, $(Ax^2 + Bx + C)$ *is negative at all values of x in case $A < 0$ and $B^2 - 4AC < 0$.* This result enables us to discover a situation like that of Illustration 3 without completing a square.

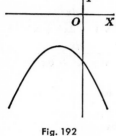

Fig. 192

ILLUSTRATION 4. In $10x - x^2 - 29$ in Illustration 3, the discriminant is $(10^2) - 4(1)(29) = -16$. Hence, immediately, we know that the radicand will be negative at all values of x.

To calculate an integral of the form

$$\int \frac{(hx + k)dx}{Ax^2 + Bx + C} \quad or \quad \int \frac{(hx + k)dx}{\sqrt{Ax^2 + Bx + C}}, \quad (2)$$

where $A \neq 0$, first express the integrand as the sum of two simpler fractions having the given denominator. For one of these fractions, we *automatically write the numerator by differentiating* $(Ax^2 + Bx + C)$, and then multiplying by a constant chosen to give hx as the coefficient of x. The integral of this fraction then is of the form $\int u^n\, du$ or $\int du/u$, perhaps multiplied by a constant. The second new fraction which is met can be integrated as in Illustrations 1–2.

ILLUSTRATION 5.
$$\int \frac{(3x + 5)dx}{4x^2 + 9} = \frac{3}{8} \int \frac{8x\, dx}{4x^2 + 9} + \frac{5}{2} \int \frac{2\, dx}{4x^2 + 9}$$

[$u = 2x$ in (XIV)]
$$= \tfrac{3}{8} \ln (4x^2 + 9) + \tfrac{5}{6} \operatorname{Arctan} \tfrac{2}{3}x + C.$$

EXAMPLE 1. Integrate:
$$\int \frac{(2x + 5)dx}{\sqrt{8 - 6x - 9x^2}}.$$

Solution. Since $D_x(8 - 6x - 9x^2) = -6 - 18x$, write

$$T = \int \frac{(2x + 5)dx}{\sqrt{8 - 6x - 9x^2}} = h \int \frac{(-6 - 18x)dx}{\sqrt{8 - 6x - 9x^2}} + \int \frac{k\, dx}{\sqrt{8 - 6x - 9x^2}}, \quad (3)$$

where h and k are to be determined. Select h so that, in (3), $2x$ on the left will equal $-18hx$ on the right, or $2 = -18h$; $h = -\tfrac{1}{9}$. Then, on the right, $-6h = \tfrac{2}{3}$ and we must have $5 = \tfrac{2}{3} + k$, or $k = \tfrac{13}{3}$. Thus,

$$T = -\frac{1}{9} \int (8 - 6x - 9x^2)^{-\frac{1}{2}}d(8 - 6x - 9x^2) + \frac{13}{3} \int \frac{dx}{\sqrt{9 - (3x + 1)^2}}$$

$$= -\frac{2}{9}(8 - 6x - 9x^2)^{\frac{1}{2}} + \frac{13}{9} \operatorname{Arcsin} \frac{3x + 1}{3} + C.$$

EXERCISE 88

Integrate.

1. $\displaystyle\int \frac{dx}{x^2 + 6x + 13}$.

2. $\displaystyle\int \frac{dx}{x^2 + 8x + 12}$.

3. $\displaystyle\int \frac{dx}{3 - x^2 - 2x}$.

4. $\displaystyle\int \frac{dx}{\sqrt{4x - x^2 - 3}}$.

5. $\displaystyle\int \frac{dx}{\sqrt{9 - x^2 - 8x}}$.

6. $\displaystyle\int \frac{dx}{\sqrt{x^2 - x - 2}}$.

7. $\displaystyle\int \frac{dx}{\sqrt{4x - x^2 - 5}}$.

8. $\displaystyle\int \frac{dy}{y^2 - y + 1}$.

9. $\displaystyle\int \frac{dt}{4t^2 - 4t + 5}$.

10. $\displaystyle\int \frac{dz}{9z^2 + 6z - 5}$.

11. $\displaystyle\int \frac{du}{9u^2 + 6u - 1}$.

12. $\displaystyle\int \frac{dx}{\sqrt{x^2 + 3x + 3}}$.

13. $\displaystyle\int \frac{dv}{3v^2 + 2v - 5}$.

14. $\displaystyle\int \frac{dx}{2x^2 - 6x + 5}$.

15. $\displaystyle\int \frac{dx}{\sqrt{1 - 2x^2 + x}}$.

16. $\displaystyle\int \frac{dw}{4w - w^2}$.

17. $\displaystyle\int \frac{dx}{4x^2 - 4x}$.

18. $\displaystyle\int \frac{dx}{\sqrt{- x^2 - 6x}}$.

19. $\displaystyle\int \frac{dx}{\sqrt{10 + 4x^2 - 4x}}$.

20. $\displaystyle\int \frac{dx}{\sqrt{15 - 9x^2 - 6x}}$.

21. $\displaystyle\int \frac{dt}{\sqrt{3t^2 + 2t + 2}}$.

22. $\displaystyle\int \frac{dx}{\sqrt{4 - 9x^2 + 6x}}$.

23. $\displaystyle\int \frac{(3 + 2x)dx}{4 + x^2}$.

24. $\displaystyle\int \frac{(4x - 2)dx}{\sqrt{x^2 - 1}}$.

25. $\displaystyle\int \frac{(3t + 5)dt}{\sqrt{9 - t^2}}$.

26. $\displaystyle\int \frac{(4z + 6)dz}{z^2 - 4}$.

27. $\displaystyle\int \frac{(3 - 4z)dz}{16 - z^2}$.

28. $\displaystyle\int \frac{(6t + 2)dt}{\sqrt{9t^2 + 5}}$.

29. $\displaystyle\int \frac{(3 - 6x)dx}{x^2 + 4x - 5}$.

30. $\displaystyle\int \frac{(13 - 5x)dx}{x^2 + 3x + 2}$.

31. $\displaystyle\int \frac{(8x + 5)dx}{\sqrt{7 - x^2 + 6x}}$.

32. $\displaystyle\int \frac{(3x - 7)dx}{\sqrt{4 - 3x^2}}$.

33. $\displaystyle\int \frac{(15 - 3x)dx}{\sqrt{4x - x^2 - 7}}$.

34. $\displaystyle\int \frac{(6x - 5)dx}{\sqrt{5x - x^2 - 6}}$.

35. $\displaystyle\int \frac{(9t + 16)dt}{\sqrt{9t^2 + 12t + 3}}$.

36. $\displaystyle\int \frac{(11 - 12y)dy}{\sqrt{24 - 9y^2 + 6y}}$.

37. $\displaystyle\int \frac{\sec^2 x\, dx}{\tan^2 x + 4 \tan x + 3}$.

38. $\displaystyle\int \frac{(4z - 5)dz}{\sqrt{4z^2 + 4z + 13}}$.

107. DIFFERENTIAL EQUATIONS SOLVABLE BY QUADRATURES *

In (7) on page 204, we saw that, if the function $f(x)$ is continuous,

$$\text{the general solution of } y' = f(x) \text{ is } y = \int f(x)dx + C. \tag{1}$$

We note that the *derivative form* $dy/dx = f(x)$ is equivalent to the *differential form* $dy = f(x)dx$. When y is a continuously differentiable function of x, from (2) on page 271 we recall that $\int dy = y + C$. Hence, (1) can be described as a consequence of integrating both sides of $dy = f(x)dx$ with respect to x:

$$\int dy = \int f(x)dx + C, \quad \text{or} \quad y = \int f(x)dx + C. \tag{2}$$

* It is essential to review Section 66 on page 202.

Note 1. The integration of a known function frequently is called a **quadrature.** Thus, the solution of $y' = f(x)$ is obtained by a single quadrature. Similarly, as on page 204, the solution of an equation $y^{(n)} = f(x)$ is obtained by n successive quadratures.

EXAMPLE 1. Solve $y'' = 4e^{2x}$, with the conditions $y = 3$ and $y' = -1$ at $x = 0$.

Solution. 1. Since $y'' = \dfrac{dy'}{dx}$, $\qquad \dfrac{dy'}{dx} = 4e^{2x}$ or $dy' = 4e^{2x}\, dx$. $\qquad$ (3)

On integrating on both sides in (3), with $\int dy' = y'$, we obtain

$$\int dy' = \int 4e^{2x}\, dx + C_1, \quad or \quad y' = 2e^{2x} + C_1, \qquad (4)$$

where C_1 is an arbitrary constant. From (4), $dy = (2e^{2x} + C_1)dx$. Then

$$\int dy = \int (2e^{2x} + C_1)dx + C_2, \quad or \quad y = e^{2x} + C_1 x + C_2, \qquad (5)$$

where C_2 is an arbitrary constant. Thus, (5) is the general solution of $y'' = 4e^{2x}$.

2. To obtain the desired particular solution, first place $y' = -1$ and $x = 0$ in (4), which gives $C_1 = -3$. Then, place $C_1 = -3$, $x = 0$, and $y = 3$ in (5), which gives $C_2 = 2$. Thus, the particular solution is $y = e^{2x} - 3x + 2$.

EXAMPLE 2. Solve: $\qquad\qquad\qquad \dfrac{d^3s}{dt^3} = e^t - t^2. \qquad\qquad (6)$

Solution. 1. Let $u = \dfrac{d^2s}{dt^2}$. Then, $\dfrac{du}{dt} = \dfrac{d^3s}{dt^3}$, or

$$\frac{du}{dt} = e^t - t^2; \quad du = (e^t - t^2)dt;$$

$$u = \int (e^t - t^2)dt, \quad or \quad \frac{d^2s}{dt^2} = e^t - \tfrac{1}{3}t^3 + C_1.$$

2. Let $v = \dfrac{ds}{dt}$. Then, $\dfrac{dv}{dt} = \dfrac{d^2s}{dt^2}$ or $\dfrac{dv}{dt} = e^t - \tfrac{1}{3}t^3 + C_1;$

$$v = \int (e^t - \tfrac{1}{3}t^3 + C_1)dt, \quad or \quad v = e^t - \tfrac{1}{12}t^4 + C_1 t + C_2 = \frac{ds}{dt};$$

$$s = \int (e^t - \tfrac{1}{12}t^4 + C_1 t + C_2)dt, \quad or \quad s = e^t - \tfrac{1}{60}t^5 + \tfrac{1}{2}C_1 t^2 + C_2 t + C_3.$$

The final expression is the general solution of (6).

108. DIFFERENTIAL EQUATION OF A GIVEN FAMILY OF CURVES

In Example 1 on page 202, we saw that a differential equation of the first order may have a general solution, say $f(x, y, c) = 0$, where c is a parameter. Conversely, if we are given an equation $f(x, y, c) = 0$ for a family of curves, we may be able to obtain a differential equation with the general solution $f(x, y, c) = 0$. To accomplish this aim, we differentiate with respect to x in $f(x, y, c) = 0$, to derive a relation between x, y, y', and c; by use of this relation and the given equation $f(x, y, c) = 0$, we then endeavor to eliminate c and obtain a differential equation involving x, y, and y'.

EXAMPLE 1. Find the differential equation of the family of curves

$$x^2 + y^2 - 2cy = c^2. \tag{1}$$

Solution. 1. Differentiate with respect to x in (1):

$$2x + 2yy' - 2cy' = 0. \tag{2}$$

2. Eliminate c between (1) and (2), by solving (2) for c and using (1):

$$c = \frac{x + yy'}{y'}; \quad x^2 + y^2 - 2y\frac{x + yy'}{y'} = \frac{(x + yy')^2}{y'^2}, \text{ or}$$

$$(x^2 - 2y^2)\left(\frac{dy}{dx}\right)^2 - 4xy\frac{dy}{dx} - x^2 = 0. \tag{3}$$

Thus, (3) is the differential equation of the family (1).

EXAMPLE 2. If P is an arbitrary constant, and k is a fixed constant, obtain a differential equation for the family of functions defined by $y = Pe^{kx}$.

Solution. On differentiating with respect to x on both sides of

$$y = Pe^{kx}, \quad \text{we obtain} \quad y' = kPe^{kx}. \tag{4}$$

Hence, from (4), $$y' = ky. \tag{5}$$

Thus, (5) is the desired differential equation.

ILLUSTRATION 1. If a principal of P dollars is invested now at compound interest at the rate of interest k, compounded m times per year, then the compound amount, y_m dollars, at the end of x years is given by

$$y_m = P\left(1 + \frac{k}{m}\right)^{mx}, \quad \text{or} \quad y_m = P\left[\left(1 + \frac{k}{m}\right)^{\frac{m}{k}}\right]^{kx}. \tag{6}$$

The limit of y_m as $m \to \infty$ is called the compound amount on P with interest at the rate k, *compounded continuously.* From (2) on page 243, if we let $y = \lim_{m \to \infty} y_m$, then $y = Pe^{kx}$, because the quantity in square brackets in (6) has the limit e as $m \to \infty$. Continuously compounded interest is of importance in the theory of life insurance. On account of the preceding details, and Example 2, it is frequently said that y obeys the **compound interest law** if $y = Pe^{kx}$, or if $y' = ky$ as in (5). This relation also is referred to as the **law of exponential growth** when $k > 0$, and of **exponential decay** when $k < 0$. These cases will be considered later.

EXERCISE 89

Verify the solution of the differential equation.

1. $y'' - 9y = 0$; solution, $y = 2e^{3x} - 3e^{-3x}$.

2. $y'' + 4y = 0$; solution, $y = c_1 \sin 2x + c_2 \cos 2x$.

Find the general solution of the differential equation. If initial conditions are given, also find the corresponding particular solution.

3. $\dfrac{ds}{dt} = -\sin t$; $s = 2$ at $t = \frac{1}{4}\pi$.   4. $\dfrac{ds}{dt} = e^{3t}$; $s = 2$ at $t = 0$.

5. $y'' = 3\cos 2x$; $y = 2$ and $y' = -\frac{3}{2}$ at $x = \frac{1}{4}\pi$.

6. $y''' = 3e^{-2x}$; $y = \frac{5}{8}$, $y' = -\frac{1}{4}$, and $y'' = \frac{3}{2}$ at $x = 0$.

7. $\dfrac{d^2u}{dx^2} = 2 \sin x + 3 \cos x.$ **8.** $\dfrac{d^3s}{dt^3} = 2t + e^{3t}.$ **9.** $\dfrac{d^3y}{dx^3} = \sin 2x.$

If c is an arbitrary constant, find the differential equation of the given family of curves.

10. $y^2 = 4(x - c).$ **11.** $x^2 = 2(c - y).$ **12.** $x^2 + y^2 = c^2.$

13. $x^2 + 4y^2 = c^2.$ **14.** $y^2 = 4cx.$ **15.** $cx^2 + y^2 = 4.$

16. $x^2 - y^2 = c.$ **17.** $xy = c.$ **18.** $y = ce^{kx}.$

19. If $\omega > 0$, prove that $s = k \sin (\omega t - \alpha)$ is a solution of $s'' = - \omega^2 s$, for all values of the constants k and α, and hence is a form for the general solution of $s'' = - \omega^2 s$. Prove the same fact for the family of functions $s = c_1 \sin \omega t + c_2 \cos \omega t$.

Note 1. The two forms in Example 19 are equivalent, as seen previously in Note 1 on page 250. The student should review Section 89 on page 249. In Problem 19, we have met the general solution of the differential equation of *simple harmonic motion* about the origin on an s-axis, $s'' = - \omega^2 s$.

By use of Problem 19, write the general solution of the differential equation in two forms. If initial conditions are given, find the corresponding particular solution.

20. $s'' = - 4s.$ **21.** $s'' = - 5s.$ **22.** $4s'' = - s.$

23. $s'' = - 25s$, with $s = 8$ and $s' = 0$ at $t = 0$.

24. $s'' = - s$, with $s = 0$ and $s' = - 5$ at $t = 0$.

25. $s'' = - 9s$, with $s = - \frac{5}{2}\sqrt{2}$ and $s' = - \frac{15}{2}\sqrt{2}$ at $t = 0$.

26. In the motion of a particle on an s-axis, the acceleration at any time t seconds is given by $a = 2t - 5$. If $s = 2$ and $v = 4$ at $t = 1$, find the equation of motion.

27. Solve Problem 26 if $a = - 4 \sin 2t$, with $s = 4$ and $v = 2$ at $t = 0$.

109. DIFFERENTIAL EQUATIONS OF THE SEPARABLE TYPE

A differential equation of the first order in the variables x and y is said to be of the *first degree* if the derivative involved, dy/dx or dx/dy, occurs only to the first degree. Thus, the equation is of the form

$$Q(x, y) \frac{dy}{dx} + P(x, y) = 0, \quad or \quad P(x, y) \frac{dx}{dy} + Q(x, y) = 0. \tag{1}$$

From either equation in (1),

$$P(x, y)dx + Q(x, y)dy = 0, \tag{2}$$

which we shall refer to as the *differential form* for (1). If each of $P(x, y)$ and $Q(x, y)$ can be expressed as a product of a function of x times a function of y, we may change (2) to the following form after dividing by appropriate factors:

$$f(x)dx = g(y)dy. \tag{3}$$

In (3), we say that *the variables are separated*. To state that (2) is of the **separable type** will mean that the equation is equivalent * to an equation (3) where the variables are separated.

---

* That is, has the same general solution as (3). The possibility of zero values for $P(x, y)$ and $Q(x, y)$ should be considered in any special case, to rule out corresponding values of x or y. As a rule, we shall omit such complications in solving (2).

ILLUSTRATION 1. The following equation is of the separable type:

$$(1 - x)(1 + y^2) + 2xy \frac{dy}{dx} = 0, \quad or \quad (1 - x)(1 + y^2)dx + 2xy \, dy = 0. \quad (4)$$

In (4), we separate the variables by dividing both sides by $x(1 + y^2)$:

$$\frac{1 - x}{x} \, dx + \frac{2y}{1 + y^2} \, dy = 0.$$

We shall consider (3) when $f(x)$ and $g(y)$ are continuous. Also, when (3) is thought of as defining y as a function of x, assume that $g(y) \neq 0$ on the domain for y, so that $y' = f(x)/g(y)$, which is continuous. Similarly, assume that $f(x) \neq 0$ on the domain for x if (3) is thought of as defining x as a function of y. Then, if $\int f(x)dx$ and $\int g(y)dy$ denote any particular indefinite integrals of the corresponding integrands, we shall show that the general solution of (3) is as follows, where * C is an arbitrary constant:

$$\int f(x)dx = \int g(y)dy + C. \quad (5)$$

ILLUSTRATION 2. By (5), the general solution of $2x \, dx = -2y \, dy$ is

$$\int 2x \, dx = -\int 2y \, dy + C, \quad or \quad x^2 + y^2 = C.$$

In this case, the domain for C is $C > 0$. Thus, $2x \, dx + 2y \, dy = 0$ is the differential equation of the family of circles $x^2 + y^2 = C$.

Proof of (5). 1. Suppose that C has a value such that there exists a function $\psi(x)$ so that $y = \psi(x)$ satisfies (5), with ψ' continuous. Then, with $y = \psi(x)$, the two sides of (5) are identical functions of x, so that

$$d\left[\int f(x)dx \right] = d\left[\int g(y)dy + C \right], \quad or \quad f(x)dx = g(y)dy,$$

because $d(C) = 0$. Hence, $y = \psi(x)$ satisfies (3).

2. Conversely, suppose that (3) has a solution $y = \psi(x)$ where ψ' is continuous. Then, with y playing the role of u in (6) and (7) on page 284, the equation

$$f(x)dx = g(y)dy$$

leads to the conclusion, from (7) on page 284, that (5) is true. Hence, (3) and (5) are satisfied by the same family of functions of x, so that (5) is the general solution of (3). Similar remarks about (5) apply if (3) is considered as defining x as a function of y.

Note 1. In place of (3), we may prefer the standard form

$$f(x)dx + g(y)dy = 0, \quad \text{whose general solution is} \quad \int f(x)dx + \int g(y)dy = C. \quad (6)$$

To obtain (5) or (6) for a differential equation of separable type, first separate the variables, and then integrate on both sides, with an arbitrary constant added on just one side. In this operation it is not necessary to group together the terms involving dx and those involving dy.

---

* C may have only those values for which (5) defines x or y as a differentiable function of the other variable, with the derivative continuous.

ILLUSTRATION 3. The solution of $3\,dx - 2y\,dy = x^3\,dx$ is

$$\int 3\,dx - \int 2y\,dy = \int x^3\,dx, \quad or \quad 3x - y^2 = \tfrac{1}{4}x^4 + C.$$

EXAMPLE 1. Solve the differential equation

$$2y(1 - x)dy + (1 + y^2)dx = 0, \tag{7}$$

with the initial conditions that $y = 3$ when $x = -2$.

Solution. 1. To separate the variables, divide by $(1 - x)(1 + y^2)$:

$$\frac{2y\,dy}{1 + y^2} + \frac{dx}{1 - x} = 0. \tag{8}$$

Integrate in (8):
$$\int \frac{2y\,dy}{1 + y^2} + \int \frac{dx}{1 - x} = C, \text{ or}$$

$$\ln(1 + y^2) - \ln|1 - x| = C. \tag{9}$$

In (9), let $C = \ln K$, where $K > 0$; then

$$\ln\left|\frac{1 + y^2}{1 - x}\right| = \ln K, \quad or \quad \left|\frac{1 + y^2}{1 - x}\right| = K. \tag{10}$$

Hence, the fraction in (10) is equal to some constant C_1, where $C_1 > 0$ or $C_1 < 0$ according as $x < 1$ or $x > 1$. That is, the general solution of (7) is

$(with\ x \neq 1)$
$$1 + y^2 = C_1(1 - x). \tag{11}$$

2. On substituting $x = -2$ and $y = 3$ in (11), we obtain $C_1 = \tfrac{10}{3}$. Hence, the desired particular solution of (7) is $1 + y^2 = \tfrac{10}{3}(1 - x)$.

Comment. When $x = 1$, (8) is not defined. If we look upon (7) as defining x to be a function of y, the constant function $x = 1$ is a solution. This is true because, if $x = 1$, then $dx/dy = 0$ and $dx = 0$, so that (7) is satisfied. The solution $x = 1$ is not given by the general solution (11) for any value of C_1. For this reason, a solution such as $x = 1$ is called a *singular solution.*

In finding a particular solution of (3), frequently it is convenient to use the following result rather than (5).

Theorem II. *The solution $y = \psi(x)$ or $x = \phi(y)$ of (3) satisfying the initial conditions $y = \alpha$ when $x = a$ is defined implicitly by the equation*

$$\int_a^x f(t)dt = \int_\alpha^y g(u)du. \tag{12}$$

Proof. By Theorem VII on page 185, the integrals on the left and right in (12) are particular indefinite integrals of $f(x)$ and $g(y)$, respectively, because

$$\frac{d}{dx}\int_a^x f(t)dt = f(x); \quad \frac{d}{dy}\int_\alpha^y g(u)du = g(y).$$

Hence, (12) is a special case of (5) with $C = 0$. Also, (12) is satisfied when $x = a$ and $y = \alpha$, because then each side of (12) is equal to zero. Thus, (12) defines a solution $y = \phi(x)$, or $x = \psi(y)$, of (2) satisfying the initial conditions.

Note 2. The change to the dummy variables t and u in (12), instead of x and y as in (5), avoids two roles for x, and for y, in (12).

EXAMPLE 2. Find the particular solution of the following equation to satisfy the conditions $x = 4$ at $t = 2$:

$$\frac{dx}{dt} = 3(x - 2). \tag{13}$$

Solution. From (13),
$$\frac{dx}{x - 2} = 3\, dt.$$

Hence, from (12),
$$\int_4^x \frac{du}{u - 2} = \int_2^t 3\, dv; \quad or,$$

$$\ln |u - 2|\,\Big]_{u=4}^{u=x} = 3v\,\Big]_{v=2}^{v=t}, \quad or \quad \ln(x - 2) = 3(t - 2) + \ln 2, \ or \tag{14}$$

$$\ln(x - 2) = \ln e^{3(t-2)} + \ln 2 = \ln 2e^{3(t-2)}. \tag{15}$$

Hence,
$$x - 2 = 2e^{3(t-2)}, \quad or \quad x = 2 + 2e^{3(t-2)}. \tag{16}$$

Comment. Notice that $x = 2$ is not admissible in the preceding details. Since $x = 4$ is on the required domain for x, we are restricted to $x > 2$; thus, in (14), $u > 2$ or

$$u - 2 > 0.$$

Hence, in (14), $|u - 2| = u - 2$.

In (10) and (16), we illustrated how to obtain a form *not involving logarithms* from a simple form involving logarithms. In such an action, it is essential to remember that, if $K > 0$, then $K = e^{\ln K}$. Also, we observe that, if A, B, and C are numbers, possibly logarithms of other numbers, then $A + B = C$ is equivalent to $e^{A+B} = e^C$, or $e^A e^B = e^C$.

EXERCISE 90

1. Find the general solution of $y\, dx + x\, dy = 0$ in a form (*a*) involving logarithms; (*b*) not involving any logarithm. Obtain the particular solutions passing through the points $(-2, 3)$ and $(2, 4)$ in the xy-plane, and sketch these solution curves.

Find the general solution of the equation, or the particular solution satisfying the initial conditions. Obtain a result not involving logarithms where convenient.

2. $(1 + x)dx + (a + y)dy = 0.$

3. $\sqrt{2 + x}\, dx = \sqrt[3]{y}\, dy.$

4. $\dfrac{dy}{dx} = \dfrac{\sin x}{\cos y}.$

5. $\dfrac{ds}{dt} = \dfrac{1 + e^{2t}}{e^t}.$

6. $\dfrac{dz}{dt} = \dfrac{\cos 2t}{\sin z}.$

7. $2x\, dy = y\, dx.$

8. $(1 + y)dx + (1 + x)dy = 0.$

9. $2x(3 + y)dx = (1 + x^2)dy.$

10. $(1 + 3y)^2 dx - (2 - x)dy = 0.$

11. $\dfrac{dy}{dx} = \dfrac{y^2}{x^4}.$

12. $\dfrac{dy}{dx} = \dfrac{2 + y}{3 + x}.$

13. $\dfrac{dy}{dx} = \dfrac{\sin y}{\sin x}.$

14. $(4 + y^2)dx = (9 + x^2)dy.$

15. $y^2\, dy + \sin x\, dx = \tan y\, dy.$

16. $\csc x \cos y\, dx + \sin x \sec y\, dy = 0.$

17. $x\, dx - 4y\, dy = 0$; the solution where $y = 2$ at $x = 5$.

18. $\sqrt{y}\, dx + \sqrt{1 + x}\, dy = 0$; the solution where $y = 4$ when $x = 8$.

19. $2y + x\dfrac{dy}{dx} + 6 = 0$; the solution where $y = -1$ at $x = 2$.

20. $(1 + y^2)dx = (1 + x^2)dy$; $y = -1$ when $x = 1$.

21. $\sqrt{4 - x^2}\, dy = \sqrt{1 - y^2}\, dx$; $y = \frac{1}{2}$ when $x = 1$.

22. $3y + xy' + 9 = 0$; $y = 6$ when $x = 2$.

23. $y^2 \dfrac{dy}{dx} = \dfrac{x^2 y^3 + x^2}{x^3 + 1}$. **24.** $\dfrac{dy}{dx} = \sqrt{\dfrac{4 - y^2}{9 - x^2}}$. **25.** $\dfrac{dy}{dx} = \dfrac{4 + y^2}{2 + x^2}$.

26. $3e^z\, dy + ye^z\, dy = e^z\, dx - 3\, dy - y\, dy$.

Find an equation for the curve in the xy-plane through the given point, with the given slope at any point (x, y).

27. Slope, $-4x/9y$; through $(2, -4)$.

28. Slope, $(1 - y)/(x - 1)$; through $(2, -3)$.

29. Slope, $(2y + 1)/(6 - 2x)$; through $(2, -2)$.

30. (*a*) Without solving the equation $x\, dx + 4y\, dy = 0$, find the slope at $(-3, 2)$ on the graph of the particular solution which passes through $(-3, 2)$. (*b*) Find the specified particular solution.

110. LAWS OF EXPONENTIAL GROWTH AND DECAY

If y is a function of x, and if the rate of change of y with respect to x is *proportional to the value of y*, with $k \neq 0$ as the fixed constant of proportionality, it is customary to say that y obeys the law of **exponential growth** ($k > 0$), or **exponential decay** ($k < 0$). Then, the differential equation defining y as a function of x is

$$y' = ky, \tag{1}$$

called the differential equation of exponential growth or decay. We met (1) in Example 2 on page 292.

EXAMPLE 1. Obtain the general solution of (1) if $y = y_0$ when $x = x_0$.

Solution. From (1), $\qquad\qquad dy/y = k\, dx. \tag{2}$

Hence, the particular solution of (2) for which $y = y_0$ when $x = x_0$ is

$$\int_{y_0}^{y} \frac{dy}{y} = \int_{x_0}^{x} k\, dx, \quad or \quad \ln |y| - \ln |y_0| = k(x - x_0). \tag{3}$$

We assume that the domain for y in (2) is an interval *not including $y = 0$*. Hence, if $y_0 > 0$, we must have $y > 0$ always; if $y_0 < 0$, we must have $y < 0$ always. Therefore, in (3), $y/y_0 > 0$ and we obtain

$$\ln \left| \frac{y}{y_0} \right| = \ln \frac{y}{y_0} = k(x - x_0), \quad or \quad \frac{y}{y_0} = e^{k(x - x_0)}, \quad or$$

$$y = y_0 e^{k(x - x_0)}. \tag{4}$$

Note 1. The words "growth" and "decay," used for (1), apply to $|y|$.

We could use (4) to obtain the solution of (1) in any special case, but we agree to solve (1) afresh in each application.

EXAMPLE 2. The rate of decay of a given mass of a radioactive element is proportional to the number of atoms of the element which remain. (a) If there are x_0 atoms at the beginning of the decay, and if the half-life of the substance is 2 days, find the number of atoms remaining at the end of t days. (b) When will only one fourth of the original atoms remain?

Solution. 1. Let x be the number of atoms remaining t days after decay starts. Then, we desire to solve

$$\frac{dx}{dt} = -kx, \quad \text{or} \quad \frac{dx}{x} = -k\,dt, \tag{5}$$

with the initial conditions $x = x_0$ at $t = 0$, and find k. The use of $-k$ instead of k in (5) is for later convenience. By use of (12) on page 295,

$$\int_{x_0}^{x} \frac{dx}{x} = -\int_0^t k\,dt, \quad \text{or} \quad \ln \frac{x}{x_0} = -kt; \tag{6}$$

$$x = x_0 e^{-kt}. \tag{7}$$

From (6) with $x = \frac{1}{2}x_0$ when $t = 2$, and recollection that

$$\ln \tfrac{1}{2} = \ln 1 - \ln 2 = 0 - \ln 2,$$

by use of Table III we obtain

$$\ln \tfrac{1}{2} = -2k; \quad -\ln 2 = -2k; \quad k = \tfrac{1}{2}\ln 2 = .3466.$$

Hence, from (7), $\qquad\qquad\qquad\qquad x = x_0 e^{-.3466t}.$

2. To find t when $x = \frac{1}{4}x_0$, substitute $x = \frac{1}{4}x_0$ in (6): $\quad t = \dfrac{\ln 4}{.3466} = 4.000.$

In computing t, we used Table III for $\ln 4$, and then used logarithms to the base 10 to compute the fraction. Or, we could foresee that, since $.3466 = \frac{1}{2}\ln 2$ and $\ln 4 = \ln 2^2 = 2 \ln 2$, then $t = 4$, exactly. Or, the half-life of $\frac{1}{2}x_0$ atoms would be 2 days, which gives 4 days as the time to reduce x_0 atoms to $\frac{1}{4}x_0$ atoms.

EXERCISE 91

1. A certain radioactive element decays, with a half-life of 3 years. (a) If a mass consisting of x_0 atoms of the element is on hand, how many atoms will remain at the end of t years? (b) When will only 30% remain?

2. The population of a colony of bacteria is increasing at a time-rate proportional to the number in the population. An initial population of 2000 grew to 2,000,000 at the end of 6 days. (a) Express the population x as a function of the time t, measured in days from the instant when $x = 2000$. (b) When will $x = 10,000,000$?

3. Let τ be the temperature of a body which is cooling in a medium with constant temperature τ_0. Then, Newton's law of cooling states that the time-rate of decrease of τ is proportional to the difference $(\tau - \tau_0)$:

$$\frac{d\tau}{dt} = -k(\tau - \tau_0), \quad \text{or} \quad \frac{du}{dt} = -ku, \tag{1}$$

where $u = \tau - \tau_0$ and $k > 0$. If an object cools from 50° above to 20° above the temperature of the medium in 3 hours, when will $u = 10$?

4. The distance-rate of decrease of the intensity I of a beam of light passing through an absorbing medium is proportional to the intensity, at any point. If the intensity is reduced from I_0 to $.75I_0$ by 10 centimeters of a glass, how many centimeters of it are needed for reduction by 75%?

5. In an electric circuit, if the impressed electromotive force is removed, the time-rate of decrease of the current i is proportional to i. (a) If i changes from 30 amperes to 2 amperes in .05 second after removal of the electromotive force, express i in terms of the time t, measured in seconds from the instant when $i = 30$. (b) When will $i = .1$?

6. The important radioactive element uranium 235, employed in atomic research, has a half-life of $7.0(10^8)$ years. How long does it take for 90% of a given mass of this element to decay?

7. Assume that, if we ascend vertically from the earth, the rate of change of the atmospheric pressure, p, with respect to the altitude h above sea level is proportional to p. If the pressure p, in millimeters of mercury, is 760 at sea level and is 675 at 1000 meters above sea level, express p as a function of h, and find h where $p = 600$.

8. Let α be the amount of a substance at the beginning of a unimolecular chemical reaction and let x be the amount which will react in t time-units. Then, at any time, the speed of the reaction, or dx/dt, is proportional to the remaining amount of the substance, or $dx/dt = k(\alpha - x)$, where k depends on the reaction. Find k if $x = .75\alpha$ when $t = 3$.

9. A tank contains v gallons of a solution in which there are α pounds of salt. A solution containing β pounds of salt per gallon is run into the tank at the rate of k gallons per minute, and the contents of the tank flow out at the same rate. Let x pounds be the amount of salt in the tank t minutes after the process starts. Then, if the solution is kept uniform by being stirred, salt is added at the rate of βk pounds, and flows out at the rate of $k \cdot (x/v)$ pounds, per minute, so that $\dfrac{dx}{dt} = \beta k - \dfrac{k}{v} x.$

Solve for x in terms of t if $v = 2000$, $\alpha = 30$, $\beta = .5$, and $k = 4$. Also, show that $x \to 1000$ as $t \to \infty$.

Note 1. The following problems deal with the radioactive elements strontium 90, iodine 131, and carbon 14, with the half-lives (approximately) 28 years, 8 days, and 5600 years, respectively. Strontium 90 is one of the most dangerous parts of the fallout debris from the testing of nuclear bombs, because of the long half-life and the tendency of the element to act like calcium after entering the human body in food. Iodine 131 is another component of nuclear fallout, which contaminates pastures, and can result in badly contaminated milk. However, danger from iodine 131 in milk essentially can be eliminated during any period of high concentration in grass, if dairy animals are taken from pastures, and are fed stored forage, because of the element's short half-life. In archaeological research, a prehistoric relic containing carbon 14 (such as a wooden article or charcoal) can lead to an accurate estimate of the age of the relic. Also, a study of the concentration of carbon 14 in rocks is useful to geologists in establishing a geological timetable.

10. Suppose that the concentration of strontium 90 in the soil in a locality should become three times the safe level for food crops. How many years, without added strontium 90, would be needed for decay of the element to the safe level?

11. A piece of charcoal in the refuse of a prehistoric cooking site shows only 20% of the concentration of carbon 14 which would be normal for a fresh piece of charcoal. Estimate the age of the prehistoric charcoal.

12. Assume that the safe level of concentration (for milk production) of iodine 131 is exceeded in the grass in pastures in a certain neighborhood.* How long must hay be stored before feeding it to dairy cows, if the concentration of iodine 131 in the hay is to be only 1% of the concentration when the hay was cut?

111. INTEGRATION BY PARTS

Theorem III. *If the variables u and v are continuously differentiable functions of an independent variable x, then*

$$\int u\ dv = uv - \int v\ du, \tag{1}$$

where du and dv are understood to be expressed in terms of x and dx, and x is the variable of integration.

Proof. 1. Suppose that $u = f(x)$ and $v = g(x)$, where f and g have a common domain on which f' and g' are continuous. Then,

$$du = f'(x)dx; \quad dv = g'(x)dx; \tag{2}$$

$$\frac{d(uv)}{dx} = \frac{d[f(x)g(x)]}{dx} = f(x)g'(x) + g(x)f'(x). \tag{3}$$

2. Since f' and g' are continuous, the right-hand side of (3) is a continuous function of x, and hence uv is a continuously differentiable function of x. Therefore, by (2) on page 271,

$$uv + C = \int d(uv) = \int [f(x)g'(x) + g(x)f'(x)]dx = \int u\ dv + \int v\ du,\ or \tag{4}$$

$$\int u\ dv = uv - \int v\ du + C, \tag{5}$$

which gives (1) when C on the right in (5) is considered absorbed in the arbitrary additive constant involved implicitly in the symbol $\int v\ du$.

We refer to (1) as the formula for **integration by parts.** In a typical application of (2), we think of $\int u\ dv$ as specified for calculation, but not in a standard form, while v and $\int v\ du$ can be found easily.

EXAMPLE 1. Integrate: $\qquad\qquad\qquad\qquad \int x \sin 2x\ dx.$

Solution. Let $u = x$ and $dv = \sin 2x\ dx$. Then,

$$v = \int \sin 2x\ dx = -\tfrac{1}{2}\cos 2x; \quad du = dx; \tag{6}$$

$$\int \underbrace{x}_{u}\ \underbrace{\sin 2x\ dx}_{dv} = -\tfrac{1}{2}x \cos 2x - \int (-\tfrac{1}{2}\cos 2x)\cdot dx$$

$$= -\tfrac{1}{2}x \cos 2x + \tfrac{1}{4}\sin 2x + C. \tag{7}$$

In (6), we avoided introduction of an arbitrary constant in specifying v, because any indefinite integral v is satisfactory for use in (1).

* A conservative safe level was exceeded for a short time during the summer of 1962 in some Midwestern localities in the United States, and in the fall of 1962 in Alaska.

In making choices for u and dv in applying (1), we are guided by the following considerations, wherever possible.

1. *Choose dv so that $\int dv$ is easily obtainable.*
2. *Choose u so that du/dx is* **simpler than u,** *for integration.*

It may be necessary to apply integration by parts two or more times in obtaining an integral.

Note 1. The derivatives and integrals of e^t, $\sin t$, and $\cos t$ are as simple as the given functions. Hence, they are useful in either u or dv in applying (1). The derivatives of $\ln t$, Arcsin t, Arctan t, and t^n, with the integer $n > 0$, usually are more desirable than the given functions in integration. Hence, these functions are useful as choices for u.

EXAMPLE 2. Integrate: $\qquad\qquad \int x^2 e^{3x} \, dx.$

Solution. Let $u = x^2$ and $dv = e^{3x} \, dx;$ $v = \int e^{3x} \, dx = \frac{1}{3} e^{3x}.$

$$\int \underbrace{x^2}_{u} \cdot \underbrace{e^{3x} \, dx}_{dv} = \frac{1}{3} x^2 e^{3x} - \frac{2}{3} \int \underbrace{x}_{u} \cdot \underbrace{e^{3x} \, dx}_{dv}$$

$$= \frac{1}{3} x^2 e^{3x} - \frac{2}{3} (\frac{1}{3} x e^{3x} - \frac{1}{3} \int e^{3x} \, dx) = \frac{1}{27} e^{3x}(9x^2 - 6x + 2) + C$$

Comment. Try the inconvenient choice $dv = x^2 \, dx$ and $u = e^{3x}$.

EXAMPLE 3. Integrate: $\qquad\qquad \int x \text{ Arctan } 2x \, dx.$

Solution. With $u = $ Arctan $2x$ and $dv = x \, dx$, then $v = \int x \, dx = \frac{1}{2} x^2$, and

$$du = \frac{2 \, dx}{1 + 4x^2}; \quad \int \underbrace{(\text{Arctan } 2x)}_{u} \cdot \underbrace{x \, dx}_{dv} = \frac{1}{2} x^2 \text{ Arctan } 2x - \int \frac{x^2 \, dx}{4x^2 + 1}$$

$$= \frac{1}{2} x^2 \text{ Arctan } 2x - \frac{1}{4} \left(\int dx - \int \frac{dx}{4x^2 + 1} \right)$$

$$= \frac{1}{2} x^2 \text{ Arctan } 2x - \frac{1}{4} x + \frac{1}{8} \text{ Arctan } 2x + C.$$

EXAMPLE 4. Integrate: $\qquad\qquad I = \int e^{3x} \sin 2x \, dx.$

Solution. 1. Use (1) with $u = \sin 2x$ and $dv = e^{3x} \, dx$; then $v = \frac{1}{3} e^{3x}$ and

$$I = \frac{1}{3} e^{3x} \sin 2x - \frac{2}{3} \int e^{3x} \cos 2x \, dx. \tag{8}$$

2. With $u = \cos 2x$ and $dv = e^{3x} \, dx$ on the right in (8),

$$I = \frac{3}{9} e^{3x} \sin 2x - \frac{2}{3} (\frac{1}{3} e^{3x} \cos 2x + \frac{2}{3} \int e^{3x} \sin 2x \, dx). \tag{9}$$

In (9), the integral on the right is I. Hence,

$$I + \frac{4}{9} I = \frac{13I}{9} = \frac{e^{3x}(3 \sin 2x - 2 \cos 2x)}{9};$$

$$I = \frac{e^{3x}(3 \sin 2x - 2 \cos 2x)}{13} + C,$$

where we added an arbitrary constant to our particular indefinite integral.

From (1), by the fundamental theorem of integral calculus,

$$\int_{x=a}^{x=b} u \, dv = \left[uv - \int v \, du \right]_{x=a}^{x=b}$$

$$= uv \Big]_{x=a}^{x=b} - \int_{x=a}^{x=b} v \, du. \tag{10}$$

Thus, with limits of integration involved on the left in (1), we make use of those limits also for each term on the right.

ILLUSTRATION 1. $\int_1^2 x^2 \ln x \, dx = \int_1^2 \underbrace{(\ln x)}_{u} \underbrace{(x^2 \, dx)}_{dv}$

$$= \tfrac{1}{3} x^3 \ln x \Big]_1^2 - \tfrac{1}{3} \int_1^2 x^2 \, dx = \tfrac{8}{3} \ln 2 - \tfrac{7}{9}.$$

EXAMPLE 5. Prove the formula

$$\int \sec^3 x \, dx = \tfrac{1}{2} \sec x \tan x + \tfrac{1}{2} \ln |\sec x + \tan x| + C. \tag{XIX}$$

Solution. Let $I = \int \sec^3 x \, dx = \int (\sec x)(\sec^2 x \, dx)$, and employ integration by parts with $u = \sec x$ and $dv = \sec^2 x \, dx$, so that $v = \tan x$:

$$I = \sec x \tan x - \int \tan x \, (\sec x \tan x) dx. \tag{11}$$

Use $\tan^2 x = \sec^2 x - 1$ in the integrand in (11):

$$I = \sec x \tan x - \int \sec^3 x \, dx + \int \sec x \, dx, \tag{12}$$

where $-I$ appears on the right. Hence, by use of (X) on page 272,

$$I + I = \sec x \tan x + \ln |\sec x + \tan x| + C'. \tag{13}$$

On dividing by 2 in (13), and letting $\tfrac{1}{2} C' = C$, we obtain (XIX). In the next exercise, the student will derive the similar formula

$$\int \csc^3 x \, dx = - \tfrac{1}{2} \cot x \csc x + \tfrac{1}{2} \ln |\csc x - \cot x| + C. \tag{XX}$$

EXAMPLE 6. If m and n are integers and $m + n \neq 0$, prove that

$$\int \sin^m x \cos^n x \, dx = \frac{\sin^{m+1} x \cos^{n-1} x}{m+n} + \frac{n-1}{m+n} \int \sin^m x \cos^{n-2} x \, dx. \tag{14}$$

Solution. Let $I = \int \sin^m x \cos^n x \, dx = \int \cos^{n-1} x \sin^m x \, (\cos x \, dx)$.

Integrate by parts with $u = \cos^{n-1} x$ *and* $dv = \sin^m x \, d(\sin x)$.

Then, $v = \int \sin^m x \, d(\sin x) = \dfrac{\sin^{m+1} x}{m+1}.$

$$I = \frac{\sin^{m+1} x \cos^{n-1} x}{m+1} + \frac{n-1}{m+1} \int \sin^{m+2} x \cos^{n-2} x \, dx. \tag{15}$$

In (15), use $\sin^{m+2} x = \sin^m x \sin^2 x = \sin^m x \, (1 - \cos^2 x)$:

$$(m+1)I = \sin^{m+1} x \cos^{n-1} x + (n-1) \int \sin^m x \cos^{n-2} x \, dx - (n-1)I;$$

$$(m+1+n-1)I = \sin^{m+1} x \cos^{n-1} x + (n-1) \int \sin^m x \cos^{n-2} x \, dx. \tag{16}$$

On dividing both sides in (16) by $(m+n)$, we obtain (14).

Comment. To *verify* (14), as distinguished from *deriving* (14) as in Example 6, we could differentiate the right-hand side of (14), to see that the derivative is the integrand on the left. In differentiation, we would use $D_x(\int \sin^m x \cos^{n-2} x \, dx) = \sin^m x \cos^{n-2} x$. A result such as (14) is called a **reduction formula** because it expresses an integral of a certain type in terms of a more simple integral of similar form.

EXERCISE 92

Integrate. Letters a, k, and n represent constants.

1. $\int xe^x \, dx$.

2. $\int_1^3 xe^{2x} \, dx$.

3. $\int x \cos x \, dx$.

4. $\int x \sin 3x \, dx$.

5. $\int xe^{-x} \, dx$.

6. $\int x \sec^2 x \, dx$.

7. $\int_{\pi/4}^{\pi/3} x \sin x \, dx$.

8. $\int \ln x \, dx$.

9. $\int x \ln x \, dx$.

10. $\int x^2 e^{2x} \, dx$.

11. $\int x^2 \ln x \, dx$.

12. $\int x^2 \sin x \, dx$.

13. $\int x^n \ln x \, dx$, with $n \neq -1$.

14. $\int y \sec y \tan y \, dy$.

15. $\int x^2 \cos 2x \, dx$.

16. $\int \text{Arctan } x \, dx$.

17. $\int \text{Arcsin } 3x \, dx$.

18. $\int_{-1}^1 x \text{ Arctan } x \, dx$.

19. $\int_{-\pi/2}^0 x \sec^2 \tfrac{1}{2}x \, dx$.

20. $\int x(2^x) \, dx$.

21. $\int x \text{ Arccot } 2x \, dx$.

22. $\int (\ln x)^3 \, dx$.

23. $\int x^3 \sin x \, dx$.

24. $\int u \csc 2u \cot 2u \, du$.

25. $\int \text{Arcsin } 2x \, dx$.

26. $\int x^4 e^{-x} \, dx$.

27. $\int x \sin kx \, dx$.

28. $\int x \text{ Arctan } \tfrac{1}{2}x \, dx$.

29. $\int xa^x \, dx$.

30. $\int x \csc^2 \tfrac{1}{2}x \, dx$.

31. $\int x^2 e^{-2x} \, dx$.

32. $\int_{\pi/4}^{3\pi/4} \dfrac{x \cot x}{\sin x} \, dx$.

33. $\int \dfrac{x^3}{\sqrt{4 + x^2}} \, dx$.

34. $\int u^3 \sqrt{a^2 \pm u^2} \, du$.

35. $\int x^{-\frac{1}{2}} \text{ Arcsin } \sqrt{x} \, dx$.

36. $\int (\text{Arcsin } x)^2 \, dx$.

37. $\int \dfrac{\ln x \, dx}{(x + 2)^2}$.

38. $\int \dfrac{\ln (x + 3)}{\sqrt[3]{x + 3}} \, dx$.

39. $\int \dfrac{x \text{ Arctan } x}{\sqrt{1 + x^2}} \, dx$.

40. $\int x \text{ Arctan } \dfrac{1}{x} \, dx$.

41. $\int \dfrac{\text{Arccot } \sqrt{x}}{\sqrt{x}} \, dx$.

42. $\int \text{Arcsin } \dfrac{1}{x} \, dx$.

Obtain the integral by using successive integrations by parts.

43. $\int e^x \sin 3x \, dx$.

44. $\int e^{2x} \cos 4x \, dx$.

45. $\int e^{-2x} \sin x \, dx$.

46. $\int e^{-x} \cos 2x \, dx$.

47. $\int e^{\frac{1}{2}x} \cos \tfrac{1}{3}x \, dx$.

48. $\int \csc^3 x \, dx$.

(*a*) *Compute the area of the region R bounded by the given curves in an xy-plane.* (*b*) *Find the volume of the solid obtained if R is revolved about the x-axis.*

49. The *x*-axis, the curve $y = \ln x$, and the line $x = e^2$.

50. The *x*-axis, the curve $y = xe^{-x}$, and the lines $x = 1$ and $x = 3$.

51. The *x*-axis and the curve $y = x \sin x$ from $x = 0$ to $x = \pi$.

52. Prove formulas (125) and (126) of Table VII, and then obtain the results in Problems 43–47 by substitution in these formulas.

53. Derive the formulas (113)–(115) of Table VII.

54. Apply formula (108) of Table VII to find $\int \sec^5 x \, dx$.

112. VARIOUS INTEGRANDS INVOLVING SINES AND COSINES

Suppose that $f(x)$ involves direct trigonometric functions of x. Then, to calculate $\int f(x)dx$ when it is not immediately expressible in terms of one or more standard forms for integration, first check to see if

$$\left\{ \begin{array}{c} \textbf{substitution of a new variable } u \textbf{ for one} \\ \textbf{of the trigonometric functions of } x \end{array} \right\} \tag{1}$$

will change $\int f(x)dx$ to a form $\int g(u)du$ which can be calculated easily. If (1) is not immediately useful, then consider using trigonometric identities to alter the form of $f(x)$, with the objective of ultimately using (1). The following alterations of $f(x)$ are possibilities.

A. *Express all trigonometric function values in terms of values of sines and cosines by use of the fundamental identities below:*

$$\tan \theta = \frac{\sin \theta}{\cos \theta}; \quad \cot \theta = \frac{\cos \theta}{\sin \theta}; \quad \sec \theta = \frac{1}{\cos \theta}; \quad \csc \theta = \frac{1}{\sin \theta}. \tag{2}$$

B. *Express all trigonometric function values in terms of values of a single function.*

C. *Use the identities for the sine and cosine of 2θ in terms of the trigonometric functions of θ:*

$$1 + \cos 2\theta = 2 \cos^2 \theta; \quad 1 - \cos 2\theta = 2 \sin^2 \theta; \quad \sin 2\theta = 2 \sin \theta \cos \theta. \tag{3}$$

Also, use other identities from page 679.

ILLUSTRATION 1. To perform the following integration, finally substitute $u = \cos x$, with $du = -\sin x \, dx$:

$$\int \sin x \tan^2 x \, dx = \int \frac{\sin x \sin^2 x}{\cos^2 x} \, dx = \int \frac{(1 - \cos^2 x)\sin x \, dx}{\cos^2 x}$$

$$= -\int \frac{1 - u^2}{u^2} \, du = u + \frac{1}{u} + C = \cos x + \sec x + C.$$

Note 1. In calculus details, recall that the variable θ in (2) and (3) has a domain consisting of *numbers*, not *angles*. However, with recollection of use of (3) in studying the trigonometric functions of angles, we shall continue to refer to (3) as **double-angle identities.** When they are read from right to left, they may be called **half-angle identities.**

In order to calculate an integral of the form

$$\int \sin^m u \cos^n u \, du, \tag{4}$$

our objective is to express (1) in terms of integrals where the sine or cosine with some argument can be taken conveniently as a new variable of integration. We emphasize the following possibilities.

I. *If m is a positive odd integer in (4), use*

$$\sin^{m-1} u \cos^n u \, (\sin u \, du) = -\sin^{m-1} u \cos^n u \, d(\cos u),$$

and express $\sin^{m-1} u$ in terms of $\cos u$ by use of $\sin^2 u = 1 - \cos^2 u$.

II. *If n is a positive odd integer in* (4), *use*

$$\sin^m u \cos^{n-1} u (\cos u \, du) = \sin^m u \cos^{n-1} u \, d(\sin u),$$

and express $\cos^{n-1} u$ *in terms of* $\sin u$ *by use of* $\cos^2 u = 1 - \sin^2 u.$

III. *If m and n are nonnegative even integers in* (4), *transform the integrand by use of the double-angle identities.*

ILLUSTRATION 2. $\quad \displaystyle\int \sin^2 x \cos^3 x \, dx = \int \sin^2 x \cos^2 x \, (\cos x \, dx)$

$$= \int \sin^2 x \, (1 - \sin^2 x) \, d(\sin x) = \tfrac{1}{3} \sin^3 x - \tfrac{1}{5} \sin^5 x + C.$$

ILLUSTRATION 3. $\quad \displaystyle\int \sin^5 2x \, dx = \tfrac{1}{2}\int \sin^4 2x \, [(\sin 2x)(2 \, dx)]$

$$= -\tfrac{1}{2}\int (\sin^2 2x)^2 \, d(\cos 2x) = -\tfrac{1}{2}\int (1 - \cos^2 2x)^2 \, d(\cos 2x)$$

$$= -\tfrac{1}{2}\int d(\cos 2x) + \int \cos^2 2x \, d(\cos 2x) - \tfrac{1}{2}\int \cos^4 2x \, d(\cos 2x)$$

$$= -\tfrac{1}{2} \cos 2x + \tfrac{1}{3} \cos^3 2x - \tfrac{1}{10} \cos^5 2x + C.$$

ILLUSTRATION 4. $\quad \displaystyle\int \frac{\cos^3 x \, dx}{\sin x} = \int \frac{(1 - \sin^2 x)(\cos x \, dx)}{\sin x}$

$$= \int \frac{d(\sin x)}{\sin x} - \int \sin x \, d(\sin x) = \ln |\sin x| - \frac{1}{2} \sin^2 x + C.$$

ILLUSTRATION 5. $\quad \displaystyle\int \sin^4 x \cos^2 x \, dx = \int \sin^2 x \, (\sin^2 x \cos^2 x) dx$

[formulas (3), page 304] $\qquad = \int \tfrac{1}{2}(1 - \cos 2x)(\tfrac{1}{4} \sin^2 2x) dx$

$$= \tfrac{1}{8}\int \tfrac{1}{2}(1 - \cos 4x) dx - \tfrac{1}{16}\int \sin^2 2x \, [(\cos 2x)(2 \, dx)]$$

$$= \tfrac{1}{16}x - \tfrac{1}{64} \sin 4x - \tfrac{1}{48} \sin^3 2x + C.$$

In (4), if *m* and *n* are *even integers* and at least *one is negative*, use of (3) may lead to an inconvenient form. Then, we may try simple devices employing $\sin^2 \theta + \cos^2 \theta = 1$, as in the details of Illustration 1.

With integrals of the form (4), when preceding methods lead to inconvenient details, the reduction formulas (112)–(115) in Table VII may apply.

ILLUSTRATION 6. In the following integration, we apply (X) of page 679.

$$\int \sin 3t \cos 4t \, dt = \tfrac{1}{2}\int [\sin 7t + \sin (-t)] dt$$

$$= \tfrac{1}{2}\int (\sin 7t - \sin t) dt = -\tfrac{1}{14} \cos 7t + \tfrac{1}{2} \cos t + C.$$

EXERCISE 93

Integrate without introducing a radical.

1. $\displaystyle\int \sin^3 x \cos x \, dx.$
2. $\displaystyle\int \cos^2 x \sin x \, dx.$
3. $\displaystyle\int \tan^3 x \csc^2 x \, dx.$

4. $\displaystyle\int \cot^2 x \sec x \, dx.$
5. $\displaystyle\int \sin^3 x \cos^2 x \, dx.$
6. $\displaystyle\int \sin^4 x \cos^3 x \, dx.$

7. $\displaystyle\int \sin \tfrac{1}{3}x \cos \tfrac{1}{3}x \, dx.$
8. $\displaystyle\int \sin 2x \cos^3 2x \, dx.$
9. $\displaystyle\int \sin^3 hx \, dx.$

10. $\displaystyle\int \cos^2 \tfrac{1}{2}x \, dx.$
11. $\displaystyle\int \sin^2 3x \, dx.$
12. $\displaystyle\int \cos^2 2x \, dx.$

13. $\int \cos^3 x \, dx.$ **14.** $\int \sin^5 x \, dx.$ **15.** $\int \sin^4 x \, dx.$

16. $\int \dfrac{\sin^3 x}{\cos^2 x} \, dx.$ **17.** $\int \dfrac{\sin^5 x}{\cos^4 x} \, dx.$ **18.** $\int \dfrac{\sin^2 2x}{\cot 2x} \, dx.$

19. $\int \sin^2 x \cos^2 x \, dx.$ **20.** $\int \sin^2 x \cos^4 x \, dx.$ **21.** $\int \sin^4 x \cos^6 x \, dx.$

22. $\int \sin^2 \tfrac{1}{2}x \cos^2 \tfrac{1}{2}x \, dx.$ **23.** $\int \sin^4 2x \cos^2 2x \, dx.$

24. $\int \sin^4 3x \cos^4 3x \, dx.$ **25.** $\int \sin 2x \cos 4x \, dx.$

26. $\int \sin 2x \sin 4x \, dx.$ **27.** $\int \cos 4x \cos 6x \, dx.$

28. $\int \dfrac{\cos^4 2x}{\sin^2 2x} \, dx.$ **29.** $\int \dfrac{\tan^3 2x}{\cos^2 2x} \, dx.$ **30.** $\int \dfrac{\cot 2x}{\csc^4 2x} \, dx.$

31. $\int \dfrac{dx}{1 - \cos 2x}.$ **32.** $\int \dfrac{dy}{1 + \cos y}.$ **33.** $\int \dfrac{dz}{1 - \cos z}.$

34. $\int \dfrac{dx}{\sqrt{1 + \cos x}}.$ **35.** $\int \dfrac{dx}{\sqrt{1 - \cos 4x}}.$ **36.** $\int \dfrac{dx}{1 + \sin x}.$

37. $\int_0^{2\pi} \sqrt{1 - \cos x} \, dx.$ **38.** $\int_0^{\pi/2} \sqrt{1 - \cos 4x} \, dx.$

39. $\int_0^{2\pi} \sqrt{1 + \cos x} \, dx.$ **40.** $\int \sin^3 x \sqrt[3]{\cos x} \, dx.$

Hint for Problem 39. If $\pi \leqq x \leqq 2\pi$, then $\sqrt{1 + \cos x} = -\sqrt{2} \cos \tfrac{1}{2}x.$

41. Calculate $\int dx/(\sin^2 x \cos^4 x)$ by first applying (114) on page 708 with $m = -4$ and $n = -2$, to increase the exponent of $\cos x$ by 2.

113. INTEGRANDS OF TYPES $\tan^m u \sec^n u$ AND $\cot^m u \csc^n u$

In order to perform integrations of the types

$$\int \tan^m u \sec^n u \, du \quad and \quad \int \cot^m u \csc^n u \, du, \tag{1}$$

we frequently employ the identities

$$\tan^2 \theta + 1 = \sec^2 \theta \quad and \quad \cot^2 \theta + 1 = \csc^2 \theta, \tag{2}$$

with the aim of obtaining integrands where $\tan u$, $\sec u$, $\cot u$, or $\csc u$ can be taken conveniently as a new variable.

I. *To obtain* $\int \tan^m u \, du$ *and* $\int \cot^m u \, du$, *if m is an integer greater than* 1, *use*

$$\tan^m u = \tan^{m-2} u \tan^2 u = \tan^{m-2} u \, (\sec^2 u - 1);$$
$$\cot^m u = \cot^{m-2} u \cot^2 u = \cot^{m-2} u \, (\csc^2 u - 1).$$

ILLUSTRATION 1. $\int \tan^4 x \, dx = \int \tan^2 x \, (\sec^2 x - 1) dx$

$$= \int \tan^2 x \, d(\tan x) - \int \tan^2 x \, dx = \tfrac{1}{3} \tan^3 x - \int (\sec^2 x - 1) dx$$

$$= \tfrac{1}{3} \tan^3 x - \tan x + x + C.$$

ILLUSTRATION 2. $\int \cot^5 x \, dx = \int \cot^3 x \, (\csc^2 x - 1) dx$

$$= -\int \cot^3 x \, d(\cot x) - \int \cot^3 x \, dx = -\tfrac{1}{4} \cot^4 x - \int \cot x \, (\csc^2 x - 1) dx$$

$$= -\tfrac{1}{4} \cot^4 x + \tfrac{1}{2} \cot^2 x + \ln |\sin x| + C.$$

II. *If n is a positive even integer in* (1), *use*

$$\tan^m u \sec^n u \, du = \tan^m u \sec^{n-2} u \, (\sec^2 u \, du) = \tan^m u \sec^{n-2} u \, d(\tan u),$$

and express $\sec^{n-2} u$ *in terms of* $\tan u$ *by use of* (2). *Similarly, express* $\cot^m u \csc^n u \, du$ *in terms of* $\cot u$ *and* $d(\cot u)$.

ILLUSTRATION 3. $\displaystyle \int \tan^3 2x \sec^4 2x \, dx = \frac{1}{2}\int \tan^3 2x \sec^2 2x \, [(\sec^2 2x)(2 \, dx)]$

$$= \frac{1}{2}\int \tan^3 2x \, (\tan^2 2x + 1) \, d(\tan 2x) = \frac{1}{12} \tan^6 2x + \frac{1}{8} \tan^4 2x + C.$$

ILLUSTRATION 4. $\displaystyle \int \frac{\sec^4 x \, dx}{\tan^5 x} = \int \frac{(\tan^2 x + 1)(\sec^2 x \, dx)}{\tan^5 x}$

$$= -\frac{1}{2 \tan^2 x} - \frac{1}{4 \tan^4 x} + C.$$

III. *If m is a positive odd integer in* (1), *use*

$$\tan^m u \sec^n u \, du = \tan^{m-1} u \sec^{n-1} u \, (\tan u \sec u \, du)$$

$$= \tan^{m-1} u \sec^{n-1} u \, d(\sec u),$$

and express $\tan^{m-1} u$ *in terms of* $\sec u$ *by use of* (2). *Similarly, express* $\cot^m u \csc^n u \, du$ *in terms of* $\csc u$ *and* $d(\csc u)$.

ILLUSTRATION 5. $\displaystyle \int \cot^5 x \csc^3 x \, dx = \int \cot^4 x \csc^2 x \, (\cot x \csc x \, dx)$

$$= -\int (\csc^2 x - 1)^2 \csc^2 x \, d(\csc x) = -\frac{1}{7} \csc^7 x + \frac{2}{5} \csc^5 x - \frac{1}{3} \csc^3 x + C.$$

ILLUSTRATION 6. $\displaystyle \int \frac{\csc^3 x}{\cot x} \, dx = \int \frac{\csc^2 x}{\cot^2 x} \, (\csc x \cot x \, dx)$

(let $u = \csc x$) $\displaystyle = \int \frac{u^2 \, du}{1 - u^2} = -\int du + \int \frac{du}{1 - u^2}$

$$= -u + \frac{1}{2} \ln\left|\frac{1 + u}{1 - u}\right| + C = -\csc x + \frac{1}{2} \ln\left|\frac{1 + \csc x}{1 - \csc x}\right| + C.$$

ILLUSTRATION 7. $\displaystyle \int \frac{\sin^2 x}{\cos^4 x} \, dx = \int \tan^2 x \sec^2 x \, dx = \frac{1}{3} \tan^3 x + C.$

To obtain $\int \sec^n x \, dx$ if n is an odd integer greater than 1, use (102) or the reduction formula (108) of Table VII.

EXERCISE 94

Integrate without introducing radicals.

1. $\displaystyle \int \tan^2 2x \, dx.$ 2. $\displaystyle \int \tan^3 x \, dx.$ 3. $\displaystyle \int \cot^3 y \, dy.$

4. $\displaystyle \int \cot^4 x \, dx.$ 5. $\displaystyle \int \tan^5 x \, dx.$ 6. $\displaystyle \int \tan^6 2z \, dz.$

7. $\displaystyle \int \cot^5 \tfrac{1}{2}x \, dx.$ 8. $\displaystyle \int \sec^4 x \, dx.$ 9. $\displaystyle \int \csc^6 x \, dx.$

10. $\displaystyle \int \csc^4 2x \, dx.$ 11. $\displaystyle \int \sec^4 3x \, dx.$ 12. $\displaystyle \int \csc^6 \tfrac{1}{2}x \, dx.$

13. $\displaystyle \int \tan^2 t \sec^4 t \, dt.$ 14. $\displaystyle \int \cot^4 y \csc^4 y \, dy.$ 15. $\displaystyle \int \cot 2t \csc^4 2t \, dt.$

16. $\displaystyle \int \cot^3 x \csc^6 x \, dx.$ 17. $\displaystyle \int \tan^3 \theta \sec^3 \theta \, d\theta.$ 18. $\displaystyle \int \tan^5 z \sec^3 z \, dz.$

19. $\displaystyle \int \cot^4 2x \csc^6 2x \, dx.$ 20. $\displaystyle \int \cot^3 \tfrac{1}{2}x \csc^3 \tfrac{1}{2}x \, dx.$

21. $\int \dfrac{\sec^4 x}{\tan^2 x}\, dx.$ **22.** $\int \dfrac{\csc^4 x}{\sqrt{\cot x}}\, dx.$ **23.** $\int \dfrac{\csc^4 2x}{\cot^5 2x}\, dx.$

24. $\int \dfrac{\csc^2 x}{\cot^5 x}\, dx.$ **25.** $\int \dfrac{\sec^2 \frac{1}{2}x}{\tan^3 \frac{1}{2}x}\, dx.$ **26.** $\int \dfrac{\sec^6 x}{\cot^3 x}\, dx.$

27. $\int \dfrac{\sin^4 x}{\cos^6 x}\, dx.$ **28.** $\int \dfrac{\sin^3 x}{\cos^7 x}\, dx.$ **29.** $\int \dfrac{\sec^3 x}{\tan x}\, dx.$

30. $\int \dfrac{\sec^4 x}{\tan x}\, dx.$ **31.** $\int \dfrac{\sec^4 2x}{\tan^4 2x}\, dx.$ **32.** $\int \dfrac{\tan^3 x}{\sec^3 x}\, dx.$

33. $\int \tan^3 x \sqrt{\sec x}\, dx.$ **34.** $\int \csc^6 2x \sqrt{\cot 2x}\, dx.$

35. $\int \sec^3 2x\, dx.$ **36.** $\int \sec^5 2x\, dx.$ **37.** $\int \sec^{-3} \frac{1}{2}x\, dx.$

38. $\int x \sec^4 x\, dx.$ **39.** $\int x \csc^4 2x\, dx.$ **40.** $\int x \tan^2 x\, dx.$

41. $\int z \sec^3 z \tan z\, dz.$ **42.** $\int x \csc^4 2x \cot 2x\, dx.$

114. RATIONALIZATION BY TRIGONOMETRIC SUBSTITUTION

In $\int f(x)dx$, suppose that $f(x)$ is an irrational function of x, and that $f(x)$ is a rational function of x and the square root of a quadratic function of x. Then, by a suitable trigonometric substitution, it is possible to alter the radical to a constant times a trigonometric function of a new variable, without introducing any new radical in the integrand. Hence, the change of variable is called a *rationalizing substitution*. We are led to the desired change in such cases by recollection of the following identities:

$$\cos^2 \theta = 1 - \sin^2 \theta; \quad \sec^2 \theta = 1 + \tan^2 \theta; \quad \tan^2 \theta = \sec^2 \theta - 1. \quad (1)$$

For radicals of the following forms, we use the indicated substitutions.

$$\sqrt{a^2 - u^2}: \qquad substitute\ \boldsymbol{u = a \sin \theta}. \qquad (2)$$

$$\sqrt{a^2 + u^2}: \qquad substitute\ \boldsymbol{u = a \tan \theta}. \qquad (3)$$

$$\sqrt{u^2 - a^2}: \qquad substitute\ \boldsymbol{u = a \sec \theta}. \qquad (4)$$

EXAMPLE 1. Integrate: $\int \dfrac{du}{(a^2 + u^2)^{\frac{3}{2}}}.$ $(a > 0)$

Solution. 1. Let $u = a \tan \theta$, where $-\frac{1}{2}\pi < \theta < \frac{1}{2}\pi$. Then, from the identity $\sec^2 \theta = 1 + \tan^2 \theta$, we obtain $\sec \theta = +\sqrt{1 + \tan^2 \theta}$, where the "+" sign is used because $\sec \theta > 0$ on the domain of θ.

2. From $u = a \tan \theta$, we find $du = a \sec^2 \theta\, d\theta$;

$$(\sqrt{a^2 + u^2})^3 = (\sqrt{a^2 + a^2 \tan^2 \theta})^3 = a^3(\sqrt{1 + \tan^2 \theta})^3 = a^3 \sec^3 \theta;$$

$$\int \frac{du}{(a^2 + u^2)^{\frac{3}{2}}} = \frac{1}{a^2} \int \frac{\sec^2 \theta}{\sec^3 \theta}\, d\theta = \frac{1}{a^2} \int \cos \theta\, d\theta = \frac{1}{a^2} \sin \theta + C. \quad (5)$$

3. The problem (asking for an *indefinite* integral) requires us to express (5) in terms of u on the right. To obtain $\sin \theta$ in terms of u, now interpret θ as a symbol

for the *angle* θ radians and act, in Figure 193, as if $u > 0$ with θ acute, and

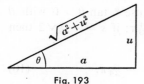

Fig. 193

$\tan \theta = u/a$. From Figure 193, $\sin \theta = u/\sqrt{a^2 + u^2}$. This result applies also if $u < 0$, because then $(u/a) < 0$, $\theta < 0$, and $\sin \theta < 0$. Hence, from (5),

$$\int \frac{du}{(a^2 + u^2)^{\frac{3}{2}}} = \frac{u}{a^2\sqrt{a^2 + u^2}} + C. \tag{6}$$

Note that (6) is (55) on page 704 for $(u^2 + a^2)$, with $m = 0$ and $n = 3$.

EXAMPLE 2. Integrate:

$$\int \frac{x^2\, dx}{(4 - x^2)^{\frac{3}{2}}}.$$

Solution. 1. Let $x = 2 \sin \theta$, with $-\frac{1}{2}\pi < \theta < \frac{1}{2}\pi$. Then $\cos \theta > 0$ on the domain for θ and $\cos \theta = +\sqrt{1 - \sin^2 \theta}$.

2. From $x = 2 \sin \theta$, we obtain $dx = 2 \cos \theta\, d\theta$;

$$(4 - x^2)^{\frac{1}{2}} = \sqrt{4 - 4 \sin^2 \theta} = 2\sqrt{1 - \sin^2 \theta} = 2 \cos \theta;$$

$$\int \frac{x^2\, dx}{(4 - x^2)^{\frac{3}{2}}} = \int \frac{\sin^2 \theta \cos \theta\, d\theta}{\cos^3 \theta} = \int \tan^2 \theta\, d\theta$$

$$= \int (\sec^2 \theta - 1)d\theta = \tan \theta - \theta + C. \tag{7}$$

Fig. 194

3. To express (7) in terms of x, we use Figure 194 and $\theta = \text{Arcsin } \frac{1}{2}x$:

$$\tan \theta = \frac{x}{\sqrt{4 - x^2}}; \quad \int \frac{x^2\, dx}{(4 - x^2)^{\frac{3}{2}}} = \frac{x}{\sqrt{4 - x^2}} - \text{Arcsin } \frac{x}{2} + C. \tag{8}$$

ILLUSTRATION 1. To rationalize the integrand in $\int \sqrt{5 - x^2 + 4x}\, dx$, we would complete a square and apply (2):

$$\sqrt{5 - x^2 + 4x} = \sqrt{9 - (x - 2)^2}; \quad then,\ let\quad x - 2 = 3 \sin \theta.$$

The preceding method applies *more easily when a definite integral is involved.* In this case, the limits of integration should be changed to correspond to the change of variable. This *avoids changing back to the original variable* of integration, as in (6) and (8).

EXAMPLE 3. Compute:

$$\int_{-1}^{\sqrt{3}} \frac{x^2\, dx}{(4 - x^2)^{\frac{3}{2}}}.$$

Solution. Let $x = 2 \sin \theta$, with $\theta = \text{Arcsin } \frac{1}{2}x$. If $x = -1$, then $\theta = -\frac{1}{6}\pi$; if $x = \sqrt{3}$, then $\theta = \frac{1}{3}\pi$. Hence, from (7), with *no necessity for the work in* (8),

$$\int_{-1}^{\sqrt{3}} \frac{x^2\, dx}{(4 - x^2)^{\frac{3}{2}}} = \int_{-\pi/6}^{\pi/3} \tan^2 \theta\, d\theta = \tan \theta - \theta \Big]_{-\pi/6}^{\pi/3} = \tfrac{4}{3}\sqrt{3} - \tfrac{1}{2}\pi.$$

EXAMPLE 4. Calculate the integral:

$$I = \int_{-4/3}^{-2\sqrt{2}/3} \frac{ds}{s\sqrt{9s^2 - 4}}.$$

Solution. In I, let s have the domain $3s < -2$ or $s < -\frac{2}{3}$, so that $\sqrt{9s^2 - 4}$ is a real number. We recall $\tan^2 \theta = \sec^2 \theta - 1$ and write $9s^2 - 4 = (3s)^2 - 4$.

Hence, we substitute $\qquad 3s = 2 \sec \theta, \quad with \quad \pi \leqq \theta < \tfrac{3}{2}\pi.$ $\qquad$ (9)

Then, $+ \sqrt{9s^2 - 4} = + 2\sqrt{\sec^2 \theta - 1} = 2 \tan \theta$, because * $\tan \theta > 0$ with θ as in (9). Also, if $s = -\tfrac{4}{3}$ then $\sec \theta = -2$ and $\theta = \tfrac{4}{3}\pi$; if $s = -\tfrac{2}{3}\sqrt{2}$ then $\theta = \tfrac{5}{4}\pi$. From (9), $3\,ds = 2 \sec \theta \tan \theta\,d\theta$;

$$I = \tfrac{1}{2} \int_{4\pi/3}^{5\pi/4} d\theta = \tfrac{1}{2}\theta\Big]_{4\pi/3}^{5\pi/4} = \tfrac{1}{2}\pi(\tfrac{5}{4} - \tfrac{4}{3}) = -\tfrac{1}{24}\pi. \qquad (10)$$

Substitutions (2), (3), and (4) also apply conveniently with integrals of the following types, where n is a positive integer: $\quad \displaystyle\int \frac{du}{(u^2 + a^2)^n}; \quad \int \frac{du}{(u^2 - a^2)^n}.$

EXERCISE 95

Integrate; perhaps use formulas (27) *and* (41), *Table* VII, *after deriving them.*

1. $\displaystyle\int \frac{dx}{(9 - x^2)^{\frac{3}{2}}}.$

2. $\displaystyle\int \frac{dx}{x^2\sqrt{4 + x^2}}.$

3. $\displaystyle\int \frac{\sqrt{x^2 - 9}}{x}\,dx.$

4. $\displaystyle\int \frac{\sqrt{t^2 - 16}}{t^2}\,dt.$

5. $\displaystyle\int \frac{dy}{y\sqrt{9 + 4y^2}}.$

6. $\displaystyle\int \frac{dt}{t\sqrt{t^2 - 16}}.$

7. $\displaystyle\int \frac{dy}{y\sqrt{1 - 9y^2}}.$

8. $\displaystyle\int \frac{u^2\,du}{(a^2 + u^2)^{\frac{3}{2}}}.$

9. $\displaystyle\int \frac{x^2\,dx}{\sqrt{25 - x^2}}.$

10. $\displaystyle\int_0^{3/7} \frac{dy}{(9 + 49y^2)^{\frac{3}{2}}}.$

11. $\displaystyle\int_{\sqrt{2}/2}^{1} \frac{u^3\,du}{\sqrt{2 - u^2}}.$

12. $\displaystyle\int_{-1/4}^{0} \frac{z^2\,dz}{\sqrt{1 - 4z^2}}.$

13. $\displaystyle\int \frac{dx}{(x^2 + 9)^2}.$

14. $\displaystyle\int \frac{du}{(a^2 + u^2)^2}.$

15. $\displaystyle\int \frac{dy}{y^2\sqrt{9 + y^2}}.$

16. $\displaystyle\int_{-2\sqrt{5}}^{-\sqrt{10}} \frac{dy}{y\sqrt{y^2 - 5}}.$

17. $\displaystyle\int_{-2}^{2\sqrt{3}} \frac{x^2\,dx}{(16 - x^2)^{\frac{3}{2}}}.$

18. $\displaystyle\int_{-4/3}^{4\sqrt{3}/3} \frac{dz}{(9z^2 + 16)^{\frac{3}{2}}}.$

19. $\displaystyle\int \sqrt{a^2 + 9x^2}\,dx.$

20. $\displaystyle\int \sqrt{4x^2 - a^2}\,dx.$

21. $\displaystyle\int \sqrt{4a^2 - x^2}\,dx.$

22. $\displaystyle\int_{1/6}^{\sqrt{2}/6} \frac{dx}{x^2\sqrt{1 - 9x^2}}.$

23. $\displaystyle\int \frac{(3x + 5)dx}{(9 + 4x^2)^2}.$

24. $\displaystyle\int \frac{(3 - 6x)dx}{(25 + 4x^2)^{\frac{3}{2}}}.$

25. $\displaystyle\int \frac{dx}{(5 - x^2 - 4x)^{\frac{3}{2}}}.$

26. $\displaystyle\int \frac{(2x - 3)dx}{(9x^2 + 12x + 5)^{\frac{3}{2}}}.$

27. $\displaystyle\int \frac{\sec^2 t\,dt}{(4 - \tan^2 t)^{\frac{3}{2}}}.$

28. $\displaystyle\int \frac{e^{-x}\,dx}{(9 + 4e^{-2x})^{\frac{3}{2}}}.$

29. $\displaystyle\int \frac{u^3\,du}{\sqrt{a^2 - u^2}}.$

30. $\displaystyle\int \frac{(16x + 5)dx}{(4x^2 + 12x + 25)^2}.$

31. $\displaystyle\int \frac{dy}{(y - 2)\sqrt{y^2 - 4y - 5}}.$

32. $\displaystyle\int (8x - 5)\sqrt{4x^2 - 4x}\,dx.$

33. $\displaystyle\int \sqrt{x^2 - 2ax}\,dx.$

34. Obtain the area of a circle of radius r by integration.

35. Find the area of the ellipse $4x^2 + 9y^2 = 36$.

36. Find the area of the ellipse $b^2x^2 + a^2y^2 = a^2b^2$.

* This fact, $\tan \theta > 0$, influenced the choice of domain for θ in (9). In (2), (3), and (4), it is convenient to specify the domain for θ so that the radical, with a plus sign attached, is equal to a function of θ. If we had specified $-\pi \leqq \theta < -\tfrac{1}{2}\pi$, in (9), then $\theta = \text{Arcsec } (3s/2)$, from (3) on page 237.

EXERCISE 96 (*Review of Chapter Eleven*)

1. Verify by calculating the differential of the right-hand side:

$$\int e^t \, dt/(1 + e^{2t}) = \text{Arctan } e^t + C.$$

Integrate.

2. $\int \dfrac{1}{5x^7} \, dx.$ **3.** $\int \dfrac{x^3}{x^{\frac{2}{3}}} \, dx.$ **4.** $\int \dfrac{dx}{\cos 3x}.$ **5.** $\int \dfrac{dv}{4 + 5v}.$

6. $\int \dfrac{(2 + t)^2}{\sqrt{t}} \, dt.$ **7.** $\int \dfrac{(2 - \sqrt{x})^2}{x^2} \, dx.$ **8.** $\int \dfrac{z^2 \, dz}{(2z^3 + 3)^4}.$

9. $\int \sin 4x \, dx.$ **10.** $\int \tan \frac{1}{2}x \, dx.$ **11.** $\int 10^{4x} \, dx.$ **12.** $\int e^{3+5t} \, dt.$

13. $\int \sec^2 (1 + x) \, dx.$ **14.** $\int \cos^3 u \sin u \, du.$ **15.** $\int_{-\pi}^{3\pi/2} \sin \frac{1}{2}x \, dx.$

16. $\int \cot^2 2x \, dx.$ **17.** $\int_{-\pi/2}^{\pi} \cos^2 3x \, dx.$ **18.** $\int \tan^2 4x \, dx.$

19. $\int (e^{2x} + 3)^5 e^{2x} \, dx.$ **20.** $\int (\ln x)^2 (x^{-1} \, dx).$ **21.** $\int_{-2}^{1} 2x^2 e^{-x^3} \, dx.$

22. $\int e^{\sin 3x} \cos 3x \, dx.$ **23.** $\int e^{4 \ln x} (2x^5 + 3) dx.$

24. $\int \dfrac{dt}{1 + 121t^2}.$ **25.** $\int \dfrac{dx}{49 - 9x^2}.$ **26.** $\int_{-2\sqrt{3}/3}^{2/3} \dfrac{du}{\sqrt{16 - 9u^2}}.$

27. $\int_{-2\sqrt{3}/5}^{2/5} \dfrac{dx}{4 + 25x^2}.$ **28.** $\int \dfrac{\cos x \, dx}{\sqrt{\sin^2 x + 9}}.$ **29.** $\int \dfrac{(2x - 3)dx}{\sqrt{4 + 49x^2}}.$

30. $\int \dfrac{(x + 3)dx}{\sqrt{1 + 2x}}.$ **31.** $\int_{-4}^{2} \dfrac{(3x - 2)dx}{(9 - 4x)^{\frac{3}{2}}}.$ **32.** $\int \dfrac{(3x + 4)dx}{\sqrt{4x - x^2}}.$

33. $\int \dfrac{(2x^2 + 3x)dx}{x^2 + 16}.$ **34.** $\int \dfrac{dx}{\sqrt{5 - x^2 - 4x}}.$ **35.** $\int \dfrac{(13 - x)dx}{7x - 3 - 2x^2}.$

36. $\int x(2 + 3x)^{\frac{1}{3}} \, dx.$ **37.** $\int_{5}^{8} x\sqrt{3x + 1} \, dx.$ **38.** $\int (3 - 5z)^{-\frac{3}{2}} \, dz.$

39. $\int x \cos x \, dx.$ **40.** $\int x^3 \ln x \, dx.$ **41.** $\int \text{Arcsin } 2x \, dx.$

42. $\int_{1}^{-2} xe^{3x} \, dx.$ **43.** $\int e^{2x} \sin x \, dx.$ **44.** $\int x^2 \sin 2x \, dx.$

45. $\int \sin^4 2x \, dx.$ **46.** $\int \cot^3 x \sec^2 x \, dx.$ **47.** $\int \tan^4 y \sec^4 y \, dy.$

48. $\int \dfrac{dx}{1 + \cos 3x}.$ **49.** $\int \dfrac{\sin^2 x}{\cos^6 x} \, dx.$ **50.** $\int \dfrac{\cos x}{\tan x} \, dx.$

51. $\int \dfrac{\sqrt{u^2 - 9}}{u^2} \, du.$ **52.** $\int_{-2/3}^{2\sqrt{3}/3} \dfrac{dz}{z\sqrt{4 + 9z^2}}.$ **53.** $\int_{-1/2}^{\sqrt{2}/2} \dfrac{z^2 \, dz}{\sqrt{1 - z^2}}.$

54. $\int \dfrac{(4x - 3)dx}{(4 - x^2 + 2x)^{\frac{1}{2}}}.$ **55.** $\int \dfrac{(8x - 2)dx}{(4x^2 + 4x + 2)^{\frac{3}{2}}}.$

56. Find an equation for the curve in an xy-plane whose slope at any point (x, y) is $4/y$, if the curve passes through the point $(2, -3)$.

57. Find the general solution of $y''' = \sin 2x.$

58. If c is an arbitrary constant, find the differential equation of the family of curves with the equation $y^2 - 2x^2 = cx.$

59. Find the solution of $2y \, dx + x \, dy + 6 \, dx = 0$ where $x = 2$ when $y = 6.$

60. Find the general solution of $y(x + 2)dy = x(y + 3)dx$ in a form not involving logarithms.

★SUPPLEMENT FOR CHAPTER ELEVEN

61. A certain radioactive element has a half-life of 85 hours. How long does it take for 80% of a given number of atoms of the element to decay?

62. Find the area of the region in the xy-plane bounded by the loop of the curve

$$y^2 = x^2(2 - x).$$

63. The population of a colony of insects in an experiment is increasing at a time rate, at any instant, proportional to the number in the population at the instant. An initial population of 1000 grows to 1,500,000 at the end of 5 days. (*a*) Express the population as a function of the time measured in days from the instant when there are 1000 insects. (*b*) Find when there will be 4,000,000 insects.

64. Prove the following formulas in Table VII: (80) and then (82); (81) and then (83); (106)–(109); (53)–(56); (26).

65. By mathematical induction, prove that, if k is a positive integer,

$$\int_0^{\pi/2} \sin^k x\, dx = \int_0^{\pi/2} \cos^k x\, dx = \frac{1 \cdot 3 \cdot 5 \cdots (k - 1)}{2 \cdot 4 \cdot 6 \cdots k} \cdot \frac{\pi}{2}, \text{ if } k \text{ is even;}$$

$$= \frac{2 \cdot 4 \cdot 6 \cdots (k - 1)}{1 \cdot 3 \cdot 5 \cdots k}, \text{ if } k \text{ is odd and } k > 1.$$

66. Let the "*natural logarithm function* ln x," whose domain is all $x > 0$ be *defined* by

$$\ln x = \int_1^x \frac{dt}{t}. \tag{1}$$

Prove as many properties of ln x as occur to you in identifying "ln x" of (1) with "ln x" as introduced previously.

Hint. To calculate ln xy, use $\int_1^{xy} f(t)dt = \int_1^x f(t)dt + \int_x^{xy} f(t)dt.$

67. Prove that the function ln x of Problem 66 has an *inverse* and then define the function "**exp.** (**x**)" as this inverse. Also, prove that D_x exp. (x) = exp. (x).*

Note 1. As in Problems 66 and 67, the direct and inverse trigonometric functions can be introduced, starting with the definition

$$(-1 < x < 1) \qquad\qquad \text{Arcsin } x = \int_0^x \frac{dt}{\sqrt{1 - t^2}}.$$

Next, the sine function would be introduced as the inverse of the Arcsine function. The details of the complete development are rather elaborate.†

---

* For a more extensive study of exp. (x) and its identification with e^x, see page 188 in *Real Variables*, by J. M. H. Olmsted (New York: Appleton-Century-Crofts, Inc., 1959).

† See Olmsted, *op. cit.*, page 192.

CHAPTER TWELVE

Advanced Topics in Plane Analytic Geometry*

115. DISTANCE BETWEEN A LINE AND A POINT

Let $h \geqq 0$ be the perpendicular distance between a point $P_1:(x_1, y_1)$ and a line $l:[Ax + By + C = 0]$, where at least one of A and B is *not zero*. We shall prove the following result:

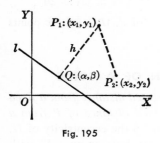

Fig. 195

$$h = \frac{|Ax_1 + By_1 + C|}{\sqrt{A^2 + B^2}}. \tag{1}$$

Proof. 1. Suppose that $AB \neq 0$. Then l has the slope $-A/B$. Let $Q:(\alpha, \beta)$ be the foot of the perpendicular from P_1 to l, as in Figure 195. Since $P_1Q \perp l$, line P_1Q has the slope B/A and the equation

$$y - y_1 = \frac{B}{A}(x - x_1), \text{ or}$$

$$B(x - x_1) = A(y - y_1). \tag{2}$$

2. Let $h = |\overline{P_1Q}|$. Then,

$$h^2 = (\alpha - x_1)^2 + (\beta - y_1)^2. \tag{3}$$

3. The equations of l and P_1Q are satisfied by $(x = \alpha, y = \beta)$, or

$$A\alpha + B\beta + C = 0 \quad and \quad B(\alpha - x_1) = A(\beta - y_1). \tag{4}$$

Then, $(\alpha - x_1) = A(\beta - y_1)/B$, and (3) gives

$$h^2 = (\beta - y_1)^2 \frac{A^2 + B^2}{B^2}. \tag{5}$$

4. On solving the equation at the right in (4) for α, substituting the result in the equation at the left in (4), and then solving it for β, we find

* Sections 115–116 will be used in Chapter 13 on Polar Coordinates. In the remainder of the text, in any plane or in space, a single unit will be used for distance in any direction, and for the number scale on any coordinate axis, except when specified otherwise.

$$\beta = \frac{A^2 y_1 - BC - ABx_1}{A^2 + B^2}, \quad and \quad \beta - y_1 = -\frac{B(Ax_1 + By_1 + C)}{A^2 + B^2}. \tag{6}$$

When (6) is used in (5), we obtain $\qquad h^2 = \frac{(Ax_1 + By_1 + C)^2}{A^2 + B^2},$

which proves (1) when neither A nor B is zero. Very simple details, which we shall omit, would prove (1) if $A = 0$ and $B \neq 0$, or if $B = 0$ and $A \neq 0$.

ILLUSTRATION 1. The distance between $l:[3x - 4y + 3 = 0]$ and $(3, -2)$ is

$$h = \frac{|\, 3(3) - 4(-2) + 3\,|}{\sqrt{3^2 + 4^2}} = 4.$$

EXERCISE 97

Find the distances between the given line and the given points.

1. $3x + 4y - 10 = 0$ and $(-3, 1)$; $(5, 3)$; $(0, 0)$.
2. $4x - 3y + 15 = 0$ and $(-1, -2)$; $(-2, 6)$; $(0, 0)$.
3. $8x + 15y = 0$ and $(3, 5)$; $(-2, -3)$.

Find the distance between the parallel lines, by starting with some convenient point on one of the lines.

4. $\begin{cases} 3x + 4y = 8. \\ 6x + 8y = 5. \end{cases}$ 5. $\begin{cases} 5x - 12y = 7. \\ 5x - 12y = 25. \end{cases}$ 6. $\begin{cases} 7x + 24y = 8. \\ 7x + 24y = 49. \end{cases}$

7. Find the distance between line AB and C, and the area of $\triangle ABC$, for the points $A:(-2, -2)$; $B:(2, 1)$; $C:(2, 6)$.

116. ECCENTRICITY–FOCUS–DIRECTRIX DEFINITION OF A CONIC

In a plane, let H be the locus of a point P whose *undirected distance from a fixed point T is equal to a constant $\eta > 0$ times the undirected distance of P from a fixed line D*, called a **directrix**, not through P. Let us call η the **eccentricity** of H. When $\eta = 1$, the description of H is the same as for a parabola on page 47, with T as the focus. We shall prove now that H is an *ellipse if $\eta < 1$*, and a *hyperbola if $\eta > 1$*, with T as a focus, where *ellipse* and *hyperbola* are defined on pages 49 and 53. Conversely, we shall prove that *every ellipse and hyperbola is of type H.*

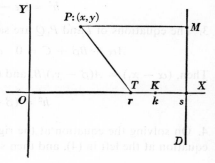

Fig. 196

Let coordinate axes be chosen so that T is the point $(r, 0)$ and D is the line $x = s$, as in Figure 196. Let $P:(x, y)$ be any point in the plane, with MP perpendicular to D. From (5) on page 5, $|\overline{MP}| = |x - s|$. Then, P is on H *if and only if*

$$(\overline{TP})^2 = \eta^2 (\overline{MP})^2, \quad or$$

$$(x - r)^2 + y^2 = \eta^2 (x - s)^2, \quad or$$

$$x^2(1 - \eta^2) + y^2 + 2x(\eta^2 s - r) + (r^2 - \eta^2 s^2) = 0. \tag{1}$$

Case I; $\eta < 1$. *To prove that* (1) *represents an ellipse with T as a focus and, conversely, that any ellipse with center at the origin in an xy-plane has an equation* (1).

1. Suppose that the axes are located so that $0 < r < s$, as in Figure 196 (or, $s < r < 0$). Then, by moving the y-axis to the left, or right, we can locate the origin so that $r = \eta^2 s$, because $\eta < 1$. Then, (1) becomes

$$x^2(1 - \eta^2) + y^2 = \eta^2 s^2 - r^2. \tag{2}$$

Since $\eta < 1$, there is a point $K{:}(k, 0)$ on H where $r < k < s$ (thus, if $\eta = \frac{1}{2}$, then k would be $\frac{1}{3}$ of the way from r to s).

2. In (2), $(1 - \eta^2) > 0$. Hence, also, $\eta^2 s^2 - r^2 > 0$ because the left-hand side of (2) is *positive* if $x = k$ and $y = 0$. On multiplying in (2) by $(\eta^2 s^2 - r^2)/(1 - \eta^2)$, we obtain $\qquad\qquad b^2 x^2 + a^2 y^2 = a^2 b^2$, *where* $\qquad\qquad\qquad$ (3)

$$a^2 = \frac{\eta^2 s^2 - r^2}{1 - \eta^2}; \quad b^2 = \eta^2 s^2 - r^2; \quad r = \eta^2 s. \tag{4}$$

In (4), $a > 0$, $b > 0$, and $a^2 > b^2$ because $1 - \eta^2 < 1$. Let $c = \sqrt{a^2 - b^2}$. Then, from (4), we find that $c^2 = a^2 \eta^2$, or $c = a\eta$; $s = r/\eta^2$, and

$$c^2 = \frac{\eta^4 s^2 - r^2 \eta^2}{1 - \eta^2} = \left(\frac{\eta^4 r^2}{\eta^4} - r^2 \eta^2\right) \cdot \frac{1}{1 - \eta^2}, \text{ or} \tag{5}$$

$c^2 = r^2$ and $c = r$. Hence, from (3), and (8) on page 51, locus H is an *ellipse* with foci $(\pm c, 0)$, or $(\pm r, 0)$, so that T is one of the two foci of the ellipse. If we had arranged to have $s < r < 0$, we would have obtained (3) and (4) again, with T as the other focus, $(- c, 0)$.

3. (*Converse for Case I*). Let W be an ellipse with center at the origin and foci on the x-axis, $b^2 x^2 + a^2 y^2 = a^2 b^2$ where $a > b$. Consider (4) as a system of equations for determining $(\eta > 0, r, s)$ with a and b known and $a > b$. Let $c^2 = a^2 - b^2$. Then, with details similar to those leading to (5), it is found that (4) has the following two solutions for (η, r, s):

$$\left(\eta = \frac{c}{a}, r = c, s = \frac{a^2}{c}\right) \quad and \quad \left(\eta = \frac{c}{a}, r = -c, s = -\frac{a^2}{c}\right). \tag{6}$$

Hence, by the details leading to (4), any ellipse $b^2 x^2 + a^2 y^2 = a^2 b^2$ is a special case of locus H, with two different choices for T and D, as given by r and s in (6), and with T as a focus of the ellipse. In (6), $s = \pm a/\eta$.

Case II; $\eta > 1$. We first consider the locus H with r and s chosen so that $0 < s < r$ (or, $r < s < 0$) and locate the origin so that $r = \eta^2 s$. Then, (1) becomes

$$b^2 x^2 - a^2 y^2 = a^2 b^2,$$

where we have

$$r = \eta^2 s; \quad a^2 = \frac{r^2 - \eta^2 s^2}{\eta^2 - 1}; \quad b^2 = r^2 - \eta^2 s^2, \tag{7}$$

and $r^2 - \eta^2 s^2 > 0$. With $c = \sqrt{a^2 + b^2}$, we may verify that $c = a\eta = r$. Hence, H is a hyperbola with center $(0, 0)$ and foci $(\pm r, 0)$, where $T{:}(r, 0)$ is one of the foci.

Conversely, let any hyperbola $a^2x^2 - b^2y^2 = a^2b^2$ be given, with $c = \sqrt{a^2 + b^2}$. If we consider r, s, and $\eta > 0$ as unknown numbers, (7) has the solution $\eta = c/a$, with $(r = c, s = a/\eta)$ or with $(r = -c, s = -a/\eta)$. Hence, every hyperbola is a special case of H, with two different choices for T and D, and with T as a focus of the hyperbola.

Our discussion has shown that the following definition is equivalent to the three separate definitions previously given for the nondegenerate conics (with an exception relating to circles, as mentioned later).

Definition I. *A **conic section** is the locus of a point P whose undirected distance from a fixed point F, called the **focus**, is equal to a constant $\eta > 0$ times the undirected distance of P from a fixed line D, called the **directrix**, which does not go through F. The constant η is referred to as the **eccentricity** of the conic, which is called an ellipse if $0 < \eta < 1$, a parabola if $\eta = 1$, and a hyperbola if $\eta > 1$.*

EXAMPLE 1. Use Definition I to obtain the equation of the hyperbola with $\eta = 2$, focus $F:(-8, 0)$, and corresponding directrix $D:[x = -2]$.

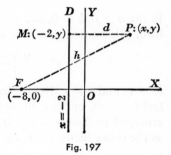

Solution. Let $P:(x, y)$ be any point, with d as the absolute value of the distance of P from D, and h as the length of PF, as illustrated in Figure 197. Then, P is on the hyperbola if and only if $h = 2d$, which is equivalent to $h^2 = 4d^2$, or

$$(x + 8)^2 + y^2 = 4(x + 2)^2, \text{ or}$$
$$3x^2 - y^2 = 48.$$

Fig. 197

From (6) for the ellipse, and corresponding items for the hyperbola, we have the following results, illustrated in Figures 198 and 199, respectively. In either case, there are two foci and corresponding directrices.

Ellipse: $b^2x^2 + a^2y^2 = a^2b^2$; $\eta = c/a$ *where* $c = \sqrt{a^2 - b^2}$.   (8)

Hyperbola: $b^2x^2 - a^2y^2 = a^2b^2$; $\eta = c/a$ *where* $c = \sqrt{a^2 + b^2}$.   (9)

$$\begin{cases} focus \quad (a\eta, 0) \quad with\ directrix \quad x = a/\eta; \\ focus \quad (-a\eta, 0) \quad with\ directrix \quad x = -a/\eta. \end{cases} \quad (10)$$

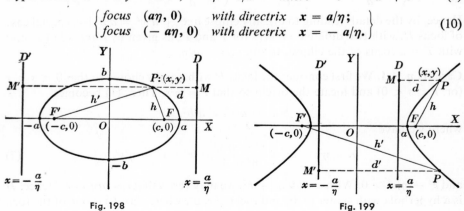

Fig. 198   Fig. 199

ILLUSTRATION 1. Figure 198 shows the ellipse $b^2x^2 + a^2y^2 = a^2b^2$ with indication of the foci and corresponding directrices as given by (10), with $c = a\eta$. Figure 199 exhibits corresponding items for the hyperbola $b^2x^2 - a^2y^2 = a^2b^2$. In either figure, $h^2 = \eta^2d^2$ and $h'^2 = \eta^2d'^2$ where $h' = |\overline{M'P}|$.

Note 1. We ruled out the case $\eta = 0$ in discussing H, because then T would be the only point on H. Now, for the case of an ellipse, adopt the viewpoint that a *shape constant* η, called the *eccentricity*, is *defined outright* by $\eta = c/a$, without any discussion of H. Then, $\eta = 0$ means that $c^2 = a^2 - b^2 = 0$, or $a = b$, so that the ellipse is a circle. From this viewpoint, a circle thus is described as an ellipse with eccentricity zero. In any case, if η is near zero then a is near b, and the ellipse has a shape close to that of a circle.

EXERCISE 98

Graph the equation, showing each focus and directrix.

1. $4x^2 + 25y^2 = 400.$ **2.** $9x^2 + 4y^2 = 36.$ **3.** $y^2 = -8x.$

4. $\dfrac{x^2}{16} - \dfrac{y^2}{4} = 1.$ **5.** $\dfrac{y^2}{25} - \dfrac{x^2}{144} = 1.$ **6.** $x^2 = 6y.$

Use the locus method of Example 1 on page 316 to derive the equation of the conic.

7. $F{:}(0, 3); D{:}[y = 12]; \eta = \frac{1}{2}.$ **8.** $F{:}(-9, 0); D{:}[x = -4]; \eta = \frac{3}{2}.$

9. $F{:}(3, 1); D{:}[x = 8]; \eta = \frac{2}{3}.$ **10.** $F{:}(3, 1); D{:}[x = 8]; \eta = \frac{3}{2}.$

11. $F{:}(2, -3); D{:}[y = 1]; \eta = 3.$ **12.** $F{:}(2, -4); D{:}[y = 2]; \eta = \frac{1}{2}.$

13. $F{:}(-3, 4); D{:}[x - 2y + 2 = 0]; \eta = \frac{1}{2}.$

14. $F{:}(4, -1); D{:}[x - 2y - 3 = 0]; \eta = 2.$

★*By use of a standard form and* (10) *on page* 316, *find the equation of the ellipse or hyperbola with axes along OX and OY which satisfies the data.*

15. *Ellipse:* vertices $(\pm 6, 0)$; one directrix is the line $x = 18.$

16. *Hyperbola:* vertices $(0, \pm 12)$; one directrix is the line $y = 9.$

17. Foci $(0, \pm 4)$; directrices $y = \pm 9.$ **18.** Foci $(\pm 8, 0)$; directrices $x = \pm 2.$

19. Foci $(\pm 2, 0)$; eccentricity 2.   **20.** Foci $(0, \pm 4)$; eccentricity $\frac{3}{4}.$

★117. TRANSFORMATION BY ROTATION OF AXES

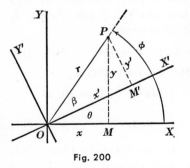

Fig. 200

Let the axes of an xy-system of coordinates be rotated about the origin through an angle θ, positive or negative, to give a new $x'y'$-system, in Figure 200. Let P be any point, with original coordinates (x, y) and new coordinates (x', y'). Then, we shall prove that

$$\begin{cases} x = x' \cos \theta - y' \sin \theta, & (1) \\ y = x' \sin \theta + y' \cos \theta; & (2) \end{cases}$$

$$\begin{cases} x' = x \cos \theta + y \sin \theta, & (3) \\ y' = -x \sin \theta + y \cos \theta. & (4) \end{cases}$$

Proof. 1. Let the projection of P on OX be M and on OX' be M', and let the length of OP be r. Let β be the angle with vertex at O generated by counterclockwise rotation from OX' to OP. Let ϕ be the angle with vertex at O generated by rotating OX first to the position OX', and then OX' to the position OP through the angle β. Thus, we have $\phi = \theta + \beta$.

2. From the definitions of the sine and cosine,

$$x = r \cos \phi; \quad y = r \sin \phi; \tag{5}$$

$$x' = r \cos \beta; \quad y' = r \sin \beta. \tag{6}$$

Since $\phi = \theta + \beta$, from (5) and the addition formulas on page 679,

$$x = r \cos (\theta + \beta) = r \cos \theta \cos \beta - r \sin \theta \sin \beta; \tag{7}$$

$$y = r \sin (\theta + \beta) = r \sin \theta \cos \beta + r \cos \theta \sin \beta. \tag{8}$$

On using (6) in (7), we obtain

$$r \cos \theta \cos \beta = (r \cos \beta) \cos \theta = x' \cos \theta, \text{ and}$$

$$r \sin \theta \sin \beta = (r \sin \beta) \sin \theta = y' \sin \theta.$$

Then (7) gives (1). Similarly, from (8) we obtain (2).

3. To prove (3) and (4), think of (x', y') as the *original* coordinates. Then, we obtain the xy-system by rotating the axes of the $x'y'$-system through the angle $- \theta$. Hence, we may obtain expressions for x' and y' in terms of x and y by using (1) and (2) with x and x', and y and y' interchanged, and θ replaced by $- \theta$. From (1), since $\cos (- \theta) = \cos \theta$ and $\sin (- \theta) = - \sin \theta$,

$$x' = x \cos (- \theta) - y \sin (- \theta) = x \cos \theta + y \sin \theta.$$

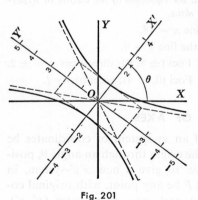

Fig. 201

Thus, (3) is obtained. Similarly, we may establish (4).

EXAMPLE 1. Transform the following equation by rotating axes through the angle θ where $0° < \theta < 90°$ and $\tan \theta = \frac{4}{3}$:

$$4x^2 + 24xy + 11y^2 = 20. \tag{9}$$

Solution. 1. From a right triangle with legs 4 and 3, we find $\cos \theta = \frac{3}{5}$ and $\sin \theta = \frac{4}{5}$. Hence, (1) and (2) become

$$x = \tfrac{1}{5}(3x' - 4y'); \quad y = \tfrac{1}{5}(4x' + 3y'). \tag{10}$$

2. On using (10) in (9), we obtain

$$\tfrac{4}{25}(3x' - 4y')^2 + \tfrac{24}{25}(3x' - 4y')(4x' + 3y') + \tfrac{11}{25}(4x' + 3y')^2 = 20; \text{ or}$$

$$20x'^2 - 5y'^2 = 20 \quad or \quad \frac{x'^2}{1} - \frac{y'^2}{4} = 1. \tag{11}$$

3. Hence, the locus of (9) is the hyperbola (11). To graph (11) in Figure 201, recall that $\tan \theta = \frac{4}{3}$. Construct OX' through O with slope $\frac{4}{3}$, and OY'. The hyperbola is sketched on the $x'y'$-system as usual, with $(x' = \pm 1, y' = 0)$ as vertices, and the corners of the associated rectangle at $(x' = \pm 1, y' = \pm 2)$.

Note 1. Observe that transformation of an equation of degree n in x and y by a rotation of axes *does not alter the degree* of the equation, because (1), (2), (3), and (4) are *linear* in the variables. On recalling the similar fact about *translation* of axes we arrive at the following result:

Transformation of an equation in x and y of degree n by any succession of translations or rotations of axes does not alter the degree of the equation.

★118. REMOVAL OF xy TERM BY ROTATION OF AXES

Consider the general equation of the 2d degree where $B \neq 0$:

$$Ax^2 + 2Bxy + Cy^2 + 2Dx + 2Ey + F = 0. \tag{1}$$

If we rotate axes through an angle θ to obtain an $x'y'$-system, then

$$\begin{cases} x = x' \cos \theta - y' \sin \theta, & (2) \\ y = x' \sin \theta + y' \cos \theta. & (3) \end{cases}$$

Substitution of (2) and (3) in (1) changes (1) to

$$A'x'^2 + 2B'x'y' + C'y'^2 + 2D'x' + 2E'y' + F = 0. \tag{4}$$

Since (2) and (3) are *linear* in x' and y', the terms of the 2d degree in (4) arise by transformation of the terms of the 2d degree in (1).

Theorem I. *If $B \neq 0$, rotation of axes through an angle θ will remove the xy term in equation* (1) *if θ satisfies the equation*

$$\cot 2\theta = \frac{A - C}{2B}. \tag{5}$$

Proof. 1. Let the functions f and f_1 be defined as follows:

$$f(x, y) = Ax^2 + 2Bxy + Cy^2; \quad f_1(x', y') = A'x'^2 + 2B'x'y' + C'y'^2.$$

Then, by use of (2) and (3), $f(x, y)$ transforms into $f_1(x', y')$, where

$$\left. \begin{aligned} f_1(x', y') &= A(x' \cos \theta - y' \sin \theta)^2 \\ &+ 2B(x' \cos \theta - y' \sin \theta)(x' \sin \theta + y' \cos \theta) + C(x' \sin \theta + y' \cos \theta)^2. \end{aligned} \right\} \tag{6}$$

2. Hence, in (4), $2B'x'y'$ represents all terms in $x'y'$ on the right in (6). On collecting terms in $x'y'$ in (6), we find that

$$2B' = 2(C - A) \sin \theta \cos \theta + 2B(\cos^2 \theta - \sin^2 \theta), \quad or \tag{7}$$

$$2B' = (C - A) \sin 2\theta + 2B \cos 2\theta. \tag{8}$$

Therefore, $B' = 0$ if $2B \cos 2\theta = (A - C) \sin 2\theta.$ (9)

On dividing by $2B \sin 2\theta$ in (9), we obtain (5).

Note 1. In (5), we may choose θ so that $0° < 2\theta \leq 90°$ if $\cot 2\theta \geq 0$, and $90° < 2\theta < 180°$ if $\cot 2\theta < 0$. Hence, in all cases, we may select θ so that $0° < \theta < 90°$.

Note 2. From (VIII) on page 679, recall that, with $0° < \theta < 90°$,

$$\cos \theta = \sqrt{\frac{1 + \cos 2\theta}{2}}; \quad \sin \theta = \sqrt{\frac{1 - \cos 2\theta}{2}}. \tag{10}$$

We use (10) to obtain $\cos \theta$ and $\sin \theta$ from (5).

EXAMPLE 1. Remove the xy term from $4x^2 + 24xy + 11y^2 = 20$ by a rotation of axes.

Solution. 1. From (5), $\cot 2\theta = -\frac{7}{24}.$ (11)

2. Then, $90° < 2\theta < 180°$. From a right triangle with legs 7 and 24, we find $\cos 2\theta = -\frac{7}{25}$. From (10), $\cos \theta = \frac{3}{5}$ and $\sin \theta = \frac{4}{5}$. We use (2) and (3), and transform the original equation, as in Example 1, page 318; the result is

$$20x'^2 - 5y'^2 = 20,$$

whose graph, a hyperbola, is in Figure 201, page 318.

For any value of θ, it can be proved (see Problem 11 in Exercise 99) that the coefficients A, B, and C in (1) and the new coefficients A', B', and C' in (4) satisfy

$$B^2 - AC = B'^2 - A'C'; \quad A + C = A' + C'. \tag{12}$$

Hence, we say that each of $(B^2 - AC)$ and $(A + C)$ is an **invariant** *under rotation of axes.* Each of these expressions is an invariant also *under translation of axes,* because such a transformation does not alter the coefficients of terms of the 2d degree in the variables. We may use (12) to check our details in rotating axes to obtain (4) for any equation (1). Thus, in the equation of Example 1, $B^2 - AC = 100$ and $A + C = 15$; in the transformed equation, $A' = 20$, $B' = 0$, and $C' = -5$; $B'^2 - A'C' = 100$ and $A' + C' = 15$, which checks.

★EXERCISE 99

Remove the xy term by a rotation of axes, and check by use of (12) on this page. Graph the final equation with both sets of axes shown.

1. $5x^2 - 6xy + 5y^2 = 32.$ **2.** $5x^2 + 5y^2 + 26xy = 72.$ **3.** $2xy = -9.$

4. $9x^2 + 24xy + 16y^2 + 40x - 30y = 0.$ **5.** $y^2 - 6xy - 7x^2 = 8.$

6. $16x^2 - 24xy + 9y^2 + 90x + 120y = 0.$ **7.** $4x^2 - 4xy + y^2 = 45.$

8. $17x^2 + 12xy + 8y^2 = 20.$ **9.** $11x^2 - 6xy + 19y^2 = 20.$

10. $2xy = k^2$, where $k > 0.$

11. From (6) on page 319, obtain expressions for A', B', and C'. Compute $(B'^2 - A'C')$ and $(A' + C')$ to verify (12) above. Simplicity is gained if $\sin 2\theta$ and $\cos 2\theta$ are introduced where appropriate.

★119. REMOVAL OF LINEAR TERMS BY A TRANSLATION OF AXES

The translation of axes defined by

$$x = x' + h \quad and \quad y = y' + k, \tag{1}$$

when applied to $Ax^2 + 2Bxy + Cy^2 + 2Dx + 2Ey + F = 0, \tag{2}$

transforms (2) into

$$Ax'^2 + 2Bx'y' + Cy'^2 + 2D'x' + 2E'y' + F' = 0, \tag{3}$$

where the coefficients of the terms of the 2d degree are the same as in (2). If h and k are chosen so that $D' = E' = 0$ in (3), we say that the translation (1) has *removed the linear terms.* If we use (1) in (2) to obtain (3), we find

$$F' = Ah^2 + 2Bhk + Ck^2 + 2Dh + 2Ek + F; \tag{4}$$

$$D' = Ah + Bk + D; \quad E' = Bh + Ck + E. \tag{5}$$

Hence, the transformed equation (3) will involve no linear terms in x', y' in case $D' = E' = 0$, which gives

$$\begin{cases} Ah + Bk + D = 0, \text{ and} & (6) \\ Bh + Ck + E = 0. & (7) \end{cases}$$

Then, the usual test shows that the $x'y'$-origin is a *center of symmetry* for (3), or the point $(x = h, y = k)$ is a center for (2), if the graph of (2) is real. We call [(6), (7)] *the equations for the center* even though the graph may be imaginary; any reference to a *center* will mean a point (h, k) satisfying [(6), (7)]. If

$$B^2 - AC \neq 0,$$

on solving [(6), (7)] we obtain $\qquad h = \dfrac{BE - CD}{AC - B^2}; \quad k = \dfrac{BD - AE}{AC - B^2}. \tag{8}$

This proves the following result:

If $B^2 - AC \neq 0$, the locus of (2) has a unique center. (9)

System [(6), (7)] may be inconsistent, and then there is no center for (2). Or, the system may have infinitely many solutions, each of which is a center. In either of these cases, $B^2 - AC = 0$.

★120. REDUCTION OF EQUATIONS OF SECOND DEGREE

The following procedure applies to the equation

$$Ax^2 + 2Bxy + Cy^2 + 2Dx + 2Ey + F = 0, \tag{1}$$

where not all of A, B, and C are zero. If (1) has a real locus, the Summary leads to a final system of coordinates where the locus is symmetric to at least one coordinate axis. The new origin is at a *center* for the locus, if there is a center, and at the *vertex* of the locus if it is a parabola.

Summary. *For simplification of an equation of the* 2d *degree:*

1. $B^2 - AC \neq 0$: *find the center; remove any linear terms by translating axes to the center as a new origin; then rotate axes to remove any xy term.*

2. $B^2 - AC = 0$: *rotate axes to remove any xy term; then, after completing a square, translate axes to change to an equation with at most one linear term.*

EXAMPLE 1. Simplify the equation by transformation of coordinates:

$$8x^2 + 4xy + 5y^2 + 28x - 2y + 20 = 0. \tag{2}$$

Solution. 1. We find $A = 8$, $B = 2$, $C = 5$, and $B^2 - AC = -36 \neq 0$. Hence, (2) has a unique center (h, k). By use of [(6), (7)] of Section 119, we obtain $(h = -2, k = 1)$. Then, we remove the linear terms in (2) by translating axes to the new origin $O':(x = -2, y = 1)$, by the equations

$$x = x' - 2; \quad y = y' + 1. \tag{3}$$

The new equation found by using (3) in (2) is as follows:

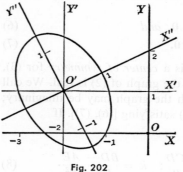

Fig. 202

$$8x'^2 + 4x'y' + 5y'^2 = 9. \tag{4}$$

2. To remove the term in $x'y'$ in (4), by the method of Section 118, rotate the $x'y'$-axes through an angle θ where $\cot 2\theta = \frac{3}{4}$. Then $\cos 2\theta = \frac{3}{5}$; $\cos \theta = 2/\sqrt{5}$; $\sin \theta = 1/\sqrt{5}$. With the new coordinates labeled x'' and y'',

$$x' = \frac{2x'' - y''}{\sqrt{5}}; \quad y' = \frac{x'' + 2y''}{\sqrt{5}}. \tag{5}$$

On using (5) in (4), we obtain the ellipse

$$\frac{x''^2}{1} + \frac{y''^2}{\frac{9}{4}} = 1.$$

3. To draw the graph in Figure 202, first indicate $O'X'$ and $O'Y'$ through the point $O':(x = -2, y = 1)$; from $\sin \theta/\cos \theta$, obtain $\tan \theta = \frac{1}{2}$ from Step 2; construct $O'X''$ as the line through O' with slope $\frac{1}{2}$, and $O'Y''$ perpendicular to $O'X''$; draw the ellipse with center at O', semi-major axis $\frac{3}{2}$ along $O'Y''$, and semi-minor axis 1.

EXAMPLE 2. Simplify by transformation of coordinates:

$$16x^2 - 24xy + 9y^2 + 100x - 200y + 100 = 0. \tag{6}$$

Solution. 1. We find $A = 16$, $B = -12$, $C = 9$, and $B^2 - AC = 0$. Hence, we shall remove the xy term by rotating the axes through an angle θ where $\cot 2\theta = -\frac{7}{24}$. Then, $\cos 2\theta = -\frac{7}{25}$; $\cos \theta = \frac{3}{5}$; $\sin \theta = \frac{4}{5}$. With new coordinates labeled (x', y'), from page 317 we obtain

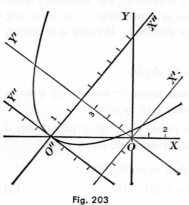

Fig. 203

$$x = \tfrac{1}{5}(3x' - 4y'); \quad y = \tfrac{1}{5}(4x' + 3y'). \tag{7}$$

Use (7) in (6):

$$25y'^2 - 200y' = 100x' - 100. \tag{8}$$

2. Divide by 25 and complete a square:

$$y'^2 - 8y' + 16 = 4x' + 12, \; or$$
$$(y' - 4)^2 = 4(x' + 3). \tag{9}$$

3. Transform (9) by translating the coordinate axes to the new origin

$$O'':(x' = -3, y' = 4),$$

by use of $\quad x'' = x' + 3; \quad y'' = y' - 4. \tag{10}$

On using (10) in (9), we obtain $y''^2 = 4x''$, whose locus is a parabola with vertex at O'' and axis along $O''X''$, given in Figure 203.

After the Summary is applied to (1), it can be verified as in Examples 1 and 2 that we obtain an equation of one of the following forms, corresponding to $B^2 - AC \neq 0$ and $B^2 - AC = 0$, respectively:

$$\left.\begin{array}{l} A'x''^2 + C'y''^2 = -F'; \\ A'x''^2 = -2E'y'' - F'; \quad C'y''^2 = -2D'x'' - F'. \end{array}\right\} \quad (11)$$

In the first equation in (11), we have $B' = 0$ and hence, from (12) on page 320, $-A'C' = B^2 - AC \neq 0$; then, by Theorem II on page 62, (1) represents an ellipse if $A'C' > 0$, or $B^2 - AC < 0$, etc. as in (13) and (14) below. In the second line in (11), we have $B' = C' = 0$, or $A' = B' = 0$, and

$$B^2 - AC = B'^2 - A'C' = 0,$$

while each of the corresponding loci in (11) represents a parabola, etc. as below in (12). Thus, we have proved the following result.

Theorem II. *The locus of any equation of the* 2d *degree in x and y is a conic, or is imaginary, with possibilities determined by the value of the* **discriminant** $(B^2 - AC)$, *as follows:*

$B^2 - AC = 0:$ *a parabola, two parallel lines, or imaginary.*   (12)

$B^2 - AC < 0:$ *an ellipse, a single point, or imaginary.*   (13)

$B^2 - AC > 0:$ *a hyperbola or two intersecting lines.*   (14)

Theorem III. (*Converse of Theorem II.*) *Any conic section in an xy-plane has an equation of the* 2d *degree in x and y.*

Proof. In the xy-plane, let a new $x'y'$-coordinate system be chosen with one axis parallel to an axis of symmetry of the conic, and with the same origin as the xy-system. By Theorem II on page 62, the conic has an equation of the 2d degree in x' and y'. Then, we may transform this equation to one in x and y by rotating axes to obtain the directions of the xy-axes. The final equation in x and y also will be of the 2d degree because the rotation does not alter the degree. This proves the theorem.

Note 1. We may call (1) the **general equation of a conic.**

Note 2. Each type of degenerate conic is associated with one of the non-degenerate conics in the references to $B^2 - AC$ in Theorem II. This fact, and other algebraic and geometric reasons which we shall not discuss, make it convenient to refer to two parallel lines, coincident or distinct, as a limiting case of a parabola; to a single point as a limiting case of an ellipse; to two intersecting lines as a limiting case of a hyperbola. Thus, if the locus of (1) is real, the locus is a parabola or limiting case of a parabola when $B^2 - AC = 0$; an ellipse or limiting case of an ellipse when $B^2 - AC < 0$; a hyperbola or a limiting case of a hyperbola when $B^2 - AC > 0$.

Note 3. Theorems II and III, as well as all preceding parts of this chapter, were developed on the basis of the assumption that the scale units were equal on the coordinate axes. In Problem 17 of the Supplement for this chapter, the interested student will have an opportunity to prove that Theorems II and III remain true in a system of rectangular coordinates having *unequal scale units on the axes.*

★EXERCISE 100

Compute $B^2 - AC$ for the equation and decide on the nature of its locus. Then, simplify the equation by transformations of coordinates and, if the locus is real, draw it in a figure showing all the coordinate axes used in the work.

1. $5x^2 + 6xy + 5y^2 - 38x - 42y + 93 = 0$.
2. $3x^2 + 10xy + 3y^2 - 14x - 2y - 13 = 0$.
3. $9x^2 - 24xy + 16y^2 + 50x - 150y + 225 = 0$.
4. $x^2 - 24xy - 6y^2 - 2x + 24y - 29 = 0$.
5. $x^2 - 4xy + 4y^2 + 10x\sqrt{5} - 10y\sqrt{5} + 5 = 0$.
6. $5x^2 + 6xy - 3y^2 + 2x - 18y - 7 = 0$.
7. $7x^2 + 48xy - 7y^2 - 82x + 76y - 17 = 0$.
8. $4x^2 - 4xy + y^2 - 20x - 40y + 100 = 0$.
9. $3x^2 + 10xy + 3y^2 - 8x + 8y - 16 = 0$.
10. $16x^2 + 24xy + 9y^2 + 20x + 15y - 50 = 0$.

Obtain the graph of the equation by use of calculus without rotating axes.

11. $2x^2 - 2xy + y^2 = 8$.   12. $3x^2 - 2xy + y^2 = 108$.

★121. ASYMPTOTES OF A HYPERBOLA

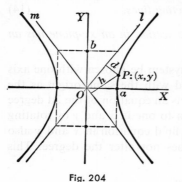

Fig. 204

Let $P:(x, y)$ be any point on the hyperbola, in Figure 204, with the equation

$$b^2x^2 - a^2y^2 = a^2b^2. \qquad (1)$$

Let the undirected distances of the point P from the asymptotes

$$l:[bx - ay = 0] \quad and \quad m:[bx + ay = 0]$$

be d and h, respectively. From (1) on page 313, we find that

$$d = \frac{|bx - ay|}{\sqrt{a^2 + b^2}}; \quad h = \frac{|bx + ay|}{\sqrt{a^2 + b^2}}. \qquad (2)$$

Hence, $$dh = \frac{|(bx - ay)(bx + ay)|}{a^2 + b^2} = \frac{|b^2x^2 - a^2y^2|}{a^2 + b^2}. \qquad (3)$$

Since $P:(x, y)$ is on (1), the numerator in (3) is equal to a^2b^2; thus,

$$d = \frac{a^2b^2}{h(a^2 + b^2)}; \quad h = \frac{a^2b^2}{d(a^2 + b^2)}. \qquad (4)$$

Suppose that $P:(x, y)$ is on the hyperbola in quadrant I. From (1),

$$y = \frac{b}{a}\sqrt{x^2 - a^2} \quad and \quad \frac{dy}{dx} = \frac{b^2x}{a^2y} = \frac{b}{a} \cdot \frac{x}{\sqrt{x^2 - a^2}}. \qquad (5)$$

Then $y \to \infty$ as $x \to \infty$, and $|\overline{OP}| \to \infty$. Also, from y' in (5), after both numerator and denominator are divided by x,

$$\lim_{x \to \infty} y' = \frac{b}{a} \left[\lim_{x \to \infty} \frac{1}{\sqrt{1 - a^2/x^2}} \right] = \frac{b}{a}, \tag{6}$$

because $\dfrac{a^2}{x^2} \to 0$ as $x \to \infty$. From (2), if $x \to \infty$ then $h \to \infty$, and (4) shows that $d \to 0$. Thus, if $|\overline{OP}| \to \infty$, with P on the hyperbola, the distance from P to l approaches zero; by (6), the slope of the hyperbola at P approaches the slope of l. Hence, l is an asymptote of the part of the curve in quadrant I. By symmetry, l and m are asymptotes for the curve in quadrants II, III, and IV.

Note 1. From (4), $dh = k$, where $k = a^2b^2/(a^2 + b^2)$. Thus, a hyperbola can be defined as *the locus of a point P:(x, y) for which the product of the undirected distances of P from two given lines (the asymptotes) is a constant.*

★122. MISCELLANEOUS LOCUS PROBLEMS

In finding the equation of a locus, it may be convenient to introduce *auxiliary parameters,* say k of them, which are related to the coordinates of the point P:(x, y) on the locus. Then, to obtain an equation involving only x, y, and any *constants* of the problem, we initially seek $(k + 1)$ equations relating x, y, and the parameters. This procedure is necessary because, as a rule, we would need k of the equations *to eliminate the k parameters.*

A **diameter** of a conic is defined as *the locus of the mid-points of a system (or family) of parallel chords.*

EXAMPLE 1. Find an equation for the diameter which bisects the chords with slope 3 for the ellipse

$$4x^2 + 9y^2 = 36. \tag{1}$$

Solution. 1. Any chord of slope 3 has the equation $y = 3x + h$, where h is a parameter. The coordinates (x_1, y_1) and (x_2, y_2) of the intersections of the chord and (1) satisfy the system of two equations

$$4x^2 + 9y^2 = 36 \quad and \quad y = 3x + h. \tag{2}$$

2. Eliminate y by use of $y = 3x + h$:

$$4x^2 + 9(3x + h)^2 = 36, \quad or \quad 85x^2 + 54hx + (9h^2 - 36) = 0. \tag{3}$$

The solutions of (3) are $x = x_1$ and $x = x_2$. By a theorem of algebra, the *sum* of the roots of $ax^2 + bx + c = 0$ is equal to $-b/a$. Hence, from (3),

$$x_1 + x_2 = -\tfrac{54}{85}h. \tag{4}$$

3. Let (X, Y) be the mid-point of the chord formed by $y = 3x + h$. Then, $Y = 3X + h$ and, by (4) on page 33, $X = \tfrac{1}{2}(x_1 + x_2)$, or

$$X = -\tfrac{27}{85}h, \quad or \quad h = -\tfrac{85}{27}X. \tag{5}$$

Hence, from $Y = 3X + h$ and (5), we obtain

$$Y = 3X - \tfrac{85}{27}X, \quad or \quad 27Y = -4X.$$

In (x, y) notation, the diameter has the equation $27y = -4x$.

★EXERCISE 101

Find an equation for the locus of a point $P:(x, y)$ which satisfies the given condition, and describe the locus.

1. P is the mid-point of an ordinate of $y^2 = 8x$.

Hint. An *ordinate* of the curve is a line segment perpendicular to OX, from OX to the curve. Similarly an *abscissa* of the curve is a line segment perpendicular to OY, from OY to the curve.

2. P is the mid-point of an ordinate of $25y^2 - 9x^2 = 225$.

3. P is the mid-point of an abscissa of $2x^2 + y^2 = 1$.

4. P is $\frac{1}{3}$ of the way, horizontally, from OY to $4x^2 - 9y^2 = 36$.

5. P is the mid-point of the line segment from $(0, 0)$ to a point on the ellipse
$$25x^2 + 9y^2 = 225.$$

6. The undirected distance of P from one fixed point is equal to 3 times the undirected distance of P from a second fixed point.

7. The sum of the squares of the distances of P from two fixed points is a constant.

8. The product of the undirected distances of P from the lines $y = mx$ and $y = -mx$ is a positive constant, k.

9. Find an equation for the diameter of $y^2 = 8x$ which bisects the chords having slope 2.

For the given conic, find an equation for the diameter which bisects the chords having slope m.

10. $y^2 = 2px$.   **11.** $b^2x^2 + a^2y^2 = a^2b^2$.   **12.** $b^2x^2 - a^2y^2 = a^2b^2$.

Note 1. If $u_1 = 0$ and $u_2 = 0$ are the equations of two conics, the family of conics (with one exception) through the intersections of the given conics has the equation $u_1 + ku_2 = 0$, where k is a parameter.

Find the equation of the conic through the intersections of the given conics and satisfying the given condition.

13. $x^2 - 2y^2 = 1$; $x^2 + 4y^2 = 25$; through $P:(1, 4)$.

14. $4x^2 + 9y^2 = 36$; $4y^2 - x^2 = 3$; through $P:(1, 0)$.

15. $x^2 + y^2 = 4$; $xy = 1$; a parabola, or limiting case of a parabola.

16. Find the equation of the conic which passes through the points $(0, 3)$, $(3, 2)$, $(1, 0)$, $(3, 0)$, and $(-1, -1)$.

Hint. Write the equations of two pairs of lines, where each pair passes through the first four points, and then a *single equation for each pair*. Consider each pair as a conic (degenerate), and obtain the conic through their intersections and the fifth point.

★SUPPLEMENT FOR CHAPTER TWELVE

17. Consider the graph of (1) on page 321 in an xy-plane where the scale unit on the x-axis is h inches and on the y-axis is k inches, with h and k not necessarily equal. Prove that Theorems II and III on page 323 remain true when $h \neq k$.

Hint. Apply the transformation $x' = hx$ and $y' = ky$, to obtain an $x'y'$-system where the scale units on the axes are both equal to one inch. By use of Theorems II and III for the corresponding $x'y'$-equation, prove the desired results.

18. Find the equation of the line, l, through the intersection of the lines $y - 2x + 4 = 0$ and $y + x = 2$, if the perpendicular distance from the origin to l is 1 unit.

19. Let $P_1:(x_1, y_1)$, $P_2:(x_2, y_2)$, and $P_3:(x_3, y_3)$ be the vertices of a triangle whose area is A. Prove that

$$A = \left| \frac{1}{2} \begin{vmatrix} x_1 & y_1 & 1 \\ x_2 & y_2 & 1 \\ x_3 & y_3 & 1 \end{vmatrix} \right|$$

20. Two diameters of an ellipse (or hyperbola) are said to be *conjugate diameters* if each bisects all chords of the curve which are parallel to the other diameter. For the ellipse $b^2x^2 + a^2y^2 = a^2b^2$, prove that, if m_1 is the slope of a diameter, the conjugate diameter exists and has slope m_2 where $m_1m_2 = -b^2/a^2$.

21. Prove that the sides of any parallelogram inscribed in an ellipse are parallel to a pair of conjugate diameters

22. Consider the graph of $x^2(a^2 + \lambda)^{-1} + y^2(b^2 + \lambda)^{-1} = 1$, where a and b are constants, with $b^2 < a^2$ and λ as a parameter. Discuss the nature of the locus or its nonexistence for all values of λ. Prove the following facts: Through every point (x_0, y_0) — with a few exceptions — there pass two conics of the system, one being an ellipse and the other a hyperbola. All conics of the system have the same foci. The two conics of the system through any point (x_0, y_0) intersect at right angles.

23. In a plane, points A, B, C, and D (distinct and no three in a line) are situated so that the lines AB and CD are perpendicular. Prove that the centers of all central conics through the points lie on a conic.

24. Let the equation of the tangent in Problem 20, page 120, be written $g(x, y, x_1, y_1) = 0$. If (x_1, y_1) is *not* on the conic, the line $g(x, y, x_1, y_1) = 0$ is called the **polar** of (x_1, y_1) with respect to the conic. If $P:(x_1, y_1)$ is on the conic, the polar of P is the tangent to the conic at P. Prove the following results, referring to any given conic: If point P_2 lies on the polar of P_1, then P_1 lies on the polar of P_2. If the polar of P_1 intersects the conic at P_2 and P_3, then P_1 is the intersection of the tangents to the conic at P_2 and P_3, respectively.

CHAPTER THIRTEEN

Derivatives, with Polar Coordinates

123. POLAR COORDINATES

In the plane, select a fixed point O, called the **pole,** and a fixed half-line or directed ray OI, called the **initial ray.** Let the whole line through OI be called the **polar axis,** drawn horizontal in the typical Figure 205, with OI directed to the right. Let P be a given point, not the pole. Let θ be any angle * whose initial side is OI and whose terminal side falls on the line OP. Let r be the corresponding value of the *directed distance* $\overline{OP}$, considered *positive* or *negative* according as P is on the terminal side of θ or on the extension of this side through O. Then, we call θ a **polar angle** for P, r the corresponding **radius vector** for P, and the pair $[r, \theta]$ a set of **polar coordinates** for P. The pole O is assigned

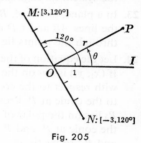

Fig. 205

the coordinates $[0, \theta]$, where θ may have *any* value. The notation $P{:}[r, \theta]$, with square brackets, will mean *"point P with polar coordinates r, θ,"* and is read simply "P, r, θ." To plot an assigned point $P{:}[r, \theta]$, lay off θ by rotation from the initial ray OI, and then locate P on the line through the terminal side of θ by use of the value of r. In applications of polar coordinates, *we cannot avoid using negative values for r.*

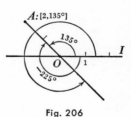

Fig. 206

> ILLUSTRATION 1. Figure 205 shows $M{:}[3, 120°]$ and $N{:}[-3, 120°]$. Figure 206 shows $A{:}[2, 135°]$; other coordinates for A are $[2, -225°]$ and $[-2, 315°]$.

A given set of polar coordinates $[r, \theta]$ locates *just one point P* with these coordinates. However, if θ, in degree measure, is any particular polar angle for P, then other possible polar angles are $(\theta + k \cdot 180°)$, where k may be any integer,

---

* Until otherwise specified, θ will be a symbol for an *angle*, not a *number*, as with trigonometric functions of angles in Note 4 of the Appendix. Thus, we may have $\theta = 45°$, or $\theta = \frac{1}{2}\pi$ radians. Later, we shall return to the viewpoint involved with trigonometric functions of numbers.

because the terminal side of any one of these angles falls on the line through OP. Thus, *P does not have a unique set of polar coordinates.* This fact causes peculiarities in the discussion of graphs in polar coordinates, as compared with the more simple situation in rectangular coordinates, where there is a one-to-one correspondence between sets of coordinates (x, y) and points P in an xy-plane.

Note 1. In the symbol P:[3, 5] where no indication of degrees is given, it is understood that $\theta = 5$ radians. In A:[2, $\frac{1}{2}\pi$], $\theta = \frac{1}{2}\pi$ radians.

Definition I. *Let the pair* [r, θ] *be interpreted as polar coordinates. Then, the graph of an equation* G(r, θ) = 0 *in an rθ-plane is the set of all points P such that there exists* **at least one set of coordinates** [r, θ] *for P satisfying* G(r, θ) = 0. *An equation for a locus in the rθ-plane is an equation* G(r, θ) = 0 *whose graph is the given locus.*

ILLUSTRATION 2. An equation for the circle with radius a and center at the pole, in Figure 207, is $r = a$. For any angle θ, P:[a, θ] is on the locus of $r = a$; as θ varies from 0° to 360°, P traces out the circle. Another equation for the circle is $r = -a$, because any point [$- a$, θ] also is on the circle. Thus, the equations $r = a$ and $r = -a$ have the same graph although they are not equivalent algebraically.

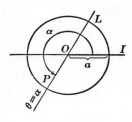

ILLUSTRATION 3. If an angle from OI to a line L through the pole is α, an equation for L is $\theta = \alpha$. Another equation for L is tan θ = tan α. Any point P:[a, α] is determined geometrically as one of the intersections of the circle $r = a$ and the line $\theta = \alpha$, as in Figure 207.

Fig. 207

ILLUSTRATION 4. The graph of the equation $\theta = \frac{1}{2}\pi$, or $\theta = \frac{3}{2}\pi$, is the whole line s perpendicular to the polar axis at the pole. We may call s the $\frac{1}{2}\pi$-line (or, the 90°-line). The polar axis has the equation $\theta = 0$, or $\theta = \pi$, or $\theta = 2\pi$, etc.

EXAMPLE 1. Graph: $$r = 4 \sin \theta. \qquad (1)$$

Solution. With degree measure used for θ, we substitute values of θ where $0° \leq \theta \leq 360°$, and compute solutions [r, θ] of (1). The graph, in Figure 208, is a circle (to be proved in Example 2, page 331). If P:[r, θ] is on the graph of (1), then P traces out the circle from the pole in the direction of the arrowheads, as θ varies from 0° to 180°. The points P obtained as θ varies from 180° to 360° repeat those just mentioned. Thus, P:[$- 2, 210°$] is the same as P:[2, 30°]. If we substitute any angle $\theta < 0°$ or $\theta \geq 360°$, we obtain a point which is the same as some point P:[r, θ] where $0° \leq \theta < 360°$, because sin θ is periodic, with the period 360°.

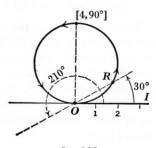

Fig. 208

$\theta =$	0°	30°	60°	90°	120°	150°	180°	210°	270°	330°	360°
$r =$	0	2	3.5	4	3.5	2	0	$- 2$	$- 4$	$- 2$	0

Note 2. Suppose that the domain of the variable θ consists of *angles*, expressed in degree measure, and assume that the function $f(\theta)$ is periodic with the period 360°, so that $f(\theta) = f(\theta \pm 360°)$ is an identity in θ. Then, if we graph $r = f(\theta)$ for $0° \leqq \theta \leqq 360°$, or for the angles θ on any interval of length 360°, we obtain all of the graph. Similarly, if the function $f(\theta)$ has the period 720°, we obtain all of the graph of $r = f(\theta)$ by use of $0° \leqq \theta \leqq 720°$. This feature was illustrated in Example 1.

Let a system of polar coordinates be given. Then, in Figure 209, introduce an xy-system of rectangular coordinates with the pole O as the origin, the polar axis as the x-axis, with its positive half along the initial ray OI, and the y-axis perpendicular to OI. Let the same unit of length be used for all distances in both systems. Any point P in the plane now has two sets of coordinates, (x, y) and $[r, \theta]$. The following relations are true, even when r is negative, except at points where a zero denominator causes rejection of tan θ.

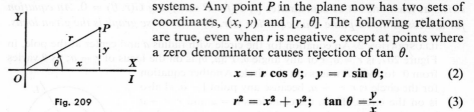

Fig. 209

$$x = r \cos \theta; \quad y = r \sin \theta; \qquad (2)$$

$$r^2 = x^2 + y^2; \quad \tan \theta = \frac{y}{x}. \qquad (3)$$

Whenever we consider rectangular and polar coordinates in the same problem, Figure 209 will apply, with relations (2) and (3).

ILLUSTRATION 5. To find (x, y) for $P:[r = 2, \theta = \frac{2}{3}\pi]$, use (2):

$$x = 2 \cos \tfrac{2}{3}\pi = -1;$$

$$y = 2 \sin \tfrac{2}{3}\pi = 2(\tfrac{1}{2}\sqrt{3}) = \sqrt{3}.$$

ILLUSTRATION 6. To obtain polar coordinates for the point $P:(-5, -12)$, we plot P in Figure 210. Then, from (3), $r^2 = 169$; $\tan \theta = \frac{12}{5} = 2.40$; if we take $r > 0$, θ is in quadrant III. From Table VI, $\tan 67.4° = 2.40$, and

$$\theta = 180° + 67.4° = 247.4°.$$

P has the polar coordinates $[13, 247.4°]$. Also, P has the coordinates $[-13, 67.4°]$, etc.

Fig. 210

If a given locus has the equation $f(x, y) = 0$, we obtain an equation $G(r, \theta) = 0$ for the locus by using (2) in $f(x, y) = 0$. If $G(r, \theta) = 0$ is a given equation for a locus, we obtain an equation $f(x, y) = 0$ for the locus by using (2) and (3) in $G(r, \theta) = 0$. In either case, we call $f(x, y) = 0$ and $G(r, \theta) = 0$ *equivalent equations* and each is said to be the *transformation* of the other into the corresponding system of coordinates. On account of the peculiarities of polar coordinates, this equivalence should be investigated with care in each special case. To study a locus, we use either $f(x, y) = 0$ or $G(r, \theta) = 0$, whichever offers the greater convenience.

ILLUSTRATION 7. To transform the circle $x^2 + y^2 = a^2$, with $a > 0$, into polar coordinates, use (2) and obtain $r^2 = a^2$, which is equivalent to $r = a$ and $r = -a$. The locus of each of these is the given circle.

ILLUSTRATION 8. The $r\theta$-equations of lines $x = a$ and $y = b$ become, respectively,

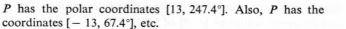

$$\boldsymbol{r \cos \theta = a} \quad \textit{and} \quad \boldsymbol{r \sin \theta = b}.$$

EXAMPLE 2. Prove that **$r = a \sin \theta$ is the equation of a circle.**

Solution. Suppose that $a > 0$. On multiplying both sides by r, we derive

$$r^2 = a(r \sin \theta).$$

By use of (2) and (3), we obtain the equivalent equation

$$x^2 + y^2 = ay \quad or \quad x^2 + (y - \tfrac{1}{2}a)^2 = \tfrac{1}{4}a^2.$$

Hence, the locus of $r = a \sin \theta$ is the circle with radius $\tfrac{1}{2}a$ and center $(0, \tfrac{1}{2}a)$, or polar coordinates $[\tfrac{1}{2}a, 90°]$. Notice that the multiplication by r at worst could have added just the locus of $r = 0$, the pole, to the original locus. However, $r = a \sin \theta$ is satisfied by $[r = 0, \theta = 0]$, or the pole is on the given locus. Thus, $r = a \sin \theta$ and $r^2 = ar \sin \theta$ are equivalent equations. Similarly, if $a < 0$, then $r = a \sin \theta$ represents a circle whose center is $[\tfrac{1}{2}a, 90°]$ and radius is $\tfrac{1}{2} \mid a \mid$.

Comment. Similarly, **$r = a \cos \theta$ represents a circle** with radius $\tfrac{1}{2} \mid a \mid$ and center $[\tfrac{1}{2}a, 0°]$.

EXAMPLE 3. Transform into polar coordinates:

$$x^2 + y^2 - 8y = 0. \tag{4}$$

Solution. By use of (2) and (3), we obtain

$$r^2 - 8r \sin \theta = 0, \quad or \quad r(r - 8 \sin \theta) = 0,$$

which is equivalent to $r = 0$ and $r = 8 \sin \theta$. The locus of $r = 0$ is just the pole O, and this point is met also as the point $[0, 0°]$ on the locus of the equation $r = 8 \sin \theta$. Hence, $r = 8 \sin \theta$ is the equation for the circle (4).

EXAMPLE 4. Transform into rectangular coordinates:

$$r = \frac{3}{2 - \cos \theta}. \tag{5}$$

Solution. 1. From (5) and then (2), $\qquad 2r - r \cos \theta = 3, \ or$

$$2r = 3 + x. \tag{6}$$

2. From (5), since $\mid \cos \theta \mid \leq 1$, we have $r > 0$ at each point $[r, \theta]$ satisfying (5). Hence, in (5), $r = + \sqrt{x^2 + y^2}$ and (6) is equivalent to

$$+ 2\sqrt{x^2 + y^2} = 3 + x. \tag{7}$$

On squaring both sides in (7), we obtain

$$4x^2 + 4y^2 = (3 + x)^2, \ or$$

$$3x^2 - 6x + 4y^2 = 9. \tag{8}$$

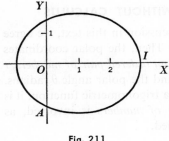

Fig. 211

The graph of (8) is the ellipse in Figure 211.

3. Since both sides of (7) were squared to obtain (8), the graph of (8) consists of the graph of (7) *and the graph, if any, of*

$$- 2\sqrt{x^2 + y^2} = 3 + x. \tag{9}$$

At each point (x, y) on the graph of (8) in Figure 211, we have $- 1 \leq x \leq 3$, so that $3 + x \geq 2$, and hence (x, y) cannot satisfy (9), where the left-hand side would be *negative*. Thus, (9) contributes *no points* to the graph of (8) or (5).

Comment. In Figure 211, notice that A has the coordinates $[\frac{3}{2}, \frac{3}{2}\pi]$, which satisfy (5), and also $[-\frac{3}{2}, \frac{1}{2}\pi]$ which do *not* satisfy (5), where $r > 0$ at all values of θ. This illustrates the fact that a point on the graph of $G(r, \theta) = 0$ may have various sets of coordinates which do *not* satisfy the equation (see "*at least one set*" in Definition I on page 329).

EXERCISE 102

Plot the point whose polar coordinates are shown, and give one other set of coordinates $[r, \theta]$ *for the point with* $0° \leq \theta \leq 360°$. *Also, find the rectangular coordinates of the point.*

1. $[3, 120°]$.   **2.** $[2, 240°]$.   **3.** $[-1, 270°]$.   **4.** $[2, -\frac{1}{4}\pi]$.

5. $[3, \frac{5}{4}\pi]$.   **6.** $[-1, \pi]$.   **7.** $[-2, \frac{3}{4}\pi]$.   **8.** $[3, \frac{5}{6}\pi]$.

Plot the point with the given rectangular coordinates and find two sets of polar coordinates for it. Use Table VI if necessary.

9. $(1, 1)$.   **10.** $(-2, 2)$.   **11.** $(1, \sqrt{3})$.   **12.** $(-\sqrt{3}, 1)$.

13. $(2\sqrt{3}, -2)$.   **14.** $(15, -8)$.   **15.** $(-4, -3)$.

First transform into rectangular coordinates and then graph.

16. $r = 5$.   **17.** $r = -4$.   **18.** $\tan \theta = 1$.

19. $r \cos \theta = 3$.   **20.** $r \sin \theta = -2$.   **21.** $r = 6 \sin \theta$.

22. $r = -4 \cos \theta$.   **23.** $r = -2 \sin \theta$.   **24.** $r = a \cos \theta$.

25. $r = \dfrac{2}{1 - \sin \theta}$.   **26.** $r = \dfrac{4}{1 + 2 \sin \theta}$.   **27.** $r = \dfrac{2}{1 - \frac{1}{2} \cos \theta}$.

Transform the equation into polar coordinates, in simple form.

28. $y = 3x$.   **29.** $x - 5 = 0$.   **30.** $x^2 + y^2 = -6y$.

Plot the locus. Make up a table of solutions $[r, \theta]$ *for Problems 36 and 37.*

31. $r = 3$.   **32.** $\theta = \frac{1}{4}\pi$.   **33.** $\theta = -\frac{2}{3}\pi$.   **34.** $r = -2$.

35. $\sin \theta = \frac{1}{2}$.   **36.** $r = 4 \cos \theta$.   **37.** $r = -2 \sin \theta$.

38. Give *two* equations of the form $\theta = c$, where c is a constant, θ is the measure of an angle in radians, and the graph of each equation forms the graph in Problem 35.

39. What is the graph of $\tan \theta = 1$? Of $\tan \theta = k$, where k is any constant?

124. GRAPHING IN POLAR COORDINATES, WITHOUT CALCULUS

Hereafter, when polar coordinates occur in any discussion in this text, we agree that the polar angle will be measured in radians.* Then, the polar coordinates $[r, \theta]$ for any point P will be considered simply as *an ordered pair of numbers,* r and θ, specifying that P has the polar distance r, and the polar angle θ radians. With this viewpoint, if θ occurs in the argument of a trigonometric function, it is understood that *a standard trigonometric function of numbers* is involved, as employed in calculus, except when otherwise specified.

---

* This does not rule out the possibility that, in graphing an equation $G(r, \theta) = 0$, the student may desire to make up a table of solutions where the equivalent in degree measure is listed in place of θ radians.

The typical equation in r and θ which we shall graph is one where we may commence by solving for r in terms of θ to obtain one or more relations of the form $r = f(\theta)$.

In Figure 212, the point $P:[r, \theta]$ is symmetric to $Q:[-r, \theta]$ or $Q:[r, \theta + \pi]$, with respect to the pole; to $R:[r, -\theta]$ or $R:[-r, \pi - \theta]$, with respect to the 0-line; to $S:[-r, -\theta]$ or $S:[r, \pi - \theta]$, with respect to the $\frac{1}{2}\pi$-line. Then, each of the following tests for symmetry amounts to showing that, if $P:[r, \theta]$ is on the locus, a symmetric point also is on it.

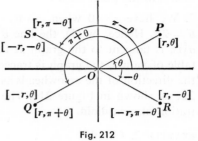

Fig. 212

Tests for symmetry. *The locus of $G(r, \theta) = 0$ is symmetric to the specified point or line if the equation is essentially unaltered by a corresponding change below.*

I. **Pole:** *replace r by $-r$; or θ by $(\pi + \theta)$.*

II. **Polar axis:** *replace θ by $-\theta$; or r by $-r$ and θ by $(\pi - \theta)$.*

III. $\frac{1}{2}\pi$-**line:** *replace r by $-r$ and θ by $-\theta$; or θ by $(\pi - \theta)$.*

Frequently, *without investigating symmetry*, we graph an equation $r = f(\theta)$ merely on the basis of a sensible selection of values for θ. Then, any symmetry will be translated into equality in the values of r, or of $|r|$, for appropriate values of θ. Sometimes we use (I), (II), and (III) simply to check the graph.

Generally, the following useful rule is valid.

$$\left\{ \begin{array}{l} \textbf{If } f(\theta) = 0 \textbf{ when } \theta = \theta_0, \textbf{ then the line } \theta = \theta_0 \\ \textbf{is tangent to the graph of } r = f(\theta) \textbf{ at the pole.} \end{array} \right\} \qquad (1)$$

Proof of (1). Let $P:[r, \theta]$ be on the graph of $r = f(\theta)$, as in Figure 213, where the equation of OT is $\theta = \theta_0$. By hypothesis, $[r = 0, \theta = \theta_0]$ satisfies $r = f(\theta)$. With the assumption that θ is a continuous function of r on the arc OP, then $\theta \to \theta_0$ when $r \to 0$. Or, the secant OP has the line OT as a limiting position when $r \to 0$. Hence, the arc OP has OT as the tangent line at the pole.

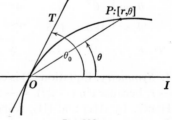

Fig. 213

EXAMPLE 1. Graph: $\qquad\qquad\qquad r = 2(1 - \cos \theta). \qquad\qquad\qquad (2)$

Solution. 1. We need use only values of θ where $0 \leq \theta < 2\pi$. The following table lists solutions $[r, \theta]$ for (2).

$\theta =$	0	$\frac{1}{12}\pi$	$\frac{1}{6}\pi$	$\frac{1}{3}\pi$	$\frac{1}{2}\pi$	$\frac{2}{3}\pi$	π	$\frac{4}{3}\pi$	$\frac{3}{2}\pi$	$\frac{5}{3}\pi$	2π
θ rad. =	0°	15°	30°	60°	90°	120°	180°	240°	270°	300°	360°
$r =$	0	.1	.3	1	2	3	4	3	2	1	0

2. If θ is replaced by $-\theta$, then (2) is unaltered because $\cos(-\theta) = \cos\theta$; hence, the graph is symmetric to the polar axis.

3. We have $r = 0$ when $\cos\theta = 1$, or $\theta = 0$ and
$\theta = 2\pi$. Hence, by (1), the line $\theta = 0$, or *the polar
axis*, is tangent to the graph at the pole. From the
table of values, the graph is traced from the pole in
the direction of the arrowheads as θ varies from 0 to
2π, as shown in Figure 214. The curve is an illustration of a **cardioid**.

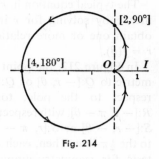

Fig. 214

EXAMPLE 2. Graph: $\qquad\qquad\qquad r = 3\sin 2\theta.$ $\qquad\qquad$ (3)

Solution. 1. *Tangents at the pole.* For convenience in graphing, all angles θ will
be described in degree measure. We have $r = 0$ when $\sin 2\theta = 0$, which gives
$\theta = 0°, 90°, 180°, 270°,$ and $360°$. Hence, the lines $\theta = 0°$ and $\theta = 90°$ are tangents at the pole, as in Figure 215. Moreover, the
graph is tangent again to the line $\theta = 0°$ at $\theta = 180°$,
and to $\theta = 90°$ at $\theta = 270°$.

2. The maximum $|r| = 3$ occurs when $\sin 2\theta = 1$,
at $\theta = 45°$ and $\theta = 225°$, and when $\sin 2\theta = -1$,
at $\theta = 135°$ and $\theta = 315°$.

3. Since the function $\sin 2\theta$ has the period $360°$,
the following table is restricted to $0° \leqq \theta \leqq 360°$.
The graph, in Figure 215, is traced from the pole in
the direction of arrowheads as θ increases from $0°$
to $360°$.

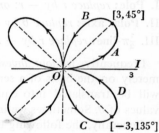

Fig. 215

$\theta =$	0°	15°	45°	75°	90°	105°	135°	165°	180°
$\theta =$	180°	195°	225°	255°	270°	285°	315°	345°	360°
$r =$	0	1.5	3	1.5	0	-1.5	-3	-1.5	0

4. *Symmetry.* Equation (3) is essentially unaltered: if θ is replaced by $-\theta$ and r by
$-r$, because $\sin(-2\theta) = -\sin 2\theta$; if r is replaced by $-r$ and θ by $(180° - \theta)$.
Hence, by (III) and (II), respectively, the graph of (3) is symmetric to the line
$\theta = 90°$ and to the polar axis. Therefore the graph also is symmetric to the pole.
The graph can be obtained by reproducing the part in quadrant I symmetrically
in the other quadrants. The graph is called a **four-leaved rose**.

Note 1. The graph of $r = a\sin n\theta$ or of $r = a\cos n\theta$, where n is a positive integer, is
called a **rose curve**. It is found that the rose has $2n$ leaves if n is even, and n leaves if
n is odd.

To graph an equation $r = f(\theta)$ which is of a familiar form, use only a few points
and general properties. Otherwise emphasize those features of the following
outline which appear useful (with aid later from calculus).

1. *Exclude values of θ for which r is imaginary or undefined.*
2. *Obtain any tangents at the pole by use of* (1) *on page* 333.
3. *Find the values of θ for which $|r|$ attains an extremum.*
4. *Perhaps transform from* $[r, \theta]$ *to* (x, y).

Note 2. If $|f(\theta)| \to \infty$ as $\theta \to \theta_0$, sometimes (but not always) the line $\theta = \theta_0$ is an asymptote of the graph of $r = f(\theta)$.

ILLUSTRATION 1. To graph $r^2 = 4 \cos 2\theta$, we must have $\cos 2\theta \geqq 0$. We use

$$\left. \begin{array}{l} 0 \leqq 2\theta \leqq \tfrac{1}{2}\pi, \quad or \quad 0 \leqq \theta \leqq \tfrac{1}{4}\pi, \; and \\[2mm] \tfrac{3}{2}\pi \leqq 2\theta \leqq 2\pi, \quad or \quad \tfrac{3}{4}\pi \leqq \theta \leqq \pi. \end{array} \right\} \tag{4}$$

All values of θ other than (4) on the interval $0 \leqq \theta \leqq \pi$ are excluded. For each value of θ in (4) except $\tfrac{1}{4}\pi$ and $\tfrac{3}{4}\pi$, the graph has two points symmetric to the pole because $r = \pm 2\sqrt{\cos 2\theta}$. From (1) on page 333, the lines $\theta = \tfrac{1}{4}\pi$ and $\theta = \tfrac{3}{4}\pi$ are tangent to the graph at the pole. The graph is called a **lemniscate** of BERNOUILLI, given by Figure 12 on page 710 with $a = 2$. Points obtained with $\pi \leqq \theta \leqq 2\pi$ duplicate those found with $0 \leqq \theta \leqq \pi$.

125. TRANSFORMATION BY ROTATION OF THE POLAR AXIS

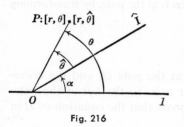

Fig. 216

Let an $r\theta$-system of polar coordinates be given in a plane. Let the polar axis OI be rotated about the pole through an angle α, to give a new $r\hat{\theta}$-system. Then, any point $P:[r, \theta]$ has new coordinates $[r, \hat{\theta}]$ where

$$\theta = \hat{\theta} + \alpha, \quad or \quad \hat{\theta} = \theta - \alpha, \tag{1}$$

as in Figure 216. Any curve $r = f(\theta)$ has a new equation $r = F(\hat{\theta})$, where $F(\hat{\theta}) = f(\hat{\theta} + \alpha)$.

ILLUSTRATION 1. The locus of $r = a \sin \theta$ is a circle, as in Figure 217. Let coordinates be transformed by rotating OI about the pole through the angle $\alpha = \tfrac{1}{2}\pi$. Then, by use of (1), the equation $r = a \sin \theta$ becomes

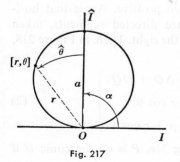

Fig. 217

$$r = a \sin (\hat{\theta} + \tfrac{1}{2}\pi), \quad or \quad r = a \cos \hat{\theta}, \tag{2}$$

and the circle now is tangent to the $\tfrac{1}{2}\pi$-line in the $r\hat{\theta}$-system, in Figure 217. Thus, assuming that we know the graph of $r = a \sin \theta$ to be a circle, we have proved that the graph of the equation $r = a \cos \theta$ also is a circle.

ILLUSTRATION 2. Let it be given that the graph of $r = a(1 - \cos \theta)$ is a cardioid, in Figure 11 on page 710. Then, rotation of OI about the pole through the angles $\alpha = \tfrac{1}{2}\pi$, π, and $\tfrac{3}{2}\pi$ shows, respectively, that the graph of each of the following equations is a cardioid with different orientation:

$$r = a(1 + \sin \theta); \quad r = a(1 + \cos \theta); \quad r = a(1 - \sin \theta). \tag{3}$$

EXERCISE 103

Graph the equation. Any line or circle should be drawn without formality. Otherwise, make use of a table of solutions $[r, \theta]$.

1. $r = 2 \cos \theta$.   **2.** $r \sin \theta = 5$.   **3.** $r = -3 \sin \theta$.   **4.** $\theta = \frac{1}{3}\pi$.

5. $\sin \theta = .2$.   **6.** $r = 3 \cos 2\theta$.   **7.** $r = 2 \sin 3\theta$.

8. $r = -2 \sin 2\theta$.   **9.** $r = 2(1 + \cos \theta)$.   **10.** $r = 2(1 + \sin \theta)$.

11. $r = 2(1 - \sin \theta)$.   **12.** $r^2 = 9 \cos 2\theta$.   **13.** $r^2 = 4 \sin 2\theta$.

14. $r^2 = \cos \theta$.   **15.** $r = 2 + 4 \cos \theta$.   **16.** $r = 4 - 2 \cos \theta$.

Note 1. The locus of $r = a + b \cos \theta$, where $a \neq 0$ and $b \neq 0$ is called a **limaçon** (see page 711). Thus, the graphs in Problems 15–16 are limaçons.

Transform the equation by rotation of the polar axis about the pole through the angle α. *Then, sketch a graph of the equation on the basis of graphs of earlier problems, showing the new polar axis* $O\hat{I}$.

17. $r = 2 \sin \theta$; $\alpha = \frac{3}{2}\pi$.   **18.** $r \cos \theta = 3$; $\alpha = \frac{1}{2}\pi$.

19. $2 = r \sin \theta$; $\alpha = \pi$.   **20.** $r^2 = a^2 \cos 2\theta$; $\alpha = \frac{1}{4}\pi$.

21. $r = 2(1 - \cos \theta)$; $\alpha = \pi$ and $\alpha = \frac{1}{2}\pi$. Use Figure 11, page 710.

22. $r = \dfrac{a}{1 - \cos \theta}$, where $a > 0$; $\alpha = \frac{1}{2}\pi$, $\alpha = \pi$, and $\alpha = \frac{3}{2}\pi$.

   Hint. Show that the curve is a parabola whose focus is at the pole, by transforming the given equation to the *xy*-form.

126. POLAR EQUATION OF A CONIC

Let H be a conic with eccentricity $\eta > 0$, focus at the pole O, and the corresponding directrix, D, perpendicular to the polar axis, to the *left* of the pole. Let $p > 0$ be the distance from D to O. We shall prove that the equation of H in the variables r and θ is

(*D at left of pole*) $$r = \frac{p\eta}{1 - \eta \cos \theta}.$$ (1)

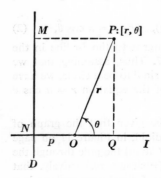

Fig. 218

Proof. 1. Let us agree that, in any coordinates $[r, \theta]$, we have $0 \leq \theta \leq 2\pi$. Let $P:[r, \theta]$ be any point at the right of D, with r taken positive. Agree that horizontal line segments are directed segments, taken positive if measured to the right. Then, in Figure 218, $\overline{MP} > 0$ and

$$\left. \begin{array}{l} \overline{MP} = \overline{NO} + \overline{OQ}; \\ \overline{OQ} = r \cos \theta; \\ \overline{MP} = p + r \cos \theta. \end{array} \right\}$$ (2)

From Definition I, page 316, P is on the conic H if and only if $r = \eta(\overline{MP})$, or

$$r = \eta(p + r \cos \theta), \quad or \quad r(1 - \eta \cos \theta) = p\eta.$$ (3)

If $1 - \eta \cos \theta \neq 0$, from (3) we obtain (1). The preceding details are complete for the cases $\eta = 1$ (a parabola), and $\eta < 1$ (an ellipse); if $\eta > 1$, the proof is complete only for the right-hand branch of the hyperbola H involved.

2. Consider the branch of H to the *left* of D in case $\eta > 1$, so that H is a hyperbola. In this case, $r < 0$ in (1) for some values of θ. With $P{:}[r,\ \theta]$ to the left of D, and the agreement that $r < 0$, the student should construct a figure to replace Figure 218, and verify that, again as in (2), $\overline{MP} = p + r \cos \theta$. Thus,

$$|r| = \eta \,|\, \overline{MP}\,|, \quad or \quad r = \eta(\overline{MP})$$

because both $r < 0$ and $\overline{MP} < 0$; then (3) is obtained again.

If we transform (1) by rotating the polar axis through π, $-\frac{1}{2}\pi$, and $\frac{1}{2}\pi$, we get the following standard forms by substituting $(\theta + \pi)$, $(\theta - \frac{1}{2}\pi)$, and $(\theta + \frac{1}{2}\pi)$, respectively, for θ in (1). In each case, the conic has the pole as a focus and p as the distance between the pole and the directrix.

(*D at right of pole*) $$r = \frac{p\eta}{1 + \eta \cos \theta}. \qquad (4)$$

(*D below pole*) $$r = \frac{p\eta}{1 - \eta \sin \theta}. \qquad (5)$$

(*D above pole*) $$r = \frac{p\eta}{1 + \eta \sin \theta}. \qquad (6)$$

To graph any special case of (1), (4), (5), and (6), first decide on the type of curve by inspection of η. Then compute r (where it exists) when $\theta = 0$, $\frac{1}{2}\pi$, π, and $\frac{3}{2}\pi$. If $\eta = 1$, in the case of a parabola, the denominator on the right will be zero for *one* of the quadrantal values of θ. In any case, these values give *each vertex* of the conic and the end points of *that latus rectum of the conic which passes through the pole* (which is a focus).

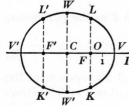

Fig. 219

ILLUSTRATION 1. From (1), as seen before in Problem 22 on page 336, the graph of $r = a/(1 - \cos \theta)$ is a parabola ($\eta = 1$).

ILLUSTRATION 2. The equation

$$r = \frac{6}{2 + \cos \theta} \qquad (7)$$

is equivalent to $$r = \frac{3}{1 + \frac{1}{2}\cos \theta}.$$

Hence, by (4), the graph of (7), in Figure 219, is an ellipse because $\eta = \frac{1}{2}$. To graph (7), we first get the points with $\theta = 0$, $\frac{1}{2}\pi$, π, and $\frac{3}{2}\pi$:

$$V{:}[2, 0]; \quad V'{:}[6, \pi]; \quad L{:}[3, \tfrac{1}{2}\pi]; \quad K{:}[3, \tfrac{3}{2}\pi].$$

The shorter resulting chord is a latus rectum of the ellipse, LK, and the longer chord is the major axis, $V'V$. Then, points L' and K' could be constructed by symmetry. Points V', V, L', K', L, and K give the basis for a fairly accurate graph. We could use (8) on page 316 with $a = 4$ and $\eta = \frac{1}{2}$ to compute $b^2 = 12$; $b = 2\sqrt{3}$. Then, C, W, and W' could be found.

ILLUSTRATION 3. The equation

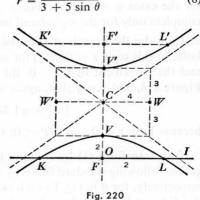

$$r = \frac{16}{3 + 5 \sin \theta} \qquad (8)$$

is a special case of (6) and represents a hyperbola H with $\eta = \frac{5}{3}$. The values $\theta = 0$, $\frac{1}{2}\pi$, π, and $\frac{3}{2}\pi$ give the points V, V', K, and L on H in Figure 220. Then, the center C for H is the mid-point of VV'; the second focus F', K', and L' can be located by symmetry. From (9) on page 316, with $a = 3$ and $\eta = \frac{5}{3}$ known, we can compute $b = 4$; this gives the data for the fundamental rectangle, whose diagonals are the asymptotes, shown in Figure 220. They correspond to the two values of θ where $3 + 5 \sin \theta = 0$, for which no value of r is given by (8).

Fig. 220

EXERCISE 104

Graph the conic whose equation is given.

1. $r = \dfrac{4}{1 - \sin \theta}$.   **2.** $r = \dfrac{3}{2 + 2 \cos \theta}$.   **3.** $r = \dfrac{8}{2 - \cos \theta}$.

4. $r = \dfrac{4}{3 + \sin \theta}$.   **5.** $r = \dfrac{18}{4 - 5 \cos \theta}$.   **6.** $r = \dfrac{12}{3 - 6 \sin \theta}$.

127. PARAMETRIC EQUATIONS RELATED TO POLAR COORDINATES

In an $r\theta$-system of polar coordinates, consider a curve $r = f(\theta)$. With the corresponding xy-system of rectangular coordinates, we have

$$x = r \cos \theta \quad and \quad y = r \sin \theta. \qquad (1)$$

Then, the curve $r = f(\theta)$ is given **in parametric form, with θ as the parameter,** by substituting $r = f(\theta)$ in (1):

$$x = f(\theta)\cos \theta \quad and \quad y = f(\theta)\sin \theta. \qquad (2)$$

With (2), we may use methods met in Section 52, page 160, to supplement the more elementary procedure used previously to graph an equation $r = f(\theta)$. However, it should be emphasized that this is not the most important feature of (2). It will be extremely useful in certain later applications not involving graphing. The following applications thus are justified in part as a means for becoming familiar with (2).

EXAMPLE 1. Find the points where the tangent is horizontal or vertical on the cardioid, and draw the graph of

$$r = 1 - \cos \theta. \qquad (3)$$

Solution. 1. Parametric equations for (3) are

$$x = (1 - \cos \theta)\cos \theta \quad and \quad y = (1 - \cos \theta)\sin \theta. \qquad (4)$$

From (4), $\dfrac{dx}{d\theta} = -\sin\theta + 2\sin\theta\cos\theta = (\sin\theta)(2\cos\theta - 1);$ (5)

$$\frac{dy}{d\theta} = \cos\theta - \cos^2\theta + \sin^2\theta = 1 + \cos\theta - 2\cos^2\theta, \text{ or}$$

$$\frac{dy}{d\theta} = (1 + 2\cos\theta)(1 - \cos\theta);$$ (6)

$$\frac{dy}{dx} = \frac{(1 + 2\cos\theta)(1 - \cos\theta)}{(2\cos\theta - 1)\sin\theta}; \quad \frac{dx}{dy} = \frac{(2\cos\theta - 1)\sin\theta}{(1 + 2\cos\theta)(1 - \cos\theta)}.$$ (7)

2. *Horizontal and vertical tangents.* From (5), $dx/d\theta = 0$ when $\sin\theta = 0$ and when $\cos\theta = \frac{1}{2}$, or when $\theta = 0$, π, 2π, $\frac{1}{3}\pi$, and $\frac{5}{3}\pi$. From (6), $dy/d\theta = 0$ when $\cos\theta = 1$ and when $\cos\theta = -\frac{1}{2}$, or when $\theta = 0$, 2π, $\frac{2}{3}\pi$, and $\frac{4}{3}\pi$. Since

$$\frac{dx}{d\theta} = \frac{dy}{d\theta} = 0$$

at $\theta = 0$ and $\theta = 2\pi$, special attention must be given to these values later, because dy/dx and dx/dy are undefined at $\theta = 0$ and $\theta = 2\pi$ in (7). Then, from (7), dy/dx is defined (denominator $\neq 0$) and is equal to zero, and thus the tangent to (3) is horizontal, when $\theta = \frac{2}{3}\pi$ and $\frac{4}{3}\pi$. Also, dx/dy is defined and is equal to zero, and thus the tangent is vertical, when $\theta = \pi$, $\frac{1}{3}\pi$, and $\frac{5}{3}\pi$.

3. When $\theta = 0$ or $\theta = 2\pi$, from (3) we obtain $r = 0$. Hence, the line $\theta = 0$, or $\theta = 2\pi$, is tangent to the cardioid at the origin; there is a cusp with a horizontal tangent at $[0, 0]$. We compute solutions $[r, \theta]$ from (3) with convenient values of θ, including the critical values from Step 2. The graph of (3) is in Figure 221.

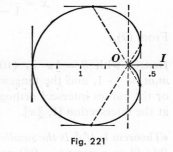

Fig. 221

The parametric form (2) may be used where the direction of a tangent is desired. "*Slope*" will relate to the corresponding xy-coordinate system.

EXAMPLE 2. Find the slope of the cardioid (3) where $\theta = \frac{5}{6}\pi$.

Solution. We refer to (4), and obtain (5) and (6). From (7),

$$\text{(slope at } \theta = \tfrac{5}{6}\pi) = \frac{dy}{dx}\bigg|_{\theta = \frac{5}{6}\pi} = \frac{(1 - \sqrt{3})(1 + \frac{1}{2}\sqrt{3})}{(-\sqrt{3} - 1)(\frac{1}{2})} = 1.$$

EXAMPLE 3. Find the smallest positive angle, ψ, formed by the tangent and the radius vector at the point on (3) where $\theta = \frac{5}{6}\pi$.

Solution. The slope of the radius vector at $P:[r, \theta]$ is $\tan\theta$. Hence, by (1) on page 30, with $m_1 = 1$ from Example 2, and $m_2 = \tan\frac{5}{6}\pi = -\frac{1}{3}\sqrt{3}$,

$$\tan\psi = \left| \frac{-\frac{1}{3}\sqrt{3} - 1}{1 - \frac{1}{3}\sqrt{3}} \right| = 2 + \sqrt{3}.$$

From Table VI, we find $\psi = 75°$.

EXAMPLE 4. Find the angle of intersection of (3) and the parabola

$$r = \frac{1}{1 - \cos \theta}. \tag{8}$$

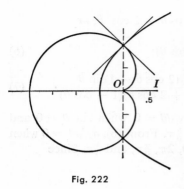

Fig. 222

Solution. 1. *Intersections.* Solve equations (3) and (8) simultaneously. In (3) and (8), r is a periodic function of θ, with the period 2π. Hence, restrict θ to the range $0 \le \theta < 2\pi$. From (3) and (8),

$$(1 - \cos \theta)^2 = 1 \quad or \quad 1 - \cos \theta = \pm 1;$$

$$\cos \theta = 0 \quad or \quad \cos \theta = 2.$$

Since $\cos \theta = 2$ is impossible, we have $\cos \theta = 0$, or $\theta = \frac{1}{2}\pi$ and $\theta = \frac{3}{2}\pi$ for intersections. If $\theta = \frac{1}{2}\pi$, then $r = 1$; if $\theta = \frac{3}{2}\pi$ then $r = 1$. The intersections are $[1, \frac{1}{2}\pi]$ and $[1, \frac{3}{2}\pi]$, as in Figure 222.

2. *Slopes at* $[1, \frac{1}{2}\pi]$. For the cardioid, from (7), the slope is $m_1 = -1$. For the parabola (8), the parametric form (2) becomes

$$x = \frac{\cos \theta}{1 - \cos \theta} \quad and \quad y = \frac{\sin \theta}{1 - \cos \theta}. \tag{9}$$

From (9),

$$\frac{dy}{dx} = \frac{1 - \cos \theta}{\sin \theta}. \tag{10}$$

Hence, with $\theta = \frac{1}{2}\pi$ in (10), the slope of the parabola is $m_2 = 1$. Thus, $m_1 m_2 = -1$, and the tangents to the cardioid and parabola are perpendicular, or the curves intersect orthogonally. From symmetry, the same situation is met at the intersection $[1, \frac{3}{2}\pi]$.

★**Theorem I.** *If ψ is the smallest positive angle made by the radius vector of a point P:$[r, \theta]$ on a curve $r = f(\theta)$ and the tangent to the curve at P, then*

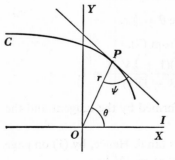

Fig. 223

$$\tan \psi = \left| \frac{r}{r'} \right|, \tag{11}$$

where $r' = \dfrac{dr}{d\theta} = f'(\theta)$.

Proof. 1. Let C be the curve $r = f(\theta)$. Angle ψ is shown in Figure 223. A parametric form for C is

$$x = r \cos \theta \quad and \quad y = r \sin \theta, \tag{12}$$

where we understand that $r = f(\theta)$. Then,

$$\frac{dx}{d\theta} = r' \cos \theta - r \sin \theta;$$

$$\frac{dy}{d\theta} = r' \sin \theta + r \cos \theta;$$

$$\left\{ \begin{matrix} \text{slope of tangent} \\ \text{to curve } r = f(\theta): \end{matrix} \right\} \qquad \frac{dy}{dx} = \frac{r' \sin \theta + r \cos \theta}{r' \cos \theta - r \sin \theta}. \tag{13}$$

2. In Figure 223, the slope of the line OP is $\tan \theta$, or $\sin \theta / \cos \theta$. To find $\tan \psi$, we use (1) from page 30,

$$\tan \psi = \left| \frac{m_2 - m_1}{1 + m_1 m_2} \right|, \tag{14}$$

with $m_1 = dy/dx$ from (13) and $m_2 = \tan \theta$. After elementary simplification, by use of $\sin^2 \theta + \cos^2 \theta = 1$, we obtain (11) from (14).

★*Note 1.* We could use (11) to solve Example 3, and (13) to solve Example 2.

EXERCISE 105

Write parametric equations in the associated xy-plane for the curve whose equation in polar coordinates is given. Also, find the slope of the curve at the specified point, and the xy-equation of the tangent at the point.

1. $r = 6 \cos \theta$; where $\theta = \frac{1}{4}\pi$.   **2.** $r = 4 \sin \theta$; where $\theta = \frac{1}{3}\pi$.

3. $r = 2 \cos 3\theta$; where $\theta = \frac{1}{3}\pi$.   **4.** $r = 3 \sin 2\theta$; where $\theta = \frac{3}{4}\pi$.

5. $r = 2(1 - \cos \theta)$; where $\theta = \frac{2}{3}\pi$.   **6.** $r = 3(1 + \sin \theta)$; where $\theta = \pi$.

7. $r = \dfrac{4}{1 - \cos \theta}$; where $\theta = \frac{2}{3}\pi$.   **8.** $r = \dfrac{2}{1 + \sin \theta}$; where $\theta = \frac{1}{3}\pi$.

9. $r = \tan \theta$; where $\theta = \frac{3}{4}\pi$.   **10.** $r = \cot \theta$; where $\theta = \frac{1}{4}\pi$.

By use of calculus, applied to the corresponding parametric form, and by use of (1) *on page 333, find the points on the curve where the tangent is horizontal or vertical and plot the curve.*

11. $r = 3(1 + \cos \theta)$.   **12.** $r = \dfrac{3}{1 + \sin \theta}$.   **13.** $r = \tan \theta$.

Hint for Problem 13. If $\theta \to \frac{1}{2}\pi -$, we find $x \to 1$, $y \to + \infty$, and $D_x y \to + \infty$. Thus, the line $x = 1$ is a vertical asymptote. There is another asymptote. The graph is called a **kappa curve.**

14. The graph of $r = a\theta$, with $a > 0$, in an $r\theta$-system of polar coordinates is called a **spiral of Archimedes;** any *number* θ in a solution $[r, \theta]$ of the equation $r = a\theta$ is interpreted as the measure in radians of the polar angle of the point $P:[r, \theta]$. Find the slope of the spiral at the points where $\theta = 0$, $\frac{1}{2}\pi$, π, and $\frac{3}{2}\pi$, and plot the curve for θ on the interval $-2\pi \leqq \theta \leqq 2\pi$.

Find the angle of intersection of the curves at each common point. If desired, use (13) *on page* 340 *in finding slopes. Draw a figure showing each angle.*

15. $r = 2 \cos 2\theta$ and $r = 1$.   **16.** $r^2 = 4 \cos 2\theta$ and $r = 2 \cos \theta$.

17. $r = 2(1 + \sin \theta)$ and $r = \dfrac{2}{1 + \sin \theta}$.

18. By use of a rotation of the polar axis, and Problem 14, graph $r = \cot \theta$.

★128. ANGULAR VELOCITY AND ACCELERATION

Suppose that a particle P is moving in a plane. Let O be a fixed point, and set up an $r\theta$-system of polar coordinates with O as the pole and any directed ray radiating from O as the polar axis. At any instant, P has coordinates r and θ which are functions of the time, t; or $r = g(t)$ and $\theta = h(t)$, where we assume that g and h have continuous second derivatives. Then, the *time-rate of change of θ*, or $d\theta/dt$, is called the **angular velocity** of P with respect to O. If $\omega = d\theta/dt$, the time-rate of change of ω, or $d\omega/dt$, is called the **angular acceleration** of P with respect to O. Thus, ω is the time-rate of revolution of the radius vector OP about the pole, or ω can be called the *angular velocity of the radius vector to P*. At present, we shall refer to dr/dt merely as the time-rate of change of the radius vector of P, and we shall not use $D_t^2 r$.

Note 1. When we consider a particle P moving in an *xy*-plane, we imply use of the related polar coordinates $[r, \theta]$ in any reference to angular velocity or acceleration for P.

EXAMPLE 1. A particle P moves on the cardioid $r = a(1 - \cos\theta)$ with constant angular velocity, k radians per second. (*a*) Find the time-rate of change of the radius vector when $\theta = \frac{1}{4}\pi$. (*b*) Find v_x, v_y, and the speed when $\theta = \frac{1}{2}\pi$. Figure 11 on page 710 shows the nature of the path.

Solution. 1. Since $\dfrac{d\theta}{dt} = k,$ $\qquad\qquad\qquad \dfrac{dr}{dt} = \dfrac{dr}{d\theta}\cdot\dfrac{d\theta}{dt} = ak\sin\theta.$

Hence, at $\theta = \frac{1}{4}\pi$, we have $\dfrac{dr}{dt} = \frac{1}{2}ak\sqrt{2}$ feet per second.

2. Parametric equations for the path are

$$x = a(1 - \cos\theta)\cos\theta \quad and \quad y = a(1 - \cos\theta)\sin\theta. \tag{1}$$

Hence, $\qquad\qquad v_x = \dfrac{dx}{dt} = \dfrac{dx}{d\theta}\cdot\dfrac{d\theta}{dt} = -ak(\sin\theta - 2\sin\theta\cos\theta);$

$$v_y = ak(\cos\theta - \cos^2\theta + \sin^2\theta).$$

Or, $\qquad\qquad v_x = ak(\sin 2\theta - \sin\theta); \quad v_y = ak(\cos\theta - \cos 2\theta).$

The student may verify that, with v as the speed, $a > 0$, and $k > 0$,

$$v^2 = v_x^2 + v_y^2 = 4a^2k^2 \sin^2 \tfrac{1}{2}\theta.$$

Thus, if $0 \leq \theta \leq 2\pi$ so that $\sin \frac{1}{2}\theta \geq 0$, we have $v = 2ak\sin\frac{1}{2}\theta$. If $\theta = \frac{1}{2}\pi$, then $v = ak\sqrt{2}$ feet per second.

★EXERCISE 106

A particle P moves on the given curve so that the radius vector of P revolves with constant angular velocity, k radians per second. Sketch the path. For the specified values of θ, (a) find v_x, v_y, a_x, and a_y; (b) construct the velocity $\mathbf{V}$ and acceleration $\mathbf{A}$; (c) compute dr/dt.

1. The circle $r = 4\cos\theta$; at $\theta = 0$, $\frac{1}{8}\pi$, $\frac{1}{4}\pi$; $k = \frac{1}{2}$.
2. The three-leaved rose $r = 5\sin 3\theta$; at $\theta = 0$, $\frac{1}{6}\pi$, and $\frac{1}{3}\pi$; $k = \frac{1}{4}$.
3. The cardioid $r = 2(1 + \sin\theta)$; at $\theta = \frac{1}{4}\pi$, $\frac{1}{2}\pi$, π; $k = \frac{1}{4}$.
4. The parabola $r = \dfrac{4}{1 + \cos\theta}$, with $-\pi < \theta < \pi$; at $\theta = -\frac{1}{2}\pi$, 0, $\frac{1}{2}\pi$; $k = \frac{1}{4}$.
5. The limaçon $r = 3 + \cos\theta$; at $\theta = 0$, $\frac{1}{2}\pi$, π; $k = \frac{1}{10}$.
6. The limaçon $r = 1 - 2\sin\theta$; at $\theta = 0$, $\frac{1}{6}\pi$, $\frac{1}{2}\pi$, $\frac{3}{2}\pi$; $k = \frac{1}{10}$.

★SUPPLEMENT FOR CHAPTER THIRTEEN

Find the coordinates of the points on the curve where the tangent is vertical or horizontal, and plot the curve.

7. $r = 4 - 2 \cos \theta$.   **8.** $r = 2 + 4 \sin \theta$.   **9.** $r^2 = \sin \theta$.

10. $r = \dfrac{6}{2 - \sin \theta}$.   **11.** $r = \dfrac{6}{3 - 2 \cos \theta}$.

12. In an $r\theta$-system of polar coordinates, find the slope of the parabola $r = \dfrac{3}{1 - \cos \theta}$ where $\theta = \frac{1}{2}\pi$. Also, find the tangent of the acute angle of intersection between the parabola and the line $y = 3 + 2x$ where they intersect.

13. Find the tangent of the acute angle of intersection of the curves $r = 2(1 - \cos \theta)$ and $r = 2 \cos \theta$, in an $r\theta$-system of polar coordinates.

14. In a given plane, supplied with a system of polar coordinates, derive a formula for the distance between two points in terms of their polar coordinates.

15. In the plane of Problem 14, derive a formula not involving a determinant for the area of a triangle with three given points as vertices, in terms of the polar coordinates of the points.

16. Find polar coordinates of the points where the curves $r^2 = h^2 \cos \theta$ and $r = \frac{1}{2}h\sqrt{2}$ intersect, if $h > 0$. Also, find the angle of intersection of the curves.

17. Discuss the graph of the **conchoid of Nicomedes,** $r = h \csc \theta + b$, where $0 < h < b$ and $[r, \theta]$ are polar coordinates. Prove the existence of the asymptote and use calculus to establish various features. See page 713.

18. Derive an equation in polar coordinates for the **ovals of Cassini.** The general case is described as *the locus of a point P such that the product of its undirected distances from two fixed points is a constant, k^2.* If these points are $H:[a, 0]$ and $T:[a, \pi]$, $a > 0$, prove that the equation of the locus is

$$k^4 = a^4 + r^4 - 2a^2r^2 \cos 2\theta. \tag{1}$$

With k taken positive, if $k = a$, the locus is also called a **lemniscate.** If $k < a$, the locus consists of two ovals about H and T, respectively. Discuss and draw the graph with the aid of calculus for the cases $k = 2a$ and $k = \frac{1}{2}a$.

19. A particle P moves clockwise on the cardioid $r = 4(1 - \cos \theta)$ with constant speed, 16 linear units per minute. Find the angular velocity, and the time-rate of change of r when P is at the point (a) $[4, -\frac{1}{2}\pi]$; (b) $[6, \frac{2}{3}\pi]$.

20. Find the base and the altitude of the isosceles triangle of maximum area which can be inscribed in the curve $r^2 = a^2 \cos 2\theta$, with one vertex of the triangle at the pole, and the vertices of the equal angles to the right of the pole.

CHAPTER FOURTEEN

Applications of Definite Integrals

129. AREA, WITH A BOUNDARY POSSIBLY IN PARAMETRIC FORM

On pages 193 and 194, we met the following formulas for the area, A, of a region R in various situations, where the function f below is continuous.

$$\left.\begin{array}{l} R \text{ bounded by } x = a, \ x = b, \\ \text{and } y = f(x); \ a < b \text{ and } f(x) \geqq 0 \end{array}\right\} \qquad A = \int_a^b y \, dx. \qquad (1)$$

$$\left.\begin{array}{l} R \text{ bounded by } y = c, \ y = d, \\ \text{and } x = f(y); \ c < d \text{ and } f(y) \geqq 0 \end{array}\right\} \qquad A = \int_c^d x \, dy. \qquad (2)$$

$$\left.\begin{array}{l} R \text{ bounded by } x = a, \ x = b, \ y_1 = f(x), \\ \text{and } y_2 = g(x); \ a < b \text{ and } y_1 \leqq y_2 \end{array}\right\} \qquad A = \int_a^b (y_2 - y_1) dx. \qquad (3)$$

$$\left.\begin{array}{l} R \text{ bounded by } y = c, \ y = d, \ x_1 = f(y) \\ \text{and } x_2 = g(y); \ c < d \text{ and } x_1 \leqq x_2 \end{array}\right\} \qquad A = \int_c^d (x_2 - x_1) dx. \qquad (4)$$

EXAMPLE 1. Find the area, A, of the region bounded by $y = \tan x$ and $y = \sin x$, and the lines $x = 0$ and $x = \frac{1}{3}\pi$.

Solution. A graph of $y_1 = \sin x$ and $y_2 = \tan x$ is given in Figure 224. We shall use (3). Figure 224 exhibits a typical elementary rectangle, whose area is $(y_2 - y_1)\Delta x$. This recalls the form of the element of area when (3) is expressed as the limit of a finite sum. From (3),

$$A = \int_0^{\pi/3} (\tan x - \sin x) dx = .1932.$$

Suppose that a curve, H, is defined parametrically by

(*curve H*) $x = \phi(t)$ *and* $y = \psi(t)$, *with t on* $I = \{\alpha \leqq t \leqq \beta\}$, *where*   (5)

ϕ' *and* ψ' *are continuous,* $\psi(t) \geqq 0$, *and*   (6)

ϕ *is an* **increasing** *function with* $\phi(\alpha) = a$ *and* $\phi(\beta) = b$, *or*   (7)

ϕ *is a* **decreasing** *function with* $\phi(\alpha) = b$ *and* $\phi(\beta) = a$.   (8)

344

Then, by the discussion in Section 34 on page 103, ϕ defines a continuous inverse function g such that, if $a \leq x \leq b$,

$$x = \phi(t) \quad \textit{is equivalent to} \quad t = g(x). \tag{9}$$

With $t = g(x)$, from $y = \psi(t)$ we obtain $y = f(x)$ where $f(x) = \psi(g(x))$, and f is continuous when $a \leq x \leq b$ because $\psi(g(x))$ is a continuous function of a continuous function of x. Hence, H of (5) is defined by $y = f(x) \geq 0$, and (1) applies. If the substitution $x = \phi(t)$ is carried out in (1) by use of (2) on page 283, when (7) is true, we obtain

$$A = \int_{x=a}^{x=b} y \, dx = \int_{t=\alpha}^{t=\beta} \psi(t)\phi'(t)\,dt. \tag{10}$$

The discussion related to (5)–(9) and $y = \psi(g(x))$ was given to justify (10), but does not enter in the simple details involved in using (10). If (8) applies, then

$$A = \int_{t=\beta}^{t=\alpha} \psi(t)\phi'(t)\,dt,$$

instead of (10). Thus we have justified the following simple routine.

Summary. *If the boundary $y = f(x)$ of R in (1) is defined as in (5)–(8), the area A of R can be obtained by first formulating A in terms of x and y as in (1), and then applying the substitution $x = \phi(t)$, as dictated by (2) on page 283, with $y = f(x) = \psi(t)$ in the integrand.*

A similar routine applies to use of (2) when the roles of (x, ϕ) and (y, ψ) in (5)–(8) are interchanged.

EXAMPLE 2. Obtain the area of the ellipse defined by

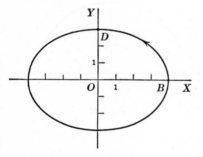

Fig. 225

$$x = 4 \cos t \quad \textit{and} \quad y = 3 \sin t. \tag{11}$$

First solution. 1. The ellipse, in Figure 225, is traced out from B to D as t varies from $t = 0$ to $t = \frac{1}{2}\pi$. The area A of the ellipse is equal to four times the area of the region bounded by the x-axis, the curve (7), and the lines $x = 0$ and $x = 4$. Thus, from (1),

$$A = 4 \int_0^4 y \, dx. \tag{12}$$

2. *Transform (12) by substituting $x = 4 \cos t$.* We obtain $dx = -4 \sin t \, dt$; $y = 3 \sin t$; if $x = 0$ in (11) then $t = \frac{1}{2}\pi$; if $x = 4$ then $t = 0$.

From (12), $A = 4 \int_{t=\pi/2}^{t=0} (3 \sin t)(- 4 \sin t)\,dt = - 48 \int_{\pi/2}^{0} \sin^2 t \, dt$, *or*

$$A = 48 \int_0^{\pi/2} \sin^2 t \, dt = 48 \int_0^{\pi/2} \tfrac{1}{2}(1 - \cos 2t)\,dt = 12\pi. \tag{13}$$

Second solution. By use of (2), and the substitution $y = 3 \sin t$,

$$A = 4 \int_0^3 x \, dy = 4 \int_{t=0}^{t=\pi/2} (4 \cos t)(3 \cos t)\,dt = 12\pi. \tag{14}$$

EXERCISE 107

Find the area of the specified region in an xy-plane.

1. Bounded by $y = \sqrt[3]{x}$, the x-axis, and the lines $x = 0$ and $x = 8$.
2. Bounded by $y = x^3$, the x-axis, and the lines $x = -2$ and $x = 3$.
3. Bounded by $x = \ln y$, the y-axis, and the lines $y = 2$ and $y = 4$.
4. Bounded by $xy = 4$, the y-axis, and the lines $y = 1$ and $y = 3$.
5. Between $y = x^3 + x^2 - 6x$ and $y = 6x$.
6. Between $y^2 = 12 - 3x$ and $y = 3x$.
7. Bounded by $y = e^{2x}$, the y-axis, and the lines $y = 1$ and $y = e$.
8. Enclosed by the loop of the curve $y^2 = x(x - 2)^2$.
9. Enclosed by the loop of the curve $y^2 = x^2(x + 2)$.
10. Bounded below by the line $y = \frac{1}{2}$ and above by one arch of $y = \sin x$.
11. Between the line $y = 2$ and one branch of $y = \sec x$.

In the following problems, t or θ is a parameter, a > 0, and b > 0.

12. Find the area of the ellipse defined by $x = a \cos t$ and $y = b \sin t$.
13. Find the area of the hypocycloid of four cusps ($x = a \cos^3 t$, $y = a \sin^3 t$).
14. Find the area of the region between the x-axis and one arch of the cycloid defined by $x = a(\theta - \sin \theta)$ and $y = a(1 - \cos \theta)$.
15. Find the area of the region between the x-axis and the witch, defined by $x = 2a \tan t$ and $y = 2a \cos^2 t$, from $x = -2a$ to $x = 2a$.
16. Find the area of the region bounded by the line $x = 3$ and the semicubical parabola ($x = \frac{27}{4}t^2$, $y = \frac{27}{4}t^3$).
17. Find the area of the loop of the curve defined by $x = 6t - \frac{1}{2}t^3$ and $y = \frac{1}{2}t^2 - 6$.
18. Figure 226 shows a sector of a circle of radius r corresponding to an angle of θ radians. Find the sector's area by subtracting the area of a triangle from the area of some region. Use ($x = r \cos t$, $y = r \sin t$) for the circle. The result proves (1) of page 224, previously based on a foundation from elementary geometry.

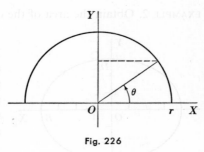

Fig. 226

130. AREAS, IN POLAR COORDINATES

Let a curve C be defined in an $r\theta$-system of polar coordinates by the equation $r = f(\theta)$, where f is continuous. Let R be the region, as in Figure 227 on page 347, bounded by C and two rays from the pole, $\theta = \alpha$ and $\theta = \beta$, respectively, where $\alpha \leq \beta$. We wish to define the area of R. Let σ be a partition of $\alpha \leq \theta \leq \beta$:

Partition σ: $\alpha = \theta_0 < \theta_1 < \cdots < \theta_{i-1} < \theta_i < \cdots < \theta_n = \beta.$ (1)

Let $r_i = f(\theta_i)$, and let τ_i be the point $[r_i, \theta_i]$ on C. Draw a ray from the pole to each point τ_i; the ith ray has the equation $\theta = \theta_i$. The rays divide R into irregular sectors, where the ith sector has the angle $\Delta_i\theta = \theta_i - \theta_{i-1}$. For the ith piece of R,

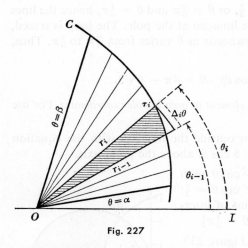

Fig. 227

construct an arc of a circle with radius *
$|r_i| = |f(\theta_i)|$, and thus form a sector
of a circle with the angle $\Delta_i\theta$. From
page 224, the area of this sector is
$\frac{1}{2}r_i^2\Delta_i\theta$. Let S_σ be the sum of the areas
of all sectors thus formed, correspond-
ing to the partition σ:

$$S_\sigma = \sum_{i=1}^{n} \tfrac{1}{2}r_i^2\Delta_i\theta = \sum_{i=1}^{n} \tfrac{1}{2}[f(\theta_i)]^2\Delta_i\theta. \quad (2)$$

Then, we define the area, A, of the
region R as *the limit, if it exists, of S_σ*
as all $\Delta_i\theta$ tend to zero, or

$$A = \lim_{(as\ all\ \Delta_i\theta \to 0)} \sum_{i=1}^{n} \tfrac{1}{2}[f(\theta_i)]^2\Delta_i\theta. \quad (3)$$

Compare the preceding details with those on page 178 leading to the definition
of a definite integral. It is verified that S_σ in (2) is a special instance (with $\xi_i = \theta_i$)
of S_σ on page 178, for the case of the function $\frac{1}{2}[f(\theta)]^2$. Hence,

$$A = \tfrac{1}{2}\int_\alpha^\beta [f(\theta)]^2\, d\theta,\ or$$

[*with $r = f(\theta)$*]
$$A = \frac{1}{2}\int_\alpha^\beta r^2\, d\theta. \quad (4)$$

EXAMPLE 1. Find the area of the region bounded by the curve $r = 2(1 - \sin \theta)$.

Solution. The cardioid is shown in Figure 228. The right-hand half of the curve
is traced as θ varies from $\theta = -\frac{1}{2}\pi$ to $\theta = \frac{1}{2}\pi$. The area A is equal to twice
that of the region bounded by the line $\theta = \frac{1}{2}\pi$ and the right-hand half of the curve:

$$A = \int_{-\pi/2}^{\pi/2} [2(1 - \sin \theta)]^2\, d\theta = 6\pi.$$

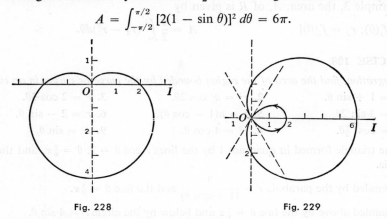

Fig. 228   Fig. 229

EXAMPLE 2. Find the area of the region bounded by the inner loop of the limaçon
whose equation is $r = 2 + 4 \cos \theta$, shown in Figure 229.

* Perhaps $f(\theta_i) < 0$. Hence, the absolute value signs are necessary.

Solution. Since $r = 0$ when $\cos \theta = -\frac{1}{2}$, or $\theta = \frac{2}{3}\pi$ and $\theta = \frac{4}{3}\pi$, hence the lines $\theta = \frac{2}{3}\pi$ and $\theta = \frac{4}{3}\pi$ are tangents to the limaçon at the pole. The loop is traced, with $r \leq 0$, in the direction of the arrowheads as θ varies from $\frac{2}{3}\pi$ to $\frac{4}{3}\pi$. Thus, the desired area, A, is given by

$$A = \int_{2\pi/3}^{4\pi/3} \tfrac{1}{2}(2 + 4\cos\theta)^2 \, d\theta = 4\pi - 6\sqrt{3}.$$

Note 1. In (2), we refer to "$\frac{1}{2}r_i^2 \Delta_i \theta$" as the *element of area in polar coordinates.* For use in (4), we may abbreviate this to "$\frac{1}{2}r^2 d\theta$."

EXAMPLE 3. Find the area of the region outside the limaçon with the equation $r = 3 - \cos\theta$ and inside the circle $r = 5\cos\theta$, above the polar axis.

Partial solution. 1. On solving $r = 3 - \cos\theta$ with $r = 5\cos\theta$, we obtain $6\cos\theta = 3$ or $\cos\theta = \frac{1}{2}$; hence $\theta = \frac{1}{3}\pi$, in quadrant I. The point of inter-section, P, as in Figure 230, is $[r = \frac{5}{2}, \theta = \frac{1}{3}\pi]$.

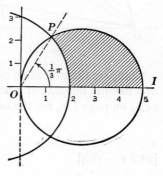

2. The specified region, R, is ruled in Figure 230. The area, A, of R is equal to the area of the region swept out by the radius vector from the origin to the point $[r, \theta]$ on the circle, minus the area of the corresponding region for the limaçon, as θ varies from 0 to $\frac{1}{3}\pi$. Thus,

$$A = \tfrac{1}{2}\int_0^{\pi/3} 25\cos^2\theta \, d\theta - \tfrac{1}{2}\int_0^{\pi/3} (3 - \cos\theta)^2 \, d\theta$$

$$= \tfrac{1}{2}\int_0^{\pi/3} (24\cos^2\theta + 6\cos\theta - 9)d\theta.$$

Fig. 230

Let R be the region bounded by the lines $\theta = \alpha$ and $\theta = \beta$, with $\alpha < \beta$, and the curves $r = f_1(\theta)$ and $r = f_2(\theta)$, where $0 \leq f_1(\theta) \leq f_2(\theta)$. Then, by the method of Example 3, the area, A, of R is given by

$[r_1 = f_1(\theta); r_2 = f_2(\theta)]$ $A = \dfrac{1}{2}\displaystyle\int_\alpha^\beta (r_2^2 - r_1^2)d\theta.$ (5)

EXERCISE 108

By integration, find the area of the region bounded by the curve or curves in an $r\theta$-plane.

1. $r = 1 + \sin\theta.$ **2.** $r^2 = a^2\cos 2\theta.$ **3.** $r = 2\cos 3\theta.$

4. $r = 3\sin 2\theta.$ **5.** $r = a(1 - \cos\theta).$ **6.** $r = 2 - \sin\theta.$

7. $r = \cos^2\frac{1}{2}\theta.$ **8.** $r^2 = 4\cos\theta.$ **9.** $r^2 = \sin\theta.$

10. The triangle formed in quadrant I by the lines $r\cos\theta = 2$, $\theta = \frac{1}{6}\pi$, and the polar axis.

11. Bounded by the parabola $r = \dfrac{3}{(1 + \cos\theta)}$ and the line $\theta = \frac{1}{2}\pi$.

12. Bounded above by the line $\theta = \frac{1}{6}\pi$ and below by the circle $r = 4\sin\theta$.

Find the area of the region swept out by the radius vector from the pole to the point $[r, \theta]$ on the curve when θ varies as specified.

13. The *spiral* of ARCHIMEDES $r = k\theta$, with $k > 0$; θ varies from 0 to π.

14. The *logarithmic spiral* $r = e^{k\theta}$, with $k > 0$; θ varies from 0 to 2π.

15. The *hyperbolic spiral* $r\theta = a$, with $a > 0$; θ varies from $\frac{1}{2}\pi$ to $\frac{3}{2}\pi$.

16. The hyperbola $r^2 \cos 2\theta = 4$; θ varies from 0 to $\frac{1}{6}\pi$, with $r > 0$.

Find the area of the region which is described.

17. The smaller segment of the circle $r = 4 \cos \theta$ cut off by the line $r \cos \theta = 3$.

18. The region bounded above by the cardioid $r = 2(1 + \sin \theta)$ and below by the circle $r = 2$, with $0 \leqq \theta \leqq \pi$.

19. The region in quadrant I inside the circle $r = \cos \theta$ and the cardioid $r = 1 - \cos \theta$.

20. The three-sided region above the polar axis bounded by the circle $r = -2 \cos \theta$, the parabola $r = 2 \csc^2 \frac{1}{2}\theta$, and the line $\theta = \frac{1}{2}\pi$.

21. The region interior to the lemniscate $r^2 = 2 \sin 2\theta$ and exterior to the circle $r = 1$.

22. The region in quadrant I bounded by the polar axis, the line $r \cos \theta = \frac{1}{2}a$, and the *kappa curve* $r = a \tan \theta$, where $a > 0$.

Find the area of the region interior to both of the curves.

23. $r = \sqrt{3} \cos \theta$; $r = \sin \theta$.   **24.** $r^2 = 4 \cos 2\theta$; $r^2 = 4 \sin 2\theta$.

131. INFINITE INTERVAL OF INTEGRATION

In the definition of a definite integral on page 178, the interval of integration is specified to be finite. Now, we shall introduce symbols such as $\int_a^\infty f(x)dx$, which we call an **improper integral,** and which we read as *"the integral of $f(x)$ from $x = a$ to infinity,"* where the domain of x is an *infinite interval.* For contrast, sometimes we shall refer to an integral as a *proper definite integral,* if it exists according to Definition II on page 178.

Definition I. *Let a be a fixed number, and suppose that the function $f(x)$ is continuous on any domain involved for x. Then, we define the value of each of the following improper integrals as the limit on the right in the corresponding equation, provided that this limit exists:*

$$\int_a^\infty f(x)dx = \lim_{h \to \infty} \int_a^h f(x)dx. \tag{1}$$

$$\int_{-\infty}^a f(x)dx = \lim_{h \to -\infty} \int_h^a f(x)dx. \tag{2}$$

In (1) or (2), if the limit on the right exists (is *finite*), we say that the improper integral on the left *exists,* or **converges,** and that it *converges to the specified limit.* Otherwise, we say that the improper integral **diverges,** or that it *fails to exist.*

ILLUSTRATION 1. By Definition I,

$$\int_2^\infty \frac{dx}{x^3} = \lim_{h \to \infty} \int_2^h \frac{dx}{x^3} = \lim_{h \to \infty} \left(-\frac{1}{2x^2}\right)\Big]_2^h = \lim_{h \to \infty} \left(\frac{1}{8} - \frac{1}{2h^2}\right) = \frac{1}{8} - 0 = \frac{1}{8}.$$

ILLUSTRATION 2. By equation (1),

$$\int_1^\infty \frac{dx}{\sqrt{x}} = \lim_{h \to \infty} \int_1^h \frac{dx}{\sqrt{x}} = \lim_{h \to \infty} 2\sqrt{x}\Big]_1^h = \lim_{h \to \infty} (2\sqrt{h} - 2) = \infty.$$

Hence, the improper integral diverges, or has no value.

Definition II. *If the function* $f(x)$ *is continuous when* $-\infty < x < \infty$, *and* a *is any number, we define the improper integral* $\int_{-\infty}^{\infty} f(x)dx$ *as follows, provided that both integrals on the right converge:*

$$\int_{-\infty}^{\infty} f(x)dx = \int_{-\infty}^{a} f(x)dx + \int_{a}^{\infty} f(x)dx. \tag{3}$$

If either integral on the right in (3) fails to exist, we say that the integral on the left fails to exist, or that it diverges.

EXAMPLE 1. Test for convergence: $\qquad\qquad\qquad\qquad \int_{-\infty}^{\infty} x^3\, dx.$

Solution. By Definition II, $\qquad\qquad \int_{-\infty}^{\infty} x^3\, dx = \int_{-\infty}^{0} x^3\, dx + \int_{0}^{\infty} x^3\, dx,$

provided that both integrals on the right converge. We obtain

$$\int_{0}^{\infty} x^3\, dx = \lim_{h\to\infty} \int_{0}^{h} x^3\, dx = \lim_{h\to\infty} \tfrac{1}{4}x^4 \Big]_{0}^{h} = \lim_{h\to\infty} \tfrac{1}{4}h^4 = \infty.$$

Hence, $\int_{0}^{\infty} x^3\, dx$ does not exist. Thus, without considering $\int_{-\infty}^{0} x^3\, dx$, we may state that $\int_{-\infty}^{\infty} x^3\, dx$ does not exist.

Comment. Notice the fallacy which arises when, *incorrectly,** we act as if the given improper integral could be defined as follows:

$$\int_{-\infty}^{\infty} x^3\, dx = \lim_{h\to\infty} \int_{-h}^{h} x^3\, dx = \lim_{h\to\infty} \tfrac{1}{4}x^4 \Big]_{-h}^{h} = \lim_{h\to\infty} 0 = 0, \tag{4}$$

which is not true. Thus, we must avoid thinking of $\int_{-\infty}^{\infty} f(x)dx$ as a *single limit* of an integral over a *finite interval* of the x-axis.

By use of improper integrals, we may define the notion of area for certain *unbounded* regions in an xy-plane. This seemingly unrealistic concept has fundamental applications, particularly in mathematical statistics. Apart from such applications, this area notion clarifies the definitions in (1) and (2).

Assume that $f(x) \geqq 0$ and f is continuous when $x \geqq a$. Let R be the unbounded region between the x-axis and the graph of $y = f(x)$ when $x \geqq a$. For any number $h > a$, let R_h be the ruled region in Figure 231, between $x = a$ and $x = h$, and let A_h be the area of R_h. Then, we define the area, A, of the unbounded region R as *the limit of* A_h *as* $h \to \infty$, provided that this limit exists. Or, by definition,

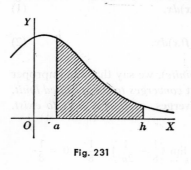

Fig. 231

$$A = \lim_{h\to\infty} A_h = \lim_{h\to\infty} \int_{a}^{h} f(x)dx, \text{ or}$$

from (1), $\qquad\qquad A = \int_{a}^{\infty} f(x)dx. \tag{5}$

If the limit in (5) is ∞, we say that *the area of* R *is infinite*, which is a convenient way of remarking that the area of R does not exist, and that $\lim_{h\to\infty} A_h = \infty$. If

---

* In more advanced mathematics, sometimes a limit as in (4) is used in connection with an improper integral, and then is called its *Cauchy principal value.*

$f(x) \geqq 0$ when $x \leqq a$, or when $-\infty < x < \infty$, similar remarks apply to the areas of the regions between the graph of $y = f(x)$ and the x-axis.

EXAMPLE 2. Find the area of the region bounded by the x-axis and the curve $y = 3/(1 + x^2)$, on the domain $0 \leqq x < \infty$.

Solution. The curve is shown in Figure 232. With notation such as was used in (5),

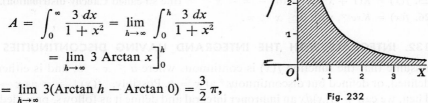

$$A = \int_0^\infty \frac{3\ dx}{1 + x^2} = \lim_{h \to \infty} \int_0^h \frac{3\ dx}{1 + x^2}$$

$$= \lim_{h \to \infty} 3\ \text{Arctan}\ x \Big]_0^h$$

$$= \lim_{h \to \infty} 3(\text{Arctan}\ h - \text{Arctan}\ 0) = \frac{3}{2}\ \pi,$$

Fig. 232

because Arctan $0 = 0$ and Arctan $h \to \frac{1}{2}\pi$ when $h \to \infty$, as seen on page 236.

ILLUSTRATION 3.
$$\int_{-\infty}^0 \sin x\ dx = \lim_{h \to -\infty} \int_h^0 \sin x\ dx$$

$$= \lim_{h \to -\infty} - \cos x \Big]_h^0 = \lim_{h \to -\infty} (\cos h - 1). \tag{6}$$

In (3), cos h oscillates between -1 and $+1$ as $h \to -\infty$, and thus *does not have a limit*, finite or infinite, or the improper integral diverges.

EXERCISE 109

Find the value of the integral, or demonstrate that it diverges.

1. $\int_1^\infty \dfrac{dx}{x^4}.$ **2.** $\int_1^\infty \dfrac{dx}{\sqrt[3]{x}}.$ **3.** $\int_1^\infty \dfrac{dx}{x}.$

4. $\int_1^\infty e^{-2x}\ dx.$ **5.** $\int_0^\infty \cos 2x\ dx.$ **6.** $\int_0^\infty xe^{-x^2}\ dx.$

7. $\int_2^\infty \dfrac{dx}{4 + x^2}.$ **8.** $\int_{-\infty}^\infty \dfrac{du}{1 + u^2}.$ **9.** $\int_4^\infty \dfrac{dx}{(x - 3)^{\frac{3}{2}}}.$

10. $\int_0^\infty \dfrac{dx}{(2x + 3)^2}.$ **11.** $\int_1^\infty \dfrac{dx}{x^2 + 2x + 2}.$ **12.** $\int_3^\infty \dfrac{du}{u^2 - 4}.$

13. $\int_1^\infty \dfrac{dx}{x^n},$ where $n < 1.$ **14.** $\int_1^\infty \dfrac{dx}{x^n},$ where $n > 1.$

15. $\int_0^\infty \dfrac{x^2\ dx}{1 + x^3}.$ **16.** $\int_{3/2}^\infty \dfrac{dt}{9 + 4t^2}.$ **17.** $\int_{-\infty}^\infty \dfrac{du}{4u^2 + 4u + 5}.$

18. $\int_{-\infty}^\infty \sin 2x\ dx.$ **19.** $\int_{-\infty}^\infty x^2e^{-x^3}\ dx.$ **20.** $\int_{-\infty}^\infty x\sqrt{x^2 + 3}\ dx.$

Find the area of the specified unbounded region, if the area exists.

21. Between the x-axis and the curve $y = e^x$ on the interval $x \leqq 0.$

22. Between the x-axis and the curve $y = 1/(9 + x^2),$ with $-\infty < x < \infty.$

23. Between the x-axis and the curve $y = 1/x^2,$ where $1 \leqq x.$

24. Between the x-axis and the curve $y = 1/(2x + 1)^3,$ where $x \geqq 0.$

★*Note 1.* In statistics, a function $f(x)$, with $-\infty < x < \infty$, is acceptable as a **probability density function** for the probability distribution of a random variable X, with values x, if and only if $f(x) \geqq 0$ at all x and there exists $\int_{-\infty}^{\infty} f(x)dx = 1$. Then, we define

$$\text{(the probability of } X \leqq t) = \int_{-\infty}^{t} f(x)dx = F(t). \tag{1}$$

Similar terminology applies if the domain of x is $-\infty < x \leqq a$, or $a \leqq x < \infty$.

★*Prove that the function $f(x)$ is acceptable as a probability density function with x on the specified domain. Find the proper value of K for this purpose.*

25. $f(x) = K(1 + x^2)^{-1}$, with $-\infty < x < \infty$ (the so-called **Cauchy distribution**).

26. $f(x) = Kxe^{-x}$, with $0 \leqq x < \infty$.

132. INTEGRALS WITH THE INTEGRAND HAVING DISCONTINUITIES

Assume that the function $f(x)$ is continuous where $a \leqq x < b$, and is either undefined, or defined but discontinuous* at $x = b$. Possibly, $|f(x)| \to \infty$ as $x \to b-$. Then, we call $\int_a^b f(x)dx$ an **improper integral** and define it as follows, provided that the limit on the right exists. In (2), we let $h = b - \epsilon$ in (1) for different notation.

$$\int_a^b f(x)dx = \lim_{h \to b-} \int_a^h f(x)dx; \; or \tag{1}$$

$$\int_a^b f(x)dx = \lim_{\epsilon \to 0+} \int_a^{b-\epsilon} f(x)dx. \tag{2}$$

Similarly, if $f(x)$ is continuous when $a < x \leqq b$, we define the improper integral $\int_a^b f(x)dx$ as follows:

$$\int_a^b f(x)dx = \lim_{h \to a+} \int_h^b f(x)dx = \lim_{\epsilon \to 0+} \int_{a+\epsilon}^b f(x)dx. \tag{3}$$

We employ terminology about *convergence* or *divergence* with improper integrals of the present type similarly as in Section 131. Also, we define the areas of unbounded regions related to (1) and (3) by improper integrals.

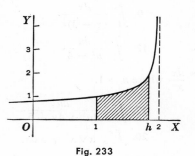

Fig. 233

EXAMPLE 1. Obtain the area, A, of the unbounded region, in Figure 233, between the x-axis and $y = 1/\sqrt[3]{2 - x}$ from $x = 1$ to $x = 2$.

Solution. We define A by

$$A = \int_1^2 \frac{dx}{\sqrt[3]{2 - x}},$$

which is improper because the denominator is zero, and the integrand is undefined, at $x = 2$. From (1),

$$A = \lim_{h \to 2-} \int_1^h (2 - x)^{-\frac{1}{3}} dx$$

$$= \lim_{h \to 2-} -\tfrac{3}{2}(2 - x)^{\frac{2}{3}} \Big]_1^h = \tfrac{3}{2} - \lim_{h \to 2-} \tfrac{3}{2}(2 - h)^{\frac{2}{3}} = \tfrac{3}{2}. \tag{4}$$

* With a more elaborate foundation for the definite integral than we gave in Chapter 9, the case of $\int_a^b f(x)dx$ where f is discontinuous at $x = b$, but is bounded, sometimes might not have to be included in the *improper* category. However, our definition (1) above still would be valid. See Problem 31 on page 367.

Comment. In Figure 233 on page 352, let A_h be the area of the region between $x = 1$ and $x = h$. The proper integral from 1 to h in (4) is equal to A_h. We defined $A = \lim_{h \to 2-} A_h$. Instead of (1) we could use (2) in Example 1, to obtain

$$\int_1^2 (2 - x)^{-\frac{1}{3}} \, dx = \lim_{\epsilon \to 0+} \int_1^{2-\epsilon} (2 - x)^{-\frac{1}{3}} \, dx$$

$$= \lim_{\epsilon \to 0+} - \tfrac{3}{2}(2 - x)^{\frac{2}{3}} \Big]_1^{2-\epsilon} = \lim_{\epsilon \to 0+} (- \tfrac{3}{2}\epsilon^{\frac{2}{3}} + \tfrac{3}{2}) = \tfrac{3}{2}.$$

In $\int_a^b f(x)dx$, suppose that f is discontinuous or undefined at some point $x = c$ where $a < c < b$, and that f otherwise is continuous. Then, we shall call the integral *improper* and define it as the sum of two improper integrals, as below, if both of them exist:

$$\int_a^b f(x)dx = \int_a^c f(x)dx + \int_c^b f(x)dx. \tag{5}$$

Similarly, suppose that the function $f(x)$ is continuous when $a \leqq x \leqq b$ except at a finite number of points. Then, we define $\int_a^b f(x)dx$ as the sum of a corresponding set of improper integrals where, in each integral, f is continuous on the interval of integration except at one or both of the end points.

ILLUSTRATION 1. From (5), since $1/(x - 3)^2$ becomes infinite as $x \to 3$,

$$\int_2^4 \frac{dx}{(x - 3)^2} = \int_2^3 \frac{dx}{(x - 3)^2} + \int_3^4 \frac{dx}{(x - 3)^2}. \tag{6}$$

Then,

$$\int_2^3 \frac{dx}{(x - 3)^2} = \lim_{h \to 3-} \int_2^h \frac{dx}{(x - 3)^2} = + \infty.$$

Similarly, the second integral on the right in (6) diverges. Hence, the integral on the left in (6) does not converge. Notice the following fallacious result which is obtained by failure to start with (6):

$$\int_2^4 \frac{dx}{(x - 3)^2} = - \frac{1}{x - 3} \Big]_2^4 = - 1 - 1 = - 2!$$

We have introduced improper integrals of two types. In one case, an integral is called improper because the interval of integration is infinite, although the integrand is continuous. In the second case, an integral with a finite interval of integration is said to be improper because the integrand is not defined, or is discontinuous at certain points. An integral may exhibit both of the preceding characteristics. In such a case, the integral is defined as the sum of corresponding improper integrals where each one exhibits just one of the two characteristics by which we have earmarked improper integrals.

ILLUSTRATION 2. The integrand is undefined at $x = 2$ in the following improper integral on the left. Hence, the integral on the left is equal to the sum of the improper integrals on the right, if both exist:

$$\int_2^\infty \frac{dx}{(x - 2)^2} = \int_2^3 \frac{dx}{(x - 2)^2} + \int_3^\infty \frac{dx}{(x - 2)^2}. \tag{7}$$

By the method of Section 131, the second integral on the right in (7) converges to the value 1. However, the integral from 2 to 3 in (7) diverges. Hence, the integral on the left in (7) diverges.

EXERCISE 110

Compute the value of the integral, or prove it divergent.

1. $\int_0^2 \dfrac{dx}{\sqrt{2-x}}$.

2. $\int_0^3 \dfrac{dx}{(3-x)^2}$.

3. $\int_0^4 \dfrac{dx}{x}$.

4. $\int_0^2 \dfrac{dx}{x^{\frac{1}{3}}}$.

5. $\int_{-2}^3 \dfrac{dx}{(x-3)^{\frac{2}{3}}}$.

6. $\int_{-1}^1 \dfrac{dx}{x^2}$.

7. $\int_0^2 \dfrac{u\,du}{\sqrt{4-u^2}}$.

8. $\int_0^1 \dfrac{dx}{\sqrt{1-x^2}}$.

9. $\int_{-3/8}^{3/4} \dfrac{du}{\sqrt{9-16u^2}}$.

10. $\int_0^{\pi/4} \tan 2t\,dt$.

11. $\int_0^{\pi/2} \cot u\,du$.

12. $\int_0^{\pi/2} \sec^2 t\,dt$.

13. $\int_{-1}^3 \dfrac{du}{u-2}$.

14. $\int_0^4 \dfrac{du}{u^2-4}$.

15. $\int_3^5 \dfrac{du}{\sqrt{u^2-9}}$.

16. $\int_{-a}^a \dfrac{dx}{\sqrt{a^2-x^2}}$; $a > 0$.

17. $\int_0^1 \dfrac{du}{u^k}$; $0 < k < 1$.

18. $\int_{\pi/4}^{\pi/2} \sec 2x\,dx$.

19. $\int_{\pi/3}^{\pi/2} \csc^2 3t\,dt$.

20. $\int_0^{\pi/2} \tan^2 t \sec^2 t\,dt$.

21. $\int_{-3}^0 \dfrac{dx}{\sqrt{3-x^2-2x}}$.

22. $\int_3^6 \dfrac{dx}{\sqrt{x^2-3x}}$.

23. $\int_{a/2}^a \dfrac{x^2\,dx}{\sqrt{a^2-x^2}}$.

24. $\int_4^8 \dfrac{du}{u\sqrt{u^2-16}}$.

Hint. Introduce a trigonometric substitution.

Investigate the area of the specified unbounded region.

25. Between the x-axis and the curve $y = \tan x$ where $0 \leq x < \frac{1}{2}\pi$.

26. Between the x-axis and the curve $y = (x-3)^{-\frac{1}{2}}$ where $3 < x \leq 5$.

27. Between the x-axis and the curve $y = \dfrac{1}{\sqrt{16-9x^2}}$ where $-\frac{2}{3} \leq x < \frac{4}{3}$.

28. Between the x-axis and the curve $y = \ln x$ where $0 < x \leq 1$.

133. VOLUMES FROM KNOWN PLANE SECTIONS

Let S be a closed surface in space of three dimensions. By a *plane section* of S, or simply a *section* of S, we mean the curve of intersection of S and some plane. Consider all plane sections of S by planes perpendicular to a specified line in space, where this line is provided with a number scale, and is labeled as an x-axis. Let the closed curve C be the section of S by a plane perpendicular to the x-axis at an arbitrary point x on $a \leq x \leq b$, and assume that the area of the region bounded by C is $A(x)$, where A is a continuous function. A surface S in an xyz-system of rectangular coordinates is represented in Figure 234 on page 355. The base of S is in the xy-plane; MNU is the section of S perpendicular to the x-axis at the point x'. Let T be the region bounded by S and the planes perpendicular to the x-axis at $x = a$ and $x = b$, as in Figure 234. We shall visualize T as a *solid* in future remarks. Then, we shall define the volume, V, of T in such a way that we shall obtain

$$V = \int_a^b A(x)\,dx. \qquad (1)$$

ILLUSTRATION 1. If a curve E with the equation $y = f(x)$ in an xy-plane is revolved in space about the x-axis, then E generates a surface of revolution, S, as considered earlier. Any plane section of S perpendicular to the x-axis is a circle. Thus, for the solid represented in Figure 146 on page 197, we would have $A(x) = \pi y^2$, where $y = f(x)$, and (1) becomes $\int_a^b \pi y^2 \, dx$.

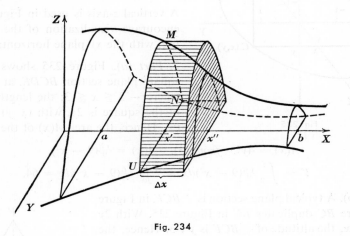

Fig. 234

Derivation of (1). Let the interval from x' to x'', as in Figure 234, be a subinterval of a partition, σ, of the interval $a \leqq x \leqq b$, with $x'' - x' = \Delta x$. Then, plane sections perpendicular to the x-axis at x' and at x'' cut out a slab with thickness Δx from the solid T. In Figure 234, one face of this slab is MNU whose area is $A(x')$. Suppose that the plane face at the point x' is moved in the direction of the x-axis to the point x''. This motion sweeps out a second slab, which we now substitute for the *actual slab* of the solid. By (II) on page 196, the volume, ΔV, of the substituted slab is

$$\Delta V = A(x')\Delta x. \tag{2}$$

For any partition σ of the interval (a, b), let S_σ be the sum of the elements of volume ΔV, as in (2), corresponding to all subintervals of P. Then, we define the volume, V, of the solid T as *the limit of S_σ as the lengths of all subintervals of σ approach zero*. From (2), we then observe that V has been defined to be the definite integral in (1).

In many problems where (1) will be used, it would be difficult to draw the solids involved. Hence, as a rule, the student is advised to concentrate on drawing just the *base of any solid*, and a *typical plane section*. If this distorts the section, then a separate undistorted sketch of the section should be drawn, for calculating the section's area, $A(x)$.

EXAMPLE 1. The base of a solid T is an ellipse with major axis 6 and minor axis 4. Find the volume, V, of T if every plane section of T perpendicular to the major axis is (a) a square; (b) an equilateral triangle.

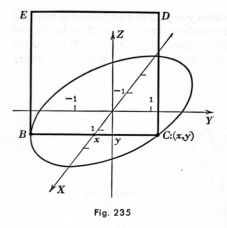

Fig. 235

Solution. 1. With *xy*-coordinates in the plane of the base, as in Figure 235, the boundary of the base becomes

$$\frac{x^2}{9} + \frac{y^2}{4} = 1, \text{ or } 4x^2 + 9y^2 = 36. \quad (3)$$

A vertical *z*-axis is used in Figure 235 to encourage visualization of the space figure, with the *xy*-plane horizontal.

2. *Part (a).* Figure 235 shows a typical square plane section *BCDE*, at a point *x* where $-3 \leq x \leq 3$; the length of a side of the square is $2y$, with (x, y) satisfying (3). Hence, the area $A(x)$ of the section is

$$A(x) = 4y^2; \quad from \text{ (3)}, \quad A(x) = \tfrac{16}{9}(9 - x^2). \quad (4)$$

By (1), $V = \int_{-3}^{3} \tfrac{16}{9}(9 - x^2)dx = 2\int_{0}^{3} \tfrac{16}{9}(9 - x^2)dx = 64. \quad (5)$

3. *Part (b).* A typical plane section is $\triangle BCF$, in Figure 236, where *BC* duplicates *BC* in Figure 235. With $2y$ as the side, the altitude of $\triangle BCF$ is $y\sqrt{3}$. Hence, the area of $\triangle BCF$ is $A(x) = y^2\sqrt{3}$; etc.

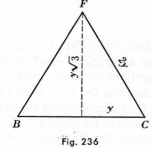

Fig. 236

EXAMPLE 2. The plane of a variable isosceles right triangle is perpendicular to the *x*-axis of an *xy*-plane, the vertex of the 90° angle is on the *x*-axis, one side is in the *xy*-plane, and a vertex is on the curve $y = \sin x$. Find the volume of the region *T* in space swept out by the region bounded by the triangle as its 90° vertex moves from $x = 0$ to $x = \pi$ on the *x*-axis.

Partial solution. In Figure 237, *CB* is the base of the triangle in a typical position, with *C* as the vertex of the right angle. Figure 237 also shows the complete triangle *BCF*. Its area is $\tfrac{1}{2}y^2$ where we have $y = \sin x$. Hence, in (1), we use $A(x) = \tfrac{1}{2}\sin^2 x$, with $a = 0$ and $b = \pi$.

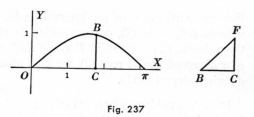

Fig. 237

EXERCISE 111

Find the volume of the solid, T, which is described. For convenience in a figure, it can be assumed that the base of T is in a horizontal xy-plane.

1. The base is the region bounded by the ellipse $4x^2 + 9y^2 = 36$. Every plane section of *T* perpendicular to the minor axis of the ellipse is an isosceles triangle whose altitude is twice its base in the *xy*-plane.

2. The base is the region bounded by the x-axis, the curve $x^2 = 6y$, and the line $x = 6$. Every section of T perpendicular to the x-axis is (a) an isosceles right triangle with the 90°-vertex on the x-axis; (b) a quadrant of a circle with its center on the x-axis.

3. The base is a circle with radius 6. Every plane section of T perpendicular to a particular diameter of the base is (a) a semicircle; (b) a rectangle whose altitude is twice the base in the plane of the given circle; (c) an equilateral triangle.

4. The base is the region bounded by the x-axis, the curve $y = \tan x$, and the line $x = \frac{1}{4}\pi$. Every plane section perpendicular to the x-axis is (a) an isosceles right triangle with its hypotenuse in the xy-plane; (b) an isosceles triangle with altitude 10, and base in the xy-plane.

5. The base is the triangle in quadrant I bounded by the x-axis, the y-axis, and the line $4x + 3y = 12$. Every plane section perpendicular to the y-axis is (a) an equilateral triangle; (b) a semicircle; (c) a sector of a circle with the angle $\frac{1}{4}\pi$.

6. The base is bounded by the axes, the curve $y = e^x$, and the line $x = 3$. Every plane section perpendicular to the x-axis is a semicircle.

7. The plane of a variable isosceles triangle is perpendicular to the x-axis in an xy-plane. The altitude of the triangle is 12, one end of the base is on the x-axis, and the other end is on the line $2y - 3x = 0$. Find the volume swept out by the region bounded by the triangle as the base moves from $x = 0$ to $x = 8$.

8. Find the volume of a pyramid with altitude 50′ and a square base whose side is 20′.

9. A variable circle has its plane perpendicular to the x-axis of an xy-plane, with a diameter of the circle joining two points on the curve $8y^2 = 9x^3$. Find the volume of the horn which is swept out by the region bounded by the circle as its center moves from $x = 0$ to $x = 2$.

10. The plane of a variable circular disk is perpendicular to the y-axis of an xy-plane, and the ends of a diameter are on the lines $y = x$ and $y = \frac{1}{3}x$. Find the volume of the region swept out by the disk as it moves from $y = 0$ to $y = 8$.

11. The base of a solid is a circle with radius r. Every plane section perpendicular to a particular diameter is an isosceles triangle whose base is a chord of the circle and altitude is 10. Find the volume of the solid.

12. Find the volume of an elliptical cone with altitude 25′ whose base is an ellipse with major axis 8′ and minor axis 6′.

13. The base-radius is 5′ and the altitude is 20′ in a solid circular cone. A wedge is cut from the cone by two half-planes through the cone's axis. If the angle between the planes is $\frac{1}{6}\pi$, find the volume of the wedge.

14. In chopping down a tree with a cylindrical trunk, a lumberjack saws a horizontal cut perpendicular to the axis halfway through the tree. Then, he makes a second cut along a plane meeting the first cut at the axis of the tree. If the tangent of the angle between the planes of the two cuts is $\frac{2}{3}$, find the volume of the wedge cut out, if the tree's diameter is 2′. Solve by use of (a) triangular sections; (b) rectangular sections.

★15. The plane of a variable isosceles right triangle is perpendicular to the y-axis of a horizontal xy-plane, the vertex of the 90°-angle is on the y-axis, and another vertex is on the curve $xy = 4$. Find the volume of the region T swept out by the triangular region as the 90°-vertex moves (a) from $y = 1$ to $y = 3$; (b) from $y = 1$ through all values of $y \geq 1$. (c) For part (b), find the area (if it exists) of the xy-base of the solid. The volume is finite in (b) but the area is infinite in (c).

134. VOLUMES BY USE OF CYLINDRICAL SLABS OR WASHERS

In an xy-plane, let R be the region bounded by the x-axis, the lines $x = a$ and $x = b$, and a curve $y = f(x)$, where f is continuous when $a \leqq x \leqq b$. Let V be the volume of the solid generated by revolving R about the x-axis. Then, on page 197, we defined V as the limit of a sum of the volumes of elementary cylindrical slabs, and obtained

$$[\textit{with } y = f(x)] \qquad\qquad V = \pi \int_a^b y^2 \, dx. \qquad\qquad (1)$$

We mentioned in Section 133 that (1) is equivalent to use of the method of plane sections, with each section as a circle. Similarly, let R be the region bounded by the y-axis, the lines $y = c$ and $y = d$, and the curve $x = g(y)$. Then, if R is revolved about the y-axis, the volume, V, of the solid thus generated is given by

$$[\textit{with } x = g(y)] \qquad\qquad V = \pi \int_c^d x^2 \, dy. \qquad\qquad (2)$$

ILLUSTRATION 1. Let R be the region bounded by the x-axis, the lines $x = \pm 2$ and the catenary (see Figure 27 on page 713) $y = \frac{1}{4}(e^{2x} + e^{-2x})$. From (1), the volume of the solid generated by revolving R about the x-axis is

$$V = \pi \int_{-2}^{2} \tfrac{1}{16}(e^{2x} + e^{-2x})^2 \, dx.$$

EXAMPLE 1. By use of the parametric form

$$x = a \cos t \quad \textit{and} \quad y = b \sin t \qquad\qquad (3)$$

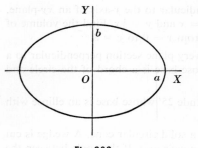

Fig. 238

for an ellipse, find the volume of the solid generated if the region bounded by the ellipse is revolved about the x-axis (the bounding surface is called an **ellipsoid**; see page 449).

Solution. 1. By symmetry, as verified in Figure 238, the volume, V, is twice that which is obtained if we revolve just the region in quadrant I bounded by the ellipse and the coordinate axes. Hence, from (1),

$$V = 2\pi \int_0^a y^2 \, dx. \qquad\qquad (4)$$

2. In (4), transform the variable of integration from x to t by use of (3). If x goes from 0 to a, then t goes from $\frac{1}{2}\pi$ to 0. Hence,

$$V = 2\pi \int_{\pi/2}^{0} b^2(\sin^2 t)(-a \sin t)dt = 2\pi a b^2 \int_0^{\pi/2} (\sin t)(1 - \cos^2 t)dt$$

$$= 2\pi a b^2 (-\cos t + \tfrac{1}{3}\cos^3 t)\Big]_0^{\pi/2} = \tfrac{4}{3}\pi a b^2.$$

If a region in an xy-plane is revolved about a line other than the x-axis or the y-axis, then (1) and (2) do not apply. However, in such a case, it may be possible to obtain the corresponding volume by the method involving plane sections, or equivalent reasoning about elements of volume.

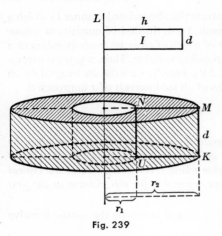

Fig. 239

Note 1. In Figure 239, revolution of the region bounded by the narrow rectangle (I) about the line L would generate a *cylindrical slab* with volume $\pi h^2 d$. Rectangle $KMNU$ has two sides parallel to L. Revolution of the rectangular region $KMNU$ about L would generate a cylindrical "washer," whose volume is

$$(\pi r_2^2 d - \pi r_1^2 d), \quad or \quad \pi d(r_2^2 - r_1^2). \quad (5)$$

EXAMPLE 2. Find the volume of the solid which is generated if the region R in an xy-plane bounded by the line $x = 2$ and the parabola $y^2 = 8x$ is revolved about the line $x = 2$.

Solution. 1. The line $x = 2$ intersects the parabola where $y = \pm 4$.

2. Let $D:(x, y)$ be any point on the curve $y^2 = 8x$, in Figure 240. Let Δy be a

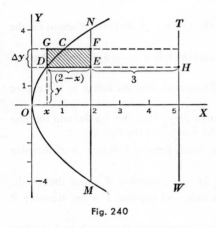

Fig. 240

subinterval of a partition σ of the interval $-4 \leqq y \leqq 4$. When the strip $CDEF$ of R is revolved about MN, a slab is generated. As a substitute for $CDEF$, introduce the rectangular region $DEFG$, whose revolution about MN produces a cylindrical slab with volume ΔV. Since $\overline{DE} = 2 - x$,

$$\Delta V = \pi(\overline{DE})^2 \Delta y = \pi(2 - x)^2 \Delta y. \quad (6)$$

The volume, V, of the solid obtained by revolving R is defined as the limit of the sum of all elements (6), for the partition σ, as the lengths of all subintervals of σ approach zero. From symmetry, the volume of the solid will be twice that obtained when $0 \leqq y \leqq 4$. From (6),

$$(\textit{with } y^2 = 8x) \qquad V = 2\pi \int_0^4 (2 - x)^2 \, dy = 2\pi \int_0^4 (2 - \tfrac{1}{8}y^2)^2 \, dy = \tfrac{256}{15}\pi.$$

EXAMPLE 3. Find the volume of the solid generated by revolving the region R of Example 2 about the line $x = 5$.

Solution. Revolution of the elementary region $DEFG$ of Figure 240 about the line WT generates a cylindrical washer, with inner radius $\overline{EH} = 3$, outer radius $\overline{DH} = 5 - x$, and volume ΔV. From (5),

$$(\textit{with } y^2 = 8x) \qquad\qquad \Delta V = \pi[(5 - x)^2 - 3^2]\Delta y. \quad (7)$$

Then, by inspection of the element of volume ΔV, we obtain

$$V = 2\pi \int_0^4 (16 - \tfrac{5}{4}y^2 + \tfrac{1}{64}y^4)dy = \textit{etc.} \quad (8)$$

Note 2. The solutions of Examples 2 and 3 illustrate the abbreviated manner in which a definite integral frequently is introduced for a result. First, the desired quantity (a *volume* in Examples 2 and 3) is recognized as *the limit of a sum of elements* corresponding to a partition, σ, of an interval of values of a corresponding variable. Then, a general expression is obtained for the *typical element* (such as ΔV). Finally, we write the integral which is the limit of the sum of elements as the lengths of all subintervals of σ approach 0.

EXERCISE 112

The specified region R is in an xy-plane. Compute the volume of the solid obtained by revolving R as indicated. Use a figure showing an interval Δx, or Δy, of the interval of integration, and a corresponding rectangular region whose revolution produces the typical element of volume for the integral. Also, write an expression for this element as the first step in the solution.

1. R is bounded above by the parabola $y = 4 - x^2$ and below by the x-axis. Revolve R about the line $y = 4$.

2. R is bounded by the curve $y = \cos x$ and the coordinate axes, from $x = 0$ to $x = \frac{1}{2}\pi$. Revolve R about the line $y = 2$.

3. R is bounded by the parabola $y = (x + 3)(1 - x)$ and the line $y = 3$. Revolve R about (*a*) the line $y = 3$; (*b*) the line $y = 0$.

4. R is bounded by the curve $y = 6x - x^2$ and the line $y = 5$. Revolve R about (*a*) the x-axis; (*b*) the line $y = 5$.

5. R is bounded by the parabola $x = y(4 - y)$ and the line $x = -5$. Revolve R about the line $x = -5$.

6. R is bounded by the curve $y = e^x$, the coordinate axes, and the line $x = 1$. Revolve R about the line $y = e$.

7. R is in quadrant I and is bounded by the curve $8y^2 = 9x^3$, the x-axis, and the line $x = 2$. Revolve R about (*a*) the x-axis; (*b*) the y-axis; (*c*) the line $x = 2$.

8. R is bounded by the curve $y = \sin x$ and the x-axis from $x = 0$ to $x = \pi$. Revolve R about the line $y = 1$.

9. R is bounded by the curves $y = x$ and $y = 4x - x^2$. Revolve R about the x-axis.

10. R is bounded by the curve $y = \tan x$, the x-axis, and the line $x = \frac{1}{4}\pi$. Revolve R about the line $y = 1$.

11. R is bounded by one branch of the curve $y = \csc x$ above the x-axis and the line $y = 2$. Revolve R about the line $y = 2$.

12. R is bounded on the right by the curve $4x^2 + 25y^2 = 100$ and on the left by the curve $x = 4 - y^2$. Revolve R about the y-axis.

13. R is bounded by the hypocycloid defined by $(x = a \cos^3 t, y = a \sin^3 t)$, where $a > 0$. Revolve R about the y-axis. Use an integral with respect to t.

14. R is bounded by the x-axis and one arch of the cycloid defined parametrically by $x = a(t - \sin t)$ and $y = a(1 - \cos t)$, where $a > 0$. Revolve R about the x-axis.

15. R is bounded by the loop of $y^2 = x(x - 1)(x - 3)$. Revolve R about the x-axis.

16. R is the smaller segment of the circle $x^2 + y^2 = 25$ cut off by the line $x = 3$. Revolve R about the line $x = 3$.

17. A region R is bounded by the parabola $x^2 + y - 2x = 1$, the y-axis, and the line $y = 2$. Find the volume of the solid obtained by revolving R about the line $y = 2$.

★*A region R is described in an rθ-system of polar coordinates. Express the given curve in parametric form in rectangular coordinates as on page 338. Then, compute the volume of the solid obtained on revolving the region as specified.*

18. R is bounded by the circle $r = a \cos \theta$, the polar axis, and the line $\theta = \frac{1}{4}\pi$, with $a > 0$. Revolve R about the x-axis.

19. R is bounded by the polar axis, the curve $r = \tan \theta$, and the line $r \cos \theta = \frac{1}{2}$. Revolve R about the x-axis.

20. R is bounded by that part of the cardioid $r = a(1 - \sin \theta)$ which is in quadrant I, and the polar axis. Revolve R about the polar axis.

135. VOLUMES BY USE OF CYLINDRICAL SHELLS

In Figure 241 below, line L lies in the plane of the slender rectangle $CDEF$, with two sides parallel to L. Revolution of region $CDEF$ about L generates a cylindrical shell. We shall use the following result.

$$\left\{ \begin{array}{l} \textit{The volume of a cylindrical shell of inner radius } r_1, \\ \textit{outer radius } r_2, \textit{ altitude h, and thickness k, is } 2\pi\rho hk, \\ \textit{where } \rho = \frac{1}{2}(r_1 + r_2), \textit{ which is the average of } r_1 \textit{ and } r_2. \end{array} \right\} \qquad (1)$$

Proof of (1). In Figure 241, let $\overline{WD} = r_1$ and $\overline{WC} = r_2$. The volume, V, of the shell is the difference of the volumes of two cylinders, or

$$V = \pi r_2^2 h - \pi r_1^2 h = \pi h(r_2^2 - r_1^2)$$

$$= \pi h(r_2 - r_1)(r_2 + r_1) = 2\pi h(r_2 - r_1)\frac{r_1 + r_2}{2} = 2\pi\rho hk,$$

where we let $k = r_2 - r_1$ and $\rho = \frac{1}{2}(r_1 + r_2)$. (We notice that $2\pi\rho$ is the circumference of a circle midway between the inner and outer circles at the base of the cylindrical shell.)

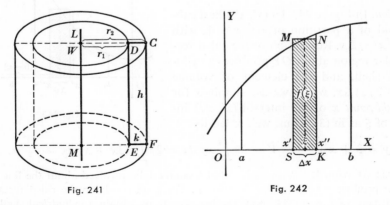

Fig. 241   Fig. 242

In Figure 242, let R be the region bounded by the curve $y = f(x)$, the x-axis, and the lines $x = a$ and $x = b$. We assume that the function $f(x)$ is continuous and $xf(x) \geqq 0$ when $a \leqq x \leqq b$. Let T be the solid obtained by revolving R about the y-axis. Then, we shall define the volume, V, of T in such a way that

$[with \ xy = xf(x) \geqq 0]$ $V = 2\pi \int_a^b xy \ dx.$ (2)

Derivation of (2). Let the interval from x' to x'', as in Figure 242, be a sub-interval of a partition of the interval $a \leqq x \leqq b$, with $x' < x''$ and $x'' - x' = \Delta x$. The ordinates of the graph of $y = f(x)$ at x' and x'' cut a vertical strip from the region R. Let ξ be the mid-point of the interval $x' \leqq x \leqq x''$, and construct a rectangle $MNKS$ having the altitude $f(\xi)$, on this interval as a base. In the following limiting process, take region $MNKS$ as a substitute for the strip of R with the interval (x', x'') as the base. Revolution of $MNKS$ about the y-axis generates a cylindrical shell with thickness Δx whose volume, ΔV, is obtained from (1) with $\rho = \xi$:

$$\Delta V = 2\pi \xi f(\xi) \Delta x.$$ (3)

For any partition σ of interval (a, b), let S_σ be the sum of the elements of volume ΔV, as in (3), corresponding to all subintervals of σ. Then, we define the volume, V, of the solid T as the limit of S_σ as the lengths of all subintervals of σ approach zero. Hence, by inspection of the element of volume in (3), we conclude that V has been defined as the integral in (2).

Note 1. In (2) and its derivation, for convenience we assumed that $xf(x) \geqq 0$, so that (3) would be positive. If we do not have $xf(x) \geqq 0$, then we alter (2) by using $|xy|$ in place of xy in the integrand. For rapid recollection later, we may rewrite the element of volume in (3) as $\Delta V = 2\pi xy \Delta x$.

EXAMPLE 1. The region R bounded by the curve $y = 3 + x^2$, the x-axis, and the lines $x = 1$ and $x = 4$ is revolved about the y-axis to generate a solid T. Obtain the volume, V, of T by integration with respect to the variable x.

Solution. In Figure 243, let (x', x'') be a sub-interval of a partition of $1 \leqq x \leqq 4$, with $x'' - x' = \Delta x$. Revolution of the ruled rectangular region about OY produces a cylindrical shell, and the element of volume $\Delta V = 2\pi xy \Delta x$, where we use simply x for the *mid-point* x of the interval (x', x'') instead of ξ as in (3). Thus, we are led to

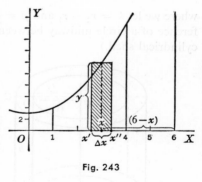

Fig. 243

$(with \ y = 3 + x^2)$ $V = 2\pi \int_1^4 xy \ dx = 2\pi \int_1^4 (3x + x^3)dx = \frac{345}{2}\pi.$

ILLUSTRATION 1. Let the region R of Example 1 be revolved about the line $x = 6$, to produce a solid T with volume V. Then, on revolving the ruled rectangular element of Figure 243 about the line $x = 6$, we obtain a cylindrical shell where the radius to the mid-point of the base is $(6 - x)$. Thus, the element of volume for the integral is $\Delta V = 2\pi(6 - x)y \Delta x$ and

$$V = 2\pi \int_1^4 (6 - x)y \ dx, \quad with \quad y = 3 + x^2.$$

EXERCISE 113

*Region R is in an xy-plane. Compute the volume of the solid obtained by revolving R as indicated. Base the integral on use of a **cylindrical shell** in obtaining the element of volume.*

1. R is bounded by the curve $y = 3x^2$, the x-axis, and the lines $x = 1$ and $x = 3$. Revolve R about (a) the y-axis; (b) the line $x = 5$. Use integrals with respect to x.

2. R is the region in quadrant I bounded by the curve $y^2 = 4x$, the x-axis, and the line $x = 4$. Revolve R about (a) the y-axis; (b) the line $x = 6$.

3. R is bounded by the parabola $y = x(x - 6)$ and the x-axis. Revolve R about (a) the y-axis; (b) the line $x = -2$.

4. R is bounded by the parabola $x = (y - 2)(y - 4)$ and the y-axis. Revolve R about (a) the x-axis; (b) the line $y = -1$. Use integrals with respect to y.

5. R is bounded by the curve $y = e^x$, the x-axis, and the lines $x = 1$ and $x = 4$. Revolve R about the y-axis. Integration by parts is available.

6. R is bounded by the curve $x = \ln y$, the y-axis, and the line $y = e^2$. Revolve R about the x-axis.

7. R is the region bounded by the hyperbola $x^2 - y^2 = 9$ and the lines $y = 1$ and $y = 4$. Revolve R about the x-axis.

8. R is bounded by the curve $y = \sin 2x$, the x-axis, and the lines $x = \frac{1}{4}\pi$ and $x = \frac{1}{2}\pi$. Revolve R about the y-axis.

9. R is the region bounded by the circle $x^2 + y^2 = a^2$, with $a > 0$. Revolve R about the line $x = a$. That is, obtain the volume of the solid generated by revolution of a circle about one of its tangents.

10. R is the region bounded by the cycloid $(x = \theta - \sin \theta, \ y = 1 - \cos \theta)$, with $0 \leq \theta \leq 2\pi$, and the x-axis. Revolve R about the y-axis.

Find the volume of the solid generated by revolution of the specified region R in an xy-plane. Use whichever method of the chapter is desirable.

11. R is the region bounded by the curve $y = x^3 - 8$, and the lines $y = -8$, $x = 1$, and $x = 2$. Revolve R about the line $x = 2$.

12. R is the region bounded by the curve $xy = 8$ and the line $x + y = 6$. Revolve R about the x-axis, and use integration (a) with respect to x; (b) with respect to y.

13. R is the region bounded by the curves $x^2 = 2y$ and $x^2 = 4y - 8$. Revolve R about (a) the x-axis; (b) the y-axis.

14. If a circle is revolved in space about a line in the plane of the circle but not intersecting it, the surface thus generated is called a **torus**, which is like an anchor ring, or a doughnut. Find the volume of the region bounded by the torus generated by revolving the circle $x^2 + y^2 = a^2$ about the line $x = h$, where $a > 0$ and $h > a$.

15. Solve Problem 14 by use of a parametric form $x = a \cos t$ and $y = a \sin t$.

16. R is the region bounded by the curve $y = \text{Arctan } x$, the x-axis, and the line $x = 1$. Revolve R about the y-axis.

17. R is the smaller segment of the circle $x^2 - 2ax + y^2 = 0$ cut off by the line $x = \frac{3}{2}a$, where $a > 0$. Revolve R about the y-axis.

★18. R is the region bounded by the witch $y = 8/(4 + x^2)$, the lines $x = 2$ and $x = 4$, and the x-axis. Revolve R about (a) the y-axis; (b) the x-axis. For Part (b), use a trigonometric substitution when integrating.

136. APPLICATIONS INVOLVING WORK, AND CENTER OF MASS

If a force $f(x)$ acts along an x-axis from $x = a$ to $x = b$, the work, W, done by the force was defined in such a manner on page 200 that

$$W = \int_a^b f(x)dx. \tag{1}$$

EXAMPLE 1. A tank is a vertical elliptic cylinder 40' high, and is full of water. Any horizontal plane section of the tank is an ellipse with major axis 10' and minor axis 8'. Find the work done in pumping the water over the top of the tank.

Solution. 1. Conceive of an imaginary piston whose face is bounded by a horizontal section of the tank, where this piston moves upward from the bottom and empties the tank.

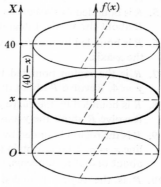

2. Insert an x-axis,* as in Figure 244, where the vertical scale is distorted. When the piston is at elevation x feet, the height of the water is $(40 - x)$ feet and its volume † is $\pi \cdot 4 \cdot 5 \cdot (40 - x)$ cubic feet; the weight of the water in pounds is $f(x) = 20\pi\tau(40 - x)$, where τ is the weight in pounds of one cubic foot of water ($\tau = 62.4$, approximately). Then, $f(x)$ is the force in pounds applied at the piston at elevation x. The work, W, done by the force $f(x)$ in emptying the tank is

$$W = 20\pi\tau \int_0^{40} (40 - x)dx = 16,000\pi\tau, ft.\text{-}lb.$$

Fig. 244

Without using the notion of an imaginary piston, we can obtain a convenient formula for the solution of a problem like Example 1. For this purpose, consider a tank with a horizontal base and top, containing liquid weighing τ pounds per

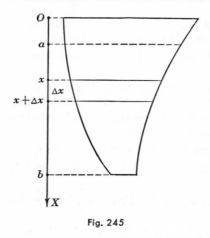

Fig. 245

cubic foot. Insert a vertical x-axis, with its positive direction downward, and the origin at the level of the top of the tank, as in the vertical section of the tank in Figure 245. Let $A(x)$ be the area of the horizontal cross section of the liquid at the level x on the x-axis, and assume that the function A is continuous. We propose defining the work done by pumping out, over the top of the tank, all of the liquid between the levels $x = a$ and $x = b$, where $a < b$. Let the interval from x to $(x + \Delta x)$, in Figure 245, be a subinterval of a partition, σ, of the interval

$$a \leqq x \leqq b.$$

* We assume that the scale unit is one foot on any coordinate axis in this section.
† The area of an ellipse with axes $2a$ and $2b$ is πab.

As a substitute for the slab of liquid between the horizontal plane sections of the liquid at depths x and $(x + \Delta x)$, take a slab with the element of volume

$$\Delta V = A(x)\Delta x,$$

as on page 355, and the element of weight $\tau \Delta V$. If this weight were concentrated at depth x, the element of work, ΔW, done in raising the weight through the distance x would be

$$\Delta W = x\tau\Delta V = \tau x A(x)\Delta x. \tag{2}$$

Let S_σ be the sum of the elements of type (2) for all subintervals of the partition σ. Then, physical intuition leads us to define the work, W, done in emptying the specified liquid, as *the limit of S_σ as the lengths of all subintervals of σ approach zero.* That is, we obtain

$\left\{\begin{array}{l} \textit{empty tank from} \\ \textit{depth a to depth b} \end{array}\right\}$
$$W = \tau \int_a^b x A(x)dx. \tag{3}$$

ILLUSTRATION 1. In Example 1, we may use (3) with $A(x) = 20\pi$, $a = 0$, and $b = 40$, to obtain

$$W = 20\pi\tau \int_0^{40} x\, dx = 10\pi\tau x^2 \Big]_0^{40} = 16{,}000\pi\tau, \textit{ft.-lb.}$$

EXAMPLE 2. Mass is spread on the x-axis with the density $\delta(x) = 3e^{-x}$. Find the mass and center of mass for the mass on $0 \le x \le 5$.

Solution. From pages 208 and 212, the total mass, m, and center of mass, $\bar{x}$, for $0 \le x \le 5$ are

$$m = 3 \int_0^5 e^{-x}\, dx; \qquad \bar{x} = \frac{3\int_0^5 xe^{-x}\, dx}{m}. \tag{4}$$

To compute the integral at the right in (4), we use integration by parts:

$$\int_0^5 xe^{-x}\, dx = (-xe^{-x} - e^{-x})\Big]_0^5 = 1 - 6e^{-5};$$

$$m = 3(1 - e^{-5}); \qquad \bar{x} = \frac{e^5 - 6}{e^5 - 1} = .966 \text{ (Tables V and II)}.$$

EXERCISE 114

1. A rectangular tank has a base 4′ square, is 20′ high, and is full of water. Find the work done in pumping all of the water out over the top of the tank. Use 62 pounds as the weight of a cubic foot of water.

2. A vertical tank is a right circular cylinder with height 30′ and base-radius 10′, and contains liquid weighing 80 pounds per cubic foot. Find the work done in pumping all of the liquid out over the top of the tank if the liquid is (*a*) 30′ deep; (*b*) 20′ deep.

3. A vertical tank is a right circular cone with altitude 60′, base-radius 8′, vertical axis, and vertex at the bottom. The tank is filled with water to a depth of 40′. Find the work done in pumping all of the water out over the top of the tank.

4. A tank is a hemisphere with the plane face horizontal, at the top, and diameter 30′. The tank is filled with liquid weighing 90 pounds per cubic foot. Find the work done in pumping out liquid over the top, to reduce the depth to 5′.

5. The surface of a tank is formed by revolving a parabola about its axis, which is vertical. The vertex of the parabola is at the bottom of the tank, which is 64′ high and has the diameter 16′ at the top. The tank is filled to a depth of 40′ by a liquid weighing 75 pounds per cubic foot. Find the work done in pumping all of the liquid out over the top.

6. The outside surface of a tank with an open top is formed by revolving the lower half of an ellipse with horizontal major axis and vertical minor axis about this axis. The lengths of the axes are 30′ and 20′. If the tank is full of a liquid weighing 80 pounds per cubic foot, find the work done in pumping all of the liquid out over the top.

7. A uniform wire cable weighs 6 pounds per foot, and 100′ of the cable hangs down, without stretching, in a shaft. By increment reasoning, as in the background for (3) on page 365, obtain an integral for the work, W, done in raising all of the cable to the top. Then, compute W.

8. Mass is distributed on the interval $0 \leq x \leq 2$ with the density $\delta(x) = e^{-2x}$. Find the total mass and center of mass.

9. Mass is distributed over the x-axis, with the density $\delta(x) = 2/(1 + x^2)$. Find the mass and center of mass (if it exists) for the mass on the interval $(a) - \sqrt{3} \leq x \leq 1$; $(b)\ 0 \leq x < \infty$; $(c) - \infty < x < \infty$.

★10. In Example 2 on page 365, find the mass and center of mass on the infinite interval $0 \leq x < \infty$.

★*Find the centroid of the region with the specified boundary.*

11. Bounded by $y = \sin x$ and the line $y = 0$, for $0 \leq x \leq \pi$.

12. Bounded by $y = e^x$ and the lines $x = 0$, $x = 3$, and $y = 0$.

13. Bounded by $y = x + \sin x$ and the line $y = x$, for $0 \leq x \leq \pi$.

14. Bounded by $y = x \ln x$, the x-axis, and the line $x = e$.

★SUPPLEMENT FOR CHAPTER FOURTEEN

15. Find the area of the region between the inner loop and the outer part of the limaçon in Example 2 on page 347. Use the result of that example.

16. Find the area of the loop of the *conchoid* of NICOMEDES, $r = \csc \theta + 2$, in polar coordinates. See Figure 26, page 713.

Find the area of the region bounded by the curve, in polar coordinates.

17. $r = 3 + 2 \cos 2\theta$.   18. $r = 3 + \sin 3\theta$.

19. A region R is bounded by the curve $r = a(1 + \cos \theta)$ in polar coordinates in quadrant I, the polar axis, and the line $\theta = \frac{1}{2}\pi$. Find the volume of the solid generated by revolving R about the polar axis.

20. A given quantity of a certain gas is confined in a right circular cylinder with a piston free to move at one end. When the volume of the gas is 1500 cubic inches, the gas exerts a pressure (a force) of 10 pounds per square inch on the walls of the container. Find the work done when the gas expands from 500 cubic inches to 1500 cubic inches. Assume that conditions justify use of the law that pressure times volume is a constant. (Carry heights as unknown constants.)

21. Use the parametric form $(x = a \cos t, y = a \sin t)$, and integrals with respect to t, to solve Problem 9 on page 363.

22. Find the centroid of the region of Problem 14, page 346.

23. A cylindrical tank is 60 feet long and has a diameter of 12 feet. The tank lies with its circular ends vertical, and is filled to a depth of 9 feet with fluid weighing w pounds per cubic foot. Find the work done by a pump in moving the fluid through a pipe reaching from the bottom of the tank to a point 18 feet above the tank.

24. Consider a vertical xy-plane, where the unit for distance is one foot, with the x-axis vertical, directed downward; let $y = f(x)$ be the equation of a curve in the plane, with $f(x) \geq 0$. A tank has a circular horizontal bottom and its side wall is the surface formed by revolving the curve $y = f(x)$ about the x-axis; for $0 \leq x \leq k$. The tank is filled with liquid weighing w pounds per cubic foot. Find the work done in pumping the fluid from the tank to a point h feet above its top. Prove that this work is equal to the work done in raising the whole weight of the liquid for h feet plus the work done in moving this weight from the centroid of the tank to its top.

25. A region R in quadrant I of an $r\theta$-plane is bounded by the kappa curve $r = \tan \theta$, the polar axis, and the line $r \cos \theta = \frac{1}{2}\sqrt{3}$. Find the volume of the solid generated if R is revolved about the associated y-axis.

26. A region R in an $r\theta$-plane is bounded by the polar axis and the rose curve

$$r = 3 \cos 2\theta \quad for \quad 0 \leq \theta \leq \tfrac{1}{4}\pi.$$

Find the volume of the solid generated by revolution of R about the line $\theta = \frac{1}{2}\pi$.

Find the volume of the unbounded solid obtained by revolving the specified region R as indicated, or prove that the volume does not exist. It is understood that the volume is defined by an improper integral.

27. R is bounded by the curve $y = e^x$, the y-axis, and the x-axis where $x \leq 0$. Revolve R about the x-axis.

28. R is bounded by the x-axis where $x \geq a$, the line $x = a$, and the hyperbola defined parametrically by $x = a \cot \theta$ and $y = a \tan \theta$, with $a > 0$. Revolve R about the x-axis, and use an integral with respect to θ.

29. R is bounded by the curve $x = 1/\sqrt{y - 3}$, the y-axis, and the lines $y = 3$ and $y = 5$. Revolve R about the y-axis.

30. R is the region in quadrant I bounded by the coordinate axes and the *witch* of AGNESI, $(x = 2a \tan t, y = 2a \cos^2 t)$. Revolve R about the y-axis.

31. Assume that the function $f(x)$ is bounded when $a \leq x \leq b$, and continuous except possibly at c, where $a \leq c \leq b$. Suppose that there exist $\lim_{x \to c+} f(x)$ and $\lim_{x \to c-} f(x)$ (where one of these limits is not involved when $a = c$ or $b = c$). Prove that $\int_a^c f(x)dx$, $\int_c^b f(x)dx$, and $\int_a^b f(x)dx$ exist, and that the last integral is the sum of the first two. Use Definition II on page 178 and Theorem I on page 179. This result extends to the case where f has just a finite number of discontinuities, of the type mentioned at $x = c$, on interval (a, b).

32. If $a > 0$, evaluate $\int_0^a [x]dx$ by use of Problem 31, with $[x]$ representing the greatest integer at most equal to x.

33. Prove that $\left| |a| - |b| \right| \leq |a - b|$. Then, prove that, if $f(x) \to L$ as $x \to c$, $|f(x)| \to |L|$ as $x \to c$. Also, prove that, if the function $f(x)$ is continuous at $x = c$, then the function $|f(x)|$ is continuous at $x = c$. Prove or disprove the converse of the preceding statement. Prove that, if f is continuous, then $\int_a^b |f(x)| \, dx$ exists.

CHAPTER FIFTEEN

Advanced Integration

137. PARTIAL FRACTIONS

Let $f(x)$ represent any polynomial of degree n in a variable x,

$$f(x) = a_0 + a_1 x + a_2 x^2 + \cdots + a_{n-1} x^{n-1} + a_n x^n, \tag{1}$$

where the coefficients a_0, a_1, etc., are any complex numbers and $a_n \neq 0$. Then, in algebra, it is proved that *there exist n numbers r_1, r_2, $\cdots$, r_n, real or imaginary,* so that

$$f(x) = a_0(x - r_1)(x - r_2) \cdots (x - r_n). \tag{2}$$

Each of r_1, r_2, $\cdots$, r_n, and no other number, is a solution of the equation $f(x) = 0$. Thus, any polynomial equation of degree $n > 0$ has *at most n distinct solutions*. This leads to the following useful result.

Theorem I. *If each of two polynomials in x is of degree n at most, and if the polynomials are equal for more than n distinct values of x, then the polynomials are identical term by term, and hence are equal for all values of x.*

Proof. Suppose that $g(x) = b_0 + b_1 x + \cdots + b_n x^n$, and $f(x)$ has the form (1). By hypothesis, the equation $f(x) = g(x)$, or $f(x) - g(x) = 0$, or

$$(a_0 - b_0) + (a_1 - b_1)x + \cdots + (a_{n-1} - b_{n-1})x^{n-1} + (a_n - b_n)x^n = 0, \tag{3}$$

has more than n distinct solutions. If $a_n - b_n \neq 0$, or $a_n \neq b_n$, then (3) is of degree n and hence has *at most* n distinct solutions. This contradicts our hypothesis; therefore $a_n = b_n$, and (3) is of degree $(n - 1)$ at most. Similarly, $a_{n-1} = b_{n-1}$, etc., as stated in the theorem.

Hereafter, let us assume that the coefficients a_0, a_1, $\cdots$, a_n in (1) are real numbers, and $n > 0$. Then, we recall that *any imaginary solutions of $f(x) = 0$ occur in conjugate imaginary pairs*, say $r_1 = b + ci$ and $r_2 = b - ci$, where b and c are real, $c \neq 0$, and $i = \sqrt{-1}$. When the corresponding factors in (2) are multiplied, we obtain a real quadratic factor for $f(x)$,

$$[x - (b + ci)][x - (b - ci)] = x^2 - 2bx + b^2 + c^2. \tag{4}$$

Then, in (2), after any imaginary factors are grouped in conjugate pairs as in (4), we may combine any identical factors into a power of the factor. Thus, we reach the following result.

Theorem II. *Any polynomial of degree $n > 0$ in x, with real coefficients, is expressible as the product of powers of distinct real factors, where each factor is linear, or is quadratic and is not a product of real linear factors.*

Note 1. If $p \neq 0$, we recall that the quadratic equation $px^2 + qx + r = 0$ has *real roots*, or $px^2 + qx + r$ has *real linear factors, if and only if the discriminant* $q^2 - 4pr \geqq 0$. If $q^2 - 4pr < 0$, the linear factors of $px^2 + qx + r$, as given by (2), are imaginary.

If $N(x)$ and $D(x)$ are polynomials in x, we have agreed to call the function $N(x)/D(x)$ a rational function. Sometimes, $N(x)/D(x)$ is referred to as a **rational fraction.** It is called a **proper fraction** if and only if the degree of $N(x)$ is *less than* the degree of $D(x)$; otherwise, $N(x)/D(x)$ is said to be an **improper fraction.** We say that $N(x)/D(x)$ is in its *lowest terms* if $N(x)$ and $D(x)$ have no common polynomial factor which is not a mere constant. If $N(x)/D(x)$ is an improper fraction, it can be expressed as a polynomial plus a proper fraction, by dividing $N(x)$ by $D(x)$ until the remainder is of lower degree than $D(x)$.

ILLUSTRATION 1.
$$\frac{4x^3 + 5}{2x^2 + x} = 2x - 1 + \frac{x + 5}{2x^2 + x}.$$

In integration, we may find it desirable to decompose a given rational fraction into a sum of more simple fractions, called *partial fractions*. This process is spoken of as the resolution of the given fraction into its partial fractions. We obtain them by applying the following theorem, whose proof will be omitted. In each application, the results automatically will be verified by the details involved.

Note 2. At present, in any reference to a *fraction*, we shall mean a *rational fraction*. In connection with any polynomial in a variable x, any factor to which we refer will have real coefficients; any quadratic factor which is mentioned will have no real linear factors, although this assumption is not necessary as a basis for some of the results.

Theorem III. *Let $N(x)/D(x)$ be a proper fraction in lowest terms. Then, there exist partial fractions, made up as follows, whose sum is $N(x)/D(x)$ wherever $D(x) \neq 0$:*

If a linear factor $(\alpha x + \beta)$ occurs just k times as a factor of $D(x)$, then there are k partial fractions,

$$\frac{A_1}{\alpha x + \beta} + \frac{A_2}{(\alpha x + \beta)^2} + \cdots + \frac{A_k}{(\alpha x + \beta)^k}, \tag{5}$$

where $A_1, A_2, \cdots, A_k$ are constants and $A_k \neq 0$.

If a quadratic factor $(px^2 + qx + r)$ occurs just h times as a factor of $D(x)$, there are h partial fractions,

$$\frac{B_1 x + C_1}{px^2 + qx + r} + \frac{B_2 x + C_2}{(px^2 + qx + r)^2} + \cdots + \frac{B_h x + C_h}{(px^2 + qx + r)^h}, \tag{6}$$

where the B's and C's are constants and $B_h x + C_h \not\equiv 0$.

In order to calculate $\int f(x)dx$ when $f(x)$ is a *proper* fraction, first we may resolve it into its partial fractions, and then add their integrals. If $f(x)$ is an *improper* fraction, by division we may express it as the sum of a polynomial and a proper fraction, which then may be integrated to obtain $\int f(x)dx$.

As a consequence of (5), two cases will arise, Case I where $k = 1$ in (5), and Case II where $k > 1$. From (6), we shall meet Case III where $h = 1$, and Case IV where $h > 1$. Two or more of these cases may arise simultaneously with a given fraction $N(x)/D(x)$.

138. CASES I AND II FOR PARTIAL FRACTIONS

Case I. *Resolution of $N(x)/D(x)$ into partial fractions when $D(x)$ is a product of distinct linear factors: For each factor $(\alpha x + \beta)$, there is a partial fraction of the form $A/(\alpha x + \beta)$.*

EXAMPLE 1. Resolve into partial fractions: $\dfrac{7x^2 - 23x + 10}{(3x - 1)(x - 1)(x + 2)}$.

First solution. 1. By Theorem III, there exists just one set of constants A, B, and C such that, at all values of x except those for which some denominators are zero,

$$\frac{7x^2 - 23x + 10}{(3x - 1)(x - 1)(x + 2)} = \frac{A}{3x - 1} + \frac{B}{x - 1} + \frac{C}{x + 2}. \tag{1}$$

2. In (1), multiply both sides by $(3x - 1)(x - 1)(x + 2)$:

$$\left. \begin{aligned} 7x^2 - 23x + 10 = \qquad\qquad\qquad\qquad\qquad\qquad\qquad\\ A(x - 1)(x + 2) + B(x + 2)(3x - 1) + C(x - 1)(3x - 1). \end{aligned} \right\} \tag{2}$$

3. On account of (1), equation (2) is true at all values of x except possibly $x = 1$, $x = -2$, and $x = \frac{1}{3}$, for which denominators vanish in (1). Hence, (2) is true for *infinitely many values of x.* Therefore, by Theorem I of page 368, (2) is true for *all* values of x, *including* $x = 1$, $x = -2$, and $x = \frac{1}{3}$. Thus, from (2),

when $x = 1$, $-6 = A \cdot 0 + 6B + C \cdot 0$, *or* $B = -1$;

when $x = -2$, $84 = 21C$, *or* $C = 4$;

when $x = \frac{1}{3}$, $\frac{28}{9} = -\frac{14}{9}A$, *or* $A = -2$.

4. On substituting for A, B, and C in (1), we obtain

$$\frac{7x^2 - 23x + 10}{(3x - 1)(x - 1)(x + 2)} = -\frac{2}{3x - 1} - \frac{1}{x - 1} + \frac{4}{x + 2}. \tag{3}$$

Second solution. (This method is *not recommended in Case* I.) By Theorem I, like powers of x on the two sides of (2) have equal coefficients. Hence,

for x^2: $7 = A + 3B + 3C$;

for x: $-23 = A + 5B - 4C$;   (4)

for the constant term: $10 = -2A - 2B + C$.

On solving system (4), we obtain $A = -2$; $B = -1$; $C = 4$.

ILLUSTRATION 1. By use of (3),

$$\int \frac{(7x^2 - 23x + 10)dx}{(3x - 1)(x - 1)(x + 2)} = -\int \frac{2\,dx}{3x - 1} - \int \frac{dx}{x - 1} + \int \frac{4\,dx}{x + 2}$$

$$= -\tfrac{2}{3} \ln |\, 3x - 1\,| - \ln |\, x - 1\,| + 4 \ln |\, x + 2\,| + C, \text{ or}$$

$$= \ln \frac{k(x + 2)^4}{|\, x - 1\,|\,(3x - 1)^{\frac{2}{3}}} \quad \text{where} \quad C = \ln k, \text{ with } k > 0.$$

Case II. *Resolution of $N(x)/D(x)$ into partial fractions when $D(x)$ has just linear factors, some repeated:* If $(\alpha x + \beta)^k$ *is a factor, there are k partial fractions,*

$$\frac{A_1}{\alpha x + \beta} + \frac{A_2}{(\alpha x + \beta)^2} + \cdots + \frac{A_k}{(\alpha x + \beta)^k}. \tag{5}$$

EXAMPLE 2. Resolve into partial fractions: $\dfrac{4x^3 + 16x^2 - 5x + 3}{(x - 1)^2(x + 2)^2}$.

Solution. 1. There exists just one set of numbers A, B, C, and D such that, for all values of x except $x = 1$ and $x = -2$,

$$\frac{4x^3 + 16x^2 - 5x + 3}{(x - 1)^2(x + 2)^2} = \frac{A}{(x - 1)^2} + \frac{B}{x - 1} + \frac{C}{(x + 2)^2} + \frac{D}{x + 2}. \tag{6}$$

2. On clearing of fractions in (6), we obtain

$$4x^3 + 16x^2 - 5x + 3 \tag{7}$$

$$= A(x + 2)^2 + B(x - 1)(x + 2)^2 + C(x - 1)^2 + D(x + 2)(x - 1)^2 \tag{8}$$

$$\left. \begin{aligned} &= (B + D)x^3 + (A + 3B + C)x^2 \\ &\qquad + (4A - 2C - 3D)x + (4A - 4B + C + 2D). \end{aligned} \right\} \tag{9}$$

In (9), we expanded (3) and collected corresponding powers of x.

3. By Theorem I of page 368, (7) and (8) are equal for all values of x, *even when $x = 1$ and $x = -2$.* Thus, we obtain two of A, B, C, and D by substituting $x = 1$ and $x = -2$ in (7) and (8). Also, we find the necessary two additional equations involving A, B, C, and D by equating coefficients for *two pairs of like powers of x* in (7) and (8).

Place $x = 1$ in (7) and (8): $18 = 9A$,   *or* $A = 2$. $\tag{10}$

Place $x = -2$ in (7) and (8): $45 = 9C$,   *or* $C = 5$. $\tag{11}$

Place $x = 0$ in (7) and (8): $3 = 4A - 4B + C + 2D$. $\tag{12}$

Equate coefficients of x^3 in (7) and (8): $4 = B + D$. $\tag{13}$

On using $A = 2$ and $C = 5$, from (12) and (13) we obtain

$$B + D = 4 \quad and \quad -2B + D = -5. \tag{14}$$

The solution of (14) gives $B = 3$ and $D = 1$. Thus,

$$\frac{4x^3 + 16x^2 - 5x + 3}{(x - 1)^2(x + 2)^2} = \frac{2}{(x - 1)^2} + \frac{3}{x - 1} + \frac{5}{(x + 2)^2} + \frac{1}{x + 2}. \tag{15}$$

Comment. By placing $x = 0$ in (7) and (8), we obtain the equivalent of equating constant terms in (7) and (9). Notice that (9) was not used in the solution. We could have used (9) to write *four* equations for A, B, C, and D, by equating the coefficients of like powers of x in (7) and (9).

ILLUSTRATION 2. By use of (15),

$$\int \frac{4x^3 + 16x^2 - 5x + 3}{(x - 1)^2(x + 2)^2} dx = \int \frac{2\,dx}{(x - 1)^2} + \int \frac{3\,dx}{x - 1} + \int \frac{5\,dx}{(x + 2)^2} + \int \frac{dx}{x + 2}$$

$$= -\frac{2}{x - 1} + 3\ln|x - 1| - \frac{5}{x + 2} + \ln|x + 2| + C.$$

The problem of factoring a denominator $D(x)$ in a rational fraction $N(x)/D(x)$ is equivalent to the problem of solving the equation $D(x) = 0$. This is true because, *if $x = r$ is a solution of $D(x) = 0$, then $(x - r)$ is a factor of $D(x)$.* Solutions of $D(x) = 0$ sometimes can be obtained by use of the following familiar theorem from algebra, with synthetic division as an aid.

If an equation $a_0 + a_1x + a_2x^2 + \cdots + a_{n-1}x^{n-1} + a_nx^n = 0,$

with integral coefficients, has a rational root c/d, where c/d is in lowest terms, then c is a factor of a_0 and d is a factor of a_n.

EXERCISE 115

Integrate. Use Table III *if necessary.*

1. $\displaystyle\int \frac{(5x + 16)dx}{(x - 4)(2x + 1)}.$

2. $\displaystyle\int \frac{(13x + 18)dx}{(3x + 2)(x - 4)}.$

3. $\displaystyle\int_8^{10} \frac{(2x - 5)dx}{x^2 - 5x - 14}.$

4. $\displaystyle\int_0^4 \frac{(7x - 14)dx}{x^2 - 3x - 10}.$

5. $\displaystyle\int_2^5 \frac{(2x^2 - 13x - 16)dx}{(x + 2)(x - 1)(2x + 1)}.$

6. $\displaystyle\int \frac{(2x^2 - 16x + 6)dx}{x(2x^2 - 5x + 2)}.$

7. $\displaystyle\int \frac{2x^2 + 8x - 12}{x^2 - 4} dx.$

8. $\displaystyle\int \frac{9x^2 + 14x + 3}{2x^3 + 5x^2 + 3x} dx.$

9. $\displaystyle\int \frac{(x^2 + 1)dx}{(x - 1)^3}.$

10. $\displaystyle\int_1^3 \frac{x^2 - 4x + 3}{x(x + 1)^2} dx.$

11. $\displaystyle\int_1^4 \frac{8\,dx}{(x + 2)^4}.$

12. $\displaystyle\int \frac{3t^2 + 10t + 9}{(t + 2)^3} dt.$

13. $\displaystyle\int \frac{(5x^2 - 11x + 5)dx}{(x - 1)(x^2 - 3x + 2)}.$

14. $\displaystyle\int \frac{x^3 - 3x^2 + 2x - 2}{(x^2 - x)(x - 1)^2} dx.$

15. $\displaystyle\int \frac{x^4 - 4x^3 + x + 27}{x(x^2 - 6x + 9)} dx.$

16. $\displaystyle\int \frac{(6x^2 + 6)dx}{2x^3 - 5x^2 - 4x + 3}.$

17. $\displaystyle\int \frac{17 + 52x + 30x^2 - 24x^3}{(3x^2 - x - 2)^2} dx.$

18. Find the area of the region R bounded by the x-axis, the lines $x = -4$ and $x = -6$, and the curve $y = \dfrac{x + 2}{(x - 1)(x + 3)}.$

19. In a bimolecular chemical reaction, let α and β be the original amounts of the two reacting substances, and let x be the amount of each which will react in t time-units. Then, $dx/dt = k(\alpha - x)(\beta - x)$, where $k > 0$. Find t in terms of x if $k = 4$, $\alpha = 3$, and $\beta = 2$.

139. CASES III AND IV FOR PARTIAL FRACTIONS

Case III. *Resolution of $N(x)/D(x)$ into partial fractions when $D(x)$ has one or more quadratic factors, not repeated: If $(px^2 + qx + r)$ occurs just once as a factor, then there is a partial fraction*

$$\frac{Bx + C}{px^2 + qx + r}. \tag{1}$$

EXAMPLE 1. Resolve into partial fractions: $\dfrac{3x^2 - x + 1}{(x + 1)(x^2 - x + 3)}$.

Solution. 1. We seek A, B, and C so that

$$\frac{3x^2 - x + 1}{(x + 1)(x^2 - x + 3)} = \frac{A}{x + 1} + \frac{Bx + C}{x^2 - x + 3}. \tag{2}$$

2. On clearing of fractions in (2), we obtain

$$3x^2 - x + 1 = A(x^2 - x + 3) + (Bx + C)(x + 1). \tag{3}$$

Place $x = -1$ in (3): $\qquad\qquad 5 = 5A$, $\quad$ or $\quad A = 1$.

Place $x = 0$ in (3): $\qquad 1 = 3A + C$; $\quad$ hence $\quad C = 1 - 3 = -2$.

Equate coefficients of x^2 in (3): $\qquad 3 = A + B$; $\quad$ hence $\quad B = 2$.

Thus, $\qquad \dfrac{3x^2 - x + 1}{(x + 1)(x^2 - x + 3)} = \dfrac{1}{x + 1} + \dfrac{2x - 2}{x^2 - x + 3}. \tag{4}$

ILLUSTRATION 1. To obtain the following integral, we resolve the integrand into its partial fractions, as in (4), and then use the method of Example 1 of page 289:

$$\int \frac{(3x^2 - x + 1)dx}{(x + 1)(x^2 - x + 3)} = \int \frac{dx}{x + 1} + \int \frac{(2x - 2)dx}{x^2 - x + 3} \tag{5}$$

$$= \ln |x + 1| + \int \frac{(2x - 1)dx}{x^2 - x + 3} - \int \frac{dx}{(x - \frac{1}{2})^2 + \frac{11}{4}}$$

$$= \ln |x + 1| + \ln |x^2 - x + 3| - \frac{2}{\sqrt{11}} \text{Arctan} \frac{2x - 1}{\sqrt{11}} + C.$$

Case IV. *Resolution of $N(x)/D(x)$ into partial fractions when $D(x)$ has one or more repeated quadratic factors: If $(px^2 + qx + r)$ occurs just h times as a factor, then there are h partial fractions as given in (6) on page 369.*

EXAMPLE 2. Resolve into partial fractions: $\dfrac{2x^4 - 7x^2 - 37x - 28}{(x + 2)(x^2 + 2x + 5)^2}$.

Solution. 1. We seek A, B, C, D, and E so that

$$\frac{2x^4 - 7x^2 - 37x - 28}{(x + 2)(x^2 + 2x + 5)^2} = \frac{A}{x + 2} + \frac{Bx + C}{(x^2 + 2x + 5)^2} + \frac{Dx + E}{x^2 + 2x + 5}. \tag{6}$$

On clearing of fractions in (6), we find

$$\left. \begin{array}{l} 2x^4 - 7x^2 - 37x - 28 = \\[4pt] A(x^2 + 2x + 5)^2 + (Bx + C)(x + 2) + (Dx + E)(x + 2)(x^2 + 2x + 5). \end{array} \right\} \tag{7}$$

2. We obtain five equations involving A, B, C, D, and E from (7):

Place $x = -2$: $50 = 25A$.   (8)

Place $x = 0$: $-28 = 25A + 2C + 10E$.   (9)

Equate coefs. of x^4: $2 = A + D$.   (10)

Equate coefs. of x^3: $0 = 4A + 4D + E$.   (11)

Equate coefs. of x^2: $-7 = 14A + B + 9D + 4E$.   (12)

3. From (8)–(12), we obtain $A = 2; B = -3; C = 1; D = 0; E = -8$;

$$\frac{2x^4 - 7x^2 - 37x - 28}{(x + 2)(x^2 + 2x + 5)^2} = \frac{2}{x + 2} + \frac{1 - 3x}{(x^2 + 2x + 5)^2} - \frac{8}{x^2 + 2x + 5}. \quad (13)$$

In Case IV, we meet integrals of the type $\int du/(a^2 + u^2)^n$, where n is an integer and $n > 1$. Then, we may apply the reduction formula *

$$\int \frac{du}{(a^2 + u^2)^n} = \frac{1}{(2n - 2)a^2}\left[\frac{u}{(a^2 + u^2)^{n-1}} + (2n - 3)\int \frac{du}{(a^2 + u^2)^{n-1}}\right], \quad (14)$$

which gives a new integral with the exponent of $(a^2 + u^2)$ reduced by 1. By use of (14), repeated if $n > 2$, we arrive where the exponent of $(a^2 + u^2)$ is 1 and the final integral is a fundamental form. With a denominator $(px^2 + qx + r)^n$, we apply a method like that of Example 1 on page 289, and then use (14).

ILLUSTRATION 2. To integrate the fraction in Example 2, we integrate the right-hand side in (13), where the major problem is to integrate the second fraction. If I represents its integral,

$$I = \int \frac{(1 - 3x)dx}{(x^2 + 2x + 5)^2} = -\frac{3}{2}\int \frac{(2x + 2)dx}{(x^2 + 2x + 5)^2} + 4\int \frac{dx}{[(x + 1)^2 + 4]^2}; \quad (15)$$

$$I = \frac{3}{2} \cdot \frac{1}{x^2 + 2x + 5} + 4\int \frac{du}{(u^2 + 4)^2}, \quad (16)$$

where $u = x + 1$. From (14) with $n = 2$ and $a^2 = 4$,

$$\int \frac{du}{(u^2 + 4)^2} = \frac{1}{8}\left(\frac{u}{u^2 + 4} + \frac{1}{2}\operatorname{Arctan}\frac{u}{2}\right).$$

Hence, $I = \dfrac{x + 4}{2(x^2 + 2x + 5)} + \dfrac{1}{4}\operatorname{Arctan}\dfrac{x + 1}{2} + C.$

If f is a rational function, then $f(x)$ is equal to the sum of a polynomial in x and possibly a set of partial fractions, of types met in the preceding Cases I–IV. The indefinite integral of a polynomial is a polynomial. Apart from constant factors, the indefinite integral of a partial fraction is a logarithmic function in Case I; either a logarithmic function or a rational fraction in Case II; an arctangent function, perhaps plus a rational function, in Cases III and IV. Hence, there exists an expression for $\int f(x)dx$ as a sum of elementary functions of the preceding types. Thus, we have proved the following result.

Theorem IV. *If f is a rational function, then there exists† an expression for $\int f(x)dx$ in terms of elementary functions of x.*

---

* Instead of applying (14), we may use a trigonometric substitution, $u = a \tan t$.
† The expression can be found only if we are able to factor all denominators involved.

EXERCISE 116

Integrate.

1. $\int \dfrac{3x^2 + 5x + 6}{(x + 1)(x^2 + 3)}\, dx.$

2. $\int \dfrac{x^2 - 8x - 4}{(x - 2)(x^2 + 4)}\, dx.$

3. $\int \dfrac{2x^2 + 11x - 7}{(2x - 5)(x^2 + 2)}\, dx.$

4. $\int \dfrac{(z^2 - 7z + 8)dz}{(z + 2)(2z^2 + 5)}.$

5. $\int \dfrac{4x^2 + 3x + 14}{x^3 - 8}\, dx.$

6. $\int \dfrac{4x^3 + 4x^2 + 54x + 18}{x^4 - 81}\, dx.$

7. $\int \dfrac{8x^3 + x^2 + 19x + 5}{(2x^2 + 3)(x^2 + 5)}\, dx.$

8. $\int \dfrac{x^3 + x^2 + 7x + 5}{x^4 + 4x^2 + 3}\, dx.$

9. $\int \dfrac{(4x + 5)dx}{(x^2 + 9)^2}.$

10. $\int \dfrac{(6t + 3)dt}{(4t^2 + 1)^2}.$

11. $\int \dfrac{dy}{(4y^2 + 9)^2}.$

12. $\int \dfrac{2x^3 + x + 3}{(x^2 + 1)^2}\, dx.$

13. $\int \dfrac{x^3 + x^2 + 2}{(x^2 + 2)^2}\, dx.$

14. $\int \dfrac{(3x^2 - 5x + 6)dx}{(1 + 3x)(1 - 2x - 15x^2)}.$

15. $\int \dfrac{3x^4 + 20x^2 + 25x}{(x^2 + 3)^2(x - 1)}\, dx.$

16. $\int_{-1}^{2} \dfrac{6x^2 - 9x + 27}{x^3 + 27}\, dx.$

17. $\int_{0}^{3} \dfrac{6x^2 + 5x + 12}{(x + 2)(x^2 + 9)}\, dx.$

18. $\int \dfrac{4x^3 + 6x - 36}{(x^2 + 2x + 5)^2}\, dx.$

19. $\int_{-\pi/4}^{\pi/3} \dfrac{4 \sec \theta \tan \theta \, d\theta}{\sec^3 \theta + 4 \sec \theta}.$

20. $\int \dfrac{(2 + 5x^2)dx}{20 + x^2 - x^4}.$

21. $\int \dfrac{(x^2 + 33)dx}{2x^4 - 15x^2 - 27}.$

140. HALF–ANGLE SUBSTITUTION

If $f(u)$ is a rational function of direct trigonometric functions of u, then the half-angle substitution

$$z = \tan \tfrac{1}{2}u \tag{1}$$

changes $\int f(u)du$ into the form $\int R(z)dz$, where R is a rational function of z.

To make use of (1), we employ the identities

$$\sin u = 2 \sin \tfrac{1}{2}u \cos \tfrac{1}{2}u; \quad \cos u = \cos^2 \tfrac{1}{2}u - \sin^2 \tfrac{1}{2}u. \tag{2}$$

From (1), we choose the solution u where

$$\tfrac{1}{2}u = \text{Arctan } z \quad or \quad u = 2 \text{ Arctan } z. \tag{3}$$

By use of (1) and a sketch like Figure 193 on page 309, we find

$$\sin \tfrac{1}{2}u = \frac{z}{\sqrt{1 + z^2}}; \quad \cos \tfrac{1}{2}u = \frac{1}{\sqrt{1 + z^2}}. \tag{4}$$

Hence, from (2), (3), and (4),

$$du = \frac{2\, dz}{1 + z^2}; \tag{5}$$

$$\sin u = \frac{2z}{1 + z^2}; \quad \cos u = \frac{1 - z^2}{1 + z^2}. \tag{6}$$

In using (1), first express sec u, csc u, tan u, and cot u, if they occur, in terms of sin u and cos u, and then use (5) and (6).

EXAMPLE 1. Obtain
$$I = \int \frac{dx}{\tan 2x + \sin 2x}.$$

Solution. If we let $u = 2x$, then
$$I = \frac{1}{2} \int \frac{\cos 2x\,(2\,dx)}{\sin 2x\,(1 + \cos 2x)} = \frac{1}{2} \int \frac{\cos u\,du}{\sin u\,(1 + \cos u)}.$$

To integrate, substitute $z = \tan \frac{1}{2}u$, or $z = \tan x$. Then, from (5) and (6),
$$I = \frac{1}{2} \int \frac{\dfrac{1 - z^2}{1 + z^2} \cdot \dfrac{2\,dz}{1 + z^2}}{\dfrac{2z}{1 + z^2} \cdot \dfrac{2}{1 + z^2}} = \frac{1}{4} \int \frac{dz}{z} - \frac{1}{4} \int z\,dz$$

$$= \tfrac{1}{4} \ln |z| - \tfrac{1}{8}z^2 + C = \tfrac{1}{4} \ln | \tan x | - \tfrac{1}{8} \tan^2 x + C.$$

Comment. Instead of introducing u in the preceding solution, we could have substituted $z = \tan x$ immediately.

By use of (1), and Theorem IV on page 374, we justify the following statement.

If $f(u)$ is a rational function of direct trigonometric functions of u, then there exists an expression for $\int f(u)du$ in terms of elementary functions of u.

It should be noted that (1) is useless from a practical standpoint unless the associated function R can be expanded conveniently into partial fractions. Thus the integrands in the next exercise had to be chosen with great care in order to offer reasonable problems.

EXERCISE 117

Integrate by use of a half-angle substitution.

1. $\displaystyle\int \frac{dy}{3 + 5 \cos y}.$

2. $\displaystyle\int \frac{dx}{13 + 5 \cos x}.$

3. $\displaystyle\int \frac{dx}{1 - \sin x}.$

4. $\displaystyle\int \frac{dw}{1 + 3 \sin 2w}.$

5. $\displaystyle\int_0^{\pi/2} \frac{dx}{13 + 12 \cos x}.$

6. $\displaystyle\int \frac{dx}{1 - \sin 2x}.$

7. $\displaystyle\int \frac{dx}{\tan 3x + \sin 3x}.$

8. $\displaystyle\int \frac{dx}{2 \sin x + \cos x}.$

9. $\displaystyle\int_{-\pi/3}^{\pi/2} \frac{dx}{1 + 2 \cos x}.$

10. $\displaystyle\int \frac{dx}{1 + \sin 3x}.$

11. $\displaystyle\int \frac{dx}{1 + 3 \cos 2x}.$

12. $\displaystyle\int \frac{dy}{5 \sin y + 1}.$

13. $\displaystyle\int_0^{\pi/2} \frac{du}{4 + 5 \sin u}.$

14. $\displaystyle\int \frac{dx}{\cot 2x + \cos 2x}.$

15. $\displaystyle\int \frac{dz}{5 \sec z - 4}.$

16. $\displaystyle\int_{-\pi/2}^{\pi/2} \frac{dw}{5 + 3 \sin w + 4 \cos w}.$

17. $\displaystyle\int \frac{dx}{5 \sin \frac{1}{2}x + 12 \cos \frac{1}{2}x + 13}.$

18. In an $r\theta$-system of polar coordinates, a region R is bounded by the polar axis and the parabola $r = 1/(1 - \sin \theta)$. Find the area of R.

141. MISCELLANEOUS ALGEBRAIC RATIONALIZATION

I. *If $f(x)$ is a rational function of powers of x with rational exponents, then a rationalizing substitution for $\int f(x)dx$ is*

$$u = x^{\frac{1}{n}} \quad or \quad x = u^n,$$

where the positive integer n is the lowest common denominator of the exponents of x in $f(x)$.

EXAMPLE 1. Integrate: $\qquad I = \int \dfrac{x^{\frac{1}{4}}\,dx}{1 + x^{\frac{1}{2}}}.$

Solution. Let $x^{\frac{1}{4}} = u$, or $u^4 = x$. Then, $dx = 4u^3\,du$;

$$I = \int \frac{4u^4\,du}{1 + u^2} = 4\int (u^2 - 1)du + 4\int \frac{du}{1 + u^2}$$

$$= \tfrac{4}{3}u^3 - 4u + 4\,\text{Arctan}\,u + C = \tfrac{4}{3}x^{\frac{3}{4}} - 4x^{\frac{1}{4}} + 4\,\text{Arctan}\,x^{\frac{1}{4}} + C.$$

II. *If n is a positive integer greater than 1, and if $f(x)$ is a rational function of x and $\sqrt[n]{a + bx}$, then a rationalizing substitution for $\int f(x)dx$ is*

$$u = \sqrt[n]{a + bx}, \quad or \quad u^n = a + bx. \tag{1}$$

A simple case of (II) was introduced on page 285. Also, (I) is a special case of (II), with simply x in place of $(a + bx)$.

ILLUSTRATION 1. The substitution $u = \sqrt{2t + 3}$ simplifies $\int \dfrac{(6t + 4)dt}{(5t - 1)\sqrt{2t + 3}}.$

Sometimes, a substitution which *simplifies the appearance* of a radicand $f(x)$ also may change $\int f(x)dx$ to a form which can be integrated easily. This elementary approach suggests (I) and (II), and also other useful substitutions.

ILLUSTRATION 2. The substitution $u = \sqrt{2 + x^3}$ simplifies $\int \dfrac{x^5\,dx}{\sqrt{2 + x^3}}.$

If $f(x)$ is an irrational algebraic integrand involving different radicals, it may be possible to obtain $\int f(x)dx$ by making a sequence of substitutions, where each one rationalizes one radical. Or, by algebraic manipulation, $f(x)$ may be placed in a new form which is more favorable for integration.

ILLUSTRATION 3. To obtain $\qquad I = \int \dfrac{x\,dx}{\sqrt{x} + \sqrt{x + 1}},$

we would first rationalize the denominator:

$$I = \int \frac{x(\sqrt{x + 1} - \sqrt{x})dx}{x + 1 - x} = \int x\sqrt{x + 1}\,dx - \int x^{\frac{3}{2}}\,dx.$$

Most of the formulas in a table of integrals, such as Table VII, can be derived by the methods presented previously in this text. However, special devices are essential for obtaining certain integration formulas, particularly various reduction formulas. Any formula in Table VII can be verified by showing that the derivatives of the two sides of the equality are equal.

When speed rather than fundamental training in methods is an essential, frequently it is desirable to use Table VII. Also, on certain occasions when our previous methods do not lead to convenient integration, some formula from Table VII may be indispensable. The details involved in applying Table VII are similar to those used with the standard forms of Chapter Eleven. Hereafter, use Table VII to the extent directed by the instructor.

ILLUSTRATION 4. The following integration uses (51) of Table VII:

$$\int \frac{dx}{(4x^2 - 9)^{\frac{3}{2}}} = \frac{1}{2}\int \frac{2\,dx}{(4x^2 - 9)^{\frac{3}{2}}} = \frac{1}{2}\int \frac{du}{(u^2 - 9)^{\frac{3}{2}}} \qquad (u = 2x)$$

$$= \frac{1}{2}\cdot\frac{-u}{9\sqrt{u^2 - 9}} + C = -\frac{x}{9\sqrt{4x^2 - 9}} + C.$$

142. RECAPITULATION ABOUT INDEFINITE INTEGRATION

In early chapters, we learned how to obtain the derivative of *any* function $f(x)$ expressible in terms of the elementary functions of analysis. In contrast, it is proved at more advanced levels that many types of elementary functions $f(x)$ exist such that $\int f(x)dx$ cannot be expressed in terms of elementary functions.

Hereafter, let us say that an *elementary formula* exists for $\int f(x)dx$ if we can prove that $\int f(x)dx$ is expressible in terms of the elementary functions. In view of preceding remarks, regardless of how many special methods are developed for obtaining elementary formulas for indefinite integrals, we must anticipate meeting integrands to which the methods do not apply.

ILLUSTRATION 1. In general, if $g(x)$ is a polynomial of degree 3 or 4 in x, and if f is an irrational function which is a rational function of x and $\sqrt{g(x)}$, then $\int f(x)dx$ is called an **elliptic integral.** Thus, if $k > 0$,

$$\int \sqrt{(1 - x^2)(1 - k^2x^2)}\,dx$$

is an elliptic integral. In more advanced mathematics, it is shown that elliptic integrals cannot be expressed in terms of elementary functions. Howev r, a new class of functions, called **elliptic functions,** then is introduced and elliptic integrals are expressed in terms of these functions.

ILLUSTRATION 2. $\int \sqrt{1 - x^4}\,dx$ is an elliptic integral.

Previously, we have seen that an elementary formula for $\int f(x)dx$ exists if $f(x)$ is of one of the following types.

I. *A rational function of* x.

II. *A rational function of direct trigonometric functions of* kx, *where* k *is some constant.*

III. *A rational function of* x *and* $\sqrt{g(x)}$, *where* $g(x)$ *is a polynomial of degree 1 or 2 in* x.

By use of standard integration forms, the general method of substitution of a new variable, and integration by parts, we can find an elementary formula for $\int f(x)dx$ in many cases where $f(x)$ is not of one of types I–III.

EXERCISE 118

Integrate without using a trigonometric substitution.

1. $\int \dfrac{dx}{x^{\frac{1}{2}} + 2x^{\frac{2}{3}}}$.

2. $\int_{16}^{81} \dfrac{dx}{x^{\frac{3}{4}} - x^{\frac{1}{2}}}$.

3. $\int \dfrac{x^3\,dx}{\sqrt{9 + x^2}}$.

4. $\int \dfrac{x^3\,dx}{(4 + x^2)^{\frac{3}{2}}}$.

5. $\int \dfrac{(x + 3)\sqrt{x}}{x - 1}\,dx$.

6. $\int \dfrac{dx}{x\sqrt[3]{8 + x^3}}$.

7. $\int_6^{25} \dfrac{dx}{(x + 2)^{\frac{2}{3}} + (x + 2)^{\frac{1}{3}}}$.

8. $\int_2^{25/3} \dfrac{dx}{8 + \sqrt[3]{2 + 3x}}$.

9. $\int \dfrac{x^5\,dx}{\sqrt{4 + x^3}}$.

10. $\int \dfrac{dx}{x^2(4 + x^4)^{\frac{3}{4}}}$.

11. $\int \dfrac{(1 + x^4)^{\frac{3}{4}}\,dx}{x^8}$.

Hint for Problem 10. Substitute $x = 1/u$.

Integrate by any method.

12. $\int \dfrac{x\,dx}{(x^2 - 4)^{\frac{1}{2}} + (x^2 - 4)^{\frac{3}{2}}}$.

13. $\int \dfrac{dx}{\sqrt{2x} - \sqrt{x + 4}}$.

14. $\int \sqrt{1 - e^x}\,dx$.

15. $\int \sqrt{1 + e^{2x}}\,dx$.

16. $\int \sqrt{\dfrac{1 - u}{1 + u}}\,du$.

17. $\int \sqrt{\dfrac{4 - x}{2 + x}}\,dx$.

18. $\int \dfrac{\sqrt{1 + 2e^x}\,dx}{e^x - 1}$.

19. Obtain $\int \dfrac{dx}{x^4\sqrt{1 + 4x^2}}$ by substituting $\sqrt{1 + 4x^2} = ux$.

Prove the formula in Table VII by an algebraic substitution.

20. Formula 35.   **21.** Formula 19.   **22.** Formula 20.

23–33. By use of Table VII, obtain the results for Problems 2, 3, 4, 5, 6, 8, 10, 12, 15, 19, and 32, respectively, of Exercise 95, page 310.

★*Note 1.* An expression of the form $v^h(a + bv^k)^{\frac{p}{q}}\,dv$ where h and k are rational numbers, p and q are integers, and p/q is in lowest terms, is called a *binomial differential*. If r is the lowest common denominator of the fractions represented by h and k (possibly integers), the substitution $v = u^r$ changes the given expression into one of the form

$u^m(a + bu^n)^{\frac{p}{q}}\,du$, where m and n are integers. Then, Problems 34 and 35 apply to this normal form.

★*Prove that* $\int u^m(a + bu^n)^{\frac{p}{q}}\,du$ *can be rationalized by the substitution under the given hypothesis about the integers m, n, p, and q, where $q > 0$ and p/q is in lowest terms.*

34. If $(m + 1)/n$ is an integer, substitute $a + bu^n = w^q$.

35. If $\left(\dfrac{m + 1}{n} + \dfrac{p}{q}\right)$ is an integer, substitute $a + bu^n = w^q u^n$.

★**36.** Apply one of Problems 34 and 35 to $\int \dfrac{\sqrt{1 + 4x^4}}{x^3}\,dx$.

143. TRAPEZOIDAL RULE FOR INTEGRATION

A primary objective of indefinite integration is to provide a means for the computation of definite integrals, by use of the fundamental theorem of integral calculus,

$$\int_a^b f(x)dx = F(b) - F(a), \quad where \quad F(x) = \int f(x)dx. \tag{1}$$

The result in (1) is of utility computationally only when we have such knowledge of $F(x)$ that its values can be computed. Hence, if it is either impossible or inconvenient for us to find a formula for $F(x)$, we have recourse to numerical methods for evaluating $\int_a^b f(x)dx$ approximately, without involving $\int f(x)dx$ and (1). The ideal, then, is to employ a method which is capable of obtaining $\int_a^b f(x)dx$ with any specified degree of accuracy, provided that sufficient computation is performed. The advent of electronic digital computing machines has made it possible to employ various methods of numerical integration with great convenience. Most of these methods were well known, although cumbersome to apply, before modern high speed computing machines were invented. The most obvious method of numerical integration is to use directly the definition of a definite integral as a limit of approximating sums, as illustrated in Exercise 51 on page 181. In the present section, we shall discuss the so-called **trapezoidal method** for approximate integration.

As a basis for numerical integration, let us interpret $\int_a^b f(x)dx$ as an area. For illustration in figures, we shall assume that $f(x) \geqq 0$. If $f(x) < 0$ on a part of the interval (a, b), our future remarks should be interpreted as assigning a negative measure for the area of any region below the x-axis.

Let f be a function which is continuous on an interval $a \leqq x \leqq b$. Let σ be a partition of (a, b) into n equal subintervals, with the division points $\{x_i\}$, where

$$a = x_0 < x_1 < x_2 < \cdots < x_n = b, \tag{2}$$

and the length of each interval of σ is Δx. Consider the graph of $y = f(x)$ in Figure 246, where $y_i = f(x_i)$, and Q_i is the point (x_i, y_i). Construct the ordinate of each point Q_i, and join each pair (Q_{i-1}, Q_i) by a line segment. Thus, n trapezoids are formed with their bases on the x-axis and the opposite sides as chords of the graph of $y = f(x)$. Let R be the region bounded by the x-axis, the curve

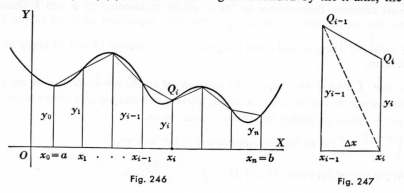

Fig. 246

Fig. 247

$y = f(x)$, and the lines $x = a$ and $x = b$. We consider the sum, τ_σ, of the areas of the n trapezoids as an approximation to the area, A, of R. That is, we shall compute τ_σ as an approximation to $\int_a^b f(x)dx$.

The nature of the typical trapezoid of Figure 246 is shown in Figure 247. On cutting this trapezoid into two triangles, its area is seen to be

$$\tfrac{1}{2}y_{i-1}\Delta x + \tfrac{1}{2}y_i\Delta x, \quad or \quad \tfrac{1}{2}(y_{i-1} + y_i)\Delta x. \tag{3}$$

Hence, with $i = 1, 2, \cdots, n$ in (3), we obtain

$$\tau_\sigma = \tfrac{1}{2}\Delta x[(y_0 + y_1) + (y_1 + y_2) + \cdots + (y_{n-2} + y_{n-1}) + (y_{n-1} + y_n)]. \tag{4}$$

Each ordinate y_i, except for y_0 and y_n, occurs *twice* in (4). Hence,

$$\tau_\sigma = \tfrac{1}{2}(y_0 + 2y_1 + 2y_2 + \cdots + 2y_{n-1} + y_n)\Delta x. \tag{5}$$

When a particular sum τ_σ is accepted as an approximation to $\int_a^b f(x)dx$, it is said that the *trapezoidal rule* is being used.

Note 1. The trapezoid of Figure 247 has the same area as some rectangle on the same base with an altitude η_i where $y_{i-1} \leqq \eta_i \leqq y_i$. This altitude would be the value of $f(x)$ at some point ξ_i where $x_{i-1} \leqq \xi_i \leqq x_i$. Then, in place of (3), we could use $f(\xi_i)\Delta x$, and $\tau_\sigma = \sum_{i=1}^{n} f(\xi_i)\Delta x$. Thus, each sum τ_σ has the same value as a *related sum S_σ*, as met in (3) on page 178, and we are assured that $\tau_\sigma \to \int_a^b f(x)dx$ as $n \to \infty$.

ILLUSTRATION 1. Usually, if $Q(x)$ is a polynomial of degree 3 in x, then $\int_a^b \sqrt{Q(x)}dx$ is an **elliptic integral** and we cannot express $\int \sqrt{Q(x)}\, dx$ in terms of known functions, at the level of this text. Let $H = \int_0^2 \sqrt{1 + x^3}\, dx$, which is an elliptic integral. We shall compute H by the trapezoidal rule, with the interval $0 \leqq x \leqq 2$ divided into 8 equal parts, so that $n = 8$ in (5). We obtain the following ordinates of the graph of $y = \sqrt{1 + x^3}$; $\Delta x = \tfrac{1}{4}$ for (5).

i	0	1	2	3	4	5	6	7	8
x_i	0	$\tfrac{1}{4}$	$\tfrac{1}{2}$	$\tfrac{3}{4}$	1	$\tfrac{5}{4}$	$\tfrac{3}{2}$	$\tfrac{7}{2}$	2
y_i	1.000	1.008	1.061	1.192	1.414	1.718	2.092	2.522	3

Then, from (5), we obtain the following approximation to H:

$$\tau = \tfrac{1}{2} \cdot \tfrac{1}{4}(1 + 2.016 + 2.122 + 2.384 + 2.828 + 3.436 + 4.184 + 5.044 + 3).$$

Thus, $\tau = 3.26$, where we round off that place in which there is a possibility of an error due to rounding off in the table.

144. SIMPSON'S RULE, OR THE PARABOLIC RULE

As a preliminary, consider three points $K_0:(-h, y_0)$, $K_1:(0, y_1)$, and $K_2:(h, y_2)$, where $h > 0$; for convenience in Figure 248 on page 382, assume that y_0, y_1, and y_2 are positive. Then, in general,* there exists just one set (a, b, c) so that the parabola $y = ax^2 + bx + c$ passes through K_0, K_1, and K_2, as seen in Figure 248. We

* See Problem 48 on page 386 later.

desire to compute the area, α, of the region bounded by this parabola, the x-axis, and the ordinates $x = -h$ and $x = h$; the result is to be expressed in terms of y_0, y_1, y_2, and h. We find

$$\alpha = \int_{-h}^{h} (ax^2 + bx + c)\,dx = \left(\frac{ax^3}{3} + \frac{bx^2}{2} + cx\right)\Big]_{-h}^{h} = \frac{2ah^3}{3} + 2ch. \quad (1)$$

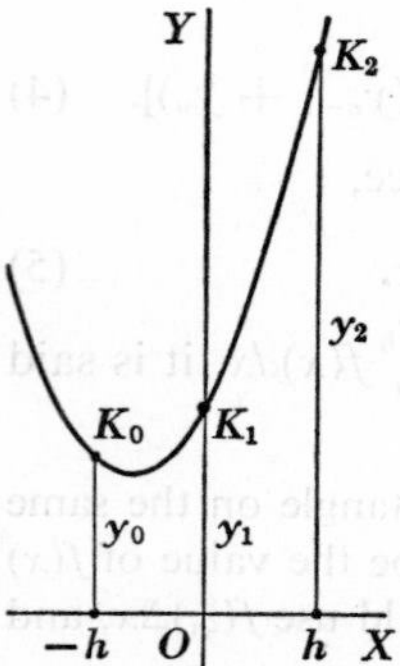

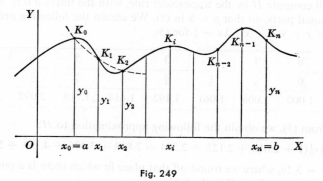

On the parabola, when $x = -h$, $x = 0$, and $x = h$, we obtain the following values for y, respectively:

$$\left.\begin{array}{ll} y = ah^2 - bh + c, \text{ or } & y_0 = ah^2 - bh + c; \\ y = c, \text{ or } & y_1 = c; \\ y = ah^2 + bh + c, \text{ or } & y_2 = ah^2 + bh + c. \end{array}\right\} \quad (2)$$

We verify that $y_0 + 4y_1 + y_2 = 2ah^2 + 6c$. From (1),*

$$\alpha = \tfrac{1}{3}h(y_0 + 4y_1 + y_2). \quad (3)$$

Now, let the function $f(x)$ be continuous, and consider approximating $\int_a^b f(x)\,dx$ as follows. Let σ be any partition of the interval (a, b), where σ has an *even number of subintervals*, and the division points

Fig. 248

$$a = x_0 < x_1 < x_2 < \cdots < x_n = b,$$

where n is an *even integer*, and where $x_i - x_{i-1} = \Delta x$, a constant, for all integers $i \geqq 1$. Let $y_i = f(x_i)$, and let K_i be the point (x_i, y_i) on the graph of $y = f(x)$, as in Figure 249. Then, pass a parabola through the points (K_0, K_1, K_2), as shown

Fig. 249

by the broken curve in Figure 249. The area of the region bounded by this curve, the x-axis, and the ordinates $x = x_0$ and $x = x_2$ is found from (3) with $h = \Delta x$:

$$\tfrac{1}{3}\Delta x(y_0 + 4y_1 + y_2). \quad (4)$$

Next, pass a parabola through (K_2, K_3, K_4). The area of the region bounded by this parabola, the x-axis, and the ordinates $x = x_2$ and $x = x_4$ is found from (3)

* It is easy to show by an independent discussion that (3) remains true if K_0, K_1, and K_2 lie on a line. In this case it is impossible to construct a parabola through the points.

with $h = \Delta x$, and (y_0, y_1, y_2) replaced by (y_2, y_3, y_4):

$$\tfrac{1}{3}(\Delta x)(y_2 + 4y_3 + y_4). \tag{5}$$

Thus, pass parabolas in succession through the sets of three successive points (K_4, K_5, K_6), (K_6, K_7, K_8), $\cdots$, (K_{n-2}, K_{n-1}, K_n), and obtain the areas of the regions between these parabolas and the x-axis, over the corresponding double intervals of the partition σ. Let τ_σ be the sum of the areas corresponding to these $n/2$ parabolas. Then,

$$\tau_\sigma = \tfrac{1}{3}\Delta x[(y_0 + 4y_1 + y_2) + (y_2 + 4y_3 + y_4) + \cdots + (y_{n-2} + 4y_{n-1} + y_n)];$$
$$\tau_\sigma = \tfrac{1}{3}\Delta x(y_0 + 4y_1 + 2y_2 + 4y_3 + \cdots + 2y_{n-2} + 4y_{n-1} + y_n). \tag{6}$$

In (6), aside from the coefficients 1 for y_0 and y_n, the coefficient is 4 for y_i if i is *odd* and is 2 if i is *even*. We take τ_σ as an approximation to $\int_a^b f(x)dx$, and refer to the preceding method as *Simpson's rule* (or, the *parabolic rule*).

EXAMPLE 1. Compute $\int_0^2 \sqrt{1 + x^3}\, dx$ by Simpson's rule, with 8 intervals.

Solution. Let H represent the integral. From the table of values for Illustration 1 on page 381, we obtain the following values, with $\Delta x = \tfrac{1}{4}$:

$$
\begin{array}{lll}
y_1 = 1.008 & y_2 = 1.061 & y_0 = 1.000 \\
y_3 = 1.192 & y_4 = 1.414 & y_8 = 3.000 \\
y_5 = 1.718 & y_6 = 2.092 & \text{sum} = 4.000 \\
y_7 = 2.522 & \text{sum} = 4.567 & \\
\text{sum} = 6.440 & &
\end{array}
$$

From (6), $\qquad \tau = \tfrac{1}{3} \cdot \tfrac{1}{4}[4.000 + 4(6.440) + 2(4.567)] \approx 3.24$,

to two decimal places. This may be compared with $\tau = 3.26$ in Illustration 1 on page 381. It is beyond our scope * to discuss the relative accuracy of these two results, although intuition leads us to consider $\tau = 3.24$ as the more accurate.

EXERCISE 119

Perform computation with accuracy to two decimal places.

1. Compute $\int_0^3 x^2\, dx$ by use of the trapezoidal rule, and Simpson's rule, with 12 intervals. Compare with the exact value.

Compute the integral approximately by use of the trapezoidal rule and Simpson's rule, with the specified number of intervals. Use logarithms where desirable.

2. $\int_0^2 \sqrt{4 + x^3}\, dx$; 8 intervals.   3. $\int_0^2 \sqrt{1 + x^4}\, dx$; 6 intervals.

4. $\int_0^1 \dfrac{dx}{1 + x^2}$; (just Simpson's rule) 10 intervals, and obtain the resulting approximation to π by knowledge of the integral.

5. $\int_0^2 \dfrac{dx}{\sqrt{1 + x^3}}$; 8 intervals.   6. $\int_0^{2.8} \dfrac{dx}{e^{x^2}}$; 14 intervals.

---

* For a full discussion of approximate integration, including error analysis, see *Numerical Calculus*, by William E. Milne (Princeton, N. J.: Princeton University Press, 1949).

EXERCISE 120 (*Review of Chapters Thirteen, Fourteen, and Fifteen*)

With $[r, \theta]$ *as polar coordinates, graph the equation without use of calculus. Draw any line or circle without computing solutions of the equation.*

1. $r = 5 \sin \theta$. **2.** $r \sin \theta = -4$. **3.** $r \cos \theta = -5$.

4. $r = 3(1 + \sin \theta)$. **5.** $r^2 = 25 \cos 2\theta$. **6.** $r = 6 \cos 2\theta$.

7. $r = \dfrac{4}{3 - 3 \sin \theta}$. **8.** $r = \dfrac{6}{2 - \cos \theta}$. **9.** $r = \dfrac{8}{2 - 4 \sin \theta}$.

Write parametric equations, in an xy-plane, for the curve with the given equation in polar coordinates, by use of θ *as the parameter. Also find the specified items.*

10. $r = -3 \cos \theta$; find the slope where $\theta = \frac{5}{6}\pi$.

11. $r = 2(1 + \cos \theta)$; find the slope where $\theta = \frac{7}{4}\pi$; find where the tangent is horizontal or vertical.

12. Transform $r^2 = 4 \sin 2\theta$ by rotating the polar axis through the angle $\frac{1}{4}\pi$.

Find the area of the specified region in an xy-plane or an rθ-plane.

13. Bounded by $y = x^2 + 6x - x^3$ and $y = 4x$.

14. Bounded by the line $y = 4$, the y-axis, and the curve $y = e^{-2x}$.

15. Bounded above by the curve in parametric form ($x = 3 \sin t, y = 4 \cos t$), and below by the line $y = 2$. Use an integral with respect to t.

16. Bounded by the curve $r = 3(1 + \sin \theta)$.

17. Bounded by the parabola $r = 2/(1 + \cos \theta)$ and the line $\theta = \frac{1}{2}\pi$.

18. The region interior to the curves $r = \sqrt{3} \sin \theta$ and $r = \cos \theta$.

Compute the value of the integral or prove it to be divergent.

19. $\displaystyle\int_0^3 \dfrac{dx}{\sqrt{3 - x}}$. **20.** $\displaystyle\int_1^4 \dfrac{dx}{(x - 4)^2}$. **21.** $\displaystyle\int_{-3}^5 \dfrac{dx}{x - 2}$.

22. $\displaystyle\int_0^\infty \dfrac{du}{(2u + 1)^2}$. **23.** $\displaystyle\int_{-5/2}^\infty \dfrac{dx}{4x^2 + 25}$. **24.** $\displaystyle\int_{-3/4}^{3/2} \dfrac{dz}{\sqrt{9 - 4z^2}}$.

25. $\displaystyle\int_0^\infty \dfrac{dx}{\sqrt[3]{1 + x}}$. **26.** $\displaystyle\int_{-\infty}^\infty e^{-3x} \, dx$. **27.** $\displaystyle\int_{-\infty}^0 xe^x \, dx$

28. The base of a solid T is the region in an xy-plane bounded by the curve $y = e^{-x}$, the axes, and the line $x = 2$. Every plane section of T perpendicular to the x-axis is an isosceles triangle whose base is in the xy-plane and altitude is twice the length of the base. Find the volume of T.

Find the volume of the solid T obtained if the specified region R in an xy-plane is revolved as indicated.

29. R is bounded by one branch of the curve $y = \sec x$ above the x-axis, and the line $y = \sqrt{2}$. Revolve R about (*a*) the x-axis; (*b*) the line $y = \sqrt{2}$.

30. R is bounded by the curve $x^2 = 6y$ and the line $y = 6$. Revolve R about (*a*) the y-axis; (*b*) the x-axis, using an integral with respect to y; (*c*) the line $y = 6$, by use of two different integrals; (*d*) the line $y = 8$.

31. R is bounded by the loop of the curve $x^2 = y(y - 1)(y - 4)$. Revolve R about the y-axis.

32. R is in quadrant I, bounded by $r = 2 \cos \theta$, in polar coordinates, and the polar axis. Revolve R about the polar axis, and use an integral with respect to θ.

33. A vertical tank is a right circular cylinder with height 20′ and base radius 30′, and contains liquid weighing 75 pounds per cubic foot. Find the work done in pumping all of the liquid over the top of the tank if the liquid is 18′ deep.

Integrate.

34. $\int \dfrac{4y^2 + 14y + 18}{y(y + 3)^2}\, dy.$

35. $\int \dfrac{7x^3 + 2x^2 + 13x + 2}{4x^4 + 11x^2 + 7}\, dx.$

36. $\int \dfrac{\csc x\, dx}{\csc x - 1 - \cot x}.$

37. $\int_0^{\pi/2} \dfrac{dx}{1 + \sin x + \cos x}.$

38. $\int_1^{64} \dfrac{dx}{x^{\frac{1}{2}} + 4x^{\frac{1}{3}}}.$

39. $\int \dfrac{dy}{y\sqrt[3]{27 + y^3}}.$

40. $\int \dfrac{1 - 2u}{1 + 2u}\, du.$

41. Compute the integral approximately by use of both Simpson's method and the trapezoidal rule, employing a partition of the interval of integration with 10 subintervals and Table V: $\int_0^1 e^{z^2}\, dx.$

★SUPPLEMENT FOR CHAPTER FIFTEEN

42. Prove (14) on page 374 by use of integration by parts.

43. The hyperbola $y^2 - x^2 = 1$, call it C, has the asymptotes $y = \pm x$. For any value of u, not 0, the line $y = x + u$, parallel to the asymptote $y = x$, cuts C in just one point. Thus, the coordinates (x, y) on C are functions of the variable u, whose domain is all real numbers, not 0. Obtain x and y in terms of u and notice that these parametric equations involve just rational functions of u. It is customary, then, to say that C has been *rationalized*, in terms of the parameter u.

44. If $y = \sqrt{1 + x^2}$, then $y^2 - x^2 = 1$. Suppose that $x = g(u)$ and $y = h(u)$ are parametric equations for the hyperbola with g and h as rational functions of u. Then, the substitution $x = g(u)$ will rationalize the integrand in any integral where the integrand is a rational function of x and $\sqrt{1 + x^2}$, that is, a rational function $f(x, y)$ with $y = \sqrt{1 + x^2}$. Use the rationalizing substitution determined by

$$x + u = \sqrt{1 + x^2},$$

from Problem 43, to calculate

$$\int \frac{dx}{(1 + x)\sqrt{1 + x^2}}.$$

Note 1. Let C be any conic $f(x, y) = 0$ in an xy-plane, where $f(x, y)$ is a polynomial of degree 2 in x and y. Let (α, β) be any point on C. Then, C can be rationalized in terms of a parameter u where, for each value of u, the corresponding point (x, y) on C, with $x = g(u)$ and $y = h(u)$, is the second point of intersection of C and the line

$$y - \beta = u(x - \alpha)$$

through (α, β). We find $g(u)$ and $h(u)$ by solving the system

$$f(x, y) = 0 \quad and \quad y - \beta = u(x - \alpha) \tag{1}$$

for x and y in terms of u. With an ellipse $f(x, y) = 0$, a convenient choice for (α, β) is any end point of an axis of the ellipse. With a hyperbola, a convenient choice is either end point of the transverse axis. Or, for a hyperbola, a family of lines $\phi(x, y, u) = 0$ parallel to an asymptote may be used to rationalize the curve instead of employing a *pencil* of lines (that is, a family of *concurrent* lines). To calculate $\int R(x, y)dx$, where $y = \sqrt{ax^2 + bx + c}$ with $a \neq 0$, and R is a rational function of x and y, we may employ (1) with $f(x, y) = 0$ as $y^2 = ax^2 + bx + c$. Then, the rational substitution $x = g(u)$

obtained from $y - \beta = u(x - \alpha)$ of (1), or

$$\sqrt{ax^2 + bx + c} = u(x - \alpha) + \beta,$$

makes $y = h(u)$, or $\sqrt{ax^2 + bx + c} = h(u)$, and thus transforms $\int R(x, y)dx$ into $\int W(u)du$, where $W(u)$ is a rational function of u.

45. Carry out the solution of (1) to find $x = g(u)$ and $y = h(u)$ for the conic $x^2 + 4y^2 = 4$ with (α, β) as the point (2, 0).

46. Show that the substitution $z = \tan \frac{1}{2}u$ of page 375 essentially amounts to a rationalization of the circle $x^2 + y^2 = 1$ by means of a pencil of lines.

47. Calculate by rationalizing the hyperbola $y^2 = 1 + x^2$:

$$\int \frac{dx}{(1 + 4x^2)\sqrt{1 + x^2}}.$$

48. Let $P_1:(x_1, y_1)$, $P_2:(0, y_2)$, and $P_3:(x_3, y_3)$ be any three points in an xy-plane such that $x_1 < 0 < x_3$. Prove that there is just one set (a, b, c) with $a \neq 0$ such that the points lie on the parabola $y = ax^2 + bx + c$, except when the points lie on a line. Then, by translation of axes, give reasoning to show that, if P_1, P_2, and P_3 are any three distinct points in the plane, the same result can be stated. (This result was assumed in the discussion of Simpson's rule.)

Note 2. Any reduction formula in Table VII can be *verified* by showing that the derivatives, or differentials, of the two sides are identical. "*To derive,*" as contrasted with "*to verify,*" a reduction formula, no routine procedure covering all cases can be specified. Only the method of ingenious devices can be mentioned as applicable. Sometimes, to prove a reduction formula, we may start by setting up a function $f(x)$ such that $df(x)$ involves two differentials, $dg_n(x)$ and $dg_{n-1}(x)$, where $g_k(x)$, for any integer $k > 0$ is the integrand in the kth case of the integral for which the formula is to be obtained. Then, $\int df(x)$ may give the desired formula. A proof involving integration by parts may be a special case of the preceding method. In the following problems, any letter used in an exponent represents an integer (positive when the context makes this desirable).

49. By calculating $d[u(a^2 + u^2)^{-k}]$, then using $u^2 = a^2 + u^2 - a^2$ in one place, and finally integrating on both sides of the equality involved, prove (26) in Table VII.

50. By starting with $d(\sin^h u \cos^k u)$, and then introducing $n = h - 1$ and $m = k + 1$, prove (112) in Table VII.

51–65. In Table VII, prove (106)–(111), (113)–(117), and (80)–(83).

66. Suppose that $H(x) = ax^2 + bx + c$ where $a \neq 0$, n is a positive integer greater than 1, $P_1(x)$ and $P_2(x)$ are polynomials of degrees at most $(2n - 1)$ and $(2n - 3)$, respectively, and $P_3(x) = cx + d$. Verify that, by differentiation of both sides of the following equation, and comparing coefficients after clearing of fractions, equations can be written which determine the coefficients in $P_1(x)$, $P_2(x)$, and $P_3(x)$ to make the equation true. (This method is a substitute for some of the routine of Case IV on page 373.)

$$\int \frac{P_1(x)dx}{[H(x)]^n} = \frac{P_2(x)}{[H(x)]^{n-1}} + \int \frac{P_3(x)dx}{H(x)} \qquad (2)$$

In (2), it is understood that $P_1(x)/[H(x)]^n$ is in lowest terms. Apply the preceding method in Problems 12, 13, and 18 on page 375.

CHAPTER SIXTEEN

Length of Arc and Applications

145. LENGTH OF ARC

In an xy-plane, consider a curve, C, defined parametrically by

$$x = \phi(t) \quad and \quad y = \psi(t), \tag{1}$$

where the domain of the parameter t is an interval, finite or infinite, and the functions ϕ and ψ are continuous. An *arc AB* of C is defined to be the curve obtained from (1) if the domain of t is restricted to be some closed interval $I = \{a \leq t \leq b\}$, where point A results from (1) for $t = a$, and point B for $t = b$.

Let M represent any partition of the interval I:

Partition M: $\qquad a = t_0 < t_1 < t_2 < \cdots < t_{n-1} < t_n = b, \tag{2}$

as in Figure 250 on page 388. Let $\Delta_i t = t_i - t_{i-1}$, and let d_M be the norm of M, or the maximum of the lengths $\{\Delta_i t\}$. For each value of i, a point $P_i:(x_i, y_i)$ is obtained on AB, as in Figure 251 on page 388, where $x_i = \phi(t_i)$ and $y_i = \psi(t_i)$. Join neighboring points in the sequence $P_0, P_1, \cdots, P_n$, to obtain a *polygonal line* inscribed in AB. Let $\left| \overline{P_{i-1}P_i} \right|$ be the length of the chord $P_{i-1}P_i$. Then, we define the concept of *length* for an arc AB as follows.

Definition I. *The length, L, of arc AB is the limit of the sum of the lengths of the chords of the inscribed polygonal line corresponding to a partition M of the domain of the parameter t as $d_M \to 0$, if this limit exists. Or,*

$$L = \lim_{d_M \to 0} \sum_{i=1}^{n} \left| \overline{P_{i-1}P_i} \right|. \tag{3}$$

Theorem I. *If ϕ and ψ in (1) have continuous derivatives, then the arc length L from $t = a$ to $t = b$ exists, and*

$$\left\{ \begin{matrix} arc: \\ x = \phi(t),\, y = \psi(t) \end{matrix} \right\} \qquad L = \int_a^b \sqrt{\left(\frac{dx}{dt}\right)^2 + \left(\frac{dy}{dt}\right)^2}\, dt. \tag{4}$$

Proof. 1. Let $\qquad \Delta_i x = \phi(t_i) - \phi(t_{i-1}); \quad \Delta_i y = \psi(t_i) - \psi(t_{i-1}).$

387

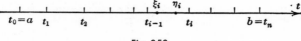

Fig. 250

From Figure 252,

$$|\overline{P_{i-1}P_i}| = \sqrt{(\Delta_i x)^2 + (\Delta_i y)^2}. \tag{5}$$

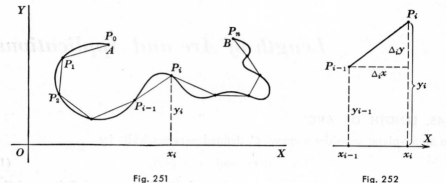

Fig. 251   Fig. 252

2. By the mean value theorem on page 173, there exist points ξ_i and η_i on the interval $t_{i-1} \leqq t \leqq t_i$, as in Figure 250, so that

$$\Delta_i x = \phi(t_i) - \phi(t_{i-1}) = \phi'(\xi_i)(t_i - t_{i-1}); \tag{6}$$

$$\Delta_i y = \psi(t_i) - \psi(t_{i-1}) = \psi'(\eta_i)(t_i - t_{i-1}); \tag{7}$$

$$(\Delta_i x)^2 + (\Delta_i y)^2 = \{[\phi'(\xi_i)]^2 + [\psi'(\eta_i)]^2\}\,(\Delta_i t)^2. \tag{8}$$

From (5),

$$|\overline{P_{i-1}P_i}| = \sqrt{[\phi'(\xi_i)]^2 + [\psi'(\eta_i)]^2}\,\Delta_i t. \tag{9}$$

From (3),

$$L = \lim_{d_M \to 0} \sum_{i=1}^{n} \sqrt{[\phi'(\xi_i)]^2 + [\psi'(\eta_i)]^2}\,\Delta_i t. \tag{10}$$

3. In (10), ξ_i and η_i lie on an interval of length $\Delta_i t$, and thus the distance between ξ_i and η_i approaches zero when all $\Delta_i t \to 0$. Hence, since ϕ' and ψ' are continuous, we accept the fact * that the limit in (10), if this limit exists, would not be changed if we should replace η_i by ξ_i, which gives

$$L = \lim_{d_M \to 0} \sum_{i=1}^{n} \sqrt{[\phi'(\xi_i)]^2 + [\psi'(\xi_i)]^2}\,\Delta_i t. \tag{11}$$

By comparison with (9) on page 178, the sum in (11) is recognized as an approximating sum, S_M, for an integral of the function $\sqrt{[\phi'(t)]^2 + [\psi'(t)]^2}$. Hence, the limit in (11) exists and is equal to the integral in (4).

EXAMPLE 1. Find the arc length from $t = 2$ to $t = 4$ on the path $(x = 3t^2, y = t^3)$.

Solution. From (4), $L = \int_2^4 \sqrt{(6t)^2 + (3t^2)^2}\,dt = 3\int_2^4 t\sqrt{4 + t^2}\,dt = 66.8.$

* It could be proved by reasoning of the type suggested in the footnote on page 212.

Note 1. On a curve C defined by (1), any specified point P might be obtained by use of more than one value of t in (1). Thus, with t having the domain $0 \leqq t \leqq 6\pi$, the equations $(x = \cos t, y = \sin t)$ give all points of the circle $x^2 + y^2 = 1$ three times and the point $(1, 0)$ four times. Then, from (4), $L = \int_0^{6\pi} dt = 6\pi$, which is three times the circumference of the circle. Hereafter, unless otherwise specified, in use of (1), we shall restrict the domain of t so that (1) yields at most a finite number of points of C more than once.

If a curve C is the graph of an equation $y = f(x)$ where f has a continuous derivative f', *we may think of C as given by parametric equations* $[x = x, y = f(x)]$, *with x as the parameter*. Then, with t replaced by x in (4), the length of arc L between $x = a$ and $x = b$ is

$$\begin{Bmatrix} \text{curve:} \\ y = f(x) \end{Bmatrix} \qquad L = \int_a^b \sqrt{1 + \left(\frac{dy}{dx}\right)^2}\, dx, \qquad (12)$$

because $dx/dx = 1$. If C is defined by $x = g(y)$, where g' is continuous, then C *is given by parametric equations* $[x = g(y), y = y]$, *with y as the parameter*. The length of arc L from $y = c$ to $y = d$, with $c < d$, then is obtained from (4) with t replaced by y:

$$\begin{Bmatrix} \text{curve:} \\ x = g(y) \end{Bmatrix} \qquad L = \int_c^d \sqrt{\left(\frac{dx}{dy}\right)^2 + 1}\, dy. \qquad (13)$$

EXAMPLE 2. Write integrals for the length of arc on the parabola $y^2 = 4x$ between $(0, 0)$ and $(1, 2)$ by use of an integral in two ways.

Solution. (a) From (12), since $dy/dx = x^{-\frac{1}{2}}$,

$$L = \int_0^1 \sqrt{1 + \frac{1}{x}}\, dx. \qquad (14)$$

(b) Since $x = \frac{1}{4}y^2$ and $dx/dy = \frac{1}{2}y$, from (13),

$$L = \int_0^2 \sqrt{1 + \frac{1}{4}y^2}\, dy. \qquad (15)$$

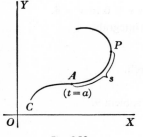

On a curve C, in (1), let s be the directed distance from A, at $t = a$, to an arbitrary point P:$[\phi(t), \psi(t)]$, as in Figure 253, where we agree that $s \geqq 0$ if $t \geqq a$ and $s \leqq 0$ if $t \leqq a$. Then, we have proved that

$$s = \int_a^t \sqrt{\left(\frac{dx}{dt}\right)^2 + \left(\frac{dy}{dt}\right)^2}\, dt. \qquad (16)$$

Fig. 253   From Theorem VII on page 185, and (16),

$$\frac{ds}{dt} = \sqrt{\left(\frac{dx}{dt}\right)^2 + \left(\frac{dy}{dt}\right)^2}, \quad or \quad ds = \sqrt{\left(\frac{dx}{dt}\right)^2 + \left(\frac{dy}{dt}\right)^2}\, dt. \qquad (17)$$

We refer to ds as the **differential of arc.** On squaring both sides in (17), we obtain

$$(ds)^2 = (dx)^2 + (dy)^2. \qquad (18)$$

Notice that dx, dy, and ds are related *formally* as if dx and dy were the legs, and ds

the hypotenuse in a right triangle, as suggested by Figure 254. On dividing by $(dx)^2$ on the right in (18), and then multiplying by $(dx)^2$, and acting similarly with $(dy)^2$, we obtain

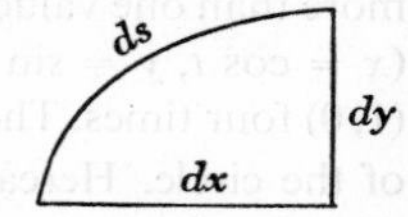

$$(ds)^2 = \left[1 + \left(\frac{dy}{dx}\right)^2\right](dx)^2, \quad and \quad (ds)^2 = \left[\left(\frac{dx}{dy}\right)^2 + 1\right](dy)^2;$$

Fig. 254

$$ds = \pm \sqrt{1 + \left(\frac{dy}{dx}\right)^2}\, dx; \quad ds = \pm \sqrt{\left(\frac{dx}{dy}\right)^2 + 1}\, dy. \tag{19}$$

In (19), we use "$+$" if s is to increase when x (or, y) increases. We write

$$L = \int_{t=a}^{t=b} ds, \quad L = \int_{x=a}^{x=b} ds, \quad and \quad L = \int_{y=c}^{y=d} ds, \tag{20}$$

where ds is expressed in terms of t, x, or y, respectively, as indicated by the limits.

★*Note 2.* At an advanced level, it is proved that the limit on the right in (3) exists, finite or infinite, if ϕ and ψ in (1) are continuous. Also, the limit is shown to be finite under hypotheses not including the assumption that ϕ and ψ have derivatives. If we substitute $\tau = h(t)$ as a new parameter in (1), this may alter L as obtained from Definition I. To avoid such a change, in advanced treatments it is found desirable to restrict the admissible changes in the parameter t. The length L obtained from (4) is unaltered if, in (1), we substitute $\tau = h(t)$ where h' is continuous and $h'(t) \geqq 0$. Such a change results merely in the corresponding substitution $\tau = h(t)$ in the integrand of (4).

EXERCISE 121

Find the length of the arc of the curve in an xy-plane defined by the given xy-equation or parametric equations. Any constant a or b is positive.

1. $x = 3t^2$ and $y = 2t^3$. From $t = 0$ to $t = 3$.
2. $x = a \cos t$ and $y = a \sin t$. Complete length.
3. $x = 2 - t$ and $y = t^2$. From $t = 0$ to $t = 3$.
4. $x^2 + y^2 = a^2$. Complete length.　　　5. $8y = x^2$. From $x = 0$ to $x = 4$.
6. $y^3 = x^2$. From $y = 0$ to $y = 4$. Inspect the two possible integrals.
7. $y = \frac{1}{2}a(e^{\frac{x}{a}} + e^{-\frac{x}{a}})$. From $x = -a$ to $x = a$.
8. $x = a(t - \sin t)$ and $y = a(1 - \cos t)$. Length of one arch.
9. $x = a \cos^3 t$ and $y = a \sin^3 t$. Complete length.
10. $x^{\frac{2}{3}} + y^{\frac{2}{3}} = a^{\frac{2}{3}}$. Length in one quadrant, without using Problem 9.
11. $27y^2 = x(x - 9)^2$. The loop from $x = 0$ to $x = 9$.
12. $x = \ln(y^2 - 1)$. From $y = 2$ to $y = 10$.
13. $6xy = y^4 + 3$. From $y = 1$ to $y = 3$.
14. $x = a(\cos \theta + \theta \sin \theta)$ and $y = a(\sin \theta - \theta \cos \theta)$; from $\theta = 0$ to $\theta = 2\pi$.
15. $y = x - x^2$. From $x = 0$ to $x = 1$.　　　16. $y = \ln \cos x$. From $x = 0$ to $x = \frac{1}{3}\pi$.
17. $x = e^t \sin t$ and $y = e^t \cos t$. From $t = -1$ to $t = 1$.
★18. Obtain the length of arc for one quadrant of the ellipse $x = 2 \cos t$ and $y = \sin t$, where t is a parameter, approximately by use of Simpson's rule with 10 intervals. A so-called **elliptic integral** is involved.

146. LENGTH OF ARC IN POLAR COORDINATES

Consider a curve C defined by the equation $r = f(\theta)$ in an $r\theta$-system of polar coordinates. Then, as on page 338, by use of the relations

$$x = r \cos \theta \quad and \quad y = r \sin \theta, \tag{1}$$

we may write parametric equations for C in the related rectangular coordinates, with θ as the parameter and r replaced by $f(\theta)$ in (1):

$$x = f(\theta) \cos \theta \quad and \quad y = f(\theta) \sin \theta. \tag{2}$$

With $r = f(\theta)$, we obtain ds from (1), thought of as abbreviating (2):

$$dx = (\cos \theta)dr - r(\sin \theta)d\theta; \quad dy = (\sin \theta)dr + r(\cos \theta)d\theta;$$

$$(ds)^2 = [(\cos \theta)dr - r(\sin \theta)d\theta]^2 + [(\sin \theta)dr + r(\cos \theta)d\theta]^2, \; or \tag{3}$$

$$(ds)^2 = (dr)^2 + r^2(d\theta)^2. \tag{4}$$

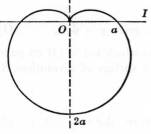

From (4), since $dr = f'(\theta)d\theta = r'\,d\theta$,

$$(ds)^2 = (r'^2 + r^2)(d\theta)^2, \; or \; ds = \sqrt{r^2 + r'^2}\; d\theta, \tag{5}$$

where we choose the positive radical with the convention that s will increase when θ increases.

Fig. 255

EXAMPLE 1. Find the perimeter, L, of the cardioid $r = a(1 - \sin \theta)$.

Solution. The right-hand half of the curve, in Figure 255, is traced as θ varies from $-\frac{1}{2}\pi$ to $\frac{1}{2}\pi$.

$$(ds)^2 = a^2[\cos^2 \theta + (1 - \sin \theta)^2](d\theta)^2 = 2a^2(1 - \sin \theta)(d\theta)^2. \tag{6}$$

Since $1 - \sin \theta = (\cos \frac{1}{2}\theta - \sin \frac{1}{2}\theta)^2$, then $ds = a\sqrt{2}(\cos \frac{1}{2}\theta - \sin \frac{1}{2}\theta)d\theta$. Hence,

$$L = 2 \int_{-\pi/2}^{\pi/2} a\sqrt{2}(\cos \tfrac{1}{2}\theta - \sin \tfrac{1}{2}\theta)d\theta = 8a.$$

Divide, and then multiply by $(dr)^2$ on the right in (4):

$$(ds)^2 = \left[1 + r^2\left(\frac{d\theta}{dr}\right)^2\right](dr)^2, \quad or \quad ds = \sqrt{1 + r^2\left(\frac{d\theta}{dr}\right)^2}\; dr. \tag{7}$$

We may use (7) to find s by integration with respect to r, but rarely do so.

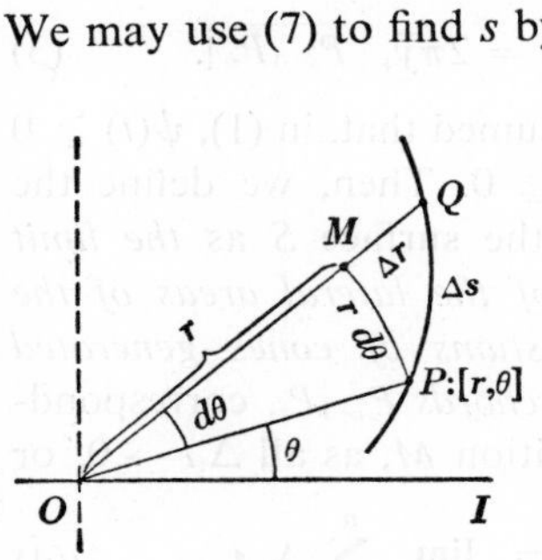

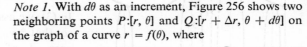

Note 1. With $d\theta$ as an increment, Figure 256 shows two neighboring points $P:[r, \theta]$ and $Q:[r + \Delta r, \theta + d\theta]$ on the graph of a curve $r = f(\theta)$, where

$$(arc\; PQ) = \Delta s; \quad |\overline{MQ}| = |\Delta r|; \quad \overset{\frown}{PM} = r\, d\theta. \tag{8}$$

The "curvilinear" triangle PQM reminds us of a right triangle with hypotenuse PQ, and suggests that $(\Delta s)^2$ is approximately equal to $(\Delta r)^2 + (r\, d\theta)^2$. Also, with Δr and Δs approximated by dr and ds, respectively, the "curvilinear" triangle PQM is a convenient device for recalling (4), in the form

Fig. 256

$$(ds)^2 = (dr)^2 + (r\, d\theta)^2.$$

EXERCISE 122

Find the length of the specified arc of the given curve in an rθ-system of polar coordinates. Integrate with respect to r or θ. Any constant a or k is positive.

1. The circle $r = 2a \cos \theta$. Complete length.

2. The cardioid $r = k \cos^2 \frac{1}{2}\theta$. Complete length.

3. The cardioid $r = a(1 - \cos \theta)$. Complete length.

4. The curve $r = k \sin^3 \frac{1}{3}\theta$. Complete length.

5. The circle $r = a(\cos \theta + \sin \theta)$. Complete length.

6. The spiral $r = a\theta$. From $\theta = 0$ to $\theta = \pi$.

7. The spiral $r = e^{k\theta}$. From $\theta = 0$ to $\theta = 1$.

★8. The parabola $r = a/(1 + \sin \theta)$. From $\theta = 0$ to $\theta = \pi$.

★9. The cissoid $r = 2a \tan \theta \sin \theta$. From $\theta = 0$ to $\theta = \frac{1}{3}\pi$.

147. AREA OF A SURFACE OF REVOLUTION

In an xy-plane, let C be the curve $\qquad x = \phi(t) \quad and \quad y = \psi(t),$ $\qquad$ (1)

with $a \leq t \leq b$, where ϕ and ψ satisfy the hypotheses which led to (4) on page 387. Let C be revolved about the x-axis to generate a surface of revolution, S. We proceed to define the notion of *area* for S.

Let M be any partition of the interval $a \leq t \leq b$:

$$a = t_0 < t_1 < \cdots < t_{i-1} < t_n < \cdots < t_n = b, \quad where \quad \Delta_i t = t_i - t_{i-1}. \quad (2)$$

When $t = t_i$, point $P_i:(x_i, y_i)$ is obtained on C, with $x_i = \phi(t_i)$ and $y_i = \psi(t_i)$. In Figure 257, $\alpha = \phi(a)$ and $\beta = \phi(b)$. Then, inscribe a polygonal line

$$P_0 P_1 \cdots P_{i-1} P_i \cdots P_n$$

in C, as in Figure 251 on page 388. The representative chord $P_{i-1}P_i$, corresponding to the interval $T_i:(t_{i-1} \leq t \leq t_i)$, is shown in Figure 257. When C is revolved about the x-axis, chord $P_{i-1}P_i$ generates a *frustum of a cone*. For this frustum, the slant height is $|\overline{P_{i-1}P_i}|$; the circumference of a midsection is $2\pi \bar{y}_i$ where

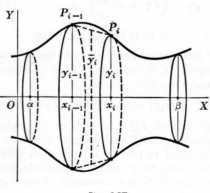

$\bar{y}_i = \frac{1}{2}(y_i + y_{i-1})$; from Note 13 of the Appendix, the lateral area, $\Delta_i A$, is

$$\Delta_i A = 2\pi \bar{y}_i |\overline{P_{i-1}P_i}|. \quad (3)$$

In (3), we assumed that, in (1), $\psi(t) \geq 0$ so that * $\bar{y}_i \geq 0$. Then, we define the area, A, of the surface S as *the limit of the sum of the lateral areas of the inscribed frustums of cones generated by all of the chords $P_{i-1}P_i$, corresponding to a partition M, as all $\Delta_i t \to 0$,* or

Fig. 257

$$A = \lim_{d_M \to 0} \sum_{i=1}^{n} \Delta_i A. \quad (4)$$

* If $\psi(t) < 0$, we would use $|\bar{y}_i|$.

Since $y_{i-1} \leqq \bar{y}_i \leqq y_i$, or $y_i \leqq \bar{y}_i \leqq y_{i-1}$, there is a point σ_i on T_i where

$$y = \psi(\sigma_i) = \bar{y}_i.$$

Also, there exist points ξ_i and η_i on T_i so that $|\overline{P_{i-1}P_i}|$ can be expressed as in (9) on page 388, and thus (3) gives

$$\sum_{i=1}^{n} \Delta_i A = 2\pi \sum_{i=1}^{n} \psi(\sigma_i)\sqrt{[\phi'(\xi_i)]^2 + [\psi'(\eta_i)]^2}\,\Delta_i t. \tag{5}$$

It is seen in Figure 258 that the distances between ξ_i and σ_i, and ξ_i and η_i, approach zero when $\Delta_i t \to 0$. Hence, since ψ, ϕ', and ψ' are continuous, we accept the fact that the limit in (4), if it exists, would not be changed if we should replace σ_i and η_i by ξ_i. With this replacement, (4) and (5) give

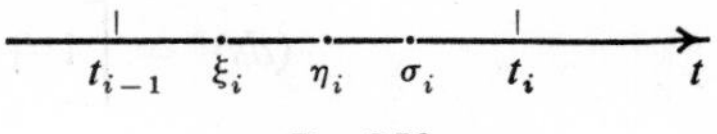

Fig. 258

$$A = 2\pi \lim_{d_M \to 0} \sum_{i=1}^{n} \psi(\xi_i)\sqrt{[\phi'(\xi_i)]^2 + [\psi'(\xi_i)]^2}\,\Delta_i t. \tag{6}$$

By comparison with (9) on page 178, the sum in (6) is recognized as an approximating sum for the integral which appears below. Hence,

$$A = 2\pi \int_a^b \psi(t)\sqrt{[\phi'(t)]^2 + [\psi'(t)]^2}\, dt, \text{ or}$$

$$\left\{ \begin{array}{l} \textit{revolve about x-axis:} \\ x = \phi(t),\ y = \psi(t) \end{array} \right\} \qquad A = 2\pi \int_{t=a}^{t=b} y\, ds, \tag{7}$$

where $$ds = \sqrt{\left(\frac{dx}{dt}\right)^2 + \left(\frac{dy}{dt}\right)^2}\, dt. \tag{8}$$

If the curve C defined by (1) is revolved about the y-axis, to generate a surface S, similarly we define the area, A, of S so that

$$\left\{ \begin{array}{l} \textit{revolve about y-axis:} \\ x = \phi(t),\ y = \psi(t) \end{array} \right\} \qquad A = 2\pi \int_{t=a}^{t=b} x\, ds. \tag{9}$$

With ds expressed in terms of dx, or dy, as in (19) on page 390,

$$\left\{ \begin{array}{l} \textit{revolve } y = f(x) \\ \textit{about x-axis} \end{array} \right\} \qquad A = 2\pi \int_{x=a}^{x=b} y\, ds, \quad \textit{or} \quad A = 2\pi \int_{y=c}^{y=d} y\, ds; \tag{10}$$

$$\left\{ \begin{array}{l} \textit{revolve } x = g(y) \\ \textit{about y-axis} \end{array} \right\} \qquad A = 2\pi \int_{x=a}^{x=b} x\, ds, \quad \textit{or} \quad A = 2\pi \int_{y=c}^{y=d} x\, ds. \tag{11}$$

In (10) or (11), $ds = \sqrt{1 + y'^2}\, dx$ with $y' = dy/dx$, or $ds = \sqrt{1 + x'^2}\, dy$ with $x' = dx/dy$, according as the limits are values of x or of y. If the curve C of (7) and (9) is defined by $r = f(\theta)$ in polar coordinates, usually we employ ds in terms of $d\theta$, as in (5) on page 391. In (7), we use $|y|$ instead of y if $\psi(t)$ is negative at some values of t. A similar change may occur in (9), (10), and (11).

EXAMPLE 1. The arc of the semicubical parabola ($x = t^2$, $y = t^3$), from $t = 0$ to $t = \sqrt{8}$ is revolved about the y-axis. Find the area of the surface which is generated. See Table VIII for a similar curve.

Solution. 1. Since $dx = 2t\, dt$ and $dy = 3t^2\, dt$,

$$(ds)^2 = (4t^2 + 9t^4)(dt)^2, \quad or \quad ds = t\sqrt{4 + 9t^2}\, dt.$$

From (9), $$A = 2\pi \int_0^{\sqrt{8}} t^3 \sqrt{4 + 9t^2}\, dt. \tag{12}$$

2. To integrate in (12), substitute $\sqrt{4 + 9t^2} = u$. Then $A = 713$, sq. units.

EXAMPLE 2. Find the area of the surface generated by revolving the arc of the parabola $x^2 = 8y$ from $y = 0$ to $y = 2$ in quadrant I about OY.

Solution. If $y = 0$ then $x = 0$; if $y = 2$ then $x = 4$.

$$(ds)^2 = \left[1 + \left(\frac{dy}{dx}\right)^2\right](dx)^2 = \frac{16 + x^2}{16}(dx)^2.$$

From (11), $$A = 2\pi \int_0^4 \tfrac{1}{4}x\sqrt{16 + x^2}\, dx = \tfrac{32}{3}\pi(2\sqrt{2} - 1).$$

EXAMPLE 3. Find the area of the surface generated by revolving the cardioid $r = a(1 - \cos \theta)$ about the x-axis.

Solution. From (5) on page 390, $(ds)^2 = 4a^2(\sin^2 \tfrac{1}{2}\theta)(d\theta)^2.$

The upper half of the cardioid, as in Figure 11 on page 710, is traced as θ varies from 0 to π. Hence, from (7) with t replaced by θ, and

$$y = r \sin \theta = a(1 - \cos \theta)\sin \theta,$$

we obtain $$A = 4\pi a^2 \int_0^\pi (\sin \theta - \sin \theta \cos \theta)\sin \tfrac{1}{2}\theta\, d\theta = \tfrac{32}{5}\pi a^2. \tag{13}$$

EXERCISE 123

Find the area of the surface obtained by revolving each curve about the indicated axis, OX or OY, in an xy-plane. The constants a and b are positive.

1. $y = x^3$, from $x = 0$ to $x = 2$. Revolve about OX.

2. $3y = 4x$, from $x = 0$ to $x = 3$. Revolve about OX. Check the result by the formula for the lateral area of a cone.

3. A line segment joins the points $(0, 12)$ and $(5, 0)$ in the xy-plane. Revolve the segment about OY. Check as in Problem 2.

4. $x = a \cos t$ and $y = a \sin t$. Revolve about OX, to find the surface area of a sphere.

5. A circle with center $(x = a, y = 0)$ and radius b, where $b < a$, with the parametric equations $x = a + b \cos \theta$ and $y = b \sin \theta$. Revolve about OY, to form a *torus*. Find its complete area.

6. $y = \tfrac{1}{2}(e^x + e^{-x})$, from $x = -1$ to $x = 1$. Revolve about OX.

7. $x^2 + y^2 = a^2$, complete curve. Revolve about OY.

8. $y^2 = 4x$, from $x = 0$ to $x = 4$. Revolve about (a) OX; (b) OY.

9. $x^2 = 8 - 4y$, from $y = \tfrac{3}{4}$ to $y = 2$. Revolve about OY.

10. $x = y^3$, from $y = 0$ to $y = 2$. Revolve about OX.

11. $x^{\frac{2}{3}} + y^{\frac{2}{3}} = a^{\frac{2}{3}}$. Revolve about OY. Use an integral with respect to x.

12. Repeat Problem 11, with the parametric form $(x = a \cos^3 t, y = a \sin^3 t)$.

13. $x = a(t - \sin t)$ and $y = a(1 - \cos t)$. Revolve one arch about OX.

14. The cardioid $r = 1 - \sin \theta$. Revolve about OY.

15. $y = \sin x$, from $x = 0$ to $x = 2\pi$. About OX.

16. $3x^2 + 4y^2 = 12$. Revolve about OX.

17. $x^2 - y^2 = 16$, from $x = 4$ to $x = 8$. Revolve about OX.

18. $x = 1 - 3t^2$ and $y = t - 3t^3$. Revolve from $x = 0$ to $x = 1$ about OX.

19. $y^3 = x^2$, from $y = 0$ to $y = \frac{4}{3}$. Revolve about OX.

20. $x = \ln (y^2 - 1)$, from $y = \sqrt{2}$ to $y = 3$. Revolve about OX.

21. The complete circle $r = 2a \cos \theta$. Revolve about OY.

22. The lemniscate $r^2 = a^2 \cos 2\theta$. Revolve about (a) OX; (b) OY.

23. A region R in an xy-plane is bounded below by $x^2 = 2y + 3$ and above by $x^2 = 8y$. Find the area of the surface of the solid generated if R is revolved about OY.

148. REGULAR CURVES

In an xy-plane, let C be the curve $\qquad x = \phi(t) \quad and \quad y = \psi(t),$ (1)

where the derivatives ϕ' and ψ' are continuous and

$$[\phi'(t)]^2 + [\psi'(t)]^2 \neq 0 \tag{2}$$

at each value of t. Then, we shall call C a *regular curve*.

If a curve C has the equation $y = f(x)$ where f' is continuous, and if C is thought of in the parametric form $[x = x \text{ and } y = f(x)]$, where x replaces t,

$$\{[\phi'(t)]^2 + [\psi'(t)]^2\} \quad becomes \quad \{1 + [f'(x)]^2\},$$

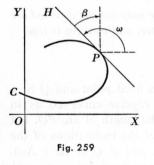

Fig. 259

which is never zero. Thus, C is a regular curve. Similarly, $x = g(y)$ defines a regular curve if g' is continuous. Also, the equation $r = f(\theta)$, where f' is continuous, defines a regular curve in polar coordinates, except where $r = 0$ and $f'(\theta) = 0$.

At any point P on a regular curve C, by Theorem II on page 158, at least one of the derivatives dy/dx and dx/dy exists, with

$$\frac{dy}{dx} = \frac{\psi'(t)}{\phi'(t)} \quad and \quad \frac{dx}{dy} = \frac{\phi'(t)}{\psi'(t)}, \tag{3}$$

because (2) shows that $\phi'(t)$ and $\psi'(t)$ cannot equal zero simultaneously. Hence, by results on page 117, C has a tangent PH at each point P, as in Figure 259. If $t = t_0$ at P and $\phi'(t_0) \neq 0$, then the slope dy/dx of PH is a continuous function of t, and thus the tangent PH turns continuously when t is near $t = t_0$. Similarly, with the roles of x and y interchanged, if $\psi'(t_0) \neq 0$, dx/dy is a continuous function of t and the tangent PH turns continuously when t is near $t = t_0$. Hence, along the whole of a regular curve (1), the tangent turns continuously.

On a regular curve C, let s be the arc distance on C, measured from any fixed point A where $t = a$. Then, with $s \geq 0$ when $t \geq a$ and $s \leq 0$ when $t \leq a$,

$$s = h(t), \quad where \quad h(t) = \int_a^t \sqrt{[\phi'(t)]^2 + [\psi'(t)]^2} \, dt. \tag{4}$$

Hence, $$\frac{ds}{dt} = h'(t) = \sqrt{[\phi'(t)]^2 + [\psi'(t)]^2}, \tag{5}$$

where $h'(t) > 0$ because of (2), and thus the graph of $s = h(t)$ has the nature shown in Figure 260. For each number $s = k$, there exists just one number t_0 such that $k = h(t_0)$, or the graph of $s = h(t)$ is met in just one point by the line $s = k$. That is, by Definition III on page 104, there exists a function g which is the *inverse* of h, and $s = h(t)$ is equivalent to $t = g(s)$. On using $t = g(s)$ in (1), we obtain a new parametric form for C with s as the parameter,

$$x = \Phi(s) \quad and \quad y = \Psi(s). \tag{6}$$

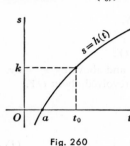

Fig. 260

Moreover, by Theorem II on page 104, there exists

$$\frac{dt}{ds} = g'(s) = \frac{1}{h'(t)}, \tag{7}$$

where g' is continuous because h' is continuous and $h'(t) \neq 0$. Hence, dy/ds and dx/ds exist and are continuous functions of s, with

$$\frac{dx}{ds} = \frac{dx}{dt} \cdot \frac{dt}{ds} \quad and \quad \frac{dy}{ds} = \frac{dy}{dt} \cdot \frac{dt}{ds}. \tag{8}$$

Then, from $(dx)^2 + (dy)^2 = (ds)^2$, on dividing by $(ds)^2$ we obtain

$$\left(\frac{dx}{ds}\right)^2 + \left(\frac{dy}{ds}\right)^2 = 1. \tag{9}$$

Summary. *On a curve* (1) *where* $[\phi'(t)]^2 + [\psi'(t)]^2 \neq 0$, *we may use the directed arc distance,* s, *measured from any fixed point, as a parameter, and then* (9) *is true.*

149. CURVATURE AND CIRCLE OF CURVATURE

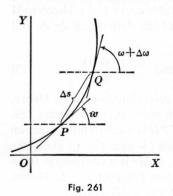

Fig. 261

In an xy-plane, let P be a fixed point and Q be a neighboring point on a regular curve C, as in Figure 261, with Δs as the length of arc PQ. Let the measures in radians of the inclinations of the tangent to C at P be * ω, and at Q be $(\omega + \Delta\omega)$. Then, $\Delta\omega/\Delta s$ is the *average rate of change of ω with respect to distance along PQ*. The *instantaneous rate of change*, $d\omega/ds$, can be taken as a *measure of the bending of C at P*, if $d\omega/ds$ exists. Let a number k be defined by the equation

$$k = \frac{d\omega}{ds} = \lim_{\Delta s \to 0} \frac{\Delta\omega}{\Delta s}. \tag{1}$$

* To obtain a continuous variation of ω, if the tangent is nearly horizontal along PQ, we would use the interval $-\frac{1}{2}\pi < \omega \leqq \frac{1}{2}\pi$ instead of $0 \leqq \omega < \pi$.

For many purposes, the sign of k is immaterial, because it depends on an arbitrary selection of the direction on C in which s increases. Reversal of this direction would alter the sign of k. Hence we shall replace k by $|k|$ below.

Definition II. *At a point P on a regular curve C, the* **curvature**, *K, of C is the absolute value of the rate of change of the * direction angle ω of the tangent with respect to distance on C:*

$$K = \left| \frac{d\omega}{ds} \right|.$$ (2)

Note 1. In (2), K is a measure in *radians per unit distance* measured along the curve.

ILLUSTRATION 1. If C is a straight line, then $K = 0$ at all points of C, because ω is a constant, and hence $d\omega/ds = 0$.

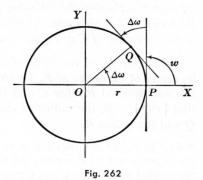

ILLUSTRATION 2. To find the curvature at any point P on a circle of radius r, let the coordinate axes be located as in Figure 262, with P on the x-axis. Then, with arc PQ as Δs, we have $\Delta s = r\Delta\omega$. Hence,

$$\frac{\Delta\omega}{\Delta s} = \frac{1}{r}; \quad K = \frac{d\omega}{ds} = \lim_{\Delta s \to 0} \frac{\Delta\omega}{\Delta s} = \frac{1}{r},$$

or *the curvature K is a constant, the reciprocal of the radius.*

Fig. 262

Let the curve C be defined by $y = f(x)$, where the derivatives f' and f'' exist. Then, at $P:(x, y)$ on C,

$$\tan \omega = y'.$$ (3)

On differentiating with respect to s on both sides of (3), with y' as a function of x, and x as a function of s, we obtain

$$(\sec^2 \omega) \frac{d\omega}{ds} = \frac{dy'}{dx} \cdot \frac{dx}{ds}, \; where$$ (4)

$$\sec^2 \omega = 1 + \tan^2 \omega = 1 + y'^2; \quad \frac{dy'}{dx} = y'';$$ (5)

$$\left| \frac{dx}{ds} \right| = \frac{|dx|}{\sqrt{(dx)^2 + (dy)^2}} = \frac{1}{\sqrt{1 + y'^2}}.$$ (6)

In (6), we divided the numerator and denominator in dx/ds by $|dx|$, or $(dx)^2$ under the radical, and used $y' = dy/dx$. Hence, from (4), (5), and (6), with $K = |d\omega/ds|$,

$$K = \frac{|y''|}{\sqrt{(1 + y'^2)^3}}.$$ (7)

The following terminology is in harmony with the fact that, for a circle, the curvature is the reciprocal of the radius.

---

* We used the *inclination* as a *direction angle* in the discussion. Any other direction angle would have been equally satisfactory.

Definition III. *At any point $P:(x, y)$ on a curve C, the* **radius of curvature,** *R, is defined as the reciprocal of the curvature:*

$$R = \frac{1}{K}. \tag{8}$$

On a curve $y = f(x)$ as involved in (7), R is not defined where $y'' = 0$ because then $K = 0$. Otherwise, from (7),

$$R = \frac{(1 + y'^2)^{\frac{3}{2}}}{|y''|}. \tag{9}$$

Definition IV. *The* **circle of curvature** *at $P:(x, y)$ on a curve C is that circle, T, through P satisfying the following conditions: T has the same tangent as C at P; the radius of T is the radius of curvature of C at P, or the curvature of T is the same as the curvature of C at P; the center of T is on the concave side of C.*

The center, Q, of the circle of curvature T at a point P on a curve C is called its **center of curvature** at P. To construct T, as in Figure 263, draw the tangent PM and normal PN for C and locate Q on PN, on the concave side of C, so that $|\overline{PQ}| = R$, the radius of curvature. Then T is constructed with the center Q and the radius R.

Note 2. In Figure 263, the circle of curvature at P crosses the given curve C at P because the rate of revolution of the tangent (or, the curvature) remains constant on the circle, but increases as we move to the right on C. In any case, the circle of curvature at a point P crosses C at P unless the curvature attains a relative maximum or minimum at P.

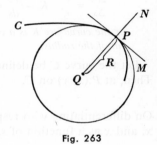

Fig. 263

EXAMPLE 1. Compute the curvature and radius of curvature at $P:(\frac{1}{2}, \frac{1}{4})$ on the curve $y = x^2$.

Solution. $y' = 2x$ and $y'' = 2$. At $x = \frac{1}{2}$,

$$y' = 1; \quad y'' = 2; \quad 1 + y'^2 = 2; \quad K = \frac{2}{2\sqrt{2}}; \quad R = \sqrt{2} = 1.4.$$

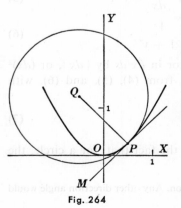

Fig. 264

In Figure 264, the tangent PM with slope 1, and the normal with slope -1, were drawn through P. Q was located so that $|\overline{PQ}| = 1.4$, and then the circle of curvature was drawn.

If the reasoning leading to (7) and (9) were repeated with the roles of x and y interchanged, we would obtain

$$K = \frac{|x''|}{(1 + x'^2)^{\frac{3}{2}}} \quad and \quad R = \frac{(1 + x'^2)^{\frac{3}{2}}}{|x''|}, \tag{10}$$

where $\quad x' = \dfrac{dx}{dy} \quad and \quad x'' = \dfrac{d^2x}{dy^2}.$

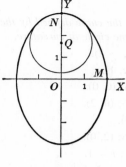

Fig. 265

EXAMPLE 2. Obtain the curvature of the ellipse

$$x = 2 \cos t \quad and \quad y = 3 \sin t \qquad (11)$$

at the extremities of its axes.

Solution. 1. At N in Figure 265, $t = \frac{1}{2}\pi$. We find that

$$y' = \frac{dy}{dx} = -\frac{3 \cos t}{2 \sin t} = -\frac{3}{2} \cot t;$$

$$y'' = \frac{d^2y}{dx^2} = \frac{dy'}{dx} = -\frac{3}{2} \cdot \frac{d(\cot t)}{d(2 \cos t)}$$

$$= -\frac{3}{2} \cdot \frac{\csc^2 t}{2 \sin t} = -\frac{3}{4} \csc^3 t.$$

When $t = \frac{1}{2}\pi$, $y' = 0$ and $y'' = -\frac{3}{4}$. From (7) and (9), $K = \frac{3}{4}$ and $R = \frac{4}{3}$. The circle of curvature, with center Q, is in the figure. The curvature attains a maximum at N, and thus the circle of curvature at N does not cross the ellipse.

2. At M in Figure 265, $t = 0$ and the tangent is vertical, so that dy/dx does not exist. Hence, (7) cannot be used. Then, we calculate

$$x' = \frac{dx}{dy} = -\frac{2}{3} \tan t; \quad x'' = \frac{d^2x}{dy^2} = \frac{dx'}{dy} = -\frac{2}{9} \cdot \frac{\sec^2 t}{\cos t} = -\frac{2}{9} \sec^3 t.$$

At M, with $t = 0$, $x' = 0$ and $x'' = -\frac{2}{9}$. From (10), $K = \frac{2}{9}$ and $R = \frac{9}{2}$.

EXAMPLE 3. Find the curvature at $(3, 2)$ on $x^2 + 4y^2 = 25$.

Solution. On differentiating with respect to x, we obtain

$$x + 4y \frac{dy}{dx} = 0, \quad or \quad y' = -\frac{x}{4y};$$

$$\frac{d^2y}{dx^2} = \frac{dy'}{dx} = -\frac{1}{4} \frac{y - xy'}{y^2} = -\frac{4y^2 + x^2}{16y^3} = -\frac{25}{16y^3}.$$

At $(3, 2)$, we find $y' = -\frac{3}{8}$ and $y'' = -\frac{25}{128}$. From (7), $K = \frac{100}{5329}\sqrt{73}$.

★*Note 3.* Let a regular curve C be defined by $x = \phi(t)$ and $y = \psi(t)$, where the second derivatives ϕ'' and ψ'' exist. Then,

$$K = \frac{|x'y'' - y'x''|}{(x'^2 + y'^2)^{\frac{3}{2}}}, \qquad (12)$$

where x', y', x'', and y'' represent derivatives with respect to t. We could use (12) instead of (7) or (10) in a problem such as Example 2. In an $r\theta$-system of polar coordinates, if C is defined by $r = f(\theta)$ where $f'(\theta)$ and $f''(\theta)$ exist,

$$K = \frac{|r^2 + 2r'^2 - rr''|}{(r^2 + r'^2)^{\frac{3}{2}}}, \qquad (13)$$

with $r' = f'(\theta)$ and $r'' = f''(\theta)$. We obtain (12) by applying the method of Example 2 to the general curve $[x = \phi(t), y = \psi(t)]$, where at least one of $\phi'(t)$ and $\psi'(t)$ is not zero at each value of t. Then (13) is derived from (12) by writing the curve $r = f(\theta)$ in parametric form as on page 338.

EXERCISE 124

Find the curvature and radius of curvature at the given point on the curve defined by the xy-equation, or parametric equations. Where convenient, sketch the circle of curvature.

1. $4y = x^2 - 4x + 4$; $(2, 0)$.   **2.** $xy = 4$; $(-2, -2)$.

3. $xy = 12$; $(6, 2)$.   **4.** $y = \sin x$; $(\frac{1}{2}\pi, 1)$.

5. $2x = y^2 - 2y + 1$; $(0, 1)$.   **6.** $x = y^2(2 - y)$; $(0, 0)$.

7. $y = \ln x$; $(1, 0)$.   **8.** $x^2 + 4y^2 = 16$; $(0, 2)$.

9. $y = \tan x$; $(\frac{1}{4}\pi, 1)$.   **10.** $3y = x^3$; $(3, 9)$.

11. $4x^2 + 9y^2 = 36$; $(3, 0)$; $(0, 2)$.   **12.** $4x^2 - y^2 = 16$; $(2, 0)$.

13. $x = t^2 - 4$, $y = 2t$; $t = 2$.   **14.** $x = t^2$, $y = t^3$; $t = 1$.

15. $x = \cos t$, $y = 2 \sin t$; $t = \frac{1}{4}\pi$.   **16.** $x = 2 \cos^3 t$, $y = 2 \sin^3 t$; $t = \frac{1}{4}\pi$.

17. $x = 2 \cos t$, $y = \cos 2t$; $t = \frac{1}{4}\pi$.   **18.** $x = 1 - \cos t$, $y = t - \sin t$; $t = \pi$.

Find the point on the curve where the curvature attains a maximum. Use K^2.

19. $y = \ln x$.   **20.** $y = e^x$.   **21.** $y = \sin x$.

Find the curvature of the curve at an arbitrary point (x_1, y_1).

22. $y = ax^3$.   **23.** $y^2 = 2px$.   **24.** $b^2x^2 + a^2y^2 = a^2b^2$.

25. $x = a \cos^3 t$ and $y = a \sin^3 t$; at (x_1, y_1) where $t = t_1$.

26. By use of a differential, find approximately the angle through which the tangent at a point P turns as P moves a distance $\Delta s = .4$ from $(2, \frac{4}{3})$ on the parabola $3y = x^2$.

★27. Prove (12) and then (13) on page 399.

★Find the curvature and radius of curvature of the given curve in an $r\theta$-system of polar coordinates, at the given point. Any constant h is positive.

28. $r = 6 \cos \theta$, at any value of θ.   **29.** $r = h \sec \theta$, at any value of θ.

30. $r = 1 - \cos \theta$, where (a) $\theta = \pi$; (b) $\theta = \frac{1}{2}\pi$.

31. $r = h(1 + \sin \theta)$, where (a) $\theta = \frac{1}{2}\pi$; (b) $\theta = \frac{11}{6}\pi$.

32. $r^2 = 4 \cos 2\theta$, where (a) $\theta = 0$; (b) $\theta = \frac{1}{6}\pi$.

★33. On a regular curve $y = f(x)$ in an xy-plane, let $P:(x_0, y_0)$ be a fixed point and Q be a neighboring point. Let the length of chord PQ be $|\overline{PQ}|$ and of arc PQ be $\overset{\frown}{PQ}$. Prove that $|\overline{PQ}/\overset{\frown}{PQ}| \to 1$ as $\overset{\frown}{PQ} \to 0$.

150. LOCATION OF CENTER OF CURVATURE

Suppose that a curve C in an xy-plane is defined by $y = f(x)$, and that $P:(x, y)$ is a point on C with x on an interval where y'' exists, is continuous, and is not zero. Then, we shall prove the following result.

$$\left\{ \begin{array}{l} \textit{The circle of curvature for } C \textit{ at } P \textit{ is that circle } T \textit{ through } P \\ \textit{on which } y' \textit{ and } y'' \textit{ have the same values at } P \textit{ as on the curve } C. \end{array} \right\} \quad (1)$$

Proof of (1). Suppose that T satisfies (1). Then, at P, T has the *same tangent* as C, and the *same curvature* as C because (7) on page 397 involves just y' and y''. Also, at P, the center of T is on the concave side of T, which also is the concave side for C, because y'' is the same on T and C. Hence, T satisfies Definition IV, page 398, and thus is the circle of curvature.

At any point $P:(x, y)$ on the curve C defined by $y = f(x)$, let the radius and center of curvature be R and $Q:(\alpha, \beta)$, respectively. Then, the first of the following equations is an equation for the circle of curvature, T. The next two equations are obtained by differentiating, successively, with respect to x in the equation of T.

$$(x - \alpha)^2 + (y - \beta)^2 = R^2; \tag{2}$$

$$(x - \alpha) + y'(y - \beta) = 0; \tag{3}$$

$$1 + y''(y - \beta) + y'^2 = 0. \tag{4}$$

Statement (1) shows that, corresponding to any point $P:(x, y)$ on C, we may insert in (3) and (4) the values of y' and y'' as determined from the equation $y = f(x)$ for C. Then, [(2), (3), (4)] become three equations for the unknowns R, α, and β, obtained on the basis of just (1) and (2).

EXAMPLE 1. Obtain an equation for the circle of curvature, and find the curvature, K, of the curve $xy = 2$ at the point $P:(1, 2)$.

Solution. 1. $y' = -\dfrac{2}{x^2}$; $y'' = \dfrac{4}{x^3}$; at $x = 1$, $y = 2$, $y' = -2$, and $y'' = 4$.

2. From (2), (3), and (4) with the values above,

$$\begin{cases} (1 - \alpha)^2 + (2 - \beta)^2 = R^2; & \tag{5} \\ (1 - \alpha) - 2(2 - \beta) = 0; & \tag{6} \\ 1 + 4(2 - \beta) + 4 = 0. & \tag{7} \end{cases}$$

By use of (7), $\beta = \frac{13}{4}$. Then (6) gives $\alpha = \frac{7}{2}$. Finally (5) gives $R^2 = \frac{125}{16}$, or $R = \frac{5}{4}\sqrt{5}$. From (2), the circle of curvature is

$$(x - \tfrac{7}{2})^2 + (y - \tfrac{13}{4})^2 = \tfrac{125}{16}.$$

3. Since $K = \dfrac{1}{R}$, we have $K = \frac{4}{25}\sqrt{5} = .36$ in radians per unit distance.

Note 1. Suppose that y'' does not exist at a point P on C, which is the case where the tangent is vertical. Then, in place of (3) and (4) we use equations obtained from (2) on differentiating twice with respect to y.

EXAMPLE 2. Obtain the circle of curvature of the ellipse $x = 2 \cos t$ and $y = 3 \sin t$, at an extremity of the minor axis.

Solution. 1. We desire the circle of curvature at $M:(2, 0)$ where $t = 0$, in Figure 265 on page 399. The tangent is vertical at M. Hence, we start from (2) and differentiate twice with respect to y:

$$\begin{cases} (x - \alpha)^2 + (y - \beta)^2 = R^2, & \tag{8} \\ (x - \alpha)\dfrac{dx}{dy} + (y - \beta) = 0, & \tag{9} \\ \left(\dfrac{dx}{dy}\right)^2 + (x - \alpha)\dfrac{d^2x}{dy^2} + 1 = 0. & \tag{10} \end{cases}$$

2. From $x = 2 \cos t$ and $y = 3 \sin t$,

$$x' = \frac{dx}{dy} = -\frac{2}{3} \tan t; \quad x'' = \frac{d^2x}{dy^2} = \frac{dx'}{dy} = -\frac{2}{3}\frac{\sec^2 t}{3 \cos t} = -\frac{2}{9} \sec^3 t.$$

At $t = 0$, $x' = 0$ and $x'' = -\frac{2}{9}$. Then, on substituting $x = 2$, $y = 0$, $x' = 0$, and $x'' = -\frac{2}{9}$ in [(8), (9), (10)], we obtain a system whose solution is found to be $\alpha = -\frac{5}{2}$, $\beta = 0$, and $R^2 = \frac{81}{4}$. The circle of curvature has the equation $(x + \frac{5}{2})^2 + y^2 = \frac{81}{4}$.

151. EVOLUTES AND INVOLUTES

At any point $P:(x, y)$ on a curve C where y has the derivatives y' and y'' with respect to x, (3) and (4) of the preceding section form a system of two equations for the unknowns α and β. Then, we solve (4) for β and use (3) to obtain α, with the following results:

$$\alpha = x - \frac{y'(1 + y'^2)}{y''}; \quad \beta = y + \frac{1 + y'^2}{y''}. \tag{1}$$

ILLUSTRATION 1. In Example 1 on page 401, with $x = 1$, $y = 2$, $y' = -2$, and $y'' = 4$, from (1) we obtain $\alpha = \frac{7}{2}$ and $\beta = \frac{13}{4}$.

For every point $P:(x, y)$ on a curve C where (1) applies, we obtain a center of curvature $Q:(\alpha, \beta)$. If a moving point P traces out C, then Q traces out a corresponding curve, described as follows.

Definition V. The **evolute**, E, *of a given curve C is the locus of the centers of curvature $Q:(\alpha, \beta)$ for all points of C.*

If C is defined by parametric equations $x = \phi(t)$ and $y = \psi(t)$, then (1) gives *parametric equations*, in terms of the parameter t, for the rectangular coordinates (α, β) of the general point on the evolute. If C is defined by an equation $y = f(x)$, then (1) gives parametric equations for the evolute in terms of x as a parameter. Elimination of the parameter, t or x, between equations (1) would give an $\alpha\beta$-equation for the evolute, where the former x-axis becomes the α-axis and the y-axis becomes the β-axis.

ILLUSTRATION 2. In Figure 266, the evolute of the ellipse is the curve with four cusps, as obtained in the next example. In Figure 266, centers of curvature Q_1, Q_2, etc. are shown for P_1, P_2, etc., respectively, on the ellipse. The lines P_iQ_i are normals to the ellipse; $|\overline{P_iQ_i}|$ is the radius of curvature at P_i on the ellipse. Notice that P_iQ_i is tangent to the evolute.

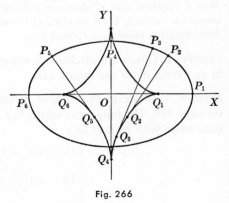

Fig. 266

EXAMPLE 1. Find the evolute of the ellipse

$$x = a \cos t \quad and \quad y = b \sin t, \quad where \quad a > 0 \quad and \quad b > 0. \tag{2}$$

Solution. 1. From (2), and from (1),

$$y' = \frac{dy}{dx} = -\frac{b}{a}\cot t; \quad y'' = \frac{d^2y}{dx^2} = -\frac{b}{a^2}\csc^3 t; \tag{3}$$

$$\alpha = \frac{a^2 - b^2}{a}\cos^3 t; \quad \beta = \frac{b^2 - a^2}{b}\sin^3 t. \tag{4}$$

2. To eliminate t from the parametric equations for the evolute in (4), solve for sin t and cos t, square the results, and add:

$$\alpha^{\frac{2}{3}}\left(\frac{a}{a^2 - b^2}\right)^{\frac{2}{3}} + \beta^{\frac{2}{3}}\left(\frac{b}{a^2 - b^2}\right)^{\frac{2}{3}} = 1, \quad or \quad a^{\frac{2}{3}}\alpha^{\frac{2}{3}} + b^{\frac{2}{3}}\beta^{\frac{2}{3}} = (a^2 - b^2)^{\frac{2}{3}}.$$

Finally, we may replace (α, β) by (x, y) to obtain

$$(ax)^{\frac{2}{3}} + (by)^{\frac{2}{3}} = (a^2 - b^2)^{\frac{2}{3}} \tag{5}$$

as the equation of the evolute in the given xy-system of coordinates. The graph of (5) is the curve with 4 cusps in Figure 266 on page 402.

EXAMPLE 2. Find the evolute of the parabola $y^2 = 4x$.

Solution. We have $\quad y' = \frac{2}{y}; \quad y'' = -\frac{4}{y^3}; \quad 1 + y'^2 = 1 + \frac{4}{y^2} = \frac{x+1}{x}.$

From (1), $\qquad\qquad\qquad \alpha = 3x + 2; \quad \beta = -\frac{y^3}{4}. \tag{6}$

With $y^2 = 4x$, (6) gives parametric equations for the evolute, where x is the parameter. In (6), solve for x and y and substitute in $y^2 = 4x$:

$$x = \tfrac{1}{3}(\alpha - 2) \quad and \quad y = -(4\beta)^{\frac{1}{3}}, \quad or \quad y^2 = (4\beta)^{\frac{2}{3}}.$$

From $y^2 = 4x$, $\qquad (4\beta)^{\frac{2}{3}} = \tfrac{4}{3}(\alpha - 2), \quad or \quad 16\beta^2 = [\tfrac{4}{3}(\alpha - 2)]^3; \ or,$

$$\beta^2 = \tfrac{4}{27}(\alpha - 2)^3. \tag{7}$$

On replacing (α, β) by (x, y) in (7), we obtain the xy-equation of the evolute, $y^2 = \tfrac{4}{27}(x - 2)^3$, which is a semicubical parabola with its cusp at $(x = 2, y = 0)$. The student should check the graphs of $y^2 = 4x$ and $y^2 = \tfrac{4}{27}(x - 2)^3$.

The evolute E of a curve C, defined by $y = f(x)$, has the following characteristics; Property I was illustrated in Figure 266 on page 402.

I. *The normal to a curve C at a point $P:(x, y)$ is tangent to the evolute of C at the center of curvature $Q:(\alpha, \beta)$ for P.*

II. *Let P_1 and P_2 be two points on C where the radii of curvature are R_1 and R_2, and the centers of curvature are $Q_1:(\alpha_1, \beta_1)$ and $Q_2:(\alpha_2, \beta_2)$, respectively. Let L be the length of arc $Q_1 Q_2$ on E. Then,* L = | R_1 - R_2 |.*

Proof of (**I**). Let C be defined by $y = f(x)$. Then, (1) specifies parametric equations for the evolute with x as the parameter. From (1),

* We assume that the radius of curvature on C continually increases (or, decreases) as a point P moves on C from P_1 to P_2. Also, we assume that f''' is continuous.

$$\frac{d\alpha}{dx} = \frac{y'(1 + y'^2)y''' - 3y'^2 y''^2}{y''^2}; \quad \frac{d\beta}{dx} = \frac{3y'y''^2 - (1 + y'^2)y'''}{y''^2}. \tag{8}$$

Let $Q:(\alpha, \beta)$ be the center of curvature on E corresponding to $P:(x, y)$ on C. Then, PQ is the normal to C at P, and the slope of PQ is $-1/y'$. From (8), the slope of the tangent to E at Q simplifies to give

$$\frac{d\beta}{d\alpha} = \frac{d\beta}{dx} \bigg/ \frac{d\alpha}{dx} = -\frac{1}{y'}. \tag{9}$$

Hence, the tangent to E at Q has the same slope as PQ, or PQ is tangent to E at Q, as we wished to prove.

Note 1. In problem 38 on page 405, the student may prove **(II)** by showing that, if σ represents arc distance on the evolute of a curve $y = f(x)$, then $|\,d\sigma/dx\,| = |\,dR/dx\,|$.

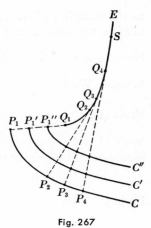

Fig. 267

ILLUSTRATION 3. In Figure 267, E is the evolute of C, where the radius of curvature increases if we move to the right on C. Conceive of a string anchored at S on E, stretched tightly on E up to a point Q_1, and then extended along the tangent to E, up to P_1 on C. By (I) and (II), if the string is unwound and remains tangent to E, the free end traces out C. From Q_1 to Q_2, the increase in free length, $(\overline{P_2 Q_2} - \overline{P_1 Q_1})$, is the length of arc $Q_1 Q_2$ on E. Suppose, now, that A is any point on the segment $P_1 Q_1$, or its extension through P_1. Then, as the string is unwound from E, A would trace out a curve which also has E as its evolute. Figure 267 shows two other curves C' and C'' obtained in this way, with E as their evolute.

If a curve C has E as the evolute, we call C an **involute** of E. Then, from Illustration 3, we observe that there are infinitely many involutes for any given curve E which is known to be an evolute of some curve. In particular, Figure 267 shows three involutes of the given curve E.

EXERCISE 125

Find the center and radius of curvature, and the curvature for the curve at the given point; write an equation for the circle of curvature. Solve on the basis of (1) *and* (2) *in Section* 150.
1–18. Problems 1–18, respectively, in Exercise 124 on page 400.

Obtain parametric equations, or an xy-equation for the evolute of the curve.
19. $x^2 = y$.   **20.** $y^2 = 6x$.   **21.** $y^2 = 2px$.
22. $x = 3 \cos t$ and $y = 2 \sin t$.   **23.** $4x^2 + 9y^2 = 36$.
24. $x = a \cos^3 t$ and $y = a \sin^3 t$.   **25.** $x = 2t$ and $y = t^2 + 2$.
26. $x = 8t$ and $y = 4/t$.   **27.** $x = a \sec t$ and $y = b \tan t$.
28. $x = a(\cos t + t \sin t)$ and $y = a(\sin t - t \cos t)$. (Involute of a circle.)
29. $x = a(\theta - \sin \theta)$ and $y = a(1 - \cos \theta)$.

★SUPPLEMENT FOR CHAPTER SIXTEEN

Obtain parametric equations, or an equation for the evolute of the curve.

30. $b^2x^2 - a^2y^2 = a^2b^2$.   **31.** $b^2x^2 + a^2y^2 = a^2b^2$.

32. $2xy = a^2$.   **33.** $x^{\frac{2}{3}} + y^{\frac{2}{3}} = a^{\frac{2}{3}}$.

34. Prove that the area of the region in the xy-plane bounded by the x-axis, arbitrary lines $x = x_1$ and $x = x_2$, and the catenary of Figure 27 on page 713 is proportional to the length of arc on the catenary between the points where $x = x_1$ and $x = x_2$.

35. The region bounded by the x-axis, arbitrary lines $x = x_1$ and $x = x_2$, and the catenary of Problem 34 is revolved about the x-axis. Prove that the volume of the solid thus generated is proportional to its surface area, omitting the circular ends.

36. Let C be a circle of radius a. Prove that the *average* with respect to arc length (or *mean value*) of the distances from the points of C to a fixed point on C is $4a/\pi$.

Hint. Use parametric form with s as the parameter. See Note 1 on page 195. With $(a, 0)$ as the fixed point and $f(x, y)$ as the distance to $P:(x, y)$, the problem requests $\lim_{\Delta s \to 0} \left[\sum_i f(x_i, y_i) \Delta s \right]/L$, where L is the circumference.

37. Let C be a cardioid where the distance from the cusp to the point of the cardioid farthest from the cusp is $2b$. Prove that the average with respect to arc length of the distances from the cusp to the points of C is $4b/3$.

38. On the evolute E involved in (I) and (II) on page 403, let σ represent the length of arc measured from the point where $x = x_0$ to the point (x, y), with $x \geq x_0$ and $f''(x) \neq 0$ at any point. Prove that $|\, d\sigma/dx\,| = |\, dR/dx\,|$, where R is the radius of curvature at (x, y), and thus establish (II) on page 403.

39. Find the surface area of the prolate spheroid obtained by revolving the ellipse $(x = a \cos t, y = b \sin t)$ about OX, with $0 < b < a$. To simplify, recall that the eccentricity η is defined by $\eta^2 = (a^2 - b^2)/a^2$.

40. Find the area of the curved surface of a zone cut from a sphere by two parallel planes k units apart.

41. If f' is continuous, and C is a curve whose equation in polar coordinates is $r = f(\theta)$, prove that C is a regular curve, as defined on page 395, except where

$$|f(\theta)| + |f'(\theta)| = 0.$$

42. Let C be the curve in an xy-plane given in parametric form by

$$x = e^t \sin t \quad and \quad y = e^t \cos t.$$

Let s be the length of arc on C measured in the direction of increasing values of t from the point $(0, 1)$ on C. Obtain parametric equations for C in terms of s as the parameter.

CHAPTER SEVENTEEN

Vectors and Direction Cosines

152. RECTANGULAR COORDINATES IN SPACE

The main objectives in this chapter are certain applications of vectors in a plane. However, we shall commence with content about vectors in *three-space* (abbreviated as *space*) including as a special case topics in a plane.

We shall have need for rectangular coordinates in space. To define coordinates, first specify a unit for length, to be used for measuring distance in any direction, and for setting up any number scale involved. Then, through a fixed point, O, called the *origin*, construct three mutually perpendicular directed lines OX, OY, and OZ, named the x-axis, y-axis, and z-axis, respectively. On each axis, lay off a number scale, with O as the zero point. These axes determine three mutually perpendicular coordinate planes, the xy-plane OXY, the xz-plane OXZ, and the yz-plane OYZ. Think of the yz-plane as vertical, facing you, with the positive direction on OX projecting toward you,* as in Figure 268, so that the xy-plane is horizontal. We agree that any line segment or distance parallel to a coordinate axis will be directed, with the same positive direction as on the axis. Then, the coordinates (x, y, z) of a point P are defined as the directed perpendicular dis-

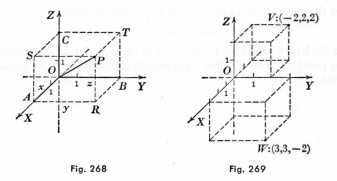

Fig. 268   Fig. 269

---

* This gives a **right-handed system,** in the order (x, y, z), in harmony with custom in applications. A right-handed screw with its head at O and screw point on the positive part of OZ would advance along OZ if rotated from OX to OY.

406

tances of P from the yz-plane, xz-plane, and xy-plane, respectively. To construct Figure 268, draw OX with $\angle XOY$ chosen (arbitrarily) as $135°$. On OX, take a foreshortened unit of length, about $\frac{2}{3}$ of the actual unit on OY. Then, locate $P{:}(x, y, z)$ with $\overline{OA} = x$, $\overline{AR} = y$, and $\overline{RP} = z$, where AR and RP are parallel to OY and OZ, respectively. We call $\overrightarrow{OP}$ the **radius vector** of P.

  ILLUSTRATION 1. Figure 269 on page 406 shows $W{:}(3, 3, -2)$; $V{:}(-2, 2, 2)$.

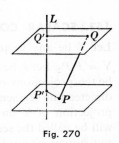

Fig. 270

 The **projection** (perpendicular) of a point P on a line L is defined as the point where a plane (or line) through P perpendicular to L meets L. The projection of a line segment PQ onto L is the segment $P'Q'$ joining the projections of P and Q on L, as in Figure 270. If PQ is a directed segment, we may consider $P'Q'$ as a directed segment.

  ILLUSTRATION 2. In Figure 268, page 406, A, B, and C are the projections of P on the axes. The coordinates x, y, and z of P are the values of the directed line segments OA, OB, and OC, respectively.

The coordinate planes divide space into eight **octants**. The *visible octant*, where all coordinates are positive, is called the *first octant*.

Note 1. In Problem 16 on page 462, the interested student will have an opportunity to prove that the agreements for Figure 268 on page 406 are equivalent to projecting all points of space onto the yz-plane by a family of parallel lines. This method is called

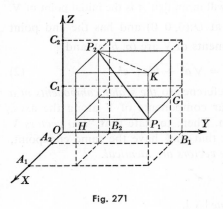

Fig. 271

parallel projection. Configurations in any plane parallel to the yz-plane are *undistorted* in such projection. Any line in space is represented by a line on the figure. Lines parallel in space become parallel lines in the figure.

 Through each of two points $P_1{:}(x_1, y_1, z_1)$ and $P_2{:}(x_2, y_2, z_2)$, as in Figure 271, pass a plane parallel to each coordinate plane. The planes intersect to form a rectangular parallelepiped, or box, with P_1P_2 as a diagonal and each edge parallel to a coordinate axis. Figure 271 shows the projections A_1A_2, B_1B_2, and C_1C_2 of the directed segment P_1P_2 on the axes. Since $\overline{OA_1} = x_1$, $\overline{OA_2} = x_2$, etc.,

$$\overline{A_1A_2} = x_2 - x_1, \quad \overline{B_1B_2} = y_2 - y_1, \quad and \quad \overline{C_1C_2} = z_2 - z_1.$$

On the box, observe that $\overline{P_1G} = \overline{A_1A_2}$, etc. Thus, the dimensions (positive) of the box are the *lengths* of the projections of P_1P_2 on the axes:

$$|x_2 - x_1|; \quad |y_2 - y_1|; \quad |z_2 - z_1|. \tag{1}$$

Hence, if d represents the length of the diagonal of the box, or the distance between P_1 and P_2, we obtain

$$|\overline{P_1P_2}| = d = \sqrt{(x_2 - x_1)^2 + (y_2 - y_1)^2 + (z_2 - z_1)^2}. \tag{2}$$

ILLUSTRATION 3. The distance between $(1, 1, -3)$ and $(-1, -2, 1)$ is

$$d = \sqrt{(-2)^2 + (-3)^2 + 4^2} = \sqrt{29}.$$

The magnitude, ρ, of the vector $\overrightarrow{OP}$ in Figure 268, page 406, is

$$\rho = \sqrt{x^2 + y^2 + z^2}. \tag{3}$$

153. SCALAR COMPONENTS OF A VECTOR

Let $\mathbf{V}$ be any vector in space, with initial point P_1 and terminal point P_2, or $\mathbf{V} = \overrightarrow{P_1P_2}$. Let L be any directed line in space, as in Figure 272, and let A_1 and A_2 be the projections of P_1 and P_2, respectively, on L. Then, the directed line segment A_1A_2 will be referred to as the directed projection of $\mathbf{V}$ on L, and the value, $\overline{A_1A_2}$, of the segment will be called the **scalar component of V along L**. Now, let an xyz-system of coordinates be imposed on space and let the end points of $\mathbf{V}$ be $P_1{:}(x_1, y_1, z_1)$ and $P_2{:}(x_2, y_2, z_2)$, with $\mathbf{V} = \overrightarrow{P_1P_2}$. Then, from Figure 271 on page 407, the scalar components of $\mathbf{V}$ along the axes are $(x_2 - x_1)$, $(y_2 - y_1)$, and $(z_2 - z_1)$, respectively, and

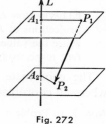

Fig. 272

$$|\mathbf{V}| = \sqrt{(x_2 - x_1)^2 + (y_2 - y_1)^2 + (z_2 - z_1)^2}. \tag{1}$$

Note 1. To state that $\mathbf{V}$ is **based** at a point A will mean that A is the initial point of $\mathbf{V}$.

As a special case of (1), if $\mathbf{V}$ is based at $O{:}(0, 0, 0)$ and has the end point $P{:}(a, b, c)$, then $\mathbf{V} = \overrightarrow{OP}$, the scalar components of $\mathbf{V}$ are (a, b, c), and

$$[\mathbf{V} = \overrightarrow{OP}; \quad P{:}(a, b, c)] \qquad\qquad |\mathbf{V}| = \sqrt{a^2 + b^2 + c^2}. \tag{2}$$

Hereafter, unless otherwise specified, a reference to *the scalar components of a vector* $\mathbf{V}$ in xyz-space will mean the scalar components of $\mathbf{V}$ along the axes. Now, let all vectors be based at the origin. Then, to state that "*two vectors* $\mathbf{V}$ *and* $\mathbf{W}$ *are equal*," is equivalent to saying that they have the same end point, and hence that *the scalar components of the vectors are identical*.

EXERCISE 126

Plot the point P, construct $\mathbf{V} = \overrightarrow{OP}$, *and compute* $|\mathbf{V}|$.

1. $(2, 3, 4)$.   **2.** $(2, -2, -3)$.   **3.** $(-2, -1, 2)$.   **4.** $(2, -3, -4)$.
5. $(-3, 4, 0)$.   **6.** $(-5, -12, 0)$.   **7.** $(2, -5, 0)$.   **8.** $(-3, 0, 0)$.

If P and Q are the points in the listed order, construct $\overrightarrow{PQ}$, *state the scalar components of* $\overrightarrow{PQ}$, *and find its magnitude*.

9. $(0, 0, 0);\ (2, 4, 5)$.   **10.** $(0, 0, 0);\ (3, 5, -1)$.
11. $(-1, 2, 3);\ (-3, 4, 4)$.   **12.** $(-1, 2, 0);\ (2, 4, 2)$.
13. $(1, -2, -1);\ (3, 1, -2)$.   **14.** $(-1, 2, 1);\ (-1, -2, 3)$.

154. ALGEBRAIC OPERATIONS FOR VECTORS

In Section 53 on page 162, we introduced elements of the terminology for vectors, and the operation of addition for *just two* vectors. We continue with a development of an algebra for vectors.

Definition I (*multiplication by a scalar*). *If* **V** *is a vector and h is a number, not zero, then h***V** *is that vector whose magnitude is* | h | *times the magnitude of* **V** *or,*

$$| h\mathbf{V} | = | h | \cdot | \mathbf{V} |,$$

and whose direction is the same as, or is opposite to, the direction of **V** *according as* $h > 0$, *or* $h < 0$. *If* $h = 0$, *then* $h\mathbf{V} = \mathbf{O}$.

We agree that **V**h will have the same meaning as h**V**. We shall write "$+$**V**" for $(+1)$**V**, "$- p$**V**" for $(- p)$**V**, and "$- $**V**" for $(- 1)$**V**. Thus, $+ \mathbf{V} = \mathbf{V}$, or insertion of "$+$" before **V** does not alter it.

ILLUSTRATION 1. In Figure 273, where $\mathbf{V} = \overrightarrow{AP}$ and $- 2\mathbf{V} = \overrightarrow{AQ}$, we have

$$| \overline{AQ} | = 2 | \overline{AP} |,$$

and the direction of $- 2\mathbf{V}$ is opposite to that of **V**. If $h \neq 0$ and $h\mathbf{V} = \mathbf{W}$ then, by Definition I, $\mathbf{V} = \dfrac{1}{h} \mathbf{W}$.

By Definition III on page 163, to say that two vectors **U** and **V** are *collinear* means that they have the same or opposite directions, or are *parallel*. Thus, the set of all vectors collinear with a given vector $\mathbf{V} \neq 0$ is the set $\{h\mathbf{V}\}$ where the domain of h consists of all numbers.

Fig. 273

On page 163, we used "$+$" to indicate vector addition. In multiplication by scalars, the signs "$+$" and "$-$" will indicate multiplication by positive or negative numbers. To avoid ambiguity, we now specify that each symbol for a vector will have a sign "$+$" or "$-$" (indicating multiplication by $+1$ or by -1) at the left, where "$+$" is implied if no sign is written. Then, we make the following agreement.

> *To represent the sum of two* * *vectors, write their symbols, with their signs, in the given order, and show any plus sign explicitly with any symbol not at the extreme left.* (1)

ILLUSTRATION 2. By (1), $(\mathbf{U} + 2\mathbf{V})$ means the sum of **U** and $+ 2\mathbf{V}$, or simply of **U** and $2\mathbf{V}$. Thus, (1) is consistent with the use of "$+$" on page 163 to indicate vector addition. $(3\mathbf{U} - 2\mathbf{V})$ means the sum of $3\mathbf{U}$ and $- 2\mathbf{V}$.

ILLUSTRATION 3. We shall call $- \mathbf{A}$ the **negative** of **A**. In Figure 274 where $\mathbf{A} = \overrightarrow{PQ}$, we have $- \mathbf{A} = \overrightarrow{QP}$. Then,

$$\mathbf{A} - \mathbf{A} = \overrightarrow{PQ} + \overrightarrow{QP} = \mathbf{O}, or$$

Fig. 274

the sum of a vector and its negative is the zero vector.

* Later, of *any number of vectors*.

Note 1. A vector with magnitude 1 will be called a **unit vector. If V is any vector, and U is a unit vector with the same direction as V, then U = V/| V | because**

$$\left|\frac{V}{|V|}\right| = \frac{1}{|V|}|V| = 1. \tag{2}$$

Hereafter, we assume that an *xyz*-system of coordinates is imposed on space. Then, suppose that three vectors V_1, V_2, and V_3 have the scalar components (a_1, b_1, c_1), (a_2, b_2, c_2), and (a_3, b_3, c_3), respectively. In Figure 275, let $V_1 = \overrightarrow{OP}$ and $V_2 = \overrightarrow{PQ}$; by Definition IV on page 163, $\overrightarrow{OQ} = V_1 + V_2$. The scalar components of V_1, V_2, and $\overrightarrow{OQ}$ along the *y*-axis are seen to be $\overline{OB}$, $\overline{BK}$, and $\overline{OK}$, respectively, and

$$\overline{OK} = \overline{OB} + \overline{BK} = b_1 + b_2.$$

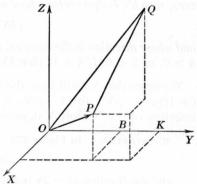

Fig. 275

Similar results are obtainable for the scalar components of $\overrightarrow{OQ}$ along the *x*-axis and the *z*-axis, and thus

$$\left\{ \begin{array}{l} \text{\textit{the scalar component of} } (V_1 + V_2) \text{ \textit{along any coordinate axis is}} \\ \text{\textit{the sum of the scalar components of} } V_1 \text{ \textit{and} } V_2 \text{ \textit{along this axis.}} \end{array} \right\} \tag{3}$$

Now consider the following vector sums:

$$[(V_1 + V_2) + V_3]; \quad [(V_1 + V_3) + V_2]; \quad [(V_2 + V_3) + V_1]. \tag{4}$$

Let S represent the sum at the left in (4). Since the scalar components of $(V_1 + V_2)$ and V_3 along the *y*-axis are $(b_1 + b_2)$ and b_3, respectively, as an application of (3) we obtain

(scalar component of S *along y-axis)* $= (b_1 + b_2) + b_3 = b_1 + b_2 + b_3.$

Similarly, the other scalar components of S are $(a_1 + a_2 + a_3)$ and $(c_1 + c_2 + c_3)$. Moreover, it is easily verified, by use of (3), that each bracketed sum in (4) has *the same scalar components as* S, or that the sums in (4) represent the *same vector.* Hence, we could define S as the sum of (V_1, V_2, V_3), and then remark that addition of three vectors is **associative,** which means that the sum is independent of the form used in (4).

We could give a similar discussion for four, five, or any number of vectors. However, to avoid the corresponding details, we decide to make a fresh start and *define* the sum of any number of vectors as follows. By (3), the new definition includes, as special cases, Definition IV on page 163 for two vectors, and the related definition for a sum of three vectors in (4).

Definition II. *The sum,* S, *of any number of vectors is the vector for which each scalar component is equal to the sum of the corresponding components of the given vectors.*

To represent the sum of a set of vectors, we agree to write their symbols in a line, as for two vectors in (1), page 409. Thus, the sum, **S**, of **T**, $- 2\mathbf{V}$, and $3\mathbf{W}$ is represented by $\mathbf{S} = \mathbf{T} - 2\mathbf{V} + 3\mathbf{W}$.

Calculation of a sum of vectors is referred to as **vector addition.** Since addition of scalar components is commutative and associative, we conclude that vector addition is **commutative** and **associative.**

At present, let all vectors be based at the origin unless otherwise specified. Let **i, j,** and **k** represent unit vectors having the directions of the x-axis, y-axis, and z-axis, respectively. Then, we shall call **i, j,** and **k** the **base vectors** for the xyz-system of coordinates. The end points of **i, j,** and **k** are $(1, 0, 0)$, $(0, 1, 0)$, and $(0, 0, 1)$, as in Figure 276.

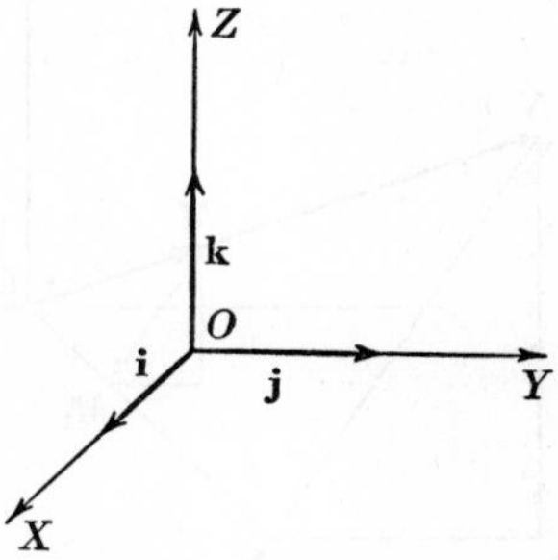

Fig. 276

Theorem I. *If a vector* **V** *has the* **scalar components** (a, b, c), *or the* **vector components** $(a\mathbf{i}, b\mathbf{j}, c\mathbf{k})$, *in the directions of the coordinate axes, then*

$$\mathbf{V} = a\mathbf{i} + b\mathbf{j} + c\mathbf{k}. \tag{5}$$

In particular, if $\mathbf{V} = \overrightarrow{P_1P_2}$, *with the end points* $P_1:(x_1, y_1, z_1)$ *and* $P_2:(x_2, y_2, z_2)$, *then*

$$\mathbf{V} = (x_2 - x_1)\mathbf{i} + (y_2 - y_1)\mathbf{j} + (z_2 - z_1)\mathbf{k}. \tag{6}$$

Proof. With the end point $P:(a, b, c)$ in Figure 277, we have $\mathbf{V} = \overrightarrow{OP}$, and the scalar components of **V** along the axes are $a = \overline{OA}$, $b = \overline{OB}$, and $c = \overline{OC}$. By Definition I on page 409,

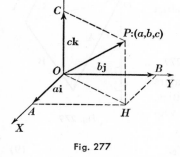

Fig. 277

$$\overrightarrow{OA} = a\mathbf{i}; \quad \overrightarrow{OB} = b\mathbf{j}; \quad \overrightarrow{OC} = c\mathbf{k}. \tag{7}$$

The scalar components of $\overrightarrow{OA}$, $\overrightarrow{OB}$, and $\overrightarrow{OC}$ are $(a, 0, 0)$, $(0, b, 0)$, and $(0, 0, c)$, respectively. By Definition II, the scalar components of the vector on the right in (5) are $(a + 0 + 0)$, $(0 + b + 0)$, and $(0 + 0 + c)$, or (a, b, c), which are the scalar components of **V**. Hence, (5) is true.* The result in (6) is obtained from (5) by recalling that $\overrightarrow{P_1P_2}$ has the scalar components $(x_2 - x_1)$, $(y_2 - y_1)$, and $(z_2 - z_1)$, respectively. We shall refer to (5), or (6), as the **component form** of the vector which is involved.

ILLUSTRATION 4. With $P_1:(- 2, 3, - 4)$ and $P_2:(1, 2, 3)$, from (5) and (6) we obtain

$$\overrightarrow{P_1P_2} = 3\mathbf{i} - \mathbf{j} + 7\mathbf{k}; \quad \overrightarrow{OP_1} = - 2\mathbf{i} + 3\mathbf{j} - 4\mathbf{k}.$$

To plot $\mathbf{V} = 2\mathbf{i} - 3\mathbf{j} + \mathbf{k}$ if **V** is based at $(0, 0, 0)$, we would locate $P:(2, - 3, 1)$, and construct $\mathbf{V} = \overrightarrow{OP}$. All scalar components of the zero vector are zero, or $\mathbf{O} = 0\mathbf{i} + 0\mathbf{j} + 0\mathbf{k}$.

* We could also demonstrate (5) by finding $(a\mathbf{i} + b\mathbf{j}) = \overrightarrow{OH}$ in Figure 277, and then the right-hand side of (5) by adding $c\mathbf{k}$, geometrically.

Let h be any number not zero, and let $\mathbf{V} = a\mathbf{i} + b\mathbf{j} + c\mathbf{k}$, where $\mathbf{V} = \overrightarrow{OM}$ in Figure 278. Then, for a case $h > 0$, we have $h\mathbf{V} = \overrightarrow{ON}$. The projections of M and N on the x-axis in Figure 278 are M_1 and N_1, respectively, where $\overline{OM_1} = a$. From Definition I on page 409 and the similar triangles OMM_1 and ONN_1 in Figure 278, we have

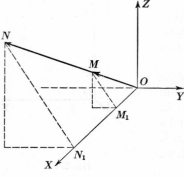

Fig. 278

$$h = \frac{|\overline{ON}|}{|\overline{OM}|} = \frac{|\overline{ON_1}|}{|\overline{OM_1}|} = \frac{\overline{ON_1}}{a}, \ or \ \overline{ON_1} = ha.$$

Thus, the scalar component of $h\mathbf{V}$ in the x-direction is ha. Similar results for $h < 0$, and for the other scalar components of $h\mathbf{V}$, lead to

$$h\mathbf{V} = ha\mathbf{i} + hb\mathbf{j} + hc\mathbf{k}. \tag{8}$$

ILLUSTRATION 5. By use of Definition II and multiplication by scalars,

$$3(2\mathbf{i} - 5\mathbf{j} + \mathbf{k}) - (\mathbf{i} - \mathbf{j} + 2\mathbf{k}) - 2(3\mathbf{i} + 2\mathbf{j} - 5\mathbf{k})$$
$$= 6\mathbf{i} - 15\mathbf{j} + 3\mathbf{k} - \mathbf{i} + \mathbf{j} - 2\mathbf{k} - 6\mathbf{i} - 4\mathbf{j} + 10\mathbf{k} = -\mathbf{i} - 18\mathbf{j} + 11\mathbf{k}.$$

By the parallelogram law, we may construct the sum of any number of vectors geometrically. We shall emphasize the construction only when all vectors are in the same plane (*coplanar vectors*).

ILLUSTRATION 6. Let $\quad \mathbf{A} = 2\mathbf{i} - 4\mathbf{j}; \quad \mathbf{B} = 2\mathbf{i} + 3\mathbf{j};$ $\mathbf{C} = -\mathbf{i} + 2\mathbf{j}.$ Since the scalar component of each vector along the z-axis is *zero*, the vectors lie in the xy-plane when based at the origin. Hence, we restrict Figure 279 to the xy-plane. Then

$$\mathbf{W} = \mathbf{A} + \mathbf{B} + \mathbf{C} = 3\mathbf{i} + \mathbf{j},$$

which checks with $\mathbf{W} = (\mathbf{A} + \mathbf{B}) + \mathbf{C}$ in Figure 279.

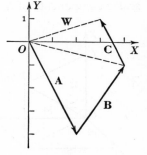

Fig. 279

The operation of multiplication of vectors by scalars has properties illustrated by the following identities. Any one of these can be proved by expressing each vector in component form and calculating both sides.

$$c(\mathbf{V_1} + \mathbf{V_2}) = c\mathbf{V_1} + c\mathbf{V_2}. \tag{9}$$

$$(c + d)\mathbf{V} = c\mathbf{V} + d\mathbf{V} = (d + c)\mathbf{V}. \tag{10}$$

$$(b + c + d)\mathbf{V} = [(b + c) + d]\mathbf{V} = [c + (b + d)]\mathbf{V} = etc. \tag{11}$$

$$b(c\mathbf{V}) = c(b\mathbf{V}) = bc\mathbf{V}. \tag{12}$$

Definition III. *To* **subtract** $\mathbf{B}$ *from* $\mathbf{A}$ *means to find* $\mathbf{C}$ *such that* $\mathbf{A} = \mathbf{B} + \mathbf{C}$. *The result,* $\mathbf{C}$, *is called the* **difference** *of* $\mathbf{A}$ *and* $\mathbf{B}$.

Theorem II. *The difference of* $\mathbf{A}$ *and* $\mathbf{B}$ *is* $(\mathbf{A} - \mathbf{B})$. *That is, to find the difference of* $\mathbf{A}$ *and* $\mathbf{B}$, *add* $-\mathbf{B}$ *to* $\mathbf{A}$.

Proof. We desire to find **C** so that $\mathbf{A} = \mathbf{B} + \mathbf{C}$. On adding $-\mathbf{B}$ to both sides of this equation, we obtain the equivalent equation

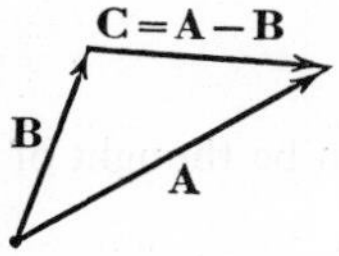

$$\mathbf{A} - \mathbf{B} = \mathbf{B} + \mathbf{C} - \mathbf{B} = \mathbf{C} + (\mathbf{B} - \mathbf{B}) = \mathbf{C} + \mathbf{O} = \mathbf{C},$$

which proves the desired result.

Fig. 280

Instead of using Theorem II to obtain $(\mathbf{A} - \mathbf{B})$, we favor the following construction where, clearly, $\mathbf{A} = \mathbf{B} + \mathbf{C}$, as seen in Figure 280.

$$\left.\begin{array}{l} \textit{To construct } \mathbf{C} = \mathbf{A} - \mathbf{B}, \textit{ base } \mathbf{A} \textit{ and } \mathbf{B} \textit{ at a common point. Then} \\ (\mathbf{A} - \mathbf{B}) \textit{ is the vector from the end point of } \mathbf{B} \textit{ to the end point of } \mathbf{A}. \end{array}\right\} \quad (13)$$

Any equation stating the equality of two expressions for vectors in *xyz*-space is equivalent to *three scalar equations*, stating the equality of corresponding scalar components of the expressions. Similarly, if all vectors involved lie in an *xy-plane*, the vector equation is equivalent to *two scalar equations*.

★*Note 2.* In this section, the word *vector* has had a geometric meaning. Any vector **V** can be based at the origin and then has some point $P:(x, y, z)$ as the end point. Also, just one vector, based at the origin, can have a given point P as the end point. Thus, there is a one-to-one correspondence between vectors and ordered triples of numbers (x, y, z). Hence, to form a nongeometric basis for a vector algebra, we may commence by *defining* a vector **V** simply as an ordered triple (x, y, z) and write $\mathbf{V} = (x, y, z)$. Our aim with the new basis would be to produce a mathematical structure which would yield the results of the previous geometric basis when each ordered triple is identified with the corresponding geometric vector. We shall omit the corresponding discussion. This method is essential in considering *n*-dimensional vectors.

EXERCISE 127

1–14. In component form, write the vector $\overrightarrow{OP}$, or the vector $\overrightarrow{PQ}$, as the case may be in Problems 1–14, respectively, of Exercise 126 on page 408. Also, by use of Note 1 on page 410, write the unit vector having the direction of $\overrightarrow{OP}$ or $\overrightarrow{PQ}$.

Base all vectors at the origin in an undistorted xy-plane without showing a z-axis, and perform the construction.

15. $\mathbf{V}_1 = 3\mathbf{i} + 5\mathbf{j}$; $\mathbf{V}_2 = -2\mathbf{i} + 4\mathbf{j}$: construct $2\mathbf{V}_1 + 3\mathbf{V}_2$.

16. $\mathbf{V}_1 = -2\mathbf{i} - 6\mathbf{j}$; $\mathbf{V}_2 = 2\mathbf{i} - \mathbf{j}$: construct $-\mathbf{V}_1 + 2\mathbf{V}_2$.

17. $\mathbf{V}_1 = \mathbf{i} - 5\mathbf{j}$; $\mathbf{V}_2 = -3\mathbf{i} + 2\mathbf{j}$: construct $3\mathbf{V}_1 - 2\mathbf{V}_2$.

18–20. In Problems 15–17, construct $(\mathbf{V}_1 - \mathbf{V}_2)$ as in (13) above.

Construct $(\mathbf{V}_1 + \mathbf{V}_2 + \mathbf{V}_3)$ in an undistorted xy-plane by the parallelogram law.

21. $\mathbf{V}_1$ and $\mathbf{V}_2$ from Problem 15; $\mathbf{V}_3 = -4\mathbf{i} - \mathbf{j}$.

22. $\mathbf{V}_1$ and $\mathbf{V}_2$ from Problem 16; $\mathbf{V}_3 = 7\mathbf{i} + 2\mathbf{j}$.

23. $\mathbf{V}_1$ and $\mathbf{V}_2$ from Problem 17; $\mathbf{V}_3 = -2\mathbf{i} + 6\mathbf{j}$.

*With **T**, **V**, and **W** given, solve for the unknown components $(x, y, 0)$ of **Z**.*

24. $\mathbf{T} = 3\mathbf{i} - 3\mathbf{j}$, $\mathbf{V} = -\mathbf{i} + 4\mathbf{j}$, $\mathbf{W} = 3\mathbf{i} + 5\mathbf{j}$; $\quad 2\mathbf{T} + 3\mathbf{V} - 2\mathbf{Z} = 4\mathbf{Z} + \mathbf{W}$.

25. $\mathbf{T} = -\mathbf{i} + 2\mathbf{j}$, $\mathbf{V} = 3\mathbf{i} + 2\mathbf{j}$, $\mathbf{W} = -3\mathbf{i} - \mathbf{j}$; $\quad 2\mathbf{Z} - \mathbf{T} - 3\mathbf{W} = 2\mathbf{V} + \mathbf{W}$.

Write the component form for a unit vector satisfying the condition.

26. With the direction of (a) $(7\mathbf{i} - 24\mathbf{j})$; (b) $(2\mathbf{i} - 3\mathbf{j} - 6\mathbf{k})$.

27. With the direction of $(\mathbf{T} - \mathbf{V})$ if $\mathbf{T} = -\mathbf{i} + 3\mathbf{j}$ and $\mathbf{V} = 4\mathbf{i} + 5\mathbf{j}$.

28. With the direction of $(\mathbf{T} - \mathbf{V})$ if $\mathbf{T} = -2\mathbf{i} - 2\mathbf{j}$ and $\mathbf{V} = 4\mathbf{i} - 6\mathbf{j}$.

29. Prove geometrically that, if $\mathbf{T}$ and $\mathbf{V}$ are any two vectors (which can be thought of as based at a common point), then $|\mathbf{T} + \mathbf{V}| \leqq |\mathbf{T}| + |\mathbf{V}|$.

★*Use a vector method to prove the result without use of a coordinate system.*

30. In any triangle, the line segment joining the mid-points of two sides is parallel to the third side and half as long.

31. The diagonals of a parallelogram bisect each other.

32. The medians of a triangle intersect at a point $\frac{2}{3}$ of the distance from any vertex to the mid-point of the opposite side.

33. Prove the result of Problem 29 algebraically by use of scalar components, with the plane of the vectors taken as the xy-plane.

★*Note 1.* Let $\mathbf{T}$, $\mathbf{V}$, and $\mathbf{W}$ be any three vectors. Then, to state that they are **linearly dependent** means that there exist scalars c_1, c_2, and c_3, not all zero, such that

$$c_1\mathbf{T} + c_2\mathbf{V} + c_3\mathbf{W} = \mathbf{O}.$$

If $\mathbf{T}$, $\mathbf{V}$, and $\mathbf{W}$ are *not* linearly dependent, they are said to be **linearly independent.** Similar definitions of linear dependence and independence apply to n given vectors, where $n \geqq 2$.

★*Prove the following results either analytically or geometrically.*

34. If $\mathbf{T}$, $\mathbf{V}$, and $\mathbf{W}$ are linearly independent, and if $c_1\mathbf{T} + c_2\mathbf{V} + c_3\mathbf{W} = \mathbf{O}$, then $c_1 = c_2 = c_3 = 0$.

35. If one of $\mathbf{T}$, $\mathbf{V}$, and $\mathbf{W}$ is the zero vector, then $\mathbf{T}$, $\mathbf{V}$, and $\mathbf{W}$ are linearly dependent.

36. If $\mathbf{T} \neq \mathbf{O}$ and $\mathbf{V} \neq \mathbf{O}$, and if $\mathbf{T}$ and $\mathbf{V}$ are linearly dependent, then $\mathbf{T}$ and $\mathbf{V}$ are collinear, and either can be expressed as a nonzero scalar times the other vector. Conversely, if $\mathbf{T}$ and $\mathbf{V}$ are collinear, then they are linearly dependent.

★**37.** Three vectors $\mathbf{T}$, $\mathbf{V}$, and $\mathbf{W}$ are said to be **coplanar** in case they lie in a plane when based at the same point. Prove that $\mathbf{T}$, $\mathbf{V}$, and $\mathbf{W}$ are coplanar if and only if they are linearly dependent.

155. DIRECTIONS IN SPACE

We shall consider a basis for dealing with directions in space, and related matters about vectors. Frequently, we shall use Ω (read *omega*) as a symbol for a direction.

Definition IV. *The angle made by two directions Ω_1 and Ω_2 is that angle θ on the interval $0 \leqq \theta \leqq \pi$ made by any two nonzero vectors * $\mathbf{V}_1$ and $\mathbf{V}_2$ having the directions Ω_1 and Ω_2, respectively, when $\mathbf{V}_1$ and $\mathbf{V}_2$ are based at the same point.*

ILLUSTRATION 1. For $\mathbf{V}_1$ and $\mathbf{V}_2$ as observed in Figure 281 on page 415, $\theta = 140°$. In Figure 282 on page 415, $\mathbf{V}_1 = -\mathbf{V}_2$ and $\theta = \pi$. If $\mathbf{V}_1$ and $\mathbf{V}_2$ have the same direction, then $\theta = 0$.

* Or *rays* with the directions Ω_1 and Ω_2 (a *ray* is a *directed half-line*).

ILLUSTRATION 2. Let θ be the angle made by **V** and **W**, as in Figure 283, and let ϕ be the angle made by **V** and $-$ **W**. Then $\phi = \pi - \theta$. That is, *if one direction is reversed in Definition* **IV**, *the new angle, ϕ, between the directions is the supplement of θ.*

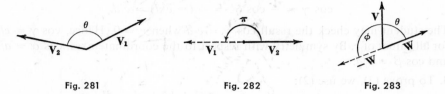

Fig. 281   Fig. 282   Fig. 283

Definition V. *The* **direction angles** *α, β, and γ of a direction Ω are the angles made with the base vectors* **i**, **j**, *and* **k**, *respectively, or with the positive rays on the coordinate axes, by any nonzero vector,* **V**, *having the direction Ω. Then* $\cos \alpha$, $\cos \beta$, *and* $\cos \gamma$ *are called the* **direction cosines** *of Ω. Also, we speak of (α, β, γ) and their cosines as the direction angles and direction cosines of* **V**.

ILLUSTRATION 3. With (α, β, γ) given for a vector **V**, let $(\alpha', \beta', \gamma')$ be the corresponding direction angles for $-$ **V**. By Illustration 2,

$$\alpha' = \pi - \alpha, \quad so \ that \quad \cos \alpha' = \cos(\pi - \alpha) = - \cos \alpha; \ etc.$$

That is, $(\alpha' = \pi - \alpha, \beta' = \pi - \beta, \gamma' = \pi - \gamma)$, and

$$\left\{ \begin{matrix} the \ direction \ cosines \ of \ a \ direction \ \Omega \ are \ the \\ \textbf{negatives} \ of \ those \ of \ the \ \textbf{opposite} \ direction. \end{matrix} \right\} \tag{1}$$

Since $0 \leqq \alpha \leqq \pi$, knowledge of $\cos \alpha$ determines just one value for α. Similar remarks apply to β and $\cos \beta$, and to γ and $\cos \gamma$.

Theorem III. *If* $\mathbf{V} = a\mathbf{i} + b\mathbf{j} + c\mathbf{k} \neq \mathbf{O}$, *the direction cosines of* **V** *are*

$$\left(\cos \alpha = \frac{a}{d}, \cos \beta = \frac{b}{d}, \cos \gamma = \frac{c}{d} \right), \quad where \quad d = \sqrt{a^2 + b^2 + c^2}. \tag{2}$$

Moreover, $$\cos^2 \alpha + \cos^2 \beta + \cos^2 \gamma = 1. \tag{3}$$

Proof. 1. **Case** $c > 0$. In Figure 284, $\mathbf{V} = \overrightarrow{OP}$, where P has the coordinates (a, b, c), and M is the projection of P on the z-axis. Hence, $\overline{OM} = c$. Also, $\angle MOP = \gamma < \frac{1}{2}\pi$; $\angle OMP = \frac{1}{2}\pi$. Triangle MOP is drawn without distortion in Figure 285, where it is seen that $\cos \gamma = c/d$.

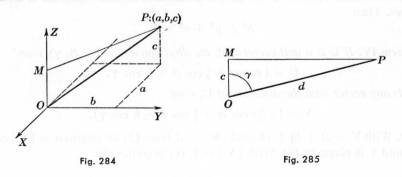

Fig. 284   Fig. 285

2. **Case $c < 0$.** Let $W = -V = -ai - bj - ck$; let γ' be the third direction angle of W. In W, $-c > 0$ and hence, by Item 1 of this proof, $\cos \gamma' = -c/d$. Since W and $-V$ have *opposite directions*, by (1) we have, again,

$$\cos \gamma = -\cos \gamma' = -(-c/d) = c/d.$$

The student may check the result $\cos \gamma = c/d$ when $c = 0$. Hence, $\cos \gamma = c/d$ for all values of c. By symmetry with respect to the coordinate axes, $\cos \alpha = a/d$ and $\cos \beta = b/d$.

3. To prove (3), we use (2):

$$\cos^2 \alpha + \cos^2 \beta + \cos^2 \gamma = \frac{a^2 + b^2 + c^2}{d^2} = \frac{d^2}{d^2} = 1.$$

Corollary 1. *If $P_1:(x_1, y_1, z_1)$ and $P_2:(x_2, y_2, z_2)$ are distinct, the direction from P_1 to P_2, or the direction of $\overrightarrow{P_1P_2}$, has the direction cosines*

$$\cos \alpha = \frac{x_2 - x_1}{d}, \quad \cos \beta = \frac{y_2 - y_1}{d}, \quad and \quad \cos \gamma = \frac{z_2 - z_1}{d}, \tag{4}$$

where $$d = \sqrt{(x_2 - x_1)^2 + (y_2 - y_1)^2 + (z_2 - z_1)^2}. \tag{5}$$

Proof. From (6) on page 411,

$$\overrightarrow{P_1P_2} = (x_2 - x_1)\mathbf{i} + (y_2 - y_1)\mathbf{j} + (z_2 - z_1)\mathbf{k}.$$

Hence, with $(a = x_2 - x_1, b = y_2 - y_1, c = z_2 - z_1)$, (2) gives (4).

ILLUSTRATION 4. With $P_1:(3, 2, -6)$ and $P_2:(1, -2, 4)$, we obtain the direction cosines of $\overrightarrow{P_1P_2}$ from (4):

$$\cos \alpha = -\frac{1}{\sqrt{30}}; \quad \cos \beta = -\frac{2}{\sqrt{30}}; \quad \cos \gamma = \frac{5}{\sqrt{30}}.$$

On account of (3), *we cannot assign* (α, β, γ) *at will.* If one of (α, β, γ) is assigned, this restricts the choice of the other two angles.

EXAMPLE 1. Obtain $\cos \beta$ and β if $\alpha = 45°$ and $\gamma = 120°$.

Solution. $\cos \alpha = \frac{1}{2}\sqrt{2}$; $\cos \gamma = -\frac{1}{2}$. Hence, from (3),

$$\cos^2 \beta = 1 - \tfrac{1}{2} - \tfrac{1}{4} = \tfrac{1}{4}; \quad \cos \beta = \pm \tfrac{1}{2}; \quad \beta = 60° \quad or \quad \beta = 120°.$$

When desired, we shall use (λ, μ, ν) as a standard notation for a set of direction cosines. Then

$$\lambda^2 + \mu^2 + \nu^2 = 1. \tag{6}$$

Theorem IV. *If U is a unit vector with the direction angles (α, β, γ), then*

$$U = \mathbf{i} \cos \alpha + \mathbf{j} \cos \beta + \mathbf{k} \cos \gamma. \tag{7}$$

If V is any vector with the direction of U, then

$$V = |V|(\mathbf{i} \cos \alpha + \mathbf{j} \cos \beta + \mathbf{k} \cos \gamma). \tag{8}$$

Proof. With $V = a\mathbf{i} + b\mathbf{j} + c\mathbf{k}$, and $|V| = d$, from (2) we obtain $a = |V| \cos \alpha$, etc., and V is given by (8). With $|V| = 1$, (8) becomes (7).

ILLUSTRATION 5. Figure 286 shows vectors **V** and **W** in the xy-plane. We have $\gamma = 90°$ for each vector because the z-axis (*not shown*) is perpendicular to each vector in the xy-plane. Observe that **W** has the direction angles $(\alpha = 120°, \beta = 30°, \gamma = 90°)$ and the direction cosines $(-\frac{1}{2}, \frac{1}{2}\sqrt{3}, 0)$. Also, the vector **V** has the direction angles $(\alpha = 120°, \beta = 150°, \gamma = 90°)$.

ILLUSTRATION 6. An admissible set of direction angles in space is $(\alpha = 120°, \beta = 60°, \gamma = 45°)$, which satisfy (3), as the student may verify.

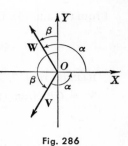

Fig. 286

Theorem V. *If θ is the angle made by two directions Ω_1 and Ω_2 having the direction angles $(\alpha_1, \beta_1, \gamma_1)$ and $(\alpha_2, \beta_2, \gamma_2)$, respectively, then*

$$\cos \theta = \cos \alpha_1 \cos \alpha_2 + \cos \beta_1 \cos \beta_2 + \cos \gamma_1 \cos \gamma_2. \tag{9}$$

Proof. 1. Let $(\lambda_1, \mu_1, \nu_1)$ and $(\lambda_2, \mu_2, \nu_2)$ be the direction cosines of Ω_1 and Ω_2, respectively. Then, by (7), the corresponding unit vectors $\mathbf{U}_1$ and $\mathbf{U}_2$ with these directions are

$$\mathbf{U}_1 = \lambda_1 \mathbf{i} + \mu_1 \mathbf{j} + \nu_1 \mathbf{k} \quad and$$
$$\mathbf{U}_2 = \lambda_2 \mathbf{i} + \mu_2 \mathbf{j} + \nu_2 \mathbf{k}.$$

With $\mathbf{U}_1$ and $\mathbf{U}_2$ based at O, as in Figure 287, the vectors have the tips $P_1:(\lambda_1, \mu_1, \nu_1)$ and $P_2:(\lambda_2, \mu_2, \nu_2)$, where $|\overline{OP_1}| = |\overline{OP_2}| = 1$.

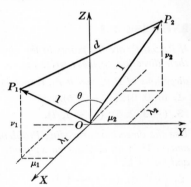

2. In $\triangle P_1 O P_2$ in Figure 287, $\theta = \angle P_1 O P_2$ and

$$d^2 = (\lambda_1 - \lambda_2)^2 + (\mu_1 - \mu_2)^2 + (\nu_1 - \nu_2)^2$$
$$= (\lambda_1^2 + \mu_1^2 + \nu_1^2) + (\lambda_2^2 + \mu_2^2 + \nu_2^2) - 2(\lambda_1\lambda_2 + \mu_1\mu_2 + \nu_1\nu_2); \tag{10}$$
$$d^2 = 2 - 2(\lambda_1\lambda_2 + \mu_1\mu_2 + \nu_1\nu_2). \tag{11}$$

Fig. 287

3. On applying the law of cosines from page 679 to $\triangle OP_1P_2$, we obtain

$$d^2 = (\overline{OP_1})^2 + (\overline{OP_2})^2 - 2|\overline{OP_1}| \cdot |\overline{OP_2}| \cos \theta, \ or$$
$$d^2 = 1 + 1 - 2 \cos \theta = 2 - 2 \cos \theta. \tag{12}$$

From (11) and (12), we obtain (9):

$$\cos \theta = \lambda_1\lambda_2 + \mu_1\mu_2 + \nu_1\nu_2.$$

Let $\mathbf{V}_1$ and $\mathbf{V}_2$ have the directions Ω_1 and Ω_2, as in Theorem V. Then, the directions of $\mathbf{V}_1$ and $\mathbf{V}_2$ are the same or are opposites (or, $\mathbf{V}_1$ and $\mathbf{V}_2$ are *parallel*) if and only if $\theta = 0$ or $\theta = \pi$, which is equivalent to $\cos \theta = \pm 1$. Since $\theta = \frac{1}{2}\pi$ is equivalent to $\cos \theta = 0$, we have

$$\left\{ \begin{array}{c} \mathbf{V}_1 \perp \mathbf{V}_2 \text{ is equivalent to} \\ \cos \alpha_1 \cos \alpha_2 + \cos \beta_1 \cos \beta_2 + \cos \gamma_1 \cos \gamma_2 = 0. \end{array} \right\} \tag{13}$$

From (2) and (9), if $V_1 = a_1\mathbf{i} + b_1\mathbf{j} + c_1\mathbf{k}$ and $V_2 = a_2\mathbf{i} + b_2\mathbf{j} + c_2\mathbf{k}$,

$$\cos\theta = \frac{a_1a_2 + b_1b_2 + c_1c_2}{\sqrt{a_1^2 + b_1^2 + c_1^2}\sqrt{a_2^2 + b_2^2 + c_2^2}}. \tag{14}$$

ILLUSTRATION 7. With $P_1:(9, -6, 2)$, $P_2:(2, -2, 1)$, $O:(0, 0, 0)$, $V_1 = \overrightarrow{OP_1}$, and $V_2 = \overrightarrow{OP_2}$, from (14), we obtain

$$\cos\theta = \frac{18 + 12 + 2}{\sqrt{121}\sqrt{9}} = \frac{32}{33}. \tag{15}$$

ILLUSTRATION 8. If $V_1 = a\mathbf{i} + b\mathbf{j}$ and $V_2 = -b\mathbf{i} + a\mathbf{j}$, then (14) gives $\cos\theta = 0$, so that $V_1 \perp V_2$.

If $V_1 \neq O$ and $V_2 \neq O$, as used in (14), then "$\cos\theta = 0$" is equivalent to the numerator being zero in (14). That is

$$V_1 \perp V_2 \quad \text{is equivalent to} \quad a_1a_2 + b_1b_2 + c_1c_2 = 0. \tag{16}$$

EXERCISE 128

If P_1 and P_2 are the points in the given order, write $\overrightarrow{P_1P_2}$ and $\overrightarrow{P_2P_1}$ in component form; find their direction cosines; write the component forms of the unit vectors U and $-U$ in the directions of $\overrightarrow{P_1P_2}$ and $\overrightarrow{P_2P_1}$, respectively.

1. $(0, 0, 0)$; $(3, -2, 6)$.   **2.** $(0, 0, 0)$; $(6, 9, -2)$.
3. $(-3, 2, 5)$; $(3, -7, 7)$.   **4.** $(1, 3, -5)$; $(4, 5, 1)$.

Use the directions preceding Problem 1. Find the desired results and draw $\overrightarrow{P_1P_2}$, $\overrightarrow{P_2P_1}$, U, and $-U$ in an undistorted xy-plane without showing a z-axis. Also, find (α, β, γ) for U and for $-U$.

5. $(0, 0, 0)$; $(-1, -1, 0)$.   **6.** $(0, 0, 0)$; $(-\sqrt{3}, 1, 0)$.
7. $(0, 3, 0)$; $(\sqrt{3}, 4, 0)$.   **8.** $(3, -2, 0)$; $(5, -4, 0)$.

Find the direction cosines of the direction from the first to the second point.

9. $(-1, 2, 3)$; $(1, 4, 2)$.   **10.** $(3, -2, 5)$; $(4, -4, 7)$.

11. Find the direction angles and direction cosines of the positive direction of the x-axis; y-axis; z-axis.

Obtain the missing direction angle and all direction cosines.

12. $\beta = 45°$; $\gamma = 45°$.   **13.** $\alpha = 60°$; $\gamma = 135°$.
14. $\alpha = 150°$; $\beta = 60°$.   **15.** $\beta = 30°$; $\gamma = 45°$.

16. If $\alpha = 30°$, find nonzero values of β and γ so that (α, β, γ) are a set of direction angles.

Suppose that all vectors lie in an xy-plane, so that $\gamma = 90°$. Construct each unit vector, U, based at the origin and having the given direction angle or cosine; read the missing direction angle from the figure, or a table; write the component form of U.

17. $\alpha = 30°$.   **18.** $\beta = 60°$.   **19.** $\beta = 135°$.   **20.** $\alpha = 135°$.
21. $\cos\alpha = \frac{1}{2}$.   **22.** $\cos\beta = -\frac{1}{2}\sqrt{2}$.   **23.** $\cos\alpha = .6$.

24-27. Let P_1 and P_2 be the points in the given order in Problems 3, 4, 7, and 8, respectively. Let $V = \overrightarrow{OP_1}$, $W = \overrightarrow{OP_2}$, and θ be the angle made by V and W. Find $\cos\theta$.

Without a figure, decide whether or not the two given vectors are $\perp$, *have the same direction, opposite directions, or no one of these characteristics. Use (14) or (16) on page 418.*

28. $(3i - 4j + 6k); (-6i + 8j - 12k).$

29. $(2i + 5j - k); (4i + 10j - 2k).$

30. $(2i - j + 3k); (-i + 13j + 5k).$

31. $(2i - j + 2k); (7i + 4j - 5k).$

32. $(i + j - k); (2i - 3j + 4k).$

33. $(-2i + 3j); (4i - 6j).$

34. $(3i + 3j); (-4i + 4j).$

35. $(-2i + 2j\sqrt{3}); (-i - j\sqrt{3}).$

36. $(4i + 5j); (2i - 3j).$

37. If $a^2 + b^2 + c^2 = 1$, prove that there is a direction Ω whose direction cosines are (a, b, c), written in any order as $(\cos \alpha, \cos \beta, \cos \gamma)$.

156. DIRECTION NUMBERS

The statement "(a, b, c) *are proportional to* (r, s, t)," abbreviated by *

$$\text{"}a : b : c = r : s : t,\text{"}$$

means that there exists a constant $h \neq 0$ such that

$$a = hr; \quad b = hs; \quad c = ht. \tag{1}$$

Whenever no denominator below is zero, (1) is equivalent to

$$\frac{a}{r} = \frac{b}{s} = \frac{c}{t}. \tag{2}$$

If all numbers on one side of $a : b : c = r : s : t$ are multiplied by $w \neq 0$, a true proportion arises. Thus, $a : b : c = rw : sw : tw$ because, from (1), $a = (rw)(h/w)$, etc., where the constant of proportionality is h/w.

ILLUSTRATION 1. If $a : b : c = \frac{2}{3} : -\frac{1}{2} : \frac{5}{6}$, we may simplify by multiplying by 6 on the right. Then, $a : b : c = 4 : -3 : 5$.

If $a_1 : b_1 : c_1 = r : s : t$ and $a_2 : b_2 : c_2 = r : s : t$, then it can be seen that $a_1 : b_1 : c_1 = a_2 : b_2 : c_2$. Thus, with constants of proportionality h_1 and h_2, we have $a_1 = h_1 r$, $a_2 = h_2 r$, and hence $a_1 = (h_1/h_2)a_2$, etc., where the constant of proportionality is h_1/h_2.

ILLUSTRATION 2. If $a_1 : b_1 : c_1 = 2 : -3 : 4$ and $a_2 : b_2 : c_2 = 2 : -3 : 4$, then $a_1 : b_1 : c_1 = a_2 : b_2 : c_2$.

If (a, b, c) are proportional to $(\cos \alpha, \cos \beta, \cos \gamma)$ for a direction Ω, we shall call (a, b, c) **direction numbers** † for Ω, or for any vector having this direction. Then, we may write

$$a : b : c = \cos \alpha : \cos \beta : \cos \gamma, \tag{3}$$

and there exists a constant of proportionality $h \neq 0$ so that

$$\cos \alpha = ha; \quad \cos \beta = hb; \quad \cos \gamma = hc. \tag{4}$$

To emphasize that (a, b, c) are direction numbers we shall write them $a : b : c$, but read them merely (a, b, c).

---

* Can be read "*a is to b is to c as r is to s is to t.*"

† Also called **direction ratios**, or **direction components**.

Theorem VI. *If* (a, b, c) *are not all zero, and* $d = \sqrt{a^2 + b^2 + c^2}$, *there exist direction cosines* (λ, μ, ν) *for two opposite directions having* (a, b, c) *as direction numbers, where*

$$\left(\lambda = \frac{a}{d}, \mu = \frac{b}{d}, \nu = \frac{c}{d}\right) \quad or \quad \left(\lambda = -\frac{a}{d}, \mu = -\frac{b}{d}, \nu = -\frac{c}{d}\right). \tag{5}$$

Proof. We desire $(h, \cos \alpha, \cos \beta, \cos \gamma)$ to satisfy (4) and

$$\cos^2 \alpha + \cos^2 \beta + \cos^2 \gamma = 1 = h^2(a^2 + b^2 + c^2). \tag{6}$$

Hence, $h = 1/\pm \sqrt{a^2 + b^2 + c^2}$. If we use the plus sign, we obtain one set of cosines in (5). We obtain the negatives of these cosines by using the negative value for h. Thus, we have obtained direction cosines for two opposite directions.

ILLUSTRATION 3. If the direction numbers are $3 : -2 : 1$,

$$\cos \alpha = \frac{3}{\pm \sqrt{14}}, \quad \cos \beta = -\frac{2}{\pm \sqrt{14}}, \quad \cos \gamma = \frac{1}{\pm \sqrt{14}}.$$

From (5), any numbers a, b, c, *not all zero* may be taken as direction numbers. One set of direction numbers for a direction is its direction cosines (λ, μ, ν). For them, $d = 1$ in (5). By Theorem III, page 415, the direction cosines of $\mathbf{V} = a\mathbf{i} + b\mathbf{j} + c\mathbf{k}$ are found on multiplying (a, b, c) by $1/\sqrt{a^2 + b^2 + c^2}$. Thus,

$$\left\{ \begin{array}{c} \textbf{a set of direction numbers for a vector} \\ \mathbf{V} = a\mathbf{i} + b\mathbf{j} + c\mathbf{k} \textbf{ are its scalar components, } a : b : c. \end{array} \right\} \tag{7}$$

In particular, if $P_1:(x_1, y_1, z_1)$ and $P_2:(x_2, y_2, z_2)$ are distinct points, then $\overrightarrow{P_1P_2} = (x_2 - x_1)\mathbf{i} + (y_2 - y_1)\mathbf{j} + (z_2 - z_1)\mathbf{k}$, and

direction numbers for $\overrightarrow{P_1P_2}$ *are* $\quad (x_2 - x_1) : (y_2 - y_1) : (z_2 - z_1).$ (8)

From (4) on page 416, the direction cosines of $\overrightarrow{P_1P_2}$ are found on dividing by $|\overrightarrow{P_1P_2}|$ in (8); division by $-|\overrightarrow{P_1P_2}|$ gives the direction cosines of $\overrightarrow{P_2P_1}$, whose direction is opposite to that of $\overrightarrow{P_1P_2}$.

Note 1. If $a : b : c$ are direction numbers for the two opposite directions on a line l, we shall call $a : b : c$ direction numbers for l. Thus, **(8) gives direction numbers for the line through points P_1 and P_2.** Occasionally, we refer to "*a direction $a : b : c$,*" meaning either of the directions having $a : b : c$ as direction numbers.

Theorem VII. *If two lines* l_1 *and* l_2 *(or, two directions* Ω_1 *and* Ω_2*) have the direction numbers* $a_1 : b_1 : c_1$ *and* $a_2 : b_2 : c_2$, *respectively, then*

$l_1 \parallel l_2$ *(or,* $\Omega_1 \parallel \Omega_2$*) is equivalent to* $\qquad a_1 : b_1 : c_1 = a_2 : b_2 : c_2;$ (9)

$l_1 \perp l_2$ *(or,* $\Omega_1 \perp \Omega_2$*) is equivalent to* $\qquad a_1a_2 + b_1b_2 + c_1c_2 = 0.$ (10)

If θ *represents any angle made by two directions chosen on* l_1 *and* l_2, *respectively, then*

$$\cos \theta = \pm \frac{a_1a_2 + b_1b_2 + c_1c_2}{\sqrt{a_1^2 + b_1^2 + c_1^2} \sqrt{a_2^2 + b_2^2 + c_2^2}}, \tag{11}$$

where the sign $\pm$ *depends on the choice of directions on* l_1 *and* l_2.

Proof. 1. Let $(\alpha_1, \beta_1, \gamma_1)$ and $(\alpha_2, \beta_2, \gamma_2)$ be the direction angles of two directions Ω_1 and Ω_2, on l_1 and l_2, respectively. Then,

$$a_1 : b_1 : c_1 = \cos \alpha_1 : \cos \beta_1 : \cos \gamma_1; \qquad (12)$$

$$a_2 : b_2 : c_2 = \cos \alpha_2 : \cos \beta_2 : \cos \gamma_2. \qquad (13)$$

To state that $\Omega_1 \parallel \Omega_2$ means that their direction cosines are the *same*, or those for Ω_2 are the *negatives* of those for Ω_1. In either case, the cosines for Ω_1 are proportional to those for Ω_2, or the right-hand sides of (12) and (13) are equal, and hence their left-hand sides are equal, as in (9).

2. By (7), vectors with the given directions are $\mathbf{V}_1 = a_1\mathbf{i} + b_1\mathbf{j} + c_1\mathbf{k}$, and $\mathbf{V}_2 = a_2\mathbf{i} + b_2\mathbf{j} + c_2\mathbf{k}$, where $\mathbf{V}_1$ has a direction on l_1 and $\mathbf{V}_2$ has a direction on l_2. Then, "$l_1 \perp l_2$" is equivalent to "$\mathbf{V}_1 \perp \mathbf{V}_2$," which is equivalent to (10), because of (16) on page 418.

3. Let $(\lambda_1, \mu_1, \nu_1)$ and $(\lambda_2, \mu_2, \nu_2)$ be the direction cosines of Ω_1 and Ω_2, respectively. Then, from (5),

$$\lambda_1 = \pm\, a_1/\sqrt{a_1^2 + b_1^2 + c_1^2}, \quad \lambda_2 = \pm\, a_2/\sqrt{a_2^2 + b_2^2 + c_2^2}, \text{ etc.}$$

Hence, by use of (9) on page 417, or (14) on page 418, we obtain (11).

ILLUSTRATION 4. From (8), direction numbers for the line through $P{:}(3, 2, -4)$ and $Q{:}(5, -4, 5)$ are $2 : -6 : 9$. From (4) on page 416, the direction cosines

of $\overrightarrow{PQ}$ are $(\frac{2}{11}, -\frac{6}{11}, \frac{9}{11})$; of $\overrightarrow{QP}$ are $(-\frac{2}{11}, \frac{6}{11}, -\frac{9}{11})$.

ILLUSTRATION 5. The directions $2 : -3 : 5$ and $-4 : 6 : -10$ are parallel. The directions $2 : -1 : 3$ and $-1 : 13 : 5$ are $\perp$ because $-2 - 13 + 15 = 0$.

EXERCISE 129

Simplify the direction numbers, if desirable. By use of (7), page 420, construct a vector $\mathbf{V}$ *having the given direction numbers. Obtain the direction cosines of* $\mathbf{V}$ *and* $-\mathbf{V}$.

1. $3 : 2 : -6$.   **2.** $-\frac{2}{5} : \frac{2}{5} : -\frac{1}{5}$.   **3.** $6 : -9 : -2$.

4. $\frac{8}{7} : -\frac{12}{7} : \frac{9}{7}$.   **5.** $-\frac{5}{2} : \frac{11}{4} : -\frac{1}{2}$.   **6.** $4 : -3 : 0$.

With the points labeled P_1 *and* P_2 *in the given order, write direction numbers for the line through* P_1P_2; *write the direction cosines of* $\overrightarrow{P_1P_2}$ *and of* $\overrightarrow{P_2P_1}$.

7. $(2, -3, 2); (-1, 2, -4)$.   **8.** $(-1, 2, -3); (-4, 2, -5)$.

9. $(0, 0, 0); (3, -2, 4)$.   **10.** $(-3, 0, -2); (0, 0, 0)$.

11. $(-3, 1, -2); (-5, 4, 7)$.   **12.** $(2, -3, -3); (4, -3, 5)$.

Are the two given directions parallel or perpendicular?

13. $-3 : 2 : -1$ and $6 : -4 : 2$.   **14.** $\frac{1}{2} : -\frac{3}{4} : 2$ and $-2 : 3 : -8$.

15. $7 : 4 : -5;\ 1 : 2 : 3$.   **16.** $2 : -1 : 2;\ -\frac{4}{3} : \frac{2}{3} : -\frac{4}{3}$.

17. $3 : 2 : -4;\ 1 : 1 : 2$.   **18.** $\frac{1}{3} : -\frac{1}{2} : \frac{1}{6};\ -4 : -1 : 5$.

Find the cosines of the two possible angles made by two directions having the given direction numbers. Also, find each of the angles from a table.

19. $2 : 3 : -4;\ -\frac{1}{2} : \frac{3}{4} : 1$.   **20.** $9 : -6 : 2;\ -8 : 12 : 9$.

157. SCALAR PRODUCT OF TWO VECTORS *

Definition VI. *If* **V** *and* **W** *are two nonzero vectors which make an angle* θ, *the scalar product* † *of* **V** *and* **W**, *written* **V·W** *or* **W·V**, *is defined by*

$$\mathbf{V\cdot W} = |\,\mathbf{V}\,|\cdot|\,\mathbf{W}\,|\cos\theta. \tag{1}$$

Separately, if **V** = **O** *or* **W** = **O**, *we define* **V·W** = 0.

From (1), on multiplying $\cos\theta$ in (14) on page 418 by $|\,\mathbf{V}_1\,|$ and $|\,\mathbf{V}_2\,|$,

$$\left.\begin{cases} \mathbf{V}_1 = a_1\mathbf{i} + b_1\mathbf{j} + c_1\mathbf{k}; \\ \mathbf{V}_2 = a_2\mathbf{i} + b_2\mathbf{j} + c_2\mathbf{k}. \end{cases}\right\} \qquad \mathbf{V_1\cdot V_2} = a_1a_2 + b_1b_2 + c_1c_2. \tag{2}$$

We observe that (2) is true also if $\mathbf{V_1}$ or $\mathbf{V_2}$ is **O**.

ILLUSTRATION 1. If $\mathbf{V} = 3\mathbf{i} - 4\mathbf{j} + \mathbf{k}$ and $\mathbf{W} = -2\mathbf{i} + 5\mathbf{j} - 2\mathbf{k}$, then $\mathbf{V\cdot W} = -28$.

ILLUSTRATION 2. Let $\mathbf{V} = a\mathbf{i} + b\mathbf{j} + c\mathbf{k}$. Then, with $\mathbf{V_1} = \mathbf{V_2} = \mathbf{V}$ in (2), we obtain

$$\mathbf{V\cdot V} = a^2 + b^2 + c^2 = |\,\mathbf{V}\,|^2.$$

On account of $\cos\theta$ in (1), we note that $\mathbf{V\cdot W} = 0$ if and only if $\theta = \frac{1}{2}\pi$, or $\mathbf{V} \perp \mathbf{W}$. This fact also appears in (2), when compared with (16) on page 418.

Let **V** and **W** be nonzero vectors, and base them at a common point O, as in Figure 288, where $\mathbf{V} = \overrightarrow{OP}$ and $\mathbf{W} = \overrightarrow{OQ}$. Let l be a directed line on OQ, where the positive direction on l is taken as the direction of **W**. Let H be the projection of P on l. Then, the value, $\overline{OH}$, of OH as a directed line segment is called *"the scalar component of* **V** *along* **W**," abbreviated *"sc. comp*$_\mathbf{W}$ **V**," and $\overrightarrow{OH}$ is called the *"vector component of* **V** *in the direction of* **W**," abbreviated *"vec. comp*$_\mathbf{W}$ **V**." From Figure 288 and (1), we observe that

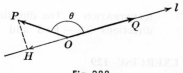

Fig. 288

$$\overline{OH} = (\text{sc. comp}_\mathbf{W}\ \mathbf{V}) = |\,\mathbf{V}\,|\cos\theta = \frac{\mathbf{V\cdot W}}{|\,\mathbf{W}\,|}. \tag{3}$$

Thus, $\overline{OH} > 0$ if $\theta < \frac{1}{2}\pi$, and $\overline{OH} < 0$ if $\theta > \frac{1}{2}\pi$ so that $\cos\theta < 0$, as in Figure 288. Let $\mathbf{U} = \mathbf{W}/|\,\mathbf{W}\,|$, the unit vector with the direction of **W**. Then,

$$(\text{vec. comp}_\mathbf{W}\ \mathbf{V}) = \overrightarrow{OH} = \overline{OH}(\mathbf{U}) = (|\,\mathbf{V}\,|\cos\theta)\frac{\mathbf{W}}{|\,\mathbf{W}\,|}. \tag{4}$$

By use of (2), the following properties of scalar products are easily proved, where h is any scalar.

(*Commutative law*) $\qquad\qquad\qquad\qquad\qquad \mathbf{V\cdot W} = \mathbf{W\cdot V}. \tag{5}$

(*Distributive law*) $\qquad\qquad\qquad\quad \mathbf{V\cdot(W + Z)} = \mathbf{V\cdot W} + \mathbf{V\cdot Z}. \tag{6}$

(*Commutative with multiplication by a scalar*) $\qquad \mathbf{V\cdot}(h\mathbf{W}) = h(\mathbf{V\cdot W}). \tag{7}$

---

* The remainder of the chapter may be omitted without loss of continuity in case the course will not include corresponding future supplementary sections and advanced content.
† Frequently called the **dot product**.

In Definition VI, we agreed that $\mathbf{V}\cdot\mathbf{W} = \mathbf{W}\cdot\mathbf{V}$, which gives (5). To prove results (6) and (7), we would introduce expansions for $\mathbf{V}$, $\mathbf{W}$, and $\mathbf{Z}$ in terms of $\mathbf{i}$, $\mathbf{j}$, and $\mathbf{k}$, and then calculate both sides of (6) and of (7) by use of (2), as requested of the student in an exercise.

EXAMPLE 1. In Figure 289, where it is unnecessary to show a z-axis, $\mathbf{V} = 3\mathbf{i} - \mathbf{j}$ and $\mathbf{W} = -\mathbf{i} - \mathbf{j}$. Find the scalar and vector components of $\mathbf{V}$ in the $\mathbf{W}$ direction.

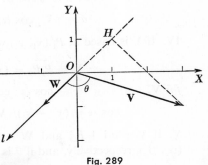

Fig. 289

Solution. $|\mathbf{V}| = \sqrt{10}$; $|\mathbf{W}| = \sqrt{2}$; $\mathbf{V}\cdot\mathbf{W} = -2$. From (14) on page 418, if θ is the angle made by $\mathbf{V}$ and $\mathbf{W}$, then $\cos\theta = -\frac{1}{5}\sqrt{5}$. From (3),

$$\overline{OH} = (\text{sc. comp}_{\mathbf{W}}\,\mathbf{V}) = -\frac{2}{\sqrt{2}} = -\sqrt{2};$$

$$\overrightarrow{OH} = (\text{vec. comp}_{\mathbf{W}}\,\mathbf{V}) = -\frac{\sqrt{2}(-\mathbf{i}-\mathbf{j})}{\sqrt{2}} = \mathbf{i} + \mathbf{j}.$$

We note that $\overrightarrow{OH}$ checks with Figure 289.

Note 1. From (3) and (4) with $|\mathbf{W}| = 1$, the scalar and vector components of $\mathbf{V}$ in the direction of a *unit vector* $\mathbf{U}$ are as follows:

$$(\text{sc. comp}_{\mathbf{U}}\,\mathbf{V}) = \mathbf{V}\cdot\mathbf{U}; \tag{8}$$

$$(\text{vec. comp}_{\mathbf{U}}\,\mathbf{V}) = (\mathbf{V}\cdot\mathbf{U})\mathbf{U}. \tag{9}$$

158. VECTORS IN A PLANE

In the remainder of this chapter, we shall deal with vector applications where all vectors will lie in a given plane, which we now stipulate as our setting. First, we remark that many preceding definitions and results about vectors in space have an analytic form which persists for vectors all in one plane. Certain other results assume simpler forms when stated for the plane. We proceed to summarize these forms. Standard notations for vectors will be used without comment.

Suppose that an xy-system of coordinates is installed in the plane. Temporarily, visualize a z-axis associated with the xy-plane and note that, for any vector $\mathbf{V}$ in the xy-plane, the z-scalar-component is zero, $\gamma = 90°$, and $\cos\gamma = 0$. We use these special values in the following summary of results for vectors (*not* $\mathbf{O}$) in the xy-plane where, in applications, it no longer will be necessary or desirable to visualize a z-axis. Only coordinates (x, y) are involved hereafter in this section.

I. If (α, β) are direction angles, $\cos^2\alpha + \cos^2\beta = 1$.

II. With $\lambda = \cos\alpha$ and $\mu = \cos\beta$, if $a : b = \lambda : \mu$ then

$$\left(\lambda = \frac{a}{\sqrt{a^2 + b^2}},\ \mu = \frac{b}{\sqrt{a^2 + b^2}}\right) \text{ or } \left(\lambda = \frac{-a}{\sqrt{a^2 + b^2}},\ \mu = \frac{-b}{\sqrt{a^2 + b^2}}\right). \tag{1}$$

III. If $V = a\mathbf{i} + b\mathbf{j}$ and V is based at the origin, the end point of V is $P:(a, b)$; direction numbers for V are $a : b$; $(\cos \alpha, \cos \beta)$ for V are at the left in (1). If U is the unit vector with the direction of V,

$$U = \mathbf{i} \cos \alpha + \mathbf{j} \cos \beta; \quad V = |V| (\mathbf{i} \cos \alpha + \mathbf{j} \cos \beta); \tag{2}$$

$$a = |V| \cos \alpha \quad \text{and} \quad b = |V| \cos \beta. \tag{3}$$

IV. If V is based at $P_1:(x_1, y_1)$ with end point $P_2:(x_2, y_2)$, then

$$V = \overrightarrow{P_1P_2} = (x_2 - x_1)\mathbf{i} + (y_2 - y_1)\mathbf{j}; \tag{4}$$

for V, $$\cos \alpha : \cos \beta = (x_2 - x_1) : (y_2 - y_1); \tag{5}$$

$$\cos \alpha = (x_2 - x_1)/|V|; \quad \cos \beta = (y_2 - y_1)/|V|.$$

V. If $V = a_1\mathbf{i} + b_1\mathbf{j}$ and $W = a_2\mathbf{i} + b_2\mathbf{j}$ with direction angles (α_1, β_1) and (α_2, β_2), respectively, and if θ is the angle made by V and W, then

$$\cos \theta = \cos \alpha_1 \cos \alpha_2 + \cos \beta_1 \cos \beta_2, \text{ or} \tag{6}$$

$$\cos \theta = (a_1a_2 + b_1b_2)/(|V| \cdot |W|). \tag{7}$$

$$V \cdot W = |V| \cdot |W| \cos \theta = a_1a_2 + b_1b_2; \tag{8}$$

$$V \parallel W \quad \text{is equivalent to} \quad a_1 : b_1 = a_2 : b_2; \tag{9}$$

$$V \perp W \quad \text{is equivalent to} \quad V \cdot W = 0, \quad \text{or} \quad a_1a_2 + b_1b_2 = 0. \tag{10}$$

ILLUSTRATION 1. If a direction Ω has the direction numbers $a : b$, then either direction perpendicular to Ω has the direction numbers $-b : a$ because $-ab + ab = 0$.

★159. NORMAL FORM FOR A LINE IN AN xy-PLANE

Let l be any line in an xy-plane. If l does not go through $O:(0, 0)$, as in Figure 290, let $\overrightarrow{ON}$ be the vector based at O, perpendicular to l, and meeting l at N. Let $p = |\overrightarrow{ON}|$. If l goes through O, define $p = 0$ and let $\overrightarrow{ON}$ be the unit vector perpendicular to l at O, directed *upward* when *not horizontal*, and directed to the *right* if *horizontal*. We shall call $\overrightarrow{ON}$ the **normal vector** from O to l. Let (α, β) be the direction angles of $\overrightarrow{ON}$. We shall prove that an equation for l, called its **normal form**, is

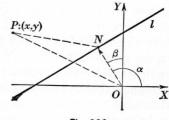

Fig. 290

$$x \cos \alpha + y \cos \beta - p = 0. \tag{1}$$

Proof of (1), *with* $p \neq 0$. 1. In Figure 290, by (2) and (3) above,

$$\overrightarrow{ON} = p(\mathbf{i} \cos \alpha + \mathbf{j} \cos \beta), \tag{2}$$

and the coordinates of N are the scalar components $(p \cos \alpha, p \cos \beta)$.

2. Let $P:(x, y)$ be any point in the plane. From (4) above,

$$\overrightarrow{NP} = (x - p \cos \alpha)\mathbf{i} + (y - p \cos \beta)\mathbf{j}. \tag{3}$$

Then, P is on l if and only if $\overrightarrow{NP} \perp \overrightarrow{ON}$, which is equivalent to $\overrightarrow{NP} \cdot \overrightarrow{ON} = 0$. Hence, from (10) on page 424, an equation for l is

$$\overrightarrow{NP} \cdot \overrightarrow{ON} = (x - p \cos \alpha)(p \cos \alpha) + (y - p \cos \beta)(p \cos \beta) = 0, \; or$$

$$x \cos \alpha + y \cos \beta - p(\cos^2 \alpha + \cos^2 \beta) = 0, \quad or \quad x \cos \alpha + y \cos \beta - p = 0,$$

which is the equation of l. [The proof of (1) when $p = 0$ is very simple.]

Theorem VIII. *If a, b, and c are any three numbers where not both of a and b are zero, the line $l:[ax + by + c = 0]$ has the normal form*

$$\frac{ax + by + c}{\pm \sqrt{a^2 + b^2}} = 0, \tag{4}$$

with "$+$" or "$-$" in (4) chosen as follows:

if $c \neq 0$:	*"$+$" or "$-$" according as $c < 0$ or $c > 0$;*	(5)
if $c = 0$ and $b \neq 0$:	*"$+$" or "$-$" according as $b > 0$ or $b < 0$;*	(6)
if $c = 0$ and $b = 0$:	*"$+$" or "$-$" according as $a > 0$ or $a < 0$.*	(7)

Moreover, $a : b$ are direction numbers for any vector (or direction) which is perpendicular (or, normal) to l.

Proof. 1. ($c \neq 0$.) From (1) on page 423, with either sign in the denominator in (4), the coefficients $\pm a/\sqrt{a^2 + b^2}$ and $\pm b/\sqrt{a^2 + b^2}$ of x and y are direction cosines, λ and μ, for some direction. To make (4) assume the form (1), we must have $\pm c/\sqrt{a^2 + b^2} < 0$ because $-p < 0$ in (1). This is accomplished if the choice is made as in (5).

2. ($c = 0$.) The choice in (6) gives $\cos \beta > 0$ so that $0 \leq \beta < \frac{1}{2}\pi$. The choice in (7) gives $\alpha = 0$. These results agree with the conventions about the normal vector $\overrightarrow{ON}$ which were made in the introduction to (1).

3. In any case, $a : b = \cos \alpha : \cos \beta$. Thus, each of the two directions perpendicular to l has the direction numbers $a : b$.

ILLUSTRATION 1. The normal form

of $3x - 4y + 20 = 0$	is	$-\frac{3}{5}x + \frac{4}{5}y - 4 = 0$;
of	$3x - 4y = 0$	is	$-\frac{3}{5}x + \frac{4}{5}y = 0$;
of	$3x + 4y = 0$	is	$\frac{3}{5}x + \frac{4}{5}y = 0$;
of	$-5x = 0$	is	$x = 0$.

ILLUSTRATION 2. Any direction perpendicular to $l:[3x - 4y - 15 = 0]$ has the direction numbers $3 : -4$, and hence the direction cosines ($\lambda = \frac{3}{5}$, $\mu = -\frac{4}{5}$) or ($\lambda = -\frac{3}{5}$, $\mu = \frac{4}{5}$).

For any line $l:[ax + by + c = 0]$, at present let us agree that each line and distance perpendicular to l is *directed*, with the *positive* direction taken as the

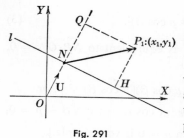

Fig. 291

direction of the normal vector $\overrightarrow{ON}$ for (1). Let **U** be the unit vector with the direction of $\overrightarrow{ON}$. Then,

$$\mathbf{U} = \mathbf{i} \cos \alpha + \mathbf{j} \cos \beta, \tag{8}$$

with (α, β) as in equation (1). Let $P_1:(x_1, y_1)$ be any point and let H be the projection (perpendicular) of P_1 on l, as in Figure 291. For any p, the point * $N:(p \cos \alpha, p \cos \beta)$ is on l, and

$$\overrightarrow{NP_1} = (x_1 - p \cos \alpha)\mathbf{i} + (y_1 - p \cos \beta)\mathbf{j}. \tag{9}$$

Theorem IX. *The directed distance, d, of $P_1:(x_1, y_1)$ from the line in (1) is*

$$d = x_1 \cos \alpha + y_1 \cos \beta - p, \tag{10}$$

and from the line $l:[ax + by + c = 0]$ is

$$d = (ax_1 + by_1 + c)/ \pm \sqrt{a^2 + b^2}, \tag{11}$$

where "+" or "−" is chosen as in (5), (6), and (7).

Proof. From Figure 291, $d = \overline{HP_1}$, which is equal to the scalar component $\overline{NQ}$ of $\overrightarrow{NP_1}$ in the direction of **U** in (8). Hence, from (8) on page 423, and (9) above,

$$d = \overline{HP_1} = (\text{sc. comp}_{\mathbf{U}} \ \overrightarrow{NP_1}) = \mathbf{U} \cdot \overrightarrow{NP_1} =$$

$$(x_1 - p \cos \alpha)\cos \alpha + (y_1 - p \cos \beta)\cos \beta = x_1 \cos \alpha + y_1 \cos \beta - p, \tag{12}$$

which proves (10). We obtain (11) by first using (4), and then (10).

Observe that (11) establishes (1) on page 313 for the *undirected* distance between l and $P_1:(x_1, y_1)$. In words, (11) states that, *to obtain the directed distance from $l:[ax + by + c = 0]$ to $P_1:(x_1, y_1)$, first change l to its normal form, and then substitute the coordinates of P_1 in the left-hand side of the equation.* In Figure 291, the student may check the fact that our agreements as to signs in (11) cause d to be *positive when P_1 and $(0, 0)$ are separated by l,* and *negative when P_1 and $(0, 0)$ are on the same side of l.*

ILLUSTRATION 3. The distance *from $l:[5x - 12y + 39 = 0]$ to $P:(2, -3)$* is

$$d = \frac{5(2) - 12(-3) + 39}{-\sqrt{25 + 144}} = -\frac{85}{13}.$$

ILLUSTRATION 4. By the last sentence in Theorem VIII, the line l through $P_1:(x_1, y_1)$ with $a : b$ as direction numbers for either direction normal to l has the equation

$$a(x - x_1) + b(y - y_1) = 0. \tag{13}$$

Note 1. From (8), $\mathbf{U} = \mathbf{i} \cos \alpha + \mathbf{j} \cos \beta$, shown in Figure 291 above. The end point of **U** is $(\cos \alpha, \cos \beta)$. With **i** and **U** both based at the origin, let ϕ be the smallest nonnegative angle obtained by revolving **i** about O to coincide with **U**. Then, ϕ is in its standard position, as on page 676, for definition of the trigonometric functions. Hence, the

* If $p = 0$, N becomes the origin.

coordinates of the end point of U also are $(\cos \phi, \sin \phi)$, and thus $\cos \alpha = \cos \phi$ and $\cos \beta = \sin \phi$. Then, (1) becomes

$$x \cos \phi + y \sin \phi - p = 0. \tag{14}$$

This notation for the normal form is used frequently, when direction cosines are not employed. With (14) replacing (1), no change occurs in (4)–(7), and (11).

EXERCISE 130

Let P and Q be the points in the listed order. Let $\mathbf{V} = \overrightarrow{OP}$ and $\mathbf{W} = \overrightarrow{OQ}$, where O is the origin. Obtain $\mathbf{V} \cdot \mathbf{W}$; sc. $\mathrm{comp_W}\ \mathbf{V}$; vec. $\mathrm{comp_W}\ \mathbf{V}$. In Problems 3–8, draw a figure.

1. $(3, -2, 6); (2, -2, -1)$.
2. $(8, -9, 12); (-10, 11, -2)$.
3. $(1, 3); (3, 3)$.
4. $(3, -1); (-1, 1)$.
5. $(1, 1); (4, -1)$.
6. $(-3, -4); (1, -2)$.
7. $(-4, -3); (3, -1)$.
8. $(-5, 12); (2, -1)$.
9. Obtain $\mathbf{i} \cdot \mathbf{i}$; $\mathbf{j} \cdot \mathbf{j}$; $\mathbf{i} \cdot \mathbf{j}$; $\mathbf{k} \cdot \mathbf{k}$; $\mathbf{i} \cdot \mathbf{k}$; $\mathbf{j} \cdot \mathbf{k}$.

★*Construct to scale the line l in an xy-plane with the given normal vector from the origin. Also, write l in its normal form.*

10. $(3\mathbf{i} + 4\mathbf{j})$.
11. $(-5\mathbf{i} + 12\mathbf{j})$.
12. $(-8\mathbf{i} - 15\mathbf{j})$.

★*Change the equation of the line l to its normal form; also, write the normal vector $\overrightarrow{ON}$ from $(0, 0)$; give the coordinates of N.*

13. $2x + 2y - 5 = 0$.
14. $3x - 3y + 4 = 0$.
15. $x + y\sqrt{3} + 4 = 0$.
16. $x\sqrt{3} + y - 6 = 0$.
17. $x - y\sqrt{3} = 0$.
18. $5x + 12y = 0$.
19. $4x + 17 = 0$.

★*Find the directed distance from the given line to each given point.*

20. $3x + 4y = 10$; to $(-3, 1); (6, 2); (0, 0)$.
21. $8x - 15y = -34$; to $(3, -1); (-2, -2)$.
22. $5x - 12y = 0$; to $(3, -2); (-4, 1)$.

★*Specify direction numbers for either normal direction for each line. If the lines are parallel, find the undirected distance between them.*

23. $\begin{cases} 3x + 4y = 8. \\ 6x + 8y = 5. \end{cases}$
24. $\begin{cases} 5x - 12y = 10. \\ 36y - 15x = -5. \end{cases}$
25. $\begin{cases} 2x + 5y = 4. \\ 3x - 2y = 8. \end{cases}$

★*Find an equation for the line l through the point with the given direction numbers for any direction perpendicular to l.*

26. Normal direction $3 : -2$; through $(2, -5)$.
27. Normal direction $-1 : -4$; through $(-1, -4)$.

★28–29. In Problems 26–27, respectively, write an equation for the line through the point perpendicular to the line previously obtained.

★*Find equations for the bisectors of the angles formed by the lines. If d_1 and d_2 are the directed distances from the lines to any point (x, y), notice that $d_1 = d_2$ gives one bisector and $d_1 = -d_2$ gives the other bisector. State which equation, $d_1 = d_2$ or $d_1 = -d_2$, corresponds to each of your results, shown in a figure.*

30. $\begin{cases} x - 7y = 4. \\ x + y = -4. \end{cases}$
31. $\begin{cases} x + 3y = 5. \\ 6x + 2y = -3. \end{cases}$
32. $\begin{cases} 8x + 15y = 7. \\ 15x + 8y = -4. \end{cases}$

★33. Prove (5), (6), and (7) on page 422.

★160. VECTOR VALUED FUNCTIONS IN A PLANE

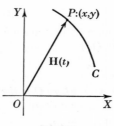

Fig. 292

Unless otherwise implied, any vector will be based at the origin in the xy-plane. Let H represent a function whose *domain* is an interval, I, of numbers, t, and *range* is a set of vectors. Thus, $H(t)$ represents a *vector*, as in Figure 292. Let $W = H(t)$, and let $W = x\mathbf{i} + y\mathbf{j}$ at point t on I. Suppose that

$$H(t) = \phi(t)\mathbf{i} + \psi(t)\mathbf{j}. \tag{1}$$

Then, $W = H(t)$ gives $x\mathbf{i} + y\mathbf{j} = \phi(t)\mathbf{i} + \psi(t)\mathbf{j}$, or

$$x = \phi(t) \quad and \quad y = \psi(t). \tag{2}$$

The end point of W is $P:(x, y)$. Thus, in (2), we have parametric equations for the curve C which is *the locus of the end point of* W, *or* $H(t)$, for t on the interval I. At any value of t, we shall call $H(t)$ the **position vector** for the corresponding point P [the end point of $H(t)$] on C. Also, we shall refer to $W = H(t)$ as a *vector equation* for C, which is defined parametrically by (2). The preceding interpretation of a vector function proves to be very useful.

ILLUSTRATION 1. Let $H(t) = \mathbf{i} \cos t + \mathbf{j} \sin t$. Then, the vector equation $W = H(t)$ defines a curve C, a circle, whose parametric form is $x = \cos t$ and $y = \sin t$.

In the following definition, we consider a function $H(t)$ defined at all points t, except possibly $t = c$, on an interval including $t = c$.

Definition VII. *To state that* **the limit of $H(t)$ is L** *(a vector) as $t \to c$ will mean that* $|H(t) - L|$ *will be as small as we please at all values of t, with $t \neq c$, sufficiently near c. Then, we write*

$$\lim_{t \to c} H(t) = L, \quad or \quad H(t) \to L \text{ as } t \to c. \tag{3}$$

Theorem X. *Suppose that $H(t) = h_1(t)\mathbf{i} + h_2(t)\mathbf{j}$ and $L = a_1\mathbf{i} + a_2\mathbf{j}$. Then, to say that $H(t) \to L$ as $t \to c$ is equivalent to stating that*

$$\lim_{t \to c} h_1(t) = a_1 \quad and \quad \lim_{t \to c} h_2(t) = a_2. \tag{4}$$

Proof. In Figure 293, we have $\overrightarrow{OP} = H(t)$, $\overrightarrow{OQ} = L$, and $|\overrightarrow{PQ}| = |H(t) - L|$. To state that $|\overrightarrow{PQ}|$ is *as small as we please* means that the tips $(h_1(t), h_2(t))$ and (a_1, a_2) of $H(t)$ and L are as close as we please. Thus, (3) means that $h_1(t)$ will be as near a_1, and $h_2(t)$ will be as near a_2 as we please, if t is sufficiently near c, with $t \neq c$. This means that (4) is true.

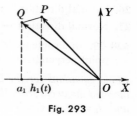

Fig. 293

ILLUSTRATION 2. If $H(t) = (3t + 2)\mathbf{i} + (9 - t^2)\mathbf{j}$, then

$$\lim_{t \to 2} H(t) = [\lim_{t \to 2} (3t + 2)]\mathbf{i} + [\lim_{t \to 2} (9 - t^2)]\mathbf{j} = 8\mathbf{i} + 5\mathbf{j}. \tag{5}$$

In the following Definitions VIII and IX, $H(t) = h_1(t)\mathbf{i} + h_2(t)\mathbf{j}$.

Definition VIII. *To state that the function* $H(t)$ *is continuous at* t_0 *means that* t_0 *is in the domain of* H *and there exists* $\lim\limits_{t \to t_0} H(t) = H(t_0)$.

By Theorem X, the condition $\lim\limits_{t \to t_0} H(t) = H(t_0)$ is equivalent to

$$\lim_{t \to t_0} h_1(t) = h_1(t_0) \quad and \quad \lim_{t \to t_0} h_2(t) = h_2(t_0). \tag{6}$$

Hence, H is continuous at t_0 if and only if each of the scalar component functions h_1 and h_2 is continuous at t_0.

Let $\quad \Delta h_1(t_0) = h_1(t_0 + \Delta t) - h_1(t_0); \quad \Delta h_2(t_0) = h_2(t_0 + \Delta t) - h_2(t_0).$

Then, we obtain

$$\Delta H(t_0) = H(t_0 + \Delta t) - H(t_0) = \Delta h_1(t_0)\mathbf{i} + \Delta h_2(t_0)\mathbf{j}. \tag{7}$$

Definition IX. *To state that the function* $H(t)$ *has a derivative at* t_0 *means that there exists*

$$\lim_{\Delta t \to 0} \frac{\Delta H(t_0)}{\Delta t} = \lim_{\Delta t \to 0} \left[\frac{\Delta h_1(t_0)}{\Delta t}\mathbf{i} + \frac{\Delta h_2(t_0)}{\Delta t}\mathbf{j} \right]. \tag{8}$$

In (8), if the limit exists, it is called the *derivative* of H at t_0, and is denoted by $H'(t_0)$. By Theorem X, existence of the limit on the right in (8) means that $\Delta h_1(t_0)/\Delta t$ and $\Delta h_2(t_0)/\Delta t$ approach limits, which would be $h_1'(t_0)$ and $h_2'(t_0)$, respectively. Hence, H has a derivative if and only if each of the *scalar component functions* h_1 and h_2 is differentiable, and then

$$H'(t) = h_1'(t)\mathbf{i} + h_2'(t)\mathbf{j}. \tag{9}$$

ILLUSTRATION 3. If $H(t) = (\sin 2t)\mathbf{i} + (\cos t)\mathbf{j}$, then
$$H'(t) = (2 \cos 2t)\mathbf{i} - (\sin t)\mathbf{j}.$$

If the scalar function $f(t)$ is differentiable and if $H(t)$ has a derivative, it is easy to prove that $f(t)H(t)$ has a derivative and

$$\frac{d}{dt} f(t)H(t) = f'(t)H(t) + f(t)H'(t). \tag{10}$$

★161. DIRECTION COSINES OF THE FORWARD TANGENT

Suppose that the domain of a vector function $H(t)$ is an interval I of values of t, and let
$$\mathbf{W} = H(t), \quad where \quad \mathbf{W} = x\mathbf{i} + y\mathbf{j}, \quad and \quad H(t) = \phi(t)\mathbf{i} + \psi(t)\mathbf{j}. \tag{1}$$

Let $H(t)$ be based at the origin, and let C be the curve having $H(t)$ as the position vector for $P{:}(x, y)$ on C corresponding to the number t on I. Then, a vector equation for C is $\mathbf{W} = H(t)$, which is equivalent to the parametric form

$$x = \phi(t) \quad and \quad y = \psi(t). \tag{2}$$

We assume that ϕ' and ψ' are continuous and that, at all values of t,

$$\phi'^2(t) + \psi'^2(t) \neq 0. \tag{3}$$

With t fixed, (2) gives $P{:}(x, y)$ on C, as in Figure 294, where $\mathbf{W} = x\mathbf{i} + y\mathbf{j}$.

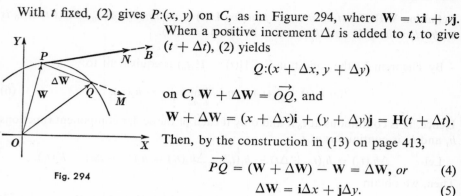

When a positive increment Δt is added to t, to give $(t + \Delta t)$, (2) yields

$$Q{:}(x + \Delta x, y + \Delta y)$$

on C, $\mathbf{W} + \Delta \mathbf{W} = \overrightarrow{OQ}$, and

$$\mathbf{W} + \Delta \mathbf{W} = (x + \Delta x)\mathbf{i} + (y + \Delta y)\mathbf{j} = \mathbf{H}(t + \Delta t).$$

Then, by the construction in (13) on page 413,

$$\overrightarrow{PQ} = (\mathbf{W} + \Delta \mathbf{W}) - \mathbf{W} = \Delta \mathbf{W}, \ or \qquad (4)$$

$$\Delta \mathbf{W} = \mathbf{i}\Delta x + \mathbf{j}\Delta y. \qquad (5)$$

Fig. 294

We call $\overrightarrow{PQ}$ a **forward chord** at P because $\Delta t > 0$. Let $\mathbf{U}(\Delta t) = \overrightarrow{PM}$ be the unit vector in the direction of $\Delta \mathbf{W}$:

$$\mathbf{U}(\Delta t) = \frac{\Delta \mathbf{W}}{|\Delta \mathbf{W}|} = \frac{\Delta x}{\sqrt{(\Delta x)^2 + (\Delta y)^2}}\mathbf{i} + \frac{\Delta y}{\sqrt{(\Delta x)^2 + (\Delta y)^2}}\mathbf{j}. \qquad (6)$$

Theorem XI. *There exists* $\quad \lim\limits_{\Delta t \to 0+} \mathbf{U}(\Delta t) = \mathbf{i}\dfrac{dx}{ds} + \mathbf{j}\dfrac{dy}{ds}, \qquad (7)$

where s is the length of arc on C.

Proof. 1. With $\Delta t > 0$, then $\Delta t = \sqrt{(\Delta t)^2}$ and

$$\sqrt{(\Delta x)^2 + (\Delta y)^2}/\Delta t = \sqrt{[(\Delta x)^2 + (\Delta y)^2]/(\Delta t)^2}. \qquad (8)$$

2. On dividing both numerator and denominator of each fraction on the right in (6) by Δt, we obtain

$$\mathbf{U}(\Delta t) = \mathbf{i}\left[\frac{\Delta x}{\Delta t} \Big/ \sqrt{\left(\frac{\Delta x}{\Delta t}\right)^2 + \left(\frac{\Delta y}{\Delta t}\right)^2}\right] + \mathbf{j}\left[\frac{\Delta y}{\Delta t} \Big/ \sqrt{\left(\frac{\Delta x}{\Delta t}\right)^2 + \left(\frac{\Delta y}{\Delta t}\right)^2}\right]. \qquad (9)$$

In (9), suppose that $\Delta t \to 0+$. Then, each difference quotient approaches a derivative as a limit and, by Theorem X,

$$\lim_{\Delta t \to 0+} \mathbf{U}(\Delta t) = \mathbf{i}\left[\frac{dx}{dt} \Big/ \sqrt{\left(\frac{dx}{dt}\right)^2 + \left(\frac{dy}{dt}\right)^2}\right] + \mathbf{j}\left[\frac{dy}{dt} \Big/ \sqrt{\left(\frac{dx}{dt}\right)^2 + \left(\frac{dy}{dt}\right)^2}\right]. \qquad (10)$$

Each radical in (10) is equal to ds/dt. Also, $(dx/dt)/(ds/dt) = dx/ds$, etc. Hence, the right-hand side of (10) proves (7).

Note 1. We shall say that a ray, τ (a directed half-line), is **on a vector** $\mathbf{V}$, based at a point P, in case the initial point of τ is at P and the directions of $\mathbf{V}$ and τ are the same.

Now define a vector $\mathbf{T} = \overrightarrow{PN}$ as a function of t, or s, by

$$\mathbf{T} = \mathbf{i}\frac{dx}{ds} + \mathbf{j}\frac{dy}{ds}, \qquad (11)$$

where $\mathbf{T}$ is a unit vector because of (9) on page 396. Figure 294 shows $\mathbf{T}$ based at P. On account of (7), we infer that the angle made by $\mathbf{T}$ and $\overrightarrow{PQ}$ approaches zero as $\Delta t \to 0$. Thus, the ray PB, which is on $\mathbf{T}$, is the limiting position of the ray from P which is on $\overrightarrow{PQ}$. Hence, we define PB as the **forward tangent** to C at P, and call $\mathbf{T}$ the **unit forward tangent vector** at P. From (11), and (2) on page 424, the direction cosines of $\mathbf{T}$, or PB, are as follows:

dir. cosines, forward tangent: $\qquad \cos \alpha = \dfrac{dx}{ds}; \quad \cos \beta = \dfrac{dy}{ds}.$ (12)

★162. VELOCITY AND ACCELERATION VECTORS IN A PLANE

Consider the motion of a particle σ in an xy-plane, where the coordinates (x, y) of σ at time t are given by

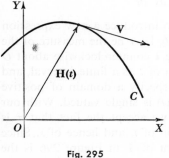

Fig. 295

$$x = \phi(t) \quad and \quad y = \psi(t), \ or$$
$$\mathbf{W} = \mathbf{H}(t), \ where \qquad (1)$$
$$\mathbf{W} = x\mathbf{i} + y\mathbf{j} \quad and \quad \mathbf{H}(t) = \phi(t)\mathbf{i} + \psi(t)\mathbf{j}, \qquad (2)$$

and where the vector $\mathbf{W}$, or $\mathbf{H}(t)$, is based at the origin, as in Figure 295. We shall call $\mathbf{H}(t)$ the **position vector** for σ at time t. We shall assume that ϕ'' and ψ'' exist and are continuous. Then, we shall initiate a new approach to velocity and acceleration for σ.

Definition X. *The **velocity** (vector) $\mathbf{V}$ and **acceleration** (vector) $\mathbf{A}$ for the motion of σ in (1) are defined by*

$$\mathbf{V} = \frac{d\mathbf{W}}{dt} \quad and \quad \mathbf{A} = \frac{d\mathbf{V}}{dt} = \frac{d^2\mathbf{W}}{dt^2}. \qquad (3)$$

Note 1. If t represents the time, we may use a notation of the field of mechanics to indicate differentiation with respect to t. Thus,

$$\dot{x} = \frac{dx}{dt}; \quad \ddot{x} = \frac{d^2x}{dt^2}; \quad \dot{y} = \frac{dy}{dt}; \quad \ddot{y} = \frac{d^2y}{dt^2}; \quad \dot{s} = \frac{ds}{dt}.$$

From (9) on page 429, (2), and (3), at time t,

$$\mathbf{V} = \dot{x}\,\mathbf{i} + \dot{y}\,\mathbf{j}, \quad and \quad \mathbf{A} = \ddot{x}\,\mathbf{i} + \ddot{y}\,\mathbf{j}. \qquad (4)$$

The scalar components of $\mathbf{V}$ along the axes are $\dot{x}$ and $\dot{y}$; the corresponding vector components of $\mathbf{V}$ are $\dot{x}\,\mathbf{i}$ and $\dot{y}\,\mathbf{j}$. Similar remarks about $\mathbf{A}$ follow from (4). Observe that $\mathbf{V}$ and $\mathbf{A}$, obtained in (4), are identical with $\mathbf{V}$ and $\mathbf{A}$ as adopted *by definition* in Section 54 on page 165. On the path, C, of σ, we agree that arc length s will be measured in the direction of increasing values of t, or that $\dot{s} \geqq 0$. Then, as in Section 54, we define the *speed*, v, of σ at any time t as the *magnitude of* $\mathbf{V}$. Thus, from (4), and (17) on page 389,

$$v = |\mathbf{V}| \quad or \quad v = \sqrt{\dot{x}^2 + \dot{y}^2} = \dot{s}, \qquad (5)$$

Or, v is the time rate of change of the distance s measured in the path of σ.

Theorem XII. *Assume that* $\dot{x}^2 + \dot{y}^2 \neq 0$ *at* $t = t_0$, *when the particle* σ *is at* $P:(x, y)$. *Then, at* $t = t_0$, $\mathbf{V}$ *has the direction of the unit forward tangent vector* $\mathbf{T}$ *to the path* (1) *at* P, *and*

$$\mathbf{V} = v\mathbf{T} \quad or \quad \mathbf{V} = v\frac{dx}{ds}\mathbf{i} + v\frac{dy}{ds}\mathbf{j}. \tag{6}$$

Proof. Since $\dot{x}$ and $\dot{y}$ are continuous functions of t, we have $\dot{x}^2 + \dot{y}^2 \neq 0$ on some t-interval including t_0. Thus, s may be used as a parameter on the path C and (11) of page 430 is available:

$$\mathbf{T} = \mathbf{i}\frac{dx}{ds} + \mathbf{j}\frac{dy}{ds}. \tag{7}$$

Then, from (4), $\mathbf{V} = \mathbf{i}\dot{x} + \mathbf{j}\dot{y} = \mathbf{i}\dfrac{dx}{ds}\cdot\dfrac{ds}{dt} + \mathbf{j}\dfrac{dy}{ds}\cdot\dfrac{ds}{dt} = \dot{s}\mathbf{T} = v\mathbf{T}. \tag{8}$

To prove certain facts about $\mathbf{A}$, it is desirable to introduce a new expression for $\mathbf{T}$. If $\mathbf{T}$ and $\mathbf{i}$ are based at $(0, 0)$ as in Figure 296, let τ be the measure of the

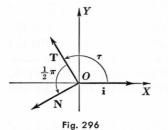

Fig. 296

angle made by rotating $\mathbf{i}$ counterclockwise about O to T. With the domain of t as a finite interval, and $\tau = f(t)$, we agree to specify a domain of positive values for τ so that $f(t)$ is single valued. With our hypotheses about (1), we accept the fact that τ is a differentiable function of t, and hence of s. Since $|\mathbf{T}| = 1$, the end point of $\mathbf{T}$ in Figure 296 is the point $(\cos \tau, \sin \tau)$ and hence

$$\mathbf{T} = \mathbf{i}\cos\tau + \mathbf{j}\sin\tau. \tag{9}$$

Let $\mathbf{N}$ be the unit vector obtained, as in Figure 296, by rotating $\mathbf{T}$ about O through the angle $\frac{1}{2}\pi$. Then,

$$\mathbf{N} = \mathbf{i}\cos(\tau + \tfrac{1}{2}\pi) + \mathbf{j}\sin(\tau + \tfrac{1}{2}\pi), \ or$$

$$\mathbf{N} = -\mathbf{i}\sin\tau + \mathbf{j}\cos\tau. \tag{10}$$

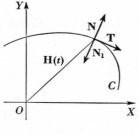

Fig. 297

In Figure 297, $\mathbf{T}$ and $\mathbf{N}$ are shown based at the corresponding point $P:(x, y)$ on C. We shall call $\mathbf{N}$ the unit normal vector at $P:(x, y)$. From (2) on page 397, we accept the fact that we could define the curvature, $K > 0$, of C by $K = |d\tau/ds|$. We recall that the radius of curvature,* R, at P is defined by $R = \dfrac{1}{K}$.

Lemma 1. *At any time* t, $\dfrac{d\mathbf{T}}{dt} = \dot{s}\dfrac{d\tau}{ds}\mathbf{N}. \tag{11}$

Proof. From (9), as an application of (9) on page 429,

$$\frac{d\mathbf{T}}{dt} = \frac{d\mathbf{T}}{ds}\cdot\frac{ds}{dt} = \dot{s}(-\mathbf{i}\sin\tau + \mathbf{j}\cos\tau)\frac{d\tau}{ds} = \dot{s}\frac{d\tau}{ds}\mathbf{N}.$$

* Whenever R is used, we assume that $K \neq 0$.

Theorem XIII. *Let a_T and a_N be the scalar components of $\mathbf{A}$ in the directions of $\mathbf{T}$ and $\mathbf{N}$, respectively. Then, at any time t, when the particle σ is at P:(x, y),*

$$a_T = \ddot{s} \quad and \quad |a_N| = v^2/R; \tag{12}$$

$$\mathbf{A} = \ddot{s}\mathbf{T} + \frac{v^2}{R}\mathbf{N_1}, \tag{13}$$

where $\mathbf{N}_1$ is the unit vector normal to C with the direction from P to the center of curvature of C at P.

Proof. 1. By use of (10) on page 429, we obtain

$$\mathbf{A} = \frac{d\mathbf{V}}{dt} = \frac{d(v\mathbf{T})}{dt} = \frac{d(\dot{s}\mathbf{T})}{dt} = \frac{d\dot{s}}{dt}\mathbf{T} + \dot{s}\frac{d\mathbf{T}}{dt}, \ or$$

[from (11)]
$$\mathbf{A} = \ddot{s}\mathbf{T} + \dot{s}^2\frac{d\tau}{ds}\mathbf{N}. \tag{14}$$

In (14), the multiples of $\mathbf{T}$ and $\mathbf{N}$ are the vector components of $\mathbf{A}$ along $\mathbf{T}$ and $\mathbf{N}$, respectively. Thus, $\ddot{s}\mathbf{T} = $ (vec. comp$_T$ $\mathbf{A}$), so that $a_T = \ddot{s}$. Also, from (14),

$$a_N = \dot{s}^2\frac{d\tau}{ds} = \pm v^2K = \pm\frac{v^2}{R}, \tag{15}$$

where "$+$" applies if $(d\tau/ds) > 0$ and "$-$" if $(d\tau/ds) < 0$, because $K > 0$.

2. *To verify $v^2\mathbf{N}_1/R$ in* (13): If $d\tau/ds < 0$, as in Figure 297 on page 432, then the unit normal $\mathbf{N}_1$, directed at the center of curvature, is obtained by clockwise rotation from $\mathbf{T}$, or $\mathbf{N}_1 = -\mathbf{N}$. Also, $d\tau/ds = -K$. Hence, in (15), the *minus sign* applies at the right; then, in (14),

$$a_N\mathbf{N} = \dot{s}^2\frac{d\tau}{ds}\mathbf{N} = \left(-\frac{v^2}{R}\right)(-\mathbf{N}_1) = \frac{v^2\mathbf{N}_1}{R}.$$

The student should be interested in constructing a figure like Figure 297 for a case where $d\tau/ds > 0$ and $\mathbf{N} = \mathbf{N}_1$. This completes the proof of Theorem XIII.

Note 2. From (8) on page 423, since $|\mathbf{T}| = |\mathbf{N}| = 1$,

$$a_T = (sc.\ comp_T\ \mathbf{A}) = \mathbf{A}\cdot\mathbf{T}; \quad a_N = (sc.\ comp_N\ \mathbf{A}) = \mathbf{A}\cdot\mathbf{N}. \tag{16}$$

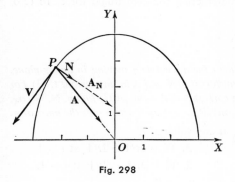

Fig. 298

We shall use (16) later. However, in the preceding proof we avoided use of (16) in order to maintain contact with the center of curvature, involved in our use of $\mathbf{N}_1$ in (13).

EXAMPLE 1. Study $\mathbf{V}$ and $\mathbf{A}$ at $t = \frac{3}{4}\pi$, if the position vector for a particle σ is $\mathbf{H}(t) = 3\mathbf{i}\cos t + 4\mathbf{j}\sin t$.

Solution. 1. From $\mathbf{W} = x\mathbf{i} + y\mathbf{j} = \mathbf{H}(t)$, parametric equations for the path C are

$$x = 3\cos t \quad and \quad y = 4\sin t, \tag{17}$$

which give the ellipse in Figure 298.

$$\mathbf{V} = \dot{\mathbf{W}} = -\,3\mathbf{i}\sin t + 4\mathbf{j}\cos t; \quad \mathbf{A} = \dot{\mathbf{V}} = -\,3\mathbf{i}\cos t - 4\mathbf{j}\sin t = -\,\mathbf{W}. \quad (18)$$

We shall base $\mathbf{V}$, $\mathbf{A}$, $\mathbf{N}$, and $\mathbf{N}_1$ at $P{:}(x, y)$, and base $\mathbf{W}$ at $(0, 0)$. From (18), $\mathbf{A}$ is directed at $(0, 0)$ for every value of t.

2. At $t = \tfrac{3}{4}\pi$: $\qquad\qquad \mathbf{V} = -\tfrac{3}{2}\mathbf{i}\sqrt{2} - 2\mathbf{j}\sqrt{2}; \quad v = |\,\mathbf{V}\,| = \tfrac{5}{2}\sqrt{2}. \qquad\qquad (19)$

$$\mathbf{A} = \tfrac{3}{2}\mathbf{i}\sqrt{2} - 2\mathbf{j}\sqrt{2}; \quad |\,\mathbf{A}\,| = \tfrac{5}{2}\sqrt{2}. \qquad\qquad (20)$$

Hence, $\qquad\qquad \mathbf{V} = v\mathbf{T} = \tfrac{5}{2}\sqrt{2}(-\tfrac{3}{5}\mathbf{i} - \tfrac{4}{5}\mathbf{j}); \quad \mathbf{T} = -\tfrac{3}{5}\mathbf{i} - \tfrac{4}{5}\mathbf{j}. \qquad (21)$

From Figure 298, $\mathbf{N}_1 = \mathbf{N}$ because $\mathbf{N}$ projects on the *concave side* of C. From $\mathbf{T}$ in (21), (9), and (10),

$$\mathbf{N} = \mathbf{N}_1 = \tfrac{4}{5}\mathbf{i} - \tfrac{3}{5}\mathbf{j}. \qquad\qquad (22)$$

3. We use (16) to obtain $a_{\mathbf{T}}$ and $a_{\mathbf{N}}$:

$$a_{\mathbf{T}} = \mathbf{A}\cdot\mathbf{T} = -\tfrac{9}{10}\sqrt{2} + \tfrac{8}{5}\sqrt{2} = \tfrac{7}{10}\sqrt{2}; \quad a_{\mathbf{N}} = \mathbf{A}\cdot\mathbf{N} = \tfrac{12}{5}\sqrt{2}.$$

Let $\mathbf{A} = \mathbf{A_T} + \mathbf{A_N}$, where $\mathbf{A_T}$ and $\mathbf{A_N}$ are the *vector components* of $\mathbf{A}$ along $\mathbf{T}$ and $\mathbf{N}$ respectively. Then $\mathbf{A} = \tfrac{7}{10}\sqrt{2}\mathbf{T} + \tfrac{12}{5}\sqrt{2}\mathbf{N}$. Figure 298 shows $\mathbf{V}$, $\mathbf{A}$, $\mathbf{N}$, and $\mathbf{A_N}$ with the scale unit for the magnitude of any vector chosen as $\tfrac{3}{4}$ of the scale unit on a coordinate axis. If m is the mass of the moving particle σ, and $\mathbf{F}_c$ is the force (a vector) acting on σ along $\mathbf{N}$ to *counteract* the force creating the acceleration $\mathbf{A_N}$, then $|\,\mathbf{F}_c\,| = \tfrac{12}{5}m\sqrt{2}$ and

$$\mathbf{F}_c = -\tfrac{12}{5}m\sqrt{2}\mathbf{N}. \qquad\qquad (23)$$

Note 3. Let all vectors in (13) be based at $P{:}(x, y)$ on C. Since $v^2\mathbf{N}_1/R$ is directed at the center of curvature, which is on the *concave side of* C, then $\mathbf{A}$ is directed to that side, as in Figure 298. If $d\tau/ds = 0$, or $K = 0$, at P, then (14), or (13), becomes simply $\mathbf{A} = \ddot{s}\mathbf{T}$. If the acceleration $\mathbf{A}$ is being experienced by a mass particle σ with mass m, the force applied to σ is

$$\mathbf{F} = m\mathbf{A} = m\ddot{s}\mathbf{T} + \frac{mv^2}{R}\mathbf{N}_1. \qquad\qquad (24)$$

The force component $\mathbf{F_N} = mv^2\mathbf{N}_1/R$ constrains σ to follow the curvilinear path C; this component counteracts an oppositely directed force $-\mathbf{F_N}$ of equal magnitude, mv^2/R, called the **centrifugal force**. Thus, for σ to follow the path C, at each point the force $\mathbf{F}$ must have a normal component counteracting the centrifugal force. In (23), $\mathbf{F}_c$ represents the centrifugal force.

★EXERCISE 131

In each problem, $\mathbf{W}$ is the position vector at time t for a particle σ moving in an xy-plane. (1) Plot the path, C, of σ. (2) Find the component forms of $\mathbf{V}$ and $\mathbf{A}$ at any instant t. (3) For the given value of t, draw $\mathbf{V}$ and $\mathbf{A}$ based at the corresponding point of C; find v, $\mathbf{N}$, $\mathbf{N}_1$, $a_{\mathbf{T}}$, $a_{\mathbf{N}}$, and the magnitude of the centrifugal force, mv^2/R, or $m\,|\,a_{\mathbf{N}}\,|$, where m is the mass of σ.

1. $\mathbf{W} = (5\cos 3t)\mathbf{i} + (5\sin 3t)\mathbf{j}$; at $t = \tfrac{1}{3}\pi$; at any value of t.

2. $\mathbf{W} = (\cos t)\mathbf{i} + (2\sin t)\mathbf{j}$; at $t = \tfrac{5}{4}\pi$.   3. $\mathbf{W} = 3t^2\mathbf{i} + 2t^3\mathbf{j}$; at $t = 1$.

4. $\mathbf{W} = 2\mathbf{i}\cos^3 t + 2\mathbf{j}\sin^3 t$; at $t = \tfrac{1}{4}\pi$.   5. $\mathbf{W} = 3t^2\mathbf{i} - 2t^3\mathbf{j}$; at $t = 1$.

6. $\mathbf{W} = -\tfrac{1}{2}t\mathbf{i} + \tfrac{1}{4}t^2\mathbf{j}$; at $t = \sqrt{3}$; at $t = -\sqrt{3}$; at $t = 0$.

★SUPPLEMENT FOR CHAPTER SEVENTEEN

7. Rewrite Definition VII of page 428 in an analytic (ϵ, δ) form. Then, prove Theorem X on page 428 analytically, by appealing finally to the analytic form of the definition of $\lim_{x \to c} f(x)$ in Note 2 on page 70.

8. Let $H(t) = ri(bt - \sin bt) + rj(1 - \cos bt)$ be the position vector for a particle σ. Verify that the path $W = H(t)$ is a cycloid where the generating circle rolls with constant angular speed. Prove that $|A|$ is a constant. If the particle σ is at $P:(x, y)$ at time t, and if A is based at P, prove that A is directed at the position of the center of the generating circle at time t.

9. Let $A = a_1 i + a_2 j \neq O$ and $B = b_1 i + b_2 j \neq O$. Let $f(z) = (A - zB) \cdot (A - zB)$. By investigating the discriminant of the quadratic function f, prove that

$$\left| \sum_{k=1}^{2} a_k b_k \right|^2 \leq \left(\sum_{k=1}^{2} a_k^2 \right)\left(\sum_{k=1}^{2} b_k^2 \right),$$

where equality occurs if and only if $a_1 : a_2 = b_1 : b_2$. This result is the **Schwarz inequality** for (a_1, a_2) and (b_1, b_2), which was met also in Problem 28 on page 150. The result, and present method of proof, extend to n-dimensional vectors.

10. Extend the definitions of Note 1 on page 414 to the case of four vectors. Then, prove that any four vectors in space are linearly dependent.

11. Prove (10) on page 429.

12. Let $\theta(t)$ be the angle made by $H(t)$ and L, where $H(t) \to L$ as $t \to c$, as in (3) on page 428. Prove that $\cos \theta(t) \to 0$ as $t \to c$, by use of Theorem X on page 428. Hence, prove that $\theta(t) \to 0$.

CHAPTER EIGHTEEN

Solid Analytic Geometry

163. SURFACES AND CURVES

On the basis of content on pages 406–421, we shall discuss certain other parts of analytic geometry in space, referred to as *solid analytic geometry*. We assume that an *xyz*-system of coordinates has been imposed on space.

The **graph** or **locus,** in an *xyz*-system of coordinates, of an equation $f(x, y, z) = 0$ is defined as the set, S, of all points $P:(x, y, z)$ whose coordinates (x, y, z) are solutions of the equation. Usually, the graph of an equation $f(x, y, z) = 0$ will impress us as deserving to be called a "*surface,*" which we accept as an undefined term. Hence, in general, we shall refer to *the surface* $f(x, y, z) = 0$, meaning the graph of the equation. An *equation for a surface* is an equation whose graph is the given surface. The intersection of two surfaces usually will be called a *space curve*. It may happen that a space curve is entirely in some plane. In referring to a *plane section*, or simply a *section* of a surface, we shall mean the curve of intersection of the surface and a plane.

ILLUSTRATION 1. Any plane section of a sphere is a circle.

The intersection of a surface and a coordinate plane is called the **trace** of the surface in that plane. We call the trace in the *xy*-plane the *xy-trace*, and similarly refer to the *yz-trace* and *xz-trace*.

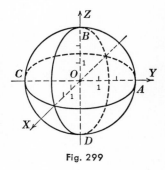

Fig. 299

ILLUSTRATION 2. The locus of $x^2 + y^2 + z^2 = 9$ is a sphere with center at the origin and radius 3, because the equation states that the square of the length of the radius vector $\overrightarrow{OP}$ from the origin to any point $P:(x, y, z)$ on the surface is equal to 9. Each trace of the surface is a circle. In Figure 299, the *xy*-trace and *xz*-trace are distorted from circles into ellipses (see Note 11 of the Appendix).

In a later section, we shall prove that *the locus of any linear equation in* (x, y, z) *is a plane* and, conversely, any plane has an equation of this type. To sketch the graph of a linear equation in (x, y, z), first find the intercepts on the axes. Then,

436

draw the traces of the plane and perhaps a few other sections parallel to coordinate planes. The aim should be to outline a triangle or quadrilateral on the
desired plane.

ILLUSTRATION 3. A graph of $3x + 2y + 2z = 6$ is in
Figure 300. With $y = z = 0$, we find the x-intercept
$x = 2$. Similarly, with $x = z = 0$, the y-intercept
is $y = 3$. The z-intercept is $z = 3$. Thus, A, B, and
C are on the plane. The xy-trace is AB, joining A
and B, etc. for the traces AC and BC.

ILLUSTRATION 4. The equation $x^2 + y^2 + z^2 = -1$
has no real solutions and hence no graph. The graph
of $3x^2 + y^2 + 5z^2 = 0$ is just *one point*, the origin.

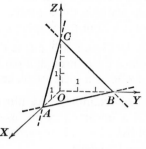

Fig. 300

A solution of a system of two equations

$$f(x, y, z) = 0 \quad and \quad g(x, y, z) = 0 \tag{1}$$

is an ordered triple of numbers (x, y, z) satisfying both equations. The graph, τ,
of a system (1) is the set of all points $P:(x, y, z)$ whose coordinates are solutions
of (1). If S_1 is the graph of $f(x, y, z) = 0$ and S_2 is the graph of $g(x, y, z) = 0$,
then τ is the set of points common to S_1 and S_2. Thus, the graph, τ, of a system
(1) is *the curve of intersection* * *of the surfaces* which are the graphs of the equations in (1). A *pair of equations* for a curve τ is any pair forming a system whose
graph is τ.

ILLUSTRATION 5. The x-axis is the intersection of the planes $y = 0$ and $z = 0$.
Hence, a system of equations for the x-axis is ($y = 0$ *and* $z = 0$). A pair of equations for the z-axis is ($x = 0$ *and* $y = 0$).

ILLUSTRATION 6. The sphere in Figure 299 on page 436 and the plane $x = 0$ intersect
in circle $ABCD$. Its *equations* are $x^2 + y^2 + z^2 = 9$ *and* $x = 0$.

ILLUSTRATION 7. In Figure 300, the xy-trace AB is the curve defined by

$$3x + 2y + 2z = 6 \quad and \quad z = 0.$$

On using $z = 0$ in the first equation, we obtain $3x + 2y = 6$ as an equation whose
locus in the xy-plane is AB.

To obtain an equation whose locus in a coordinate plane is the trace of a given
surface $f(x, y, z) = 0$ in that plane, proceed as follows:

1. *For the xy-trace:* *place* $z = 0$ *in* $f(x, y, z) = 0$.

2. *For the xz-trace:* *place* $y = 0$ *in* $f(x, y, z) = 0$.

3. *For the yz-trace:* *place* $x = 0$ *in* $f(x, y, z) = 0$.

EXAMPLE 1. Plot the plane $\qquad\qquad\qquad\qquad 3y + 2z = 6.$ $\qquad\qquad$ (2)

Solution. 1. If $y = z = 0$, then (2) gives $0 = 6$. Hence, (2) has no x-intercept,
and thus is perpendicular to the yz-plane.

* In notation from page 674, $\tau = S_1 \cap S_2$.

2. *The traces*. If $x = 0$, this does not affect (2). Hence, in Figure 301, the yz-trace is the locus, AB, of (2) in the yz-plane. With $z = 0$ in (2), we find $y = 2$ as the equation whose locus in the xy-plane is the xy-trace. The xz-trace is the locus, DB, of $z = 3$ in the xz-plane.

3. In Figure 301, CD is the intersection of (2) with the plane CDE through E parallel to the yz-plane. Rectangle $ABDC$ is a piece of plane (2).

In Example 1, we illustrated the fact that the graph of a linear equation in x, y, and z, *with one variable missing*, is a plane *perpendicular to the plane of the other two variables*.

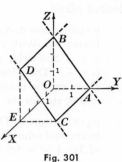

Fig. 301

164. ONE–POINT–NORMAL–DIRECTION FORM FOR A PLANE

Let τ be a given plane, and let $A : B : C$ be direction numbers for a direction perpendicular to the plane. We shall refer to $A : B : C$ as the **normal direction** for the plane. Any line perpendicular to a plane is called a **normal** to the plane.

Theorem I. *Every plane, τ, has an equation linear in x, y, and z. If the normal direction is $A : B : C$, and if point M:(x_0, y_0, z_0) is on τ, then it has the equation*

$$A(x - x_0) + B(y - y_0) + C(z - z_0) = 0. \qquad (1)$$

Proof. 1. Let $\overrightarrow{MN}$ be the vector normal to τ and based at M, with (A, B, C) as scalar components, as in Figure 302. Then, from (5) on page 411, we obtain

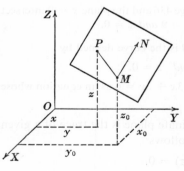

Fig. 302

$$\overrightarrow{MN} = A\mathbf{i} + B\mathbf{j} + C\mathbf{k}. \qquad (2)$$

From (7) on page 420, $\overrightarrow{MN}$ has the direction numbers $A : B : C$. Let P:(x, y, z) be any point in space, as in Figure 302. Then, from (6) on page 411,

$$\overrightarrow{MP} = (x - x_0)\mathbf{i} + (y - y_0)\mathbf{j} + (z - z_0)\mathbf{k}, \qquad (3)$$

and direction numbers for $\overrightarrow{MP}$ are

$$(x - x_0) : (y - y_0) : (z - z_0). \qquad (4)$$

2. P is on the plane τ if and only if $\overrightarrow{MP} \perp \overrightarrow{MN}$; this is equivalent to stating that the sum of the products of corresponding direction numbers of $\overrightarrow{MN}$ and $\overrightarrow{MP}$ is zero,* because of (10) on page 420. Hence, from (2) and (4), we obtain

$$A(x - x_0) + B(y - y_0) + C(z - z_0) = 0, \qquad (5)$$

as stated in (1).

* Or, is equivalent to stating that $\overrightarrow{MN} \cdot \overrightarrow{MP} = 0$, which also gives (5).

ILLUSTRATION 1. The equation of the plane through $(2, -3, 4)$ with the normal direction $4 : -1 : 2$ is

$$4(x - 2) - (y + 3) + 2(z - 4) = 0, \quad or \quad 4x - y + 2z = 19.$$

Theorem II. *If A, B, and C are not all zero, the locus of*

$$Ax + By + Cz + D = 0 \tag{6}$$

is a plane with the normal direction $A : B : C$. Thus, the locus of every linear equation in x, y, and z is a plane.

Proof. 1. If $A \neq 0$, we may assign any values $y = y_0$ and $z = z_0$ in (6) and then obtain a value $x = x_0$ which satisfies (6); etc., if $B \neq 0$, or $C \neq 0$. Thus, there exists at least one point $P:(x_0, y_0, z_0)$ on the locus of (6), and hence

$$Ax_0 + By_0 + Cz_0 + D = 0. \tag{7}$$

2. On subtracting each side in (7) from the corresponding side in (6), we obtain the following equation which is equivalent to (6):

$$A(x - x_0) + B(y - y_0) + C(z - z_0) = 0.$$

Hence, from (1), the locus of (6) is the plane described in Theorem II.

ILLUSTRATION 2. The plane $3x + 2y - 7z = 3$ has the normal direction $3 : 2 : -7$; $2x - z = 4$ has the normal direction $2 : 0 : -1$.

EXAMPLE 1. Obtain the equation of the plane T through $(2, -3, 1)$ which is parallel to the plane $S:[4x - 2y + z = 2]$.

Solution. Since S and T are parallel, they have the same normal direction, which is $4 : -2 : 1$. Hence, from (1), the equation of T is

$$4(x - 2) - 2(y + 3) + (z - 1) = 0 \quad or \quad 4x - 2y + z = 15.$$

EXERCISE 132

Obtain a graph of the equation.

1. $x = 2$.
2. $y = -3$.
3. $z = 2$.
4. $z = -2$.
5. $2x + y + z = 4$.
6. $3x - 2y - 2z + 6 = 0$.
7. $3x + 4y = 6z - 12$.
8. $x - y + 2z = 4$.
9. $3x + 4y = 12$.
10. $y + z = 2$.
11. $2x - 3z = 6$.

12. For the plane in Problem 6, what are the *equations* of the xy-trace; yz-trace?

Write an equation for the plane through the point with the given normal direction.

13. $(2, 1, -2)$; $3 : -1 : 4$.
14. $(-1, 2, -3)$; $-1 : 2 : -1$.
15. $(2, 0, -1)$; $0 : -1 : 2$.
16. $(-3, 1, 0)$; $3 : 0 : -1$.
17. $(2, 3, 0)$; $4 : -1 : 0$.
18. $(1, 0, -3)$; $-2 : 1 : -3$.

Write an equation for the specified plane.

19. Through $(-1, 2, -3)$ parallel to $2x - 3y + z = 8$.
20. Through $(0, -1, 2)$ parallel to $-x + 2y - z = 3$.
21. Through $(2, -1, 3)$ parallel to the xz-plane.
22. Through $(1, 2, -1)$ perpendicular to a line with the direction cosines $-\frac{9}{11}, \frac{2}{11}, \frac{6}{11}$.

23. Prove that the plane with x-intercept a, y-intercept b, and z-intercept c, where $abc \neq 0$, can be written in the **intercept form** $\dfrac{x}{a} + \dfrac{y}{b} + \dfrac{z}{c} = 1.$

24. Write the equation $3x - 2y - 5z = 20$ in the intercept form.

165. PROBLEMS ABOUT TWO PLANES

Consider two planes:

$$S_1:[A_1x + B_1y + C_1z + D_1 = 0]; \tag{1}$$
$$S_2:[A_2x + B_2y + C_2z + D_2 = 0]. \tag{2}$$

Their normals have the direction numbers $A_1 : B_1 : C_1$ and $A_2 : B_2 : C_2$. If S_1 and S_2 are parallel (coincide, or do not intersect), we shall say that the angle between S_1 and S_2 is 0. In this case the normals of S_1 and S_2 are parallel. If S_1 and S_2 intersect in a line l, then S_1 and S_2 form four dihedral angles, equal in pairs. These angles are measured by plane angles which are equal to those formed by the normal directions of the planes. In particular, S_1 and S_2 are perpendicular if and only if their normal directions are perpendicular.

The results summarized below are a consequence of (9) and (10) of page 420, as applied to the normals to the planes.

Summary. *To find the angles formed by planes* (1) *and* (2), *obtain the angles formed by their normal directions. The following conditions are available.*

Planes parallel: $A_1 : B_1 : C_1 = A_2 : B_2 : C_2.$ $\tag{3}$

Planes perpendicular: $A_1A_2 + B_1B_2 + C_1C_2 = 0.$ $\tag{4}$

ILLUSTRATION 1. The planes

$$3x + 4y - 2z + 5 = 0 \quad and \quad 6x + 8y - 4z - 7 = 0$$

are parallel because $3 : 4 : - 2 = 6 : 8 : - 4$.

ILLUSTRATION 2. The planes $6x - 9y + 2z = 3 \quad and \quad 6x + 2y - 9z = 8$
are perpendicular because $6(6) - 9(2) + 2(- 9) = 0$.

EXAMPLE 1. Find the angles, in degree measure, formed by the planes

$$2x - 2y + z = 3 \quad and \quad 9x - 6y + 2z = 7. \tag{5}$$

Solution. 1. The normal directions are $2 : - 2 : 1$ and $9 : - 6 : 2$, respectively. With $(\lambda_1, \mu_1, \nu_1)$ and $(\lambda_2, \mu_2, \nu_2)$ as the corresponding direction cosines, from Theorem VI on page 420 we obtain (with top signs applying together, and bottom signs applying together)

$$(\lambda_1 = \pm \tfrac{2}{3}, \mu_1 = \mp \tfrac{2}{3}, \nu_1 = \pm \tfrac{1}{3}), \quad and \quad (\lambda_2 = \pm \tfrac{9}{11}, \mu_2 = \mp \tfrac{6}{11}, \nu_2 = \pm \tfrac{2}{11}). \tag{6}$$

2. Let θ represent either one of the two angles formed by the normal directions for (5). Then, from (6), and (9) on page 417,

$$\cos \theta = \tfrac{18}{33} + \tfrac{12}{33} + \tfrac{2}{33} = \tfrac{32}{33}, \quad or \quad \cos \theta = - \tfrac{32}{33}.$$

Or, $\cos \theta = \pm .970$. From Table VI, $\theta = 14.0°$ or $\theta = 166.0°$.

166. PROJECTION PLANES FOR A LINE

A line l may be defined (or, *determined*) geometrically by specifying any two distinct planes R and S whose intersection is l. Algebraically, l is determined as the locus of a point $P:(x, y, z)$ satisfying the system of *two linear equations* whose loci are the planes R and S. Since infinitely many pairs of distinct planes R and S may be drawn through a given line l, we may have infinitely many different pairs of equations for l. We shall refer to any one of these pairs as *the* equations of l.

Let l be a given line and S be a given plane not perpendicular to l. Then, the projection of l on S is the line of intersection of S and the plane T through l perpendicular to S. If S is a coordinate plane, the plane T projecting l on S is called a *projection plane* for l. Any projection plane T for l is parallel to a coordinate axis, and hence *the corresponding variable x, y, or z is missing from the equation of T*. If a line l is determined by two given linear equations in x, y, and z, the equations of the projection planes for l can be found by *eliminating x, y, and z, in turn,* between the given equations.

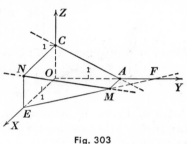

Fig. 303

ILLUSTRATION 1. The line l determined by the planes

$$U:[y + 2z = 2] \quad and \quad W:[3x + 2y = 6] \tag{1}$$

is MN in Figure 303. U and W are projection planes for l. U projects l into CA on the yz-plane and W projects l into EF on the xy-plane.

EXAMPLE 1. Obtain projection planes for the line l determined by

$$\begin{cases} 3x + 3y + 2z - 8 = 0, \ and & (2) \\ 3x + y - 2z - 4 = 0. & (3) \end{cases}$$

Solution. 1. The equation of the plane projecting l on the xy-plane will not involve z. To obtain this projection plane, eliminate z by adding in (2) and (3). We find $6x + 4y - 12 = 0$, or $3x + 2y = 6$.

2. The plane projecting l on the yz-plane is $y + 2z = 2$. Thus, (1) has been obtained from (2) and (3). The graph of the line [(2), (3)] is MN in Figure 303.

167. DIRECTION PERPENDICULAR TO TWO DIRECTIONS

We recall that two directions $a_1 : b_1 : c_1$ and $a_2 : b_2 : c_2$ are perpendicular if and only if

$$a_1 a_2 + b_1 b_2 + c_1 c_2 = 0. \tag{1}$$

EXAMPLE 1. Obtain direction numbers for a direction perpendicular to each of the directions $2 : -1 : 3$ and $3 : 1 : -2$.

Solution. Let $a : b : c$ be the desired direction numbers. Because of (1),

$$2a - b + 3c = 0 \quad and \quad 3a + b - 2c = 0. \tag{2}$$

The solution of system (2) for a and b in terms of c is $(a = -\frac{1}{5}c,\ b = \frac{13}{5}c)$. Hence, if c has any value $\neq 0$,

$$a : b : c = -\tfrac{1}{5}c : \tfrac{13}{5}c : c = -\tfrac{1}{5} : \tfrac{13}{5} : 1,\tag{3}$$

where we divided in the center by c. Hence, $a : b : c = -1 : 13 : 5$ is the desired direction. The method just used proves the following result.

Theorem III. *Let $a_1 : b_1 : c_1$ and $a_2 : b_2 : c_2$ be direction numbers for two nonparallel directions Ω_1 and Ω_2, respectively. Then, direction numbers for a direction, K, perpendicular to both Ω_1 and Ω_2 are*

$$\begin{vmatrix} b_1 & c_1 \\ b_2 & c_2 \end{vmatrix} : \begin{vmatrix} c_1 & a_1 \\ c_2 & a_2 \end{vmatrix} : \begin{vmatrix} a_1 & b_1 \\ a_2 & b_2 \end{vmatrix}.\tag{4}$$

Proof. 1. A direction $A : B : C$ is $\perp$ to both Ω_1 and Ω_2 if and only if

$$\begin{cases} Aa_1 + Bb_1 + Cc_1 = 0,\ and \tag{5} \\ Aa_2 + Bb_2 + Cc_2 = 0. \tag{6} \end{cases}$$

2. Let U, V, and W, respectively, represent the determinants from left to right in (4). If $W \neq 0$, on solving (5) and (6) for A and B in terms of C by use of determinants, we find $A = CU/W$ and $B = CV/W$. Then, if $C \neq 0$, we may divide the central numbers in (7) below by C, and

$$A : B : C = \frac{U}{W}C : \frac{V}{W}C : C = \frac{U}{W} : \frac{V}{W} : 1.\tag{7}$$

On multiplying the numbers at the right in (7) by W, we obtain the proportionality statement $A : B : C = U : V : W$, as stated in (4).

★*Note 1.* It can be proved that, if $a_1 : b_1 : c_1 \neq a_2 : b_2 : c_2$, at least one of the determinants in (4) is not zero. Thus, if the denominator in (7) is zero, we might solve (5) and (6) for B and C instead of for A and B, to obtain (4).

ILLUSTRATION 1. To solve Example 1 by use of (4), arrange $2 : -1 : 3$ and $3 : 1 : -2$ in rows, repeating the first two columns at the right:

$$\begin{bmatrix} 2: & \overbrace{-1:} & 3 & 2: & -1 \\ 3: & 1: & -2 & 3: & 1 \end{bmatrix};$$

$$a : b : c = \begin{vmatrix} -1 & 3 \\ 1 & -2 \end{vmatrix} : \begin{vmatrix} 3 & 2 \\ -2 & 3 \end{vmatrix} : \begin{vmatrix} 2 & -1 \\ 3 & 1 \end{vmatrix} = -1 : 13 : 5.$$

The line of intersection of two nonparallel planes

$$a_1x + b_1y + c_1z = d_1 \quad and \quad a_2x + b_2y + c_2z = d_2\tag{8}$$

is perpendicular to each of the normal directions $a_1 : b_1 : c_1$ and $a_2 : b_2 : c_2$. Hence, from Theorem III, the intersection of (8) has the direction numbers in (4).

ILLUSTRATION 2. By use of (4), the line of intersection of the planes

$$2x - 2y + z = 3 \quad and \quad 9x - 6y + 2z = 7$$

has the direction numbers $\begin{vmatrix} -2 & 1 \\ -6 & 2 \end{vmatrix} : \begin{vmatrix} 1 & 2 \\ 2 & 9 \end{vmatrix} : \begin{vmatrix} 2 & -2 \\ 9 & -6 \end{vmatrix}$, or $2 : 5 : 6$.

EXERCISE 133

If the two planes are parallel or perpendicular, verify this fact.

1. $\begin{cases} 2x - 6y - 2z = 5, \\ 3x - 9y - 3z = 7. \end{cases}$

2. $\begin{cases} 2x + y + 2z = 4, \\ 9x + 6y - 2z = 3. \end{cases}$

3. $\begin{cases} 3x - y + 2z = 4, \\ 2x - 3z = 9. \end{cases}$

4. $\begin{cases} 2x - y + 4z = 5, \\ x - 2y - z = 2. \end{cases}$

5. $\begin{cases} 3x - 6y - 2z = 5, \\ 2x + y - 2z = 4. \end{cases}$

6. $\begin{cases} 4x + 2y - 2z = 3, \\ -2x - y + z = 5. \end{cases}$

7. $\begin{cases} x - 3z = 1, \\ y - 4 = 0. \end{cases}$

8. $\begin{cases} 3x - 4y = 5, \\ 4x + 3y = 7. \end{cases}$

9. $\begin{cases} 2z + y = 5, \\ 3x - 2 = 0. \end{cases}$

10–11. In each of Problems 2 and 5, find the acute angle which is formed by the planes.

12. Prove that the plane $Ax + Cz + D = 0$ is perpendicular to the xz-plane, and that $By + Cz + D = 0$ is perpendicular to the yz-plane.

Graph the line l determined by the equations.

13. $\begin{cases} x + z = 4, \\ 4z + 3y = 12. \end{cases}$

14. $\begin{cases} 2x + y = 4, \\ 2x + 3y = 6. \end{cases}$

15. $\begin{cases} x + 2y = 4, \\ y + z = 3. \end{cases}$

Obtain the equations of the projection planes for the line and plot it.

16. $\begin{cases} 4x + y + 2z = 10, \\ x - 2y + 2z = -2. \end{cases}$

17. $\begin{cases} x + y + 3z = 5, \\ x - 3y - 3z = -7. \end{cases}$

18–22. In Problems 13–17, respectively, find the coordinates of the points where the line intersects the coordinate planes.

Find direction numbers and direction cosines for a direction perpendicular to two directions having the given direction numbers or cosines.

23. $1 : -2 : 2; \quad 3 : 1 : 2.$

24. $0 : -1 : 3; \quad 2 : -2 : 3.$

25. $2 : 0 : -3; \quad -3 : 2 : -5.$

26. $-3 : 1 : 4; \quad 0 : -2 : 5.$

27. Cosines: $\frac{2}{3}, -\frac{1}{3}, \frac{2}{3}; \quad \frac{3}{7}, \frac{2}{7}, \frac{6}{7}.$

28. Cosines: $\frac{3}{5}, 0, \frac{4}{5}; \quad \frac{5}{13}, \frac{12}{13}, 0.$

29–30. Find direction numbers for the line of intersection of the planes in Problems 2 and 5, respectively.

31–32. In Problems 2 and 5, respectively, obtain the equation of the plane S through $(1, 2, -1)$ perpendicular to the given planes.

168. PARAMETRIC AND SYMMETRIC EQUATIONS FOR A LINE

Let l be a line through a fixed point $P_1:(x_1, y_1, z_1)$, with Ω as either one of the directions on l; let (α, β, γ) be the direction angles of Ω. Hereafter, let l be a directed line with Ω as the positive direction in measuring line segments. If $P:(x, y, z)$ is on l, let s represent the directed distance from P_1 to P, as in Figure 304, with $\overline{P_1P} = s$. Then, we shall prove that parametric equations for l in terms of s as the parameter are as follows:

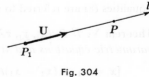

Fig. 304

$$(x = x_1 + s \cos \alpha, \quad y = y_1 + s \cos \beta, \quad z = z_1 + s \cos \gamma). \qquad (1)$$

Proof. 1. Visualize l as an s-number-scale, with $s = \overline{P_1P}$ at any point $P:(x, y, z)$ on l. Assume that P is not P_1. Then, $s > 0$ when P_1P has the direction Ω, and $s < 0$ when P_1P has the opposite direction. Let $\mathbf{U}$ be the unit vector with the direction (α, β, γ) based at P_1. From (7) on page 416 and (6) on page 411, we have

$$\mathbf{U} = \mathbf{i} \cos \alpha + \mathbf{j} \cos \beta + \mathbf{k} \cos \gamma, \text{ and} \tag{2}$$

$$\overrightarrow{P_1P} = (x - x_1)\mathbf{i} + (y - y_1)\mathbf{j} + (z - z_1)\mathbf{k}. \tag{3}$$

2. Since $|\overrightarrow{P_1P}| = |s| \cdot |\mathbf{U}|$, from Definition I on page 409 we obtain

$$\overrightarrow{P_1P} = +|s|\mathbf{U} \text{ if } \overrightarrow{P_1P} \text{ and } \mathbf{U} \text{ have the same direction;} \tag{4}$$

$$\overrightarrow{P_1P} = -|s|\mathbf{U} \text{ if } \overrightarrow{P_1P} \text{ and } \mathbf{U} \text{ have opposite directions.} \tag{5}$$

In case (4) is true, $s > 0$ and hence $+|s| = s$; if (5) is true, then $s < 0$ and $-|s| = s$. Thus, in either case, $\overrightarrow{P_1P} = s\mathbf{U}$, or

$$(x - x_1)\mathbf{i} + (y - y_1)\mathbf{j} + (z - z_1)\mathbf{k} = s(\mathbf{i} \cos \alpha + \mathbf{j} \cos \beta + \mathbf{k} \cos \gamma). \tag{6}$$

On equating the coefficients of $\mathbf{i}$, $\mathbf{j}$, and $\mathbf{k}$, respectively, from the two sides of (6), we obtain $x - x_1 = s \cos \alpha$, or $x = x_1 + s \cos \alpha$, etc., as in (1). If $s = 0$, then (1) gives $P_1:(x_1, y_1, z_1)$. Hence, (1) gives parametric equations for l, because the coordinates of each point P on l are obtained from (1) just once, with $s = \overline{P_1P}$.

Theorem IV. *If the line l through $P_1:(x_1, y_1, z_1)$ has the direction numbers $a : b : c$, then l has the parametric equations*

$$(x = x_1 + at, \quad y = y_1 + bt, \quad z = z_1 + ct), \tag{7}$$

where t is a parameter. Also, if no one of (a, b, c) is zero, then l has the xyz-equations (two are abbreviated)

$$\frac{x - x_1}{a} = \frac{y - y_1}{b} = \frac{z - z_1}{c}. \tag{8}$$

Proof. 1. A number $h \neq 0$ exists so that $\cos \alpha = ha$, $\cos \beta = hb$, and $\cos \gamma = hc$ in (1). Then, from (1), $x = x_1 + ahs$, $y = y_1 + bhs$, and $z = z_1 + chs$. If we let $t = hs$, the preceding equations yield (7).

2. To prove (8), we obtain $t = [(x - x_1)/a] = [(y - y_1)/b]$, etc., from (7).

Note 1. Equalities (8) are equivalent to the system of two equations obtained by equating any one of the fractions to each of the other two, for instance, to the system

$$\frac{x - x_1}{a} = \frac{y - y_1}{b} \quad \text{and} \quad \frac{x - x_1}{a} = \frac{z - z_1}{c}. \tag{9}$$

Equalities (8) are referred to as **symmetric equations** for the line.

Theorem V. *If $P_1:(x_1, y_1, z_1)$ and $P_2:(x_2, y_2, z_2)$ are distinct points on a line l, then parametric equations and symmetric equations, respectively, for l are as follows:*

$$[x = x_1 + (x_2 - x_1)t, \quad y = y_1 + (y_2 - y_1)t, \quad z = z_1 + (z_2 - z_1)t]; \tag{10}$$

$$\frac{x - x_1}{x_2 - x_1} = \frac{y - y_1}{y_2 - y_1} = \frac{z - z_1}{z_2 - z_1}. \tag{11}$$

Proof. From (8) on page 420, l has the direction numbers

$$(x_2 - x_1) : (y_2 - y_1) : (z_2 - z_1).$$

With these replacing $a : b : c$, we obtain (10) and (11) from (7) and (8).

If just one of (a, b, c) is *zero*, then (7) immediately gives the equation of one projection plane through l. A second projection plane then is obtained by equating two fractions from (8) where the denominators are not zero. If *two* of (a, b, c) are zero, then (7) immediately gives the equations of two projection planes for l.

ILLUSTRATION 1. From (7), the line, l, through A:(2, $- 3$, 4) with the direction numbers $4 : 3 : - 5$ has the parametric equations

$$(x = 2 + 4t, \quad y = - 3 + 3t, \quad z = 4 - 5t). \tag{12}$$

With $t = + 1$ in (12), we obtain B:(6, 0, $- 1$) on l. Recall that we used $t = hs$ in (1) to obtain (7) in the proof of Theorem IV. Hence, the point in (7) is in *one direction* on l when $t > 0$ and in *the opposite direction* when $t < 0$. Since $t = + 1$ for B, all points, P, on l where AP has the same direction as $\overrightarrow{AB}$ will result from (7) with positive values of t. Symmetric equations for l are

$$\frac{x - 2}{4} = \frac{y + 3}{3} = \frac{z - 4}{- 5}. \tag{13}$$

From (13), $$\frac{x - 2}{4} = \frac{y + 3}{3} \quad and \quad \frac{y + 3}{3} = \frac{z - 4}{5}, \; or \tag{14}$$

$$3x - 4y = 18 \quad and \quad 5y - 3z = - 27. \tag{15}$$

EXAMPLE 1. Obtain parametric equations and also the *xyz*-equations of two projection planes for the line, l, through P:(4, 3, $- 7$) and Q:($- 2$, 3, 5).

Solution. 1. Direction numbers for PQ are $- 6 : 0 : 12$, or $- 1 : 0 : 2$. Hence, from (10), parametric equations for l are

$$(x = 4 - t, \quad y = 3, \quad z = - 7 + 2t). \tag{16}$$

2. From (16), $t = 4 - x = (z + 7)/2$. Hence, l is determined by the following system, representing projection planes through l:

$$4 - x = \tfrac{1}{2}(z + 7) \quad and \quad y = 3. \tag{17}$$

Note 2. The symmetric form (8) is not algebraically "*legal*" if any denominator is zero. However, there is no serious objection to writing (8) then if it is understood merely *to abbreviate* (7). For instance, if $b = 0$ in (8), then (7) implies that $y = y_1$; that is, a zero denominator in (8) implies that the corresponding numerator is equal to zero. With such license, in Example 1, the symmetric form is

$$\frac{x - 4}{- 1} = \frac{y - 3}{0} = \frac{z + 7}{2}, \tag{18}$$

from which we obtain, as before, the projection planes

$$y - 3 = 0 \quad and \quad \frac{x - 4}{- 1} = \frac{z + 7}{2}.$$

We shall prefer to avoid such usage as (18) and base our work on (7) when any denominator is zero in (8).

EXAMPLE 2. Change the following equalities to the symmetric form; determine a point on the line l which they represent and direction numbers for l:

$$\frac{3x + 5}{2} = \frac{3 - 2y}{1} = \frac{4 - z}{-3}. \tag{19}$$

Solution. Form (8) is earmarked by the fact that, in each numerator, the coefficient is 1 for x, y, or z. To change (19) to the form (8), divide both numerator and denominator in any fraction by the coefficient of x, or y, or z, as the case may be. Thus, divide by 3, -2, and -1, respectively, in obtaining

$$\frac{x + \frac{5}{3}}{\frac{2}{3}} = \frac{y - \frac{3}{2}}{-\frac{1}{2}} = \frac{z - 4}{3}.$$

Then, multiply all denominators by 6:

$$\frac{x + \frac{5}{3}}{4} = \frac{y - \frac{3}{2}}{-3} = \frac{z - 4}{18}. \tag{20}$$

By comparing (20) with (8), we see that (20) represents a line through $(-\frac{5}{3}, \frac{3}{2}, 4)$ with the direction $4 : -3 : 18$.

EXERCISE 134

Plot the line l whose parametric equations are given, by finding two points on l by use of the equations.

1. $x = 1 + t, y = 3 - 4t, z = 4 + 3t.$ **2.** $x = 4 + 5t, y = 1 - t, z = 5 + 7t.$

Write the equations of two projection planes which determine the line.

3. $\dfrac{x - 3}{-3} = \dfrac{y}{4} = \dfrac{z - 1}{1}.$ **4.** $\dfrac{x - 1}{1} = \dfrac{y - 6}{2} = \dfrac{z - 1}{-1}.$

Write equations for the line in parametric form, in symmetric form if no direction number is zero, and finally in the form of a system of two equations defining projection planes.

5. Through $(2, 4, 2)$ with the direction $0 : 4 : 3$.

6. Through $(-3, 2, 3)$ with the direction $2 : 0 : 0$.

7. Through $(-1, 2, 3)$ with the direction $2 : -3 : 1$.

8. Through $(2, -1, \frac{3}{4})$ with the direction $-1 : 2 : -3$.

9. Through $(0, -1, 3)$ with the direction cosines $-\frac{1}{3}, -\frac{2}{3}, \frac{2}{3}$.

10. Through $(2, -1, 3)$ with the direction $2 : 0 : -1$.

11. Through $(-1, 0, -3)$ with the direction $0 : -1 : 3$.

12. Through the points $(-1, 2, -1)$ and $(3, 4, -2)$.

13. Through the points $(-3, 1, 0)$ and $(0, 1, -3)$.

14. Through the points $(-2, 3, 1)$ and $(0, -2, 1)$.

15. Through $(2, -1, 3)$ perpendicular to the plane $3x + 2y + 5z = 3$.

16. Through $(-1, 3, 0)$ perpendicular to the plane $x - 2y = 2$.

17. Through $(2, -1, 3)$ parallel to the line with the symmetric form

$$\frac{x - 2}{3} = \frac{y}{2} = \frac{z + 1}{-1}.$$

18. Through $(2, 3, -5)$ parallel to the z-axis.

19. Find a pair of projection equations for the line through $(2, -1, 2)$ parallel to the line through $(1, 3, -1)$ and $(-2, 1, 4)$.

20. Find the acute angle made by the lines in Problems 3 and 4.

21. By use of parametric equations, find where the line through $(2, -1, 3)$ with the direction $1 : 4 : -2$ intersects $2x + y - 3z = 18$.

Find direction numbers for the line defined by the equations, and a point on the line.

22. $\dfrac{2x - 1}{3} = \dfrac{2 - y}{2} = \dfrac{3z + 5}{1}.$

23. $\dfrac{3x - 2}{4} = \dfrac{5 + y}{3} = \dfrac{1 - 2z}{5}.$

24. Line with the equations

$$3 + 2x = 0 \quad and \quad \frac{4 - y}{3} = \frac{z - 2}{4}.$$

25. Line with the equations

$$\frac{2 - 5x}{3} = \frac{2z - 1}{4} \quad and \quad 3 + 4y = 0.$$

26. $\begin{cases} x + y - z = 1, \\ 4x - y + 6z = 9. \end{cases}$

27. $\begin{cases} 2x + y - z = 4, \\ 2x - 3y - 9z = -8. \end{cases}$

Hint. Find the point where $z = 0$ and use (4) on page 442 to find the direction. Or, commence by solving for x and y in terms of z; then get z in terms of x and of y, and a resulting sequence of three equal fractions.

28. $\begin{cases} x + 2y - z = 1, \\ 3x + 6y - 4z = 1. \end{cases}$

29. $\begin{cases} 2x + 4y - 3z = 10, \\ 2x - 4y + 3z = -8. \end{cases}$

30. Find direction cosines for a direction on the line which is the locus of the system of equations in Problem 27.

31. The line of Problem 1 is projected on the xy-plane. Find xyz-equations for this line of projection.

32. The line of Problem 2 is projected on the yz-plane. Find xyz-equations for this line of projection.

169. SPHERES AND CYLINDERS

Let r be the radius and let $C:(g, h, k)$ be the center of a sphere. Then, it has the equation

$$(x - g)^2 + (y - h)^2 + (z - k)^2 = r^2, \tag{1}$$

because (1) states that the square of the distance between $C:(g, h, k)$ and $P:(x, y, z)$ is equal to r^2. By completing squares with the terms in x, y, and z, respectively, we find that any equation of the form

$$x^2 + y^2 + z^2 + Rx + Sy + Tz + U = 0,$$

where R, S, T, and U are real numbers, represents a sphere, real (including a point-sphere) or imaginary.

A *cylinder* is defined as the surface swept out by a line L, with a fixed direction, which moves through all points of a plane curve C. Each position of L is called a *ruling*, and C is called a *directrix curve* of the cylinder. For any cylinder, we may choose any plane section perpendicular to the rulings as a directrix curve, and this will be taken as the situation hereafter. If the rulings are perpendicular to a coordinate plane, as will be the case usually in our applications, the directrix C may be taken as the trace of the cylinder in this plane. The cylinder will be referred to as *perpendicular to this plane,* or parallel to its normals. A cylinder frequently is named after its directrix.

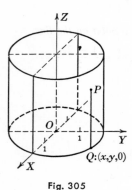

Fig. 305

ILLUSTRATION 1. A cylinder is called a circular, an elliptic, a hyperbolic, or a parabolic cylinder according as its directrix is a circle, an ellipse, etc.

ILLUSTRATION 2. Consider the surface S defined by

$$x^2 + y^2 = 4. \tag{2}$$

The xy-trace is the circle which is the graph of (2) in the xy-plane, as in Figure 305. The projection of any point P:(x, y, z) on the xy-plane is Q:$(x, y, 0)$. Point P is on S if and only if Q satisfies (2), or P is on a perpendicular to the xy-plane at a point Q on the circle $x^2 + y^2 = 4$. Thus, S is a circular cylinder perpendicular to the xy-plane. A similar discussion establishes the following result.

Theorem VI. *If an equation lacks one of the variables x, y, and z, the graph of the equation is a cylinder parallel to the axis of the missing variable, or perpendicular to the plane of the other variables.*

Note 1. A section of a cylinder by a plane parallel to the plane of a directrix curve C is a curve *congruent* to C. A section of a cylinder by a plane perpendicular to the plane of C consists of one or more rulings.

ILLUSTRATION 3. The graph S of $yz = 6$ is a hyperbolic cylinder perpendicular to the yz-plane; the directrix is the graph of $yz = 6$ in the yz-plane. Figure 306 shows a piece of S bounded by arc BD of the directrix, by arc AC of a congruent section parallel to the yz-plane, and by rulings CD and AB perpendicular to the yz-plane.

ILLUSTRATION 4. A plane is a special case of a cylinder, where the directrix curve is a line. Thus, $3x + 2y = 5$ may be referred to as a *linear cylinder,* perpendicular to the xy-plane.

To write the equation of a cylinder whose directrix is a certain curve C in a coordinate plane, *write the equation in two variables whose locus in that plane is C.*

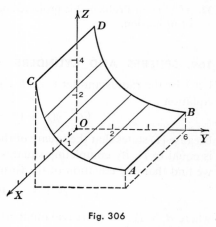

Fig. 306

ILLUSTRATION 5. Let the directrix of a cylinder be the ellipse in the xz-plane with major axis 10 along OX, minor axis 6 along OZ, and center at the origin. Then, the equation of this cylinder is $9x^2 + 25z^2 = 225$.

170. SURFACES OF REVOLUTION

If a plane curve C is revolved about a line l in its plane, the surface S thus generated is called a *surface of revolution* with l as its **axis** of revolution and C as a **generatrix**. Any section of S by a plane through l is called a **meridian section** and consists of one position of C, in its revolution, together with the symmetric reflection of C with respect to l. Any section of S by a plane perpendicular to l is a circle. If we revolve an ellipse, a hyperbola, or a parabola about an axis of symmetry of the curve, the surface obtained is called an *ellipsoid*, a *hyperboloid*, or a *paraboloid of revolution*, respectively. Suppose that, for a given ellipse, the major and minor axes are unequal. Then, the ellipsoid of revolution obtained by revolving the ellipse about its minor axis is called an **oblate spheroid** (illustrated by the earth's surface); the ellipsoid is called a **prolate spheroid** if it is obtained by revolution of the ellipse about its major axis. If the ellipse is a circle, any corresponding ellipsoid of revolution is a sphere. A prolate spheroid is illustrated in Figure 307 below.

ILLUSTRATION 1. If the ellipse C, which is the locus of

$$9y^2 + 4z^2 = 36 \tag{1}$$

in the yz-plane, is revolved about OZ, a prolate spheroid S is obtained, as in Figure 307. To derive an equation for S, consider Figure 308. Let $Q:(0, y_1, z_1)$ be a point on C, and let $P:(x, y, z)$ be any point into which Q revolves. Let $P_1:(x, y, 0)$ and $Q_1:(0, y_1, 0)$ be the projections of P and Q on the xy-plane. Since Q is on C,

$$9y_1^2 + 4z_1^2 = 36. \tag{2}$$

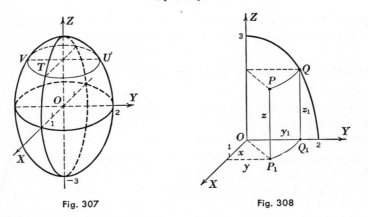

Fig. 307   Fig. 308

In Figure 308, $\overline{Q_1Q} = \overline{P_1P}$; $(\overline{OQ_1})^2 = (\overline{OP_1})^2$. Hence,

$$z_1 = z \quad and \quad y_1^2 = x^2 + y^2. \tag{3}$$

A point P is on S if and only if (2) and (3) are true. Hence, an equation for S is found by using (3) in (2), which gives

$$9(x^2 + y^2) + 4z^2 = 36. \tag{4}$$

ILLUSTRATION 2. If the ellipse (1) in the yz-plane were revolved about OY, an oblate spheroid would be obtained with the equation $4x^2 + 4z^2 + 9y^2 = 36$.

Let C be the graph of $f(y, z) = 0$, $f(x, y) = 0$, or $f(x, z) = 0$, in the coordinate plane of the two variables involved. Then, as in Illustration 1, the equation of the surface generated by revolving C about a coordinate axis, in its plane, is obtained as follows:

I. Revolution about OZ: $\begin{cases} \text{for } f(y, z) = 0, \text{ replace } y^2 \text{ by } (x^2 + y^2); * \\ \text{for } f(x, z) = 0, \text{ replace } x^2 \text{ by } (x^2 + y^2). \end{cases}$

II. Revolution about OY: $\begin{cases} \text{for } f(x, y) = 0, \text{ replace } x^2 \text{ by } (x^2 + z^2); \\ \text{for } f(y, z) = 0, \text{ replace } z^2 \text{ by } (x^2 + z^2). \end{cases}$

III. Revolution about OX: $\begin{cases} \text{for } f(x, y) = 0, \text{ replace } y^2 \text{ by } (y^2 + z^2); \\ \text{for } f(x, z) = 0, \text{ replace } z^2 \text{ by } (y^2 + z^2). \end{cases}$

ILLUSTRATION 3. If the hyperbola which is the graph of

$$y^2 - 4z^2 = 4 \tag{5}$$

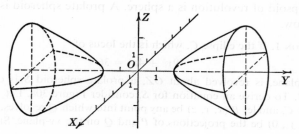

Fig. 309

in the yz-plane is revolved about OY, a hyperboloid of revolution of two sheets, S, is generated, as in Figure 309. By (II), the equation of S is

$$y^2 - 4(x^2 + z^2) = 4. \tag{6}$$

ILLUSTRATION 4. By reference to (I), we see that

$$3x^2 + 3y^2 - 7z^2 = 8 \quad or \quad 3(x^2 + y^2) - 7z^2 = 8,$$

represents a hyperboloid of revolution, which is generated by revolving about OZ the locus of $3x^2 - 7z^2 = 8$ in the xz-plane, or the locus of $3y^2 - 7z^2 = 8$ in the yz-plane.

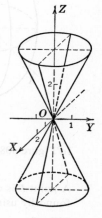

Let C be a fixed plane curve and let V be a fixed point not in the plane of C. Then, the surface generated by a line t drawn through V to a point P on C, as P moves through all positions on C, is called a *cone*. For this cone, we call V the *vertex*, any position of t a *ruling*, and C a *directrix curve*. Suppose that C can be chosen as a circle, with V on a line l perpendicular to the plane of the circle at its center. Then, the cone is a surface of revolution, generated by revolving a ruling about l as the axis of revolution. Such a cone is called a *right circular cone*. It has two *nappes*, radiating from the vertex, as illustrated in Figure 310, where the vertex is the origin, O.

Fig. 310

* That is, replace $| y |$ by $\sqrt{x^2 + y^2}$, and similarly in the other cases.

EXAMPLE 1. Obtain the equation of the cone generated by revolving about OZ the line which is the locus of $z = 2y$ in the yz-plane.

Solution. Replace $|y|$ by $\sqrt{x^2 + y^2}$, and obtain $\pm 2\sqrt{x^2 + y^2} = z$, where "+" applies if $z \geq 0$ and "−" if $z < 0$. On rationalizing, we find $4x^2 + 4y^2 = z^2$ as the equation of the cone, shown in Figure 310 on page 450.

EXERCISE 135

Graph the specified sphere and write its equation.

1. Center (2, 5, 7); radius 2.   **2.** Center (3, − 4, 6); radius 3.

Find the center and radius of the sphere.

3. $x^2 + 2x + y^2 - 6y + z^2 - 5 = 0$.   **4.** $x^2 + y^2 + z^2 - 4x + 6z + 9 = 0$.

Graph the piece of the surface between the xy-plane and the plane $z = 6$.

5. $x^2 + y^2 = 16$.   **6.** $4x^2 + 9y^2 = 36$.   **7.** $x^2 = 4y$.

8. $4x^2 - 9y^2 = 0$.   **9.** $4y - 3x + 12 = 0$.

Graph the surface represented by the equation.

10. $9y^2 + 4z^2 = 36$.   **11.** $25x^2 + 4z^2 = 100$.   **12.** $z^2 = 6x$.

13. $z^2 - y^2 = 4$.   **14.** $4z^2 - 9x^2 = 36$.   **15.** $x = \sin z$.

Sketch the surface obtained by revolving the locus of the given equation, in the plane of the variables involved, about the specified axis. Show the traces and several circular sections. Also, write the equation of the surface.

16. $z^2 = 4y$; about OY.   **17.** $9y^2 + 25z^2 = 225$; about OY.

18. $9x^2 + 4z^2 = 36$; about OX.   **19.** $x^2 = 6z$; about OZ.

20. $z = 4x$; about OZ.   **21.** $x = 3z$; about OX.

22. $4y^2 - 9z^2 = 36$; about OY.   **23.** $4y^2 - 9z^2 = 36$; about OZ.

First describe the locus of the equation as a surface of revolution, stating its axis and a generatrix. Then, sketch the surface.

24. $4(x^2 + y^2) + z^2 = 4$.   **25.** $z^2 + x^2 + 4y = 0$.

26. $4x^2 + 4y^2 = z^2$.   **27.** $16x^2 + 9y^2 + 9z^2 = 144$.

28. $x^2 - y^2 + z^2 = 4$.   **29.** $9x^2 - y^2 + 9z^2 = 0$.

171. PROJECTING CYLINDER FOR A PLANE SECTION

Let C be the section of a surface $f(x, y, z) = 0$ made by a plane $z = k$, where k is a constant. Then, C is the intersection of the plane $z = k$ and the *cylinder H* whose equation is $f(x, y, k) = 0$, obtained by using $z = k$ in $f(x, y, z) = 0$. The xy-trace of H is the projection of C onto the xy-plane, and is congruent to C. We call H the *projecting cylinder* for the plane section C.

Note 1. Two points P and Q are said to be *symmetric to a plane T* if T is perpendicular to the line segment PQ and bisects PQ.

EXAMPLE 1. Discuss the surface S with the equation

$$\frac{x^2}{4} + \frac{y^2}{9} + \frac{z^2}{25} = 1.$$

Solution. 1. Since all exponents are even, if a point (x, y, z) is on the surface S then $(-x, -y, -z)$ is on S, or S is symmetric to the origin. If (x, y, z) is on S, then $(x, y, -z)$ is on S, or S is symmetric to the xy-plane. Similarly, S is symmetric to the xz-plane and the yz-plane.

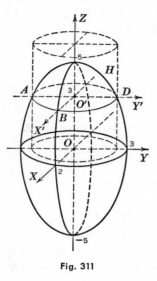

2. With $z = 0$ in (1), we obtain $9x^2 + 4y^2 = 36$ as the equation whose graph in the xy-plane is the xy-trace of S. This trace is an ellipse. Similarly, the xz-trace and yz-trace are ellipses, as shown in Figure 311.

3. The plane section C of S by the plane $z = 3$ is the locus of

$$\frac{x^2}{4} + \frac{y^2}{9} + \frac{z^2}{25} = 1 \quad and \quad z = 3, \ or \qquad (2)$$

$$\frac{x^2}{4} + \frac{y^2}{9} = 1 - \frac{9}{25} \quad and \quad z = 3. \qquad (3)$$

In (3), the quadratic equation defines an *elliptic cylinder H* perpendicular to the xy-plane. Thus, C is defined by (3) as the intersection of the *plane $z = 3$*

Fig. 311

and the *projecting cylinder H*, shown by broken lines in Figure 311, where C is ABD. Hence, C is an ellipse, congruent to the ellipse which is the xy-trace of H. Also, we may think of C as the locus of the quadratic from (3) in *a new system of xy-coordinates* with axes $O'X'$ and $O'Y'$ as shown *in the plane $z = 3$* in Figure 311.

4. If $z = k$ in (1), we obtain

$$\frac{x^2}{4} + \frac{y^2}{9} = 1 - \frac{k^2}{25}; \qquad (4)$$

in (4), the right-hand side is *negative* if $|k| > 5$, and then the locus of (4) is imaginary. Hence, the plane $z = k$ does not intersect (1) if $|k| > 5$, or the domain for z is $|z| \leq 5$. If $|k| \leq 5$, the locus of (4) is an elliptic cylinder, or the section of (1) by the plane $z = k$ is an ellipse. Similarly, the domain for x is $|x| \leq 2$ and for y is $|y| \leq 3$. Sections of (1) by planes $x = h$ or $y = g$, in the specified domains, are ellipses. The graph of (1) is in Figure 311, and is called an *ellipsoid*.

172. STANDARD QUADRIC SURFACES

The locus of any equation of the second degree in x, y, and z is called a *quadric surface*, or a *conicoid*, if the locus is real. It can be proved that a quadric surface is either a cylinder with a conic as a directrix curve, or a surface of one of the types which will now be illustrated, in convenient positions, or a corresponding degenerate type of surface. In the following standard forms, the constants a, b, and c are positive.

Ellipsoid:
$$\frac{x^2}{a^2} + \frac{y^2}{b^2} + \frac{z^2}{c^2} = 1. \tag{1}$$

Discussion of (1). The graph, S, of (1) has the origin as a center of symmetry, and each coordinate plane as a plane of symmetry, called a *principal plane*. S is illustrated in Figure 311, page 452.

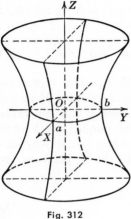

Hyperboloid of one sheet:
$$\frac{x^2}{a^2} + \frac{y^2}{b^2} - \frac{z^2}{c^2} = 1. \tag{2}$$

Discussion of (2). The surface S, in Figure 312, which is the graph of (2), has the origin as a center of symmetry and each coordinate plane as a plane of symmetry, called a principal plane. S has no z-intercept. The section of S by any plane $z = k$ is an ellipse. In (2), x and y cannot have values for which the point $(x, y, 0)$ in the xy-plane is inside the ellipse which is the xy-trace of S. Otherwise, the domains for x, y, and z are all real values. Sections by planes $x = g$ or $y = h$ are hyperbolas.

Fig. 312

Hyperboloid of two sheets:
$$-\frac{x^2}{a^2} + \frac{y^2}{b^2} - \frac{z^2}{c^2} = 1. \tag{3}$$

Discussion of (3). The surface S which is the graph of (3) is illustrated in Figure 309, page 450, for a case where $a = c$. Surface S has the origin as a center of symmetry, and each coordinate plane as a plane of symmetry. The section C of S by a plane $y = h$ is the locus of the system

$$\frac{x^2}{a^2} + \frac{z^2}{c^2} = \frac{h^2}{b^2} - 1 \quad and \quad y = h. \tag{4}$$

In (4), if $|h| \geqq b$, the quadratic equation defines an elliptic cylinder. The xz-trace of this projecting cylinder is an ellipse; hence, C is an ellipse. If $|h| < b$, the locus of (4) is imaginary. Thus, the domain for y in (3) is $|y| \geqq b$. The domain for x and for z is all real numbers. Any section of S by a plane $x = g$, or by $z = k$, is a hyperbola, whose transverse axis is parallel to the y-axis.

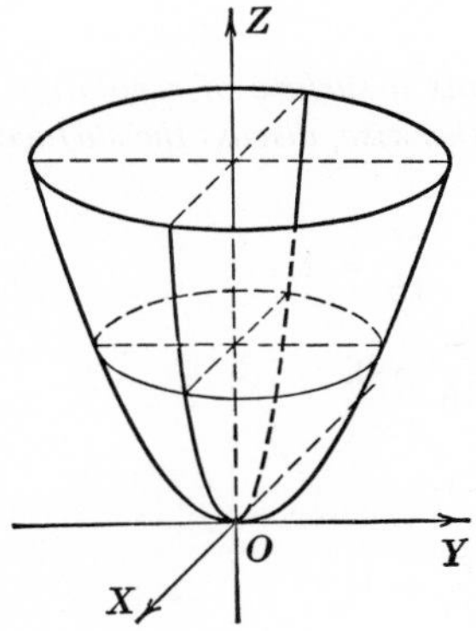

Fig. 313

Elliptic paraboloid:
$$\frac{x^2}{a^2} + \frac{y^2}{b^2} = pz. \tag{5}$$

Discussion of (5). In (5), $p \neq 0$. A graph of the surface S represented by (5) is shown in Figure 313 for a case where $p > 0$; any plane section of S by a plane $z = c \geqq 0$ parallel to the xy-plane is an ellipse. A section of S by a plane $x = g$, or a plane $y = h$, is a parabola.

Hyperbolic paraboloid: $$\frac{y^2}{b^2} - \frac{x^2}{a^2} = pz. \qquad (6)$$

Discussion of (6). In (6), $p \neq 0$. Figure 314 shows a graph of the surface S in (6) with $p > 0$. S is saddle-shaped. The xz-trace and yz-trace are parabolas. The xy-trace is the graph of $a^2y^2 - b^2x^2 = 0$ in the xy-plane, and consists of two lines (not shown) through the origin. If $k \neq 0$, the section C of S by the plane

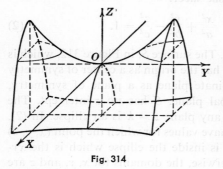

Fig. 314

$z = k$ is defined by

$$\frac{y^2}{b^2} - \frac{x^2}{a^2} = pk \quad and \quad z = k. \qquad (7)$$

In (7), the quadratic equation represents a projecting hyperbolic cylinder. Hence, if $p > 0$, the plane section C is a hyperbola with its transverse axis parallel to OY when $k > 0$, and to OX when $k < 0$. Any section of S parallel to the xz-plane or yz-plane is a parabola.

Quadric cone: $$\frac{x^2}{a^2} + \frac{y^2}{b^2} - \frac{z^2}{c^2} = 0. \qquad (8)$$

Discussion of (8). The surface S represented by (8) is illustrated in Figure 310, page 450, for a case where $a = b$. Sections by planes $z = k$ are ellipses, and by planes $x = g$ or $y = h$ are hyperbolas.

EXERCISE 136

Sketch the surface and state its name. If the equation represents a surface of revolution, or a cylinder, obtain the sketch by an elementary procedure. Otherwise, discuss the surface as done for (3) *on page* 453.

1. $\dfrac{x^2}{4} + \dfrac{y^2}{9} + \dfrac{z^2}{16} = 1.$

2. $-\dfrac{x^2}{4} + \dfrac{y^2}{9} - \dfrac{z^2}{16} = 1.$

3. $\dfrac{x^2}{4} + \dfrac{y^2}{9} - \dfrac{z^2}{16} = 1.$

4. $\dfrac{x^2}{4} + \dfrac{y^2}{9} - \dfrac{z^2}{16} = 0.$

5. $\dfrac{x^2}{9} + \dfrac{y^2}{25} = z.$

6. $\dfrac{x^2}{4} + \dfrac{z^2}{9} = 2y.$

7. $\dfrac{y^2}{9} - \dfrac{x^2}{25} = z.$

8. $\dfrac{x^2}{9} - \dfrac{y^2}{4} + \dfrac{z^2}{25} = 1.$

9. $16x^2 + 16y^2 - 25z^2 = -400.$

10. $4x^2 + 4y^2 - 9z^2 = 36.$

11. $\dfrac{x^2}{9} - \dfrac{y^2}{4} + \dfrac{z^2}{9} = 0.$

12. $\dfrac{x^2}{9} - \dfrac{y^2}{25} = z.$

13. $x^2 = 16y^2.$ 14. $z^2 - 6y = 0.$ 15. $x^2 - 4z^2 = 16.$

★16. Prove that the locus of equation (8) of Section 172 is a cone, as defined on page 450, with the origin O as the vertex.

Hint. Let C represent any section of the surface made by a plane $z = k$. Let the point $P':(x', y', k)$ be on C. Prove that every point P on the line OP' lies on the locus.

173. SPACE CURVES

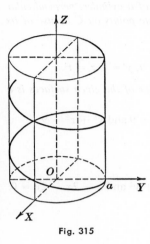

Fig. 315

A space curve may be defined parametrically, in terms of a parameter t, by a set of equations

$$x = f(t), \quad y = g(t), \quad and \quad z = h(t). \quad (1)$$

The straight-line case of the parametric form (1) was met on page 444.

ILLUSTRATION 1. Suppose that a point P:(x, y, z) moves clockwise on the cylinder $x^2 + y^2 = a^2$ with a constant angular speed of ω radians per second about the z-axis, and a constant speed of k units per second in the vertical direction. If P is at $(0, a, 0)$ when the time t (in seconds) is zero, the position of P at any time t is given by

$$x = a \sin \omega t, \ y = a \cos \omega t, \ and \ z = kt. \quad (2)$$

The path traced by P, as in Figure 315, is called a circular **helix**.

Suppose that C is the curve of intersection of two surfaces defined by

$$f(x, y, z) = 0 \quad and \quad g(x, y, z) = 0. \quad (3)$$

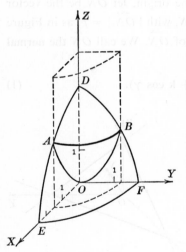

Fig. 316

Then, intersections of the traces of the surfaces in (3) determine points on C. Also, as an aid in visualizing C, it is useful to obtain the equations of one or more of the cylinders which would project C onto the coordinate planes. To find the equation of the cylinder projecting C onto the xy-plane, eliminate z between equations (3), etc. for the cylinders projecting C onto the yz-plane and xz-plane. However, sometimes the elimination just mentioned proves to be impossible or very inconvenient.

ILLUSTRATION 2. In Figure 316, arc AB in the 1st octant is a part of the curve defined by

$$z = 3 - \tfrac{1}{2}x^2 - y^2 \quad and \quad z = x^2 + y^2. \quad (4)$$

In the 1st octant in Figure 316, the paraboloid

$$z = 3 - \tfrac{1}{2}x^2 - y^2$$

is outlined by the arcs DAE, DBF, and EF, and the paraboloid

$$z = x^2 + y^2$$

by ABO. The intersection of the xz-traces is A, and of the yz-traces is B. On eliminating z in (4) by subtraction, we obtain the projecting elliptic cylinder $3x^2 + 4y^2 = 6$, shown by broken lines in Figure 316, which projects C onto the xy-plane. The coordinates of A can be checked by using $y = 0$ in (4) and solving for x and z, which gives $(\sqrt{2}, 0, 2)$. Similarly, B has the coordinates $(0, \tfrac{1}{2}\sqrt{6}, \tfrac{3}{2})$.

EXERCISE 137

By eliminating t between two equations, obtain the equation of a cylinder, perpendicular to the xy-plane, on which the given path C lies. Also, compute points on C by use of its parametric equations and draw an arc of C.

1. $x = 3 \sin t,\ y = 3 \cos t,\ z = 2t$.

2. $x = 2 \cos^2 t,\ y = 2 \sin^2 t,\ z = \sin t$.   3. $x = 3 - t,\ y = t,\ z = t^2$.

Draw an arc of the curve C defined by the equations. If neither of the given surfaces is a cylinder, draw a projecting cylinder for C.

4. $x^2 + y^2 = 9$ and $3z = y$.   5. $x^2 + y^2 = 9$ and $x^2 + z^2 = 9$.

6. $x^2 + y^2 + z^2 = 25$ and $x^2 + y^2 = 16$.

7. $x^2 + y^2 + z^2 = 25$ and $16x^2 + 16y^2 = 9z^2$.

8. $x^2 + y^2 + z^2 = 16$ and $x^2 + y^2 - 4y = 0$.

9. $y = 3 - z^2 - \frac{1}{3}x^2$ and $y = x^2 + \frac{1}{3}z^2$.   10. $z = x^2 + y^2$ and $z - 2x - 2y = 0$.

11. $4x^2 + 9y^2 - 4z^2 = 36$ and $x^2 + z^2 = 9$.

★SUPPLEMENT FOR CHAPTER EIGHTEEN

★174. NORMAL FORM FOR A PLANE

Let τ be any plane. If τ does not go through the origin, let $\overrightarrow{ON}$ be the vector based at $(0, 0, 0)$, normal to τ, and meeting τ at N, with $|\overrightarrow{ON}| = p$, as in Figure 317, and with $(\alpha,\ \beta,\ \gamma)$ as the direction angles of $\overrightarrow{ON}$. We call $\overrightarrow{ON}$ the **normal vector** to τ from the origin. Then,

$$\overrightarrow{ON} = p(\mathbf{i} \cos \alpha + \mathbf{j} \cos \beta + \mathbf{k} \cos \gamma), \tag{1}$$

and N is point $(p \cos \alpha,\ p \cos \beta,\ p \cos \gamma)$.

If τ goes through the origin, let $\overrightarrow{ON}$ be the unit vector normal to τ, where $(\alpha,\ \beta,\ \gamma)$ are the direction angles of $\overrightarrow{ON}$, directed so that $\gamma < 90°$ if $\gamma \neq 90°$; $\beta < 90°$ if $\gamma = 90°$ and $\beta \neq 90°$; $\alpha = 0°$ if $\beta = \gamma = 90°$; in these cases, we define $p = 0$. Then, the following results can be proved by a method of the same type as used with the normal form for a line in an xy-plane:

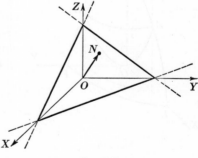

Fig. 317

Plane τ has the following equation, called the **normal form** for τ:

$$x \cos \alpha + y \cos \beta + z \cos \gamma - p = 0. \tag{2}$$

If $P_1{:}(x_1, y_1, z_1)$ is any point, and if the distance, ρ, *from τ to P_1* is taken as the measure of a *directed line segment* where the positive direction is that on $\overrightarrow{ON}$, then

$$\rho = x_1 \cos \alpha + y_1 \cos \beta + z_1 \cos \gamma - p. \tag{3}$$

If τ is the plane $ax + by + cz + d = 0$, where at least one of (a, b, c) is *not zero*, the normal form of τ is obtained on dividing both sides of the equation by $\pm \sqrt{a^2 + b^2 + c^2}$, where the sign $+$ or $-$ is chosen opposite to that of d if $d \neq 0$, etc. (as will be decided by the student in Problem 2 on page 462).

★175. CROSS PRODUCT OF TWO VECTORS

With all vectors based at a common point P, let

$$\mathbf{V}_1 = a_1\mathbf{i} + b_1\mathbf{j} + c_1\mathbf{k} \quad and \quad \mathbf{V}_2 = a_2\mathbf{i} + b_2\mathbf{j} + c_2\mathbf{k}$$

be nonzero vectors, where θ is the angle made by $\mathbf{V}_1$ and $\mathbf{V}_2$, and $0 < \theta < \pi$. Let τ be the plane containing $\mathbf{V}_1$ and $\mathbf{V}_2$. Let $\mathbf{U}_R$ and $\mathbf{U}_L$ be oppositely directed unit vectors perpendicular to τ, where

$$\left\{ \begin{array}{l} \textit{an observer standing at point P, with his head in the direction of } \mathbf{U}_R, \\ \textit{sees } \theta \textit{ as an angle obtained by } \textbf{counterclockwise} \textit{ rotation from } \mathbf{V}_1 \textit{ to } \mathbf{V}_2. \end{array} \right\} \quad (1)$$

In (1), we shall call the observer's side of τ its *right-handed* side; the opposite side of τ will be called its *left-handed* side. Let $\mathbf{V}_3$ be any vector making an angle $\phi < \frac{1}{2}\pi$ with $\mathbf{U}_R$, as in Figure 318, drawn as if the plane τ is horizontal. Then, we shall call the ordered set $(\mathbf{V}_1, \mathbf{V}_2, \mathbf{V}_3)$ a **right-handed triple** of vectors. Similarly, $(\mathbf{V}_1, \mathbf{V}_2, \mathbf{V}_3)$ will be called a **left-handed** triple if $\mathbf{V}_3$ makes an angle $\phi < \frac{1}{2}\pi$ with $\mathbf{U}_L$. It can be verified geometrically that, if $(\mathbf{V}_1, \mathbf{V}_2, \mathbf{V}_3)$ form a right-handed triple, then $(\mathbf{V}_2, \mathbf{V}_3, \mathbf{V}_1)$ and $(\mathbf{V}_3, \mathbf{V}_1, \mathbf{V}_2)$ are right-handed.

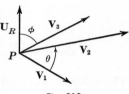

Fig. 318

ILLUSTRATION 1. The simplest right-handed triple is $(\mathbf{i}, \mathbf{j}, \mathbf{k})$, where the student may verify that $(\mathbf{j}, \mathbf{k}, \mathbf{i})$ and $(\mathbf{k}, \mathbf{i}, \mathbf{j})$ also are right-handed, while $(\mathbf{j}, \mathbf{i}, \mathbf{k})$ is left-handed.

Definition I. *Suppose that* $\mathbf{V}_1 \neq \mathbf{O}$, $\mathbf{V}_2 \neq \mathbf{O}$, *and* $\mathbf{V}_1 \neq r\mathbf{V}_2$, *where r is a scalar. Then, the* **cross product,** *or* **vector product,** *of* $\mathbf{V}_1$ *and* $\mathbf{V}_2$, *written* $\mathbf{V}_1 \times \mathbf{V}_2$, *is defined as that vector* $\mathbf{V}_3$, *satisfying the following conditions:*

$$| \mathbf{V_3} | = | \mathbf{V_1} | \cdot | \mathbf{V_2} | \sin \boldsymbol{\theta}; \quad (2)$$

$$\mathbf{V}_3 \textit{ is perpendicular to the plane of } \mathbf{V}_1 \textit{ and } \mathbf{V}_2; \quad (3)$$

$$(\mathbf{V}_1, \mathbf{V}_2, \mathbf{V}_3) \textit{ form a } \textbf{right-handed triple.} \quad (4)$$

ILLUSTRATION 2. From Definition I,

$$\mathbf{i} \times \mathbf{j} = \mathbf{k}; \quad \mathbf{j} \times \mathbf{k} = \mathbf{i}; \quad \mathbf{j} \times \mathbf{i} = -\mathbf{k}.$$

ILLUSTRATION 3. Figure 319 illustrates Definition I, with all vectors based at a point P.

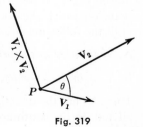

Fig. 319

Note 1. If $\mathbf{V}_1 = \mathbf{O}$ or $\mathbf{V}_2 = \mathbf{O}$, or if $\mathbf{V}_1 \neq \mathbf{O}$, $\mathbf{V}_2 \neq \mathbf{O}$, and $\mathbf{V}_1 = r\mathbf{V}_2$, where r is a scalar, we separately define $\mathbf{V}_1 \times \mathbf{V}_2 = \mathbf{O}$. These cases will be omitted in the following discussion until we mention them again.

From (4) on page 442, direction numbers for $\mathbf{V}_3$, which is perpendicular to both $\mathbf{V}_1$ and $\mathbf{V}_2$, are

$$\begin{vmatrix} b_1 & c_1 \\ b_2 & c_2 \end{vmatrix} : \begin{vmatrix} c_1 & a_1 \\ c_2 & a_2 \end{vmatrix} : \begin{vmatrix} a_1 & b_1 \\ a_2 & b_2 \end{vmatrix} . \tag{5}$$

In (5), name the determinants D_1, D_2, and D_3, respectively. Then, from (5), with $h = \sqrt{D_1^2 + D_2^2 + D_3^2}$, the direction cosines of $\mathbf{V}_3$ are either

$$\left(\lambda = \frac{D_1}{h}, \ \mu = \frac{D_2}{h}, \ \nu = \frac{D_3}{h} \right), \quad or \quad \left(\lambda' = -\frac{D_1}{h}, \ \mu' = -\frac{D_2}{h}, \ \nu' = -\frac{D_3}{h} \right). \tag{6}$$

Theorem VII. *The direction cosines of* $\mathbf{V}_1 \times \mathbf{V}_2$ *are* (λ, μ, ν) *from* (6), *and the magnitude of* $\mathbf{V}_1 \times \mathbf{V}_2$ *is* h, *of* (6), *so that*

$$\mathbf{V}_1 \times \mathbf{V}_2 = h(\lambda \mathbf{i} + \mu \mathbf{j} + \nu \mathbf{k}), \ or \tag{7}$$

(formally)
$$\mathbf{V}_1 \times \mathbf{V}_2 = \begin{vmatrix} \mathbf{i} & \mathbf{j} & \mathbf{k} \\ a_1 & b_1 & c_1 \\ a_2 & b_2 & c_2 \end{vmatrix} . \tag{8}$$

Proof. 1. Let $\mathbf{V}_3 = \mathbf{V}_1 \times \mathbf{V}_2$. From (14) on page 418,

$$\cos^2 \theta = \frac{(a_1 a_2 + b_1 b_2 + c_1 c_2)^2}{(a_1^2 + b_1^2 + c_1^2)(a_2^2 + b_2^2 + c_2^2)}; \tag{9}$$

$$\sin^2 \theta = \frac{(a_1^2 + b_1^2 + c_1^2)(a_2^2 + b_2^2 + c_2^2) - (a_1 a_2 + b_1 b_2 + c_1 c_2)^2}{|\mathbf{V}_1|^2 \cdot |\mathbf{V}_2|^2}. \tag{10}$$

The student may carry out the simple (but somewhat long) algebraic steps to prove that the numerator in (10) is equal to h^2. Since $0 < \theta < \pi$, we have

$$\sin \theta > 0.$$

Hence, from (10) and (2),

$$\sin \theta = \frac{h}{|\mathbf{V}_1| \cdot |\mathbf{V}_2|} \quad and \quad |\mathbf{V}_3| = h.$$

2. From (6), one of the following results is true.

$$\mathbf{V}_3 = \mathbf{V}_1 \times \mathbf{V}_2 = h\lambda \mathbf{i} + h\mu \mathbf{j} + h\nu \mathbf{k} = \mathbf{W}, \ or \tag{11}$$

$$\mathbf{V}_3 = \mathbf{V}_1 \times \mathbf{V}_2 = h\lambda' \mathbf{i} + h\mu' \mathbf{j} + h\nu' \mathbf{k} = \mathbf{W}'. \tag{12}$$

3. Consider each of the triples $(\mathbf{V}_1, \mathbf{V}_2, \mathbf{V}_3)$, $(\mathbf{V}_1, \mathbf{V}_2, \mathbf{W})$ and $(\mathbf{V}_1, \mathbf{V}_2, \mathbf{W}')$ as being rigidly formed, with the vectors attached to each other rigidly at a common base point. Since $(\mathbf{V}_1, \mathbf{V}_2, \mathbf{V}_3)$ is a *right-handed* triple, we accept the fact that it can be moved in xyz-space, with the end point of each vector following a continuous path, on which the coordinates are continuous functions of some parameter s, until the following situation has been reached:

A. $\mathbf{V}_1$ *is based at the origin and has the direction of the x-axis.*

B. $\mathbf{V}_2$ *is in the xy-plane with the end point of* $\mathbf{V}_2$ *to the right of the xz-plane.*

Then, $\mathbf{V}_3$ has the direction of the z-axis, and $\mathbf{V}_3 = h\mathbf{k}$, because $|\mathbf{V}_3|$ has not been altered. In the continuous motion leading to (A) and (B), the scalar components of V_1 and V_2, D_1, D_2, D_3, the direction cosines in (6), W, and W' change continuously, with the final results as follows:

$$a_1 > 0, \quad b_1 = 0, \quad c_1 = 0, \quad b_2 > 0, \quad c_2 = 0, \quad D_1 = D_2 = 0, \quad h^2 = D_3^2,$$

$$D_3 = \begin{vmatrix} a_1 & 0 \\ a_2 & b_2 \end{vmatrix} = a_1 b_2 > 0, \quad \text{and hence} \quad h = D_3;$$

$$(\lambda = 0, \ \mu = 0, \ \nu = 1) \quad \text{and} \quad (\lambda' = 0, \ \mu' = 0, \ \nu' = -1);$$

$$W = h\mathbf{k} \quad \text{and} \quad W' = -h\mathbf{k}. \tag{13}$$

Since $V_3 = h\mathbf{k} = W$ when (A) and (B) are attained, hence $V_3 = W$, as in (11), at the *initial stage*. This proves * (7).

4. We agree that the array in (8) shall be expanded according to minors of the first row, *as if the array were a determinant*. Thus, (8) abbreviates

$$\mathbf{i} \begin{vmatrix} b_1 & c_1 \\ b_2 & c_2 \end{vmatrix} - \mathbf{j} \begin{vmatrix} a_1 & c_1 \\ a_2 & c_2 \end{vmatrix} + \mathbf{k} \begin{vmatrix} a_1 & b_1 \\ a_2 & b_2 \end{vmatrix}, \quad \text{or} \quad D_1\mathbf{i} + D_2\mathbf{j} + D_3\mathbf{k}.$$

This is the right-hand side of (7), because of (6). Hence, (8) is true.

ILLUSTRATION 4. If $V_1 = 2\mathbf{i} - 3\mathbf{j} + 5\mathbf{k}$ and $V_2 = -\mathbf{i} + \mathbf{j} - 2\mathbf{k}$, from (8) we obtain

$$V_1 \times V_2 = \begin{vmatrix} \mathbf{i} & \mathbf{j} & \mathbf{k} \\ 2 & -3 & 5 \\ -1 & 1 & -2 \end{vmatrix} = \mathbf{i} - \mathbf{j} - \mathbf{k}.$$

$$V_2 \times V_1 = \begin{vmatrix} \mathbf{i} & \mathbf{j} & \mathbf{k} \\ -1 & 1 & -2 \\ 2 & -3 & 5 \end{vmatrix} = -\mathbf{i} + \mathbf{j} + \mathbf{k} = -V_1 \times V_2.$$

It is easily verified that, in all cases mentioned in Note 1 on page 457, (8) gives the zero vector. Hence, (8) is true in all cases. Also, (2) is true in all cases.

By use of (8), the following properties of the vector product can be proved. The details are left for the student, as requested in a later problem.

$$V \times V = \mathbf{O}; \quad V \times W = -(W \times V). \tag{14}$$

$$V \times (W + Z) = V \times W + V \times Z. \tag{15}$$

$$(W \times Z) \times V = W \times V + Z \times V. \tag{16}$$

$$V \times (hW) = (hV) \times W = h(V \times W), \quad \text{where } h \text{ is a scalar.} \tag{17}$$

$$\mathbf{i} \times \mathbf{j} = \mathbf{k}; \quad \mathbf{j} \times \mathbf{k} = \mathbf{i}; \quad \mathbf{k} \times \mathbf{i} = \mathbf{j}. \tag{18}$$

$$\mathbf{i} \times \mathbf{i} = \mathbf{j} \times \mathbf{j} = \mathbf{k} \times \mathbf{k} = \mathbf{O}. \tag{19}$$

By use of (17) and the distributive laws in (15) and (16), we may obtain $V_1 \times V_2$ by vector multiplication of the component forms of V_1 and V_2:

$$V_1 \times V_2 = (a_1\mathbf{i} + b_1\mathbf{j} + c_1\mathbf{k}) \times (a_2\mathbf{i} + b_2\mathbf{j} + c_2\mathbf{k})$$
$$= a_1 a_2 \mathbf{i} \times \mathbf{i} + a_1 b_2 \mathbf{i} \times \mathbf{j} + \cdots + c_1 c_2 \mathbf{k} \times \mathbf{k},$$

* For another proof, see pages 47–51 in *Advanced Calculus* by Wilfred Kaplan (Reading, Mass.: Addison-Wesley Publishing Co., Inc., 1952).

which can be verified to produce (8). However, this is not a proof of (8), because (8) is basic in proving (15) and (16).

Note 2. In solid analytic geometry, it is a matter of arbitrary choice to employ a *right-handed* rather than a *left-handed xyz*-system of axes. In this text, right-handed systems have been used partly * in order to create convenience with the vector product. In turn, its definition is dictated by a desire for convenience in various applications of vector products in physical science. Hence, our choice of a right-handed *xyz*-system of coordinates rests largely on a desire to create convenience in the use of parts of solid analytic geometry and vector analysis in fields of application.

★176. SCALAR TRIPLE PRODUCT

Definition II. *The* **scalar triple product** *of the ordered triple of vectors* $(\mathbf{A}, \mathbf{B}, \mathbf{C})$ *is defined as* $\mathbf{A} \cdot (\mathbf{B} \times \mathbf{C})$.

Let $(\mathbf{A}, \mathbf{B}, \mathbf{C})$ and $\mathbf{B} \times \mathbf{C}$ be based at the origin, and let

$$\mathbf{A} = a_1\mathbf{i} + a_2\mathbf{j} + a_3\mathbf{k}; \quad \mathbf{B} = b_1\mathbf{i} + b_2\mathbf{j} + b_3\mathbf{k}; \quad \mathbf{C} = c_1\mathbf{i} + c_2\mathbf{j} + c_3\mathbf{k}. \tag{1}$$

Theorem VIII. *For any vectors* $(\mathbf{A}, \mathbf{B}, \mathbf{C})$, *let* τ *be the parallelepiped having* $(\mathbf{A}, \mathbf{B}, \mathbf{C})$ *as coterminal edges, and let* v *be the volume of* τ.† *Then,*

$$\mathbf{A} \cdot (\mathbf{B} \times \mathbf{C}) = \begin{vmatrix} a_1 & a_2 & a_3 \\ b_1 & b_2 & b_3 \\ c_1 & c_2 & c_3 \end{vmatrix} = \pm v, \tag{2}$$

where the determinant in (2) *is* **positive** *or* **negative,** *and the sign at the right is* "+" *or* "−," *according as* $(\mathbf{A}, \mathbf{B}, \mathbf{C})$ *is a* **right-handed** *or a* **left-handed triple,** *respectively.*

Proof. 1. We assume that $(\mathbf{A}, \mathbf{B}, \mathbf{C})$ are linearly independent. Later, the student will prove the simple fact that $|\mathbf{B} \times \mathbf{C}|$ is equal to *the area of the face, σ, of τ having $\mathbf{B}$ and $\mathbf{C}$ as coterminal edges.* Let $\mathbf{W} = \mathbf{B} \times \mathbf{C}$, and let θ be the angle made by $\mathbf{A}$ and $\mathbf{W}$. Figure 320 exhibits a case where $(\mathbf{A}, \mathbf{B}, \mathbf{C})$ is a *right-handed triple.* In this case $0 < \theta < \frac{1}{2}\pi$ and $\cos \theta > 0$.

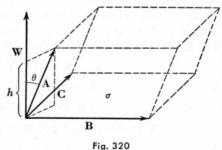

Fig. 320

2. With $0 < \theta < \frac{1}{2}\pi$, we have

$$\mathbf{A} \cdot \mathbf{W} = |\mathbf{A}| \cdot |\mathbf{W}| \cos \theta > 0,$$

where $|\mathbf{A}| \cos \theta$ is the (sc. comp$_\mathbf{W}$ $\mathbf{A}$), or is the altitude, h, of τ, from the face σ to the end point of $\mathbf{A}$, as in Figure 320. Hence,

$$\mathbf{A} \cdot (\mathbf{B} \times \mathbf{C}) = (\textit{altitude of } \tau) \cdot (\textit{area of } \sigma) = v. \tag{3}$$

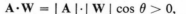

* Another reason will appear in dealing with cylindrical coordinates in space.
† It is understood that τ collapses, and $v = 0$, if and only if $(\mathbf{A}, \mathbf{B}, \mathbf{C})$ are linearly dependent. In such a case, the student may desire to prove that the determinant in (2) has the value 0.

If $(\mathbf{A}, \mathbf{B}, \mathbf{C})$ is a *negative* triple, then $\theta > \frac{1}{2}\pi$, $\cos\theta < 0$, and $|\mathbf{A}|\cos\theta$ is the *negative* of the altitude mentioned in (3). Then, $\mathbf{A}\cdot(\mathbf{B}\times\mathbf{C}) = -v$. Thus, we have proved "$\pm v$" in (2).

3. From (2) on page with 422, the "determinant" expanded,

$$\mathbf{A}\cdot(\mathbf{B}\times\mathbf{C}) = (a_1\mathbf{i} + a_2\mathbf{j} + a_3\mathbf{k})\cdot \begin{vmatrix} \mathbf{i} & \mathbf{j} & \mathbf{k} \\ b_1 & b_2 & b_3 \\ c_1 & c_2 & c_3 \end{vmatrix}$$

$$= a_1 \begin{vmatrix} b_2 & b_3 \\ c_2 & c_3 \end{vmatrix} - a_2 \begin{vmatrix} b_1 & b_3 \\ c_1 & c_3 \end{vmatrix} + a_3 \begin{vmatrix} b_1 & b_2 \\ c_1 & c_2 \end{vmatrix}$$

$$= \begin{vmatrix} a_1 & a_2 & a_3 \\ b_1 & b_2 & b_3 \\ c_1 & c_2 & c_3 \end{vmatrix} = \pm v.$$

Hence, the determinant in (2) is positive or negative according as $+v$ or $-v$ applies in (2), which completes the proof of Theorem VIII.

Note 1. The facts about the value, > 0 or < 0, of the determinant in (2) are very useful apart from (2).

Earlier in this chapter, we used vector algebra in obtaining *scalar equations* for planes and lines. If desired, we may write *vector equations* in place of scalar equations. The details involved will be similar to those met in obtaining scalar equations.

Let τ be any surface, and σ be any curve in space. Let $P:(x, y, z)$ be any point on the surface, or curve. Then, let

$$\mathbf{R} = \overrightarrow{OP} = x\mathbf{i} + y\mathbf{j} + z\mathbf{k}. \tag{4}$$

We shall call $\mathbf{R}$ the **position vector** for the arbitrary point P on the locus. Then, to find a vector equation for τ or σ, we seek to obtain an equation involving $\mathbf{R}$ which characterizes the locus.

ILLUSTRATION 1. Let τ be the plane through $P_0:(x_0, y_0, z_0)$ with $a : b : c$ as direction numbers of the direction normal to τ. Hence, the vector $\mathbf{N} = a\mathbf{i} + b\mathbf{j} + c\mathbf{k}$ is normal to τ. Let $\mathbf{R}_0 = \overrightarrow{OP_0}$. Then, a point $P:(x, y, z)$ is on τ if and only if $\mathbf{R}$, from (4), satisfies

$$(\mathbf{R} - \mathbf{R}_0)\cdot\mathbf{N} = 0, \quad or \quad \mathbf{R}\cdot\mathbf{N} = \mathbf{R}_0\cdot\mathbf{N}. \tag{5}$$

The student should draw a figure and verify (5). Let $d = \mathbf{R}_0\cdot\mathbf{N}$. Then, a vector equation for τ is of the form $\mathbf{R}\cdot\mathbf{N} = d$, with $\mathbf{N} \neq \mathbf{O}$, $\mathbf{R}$ the arbitrary position vector, and $d = \mathbf{N}\cdot\mathbf{R}_0$ where $\mathbf{R}_0$ is a particular position vector for τ. We verify that $\mathbf{R}\cdot\mathbf{N} = d$ is equivalent to $ax + by + cz = d$.

ILLUSTRATION 2. Let l be the line through $P_1:(x_1, y_1, z_1)$ with (α, β, γ) as direction angles for one direction, Ω, on l. Then, with $\mathbf{R}_1 = \overrightarrow{OP_1}$, and $\overline{P_1P} = s$, the student should draw a figure and prove that a vector equation for l, in parametric form, is $\mathbf{R} - \mathbf{R}_1 = s\mathbf{U}$, where $\mathbf{U}$ is the unit vector with the direction Ω. The corresponding scalar equations are (1) on page 443.

★EXERCISE 138

1. Obtain the equation of the plane through the points

$$A:(-1, -2, -1), \quad B:(0, -2, -3), \quad and \quad C:(1, 4, 1).$$

2. Carry out the proofs of the facts mentioned in Section 174 on page 456.

By use of Problem 2, write the normal form of the plane, and find the directed distance from it to the specified point.

3. $2x + 2y - z = 6$; $(-1, 2, 1)$.   **4.** $2x - 6y - 9z = 44$; $(2, 0, -3)$.

Find the distance between the parallel planes. Without drawing a figure decide whether or not the origin is between the planes.

5. $\begin{cases} 3x - 2y - 6z = 28. \\ 3x - 2y - 6z = 20. \end{cases}$ **6.** $\begin{cases} -2x - 9y + 6z = 33. \\ 2x + 9y - 6z = -10. \end{cases}$

7. Find the equations of the planes which bisect the dihedral angles between the planes $x - 2y - 2z = 7$ and $2x - 3y - 6z + 5 = 0$.

8. Prove that, if **A** and **B** are not collinear, then $| \mathbf{A} \times \mathbf{B} |$ is the measure of the area of a certain parallelogram.

9. Let $(\mathbf{V} = 2\mathbf{i} + \mathbf{j} - \mathbf{k}; \quad \mathbf{W} = -3\mathbf{i} + 2\mathbf{j} + \mathbf{k}; \quad \mathbf{Z} = -3\mathbf{i} - 2\mathbf{j} + 4\mathbf{k}).$ Calculate $\mathbf{V} \times \mathbf{W}$ and construct **V**, **W**, and $\mathbf{V} \times \mathbf{W}$ in a figure. Calculate $\mathbf{Z} \cdot (\mathbf{V} \times \mathbf{W})$ and $\mathbf{V} \cdot (\mathbf{W} \times \mathbf{Z})$. Draw associated parallelepipeds.

10. Prove (14)–(17) on page 459.

11. Prove $\mathbf{A} \times (\mathbf{B} \times \mathbf{C}) \neq (\mathbf{A} \times \mathbf{B}) \times \mathbf{C}$ in general, or vector multiplication is *not associative*. Search for a simple counter-example.

12. Prove $\mathbf{A} \cdot (\mathbf{B} \times \mathbf{C}) = (\mathbf{A} \times \mathbf{B}) \cdot \mathbf{C}$, or *dot and cross can be interchanged*. First, give a simple geometrical proof. Second, give an analytical proof.

13. Prove that $\mathbf{A} \times (\mathbf{B} \times \mathbf{C}) = (\mathbf{A} \cdot \mathbf{C})\mathbf{B} - (\mathbf{A} \cdot \mathbf{B})\mathbf{C}$.

Hint. If $\mathbf{V} = a\mathbf{i} + b\mathbf{j} + c\mathbf{k}$, notice that $\mathbf{i} \cdot \mathbf{V} = a$. Prove the identity by calculating a general component of each side; thus, calculate $\mathbf{i} \cdot [\mathbf{A} \times (\mathbf{B} \times \mathbf{C})]$.

14. Prove that $\mathbf{A} \cdot (\mathbf{A} \times \mathbf{B}) = \mathbf{B} \cdot (\mathbf{A} \times \mathbf{B}) = 0$.

15. Carry out the details to prove $\sin \theta = \dfrac{h}{| \mathbf{V}_1 | \cdot | \mathbf{V}_2 |}$ on page 458.

16. *(On parallel projection.)* In Figure 268 on page 406, suppose that $\angle XOY = 135°$. Conceive of all points in the figure as being located physically in the yz-plane, with the actual x-axis directed toward you. Then, our system for plotting points maps $P:(x, y, z)$ of space into $P':(0, y', z')$ in the yz-plane. Let the "*unit*" on OX in Figure 268 be $\frac{1}{2}\sqrt{2}$ times the distance unit used on OY and OZ, and on the actual axis OX in space. Verify that $Q:(2, 0, 0)$ in space is mapped into $S:(0, -1, -1)$ in the yz-plane. Then, prove that any point $P:(x, y, z)$ in space is mapped into $P':(0, y', z')$ in such a way that the lines PP' and QS are parallel. Thus, *a system of parallel lines projects space onto the yz-plane*. (Any sensible arbitrary choice for $\angle XOY$, and for the unit on OX in Figure 268 determines the directions on the family of parallel lines for the system of parallel projection.)

17. In an xyz-system of coordinates, let

$$(\mathbf{i}' = \lambda_1\mathbf{i} + \mu_1\mathbf{j} + \nu_1\mathbf{k}, \quad \mathbf{j}' = \lambda_2\mathbf{i} + \mu_2\mathbf{j} + \nu_2\mathbf{k}, \quad \mathbf{k}' = \lambda_3\mathbf{i} + \mu_3\mathbf{j} + \nu_3\mathbf{k}) \tag{1}$$

be unit vectors which are mutually perpendicular and are based at the origin. Let OX', OY', and OZ' be new coordinate axes through $\mathbf{i}'$, $\mathbf{j}'$, and $\mathbf{k}'$, respectively, where the positive direction on each new axis is that of the corresponding unit vector in (1). Let P be a point with coordinates (x, y, z) and let $\mathbf{R} = \overrightarrow{OP} = x\mathbf{i} + y\mathbf{j} + z\mathbf{k}$. Then P has new coordinates (x', y', z'). With each new coordinate known to be the scalar component of $\mathbf{R}$ along the corresponding coordinate axis, prove that

$$\begin{cases} x' = \lambda_1 x + \mu_1 y + \nu_1 z \\ y' = \lambda_2 x + \mu_2 y + \nu_2 z \\ z' = \lambda_3 x + \mu_3 y + \nu_3 z \end{cases}.$$

Then, let

$$D = \begin{vmatrix} \lambda_1 & \mu_1 & \nu_1 \\ \lambda_2 & \mu_2 & \nu_2 \\ \lambda_3 & \mu_3 & \nu_3 \end{vmatrix}.$$

Prove that $D = +1$ or $D = -1$ according as $(\mathbf{i}', \mathbf{j}', \mathbf{k}')$ form a right-handed or a left-handed triple. Prove that $\sum_{h=1}^{3} \lambda_h^2 = \sum_{h=1}^{3} \mu_h^2 = \sum_{h=1}^{3} \nu_h^2 = 1$. Find the equations expressing (x, y, z) in terms of (x', y', z').

18. Let l_1 and l_2 be nonintersecting and nonparallel lines on unit vectors $\mathbf{U}_1$ and $\mathbf{U}_2$ with direction angles $(\alpha_1, \beta_1, \gamma_1)$ and $(\alpha_2, \beta_2, \gamma_2)$, and through points $P_1:(x_1, y_1, z_1)$ and $P_2:(x_2, y_2, z_2)$, respectively, where common subscripts apply together. Prove that the shortest distance between l_1 and l_2 is equal to the absolute value of

$$\frac{\overrightarrow{P_1 P_2} \cdot (\mathbf{U}_1 \times \mathbf{U}_2)}{|\mathbf{U}_1 \times \mathbf{U}_2|}.$$

Then, use the result to find the shortest distance between the lines

$$l_1 \quad through \quad (1, -2, 5) \quad and \quad (4, -4, -1), \ and$$
$$l_2 \quad through \quad (-4, -5, 3) \quad and \quad (2, 4, 1).$$

19. On a plane τ, let $P_h:(x_h, y_h, z_h)$, $h = 1, 2, 3$, be distinct, noncollinear points. First, prove that an equation for τ is $(\overrightarrow{P_1 P_2} \times \overrightarrow{P_3 P_2}) \cdot \overrightarrow{PP_1} = 0$, where $P:(x, y, z)$ is any point on τ. Then, show that the result can be written in the determinant form

$$\begin{vmatrix} 1 & x & y & z \\ 1 & x_1 & y_1 & z_1 \\ 1 & x_2 & y_2 & z_2 \\ 1 & x_3 & y_3 & z_3 \end{vmatrix} = 0.$$

Solve Problem 1 by use of the vector equation and also by use of the preceding determinant.

CHAPTER NINETEEN

Introduction to Partial Differentiation

177. REGIONS

It will be convenient to use a small part of the standard terminology about sets of points, in a plane or in space. At present, we restrict our remarks to a plane. We define a **circular neighborhood** of a point P to be the set of all points inside a circle having P as the center. Now, let S be any set of points. Then, to state that P is an **interior point** of S means that there is some circular neighborhood of P consisting entirely of points of S. The set, I, of all interior points of S is called its **interior.** To state that S is an **open set** means that each point of S is an interior point. To state that P is a **boundary point** of S means that every circular neighborhood of P contains at least one point *of S* and at least one point *not in S*. The set, B, of all boundary points of S is called its **boundary.** Conveniently, the words *interior* and *boundary*, as applied to sets of points as met in this text, have essentially the meanings which would be expected on a colloquial basis. A *bounded set of points* is a set which lies entirely inside some rectangle.

> ILLUSTRATION 1. The set of points inside a circle is an open set whose boundary is the circle. The whole plane forms an unbounded open set.

Definition I. *In this text, to state that a set of points, R, is a* **region** *will mean that R is not empty, and consists of an open set, possibly together with part of its boundary B. To state that R is a* **closed region** *will mean that R contains all of B.*

> ILLUSTRATION 2. The set, R, consisting of the points inside and on a circle, or any other common closed curve, is a closed region. In Figure 321, the ruled part, including the boundaries B and C, is a closed region.

Definition II. *To state that a region R is* **connected** *will mean that any two points P and Q of R can be joined by a continuous curve, σ, where σ lies in R.*

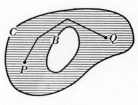

Fig. 321

> ILLUSTRATION 3. The force of Definition II is illustrated in Figure 321.

Hereafter, unless otherwise stated, if we refer to a *region R*, we shall mean a *connected region*. Our references to regions will be on an intuitional basis, where hypotheses about their boundaries will not have an opportunity to become significant. The preceding discussion about regions in a plane can be repeated for regions in space, with no essential alterations except for replacement of the notion of a *circular* neighborhood of a point *P* by a *spherical* neighborhood, consisting of the points inside a sphere with *P* as the center. The terminology extends to space of *n* dimensions where $n > 3$. These extensions will be employed occasionally on an intuitional basis.

Note 1. A *closed region* is a special case of a *closed set, S,* of points, where discussion of *S* involves the notion of a *limit point* of a set. We shall refer to closed sets only where they are closed regions, except in a chapter supplement.

178. LIMITS FOR A FUNCTION OF MORE THAN ONE VARIABLE

If *f* is a function whose domain, *D*, consists of a set of ordered pairs of numbers (x, y), we refer to *f* as a function of the two independent variables (x, y). If we let $z = f(x, y)$, then either *z* or $f(x, y)$ represents the *value* of *f* at (x, y) in *D*, and we may refer to either *z* or $f(x, y)$ as *a function of x and y*. At present, we visualize *D* as a set of points in a plane provided with an *xy*-system of rectangular coordinates.* Sometimes we may refer to "*a function f(x, y)*" as an abbreviation for "*a function f of two variables which will be represented by x and y.*" We define **the graph of a function $f(x, y)$** as *the graph of the equation $z = f(x, y)$*. In the following Definition III, we may think of the domain *D* of *f* as being a *region*,† with (x_0, y_0) possibly not in *D*. If (x_0, y_0) is not in *D*, we assume that (x_0, y_0) is on the boundary of *D*. Any pair (x, y) used as an argument in $f(x, y)$ is in *D*.

Definition III. *To say that* "**the limit of $f(x, y)$ is L as $(x, y) \rightarrow (x_0, y_0)$**" *means that, when $(x, y) \neq (x_0, y_0)$, $|f(x, y) - L|$ is as small as we please at all points (x, y) sufficiently near (x_0, y_0), and then we write*

$$f(x, y) \rightarrow L \quad as \quad (x, y) \rightarrow (x_0, y_0), \ or \tag{1}$$

$$\lim_{(x,\, y) \to (x_0,\, y_0)} f(x, y) = L. \tag{2}$$

Definition III means that, if $(x, y) \neq (x_0, y_0)$, the function value $f(x, y)$ is as close to *L* as we please when (x, y) is sufficiently near (x_0, y_0). When (1) is true, we may say that "*f has the limit L at (x_0, y_0).*"

Definition IV. *To say that a function $f(x, y)$ is* **continuous** *at (x_0, y_0) means that f is defined at (x_0, y_0), $f(x, y)$ has a limit as $(x, y) \rightarrow (x_0, y_0)$, and*

$$\lim_{(x,\, y) \to (x_0,\, y_0)} f(x, y) = f(x_0, y_0), \ or \tag{3}$$

$$\lim_{(\Delta x,\, \Delta y) \to (0,\, 0)} f(x_0 + \Delta x, y_0 + \Delta y) = f(x_0, y_0). \tag{4}$$

* Our essential remarks would remain unaltered if (x, y) were interpreted as polar coordinates.
†The definition remains essentially unaltered if *D* is of a less restricted type.

To state merely that a function $f(x, y)$ is *continuous*, will mean that f is continuous at all points of its domain.

Suppose that the surface in Figure 322 is a graph of $z = f(x, y)$, where $z_0 = f(x_0, y_0)$, and P_0 is the point (x_0, y_0, z_0). Then, (3) states that, as $(x, y) \rightarrow (x_0, y_0)$, the limit of the z-coordinate of P in Figure 322 is z_0.

The notions of a limit and continuity for a function of two variables extend to functions of any number of variables. Thus, we may refer to a function $f(x, y, z, w)$ as being continuous at a point (a, b, c, d). The theorems on page 70 about limits for functions of a single variable extend to limits of functions of any number of variables. Without proof, we accept the fact that any function of two or more variables, which is expressible in terms of the elementary functions of analysis, is continuous at any set of values of the variables where the function is defined.

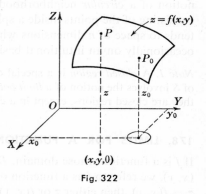

Fig. 322

Definition III involves a condition about x and y simultaneously. It is possible for a function $f(x, y)$ to be such that there exist, separately, $\lim_{x \to x_0} f(x, y_0)$ and $\lim_{y \to y_0} f(x_0, y)$, when (1) is *not true* (see Problem 25 on page 469).

Note 1. By Definition III, equation (2) means that, for every number $\epsilon > 0$ there exists a corresponding number $\delta > 0$ such that

$$\text{if} \quad 0 < \sqrt{(x - x_0)^2 + (y - y_0)^2} < \delta \quad \text{then} \quad |f(x, y) - L| < \epsilon. \tag{5}$$

In (5), the radical is equal to the distance between (x, y) and (x_0, y_0). Figure 322 shows a circular neighborhood of (x_0, y_0) of radius δ defined by the radical condition in (5), in which $|f(x, y) - L| < \epsilon$, where $L = z_0$ in Figure 322. Instead of specifying a circular neighborhood in (5), we could say

"*if* $|x - x_0| < \delta$ *and* $|y - y_0| < \delta$ *and* $(x_0, y_0) \neq (x, y)$."

This would imply that $|f(x, y) - L| < \epsilon$ at all points except possibly (x_0, y_0) inside a sufficiently small *square neighborhood* with center (x_0, y_0) and sides of length 2δ.

Note 2. A continuous function of two or more variables has properties similar to those stated in Theorem II on page 122 for a function of just one variable. Thus, if the function $f(x, y)$ is continuous when (x, y) is in a closed bounded region R, then f is bounded in R, with a least upper bound M and greatest lower bound m. Moreover, there exist points (x_1, y_1) and (x_2, y_2) in R such that $f(x_1, y_1) = m$ and $f(x_2, y_2) = M$; or, f has an absolute minimum m and absolute maximum M in R. Also, if γ is such that $m \leq \gamma \leq M$, then there exists a point (a, b) in R such that $f(a, b) = \gamma$.

179. PARTIAL DERIVATIVES

Consider a function $f(x, y)$. If y is held fast, with $y = y_0$, then $f(x, y)$ becomes a function of x alone, $f(x, y_0)$. If this function has a derivative with respect to x at $x = x_0$, the result is called "*the* **partial derivative** *of f with respect to x at*

(x_0, y_0)," and is denoted by $f_x(x_0, y_0)$, which we sometimes read simply as "f sub x at (x_0, y_0)." Thus, we have defined a function f_x, called the partial derivative of f with respect to x, with the value below at any point (x, y) where the limit exists:

$$f_x(x, y) = \lim_{\Delta x \to 0} \frac{f(x + \Delta x, y) - f(x, y)}{\Delta x}. \tag{1}$$

The numerator in (1) is the increment in $f(x, y)$ due to a change from (x, y) to $(x + \Delta x, y)$ in the (x, y) plane, which is a change parallel to the x-axis. Hence, we may call $f_x(x, y)$ the instantaneous rate of change of $f(x, y)$ in the x-direction at $P:(x, y)$. Similarly, we define the function f_y by describing $f_y(x, y)$ as follows:

$$f_y(x, y) = \lim_{\Delta y \to 0} \frac{f(x, y + \Delta y) - f(x, y)}{\Delta y}. \tag{2}$$

For contrast with partial derivatives, the derivative of a function of a single independent variable may be called an *ordinary derivative*. If we let $z = f(x, y)$, then we may use the following symbols in place of $f_x(x, y)$ and $f_y(x, y)$:

$$\frac{\partial z}{\partial x} = z_x = f_x(x, y); \quad \frac{\partial z}{\partial y} = z_y = f_y(x, y). \tag{3}$$

In (3), we read $\dfrac{\partial z}{\partial x}$ or z_x as "*the partial derivative of z with respect to x,*" etc., for $\dfrac{\partial z}{\partial y}$ or z_y. Or, we may use $\dfrac{\partial f}{\partial x}$ for $f_x(x, y)$ and $\dfrac{\partial f}{\partial y}$ for $f_y(x, y)$, \tag{4}

where we read "$\dfrac{\partial f}{\partial x}$" simply as "*the partial derivative of f with respect to x,*" and understand that "*at (x, y)*" is implied. If we wish to emphasize "*at (x, y),*" we may write, for instance,*

$$\frac{\partial f(x, y)}{\partial x} \quad or \quad \frac{\partial f}{\partial x}\bigg|_{(x, y)}. \tag{5}$$

If u is a function of x and any number of other independent variables, the partial derivative u_x is defined as the *ordinary derivative* of u with respect to x when the other independent variables are *held fast*. Thus, the usual formulas for differentiation apply in obtaining a partial derivative, because it is an ordinary derivative when certain variables are held constant.

ILLUSTRATION 1. If $\quad z = ye^x + \sin(2x + 3y), \quad$ then

$$\frac{\partial z}{\partial x} = ye^x + 2\cos(2x + 3y); \quad \frac{\partial z}{\partial y} = e^x + 3\cos(2x + 3y).$$

ILLUSTRATION 2. If $\quad f(x, y, z) = x^2y + y^2z + xz^2,$

$$f_x(x, y, z) = 2xy + z^2; \quad f_y(x, y, z) = x^2 + 2yz; \quad f_z(x, y, z) = y^2 + 2xz.$$

Then, $\qquad f_x(1, 2, -3) = \dfrac{\partial f}{\partial x}\bigg|_{(1, 2, -3)} = 4 + 9 = 13.$

---

* Established custom approves use of $\dfrac{\partial f}{\partial x}$ either for the *value* of $f_x(x, y)$, or as an optional symbol for the partial derivative *function* f_x, with the context relied on to prevent ambiguity.

For a function $f(x, y)$, in place of $\dfrac{\partial f}{\partial x}$, we may write $\left(\dfrac{\partial f}{\partial x}\right)_y$, which is read
"*the partial derivative of f with respect to x* **when y is held fast.**" This notation has
the advantage of indicating both of the independent variables involved.

In order to consider a certain geometrical interpretation for partial derivatives,

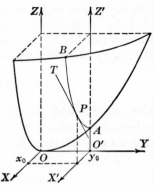

let $P:(x_0, y_0, z_0)$ be on the surface $z = f(x, y)$, in
an *xyz*-system of coordinates. The plane $y = y_0$
intersects the surface in a curve C, lettered APB
in Figure 323, and the *y*-axis at O'. In the plane
$y = y_0$, introduce new axes $O'X'$ and $O'Z'$ with the
directions of OX and OZ, respectively. Draw the
tangent line PT for C at P, and let α be the angle
from the *x'*-axis to PT. In the plane $y = y_0$, or the
x'z'-plane, the equation of C is $z' = f(x', y_0)$, or
$z = f(x, y_0)$, where we drop the primes for convenience. Think of the coordinate x as the abscissa on C.
Then, the slope of PT is $\tan \alpha = z_x$, evaluated at
$(x = x_0, y = y_0)$. Similarly, the value of z_y at P can
be interpreted as a slope.

Fig. 323

EXAMPLE 1. Find the slope of the curve of intersection of the plane $y = 2$ and the
elliptic paraboloid $z = x^2 + \frac{1}{4}y^2$ at the point $P:(1, 2, 2)$.

Solution. We find $z_x = 2x$. The plane $y = 2$ intersects the surface in a curve
whose slope at P is $\tan \alpha$, where

$$slope = \tan \alpha = \frac{\partial z}{\partial x}\Big|_{(x=1,\, y=2)} = 2x\Big|_{(x=1)} = 2.$$

With a proper choice of units, Figure 322 corresponds to the data.

To find a partial derivative of a function $f(x, y)$ means to find the *value* of the
derivative at an arbitrary point (x, y) in the domain of f.

EXERCISE 139

*Find the partial derivative of the dependent variable, u, v, or w, or of the function whose
values are defined, with respect to each of the independent variables x, y, or z which are
involved.*

1. $u = 3x^2y + 4x^3y$.   2. $u = \sin x \cos y$.   3. $w = e^{3x+2y}$.

4. $v = e^{2x} \ln y$.   5. $w = (x^2 + xy)^3$.   6. $u = \sqrt{x^2 + 4y^2}$.

7. $f(x, y) = (3x^2 - 2y)^{\frac{3}{2}}$.   8. $g(x, z) = e^{3x^2z}$.   9. $f(x, y) = \sin 4xy$.

10. $F(x, y) = \text{Arcsin } (2x + 3y)$.   11. $G(x, z) = ze^{-2x} + xe^{-3z}$.

12. $f(x, y) = \text{Arctan } x^2y$.   13. $H(x, y) = \tan (4x - 5y)^2$.

14. $f(x, y) = \dfrac{\sec 3xy}{e^y}$.   15. $g(x, z) = \dfrac{10^{2x}}{4x + 3z}$.

16. $\sin xy + \cos yz + \tan xz$.   17. $e^y \ln x + e^z \ln y$.

18. Find f_ρ and f_θ if $f(\rho, \theta) = \rho^3 \sin \theta + e^\rho \cos \theta$.

19. If $F(x, y) = 3x^2 + 7xy^3$, find $F_x(3, 1)$; $F_y(2, -1)$.

20. If $g(r, \theta) = 4r^2 \sin 2\theta$, find $g_r(-2, \frac{1}{4}\pi)$, $g_\theta(1, \frac{1}{2}\pi)$.

21. If $u = 3xy^2z$, find the rate of change of u in the direction of the y-axis in an xyz-system of coordinates, at $(-2, 1, 3)$.

22. If $u = 4x^2 + 3x\dot{y}$, find the rates of change of u in the x-direction and the y-direction at $(x = -2, y = 3)$ in the xy-plane.

23. The surface $z = x^2 + 4y^2$ is intersected by the plane $x = 2$ in a curve C_1. Find the slope of C_1 at $(2, 1, 8)$. The plane $y = 1$ intersects the surface in a curve C_2. Find the slope of C_2 at $(2, 1, 8)$.

24. The surface $z = x^2 - y^2$ is intersected in curves C_1 and C_2 by planes $x = 3$ and $y = 1$, respectively. Find the slopes of these curves at their point of intersection.

★25. Consider the function $f(x, y) = xy/(x^2 + y^2)$, which is not defined at the point $(x = 0, y = 0)$. (a) Prove that $f(x, 0) \to 0$ as $x \to 0$ and $f(0, y) \to 0$ as $y \to 0$. (b) If m is any number and $y = mx$, show that $f(x, y) \to m/(1 + m^2)$ as $x \to 0$. (c) Does $f(x, y)$ have a limit as $(x, y) \to (0, 0)$? This example is designed to show that $f(x, y)$ may have no limit as $(x, y) \to (x_0, y_0)$ although, separately, there may exist limits of $f(x, y_0)$ as $x \to x_0$, and of $f(x_0, y)$ as $y \to y_0$.

180. PARTIAL DERIVATIVES OF HIGHER ORDERS

Partial derivatives of partial derivatives may be considered. If just two successive partial differentiations are involved, the result is called a partial derivative of the *second order*. Similarly, we introduce partial derivatives of the third and higher orders. If $z = f(x, y)$, notations employed for the values of derivatives of the second order are

$$\frac{\partial^2 z}{\partial x^2} = \frac{\partial}{\partial x}\left(\frac{\partial z}{\partial x}\right) = f_{xx}(x, y) = \frac{\partial^2 f}{\partial x^2}; \quad \frac{\partial^2 z}{\partial y^2} = \frac{\partial}{\partial y}\left(\frac{\partial z}{\partial y}\right) = f_{yy}(x, y) = \frac{\partial^2 f}{\partial y^2}; \quad (1)$$

$$\left. \begin{aligned} z_{yx} &= \frac{\partial^2 z}{\partial x\, \partial y} = \frac{\partial}{\partial x}\left(\frac{\partial z}{\partial y}\right) = f_{yx}(x, y) = \frac{\partial^2 f}{\partial x\, \partial y}; \\ z_{xy} &= \frac{\partial^2 z}{\partial y\, \partial x} = \frac{\partial}{\partial y}\left(\frac{\partial z}{\partial x}\right) = f_{xy}(x, y) = \frac{\partial^2 f}{\partial y\, \partial x}. \end{aligned} \right\} \quad (2)$$

It can be proved that, if all derivatives which enter are continuous functions, the two results in (2) are identical for all values of x and y. That is, *the order of successive partial differentiations is immaterial.* This important result applies to partial derivatives of all orders, and will be taken without proof.* We read $\frac{\partial^2 z}{\partial x^2}$ as "*the second partial derivative of z with respect to x;*" $\frac{\partial^2 f}{\partial x\, \partial y}$, or $\frac{\partial^2 f}{\partial y\, \partial x}$, is "*the second partial derivative of f with respect to x and y,*" where it is immaterial which variable is mentioned first; z_{xyy} is "*the third derivative of z with respect to x once and y twice.*"

---

* For a proof that $f_{xy} = f_{yx}$, under certain conditions, see Note 15 in the Appendix. Observe that an equality statement for two *functions*, such as f_{xy} and f_{yx}, means that their function values are identical at each point of their common domain.

ILLUSTRATION 1. If $z = \tan x \sin y$, then

$$\frac{\partial z}{\partial x} = \sec^2 x \sin y; \quad \frac{\partial z}{\partial y} = \tan x \cos y;$$

$$\frac{\partial^2 z}{\partial x^2} = \frac{\partial}{\partial x}(\sec^2 x \sin y) = 2 \sec^2 x \tan x \sin y = z_{xx};$$

$$\frac{\partial^2 z}{\partial x \partial y} = \frac{\partial}{\partial x}\left(\frac{\partial z}{\partial y}\right) = \frac{\partial}{\partial x}(\tan x \cos y) = \sec^2 x \cos y; \text{ or,}$$

$$\frac{\partial^2 z}{\partial y \partial x} = \frac{\partial}{\partial y}\left(\frac{\partial z}{\partial x}\right) = \sec^2 x \cos y, \text{ as above.}$$

$$\frac{\partial^3 z}{\partial x^2 \partial y} = \frac{\partial}{\partial x}\left(\frac{\partial^2 z}{\partial x \partial y}\right) = \frac{\partial}{\partial x}(\sec^2 x \cos y) = 2 \sec^2 x \tan x \cos y; \text{ or}$$

$$\frac{\partial^3 z}{\partial x^2 \partial y} = \frac{\partial}{\partial y}\left(\frac{\partial^2 z}{\partial x^2}\right) = \frac{\partial}{\partial y}(2 \sec^2 x \tan x \sin y) = 2 \sec^2 x \tan x \cos y.$$

If we let $f(x, y) = \tan x \sin y$ above, then

$$f_{xx}(x, y) = 2 \sec^2 x \tan x \sin y; \quad f_{xy}(x, y) = f_{yx}(x, y) = \sec^2 x \cos y; \qquad (3)$$

$$f_{yy}(x, y) = -\tan x \sin y. \qquad (4)$$

EXERCISE 140

If the independent variables are x, y, and z, find all partial derivatives of the second order for each dependent variable, or for the function whose values are defined.

1. $u = x^3 y^4$.   **2.** $v = e^{x+3y}$.   **3.** $u = \sin x^2 y$.

4. $u = \sin x \cos 2y$.   **5.** $w = e^x \ln y$.   **6.** $v = \text{Arcsin } xy$.

7. $f(x, y) = x^3 + 4x^2 y - y^3$.   **8.** $f(x, y) = (x + 3x^3 y^2)^2$.

9. $g(x, y) = \sqrt{x^2 - y^2}$.   **10.** $f(x, y, z) = x^3 y^2 z^4$.

11. $g(x, y, z) = \cos xyz$.   **12.** $F(x, y, z) = e^x + ye^z + ze^y$.

13. $\text{Arctan } (x/y)$.   **14.** e^{3xyz}.   **15.** $\cos (x + 2y - 3z)$.

Obtain the third partial derivatives of z with respect to x twice and y once, and x once and y twice. That is, obtain z_{xxy} and z_{xyy}.

16. $z = x^2 y^3 + 4xy^4$.   **17.** $z = \sin x^2 y^2$.

Obtain z_{xy} by differentiating in two different orders: first with respect to x, and second with respect to y; then, with the order reversed.

18. $z = \tan x \sec y$.   **19.** $z = e^x \cos y$.

20. If $u = x^3 + x^2 y$, prove that $xu_x + yu_y = 3u$.*

21. If $u = \text{Arcsin } \dfrac{y}{x}$, prove that $x \dfrac{\partial u}{\partial x} + y \dfrac{\partial u}{\partial y} = 0$.*

The partial differential equation $\dfrac{\partial^2 u}{\partial x^2} + \dfrac{\partial^2 u}{\partial y^2} = 0$ (1)

is called **Laplace's equation,** *in two variables, and is important in applied mathematics. Prove that u, as defined, is a function of x and y satisfying* (1).

22. $u = x^3 - 3xy^2$.   **23.** $u = 3x^2 y - y^3$.   **24.** $u = e^x \cos y$.

* The use of u_x and u_y, or $\dfrac{\partial u}{\partial x}$ and $\dfrac{\partial u}{\partial y}$, indicates that x and y are independent variables and u is a function of x and y.

181. PARTIAL DERIVATIVES OF IMPLICIT FUNCTIONS

To state that an equation in three variables (x, y, z),

$$g(x, y, z) = h(x, y, z), \tag{1}$$

"has a solution $z = f(x, y)$" will have the following meaning:

$$\left\{ \begin{array}{l} \textit{There is a particular solution } (x_0, y_0, z_0) \textit{ of } (1) \textit{ with} \\ z_0 = f(x_0, y_0), \textit{ and a region } D, \textit{ of points } (x, y), \textit{ where} \\ D \textit{ includes } (x_0, y_0), \textit{ such that, for all } (x, y) \textit{ in } D, f \textit{ is con-} \\ \textit{tinuous and } (x, y, z) \textit{ is a solution of } (1) \textit{ when } z = f(x, y). \end{array} \right\} \tag{2}$$

Then, we shall call f a *solution function* of (1) for z as a function of x and y. Suppose, now, that (1) has at least one solution $z = f(x, y)$. If (1) itself is equivalent to the form $z = f(x, y)$, we say that (1) defines z *explicitly* as a function of x and y. Otherwise, we say that (1) defines z *implicitly* as a function of x and y, or defines z as an *implicit function* of x and y. In this discussion, we have earmarked z as a dependent variable and (x, y) as the independent variables. The roles could be altered, with x or y as a dependent variable and the other variables as independent. In the case of an equation relating n variables, as a rule any $(n - 1)$ of them can play the role of *independent variables*, with the privilege of assuming sets of values relatively arbitrarily as the basis for obtaining corresponding values of the single remaining variable. That is, with a single equation, usually just *one* variable at a time can play the role of a *dependent variable*.

ILLUSTRATION 1. If $x^2 + y^2 + z^2 = 25$, then we have the solutions

$$z = \sqrt{25 - x^2 - y^2} \quad and \quad z = -\sqrt{25 - x^2 - y^2}. \tag{3}$$

The graph of the equation at the left in (3) is the *upper* hemisphere, and of the equation at the right is the *lower* hemisphere, of the sphere which is the graph of the given equation.

In addition to (2), we now assume that, if $z = f(x, y)$ is a solution of (1), then the partial derivatives z_x and z_y exist, with a similar assumption if any other variable is designated as dependent. To find the partial derivatives, we use the method of Section 33 on page 101.

EXAMPLE 1. Find z_x at $(x = 2, y = -1, z = 3)$, if (x, y, z) are related by

$$x^3 + 2xz - 2yz^2 - z^3 = 11. \tag{4}$$

Solution. 1. The notation z_x specifies that x is an independent variable, and z is a dependent variable. Hence, y also is an independent variable, and z is considered as a function of x and y. Thus, z_x means the derivative of z with respect to x, *with y held fast*.

2. With y held fast in (4), differentiate both sides with respect to x:

$$3x^2 + 2z + 2x \frac{\partial z}{\partial x} - 4yz \frac{\partial z}{\partial x} - 3z^2 \frac{\partial z}{\partial x} = 0; \quad \frac{\partial z}{\partial x} (4yz + 3z^2 - 2x) = 3x^2 + 2z;$$

$$\frac{\partial z}{\partial x} = \frac{3x^2 + 2z}{4yz + 3z^2 - 2x}; \quad \frac{\partial z}{\partial x} \bigg|_{(2, -1, 3)} = \frac{18}{11}.$$

EXAMPLE 2. Find u_z if the variables u, x, and z satisfy

$$\tan (x^2 + 3u) + \tan (3z + u^2) = 5. \tag{5}$$

Solution. The problem specifies u as a dependent variable which is to be considered as a function of x and z in (5). *With x held fast*, differentiate with respect to z on both sides of (5):

$$\sec^2 (x^2 + 3u) \frac{\partial(x^2 + 3u)}{\partial z} + \sec^2 (3z + u^2) \frac{\partial(3z + u^2)}{\partial z} = 0, \; or$$

$$3[\sec^2 (x^2 + 3u)] \frac{\partial u}{\partial z} + [\sec^2 (3z + u^2)] \left(3 + 2u \frac{\partial u}{\partial z} \right) = 0, \; or$$

$$\frac{\partial u}{\partial z} = \frac{- 3 \sec^2 (3z + u^2)}{2u \sec^2 (3z + u^2) + 3 \sec^2 (x^2 + 3u)}.$$

EXERCISE 141

Find $\dfrac{\partial z}{\partial x}$ and $\dfrac{\partial z}{\partial y}$, and evaluate the derivatives at any given point.

1. $x^2 + 4y^2 + z^2 = 8$.

2. $x^3 + y^3 + z^3 = 6$.

3. $e^x + e^y + e^z = 5$.

4. $\ln x + \ln y - \ln z = e^x$.

5. $x^2 + 4y^2 - z^2 = 4$, at $(- 3, 1, 3)$.

6. $z^3 - 2xz + y^2 = 6$, at $(2, 3, 1)$.

7. $z^2 - xz^3 + 10yz = - 78$, at $(1, - 2, 3)$.

8. $(x + 2z)^7 + (3y - z^2)^5 = 2$.

9. $x^{\frac{2}{3}} + y^{\frac{2}{3}} + z^{\frac{2}{3}} = a^{\frac{2}{3}}$.

10. $\sin x + \cos y = \tan z$.

11. $\ln x - e^z = xy^2$.

12. $\sqrt{x^2 + z^2} + \sqrt{y^2 - z^2} = 5$.

13. $\sin x \cos z + \cos y \sin z = z$.

14. $e^{2x+3z} + e^{2x-4y} = 6$.

15. $xe^{z^2+x} - ye^{2z-y} = 3$.

16. $\sin (x + 2z) + \cos (3y + 4z) = 1$.

17. $\ln (2x + z) + e^{y-3z} = 4$.

18. $\ln (4x - z^2) = \tan (x + y + 3z)$.

19. $2 \tan (2x - z^2) = 1 + \cot (y^2 - 2z)$.

20. $\dfrac{x + 3z}{y^2 + z^2} = e^{4z}$.

21. $\dfrac{e^x - e^{2z}}{e^y + e^z} = 2x + 5yz$.

22. If $x^2 + y^2 + z^2 = 25$, find z_{xx} and z_{xy}.

23. Find z_{xy} at $(- 3, 1, 3)$ in Problem 5.

182. IMPLICIT FUNCTIONS DEFINED BY A SYSTEM OF EQUATIONS

Without detailed remarks, we extend the terminology of Section 181 to the case where a system of n equations in *more than* n variables is involved. As a rule, such a system defines any n of the variables, considered *dependent*, as functions of the other variables, considered as *independent*. Sometimes, certain choices for the n dependent variables will not be permissible. Under conditions as met in this text, any function thus defined implicitly by a system of equations will be continuous in a certain part of the domain of the independent variables jointly. Also, the dependent variables will possess partial derivatives of all orders which will be mentioned, except perhaps in parts of the domain of the independent variables.

Suppose, now, that the equations of a system are written in terms of elementary functions, without use of any general functional notation.* Then, the partial derivatives of the dependent variables can be obtained by an elementary method similar to that employed in the preceding section.

Note 1. In starting a solution of any problem of the type now in view, the student should commit himself definitely, by an explicit statement, in regard to the choice of variables to be considered *independent* and those to be *dependent*.

EXAMPLE 1. Find du/dx and dv/dx if (x, u, v) satisfy

$$\left.\begin{aligned} 3x^2 + 2u^2v &= 5, \text{ and} \\ ux + uv^2 &= 2. \end{aligned}\right\} \tag{1}$$

Solution. 1. The request specifies x as the sole independent variable, and (u, v) as dependent variables. Differentiate with respect to x in each equation, recognizing that u and v are functions of x alone:

$$\left.\begin{aligned} 6x + 4uv \frac{du}{dx} + 2u^2 \frac{dv}{dx} &= 0, \text{ and} \\ u + x \frac{du}{dx} + v^2 \frac{du}{dx} + 2uv \frac{dv}{dx} &= 0. \end{aligned}\right\} \tag{2}$$

Thus,

$$\left.\begin{aligned} 4uv \frac{du}{dx} + 2u^2 \frac{dv}{dx} &= -6x, \text{ and} \\ (x + v^2) \frac{du}{dx} + 2uv \frac{dv}{dx} &= -u \end{aligned}\right\} \tag{3}$$

2. Solve (3) for du/dx and dv/dx by use of determinants:

$$\frac{du}{dx} = \frac{\begin{vmatrix} -6x & 2u^2 \\ -u & 2uv \end{vmatrix}}{\begin{vmatrix} 4uv & 2u^2 \\ (x + v^2) & 2uv \end{vmatrix}} = \frac{2u^3 - 12uvx}{6u^2v^2 - 2u^2x} = \frac{u^2 - 6vx}{3uv^2 - ux}; \tag{4}$$

$$\frac{dv}{dx} = \frac{\begin{vmatrix} 4uv & -6x \\ (x + v^2) & -u \end{vmatrix}}{6u^2v^2 - 2u^2x} = \frac{3x^2 + 3v^2x - 2u^2v}{3u^2v^2 - u^2x}.$$

EXAMPLE 2. Find $\dfrac{\partial u}{\partial x}$ and $\dfrac{\partial v}{\partial x}$ if

$$\left\{\begin{aligned} u^3 + v - 2x &= 0, \text{ and} \\ v^3 + u - y &= 0. \end{aligned}\right\} \tag{5}$$

Solution. 1. The requested derivatives order us to select x as an independent variable with (u, v) as dependent variables. Hence, y also is an independent variable, because the two equations can determine only two dependent variables as functions of independent variables. Thus, we consider (5) as defining u and v as functions of x and y.

* If any equation is written in general functional notation, such as $f(x, y, u) = 0$, general theorems (to be met in Chapter Twenty-five) on partial differentiation are required to obtain results corresponding to the special cases which will be treated at present.

2. Hold y fast (that is, temporarily consider y to be a constant) and differentiate with respect to x on both sides in each equation in (5):

$$\left.\begin{array}{r}3u^2\,\dfrac{\partial u}{\partial x} + \dfrac{\partial v}{\partial x} = 2,\ and \\[2mm] \dfrac{\partial u}{\partial x} + 3v^2\,\dfrac{\partial v}{\partial x} = 0.\end{array}\right\} \tag{6}$$

On solving for the derivatives in (6) by use of determinants, we obtain

$$\left(\frac{\partial u}{\partial x}\right)_y = \frac{6v^2}{9u^2v^2 - 1}, \quad and \quad \left(\frac{\partial v}{\partial x}\right)_y = \frac{2}{1 - 9u^2v^2}. \tag{7}$$

EXAMPLE 3. In (5), find u_x if v is an independent variable.

Solution. The problem specifies (x, v) as the independent variables, and hence (u, y) as the dependent variables. Thus, with v held fast, we differentiate with respect to x in the first equation of (5) and obtain

$$3u^2\,\frac{\partial u}{\partial x} = 2, \quad or \quad \left(\frac{\partial u}{\partial x}\right)_v = \frac{2}{3u^2}. \tag{8}$$

Comment. In (8), we found u_x with v held fast. In (7), y was held fast. Thus, *the symbol for a partial derivative may have different meanings, depending on the choice of independent variables.*

EXAMPLE 4. Find x_u in (5) if v is an independent variable.

Solution. The independent variables are (u, v) and the dependent variables are (x, y). From the first equation in (5), $x = \frac{1}{2}u^3 + \frac{1}{2}v$. Hence,

$$\left(\frac{\partial x}{\partial u}\right)_v = \frac{3}{2}\,u^2. \tag{9}$$

In (9), $\dfrac{\partial x}{\partial u}$ is *not the reciprocal of* $\dfrac{\partial u}{\partial x}$ in (7), but *is the reciprocal of* $\dfrac{\partial u}{\partial x}$ in (8), which happens because the second independent variable involved is the same in (8) and (9). *This shows the futility of trying to attach separate meanings to the symbols "∂u" and "∂x" which would apply in all situations and would make* $\dfrac{\partial u}{\partial x}$ a true *quotient.* Hence, a partial derivative $\dfrac{\partial u}{\partial x}$ *always should be treated as a whole* and *never should be read like a quotient.*

EXERCISE 142

Find dy/dx and dz/dx if (x, y, z) are related by the equations.

1. $\begin{cases} 3x + 2y + 3z = 4,\ and \\ 2x - 3y + 5z = 2. \end{cases}$ 2. $\begin{cases} 6x - 3y + z = 4,\ and \\ 2x + 2y - z = 3. \end{cases}$

3. $\begin{cases} x^2 + y^2 - 2z^2 = 1,\ and \\ 3x + 2y - z = 5. \end{cases}$ 4. $\begin{cases} xy + yz + xz = 4,\ and \\ 2x + 3y - 2z = 1. \end{cases}$

5. $\begin{cases} y^2 + xz = 3x,\ and \\ z^2 - xy = x^2. \end{cases}$ 6. $\begin{cases} xy^2 - 3z = 4,\ and \\ xz^2 - yz = 3. \end{cases}$

Find the derivatives of u and v with respect to x and y, if (x, y, u, v) are related by the equations.

7. $\begin{cases} 2x + y - 3u - 5v = 2, \text{ and} \\ x - y + 2u + 3v = 1. \end{cases}$

8. $\begin{cases} 3x - y - u - v = 4, \text{ and} \\ 2x + 3y - u + 4v = 7. \end{cases}$

9. $\begin{cases} u^2 + v^2 - x = 0, \text{ and} \\ v^2 + u - y = 0. \end{cases}$

10. $\begin{cases} x = u^2 + v^2, \text{ and} \\ y = 3uv. \end{cases}$

11. $\begin{cases} ux + v^2 y = 1, \text{ and} \\ u^2 x - vy = 4. \end{cases}$

12. $\begin{cases} 3u^3 + ux + vy = 5, \text{ and} \\ v^3 + uy - vx = 1. \end{cases}$

13. $\begin{cases} x = u \cos v, \text{ and} \\ y = u \sin v. \end{cases}$

14. $\begin{cases} \sin ux + \cos vy = x, \text{ and} \\ \sin vx + \cos uy = y. \end{cases}$

15–18. Obtain $\dfrac{\partial x}{\partial u}$ and $\dfrac{\partial y}{\partial v}$ in Problems 7–10; compare with previous results.

19. Find $\dfrac{dy}{dx}$ if $\begin{cases} \sin x + y^2 - 3z = 0, \text{ and} \\ \cos x + z^2 - 2y = 0. \end{cases}$

20. Find $\left(\dfrac{\partial u}{\partial x}\right)_y$ if $\begin{cases} u^2 - v + 3x - y^2 = 4, \text{ and} \\ v^2 - u + 2y + x^2 = 1. \end{cases}$

21. In Problem 20, find $\dfrac{\partial u}{\partial x}$ with a different meaning for the symbol.

22. Find $\left(\dfrac{\partial u}{\partial x}\right)_y$ if $\begin{cases} 3 \sin (x + 2v) + \cos (y + 3u) = 1, \text{ and} \\ 2 \cos (2x - u) - \cos (y + 2v) = 1. \end{cases}$

183. TOTAL DIFFERENTIALS

Consider $u = f(x, y)$, where f_x and f_y are continuous functions. At a given point $(x = x_1, y = y_1)$, with Δx and Δy as arbitrary increments for x and y, let

$$\Delta u = f(x_1 + \Delta x, y_1 + \Delta y) - f(x_1, y_1). \tag{1}$$

Then, on page 583, it will be proved that there exist variables ϵ_1 and ϵ_2, which are functions of the variables Δx and Δy, such that

$$\Delta u = \frac{\partial u}{\partial x} \Delta x + \frac{\partial u}{\partial y} \Delta y + \epsilon_1 \Delta x + \epsilon_2 \Delta y, \tag{2}$$

where derivatives are evaluated at (x_1, y_1) and

$$\epsilon_1 \to 0 \text{ and } \epsilon_2 \to 0 \text{ as } (\Delta x, \Delta y) \to (0, 0). \tag{3}$$

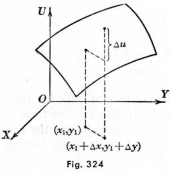

Fig. 324

In (1), Δu is the increment in the ordinate on the graph of $u = f(x, y)$, due to a change from $(x = x_1, y = y_1)$ to $(x = x_1 + \Delta x, y = y_1 + \Delta y)$, as in Figure 324. Then, from (2), it is seen that $\Delta u \to 0$ as $(\Delta x, \Delta y) \to (0, 0)$, so that u is a continuous function of x and y when (2) is true.

In (2), if Δx and Δy are sufficiently small, each of the terms $\epsilon_1 \Delta x$ and $\epsilon_2 \Delta y$ is a product of *two* small numbers, and is *small in comparison with* Δx and Δy. Hence, in general, when Δx and Δy are sufficiently small, the first two terms on the right in (2) form the *dominant part* of Δu, and should give a good approximation to Δu.* The preceding remarks motivate the following terminology.

Definition V. *Suppose that* $u = f(x, y)$, *where* f *has continuous partial derivatives* f_x *and* f_y. *Then, the* **total differential,** du [*or,* $df(x, y)$], *of* u *at any point* (x, y) *in the domain* † *of* f *corresponding to increments* Δx *and* Δy, *is defined by*

$$du = \frac{\partial u}{\partial x} \Delta x + \frac{\partial u}{\partial y} \Delta y. \tag{4}$$

We define the differentials dx and dy of the independent variables to be their increments, or $dx = \Delta x$ and $dy = \Delta y$. Then, (4) becomes

$$du = \frac{\partial u}{\partial x} dx + \frac{\partial u}{\partial y} dy, \text{ or} \tag{5}$$

$$[u = f(x, y)] \qquad du = f_x(x, y)dx + f_y(x, y)dy = df(x, y). \tag{6}$$

Similarly, if $u = f(x, y, z)$, the total differential du is

$$du = \frac{\partial u}{\partial x} dx + \frac{\partial u}{\partial y} dy + \frac{\partial u}{\partial z} dz, \tag{7}$$

etc., for functions of more than three independent variables.

ILLUSTRATION 1. If $u = 3x^2y^3$, then

$$\frac{\partial u}{\partial x} = 6xy^3; \quad \frac{\partial u}{\partial y} = 9x^2y^2; \quad du = 6xy^3\, dx + 9x^2y^2\, dy.$$

At $(x = 2, y = -1)$, when $dx = .1$ and $dy = -.2$,

$$du = -12(.1) + 36(-.2) = -8.4.$$

EXAMPLE 1. If $u = xy$, find Δu and du if $x = 3$, $y = 4$, $dx = .2$, $dy = .3$.

Solution. 1. $x + dx = 3.2$; $y + dy = 4.3$. Hence,

$$\Delta u = (x + dx)(y + dy) - xy = 3.2(4.3) - 3 \cdot 4 = 1.76.$$

2. From (5) with $u = xy$,

$$\frac{\partial u}{\partial x} = y; \quad \frac{\partial u}{\partial y} = x; \quad du = y\, dx + x\, dy.$$

Hence, we obtain $\qquad\qquad du = 4(.2) + 3(.3) = 1.7.$

Thus, the error of du as an approximation to Δu is $-.06$.

The standard forms for differentials on page 252 were proved only for functions of a single variable. Fortunately, these forms apply also for functions of more than one independent variable. We shall prove the formulas for the case where there are just two independent variables. Similar proofs apply for any number of independent variables.

---

* For the corresponding analytic statement, see Problem 24 on page 593.

† Implicitly, we imply that the point $(x + \Delta x, y + \Delta y)$ is in some circular neighborhood of (x, y) contained in the domain of f.

Note 1. Let $w = uv$, where u and v are independent variables. Then, from (5),

$$dw = \frac{\partial w}{\partial u}\,du + \frac{\partial w}{\partial v}\,dv = v\,du + u\,dv, \text{ or}$$

$$d(uv) = v\,du + u\,dv. \tag{8}$$

The force of the next example is that (8) is true *even when u and v are not the independent variables.*

EXAMPLE 2. Suppose that u and v are **differentiable** * functions of the independent variables x and y. Prove that the differential of uv with respect to x and y is given by (8), where du and dv now represent differentials with respect to x and y.

Proof. Let $w = uv$. Then, by the formula for differentiating a product,

$$\frac{\partial w}{\partial x} = v\frac{\partial u}{\partial x} + u\frac{\partial v}{\partial x}; \quad \frac{\partial w}{\partial y} = v\frac{\partial u}{\partial y} + u\frac{\partial v}{\partial y}. \tag{9}$$

Hence, by (5),
$$dw = \left(v\frac{\partial u}{\partial x} + u\frac{\partial v}{\partial x}\right)dx + \left(v\frac{\partial u}{\partial y} + u\frac{\partial v}{\partial y}\right)dy$$

$$= v\left(\frac{\partial u}{\partial x}\,dx + \frac{\partial u}{\partial y}\,dy\right) + u\left(\frac{\partial v}{\partial x}\,dx + \frac{\partial v}{\partial y}\,dy\right), \tag{10}$$

where we have du and dv in parentheses, by (5). Hence, $d(uv) = v\,du + u\,dv$.

Similarly, as in Example 2, the student will prove (IV)$_d$ and (VI)$_d$ of page 252 in the next exercise. On page 252, it was mentioned that all of the fundamental forms for differentials in the Summary on page 252 could be obtained as special cases of (VII)$_d$, which may be written

$$d\phi(u) = \phi'(u)du, \tag{11}$$

where u was assumed to be a function of just one independent variable. We proceed to prove (11) when u is a function of any number of independent variables (two for illustration). Then, it will follow that, by use of (11), all of the fundamental forms for differentials of functions of u on page 252 remain valid when u is a function of *any number of independent variables.*

Theorem I. *Let u be a differentiable function of x and y, and assume that the function $\phi(u)$ has a continuous derivative ϕ'. Then, if $w = \phi(u)$, the total differential, dw, of w with respect to x and y is given by $dw = \phi'(u)du$, where du is the total differential of u with respect to x and y as the independent variables.*

Proof. By (VII), page 98, for the derivative of a composite function,

$$\frac{\partial w}{\partial x} = \phi'(u)\frac{\partial u}{\partial x} \quad and \quad \frac{\partial w}{\partial y} = \phi'(u)\frac{\partial u}{\partial y}.$$

Hence,
$$dw = \frac{\partial w}{\partial x}\,dx + \frac{\partial w}{\partial y}\,dy = \phi'(u)\frac{\partial u}{\partial x}\,dx + \phi'(u)\frac{\partial u}{\partial y}\,dy$$

$$= \phi'(u)\left(\frac{\partial u}{\partial x}\,dx + \frac{\partial u}{\partial y}\,dy\right), \quad or \quad dw = \phi'(u)du.$$

---

* Meaning, hereafter in this text, that 1st partial derivatives with respect to the independent variables exist and are continuous.

ILLUSTRATION 2. From (8) with $u = x^2$ and $v = y$,

$$d(x^2y) = y\, d(x^2) + x^2\, dy = 2xy\, dx + x^2\, dy.$$

ILLUSTRATION 3. Since $de^u = e^u\, du$, $de^{3x-4z} = e^{3x-4z}\, d(3x - 4z) = e^{3x-4z}(3\, dx - 4\, dz)$.

ILLUSTRATION 4. From (VI)$_d$ and (XV)$_d$ on page 252, with $u = y/x$ and $x > 0$,

$$d \operatorname{Arcsin}\left(\frac{y}{x}\right) = \frac{1}{\sqrt{1 - \left(\frac{y}{x}\right)^2}}\, d\left(\frac{y}{x}\right)$$

$$= \frac{x}{\sqrt{x^2 - y^2}} \cdot \frac{x\, dy - y\, dx}{x^2} = \frac{x\, dy - y\, dx}{x\sqrt{x^2 - y^2}}. \quad (\text{Using } \sqrt{x^2} = x.)$$

EXERCISE 143

The independent variables are (x, y, z). *Find the total differential of u or v, first by use of the definition in* (5) *on page 476; second, by use of formulas from page 252.*

1. $u = 5x^3 + 3x^2y^3$.   2. $u = 2x + 4x^2y^2 - y^4$.

3. $v = \sin x \cos y$.   4. $v = x^3 - xy^2 - xz^3$.

5. $u = (\ln x)(\ln y) \ln z$.   6. $v = e^{2x+3y-4z}$.

By Theorem I *and page 252, find the total differential of the function of* (x, y) *or* (x, y, z).

7. $x^2(y^4 + 3x)$.   8. $\sin^3 (2x + 5y)$.   9. $e^{4x^2+y^2}$.

10. $\ln (3y - x^2)$.   11. $(x^2 + 3y + z^2)^4$.   12. $\tan^2 (2x - y^2)$.

13. $\sqrt{x^2 + y^2 + z^2}$.   14. $y^2 \sin (z + y^3)$.   15. xz^2e^y.

16. $\dfrac{x^2 + 2y}{z^3}$.   17. $\dfrac{\sin 2x}{1 + \cos y}$.   18. $\dfrac{e^{xz}}{(y^2 + z)^2}$.

19. $\ln \sqrt[3]{x^2 + y^2}$.   20. $\operatorname{Arcsin} xyz$.   21. $\operatorname{Arctan} xy^{-1}$.

22. If $u = 4xy^2$, compute du and Δu when $x = 3$, $y = -2$, and the increments for x and y are $dx = .2$ and $dy = -.1$.

If C is a constant, and u and v are differentiable functions of x and y, prove the result.

23. $d(u + v) = du + dv$.   24. $dC = 0$.   25. Formula (VI)$_d$, page 252.

184. TOTAL DIFFERENTIALS AS APPROXIMATIONS

Consider $u = f(x, y)$ where f_x and f_y exist and are continuous. Then, if dx and dy are arbitrary increments,

$$\Delta u = f(x + dx, y + dy) - f(x, y); \quad du = f_x(x, y)\, dx + f_y(x, y)\, dy. \quad (1)$$

If dx and dy are interpreted as *errors in data*, the corresponding error in u is Δu, and the relative error is $(\Delta u)/u$. If dx and dy are small enough, we shall consider du as an approximation to Δu. Then,

(*approximately*)   **(error in u)** $= du$;   (2)

(*approximately*)   **(relative error in u)** $= \dfrac{du}{u} = d \ln u$,   (3)

where we noticed that $d \ln u = \dfrac{d \ln u}{du}\, du = \dfrac{1}{u}\, du.$

We recall that the *relative error* in (3), when expressed as a decimal, may be referred to as the *percent of error.*

Note 1. In problems where (2) and (3) are used, we may omit stating *"approximately"* in corresponding results, as in (6) and (7) in the solution of the following Example 1.

EXAMPLE 1. The period T, in seconds, of a simple pendulum, having small oscillations, is taken as $T = 2\pi\sqrt{l/g}$, where l is the length in feet, and g is the acceleration of gravity in feet per second per second. In a certain case, measurement gives $l = 10$ and $g = 32$, with maximum possible errors of .2 in l and .1 in g. Find approximately the maximum possible absolute values for the error and percent of error in T.

Solution. 1. With l and g considered as variables,

$$dT = 2\pi \cdot \frac{1}{2}\sqrt{\frac{g}{l}} \cdot \frac{g\,dl - l\,dg}{g^2} = \frac{\pi(g\,dl - l\,dg)}{\sqrt{l}\sqrt{g^3}}; \tag{4}$$

$$\ln T = \ln 2\pi + \tfrac{1}{2}\ln l - \tfrac{1}{2}\ln g; \qquad \frac{dT}{T} = d\ln T = \frac{1}{2}\left(\frac{dl}{l} - \frac{dg}{g}\right). \tag{5}$$

2. The maximum absolute values of dT and dT/T occur when dl and dg have *opposite signs*, so that no cancellation occurs in (4) and in dT/T. Hence, we use $l = 10$, $g = 32$, $dl = .2$, and $dg = -.1$ in (4) and (5):

$$(max.\,|\,error\,|) = (max.\,|\,dT\,|) = \pi\frac{(6.4 + 1.0)}{\sqrt{10}\sqrt{32^3}} = .0406 \text{ sec.}; \tag{6}$$

$$(max.\,|\,rel.\,error\,|) = \left(max.\,\left|\frac{dT}{T}\right|\right) = \frac{1}{2}\left(\frac{.2}{10} + \frac{.1}{32}\right) = .012 = 1.2\%. \tag{7}$$

EXAMPLE 2. In Example 1, suppose that l and g are measured with errors of at most $1\tfrac{1}{2}\%$ and $\tfrac{1}{4}\%$, respectively. Find approximately the largest possible percent of error in the computed value of T.

Solution. From (3), $\qquad \begin{pmatrix} relative\ error \\ in\ T \end{pmatrix} = d\ln T = \frac{1}{2}\left(\frac{dl}{l} - \frac{dg}{g}\right). \tag{8}$

In (8), dl/l and dg/g are the relative errors in l and g due to errors dl and dg, respectively. The maximum possible absolute value of $d\ln T$ occurs if $.015 = dl/l$ and $-.0025 = dg/g$, or $(max.\,|\,d\ln T\,|) = \tfrac{1}{2}(.015 + .0025) = \tfrac{7}{8}\%.$

EXERCISE 144

Solve by use of a differential approximation. Perhaps use logarithms in computing. In the problems, "maximum error" will mean "maximum absolute value of the error."

1. The altitude of a right circular cylinder is $20''$ and its base has the radius $5''$. Find approximately the change in the volume of the cylinder if each of these dimensions is increased (*a*) by $.2''$; (*b*) by 3%.

2. The inner dimensions of a rectangular box are $10'' \times 20'' \times 5''$. The walls of the box are $.3''$ thick. Find approximately the weight of the box, if its walls weigh 6 ounces per cubic inch.

3. The radius of the base of a right circular cone was measured as 50″ and its altitude as 20″, subject to a possible error of as much as .2″ in each case. Find approximately the maximum possible error and percent of error in the computed volume of the cone.

4. For a simple pendulum, find approximately the maximum possible percent of error in the period if l and g are measured with errors possibly as large as 2% and 3%, respectively.

5. In a right triangle, we measure one acute angle as 30°, and the hypotenuse as 40″, with errors possibly as large as .5° in the angle and .3″ in the side. Find approximately the maximum possible errors in the corresponding computed legs of the triangle. Remember that any increment of an angle must be expressed in radian measure.

6. In a right triangle, we measure the two legs as 50″ and 120″, respectively, with an error possibly as large as .5″ in each case. Find approximately the interval on which the true length of the hypotenuse lies.

7. In Problem 6, find approximately, in degrees, the maximum possible error in the computed value of the acute angle which has the shorter leg as one side, if we find the angle by use of its tangent.

8. The constant C in Boyle's law for gases satisfies $pv = C$, where p is the pressure and v is the volume. If p and C are known with a possible error of 2% in p and 1% in C, find the maximum possible percent of error in v as computed by use of p and C.

9. The specific gravity s of an object is given by the equation $s = a/(a - w)$, where a and w are the weights, in pounds, of the object as measured in air and water, respectively. If a and w can be read with an accuracy limit of .05 pound, find approximately the maximum possible error and percent of error in s if observation gives $a = 3.2$ and $w = 2.7$. In the formula, we assume that $a > w$.

10. In an electric circuit where the measures of the electromotive force in volts, resistance in ohms, and current in amperes, are E, R, and I, respectively, it is known that $E = RI$. If measurements give $E = 110$ and $I = 20$, with a possible error of 2% in each case, find the maximum possible percent of error in the computed value of R.

11. On the surface which is the graph of the function $z = f(x, y)$, find approximately the increment in the value of z due to increments dx and dy in x and y, applied to given values (x_1, y_1). Compute this approximation, and also the exact increment Δz, where $x_1 = 3$ and $y_1 = 2$ on the surface $z = x^2 + 4y^2$, if $dx = .1$ and $dy = .2$.

12. The legs of a right triangle are measured as 3″ and 4″, respectively, with an error of at most 2% in each case. Find approximately the maximum possible percent of error in the computed hypotenuse.

13. In an xyz-system of rectangular coordinates, the coordinates of a point P are measured as $(6, -9, 2)$. Find the maximum possible error in the corresponding computed distance of P from the origin, if the maximum possible percent of error in each coordinate is 2%.

14. When light passes from free space into a given medium, with i and r as the angles of incidence and refraction, respectively, then $(\sin i)/\sin r = n$, where n is the refractive index of the medium. If we measure $i = 32°$ and $r = 30°$, with an error in each case of at most .1°, find approximately the maximum possible error in the computed value of n.

15. For a perfect gas, the volume v, pressure p, and absolute temperature T are connected by the relation $pv = RT$, where R is a constant. If $T = 400°$ when $p = 50$ pounds per square inch, and $v = 600$ cubic inches, find approximately the change and the percent of change in p if T increases by $10°$ and v by 18 cubic inches.

★SUPPLEMENT FOR CHAPTER NINETEEN

By use of Note 1 on page 466, prove each of the following results analytically. It may be useful to notice that $|u| + |v| \leqq 2\sqrt{u^2 + v^2}$.

16. $\displaystyle \lim_{(x,y)\to(0,0)} \frac{x^6 + y^6}{x^2 + y^2} = 0.$ **17.** $\displaystyle \lim_{(x,y)\to(0,0)} (3x^2 - 7xy + 5y^2) = 0.$

18. $\displaystyle \lim_{(x,y)\to(3,2)} \frac{4x - y}{2x + y} = \frac{5}{4}.$ **19.** $\displaystyle \lim_{(x,y)\to(2,-3)} \frac{2x + 3y}{x - 4y} = -\frac{5}{14}.$

Hint for Problem 18. If (x, y) first is restricted by $|x - 3| < 1$ and $|y - 2| < 1$, and if we let $x - 3 = u$ and $y - 2 = v$, show that

$$h(x, y) = |f(x, y) - \tfrac{5}{4}| < \tfrac{9}{20}(|u| + |v|).$$

20. Prove that $\dfrac{x^2 + y^4}{x^4 + 2y^4}$ has no limit as $(x, y) \to (0, 0)$.

21. Let $f(x, y) = \dfrac{\sin(|x| + |y|)}{|x| + |y|}$ when $(x, y) \neq (0, 0)$. How must $f(0, 0)$ be defined to make f continuous at $(0, 0)$? Prove your conclusion.

22. Prove or disprove the following statement: If a function $f(x, y)$ possesses partial derivatives $f_x(a, b)$ and $f_y(a, b)$, then f is continuous at (a, b). Assume that the domain of f contains a circular neighborhood of P.

23. If $w = f(r)$ and $r = \sqrt{x^2 + y^2}$, prove that $\left(\dfrac{\partial w}{\partial x}\right)^2 + \left(\dfrac{\partial w}{\partial y}\right)^2 = \left(\dfrac{dw}{dr}\right)^2$, where all derivatives mentioned are assumed to exist and be continuous when $r \neq 0$.

24. If $z = xy + yg(xy)$, where g is a differentiable function of a single variable, prove that z is a solution of the partial differential equation $z - xy + xz_x - yz_y = 0$.

Note 1. The following content refers to point sets in a plane. We add the following definitions. To state that a point P is a **limit point** of a set of points S means that, in every circular neighborhood of P, there exists a point of S other than P. To say that a set S is **closed** means that S contains all of its limit points. We let $\emptyset$ represent the *empty set*, and T represent the whole plane. The **complement**, S', of a set is defined as the set of all points of T not in S.

25. Give an illustration of a set S which is neither open nor closed.

26. What is the complement of T? Prove that the complement of the complement of a set S is S.

27. Prove that, if S is closed, then S' is open; if S is open, then S' is closed.

28. Prove that T and $\emptyset$ are both open and closed.

Decide whether or not the set S is closed, open, or neither, and describe the boundary of S.

29. S consists of the points (x, y) such that $|xy| \leqq 1$; such that $|xy| < 1$ and $x < 0$.

30. S consists of the points (x, y) satisfying the conditions

$$4x^2 + 9y^2 \leqq 36, \quad and \quad x > 0 \quad if \quad y = 1.$$

CHAPTER TWENTY

Double Integrals

185. DOUBLE INTEGRALS *

In this chapter, unless otherwise stated, when we refer to a *region*, we shall mean a *closed, bounded region* in a plane. Let an *xy*-system of coordinates be imposed on the plane. Let F be a function of two variables whose domain includes a region R in the *xy*-plane. We propose defining the integral of F over R.

Note 1. We define the **diameter** of any region as the length of the longest line segment which can be drawn connecting two points of the region. Thus, the diameter of a region bounded by a circle or sphere is its diameter as generally considered. The diameter of a region bounded by a rectangle is the length of its diagonal.

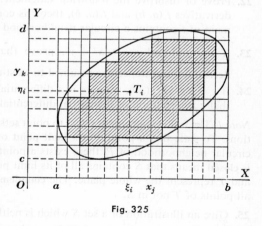

Fig. 325

In the *xy*-plane, let R be a region such that the values of x and y for points $P:(x, y)$ in R form the intervals $a \leqq x \leqq b$ and $c \leqq y \leqq d$. Thus, R lies in the rectangle † T with sides on the lines $x = a$, $x = b$, $y = c$, and $y = d$. Form a partition of the *x*-interval (a, b), as on page 177, and of the *y*-interval (c, d), as in Figure 325, with the subintervals

$$x_{j-1} \leqq x \leqq x_j, \quad \text{where we let} \quad \Delta_j x = x_j - x_{j-1}, \text{ and} \tag{1}$$

$$y_{k-1} \leqq y \leqq y_k, \quad \text{where we let} \quad \Delta_k y = y_k - y_{k-1}. \tag{2}$$

Superimpose a grid on the rectangle T by constructing a line perpendicular to the *x*-axis at each point $x = x_j$, and perpendicular to the *y*-axis at each point $y = y_k$,

---

* The student should review the parallel treatment for $\int_a^b f(x)dx$ in Section 56 on page 177.
† Frequently, as shown by the context, the word "*rectangle*" will refer to a "*region bounded by a rectangle.*" This is the case with T above.

as in Figure 325. The grid divides R into subregions, and we shall call this sub-division of R a partition, σ, of the region R. We define the **norm,** d_σ, of σ as the maximum of the diameters of the rectangles of the grid involved in σ. Suppose that just n of the subregions in σ consist of *entire* rectangles,

$$T_1, T_2, \cdots, T_i, \cdots, T_n, \tag{3}$$

which are ruled in Figure 325, except for the representative rectangle T_i. If $d_\sigma \to 0$, then $n \to \infty$ in (3).

Definition I. *Let σ be any partition of the region R. In each* **whole rectangle** T_i *of σ, select a point (ξ_i, η_i) arbitrarily, and let*

$$S_\sigma = \sum_{i=1}^{n} F(\xi_i, \eta_i)\Delta_i A, \tag{4}$$

where $\Delta_i A$ is the area * of T_i. Then, if † S_σ approaches a limit as $d_\sigma \to 0$, we call this limit "the **double integral** *of $F(x, y)$ over R," to be represented by the following symbol on the left:*

$$\iint_R F(x, y)dA = \lim_{d_\sigma \to 0} \sum_{i=1}^{n} F(\xi_i, \eta_i)\Delta_i A. \tag{5}$$

If the limit in (5) exists, F is said to be *integrable* over R. The following theorem is demonstrated at a more advanced level.

Theorem I. *If R is a region satisfying suitable hypotheses, ‡ and if the function F is continuous in R, then the double integral of F over R exists.*

Previously, we have introduced the notion of *area* for special regions in the xy-plane. Now, we shall define the area of a general region.

Definition II. *For a region R in the xy-plane, let σ be a partition created by use of a rectangular grid, as in Definition I. Then, if the sum of the areas of all of the whole rectangles in σ has a limit as $d_\sigma \to 0$, we define this limit as the area, A, of R:*

$$A = \lim_{d_\sigma \to 0} \sum_{i=1}^{n} \Delta_i A. \tag{6}$$

The sum in (6) is obtained from (5) when $F(x, y) \equiv 1$. Thus, *we have defined the area of R to be the double integral of the function "1" over R. That is,*

$$A = \iint_R 1 \, dA, \quad \text{or simply} \quad A = \iint_R dA, \tag{7}$$

provided that the integral exists. Since the function $F(x, y) = 1$ is continuous, we conclude that, if R is of such a type that Theorem I applies, then R *has an area given by* (7). Hereafter, whenever we mention a *region R*, we shall assume that it satisfies the conditions of Theorem I, so that R has an *area*, and *any continuous function is integrable over R.*

---

* At present we use the concept of area *only for rectangles*, as on page 180.
† We use Definition I on page 178 unchanged, with our new meaning for S_σ.
‡ It is beyond the level of this text to discuss these hypotheses. They will be satisfied in all cases which we consider.

Note 2. For future use, let τ_σ be the sum in (6). Then,

$$\tau_\sigma = \sum_{i=1}^{n} \Delta_i A \quad and \quad \tau_\sigma \to A \text{ if } d_\sigma \to 0. \tag{8}$$

EXAMPLE 1. By use of (4), obtain an approximation S_σ for the double integral of the function $F(x, y) = x^2$, over the region R whose boundary is the circle with radius 5 and center at the origin in the xy-plane.

Solution. Divide the x-interval, and the y-interval, into 10 equal parts and construct the corresponding rectangular grid, to obtain a partition σ for R as shown in Figure 326. Notice that $F(x, y)$ is symmetrical to the origin. In any complete square T_i of σ in quadrant I, let (ξ_i, η_i) be the lower left-hand corner, in forming the product $F(\xi_i, \eta_i)\Delta_i A$. Then, if symmetrical points (ξ_i, η_i) are chosen in the other quadrants, S_σ from (4) will be equal to four times the sum taken just for quadrant I. Each area $\Delta_i A$ is 1. Hence,

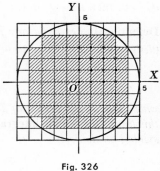

Fig. 326

$$S_\sigma = 4[F(0, 0) + F(0, 1) + F(0, 2) + F(0, 3) + F(1, 0) + \cdots + F(3, 2)]. \tag{9}$$

We obtain $F(1, 0) = 1$, $F(0, 1) = 0$, $F(2, 0) = 4$, etc., and $S_\sigma = 4(47) = 188$.

Comment. For the partition in Example 1, there are 60 complete squares inside the circle, and hence $\tau_\sigma = \sum_{i=1}^{60} \Delta_i A = 60$, as an approximation to the area. The usual formula πr^2 gives 78.54. The student will obtain a better approximation in the next exercise.

As a consequence of Definition II, we may introduce a new interpretation for the expression on the right in (5).

Theorem II. *Let σ be any partition of the region R into subregions $\{T_i\}$ of* **any shape,** *as in Figure 327 below, where T_i has an area, $\Delta_i A$, and let d_σ be the maximum of the diameters of the subregions $\{T_i\}$. Let (ξ_i, η_i) be an arbitrary point in T_i. Then, if F is continuous in R, equation (5) is valid with the new meaning for σ.*

We accept Theorem II on an intuitional basis. Our reaction is that, since the general notion of *area* is defined as the limit of a sum of areas of *rectangles*, then use of areas of irregular regions in Theorem II should lead to the same limit as obtained with *rectangular regions* in Definition I.

With the notion of a *region* replacing an *interval*, and the *area* of a region replacing the *length* of an interval, the following results could be verified by reasoning similar to that employed in establishing corresponding facts for simple integrals in Section 59 on page 183.

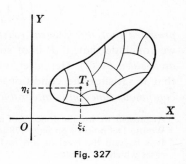

Fig. 327

If F and G are continuous in a region R, and if c is a constant,

$$\iint_R [F(x, y) + G(x, y)]dA = \iint_R F(x, y)dA + \iint_R G(x, y)dA; \quad (10)$$

$$\iint_R cF(x, y)dA = c\iint_R F(x, y)dA. \quad (11)$$

If a region R consists of two regions R′ and R″ which have only boundary points in common, and if F is continuous in R, then

$$\iint_R F(x, y)dA = \iint_{R'} F(x, y)dA + \iint_{R''} F(x, y)dA. \quad (12)$$

If F is continuous in a region R whose area is A, and if m and M are the absolute minimum and maximum, respectively, of F in R, then

$$mA \leqq \iint_R F(x, y)dA \leqq MA. \quad (13)$$

Mean value theorem. *If F is continuous in a region R whose area is A, then there exists a point (ξ, η) in R such that*

$$\iint_R F(x, y)dA = F(\xi, \eta)A. \quad (14)$$

EXERCISE 145

1. Let R be the region bounded by the circle $x^2 + y^2 = 25$. Form a partition σ of R by dividing the corresponding domains for x and y into 20 parts of equal lengths. Compute the approximation τ_σ for the area of R.

2. Let R be the region bounded by the x-axis, the curve $y^2 = 4x$, and the line $x = 2$ in quadrant I. Place a grid on R by drawing the lines $x = 0$, $x = \frac{1}{4}$, $x = \frac{1}{2}, \cdots$, $x = 1.75$, and $y = 0$, $y = \frac{1}{4}$, $y = \frac{1}{2}, \cdots$, $y = 2.75$, spaced $\frac{1}{4}$ unit apart. By use of the corresponding partition σ for R, compute approximations for (*a*) the area of R; (*b*) the double integral over R of the function $F(x, y) = xy$, with (ξ_i, η_i) in (4) on page 483 taken as the lower left-hand corner in any complete square of σ.

186. ITERATED INTEGRALS

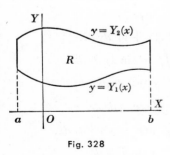

Fig. 328

Assume that the functions $Y_1(x)$ and $Y_2(x)$ have continuous derivatives * Y_1' and Y_2' when $a \leqq x \leqq b$, and let the function $F(x, y)$ be continuous in the region R of the xy-plane bounded by the curves $y = Y_1(x)$ and $y = Y_2(x)$, and the lines $x = a$ and $x = b$. Figure 328 for R is drawn as if $Y_1(x) \leqq Y_2(x)$, at all values of x, but this feature is not essential. Then, without proof we shall accept the fact that the function $G(x)$ defined by

$$G(x) = \int_{Y_1(x)}^{Y_2(x)} F(x, y)dy \quad (1)$$

is a continuous function of x. In (1), it is understood that x is a constant during

---

* A less restrictive hypothesis could be used, but the stated condition will cover all of the usual applications. For an advanced discussion of all theory in this chapter, see Chapter 13, *Real Variables*, by John M. H. Olmsted (New York: Appleton-Century-Crofts, Inc., 1959).

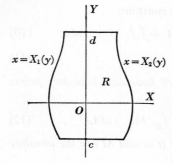

$x = X_1(y)$

$x = X_2(y)$

R

Fig. 329

the integration with respect to y. Then, $\int_a^b G(x)dx$ exists. Thus, the following symbol has a well-defined value, found by two successive integrations:

$$\int_a^b \left[\int_{Y_1(x)}^{Y_2(x)} F(x, y)dy \right] dx. \qquad (2)$$

We shall refer to (2) as a **two-fold iterated integral.** Similarly, with R bounded by curves $x = X_1(y)$ and $x = X_2(y)$, and lines $y = c$ and $y = d$, as in Figure 329, where X_1' and X_2' are continuous, we may use

$$\int_c^d \left[\int_{X_1(y)}^{X_2(y)} F(x, y)dx \right] dy. \qquad (3)$$

ILLUSTRATION 1. $\qquad \int_2^3 \left[\int_{2x}^{3x^2} xy\,dy \right] dx = \int_2^3 \tfrac{1}{2}xy^2 \Big]_{y=2x}^{y=3x^2} dx$

$$= \tfrac{1}{2} \int_2^3 (9x^5 - 4x^3)dx = \tfrac{1}{2}(\tfrac{3}{2}x^6 - x^4) \Big]_2^3 = \tfrac{1865}{4}.$$

ILLUSTRATION 2. If a and c are constants, then

$$\int_a^x \left[\int_c^y F(u, v)dv \right] du$$

is a function of x and y. By use of Theorem VII on page 185,

$$\frac{\partial}{\partial x} \left\{ \int_a^x \left[\int_c^y F(u, v)dv \right] du \right\} = \int_c^y F(x, v)dv;$$

$$\frac{\partial^2}{\partial x\,\partial y} \left\{ \int_a^x \left[\int_c^y F(u, v)dv \right] du \right\} = \frac{\partial}{\partial y} \int_c^y F(x, v)dv = F(x, y).$$

In the next section, we shall establish a connection between two-fold iterated integrals and double integrals. We may write (2) or (3) without the square brackets, with the understanding that the differentials, starting at the left, indicate the order of integration.

EXERCISE 146

Compute the iterated integral.

1. $\int_0^3 \int_1^2 (x + 2y)dy\,dx.$

2. $\int_1^2 \int_0^y 3(x + y)^2 \, dx\,dy.$

3. $\int_1^2 \int_1^{2x} x^2 e^{xy} \, dy\,dx.$

4. $\int_0^{\pi/2} \int_x^x x^2 \sin xy \, dy\,dx.$

5. $\int_{4a^2}^{9a^2} \int_1^{\sqrt{y}} dx\,dy.$

6. $\int_1^3 \int_1^x x^{-1}y^{-1} \, dy\,dx.$

7. $\int_{-\pi/2}^{\pi/2} \int_x^{3x} 2 \sin (x + 2y)dy\,dx.$

8. $\int_{-\pi/4}^{\pi/4} \int_0^r \sec^2 \theta \, d\theta\,dr.$

9. $\int_{1/2}^1 \int_0^x \sqrt{x^2 - y^2} \, dy\,dx.$

10. $\int_{1/2}^4 \int_0^x x(x^2 - y^2)^{-\frac{1}{2}} \, dy\,dx.$

11. $\int_{-\pi}^\pi \int_1^{\sin \theta} r \, dr\,d\theta.$

12. $\int_1^3 \int_{\pi/2}^{2\pi} r \sin \theta \, d\theta\,dr.$

13. $\int_0^{\pi/6} \int_1^{\sqrt{2 \cos 2\theta}} r \, dr\,d\theta.$

14. $\int_0^{\pi/6} \int_1^{2 \cos \theta} r \sin 2\theta \, dr\,d\theta.$

15. If a, b, c, and d are constants, prove that $\int_a^b \int_c^d f(x)g(y)dy\,dx$ can be expressed as a product of two simple integrals, if f and g are integrable.

187. DOUBLE INTEGRALS, BY USE OF ITERATED INTEGRALS

Hereafter, we shall refer frequently to regions of the following types in an xy-plane, as in Figures 328 and 329, respectively, on pages 485–486.

$(R \text{ of type I})$ $\qquad\qquad a \leqq x \leqq b \quad and \quad Y_1(x) \leqq y \leqq Y_2(x).$ $\qquad$ (1)

$(R \text{ of type II})$ $\qquad\qquad c \leqq y \leqq d \quad and \quad X_1(y) \leqq x \leqq X_2(y).$ $\qquad$ (2)

Theorem III. (*Fundamental theorem of integral calculus for a double integral.*) *If a function F is continuous in a region R of type* I *or type* II, *then*

$(R \text{ of type I})$ $\qquad \iint_R F(x, y)dA = \int_a^b \int_{Y_1(x)}^{Y_2(x)} F(x, y)dy\, dx;$ $\qquad$ (3)

$(R \text{ of type II})$ $\qquad \iint_R F(x, y)dA = \int_c^d \int_{X_1(y)}^{X_2(y)} F(x, y)dx\, dy.$ $\qquad$ (4)

EXAMPLE 1. Let R be the region bounded by the x-axis and the curves $y^2 = x$ and $x^2 + y^2 = 2$, where $y \geq 0$. Compute the following integral, K:

$$K = \iint_R y\, dA. \qquad (5)$$

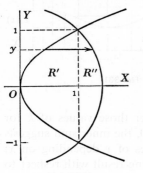

Fig. 330

Solution. 1. On solving $y^2 = x$ and $x^2 + y^2 = 2$ simultaneously, we obtain the intersection $(1, 1)$ of their graphs in quadrant I, as in Figure 330.

2. On the interval $0 \leq y \leq 1$, any perpendicular to OY meets the boundary of R in *just two points*, as shown by the arrow in Figure 330. Hence, we may consider R as of type II. The right-hand boundary is a part of $x^2 + y^2 = 2$, or $x = \sqrt{2 - y^2}$. Hence, by use of (4) with

$$X_1(y) = y^2 \quad and \quad X_2(y) = \sqrt{2 - y^2},$$

$$K = \int_0^1 \int_{y^2}^{\sqrt{2-y^2}} y\, dx\, dy = \int_0^1 xy \Big]_{x=y^2}^{x=\sqrt{2-y^2}} dy \qquad (6)$$

$$= \int_0^1 (y\sqrt{2 - y^2} - y^3)dy = \Big[-\tfrac{1}{3}(2 - y^2)^{\frac{3}{2}} - \tfrac{1}{4}y^4 \Big]_0^1 = \tfrac{2}{3}\sqrt{2} - \tfrac{7}{12}. \qquad (7)$$

We may compute K by use of (3). Then, however, the fact that two formulas are involved for y on the upper boundary forces us to divide R into two parts. Thus, we cut R into R', where $0 \leqq x \leqq 1$, and R'', where $1 \leqq x \leqq \sqrt{2}$, by drawing the line $x = 1$. Then, from (3),

$$K = \iint_{R'} y\, dA + \iint_{R''} y\, dA = \int_0^1 \int_0^{\sqrt{x}} y\, dy\, dx + \int_1^{\sqrt{2}} \int_0^{\sqrt{2-x^2}} y\, dy\, dx.$$

Intuitional discussion of (3). 1. Let the region R be of type I, as in Figure 331 on page 488. Form a partition of the interval $a \leq x \leq b$ into g pieces, and of $c \leqq y \leqq d$ into h pieces by division points as follows:

$$x_0 = a < x_1 < x_2 < \cdots < x_{j-1} < x_j < \cdots < x_g = b; \qquad (8)$$

$$y_0 = c < y_1 < y_2 < \cdots < y_{k-1} < y_k < \cdots < y_h = d. \qquad (9)$$

In (8) and (9), the typical subintervals have the lengths

$$\Delta_j x = x_j - x_{j-1} \quad and \quad \Delta_k y = y_k - y_{k-1}.$$

By use of the lines $x = x_j$ and $y = y_k$, for all values of j and k, construct a grid of rectangles, arranged in g columns and h rows, as in Figure 331. This grid produces a partition σ of R, as on page 482. To say that $d_\sigma \to 0$ is equivalent to saying that, in (8) and (9), all $\Delta_j x \to 0$ and all $\Delta_k y \to 0$.

2. To form an approximating sum S_σ for $\iint_R F(x, y)dA$ in (3), consider the typical rectangle $T_{j,k}$ of σ in the jth column where $x_{j-1} \leqq x \leqq x_j$, and kth row where $y_{k-1} \leqq y \leqq y_k$. The area of $T_{j,k}$ is $(\Delta_j x)(\Delta_k y)$. In $T_{j,k}$, select (x_j, y_k), shown by a black dot in Figure 331, as the arbitrary point referred to in Definition I on page 483, to obtain the element $F(x_j, y_k)\Delta_k y \Delta_j x$ for a sum S_σ. Then, form the sum of the elements by adding, first, all of those from the jth column of σ, and then taking the sum of the column sums, for all values of j:

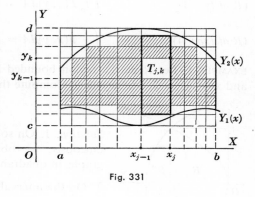

Fig. 331

$$S_\sigma = \sum_{j=1}^{g} \left[\sum_{(k)} F(x_j, y_k)\Delta_k y \right] \Delta_j x,$$

where, for each value of j, the inner sum extends over those values of k for which there is a rectangle $T_{j,k}$ in σ. In S_σ, as all $\Delta_k y \to 0$, the inner sum suggests an integral of $F(x, y)$ with respect to y, between values of y depending on x; then, the outer sum suggests the integral of the preceding result with respect to x over the interval (a, b). Hence, we are led to infer that

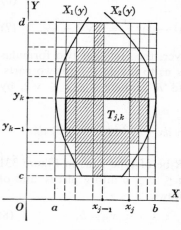

Fig. 332

$$\lim_{d_\sigma \to 0} S_\sigma = \int_a^b \int_{Y_1(x)}^{Y_2(x)} F(x, y)dy\, dx, \quad (10)$$

as in (3). Thus, we may visualize (10) as a consequence of *first summing elements by columns*, and then taking *the sum of column sums in S_σ.*

If R is of Type II as in Figure 332, we write

$$S_\sigma = \sum_{k=1}^{h} \left[\sum_{(j)} F(x_j, y_k)\Delta_j x \right] \Delta_k y, \quad (11)$$

and then would be led to (4). Thus, in (4), we may visualize the inner integration with respect to x as a consequence of first summing elements $F(x_j, y_k)\Delta_j x$ by *rows;* the outer integration can be thought of as a result of taking *the sum of row sums in* (11).

Note 1. The results in (3) and (4) are special cases of **Fubini's Theorem,** which applies to triple integrals (in Chapter 22) and also to many situations in advanced mathematics where the concept of an integral is generalized extensively. Proof of (3) and (4) is beyond the level of this text.

Note 2. In (3) and (4), we can call *"dx dy"* the differential *element of area* in rectangular coordinates, as a reminder of the area $\Delta x \Delta y$ of an elementary rectangle in an approximating sum for the corresponding double integral.

188. TWO–DIMENSIONAL DISTRIBUTION OF MASS

Consider a plane region R, and visualize mass spread over R like paint on a surface, where the mass is idealized as having no thickness. Suppose there exists a constant δ such that, if T is any subregion of R with the area ΔA area units, then the mass, Δm, of T is $\delta \Delta A$ mass units. In this case, we say that the mass over R has *uniform density*, and that the density is δ units of mass per square unit of area. Thus, we have

$$\Delta A = \iint_T dA \quad and \quad \Delta m = \delta \iint_T dA = \iint_T \delta \, dA.$$

This discussion suggests the notion of a variable density.

Definition III. *Let δ be a continuous, nonnegative function whose domain consists of all points (x, y) in a region R. Then, to state that δ is the* **density function** *for a distribution of mass over R, means that, if T is any subregion of R, the mass, Δm, of T is*

$$\Delta m = \iint_T \delta(x, y) dA.$$

In particular, the total mass, m, of R is

$$m = \iint_R \delta(x, y) dA. \tag{1}$$

Let T be any subregion of R with area ΔA and mass Δm, as in Figure 333. Then, by the mean value theorem for a double integral on page 485, there exists a point (ξ, η) in T such that

$$\Delta m = \iint_T \delta(x, y) dA = \delta(\xi, \eta) \Delta A, \ or$$

$$\delta(\xi, \eta) = \frac{\Delta m}{\Delta A}. \tag{2}$$

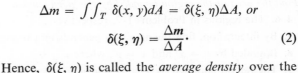

Fig. 333

Hence, $\delta(\xi, \eta)$ is called the *average density* over the region T. In (2), suppose that T is a variable region with the diameter γ, a variable, and that T always includes a certain fixed point (x_0, y_0). If $\gamma \to 0$, then $\delta(\xi, \eta) \to \delta(x_0, y_0)$, $\Delta A \to 0$, and (2) gives

$$\lim_{\gamma \to 0} \frac{\Delta m}{\Delta A} = \delta(x_0, y_0). \tag{3}$$

Because of (3), we shall call $\delta(x, y)$ the density *at the point* (x, y).

EXAMPLE 1. Find the mass of the region R bounded by the y-axis and the right-hand semicircle of the circle $x^2 + y^2 = 25$, if the density of R at the point (x, y) is $\delta(x, y) = 5\,|\,y\,|$.

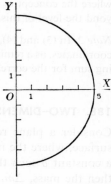
Fig. 334

Solution. 1. *Symmetry*. The region R, shown in Figure 334, is symmetric with respect to OX. Also, the density has the same value at any point (x, y_1) as at (x, y_2) where $y_2 = -y_1$, because

$$\delta(x, y_1) = 5\,|\,y_1\,| = 5\,|\,y_2\,| = \delta(x, y_2).$$

Since the *region* and the *density function values* are symmetric with respect to OX, the mass of R is twice the mass in that quadrant R' where $y \geq 0$.

2. If m is the mass of R, then

$$m = 2 \iint_{R'} 5y \, dA = 10 \int_0^5 \int_0^{\sqrt{25-x^2}} y \, dy \, dx = \tfrac{1250}{3}.$$

If the word "*mass*" in Definition III is changed to "*electric charge*," then $\delta(x, y)$ is the density of electric charge, and (1) becomes the total charge over R. In statistics, with the words "*density of mass*" changed to "*probability density*," the integral of $\delta(x, y)$ becomes a *probability*.

EXERCISE 147

Express the double integral of an arbitrary function $F(x, y)$ over the specified region R by use of an iterated integral, or more than one iterated integral.

1. R is the region in quadrant I bounded by the parabolas $3y = x^2$ and $3x = y^2$. Give the result for each order of integration.

2. R is bounded by the parabolas $y^2 = -4x$ and $y^2 = 4(x + 2)$.

3. R is bounded by the y-axis, and the curves $y = \sin x$ and $y = \cos x$, up to their first point of intersection where $x > 0$. Give two results.

First formulate the result as a double integral, and then compute by use of an iterated integral. Use symmetry. Any constant a or k is positive.

Find the area of the region bounded by the given curves.

4–6. The regions in Problems 1–3, respectively.

7. By integration, find the area of a general right triangle.

8. Bounded by $y = x^3$ and $x = y^3$, where $y \geq 0$.

9. The region bounded by $y = 7x$ and $y = x(x + 1)(x - 5)$.

10. Bounded by $y + 2x + 6 = 0$ and $y = 9 - x^2$.

11. Bounded by $y^2 = 4 + 4x$ and $y^2 = 4 - 8x$.

12. Bounded by $x^2 + y^2 = 4$ and $y^2 = 3x$.

13. Bounded by the lines $x = 0$, $y = 0$, $x = 3$, and $y = e^x$.

14. Bounded by the curve $y = f(x)$ where $f(x) \geq 0$, the x-axis, and the lines $x = a$ and $x = b$. Thus, obtain (1) on page 344 by use of a double integral.

15. Bounded by $y = \tfrac{1}{2}(e^x + e^{-x})$ and $y = \tfrac{1}{2}e^x$, with $0 \leq x \leq 1$.

16. Bounded by a circle of radius a.

17. Bounded by $x^{\frac{1}{2}} + y^{\frac{1}{2}} = 2$ and $x + y = 4$.

Find the mass of the region. $\delta(x, y)$ *is the density at* (x, y).

18. Bounded by $y = \sin x$ and $y = \cos x$, for $0 \leq x \leq \frac{1}{4}\pi$; $\delta(x, y) = ky$.

19. Bounded by the line $y = 1$ and the curve $4y^3 = x^2$; $\delta(x, y) = kx^2$.

20. Bounded by the circle $x^2 + y^2 = a^2$; $\delta(x, y) = |xy|$.

21. Bounded by $y = 1/\sqrt{9 - 25x^2}$, and the lines $y = 0$ and $x = \pm \frac{3}{10}\sqrt{2}$; the density at any point (x, y) is $\delta(x, y) = 2y|x|$.

22. The region of Problem 2, if $\delta(x, y) = 4 + x + y$.

23. Bounded by the loci $x = 0$, $y = \frac{3}{2}$, $y = 4$, and $x = \sqrt{2y + 1}$; $\delta(x, y) = 3x^2$.

24. Bounded by $y = x - \sin 2x$ and $y = x$, $0 \leq x \leq \frac{1}{2}\pi$; $\delta(x, y) = 2(x + y)$.

25. Find the area of the ellipse $b^2x^2 + a^2y^2 = a^2b^2$.

★*Draw a region R in an xy-system of coordinates so that the iterated integral is equal to a double integral over R. The limits of integration give equations for boundaries.*

26. $\displaystyle\int_{-2}^{4} \int_{y^2/4}^{(4+y)/2} F(x, y)dx\, dy$.

27. $\displaystyle\int_{-3}^{3} \int_{x^2-9}^{(9-x^2)/3} F(x, y)dy\, dx$.

★*By first obtaining a corresponding double integral, derive an expression for the given integral with the order of integration reversed.*

28. $\displaystyle\int_{0}^{2} \int_{y^2/2}^{(8-y^2)/2} F(x, y)dx\, dy$.

29. $\displaystyle\int_{-1}^{0} \int_{e^x}^{e^{-x}} F(x, y)dy\, dx$.

189. A CERTAIN VOLUME AS A DOUBLE INTEGRAL

In an xyz-system of rectangular coordinates, let R be a region in the xy-plane bounded by a curve C. Then, consider the cylinder formed by moving a line L parallel to the z-axis through all points on C, as in Figure 335. Let W be the region of points in space bounded by this cylinder, the region R, and the surface $z = F(x, y)$, where F is continuous and $F(x, y) \geq 0$ in R. We propose defining the notion of *volume* for W, shown in Figure 335, with the viewpoint that only the volume of a *parallelepiped* has been defined previously.

Form a partition σ of R by superimposing a grid of rectangles over R, as on page 482; Figure 335 shows a representative complete rectangle T_i of σ having the area $\Delta_i A$. Let d_σ be the norm of σ, as on page 483. For each rectangle T_i, construct planes perpendicular to the xy-plane on the sides of T_i, thus forming a column τ_i in W with base T_i and cap $HBDE$ on

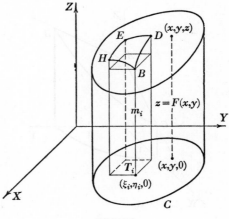

Fig. 335

the surface $z = F(x, y)$. Let γ_i be the largest parallelepiped with T_i as a base included in τ_i. If m_i is the absolute *minimum* of F at points in T_i, then m_i is the altitude of γ_i, and there exists a point $(\xi_i, \eta_i, 0)$ in T_i in the xy-plane such that $m_i = F(\xi_i, \eta_i)$. Hence, the volume $\Delta_i V$ of γ_i is given by

$$\Delta_i V = m_i \Delta_i A = F(\xi_i, \eta_i)\Delta_i A.$$

Then, we define the volume V of W as *the limit of the sum, S_σ, of the volumes of all of the maximum parallelepipeds γ_i with whole rectangles of σ for bases, as $d_\sigma \to 0$. Or,*

$$V = \lim_{d_\sigma \to 0} S_\sigma = \lim_{d_\sigma \to 0} \sum_{i=1}^{n} \Delta_i V = \lim_{d_\sigma \to 0} \sum_{i=1}^{n} F(\xi_i, \eta_i)\Delta_i A. \tag{1}$$

From Definition I and Theorem I, the limit in (1) exists and

$$\left\{ \begin{array}{l} \text{cylindrical region, } W; \\ \text{base, } R; \text{ cap, } z = F(x, y) \end{array} \right\} \qquad V = \iint_R F(x, y)dA, \tag{2}$$

which we may abbreviate by

$$[z = F(x, y)] \qquad V = \iint_R z \, dA. \tag{3}$$

EXAMPLE 1. Find the volume of the region bounded by the circular cylinder $x^2 + y^2 = 4$, the xy-plane, and the plane $x - y + 2z = 4$.

Solution. 1. Figure 336 shows the part of the solid in the 1st octant. AB is the yz-trace, and AC is the xz-trace of the plane. The equation of AB is $z = \frac{1}{2}(4 + y)$ in the yz-plane. BC is part of the curve of intersection of the plane and the cylinder.

2. We use (3) with $z = \frac{1}{2}(4 - x + y)$ and R as the region bounded by the circle $x^2 + y^2 = 4$, or $y = \pm \sqrt{4 - x^2}$. We take R as of type I in (3). The inner limits of integration are indicated by the arrow in Figure 337, where the xy-plane is shown without distortion (a recommended procedure).

$$V = \iint_R \frac{1}{2}(4 - x + y)dA = \frac{1}{2}\int_{-2}^{2} \int_{-\sqrt{4-x^2}}^{\sqrt{4-x^2}} (4 - x + y)dy \, dx = 8\pi. \tag{4}$$

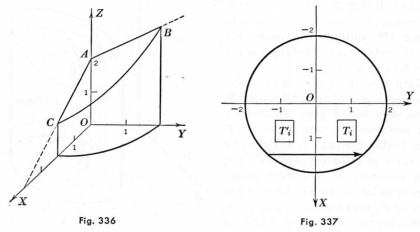

Fig. 336   Fig. 337

Comment. In Example 1, let R_1 and R_2 be the subregions of R where $y \geqq 0$ and $y \leqq 0$, respectively. Let σ_1 be a partition of R_1, with pieces $\{T_i\}$; let σ_2 be that partition of R_2 where each piece T_i' is symmetric to T_i with respect to the x-axis, as in Figure 337. In T_i, select arbitrarily a point (x_i, y_i), and in T_i' select the symmetrical point $(x_i, -y_i)$, for applying Definition I of page 483. Then, if $\Delta_i A$ is the common area of T_i and T_i',

$$\iint_{R_1} y\, dA = \lim_{d_{\sigma_1} \to 0} \sum y_i \Delta_i A; \quad \iint_{R_2} y\, dA = \lim_{d_{\sigma_1} \to 0} \sum (-y_i)\Delta_i A, \text{ or}$$

$$\iint_{R_2} y\, dA = -\iint_{R_1} y\, dA; \quad \iint_{R} y\, dA = \iint_{R_1} y\, dA + \iint_{R_2} y\, dA = 0. \quad (5)$$

Similarly, $\iint_R x\, dA = 0$. Then, from (4), $V = \iint_R 2\, dA = 2A = 2(4\pi) = 8\pi$.

ILLUSTRATION 1. If H is a constant and $F(x, y) = H$ in R, then W in (2) is a *slab* with thickness H, and (2) gives $V = HA$, where A is the area of R. Thus, from (2) we have proved (II) on page 196.

We may use (2) to obtain a fresh viewpoint about the fundamental theorem of integral calculus for a double integral. First, recall that, on page 354, the volume V of a solid such as W in (2) was defined as the limit of a sum of volumes of *slabs*, with the result in Illustration 1 taken as a definition. The volume of each slab now is defined as a limit of a sum of volumes of parallelepipeds. Hence, we accept intuitively the fact that volume as defined on page 354, and volume as obtained by use of parallelepipeds in (2), have the same value. With this basis, we shall give a new background for (3) and (4) on page 487, where $F(x, y) \geqq 0$.

Let R be a region of type II in the xy-plane, in Figure 338:

Region R: $\qquad\qquad\qquad c \leqq y \leqq d; \quad X_1(y) \leqq x \leqq X_2(y). \qquad\qquad\qquad (6)$

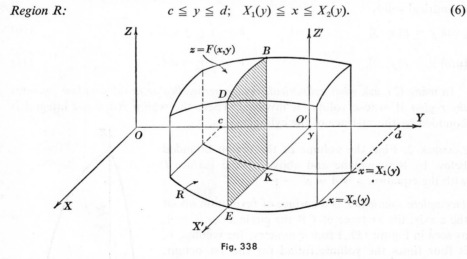

Fig. 338

Let W be the cylindrical region in space having R as a base and the surface $z = F(x, y)$ for a cap, as in Figure 338. At any point y on the y-axis, construct a plane perpendicular to the y-axis, creating the plane section $BDEK$ of W. In the plane of $BDEK$, visualize new axes $O'X'$ and $O'Z'$, as in the figure, with the directions of OX and OZ. In this new xz-plane, the equation of BD is $z = F(x, y)$, where y is fixed at the moment. At E and K, $x = X_2(y)$ and $x = X_1(y)$, respectively.

Let $A(y)$ be the area of *BDEK*. Then, from (1) on page 344,

$$A(y) = \int_{X_1(y)}^{X_2(y)} F(x, y)dx.$$

Hence, from (1) on page 354, $V = \int_c^d A(y)dy$. Then, from (2),

$$\iint_R F(x, y)dA = \int_c^d \int_{X_1(y)}^{X_2(y)} F(x, y)dx\, dy, \tag{7}$$

which gives (4) on page 487. Similarly, we could obtain (3) on page 487.

Note 1. If we do not have $F(x, y) \geqq 0$ at all points of R in (7), suppose that m is the absolute minimum for F in R. Let $G(x, y) = F(x, y) - m$, where $m < 0$. Then, $G(x, y) \geqq 0$ in R and (7) applies with G replacing F:

$$\iint_R G(x, y)dR = \iint_R [F(x, y) - m]dA = \iint_R F(x, y)dA - mA \tag{8}$$

$$= \int_c^d \int_{X_1(y)}^{X_2(y)} [F(x, y) - m]dx\, dy = \int_c^d \int_{X_1(y)}^{X_2(y)} F(x, y)dx\, dy - m \int_c^d \int_{X_1(y)}^{X_2(y)} dx\, dy$$

$$= \int_c^d \int_{X_1(y)}^{X_2(y)} F(x, y)dx\, dy - mA. \tag{9}$$

From (8) and (9), we again obtain (7), without the restriction $F(x, y) \geqq 0$.

With R as a region in the xz-plane, and then with R as a region in the yz-plane, from (3) we obtain, respectively, the following analogous formulas for volumes of cylindrical solids:

$$[with\ y = F(x, z)] \qquad\qquad V = \iint_R y\, dA. \tag{10}$$

$$[with\ x = F(y, z)] \qquad\qquad V = \iint_R x\, dA. \tag{11}$$

In using (2), ask *what cylindrical surface perpendicular to the xy-plane encloses the region W whose volume is involved.* Then, the region R for the integral is bounded by the xy-trace of the cylinder.

EXAMPLE 2. Find the volume of the region bounded below by the xy-plane and above by the surface T with the equation $z = 4 - x^2 - y^2$.

Incomplete solution. T is a surface of revolution about the z-axis; the xy-trace of T is the circle $x^2 + y^2 = 4$, as seen in Figure 339. From symmetry, the volume, V, is four times the volume found for the 1st octant. Hence, with R as the region bounded by the parabola $z = 4 - y^2$ in quadrant I of the yz-plane, from (11),

$$V = 4 \iint_R \sqrt{4 - y^2 - z}\, dA$$

$$= 4\int_0^2 \int_0^{4-y^2} \sqrt{4 - y^2 - z}\, dz\, dy.$$

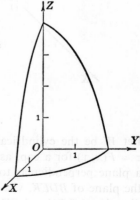

Fig. 339

EXAMPLE 3. In an *xyz*-system of rectangular coordinates, the planes $z = 0$, $x + y = 1$, $x = 1$, and $y = 1 + 3x$ intersect to form a prism with its base in the *xy*-plane. Find the volume of the region bounded by this prism and the surface $z = 2 + x + y^2$.

Incomplete solution. The prism W involved has its base in the *xy*-plane, whose equation is $z = 0$. The sides of W are in the vertical planes $x + y = 1$, $x = 1$, and $y = 1 + 3x$. No space figure is necessary. The student should verify that

$$V = \int\int_R (2 + x + y^2)dA = \int_0^1 \int_{1-x}^{1+3x} (2 + x + y^2)dy\, dx.$$

EXERCISE 148

Find the volume of the region W bounded by the given surfaces in xyz-space.

1. The surfaces $z = 0$, $2y = x$, $x = 1$, $y = 0$, and $z = x^2 + 3y + 1$.
2. Bounded by the tetrahedron in the 1st octant formed by the coordinate planes and the plane $3x + 2y + z = 6$.
3. The planes $z = 0$, $y = x$, $y = 2x$, and $y = 3$, and the surface $z = x + y^2$.
4. The cylinder $x^2 = 2y$, the planes $y = 2$ and $z = 0$, and the paraboloid $z = x^2 + 3y^2$.
5. The planes $x = 0$, $x = 1$, $y = 0$, $y = 2$, and $z = 0$, and $z = 4 - x^2$.
6. The cylinder $x^2 + y^2 = 9$ and the planes $z = 0$ and $y - x + 2z = 4$.
7. The cylinders $z = 1 - y^2$ and $x^2 = 4y$, and the *xy*-plane. (*a*) Solve by use of (2) on page 492. (*b*) Also, solve by use of (11) on page 494.
8. The surfaces $x^2 + y^2 = 25$, $y = 3$, $y = -3$, $z = 0$, and $x - y + z = 8$.
9. The surfaces $3y = 9 - x^2$, $z = 0$, $y = 0$, and $x = 3 - z$. Use two methods.
10. The plane $x = 0$ and the paraboloid $x = 16 - z^2 - 4y^2$. Use two methods.
11. The surfaces $x^2 + y^2 = k^2$, $z = 0$, and $z = k^2 - x^2$ where $k > 0$.
12. The surfaces $z = 0$, $y = 3x$, $y = x$, and $z = 16 - x^2$.
13. The cylinders $z = 4 - x^2$ and $z = 4 - y^2$, and the *xy*-plane.
14. With $a > 0$, $b > 0$, and $c > 0$, W is the region bounded by the tetrahedron formed in the first octant by the coordinate planes and the plane $bcx + acy + abz = abc$.
15. The region bounded by the cylinders $x^2 + z^2 = a^2$ and $y^2 + z^2 = a^2$.
16. Obtain the volume of a sphere of radius a by use of a double integral.

190. DOUBLE INTEGRALS IN POLAR COORDINATES

Consider a region R in a plane where we have an $r\theta$-system of polar coordinates and the associated *xy*-system of rectangular coordinates, with

$$x = r \cos \theta \quad and \quad y = r \sin \theta. \tag{1}$$

Suppose that, corresponding to each point P in R, a single number z is defined. We could express this by saying that there exists a function G whose domain consists of the set of points $\{P\}$ in R, and that $z = G(P)$. We might call G a **point-function.** Then, with minor changes in Section 185 on page 482, we could define $\int\int_R G(P)dA = \int\int_R z\, dA$. Previously, in this chapter, we have introduced

$P:(x, y)$, and then, instead of $z = G(P)$, have used $z = F(x, y)$. Now, with P having the polar coordinates $[r, \theta]$, we shall use $z = f(r, \theta)$, where

$$z = G(P) = F(x, y) = f(r, \theta),$$

and $f(r, \theta)$ can be obtained from $F(x, y)$ by using (1) in $F(x, y)$. The integral of z over R can be written in any one of the forms

$$\iint_R z\, dA, \quad \iint_R F(x, y)dA, \quad or \quad \iint_R f(r, \theta)dA. \tag{2}$$

With the form at the right in (2), it is desirable to restate briefly the essential parts of the definition of a double integral, as based on Theorem II, page 484. Let σ be a partition of R into subregions $\{T_i\}$ where T_i has the area $\Delta_i A$. Select arbitrarily a point $[r = \gamma_i, \theta = \mu_i]$ in T_i. Then, instead of (5) on page 483, the defining expression for the form at the right in (2) becomes

$$\iint_R f(r, \theta)dA = \lim_{d_\sigma \to 0} \sum_{i=1}^{n} f(\gamma_i, \mu_i)\Delta_i A. \tag{3}$$

We desire to express (3) by use of iterated integrals with respect to r and θ for regions of the following nature, where type I is illustrated in Figure 340 and type II in Figure 341. In each case, we assume that coordinates are chosen with $r \geq 0$. Also, we assume that the functions h_1, h_2, g_1, and g_2 have continuous derivatives.

(R of type I) $\qquad\qquad\qquad \alpha \leq \theta \leq \beta; \quad h_1(\theta) \leq r \leq h_2(\theta).$ \hfill (4)

(R of type II) $\qquad\qquad\qquad a \leq r \leq b; \quad g_1(r) \leq \theta \leq g_2(r).$ \hfill (5)

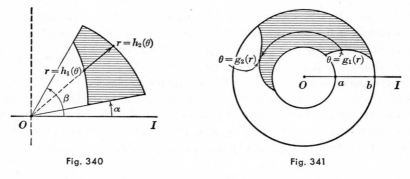

Fig. 340 $\qquad\qquad\qquad\qquad\qquad\qquad\qquad\qquad$ Fig. 341

We shall give a background later for the following result.

Theorem IV. (*Fundamental theorem of integral calculus, with polar coordinates.*) *If $f(r, \theta)$ is continuous in a region R, then*

(R of type I) $\qquad\qquad \iint_R f(r, \theta)dA = \int_\alpha^\beta \int_{h_1(\theta)}^{h_2(\theta)} rf(r, \theta)dr\, d\theta;$ \hfill (6)

(R of type II) $\qquad\qquad \iint_R f(r, \theta)dA = \int_a^b \int_{g_1(r)}^{g_2(r)} rf(r, \theta)d\theta\, dr.$ \hfill (7)

The inner limits of integration in (6) and (7) are indicated by the corresponding straight arrow in Figure 340, and curved arrow in Figure 341.

Let A be the area of the region R in Theorem IV. Also, suppose that a mass m is spread over R with $\delta(r, \theta)$ as the density of mass at the point $[r, \theta]$. Then,

(R *of type* I)
$$A = \iint_R dA = \int_\alpha^\beta \int_{h_1(\theta)}^{h_2(\theta)} r\, dr\, d\theta;$$
(8)

(R *of type* II)
$$m = \iint_R \delta(r, \theta)dA = \int_a^b \int_{g_1(r)}^{g_2(r)} r\delta(r, \theta)d\theta\, dr.$$
(9)

EXAMPLE 1. If R is the region bounded by the line $\theta = \frac{1}{2}\pi$ and the curves $r = \cos\theta$ and $r = 1 + \cos\theta$ in quadrants I and IV, find (*a*) the area of R; (*b*) its mass if $\delta(r, \theta) = k|y|$, where $y = r\sin\theta$.

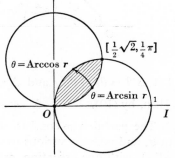

Solution. 1. R is indicated in Figure 342 and is of type I. To obtain a single interval for the variable of integration, choose θ on the interval $-\frac{1}{2}\pi \le \theta \le \frac{1}{2}\pi$. The arrow in Figure 342 indicates that the lower limit for the inner integration is $r = \cos\theta$, and the upper limit is $r = 1 + \cos\theta$.

$$A = \iint_R dA = \int_{-\pi/2}^{\pi/2} \int_{\cos\theta}^{1+\cos\theta} r\, dr\, d\theta = 2 + \frac{1}{2}\pi.$$

Fig. 342

2. At any point $[r, \theta]$, $\delta(r, \theta) = k|y| = kr|\sin\theta|$, where k is an unknown positive constant of proportionality, and $\delta(r, \theta) = \delta(r, -\theta)$. Hence, R and $\delta(r, \theta)$ are symmetric to the polar axis, so that the mass of R is twice the mass of that part, R', above the polar axis, where $|\sin\theta| = \sin\theta$. Thus,

$$M = 2\iint_{R'} kr\sin\theta\, dA$$

$$= 2k \int_0^{\pi/2} \int_{\cos\theta}^{1+\cos\theta} r^2 \sin\theta\, dr\, d\theta = \frac{7}{3}k.$$

ILLUSTRATION 1. Let R be the region bounded by $r = \cos\theta$ and $r = \sin\theta$ in Figure 343, which intersect at $[r = \frac{1}{2}\sqrt{2}, \theta = \frac{1}{4}\pi]$. R is of type II. From $r = \cos\theta$ and $r = \sin\theta$, respectively,

$$\theta = \text{Arccos } r \quad and \quad \theta = \text{Arcsin } r;$$

$$\iint_R f(r, \theta)dA = \int_0^{\sqrt{2}/2} \int_{\text{Arcsin } r}^{\text{Arccos } r} rf(r, \theta)d\theta\, dr;$$

the arrow in Figure 343 shows the inner limits.

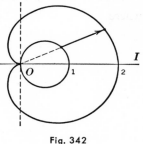

$\theta = \text{Arccos } r$

$[\frac{1}{2}\sqrt{2}, \frac{1}{4}\pi]$

$\theta = \text{Arcsin } r$

Fig. 343

Note 1. Consider the region $BCDE$ in Figure 344 between concentric circles of radii $r = r_1$ and $r = r_2$, where $r_2 = r_1 + \Delta r$. From (1) in Section 75 on page 224, the area, A, of $BCDE$ is $A = \frac{1}{2}(r_2^2\Delta\theta - r_1^2\Delta\theta)$, or

$$A = \frac{1}{2}(r_2 + r_1)(r_2 - r_1)\Delta\theta, \text{ or}$$

(with $\Delta r = r_2 - r_1$)
$$A = r'\Delta r\Delta\theta,$$
(10)

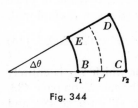

Fig. 344

where $r' = \frac{1}{2}(r_2 + r_1)$, which is the radius of a mid-section of $BCDE$. Hereafter, in an $r\theta$-plane, we shall refer to a subregion of type $BCDE$ as a **regular subregion**.

Note 2. Use of (8) to obtain A will be found equivalent to the method of page 347.

Note 3. Any type of complete proof for Theorem IV is beyond the level of this text. The following details have the objective of making (6) and (7) plausible.

Discussion of Theorem IV. 1. Let the domains for r and θ in R be

$$a \leqq r \leqq b \quad and \quad \alpha \leqq \theta \leqq \beta. \tag{11}$$

Form partitions of the intervals in (11) by points $r = r_j$ for (a, b) and $\theta = \theta_k$ for (α, β). Cover R with a grid formed by lines $\theta = \theta_k$, and circles $r = r_j$, as in Figure 345. This grid creates a partition σ of R. Let $T_{j,k}$ be the regular subregion where

$$\theta_{k-1} \leqq \theta \leqq \theta_k \quad and \quad r_{j-1} \leqq r \leqq r_j. \tag{12}$$

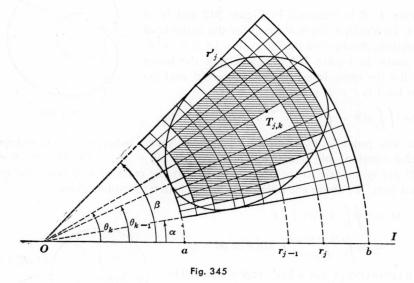

Fig. 345

Let $\Delta_k\theta = \theta_k - \theta_{k-1}$ and $\Delta_j r = r_j - r_{j-1}$, and let $\Delta_{j,k}A$ be the area of $T_{j,k}$. Then, by (10), $\qquad \Delta_{j,k}A = r_j'\Delta_j r\Delta_k\theta, \quad where \quad r_j' = \frac{1}{2}(r_{j-1} + r_j). \tag{13}$

2. The partition σ consists of certain regular subregions $T_{j,k}$ which lie wholly in σ, and perhaps various irregular subregions. In Figure 345, the regular parts $\{T_{j,k}\}$, with one exception, are ruled. Intuition convinces us that the total area of all irregular subregions of σ approaches zero if $d_\sigma \to 0$ and, hence, that they may be omitted in setting up the right-hand side of (3) for σ, without changing the equality. In any piece $T_{j,k}$ of σ, select the point $[r = r_j', \theta = \theta_k]$ to serve in place of $[\gamma_i, \mu_i]$ in (3). From (3) and (13) with only regular subregions of σ employed,

$$\iint_R f(r, \theta)dA = \lim_{d_\sigma \to 0} \sum_{(j,k)} f(r_j', \theta_k)\Delta_{j,k}A = \lim_{d_\sigma \to 0} \sum_{(j,k)} [r_j'f(r_j', \theta_k)]\Delta_j r\Delta_k\theta, \tag{14}$$

where the sum for (j, k) extends over all values (j, k) for which $T_{j,k}$ is entirely in R. We verify that the sum in (14) is of the same form as the sum S_σ on page 488, with the function "$rf(r, \theta)$" in (14) playing the role of "$F(x, y)$" on page 488, and

$[r, \theta]$ in place of (x, y). Hence, we conclude that the type of reasoning employed with S_σ in Section 187, on page 488, would lead from (14) to (6) or (7), according as "$\sum_{(j,k)}$" in (14) is evaluated by summing *first with respect to j* or *first with respect to k*. Thus, in (6), hereafter we may think of the inner integral arising as a consequence of writing

$$\sum_{(j,k)} r'_j f(r'_j, \theta_k) \Delta_j r \Delta_k \theta = \sum_{(k)} \left[\sum_{(j)} r'_j f(r'_j, \theta_k) \Delta_j r \right] \Delta_k \theta, \tag{15}$$

where we first take a sum of elements in a *fixed sector*, where k is held fast. Then, the outer integration in (6) is thought of as a consequence of taking the sum of sector sums in (15). Similar remarks apply to (7).

Note 4. For a regular subregion, in Figure 346, (13) gives $\Delta A = r\Delta r\Delta\theta$, with proper values for the factors, and this reminds us of the area of a rectangle with sides $r\Delta\theta$ and Δr. We think of "$r\Delta r\Delta\theta$" as a background for "$r\,dr\,d\theta$" in (6) and (7), and refer to "$r\,dr\,d\theta$" as the differential **element of area in polar coordinates.** The extra factor "r" in "$rf(r, \theta)$" on the right in (6) and (7) is a consequence of r'_j in expression (13) for the area $\Delta_{j,k}A$ for a regular subregion of R.

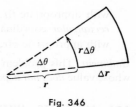

Fig. 346

EXERCISE 149

Unless otherwise specified, "$[r, \theta]$" indicates polar coordinates.

Express the double integral of $f(r, \theta)$ over R as an iterated integral.

1. R is the smaller segment of the circle $r = 4\cos\theta$ cut off by the line $r\cos\theta = 3$.

2. R is bounded by the loci $r = 1 + \sin\theta$, $r = \sin\theta$, and $\theta = 0$.

3. R is the triangle in quadrant I bounded by the lines $\theta = \frac{1}{6}\pi$, $r\cos\theta = 2$, and the polar axis. Write a result, first, where the inner integration is with respect to r. Second, divide R into two parts by drawing the circle $r = 2$, and write the result as a sum of two iterated integrals where the inner integration is with respect to θ.

4. R is bounded outside by the limaçon $r = 3 - \cos\theta$, and inside by $r = 5\cos\theta$.

5. Check the formula for the area of a circle by use of polar coordinates.

6. Check the formula for the area of a right triangle with legs u and v by use of a double integral in polar coordinates.

7. Find the mass of the region bounded by $r = 4$ if the density at $[r, \theta]$ is $\delta(r, \theta) = 5r$.

First formulate the specified area or mass as a double integral. Where mass is requested, $\delta(r, \theta)$ is the density at $[r, \theta]$. Integrate with respect to r and θ.

8. The area of R in Problem 1, and also the mass of R if $\delta(r, \theta)$ is proportional to the distance of $[r, \theta]$ from the polar axis.

9. The mass of R in Problem 4 if $\delta(r, \theta) = 2|\sin\theta|$.

10. The mass of R in Problem 3 if $\delta(r, \theta) = kr^2$.

11. The area of the region R bounded above by $r = 2(1 + \sin\theta)$ and below by the upper half of $r = 2$; the mass of R if $\delta(r, \theta) = k|\cos\theta|$.

12. R is the region bounded inside by the circle $r = 5\cos\theta$ and outside by the circle $r = \frac{5}{2}$. Find the mass of R if $\delta(r, \theta) = kr^2$.

13. R is the region bounded outside by the cardioid $r = 1 + \cos \theta$ and inside by the cardioid $r = 1 - \cos \theta$ in quadrant I. Find the mass of R if $\delta(r, \theta) = xy$.

14. R is the region above the polar axis bounded by $r = 2 \cos \theta, r = 4/(1 + \cos \theta)$, and the line $\theta = \frac{1}{2}\pi$. Find the area of R, and its mass if $\delta(r, \theta) = ky$.

15. In a region R bounded by an equilateral triangle whose side is u, the density of mass at any point is proportional to the distance from one vertex. Find the mass of R.

16. R is the region in quadrant I between the circle $r = 2$ and the parabola $r = \sec^2 \frac{1}{2}\theta$. Find the mass of R if $\delta(r, \theta) = k/r$.

17. First, interpret $[r, \theta]$ as polar coordinates, and draw R such that

$$I = \int_0^{\pi/4} \int_2^4 r^2 \cos \theta \, dr \, d\theta = \int\int_R f(r, \theta)dA,$$

with appropriate $f(r, \theta)$. Second, interpret (r, θ) as coordinates in an $r\theta$-system of *rectangular* coordinates in some plane, and draw R such that $I = \int\int_R g(r, \theta)dA$, with appropriate $g(r, \theta)$. Compute I.

Comment. This problem emphasizes that an iterated integral is an analytic expression whose value *does not depend on the geometric interpretation of the variables of integration.*

191. VOLUMES, WITH CYLINDRICAL COORDINATES

Consider an *xyz*-system of rectangular coordinates and, in the *xy*-plane, set up an *rθ*-system of polar coordinates related as usual to the rectangular coordinates (x, y). Then, the cylindrical coordinates $[r, \theta, z]$ of a point P, as in Figure 347, are defined as follows: the *z*-coordinate has its former meaning, the directed distance of P from the *rθ*-plane; *the pair (r, θ) are the polar coordinates in the rθ-plane of the projection of P on that plane.* The coordinates (x, y, z) and $[r, \theta, z]$ for a point P satisfy

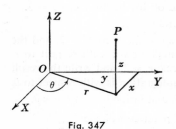

Fig. 347

$$z = z; \quad x = r \cos \theta; \quad y = r \sin \theta. \quad (1)$$

If (a, α, c) are constants, the locus of

$$\left.\begin{array}{l} r = a \text{ is a circular cylinder, axis } OZ\,; \\ \theta = \alpha \text{ is a plane through the z-axis}\,; \\ z = c \text{ is a horizontal plane.} \end{array}\right\} \quad (2)$$

The point $P:[r = a, \theta = \alpha, z = c]$ is the point of intersection of (2).

The locus of an equation $f(r, \theta) = 0$ in cylindrical coordinates is a *cylinder* whose generating lines are perpendicular to the *rθ*-plane, along the curve which is the locus of $f(r, \theta) = 0$ in the *rθ*-plane.

ILLUSTRATION 1. The space locus of $r = 3 \cos \theta$ is the circular cylinder perpendicular to the *rθ*-plane whose trace in that plane is the circle $r = 3 \cos \theta$.

To change an *xyz*-equation to cylindrical coordinates, we use (1).

ILLUSTRATION 2. The paraboloid of revolution $z = 4x^2 + 4y^2$ becomes

$$z = 4(x^2 + y^2) \quad or \quad z = 4r^2, \quad (3)$$

in cylindrical coordinates. Notice that *the equation of any surface of revolution about the z-axis involves just z and r in cylindrical coordinates.*

Note 1. With a *right-handed xyz*-system of coordinates, observe that the associated coordinate θ of (1) is measured *positive* in the *counterclockwise* direction, just as we should desire with polar coordinates in the *xy*-plane. *This would not be true in the case of a left-handed xyz-system.* This situation was one of the determining factors in our decision to use right-handed systems.

In space, install an *xyz*-system of rectangular coordinates and also the related *rθz*-system of cylindrical coordinates. Let T be a surface whose equation in

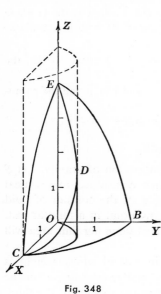

Fig. 348

cylindrical coordinates is $z = f(r, \theta)$, where $f(r, \theta) \geqq 0$. We may think of T also with the equation $z = F(x, y)$ where $F(x, y) \equiv f(r, \theta)$ when $x = r \cos \theta$ and $y = r \sin \theta$. Let V be the volume of the region W in (2) on page 492, capped by the surface T. Then,

$$\left\{ \begin{array}{l} cylindrical\ region,\ W; \\ base,\ R;\ cap,\ z = f(r,\ \theta) \end{array} \right\} \quad V = \iint_R z\ dA. \quad (4)$$

If the boundary of R consists of curves whose equations are convenient in *polar coordinates*, as is the case in Figure 348, we consider computing V in (4) by using $z = f(r, \theta)$, and obtaining an iterated integral in polar coordinates. Thus, if R is of type I as given in (4) on page 496,

$$V = \iint_R z\ dA = \int_\alpha^\beta \int_{h_1(\theta)}^{h_2(\theta)} rz\ dr\ d\theta. \quad (5)$$

EXAMPLE 1. Find the volume of the region W above the *xy*-plane within the cylinder $r = 2 \cos \theta$ and below the paraboloid $z = 4 - x^2 - y^2$.

Solution. Figure 348 shows one-half of the region W; the surfaces intersect along arc EDC, with CD on the front and DE on the back of the cylinder. Figure 349 exhibits the base of the circular cylinder $r = 2 \cos \theta$, undistorted. Let R be the half of the base in quadrant I. With $x = r \cos \theta$ and $y = r \sin \theta$, the equation of the paraboloid is $z = 4 - r^2$. Since W is symmetric to the *xz*-plane, from (5) with $z = 4 - r^2$ we obtain

$$V = 2 \iint_R z\ dA = 2 \int_0^{\pi/2} \int_0^{2\cos\theta} r(4 - r^2)dr\ d\theta = \tfrac{5}{2}\pi.$$

Comment. With knowledge that $z \geqq 0$ on $z = 4 - x^2 - y^2$, Figure 349 alone would be sufficient. The arrow checks the inner limits of integration.

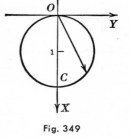

Fig. 349

EXERCISE 150

Compute by use of iterated integrals in polar coordinates in this exercise.

1. Find the volume of the sphere $x^2 + y^2 + z^2 = a^2$.

2. Find the volume of a right circular cylinder with altitude h and with base radius a.

Find the volume, V, of the region W above the rθ-plane within the given cylinder and below the specified surface, or the region bounded by the specified surfaces.

3. Within the cylinder $x^2 + y^2 = a^2$ and the sphere $x^2 + y^2 + z^2 = 4a^2$.

4. Within the cylinder $r = 2$, below the plane $y - x + 2z = 8$.

5. Within the cylinder $r = 3 \sin \theta$, below the plane $z = x$.

6. Within the cylinder $r = 1 - \cos \theta$, below the plane $z = y$.

7. Within the cylinder $x^2 + y^2 = 1$, below the cone $z^2 = 4x^2 + 4y^2$.

8. Find the volume of the wedge of the cylinder $r = a$ bounded below by the xy-plane and above by a plane through the x-axis making an angle of 30° with the xy-plane.

9. Within the cylinder $r = a$, below the cylinder $z = a^2 - x^2$.

10. W is the wedge in the first octant between the planes $\theta = \frac{1}{6}\pi$ and $\theta = \frac{1}{4}\pi$, the xy-plane, and the sphere $x^2 + y^2 + z^2 = a^2$.

11. W is bounded by the planes $x = 0, y = 0, z = 0, x = 1$, and $y = 1$, and the paraboloid $z = 4 - x^2 - y^2$, above the xy-plane.

12. W is the region inside both of the cylinders $z = 4 - x^2$ and $z = 4 - y^2$.

192. FLUID PRESSURE ON A VERTICAL SURFACE

Consider a body of fluid which is at rest under the attraction of gravity. Let S be a horizontal plane surface immersed in the fluid. Then, S is subject to a vertical force directed downward, which is equal to the weight of the column of fluid directly over S. We accept the physical fact that, at any point in a fluid at rest, it exerts a force which is *the same in all directions*. This **force per unit area** will be referred to as the **fluid pressure.**

In a vertical plane, let R be a region immersed in a fluid whose weight is w pounds per cubic unit. Set up an xy-system of rectangular coordinates in the plane, with the x-axis vertical, and the y-axis parallel to the surface of the fluid. At any point $Q:(x, y)$ in R, let $h(x)$ be the distance of Q below the surface of the fluid. Now, consider any partition σ of R. Let T be a subregion of σ with area ΔA; in Figure 350, T is represented by rectangle CD. Physical intuition convinces us

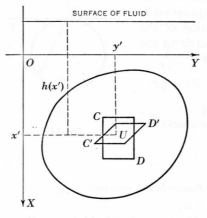

Fig. 350

that T is subject to a force due to fluid pressure which is *less* than that which would exist if all of T were at its *deepest* point, and *more* than that which would exist if all of T were at its *highest* point. Thus, by intuition, we accept the fact that there is some unknown point $U:(x', y')$ in T such that, if all of T were at the depth $h(x')$ of U, the resulting force would be equal to the actual force on T. Visualize T as tipped to the horizontal position $C'D'$, in Figure 350, at the level of U, and let ΔF be the force of fluid pressure which then acts on T. We have

$$\Delta F = wh(x')\Delta A, \qquad (1)$$

where $h(x')\Delta A$ is the volume of the column of fluid over T in horizontal position. With the preceding background, we define the force F due to fluid pressure acting on R as the limit of the sum of all elements ΔF for a partition σ as the norm $d_\sigma \to 0$:

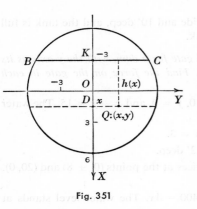

Fig. 351

$$F = \lim_{d_\sigma \to 0} \sum_{(all, \, for \, \sigma)} \Delta F. \qquad (2)$$

We recognize ΔF in (1) as the typical element of an approximating sum for the integral of $wh(x)$ over R. Hence,

$$F = w \iint_R h(x)dA. \qquad (3)$$

EXAMPLE 1. A cylindrical tank $12'$ in diameter is lying horizontally on its side and contains water to a depth of $9'$. Find the force F on one end of the tank.

Solution. 1. Figure 351 shows an end of the tank. In the plane of the circle, set up coordinates as indicated. In Figure 351, BC represents the water surface.

2. At $Q:(x, y)$ in Figure 351, the depth below the surface is the value of the directed segment KD where K is $(-3, 0)$. Hence, $\overline{KD} = h(x) = x + 3$.

3. By symmetry, the force F is equal to twice the force on the larger region R (where $y \geqq 0$) bounded by the x-axis, the line $x = -3$, and circle $x^2 + y^2 = 36$, or $y = \sqrt{36 - x^2}$. From (3),

$$F = 2w \iint_R (x + 3)dA = 2w \int_{-3}^{6} \int_0^{\sqrt{36-x^2}} (x + 3)dy \, dx = 9w(9\sqrt{3} + 8\pi).$$

With $w = 62.4$, we find $F = 2.29(10^4)$, pounds, by use of logarithms.

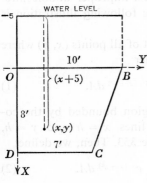

Fig. 352

EXAMPLE 2. The vertical gate in a dam $OBCD$ has the dimensions shown in Figure 352, and water is flowing over the dam with the surface $5'$ above the gate. Find the force due to water pressure on the gate.

Incomplete solution. Take the x-axis vertical, directed downward, with the origin at the top of the dam, as in the figure. Points $B:(0, 10)$ and $C:(8, 7)$ determine line BC. Its equation is

$$\frac{y - 7}{x - 8} = \frac{7 - 10}{8}, \quad or \quad 8y + 3x = 80. \qquad (4)$$

The distance of point (x, y) below the water surface is $h(x) = x + 5$. The region R on the gate is bounded by the lines $x = 0$, $x = 8$, $y = 0$, and $8y + 3x = 80$. From (3),

$$F = w \iint_R (x + 5)dA = w \int_0^8 \int_0^{(80-3x)/8} (x + 5)dy \, dx.$$

EXERCISE 151

Find the force on the vertical surface due to fluid pressure. Use 62.4 pounds as the weight of a cubic foot of water.

1. The vertical end of a rectangular tank is 8' wide and 10' deep, and the tank is full of water. Find the force on the end of the tank.

Let the x-axis and y-axis be located in the vertical gate for a dam, with the y-axis as its top, and the x-axis directed vertically downward. Find the force on the gate in each problem. The unit for each coordinate is 1'.

2. The gate is bounded by the lines $x = 0$, $x = 10$, $y = 0$, and $x + y = 15$. The water level stands at $x = 0$.

3. Solve Problem 2, if the water level stands at $x = 3$.

4. Solve Problem 2, if water flows over the gate 2' deep.

5. The gate has the shape of a triangle, with vertices at the points $(0, \pm 8)$ and $(20, 0)$. Water flows over the gate 5' deep.

6. The gate is bounded by the parabola $y^2 = 400 - 4x$. The water level stands at $x = 10$.

7. The gate is a trapezoid, with the vertices at the points $(0, -5)$, $(0, 10)$, $(20, 0)$, and $(20, 5)$. The water level is flush with the top of the gate.

8. The gate is bounded on the left by the parabola $y^2 = 100 - 2x$, on the right by the parabola $y^2 = 400 - 8x$. The water level is 10' below the top of the gate.

9. A vertical drainage gate for a swimming pool is bounded by a circle 4' in diameter. If the water level is 12' above the top of the gate, find the force on the gate.

10. A horizontal cylindrical tank is 10' in diameter and is full of oil weighing 50 pounds per cubic foot. Find the force on an end of the tank.

193. IMPROPER DOUBLE INTEGRALS

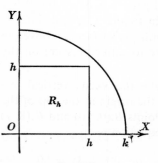

Fig. 353

In more advanced courses, improper double integrals are introduced. The following illustration is very useful.

Let the region R consist of all points (x, y) where $x \geqq 0$ and $y \geqq 0$. Consider

$$J = \iint_R e^{-(x^2+y^2)} \, dA. \qquad (1)$$

Let R_h be the square region bounded by the coordinate axes and the lines $x = h$ and $y = h$, where $h > 0$, as in Figure 353. Then, we define:

$$J = \lim_{h \to \infty} \iint_{R_h} e^{-(x^2+y^2)} \, dA. \qquad (2)$$

Thus, $\qquad J = \lim_{h \to \infty} \int_0^h \int_0^h e^{-x^2} e^{-y^2} \, dx \, dy = \lim_{h \to \infty} \left(\int_0^h e^{-x^2} \, dx \right) \left(\int_0^h e^{-y^2} \, dy \right). \qquad (3)$

Hence, $\qquad\qquad\qquad J = \lim_{h \to \infty} \left(\int_0^h e^{-x^2} \, dx \right)^2. \qquad (4)$

We shall employ (4) later. First, we shall consider a second evaluation of J.

Let S_k be the region in quadrant I bounded by the coordinate axes and the circle whose equation in polar coordinates is $r = k > 0$, as in Figure 353. Then, we define J as the following limit, if it exists:

$$J = \lim_{k \to \infty} \iint_{S_k} e^{-(x^2 + y^2)} \, dA. \tag{5}$$

Or,

$$J = \lim_{k \to \infty} \int_0^k \int_0^{\pi/2} re^{-r^2} \, d\theta \, dr = \frac{1}{2} \pi \lim_{k \to \infty} \int_0^k re^{-r^2} \, dr = \frac{\pi}{4}. \tag{6}$$

We now accept the fact that (2) should lead to the same value for J, because R_h and S_k both expand over each point in R as $h \to \infty$ and $k \to \infty$. Thus, from (4) and (6), we conclude that

$$\lim_{h \to \infty} \left(\int_0^h e^{-x^2} \, dx \right)^2 = \frac{\pi}{4}, \quad \text{or} \quad \lim_{h \to \infty} \int_0^h e^{-x^2} \, dx = \sqrt{\frac{\pi}{4}} = \int_0^\infty e^{-x^2} \, dx.$$

Therefore, by investigating (1), we have proved that

$$\int_0^\infty e^{-x^2} \, dx = \tfrac{1}{2} \sqrt{\pi}, \quad \text{or} \quad \int_{-\infty}^\infty e^{-x^2} \, dx = \sqrt{\pi}.$$

This result is especially valuable in statistics, in the study of the normal probability distribution.

★SUPPLEMENT FOR CHAPTER TWENTY

★EXERCISE 152

Any region, R, in Problems 1–2 is in an $r\theta$-, or xy-plane, and includes the boundaries.

1. R is inside the curve $r = 4(1 + \sin \theta)$ and outside $r = 3/(1 - \sin \theta)$, to the right of the line $\theta = \frac{1}{2}\pi$. If mass is spread over R with density $\delta(r, \theta) = kx$, find the mass of R.

2. R is the region between the inner loop and the outer part of the limaçon

$$r = 2 - 4 \cos \theta.$$

Find the mass of R if $\delta(r, \theta) = k|y|$.

3. Suppose that a region R in the xy-plane is symmetric to the x-axis, which divides R into two regions R_1 and R_2. Assume that $F(x, y) = F(x, -y)$, at all points (x, y) in R (that is, suppose that $F(x, y)$ also is symmetric to the x-axis). By describing how to obtain appropriate approximating sums for each integral, as in the Comment on page 493, prove that

$$\iint_{R_1} F(x, y)dA = \iint_{R_2} F(x, y)dA, \quad \text{or} \quad \iint_R F(x, y)dA = 2\iint_{R_1} F(x, y)dA.$$

With $[r, \theta]$ interpreted as polar coordinates, draw the region R in an $r\theta$-plane, so that the given iterated integral is equal to a double integral over R, and write this integral. Then, repeat with (r, θ) as **rectangular coordinates.**

4. $\displaystyle\int_2^4 \int_0^{\pi/3} r^3 \sin \theta \, d\theta \, dr.$

5. $\displaystyle\int_0^\pi \int_{\sin \theta}^{3 \sin \theta} r^4 \cos \theta \, dr \, d\theta.$

6. $\displaystyle\int_{-\pi/2}^{\pi/2} \int_{\cos \theta}^{4/(1+\cos \theta)} \sin \theta \, dr \, d\theta.$

7. $\displaystyle\int_{\pi/3}^{2\pi/3} \int_{3/(1-\cos \theta)}^{4(1+\cos \theta)} \sin \theta \, dr \, d\theta.$

Express with the order of integration interchanged, by first obtaining a double integral in some plane.

8. $\int_0^{\pi/4} \int_{\sin\theta}^{\cos\theta} \cos^4\theta \, dr \, d\theta.$

9. $\int_1^2 \int_0^{(\text{Arccos } r/2)/2} r \sin 2\theta \, d\theta \, dr.$

10. A round hole of radius $\frac{1}{2}a$ is bored through a solid sphere of radius a, with a diameter of the sphere as the axis of symmetry of the hole. Find the volume of the material cut from the sphere.

11. W is bounded by the planes $x = 0$, $y = 0$, $z = 0$, $x = 1$, and $z = 1$, and the cone $y^2 = 9x^2 + 9z^2$. Use modified cylindrical coordinates.

12. If the function $F(x, y)$ has continuous derivatives F_x, F_y, and F_{xy}, and if

$$F_{xy}(x, y) = f(x, y),$$

prove that

$$\int_a^b \int_c^d f(x, y) dy \, dx = F(b, d) - F(a, d) - F(b, c) + F(a, c).$$

13. If the function $f(x, y)$ is continuous where $a \leqq x \leqq b$ and $c \leqq y \leqq d$, and if

$$F(x, y) = \int_a^x \int_b^y f(u, v) dv \, du,$$

prove that $F_{xy}(x, y) = f(x, y)$.

Note 1. The **average value** (or **mean value**), μ, of a function $F(x, y)$ over a region R in the xy-plane is defined as $\mu = \int\int_R F(x, y) dA/A$, where A is the area of R. As a special case, in (2) on page 489, with $\mu = \delta(\xi, \eta)$, we meet the average density.

14. Let R be the region bounded by a circle, C, of radius ρ. Prove that the average of the distance from a fixed point of C to a point in R is $32\rho/9\pi$.

15. By use of Section 193, page 504, prove that, if $h > 0$, $\int_{-\infty}^{\infty} e^{-hu^2} du = \sqrt{\pi}/\sqrt{h}$.

16. Let W be the unbounded region in xyz-space bounded by the xy-plane and the **normal probability surface** of statistics,

$$z = \frac{1}{2\pi\sigma_1\sigma_2} e^{-\frac{1}{2}\left(\frac{x^2}{\sigma_1^2} + \frac{y^2}{\sigma_2^2}\right)}, \text{ where } \sigma_1 > 0 \text{ and } \sigma_2 > 0.$$

With the "volume" of W defined by an improper integral, as on page 504, prove that the volume of W is 1 unit.

CHAPTER TWENTY-ONE

Moments in a Plane

194. CENTER OF MASS IN A PLANE, VARIABLE DENSITY

Let R be a region in an xy-plane. Suppose that a total mass m is distributed over R with $\delta(x, y)$ as the density of mass at any point (x, y), where δ is a continuous function. Under these circumstances, we refer to R as a *lamina*. Its total mass is

$$m = \iint_R \delta(x, y)dA. \tag{1}$$

We shall define the notions of moments and the center of mass for R.*

First, we shall define the moments of lamina R with respect to the x-axis and y-axis. Let σ be a partition of R into subregions $\{T\}$, where the representative piece T has the area ΔA and mass Δm. Let the norm d_σ be the maximum of the diameters of the subregions. From (2) on page 489, there exists a point (x', y') in T, as in Figure 354, so that $\Delta m = \delta(x', y')\Delta A$.

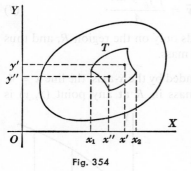 By physical intuition, we decide that the moment with respect to the y-axis of the mass of T should lie between $x_1\Delta m$ and $x_2\Delta m$, where x_1 and x_2 are, respectively, the least and the greatest values for x in T, as in Figure 354. Hence, we think of concentrating all of Δm at an arbitrary point (x'', y'') in T, where x'' lies on the interval $x_1 \leqq x \leqq x_2$, and let ΔM_y be the corresponding moment of Δm with respect to the y-axis. Then,

Fig. 354

$$\Delta M_y = x''\Delta m = x''\delta(x', y')\Delta A. \tag{2}$$

Finally, we define the moment, M_y, of the mass of R with respect to the y-axis to be the limit of the sum of all elements ΔM_y as $d_\sigma \to 0$. Or,

$$M_y = \lim_{d_\sigma \to 0} \sum \Delta M_y = \lim_{d_\sigma \to 0} \sum x''\delta(x', y')\Delta A, \tag{3}$$

* The discussion will be independent of Section 71, on page 213, where $\delta(x, y)$ is a constant. The student should review Section 69 on page 209.

where the sum "$\sum$" involves the moment elements for all subregions of σ. Since the functions x and $\delta(x, y)$ are continuous functions, we accept the fact * that the limit in (3), if it exists, will not be altered by changing x'' to x', because $|\, x'' - x' \,| \to 0$ as $d_\sigma \to 0$. Hence, we conclude that

$$M_y = \lim_{d_\sigma \to 0} \sum x'\delta(x', y')\Delta A. \qquad (4)$$

From (5) on page 483, $[x'\delta(x', y')\Delta A]$ in (4) is recognized as the typical element of an approximating sum S_σ for the double integral of $x\delta(x, y)$ over R. Thus, from (4), we arrive at the following definition for M_y, and similarly for M_x, the moment of the mass of R with respect to the x-axis:

$$M_y = \iint_R x\delta(x, y)dA; \quad M_x = \iint_R y\delta(x, y)dA. \qquad (5)$$

By Definition VII on page 210, the center of mass, $(\bar{x}, \bar{y})$, for R is that point where the whole mass m would have to be concentrated in order for it to have the same moments with respect to the axes as the mass m *when spread over R.* If a mass m were at $(\bar{x}, \bar{y})$, the moments with respect to the y-axis and x-axis would be $m\bar{x}$ and $m\bar{y}$, respectively. Hence, $\qquad m\bar{x} = M_y \quad and \quad m\bar{y} = M_x$, or

$$\left\{ \begin{matrix} \textbf{center of} \\ \textbf{mass} \end{matrix} \right\} \qquad \bar{x} = \frac{\iint_R x\delta(x, y)dA}{m}; \quad \bar{y} = \frac{\iint_R y\delta(x, y)dA}{m}. \qquad (6)$$

If, for all (x, y), $\delta(x, y)$ is a constant, which we shall represent simply by δ, then $(\bar{x}, \bar{y})$ is called the **centroid** of R. In such a case, (1) becomes $m = \delta A$, where A is the area of R, and δ divides out in (6) to give

$$\textbf{(centroid)} \qquad \bar{x} = \frac{\iint_R x \, dA}{A} \quad and \quad \bar{y} = \frac{\iint_R y \, dA}{A}. \qquad (7)$$

Since (7) does not involve δ, the centroid depends only on the region R, and thus has a geometrical significance regardless of any mass.

EXAMPLE 1. A region R in the 1st quadrant is bounded by the x-axis, the line $x = 4$, and the parabola $y^2 = 4x$. If the density of mass in R at any point (x, y) is $\delta(x, y) = 2x$, find the center of mass.

Solution. From Figure 355, (1), and (6),

$$m = \iint_R 2x \, dA = \int_0^4 \int_0^{2x^{\frac{1}{2}}} 2x \, dy \, dx = \tfrac{1}{5}(2^8);$$

$$M_x = \iint_R 2xy \, dA = \tfrac{1}{3}(2^8);$$

$$M_y = \iint_R 2x^2 \, dA = \tfrac{1}{7}(2^{10});$$

$$\bar{x} = \frac{M_y}{m} = \tfrac{20}{7}; \quad \bar{y} = \frac{M_x}{m} = \tfrac{5}{3}.$$

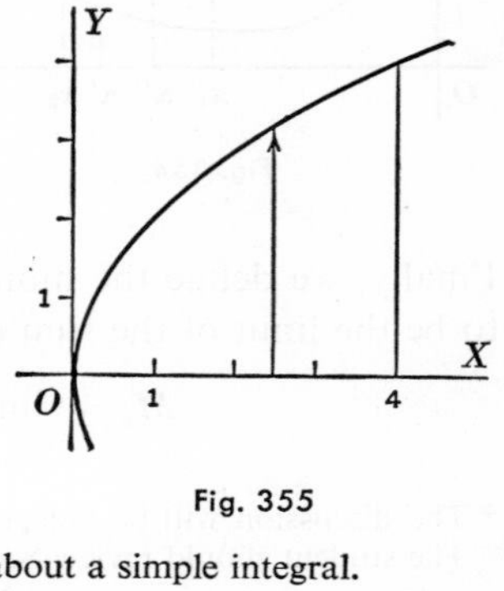

Fig. 355

* The reasoning is similar to that in the footnote on page 212 about a simple integral.

It can be proved (see Problem 35 on page 522) that the location of the center of mass in a lamina is independent of the directions of the axes and the location of the origin in the xy-plane. Also, it will be found that the point $(\bar{x}, \bar{y})$ may not lie in the lamina.

Theorem I. *If a region R has an axis of symmetry, and if the values of the density function δ also are symmetric (or, the function δ is symmetric) to this axis, then the center of mass for R lies on the axis of symmetry.*

Proof. 1. Choose the axis of symmetry as the y-axis. For any point (x, y), the point symmetric to the y-axis is $(-x, y)$. By hypothesis, $\delta(x, y) = \delta(-x, y)$, for every point (x, y) in R.

2. In the details preceding (4), let σ be restricted to consist of *pairs* of subregions, T and $\hat{T}$, symmetric to the y-axis, as in Figure 356. Then, with (x', y') as a point in T, and with the symmetric point $(-x', y')$ in $\hat{T}$, we obtain elements ΔM_y and $\Delta \hat{M}_y$, as in (2), where we choose $x'' = x'$ in (2), and finally arrive at

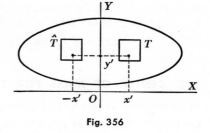

$$\Delta M_y = x'\delta(x', y')\Delta A, \text{ and}$$
$$\Delta \hat{M}_y = -x'\delta(-x', y')\Delta \hat{A}.$$

Fig. 356

Since $\delta(x', y') = \delta(-x', y')$ and $\Delta A = \Delta \hat{A}$,

we have $$\Delta M_y = -\Delta \hat{M}_y \quad \text{or} \quad \Delta M_y + \Delta \hat{M}_y = 0. \tag{8}$$

Hence, the sum in (4) is zero, because the terms cancel in pairs, as in (8). Thus, $M_y = 0$. Or, $m\bar{x} = 0$ and hence $\bar{x} = 0$, which proves Theorem I.

EXAMPLE 2. Find the center of mass for the region R bounded above by $4x^2 + 9y^2 = 36$ and below by the x-axis, if $\delta(x, y) = 3y|x|$.

Solution. 1. R is symmetric to the y-axis, in Figure 357. Also, δ is symmetric to the y-axis, or $\delta(x_1, y_1) = \delta(-x_1, y_1)$. By Theorem I, $(\bar{x}, \bar{y})$ is on the y-axis, or $\bar{x} = 0$.

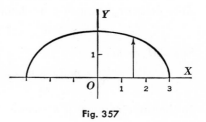

Fig. 357

2. From (1) and (6),

$$m = \iint_R 3y|x|\,dA; \quad m\bar{y} = \iint_R 3y^2|x|\,dA. \tag{9}$$

Let R_1 be that part of R where $x \geq 0$. By symmetry,

$$m = 2\iint_{R_1} 3xy\,dA = 6\int_0^3 \int_0^{(2\sqrt{9-x^2})/3} xy\,dy\,dx = 27; \tag{10}$$

$$m\bar{y} = 2\iint_{R_1} 3xy^2\,dA = 6\int_0^2 \int_0^{(3\sqrt{4-y^2})/2} y^2x\,dx\,dy = \tfrac{144}{5}. \tag{11}$$

Then, from (10) and (11), $\bar{y} = \tfrac{16}{15}$. The center of mass is $(0, \tfrac{16}{15})$.

Note 1. If $\delta(x, y)$ is a constant, then δ is symmetric to any line in the xy-plane. Also, in this case, we call the center of mass of a region R its *centroid*. Hence, by Theorem I, if a region R has *two* axes of symmetry, their intersection is the centroid of R. This result was accepted intuitively on page 214.

ILLUSTRATION 1. By Note 1, if R is bounded by a rectangle, the centroid of R is the intersection of the diagonals of the rectangle. Similarly, the center of mass of a homogeneous circular lamina R is its geometrical center.

★*Note 2.* In the field of statistics, let (X, Y) denote a *two-dimensional random vector variable*, with the particular values (x, y). Let the range of (X, Y) be the region R in the xy-plane. Then, a continuous, nonnegative function $\delta(x, y)$ is called the *probability density function* for (X, Y) in case

$$\iint_R \delta(x, y)dA = 1 \quad and \quad pr[(X, Y) \text{ in } T] = \iint_T \delta(x, y)dA, \tag{12}$$

for every subregion T of R, where "*pr*[ ]" means "*probability of* [ ]." Then, we refer to $\bar{x}$ and $\bar{y}$ of (6) as the *means*, or *expected values* of X and Y, respectively, and write $\bar{x} = E(X)$ and $\bar{y} = E(Y)$. From (6) with $m = 1$,

$$\bar{x} = E(X) = \iint_R x\delta(x, y)dA \quad and \quad \bar{y} = E(Y) = \iint_R y\delta(x, y)dA. \tag{13}$$

195. CENTER OF MASS FOR TWO OR MORE REGIONS

In an xy-plane, consider distributions of mass over two regions R_1 and R_2, which do not overlap except possibly at boundaries. In R_1 and R_2, suppose that the densities of mass are $\delta_1(x, y)$ and $\delta_2(x, y)$, the centers of mass are $(\bar{x}_1, \bar{y}_1)$ and $(\bar{x}_2, \bar{y}_2)$, the masses are m_1 and m_2, and the moments with respect to the y-axis are $M_{y,1}$ and $M_{y,2}$, respectively. Let R be the region consisting of the subregions R_1 and R_2, with R having the mass m, center of mass $(\bar{x}, \bar{y})$, and M_y as the moment with respect to the y-axis. We define the double integral of any function of x and y over R as the sum of the double integrals of the function over R_1 and R_2. Hence, since mass and moments are defined as integrals, we have

$$m = m_1 + m_2; \quad M_y = M_{y,1} + M_{y,2} = m_1\bar{x}_1 + m_2\bar{x}_2.$$

Since $M_y = m\bar{x}$, $\quad\quad\quad\quad\quad\quad\quad m\bar{x} = m_1\bar{x}_1 + m_2\bar{x}_2,$ or

$$\bar{x} = \frac{m_1\bar{x}_1 + m_2\bar{x}_2}{m}; \quad similarly, \quad \bar{y} = \frac{m_1\bar{y}_1 + m_2\bar{y}_2}{m}. \tag{1}$$

In the same manner, if n regions $\{R_i\}$ are involved, there is obtained

$$\bar{x} = \frac{\sum_{i=1}^n m_i\bar{x}_i}{\sum_{i=1}^n m_i}; \quad \bar{y} = \frac{\sum_{i=1}^n m_i\bar{y}_i}{\sum_{i=1}^n m_i}. \tag{2}$$

Comparison of (2) with (7) on page 211 justifies the following conclusion: *The center of mass of a set of regions $\{R_i\}$, with masses $\{m_i\}$, is that point $(\bar{x}, \bar{y})$ which would be the center of mass for a set of mass points $\{m_i\}$, concentrated at the centers of mass $(\bar{x}_i, \bar{y}_i)$ for the regions R_i.* If the density of mass is a constant δ, then $m_i = \delta A_i$, where A_i is the area of R_i, and (2) gives the centroid of R, where δ divides out:

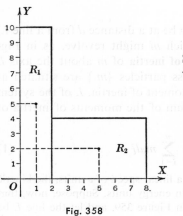

Fig. 358

$$\bar{x} = \frac{\sum_{i=1}^{n} A_i \bar{x}_i}{\sum_{i=1}^{n} A_i} \quad and \quad \bar{y} = \frac{\sum_{i=1}^{n} A_i \bar{y}_i}{\sum_{i=1}^{n} A_i}. \quad (3)$$

Sometimes, we may use (3) to find the centroid without integration.

ILLUSTRATION 1. Suppose that mass is spread uniformly over the L-shaped region R in quadrant I of Figure 358. To find the centroid of R without integration, divide R into the two rectangular regions R_1 and R_2, whose areas A_1 and A_2, and centroids (x_1, y_1) and (x_2, y_2) are found easily. Then we could use (3). The student may complete the work here in Problem 24 in the exercise below.

EXERCISE 153

Find the centroid of the region with the specified boundary. Employ double integrals. Use symmetry. Do not integrate for any familiar area.

1–12. The regions of Problems 1–12, respectively, in Exercise 61, page 216.

13. Bounded by the lines $x = 0$, $y = 0$, and $bx + ay = ab$.

14. Bounded by the x-axis and the curve $y = \sin x$ where $0 \le x \le \pi$.

15. Bounded by the x-axis, the line $x = \frac{1}{2}\pi$ and $y = \sin x$, with $0 \le x \le \frac{1}{2}\pi$.

16. Bounded by the lines $x = 0$, $y = 0$, and $x = 3$, and $y = e^x$.

Find the center of mass of the lamina with the given boundary and density.

17. Bounded by $x = 0$, $y = 0$, $x = 2$, and $y = 3$; $\delta(x, y) = x^2 y$.

18. Bounded by $x = 0$, $y = 0$, and $x + 3y = 6$; $\delta(x, y) = 4x$.

19. Bounded by $y = 0$, $y = x$, and $x + y = 4$; (a) $\delta(x, y) = 3y$; (b) $\delta(x, y) = 2x$.

20. Bounded by $y = 0$ and $y = 2x - x^2$; $\delta(x, y) = 2x^2$.

21. Bounded by $y^2 = 4 + 4x$ and $y^2 = 4 - 8x$; $\delta(x, y) = ky^2$.

22. Bounded by the parabola $y^2 = 9x$ and the line $x = 4$, with the density at any point (x, y) proportional to its distance from the line $x = 4$.

23. Bounded by the curve $x^2 = 2y + 1$ and the line $y = 4$; $\delta(x, y) = 3|x|$.

Find the centroid of the region with the specified boundary. Avoid integration if possible.

24. The region in Figure 358, above.

25. Bounded by the quadrilateral with vertices $(0, 0)$, $(3, 3)$, $(5, 1)$, and $(5, 0)$.

26. Bounded by the trapezoid with the vertices $(0, 0)$, $(1, 0)$, $(5, 4)$, and $(0, 4)$.

27. Bounded above by the ellipse whose parametric equations are $x = a \cos t$ and $y = b \sin t$, with $a > 0$ and $b > 0$, and below by the x-axis.

28. Bounded by the x-axis and the cycloid whose parametric equations are
$$x = t - \sin t \quad and \quad y = 1 - \cos t, \quad with \quad 0 \le t \le 2\pi.$$

29. Bounded by the curve $y = \sec x$ and the line $y = 2$, with x restricted to the interval $-\frac{1}{2}\pi < x < \frac{1}{2}\pi$.

30. Derive formulas (1), page 214, by use of double integrals.

196. MOMENT OF INERTIA

In three-dimensional space, let a mass particle m be at a distance d from a line L,

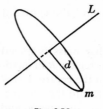

which is an axis about which m might revolve, as in Figure 359. Then, the **moment of inertia** of m about the axis L is defined as md^2. If n mass particles $\{m_i\}$ are situated at distances $\{d_i\}$ from L, the moment of inertia, I, of the system about L is defined as the sum of the moments of inertia of the particles:

Fig. 359

$$I = \sum_{i=1}^{n} m_i d_i^2 \tag{1}$$

Note 1. If a mass particle of m units is moving with a linear speed of v units, the kinetic energy, E, of the particle is defined by $E = \frac{1}{2}mv^2$, in energy units. Suppose, now, that the particle is revolving in a circle of radius d, as in Figure 359, and let the line L be perpendicular to the plane of the circle at its center. At any instant, if the angular velocity of the particle is ω radians per unit time, the speed of the particle is ωd linear units per unit time. Then, the kinetic energy in energy units is

$$E = \tfrac{1}{2}m(\omega d)^2 = \tfrac{1}{2}(md^2)\omega^2 = \tfrac{1}{2}I\omega^2, \tag{2}$$

where I is the moment of inertia of the particle with respect to the axis L. Thus, in (2), I plays the role of the *mass m* and ω the role of v, as compared to the formula $E = \frac{1}{2}mv^2$.

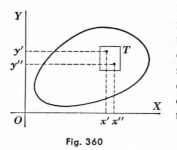

Suppose that a mass m is spread over a region R in the xy-plane, as in Figure 360, with $\delta(x, y)$ as the density of mass at any point (x, y), where δ is continuous in R. Let σ be a partition of R into subregions $\{T\}$, and let d_σ be the maximum of their diameters. Let ΔA be the area and Δm be the mass of the typical subregion T. Then, as on page 507, there exists a point (x', y') in T such that

Fig. 360

$$\Delta m = \delta(x', y')\Delta A. \tag{3}$$

If Δm is considered as concentrated at an arbitrary point (x'', y'') in T, the moment of inertia of Δm about the y-axis is

$$x''^2 \Delta m, \quad or \quad x''^2 \delta(x', y')\Delta A. \tag{4}$$

The **moment of inertia,** I_y, of the mass in R *about the y-axis* is defined as the limit of the sum, S_σ, of all elements (4) for the subregions of σ, as $d_\sigma \to 0$. By familiar reasoning, as applied in (3) on page 507, we decide that the preceding limit may be evaluated with x'' replaced by x' in (4), to give the element

$$\Delta I_y = x'^2 \delta(x', y')\Delta A, \quad and\ then \quad I_y = \lim_{d_\sigma \to 0} \sum \Delta I_y. \tag{5}$$

In (5), the sum extends over the elements ΔI_y corresponding to all subregions of σ. From (5) on page 483, we recognize ΔI_y in (5) as the typical element of an approximating sum S_σ for the integral of $x^2\delta(x, y)$ over R. Thus,

$$I_y = \iint_R x^2\delta(x, y)dA; \quad similarly, \quad I_x = \iint_R y^2\delta(x, y)dA. \tag{6}$$

Consider an axis L perpendicular to the xy-plane at the origin, as in Figure 361. Let a mass particle m be located at (x_0, y_0) in the plane. Then, the moment of inertia of m with respect to L is called the *polar moment of inertia* of m. The distance, d, of m from L is given by $d^2 = x_0^2 + y_0^2$, and thus the polar moment of

inertia of m is $\qquad md^2 \quad or \quad m(x_0^2 + y_0^2), \quad or \quad (mx_0^2 + my_0^2),$ $\qquad$ (7)

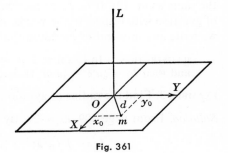

Fig. 361

which is the sum of the moments of inertia of m with respect to the x-axis and the y-axis. Similarly, if there is a *continuous* distribution of mass over a region R in the xy-plane, the moment of inertia, I_O, of this mass with respect to a line perpendicular to the plane at the origin is called the **polar moment of inertia** of the mass. When (7) is used for Δm from (3), and details similar to (5) are discussed, we obtain

$$I_O = \int\int_R (x^2 + y^2)\delta(x, y)dA.$$ (8)

From (6) and (8), $\qquad\qquad I_O = I_x + I_y.$ $\qquad$ (9)

EXAMPLE 1. For the lamina of Example 1 on page 508, find I_x, I_y, and I_O.

Solution. From (6), $\qquad I_x = \int\int_R 2xy^2\, dA \quad and \quad I_y = \int\int_R 2x^3\, dA;$

$$I_x = \int_0^4 \int_0^{2x^{\frac{1}{2}}} 2xy^2\, dy\, dx = \tfrac{4096}{21}; \quad I_y = \tfrac{4096}{9}; \quad I_O = \tfrac{4096}{21} + \tfrac{4096}{9} = \tfrac{40,960}{63}.$$

EXAMPLE 2. A homogeneous plane lamina is bounded by an isosceles right triangle. Find the moment of inertia of the lamina about an axis perpendicular to its plane at the vertex of the $90°$ angle.

Solution. 1. Let the constant density of mass be δ, and each leg of the triangle be a units long. Place the triangle on an xy-system with the $90°$ vertex at the origin, and the legs in the positive directions on the axes, as in Figure 362. Then, we desire I_O.

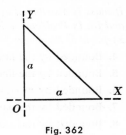

Fig. 362

2. Let R be the region bounded by the right triangle. The hypotenuse has the equation $x + y = a$. Hence,

$$I_x = \int\int_R \delta y^2\, dA = \delta \int_0^a \int_0^{a-x} y^2\, dy\, dx = \tfrac{1}{12}a^4\delta.$$

By symmetry, $I_y = I_x$. Hence, $I_O = \tfrac{1}{6}a^4\delta$.

Let L be any line in the xy-plane, and let $h(x, y)$ be the perpendicular distance (taken positive) from a point (x, y) to L. Let I be the moment of inertia about L for the mass over a region R. Then, we could derive

$$I = \int\int_R [h(x, y)]^2\delta(x, y)dA.$$ (10)

If m is the total mass over R, define a positive constant k by

$$I = mk^2. \tag{11}$$

Then, k is called the **radius of gyration** of the mass distribution with respect to the axis of rotation L. That is, by (11), if all of the mass were located at the perpendicular distance k from L, the resulting moment of inertia about L would be the same as in (10). If I_x, I_y, or I_O is written in the form (11), k is called the radius of gyration with respect to the x-axis, y-axis, or the origin, respectively. Frequently we write any moment of inertia in the form $I = mk^2$, so that k^2 is prominent.

ILLUSTRATION 1. In Example 2, $m = A\delta$ where $A = \frac{1}{2}a^2$. Thus we have $\delta = 2m/a^2$, and then $I_O = \frac{1}{6}a^4\delta = \frac{1}{3}a^2m$. Hence, $k^2 = \frac{1}{3}a^2$, or the radius of gyration is $\frac{1}{3}a\sqrt{3}$.

EXAMPLE 3. Find the radius of gyration about OX in Example 2 on page 509.

Solution. From page 509, $m = 27$. By use of (6),

$$I_x = \int\int_R 3y^2| \, x \, |y \, dA = 6\int\int_{R_1} xy^3 \, dA, \tag{12}$$

where R_1 is described on page 509. From (12), with limits of integration found from Figure 357 on page 509, we obtain

$$I_x = 6\int_0^2 \int_0^{(3\sqrt{4-y^2})/2} xy^3 \, dx \, dy = 27(\tfrac{4}{3}) = \tfrac{4}{3}m; \quad k^2 = \tfrac{4}{3} \quad or \quad k = 1.155.$$

EXERCISE 154

1. Find the moment of inertia and the radius of gyration of a homogeneous square lamina of side h and constant density, (a) about one side; (b) about the center.

2. A homogeneous lamina is bounded by an isosceles triangle with base 4 and altitude 6. Find the moment of inertia and radius of gyration of the lamina about the perpendicular bisector of the base.

3. Find the moment of inertia of a homogeneous rectangular lamina of dimensions h and k, (a) about a vertex; (b) about a side of length h. Also find the corresponding radii of gyration.

If mass is distributed over the specified region with the indicated density δ, obtain I_x, I_y, and I_O. In Problems 4–5, obtain the radius of gyration about an axis perpendicular to the xy-plane at the origin.

4. Bounded by the lines $y = 0$, $y = x$, and $x + y = 4$; δ a constant.

5. Bounded by the lines $x = 0$, $x + 2y = 4$, and $x - 2y = 4$; δ a constant.

6. Bounded by $y^2 = 4 + x$ and the lines $y = 0$ and $x = 5$, with $y \geqq 0$; δ a constant.

7. Bounded by the parabola $x^2 = 9y$ and the line $y = 1$, with $x \geqq 0$; δ a constant.

8. Bounded by the x-axis and the curve $y = 2x - x^2$; δ a constant.

9–12. The mass in Problems 17–20, respectively, of Exercise 153.

13. The region bounded below by the x-axis and above by the ellipse whose parametric equations are $x = a \cos t$ and $y = b \sin t$, where $a > 0$ and $b > 0$; δ a constant.

Hint. $\qquad\qquad I_x = \delta \int_{-a}^a \int_0^y y^2 \, dy \, dx = \tfrac{1}{3}\delta \int_{-a}^a y^3 \, dx.$

Then, use the parametric equations.

14. Mass is distributed uniformly, with the density δ, over the region in an xy-plane bounded by the circle defined by $x = a \cos^2 t$ and $y = a \sin t \cos t$, where $a > 0$. Find I_x, I_y, and I_0 for the lamina.

15. Find the polar moment of inertia for the region bounded by the whole ellipse of Problem 13; δ a constant. Notice the result then obtained for a circle of radius a.

16. A lamina R with constant density is bounded by the lines $y = 0$, $x = a$, and $x = b$, and the curve $y = f(x)$, where $f(x) \geqq 0$. By starting with double integrals, find expressions for I_x and I_y for R as simple integrals.

17. Mass is spread uniformly over the region bounded by the lines $x = 0$, $y = 0$, and $x + 3y = 6$. Find the moment of inertia of the mass about the line $x = 4$. Make an appropriate change in (6) on page 512, as suggested by (10) on page 513.

18. Mass is spread uniformly over the region bounded by the y-axis and the curve $x = 4y - y^2$. Find the moment of inertia of the mass about the line $y = 4$.

197. CENTERS OF MASS AND MOMENTS, IN POLAR COORDINATES

Suppose that the boundary of a region R in an xy-plane can be described conveniently in the associated $r\theta$-system of polar coordinates. Then, it may be desirable to find some of the quantities M_x, M_y, $\bar{x}$, $\bar{y}$, and various moments of inertia by evaluating double integrals by use of polar coordinates. In doing this, we first set up the results as double integrals in the associated xy-system of coordinates.

EXAMPLE 1. Mass is distributed uniformly over the region R bounded above by $r = 2(1 - \cos \theta)$ and below by the x-axis. Find the center of mass, and the moment of inertia with respect to the x-axis.

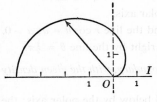

Fig. 363

Solution. 1. R is shown in Figure 363. The density of mass is a constant, δ. Let A be the area of R. Then, from (7) on page 508,

$$A\bar{x} = \int\int_R x \, dA; \quad A\bar{y} = \int\int_R y \, dA. \quad (1)$$

In (1), use $x = r \cos \theta$ and $y = r \sin \theta$. From a previous example in this text, $A = 3\pi$. Recall the element of area "$r \, dr \, d\theta$." Then, from (1),

$$3\pi\bar{x} = \int_0^\pi \int_0^{2(1-\cos \theta)} (r \cos \theta) r \, dr \, d\theta = \tfrac{8}{3} \int_0^\pi (1 - \cos \theta)^3 \cos \theta \, d\theta = -5\pi;$$

$$3\pi\bar{y} = \int_0^\pi \int_0^{2(1-\cos \theta)} r^2 \sin \theta \, dr \, d\theta = \tfrac{8}{3} \int_0^\pi (1 - \cos \theta)^3 \sin \theta \, d\theta = \tfrac{32}{3}.$$

Thus, $\bar{x} = -\tfrac{5}{3}$ and $\bar{y} = 32/9\pi$.

2. From (6) on page 512, with $y^2 = r^2 \sin^2 \theta$,

$$I_x = \delta \int\int_R y^2 \, dA = \delta \int_0^\pi \int_0^{2(1-\cos \theta)} r^3 \sin^2 \theta \, dr \, d\theta, \text{ or}$$

$$I_x = 4\delta \int_0^\pi (1 - \cos \theta)^4 \sin^2 \theta \, d\theta = \tfrac{21}{4} \pi\delta. \quad (2)$$

Since the total mass is $m = A\delta = 3\pi\delta$, we find $I_x = 7m/4$.

When polar coordinates are employed, a convenient expression arises for the polar moment of inertia. Since $x^2 + y^2 = r^2$ and $I_O = I_x + I_y$,

$$I_O = \int\int_R y^2\delta(r, \theta)dA + \int\int_R x^2\delta(r, \theta)dA = \int\int_R (x^2 + y^2)\delta(r, \theta)dA, \text{ or}$$

$$I_O = \int\int_R r^2\delta(r, \theta)dA. \tag{3}$$

EXAMPLE 2. If the density of mass at any point is proportional to its distance from the origin, obtain the polar moment of inertia of the mass over the region R bounded by the cardioid $r = a(1 - \cos\theta)$.

Incomplete solution. Inspect Figure 363 on page 515 for limits of integration. By symmetry, I_O is twice the result obtained on integrating over the upper half, R_1, of the region R. Let $\delta(r, \theta) = hr$, where h is a constant of proportionality. Then,

$$I_O = 2h\int\int_{R_1} r^2(r)dA = 2h\int_0^\pi \int_0^{a(1-\cos\theta)} r^4 \, dr \, d\theta.$$

EXERCISE 155

Use polar coordinates in evaluating integrals. Any familiar area may be taken as known without integration. Use symmetry where available.

Find the rectangular coordinates of the centroid if mass is distributed uniformly over the region with the specified boundary.

1. Bounded by the upper semicircle of the curve $r = a\cos\theta$, where $a > 0$, and the polar axis.
2. Bounded by the x-axis, the y-axis, and the circle $x^2 + y^2 = a^2$ in quadrant I.
3. Bounded by the lines $\theta = \frac{1}{3}\pi$, $r\cos\theta = 4$, and the polar axis.
4. The smaller segment bounded by the circle $r = 2a$ and the line $r\cos\theta = a$; $a > 0$.
5. Bounded on the left by $r = 3(1 - \cos\theta)$ and on the right by the line $\theta = \frac{1}{2}\pi$.

Find the center of mass for the region having the specified boundary, with the given density of mass, δ.

6. Bounded above by the circle $r = a$ where $a > 0$, and below by the polar axis; the density at any point is proportional to its distance from the center of the circle.
7. The region of Problem 1; $\delta(r, \theta) = 2r$.
8. The region of Problem 3; the density at any point is proportional to its distance from the polar axis.
9. Mass is distributed over the region bounded by the circle $r = h$, where $h > 0$. Find the polar moment of inertia and the corresponding radius of gyration, (a) if the density is a constant; (b) if the density at any point is proportional to its distance from the pole.
10. Repeat Problem 9 for the region bounded by the circle $r = h\sin\theta$. That is, find the moment of inertia and radius of gyration about an axis perpendicular to the plane of the circle at a point on its circumference.
11. Mass is distributed uniformly over the region bounded by $r^2 = 4\cos 2\theta$. Find the moment of inertia with respect to the line $\theta = \frac{1}{2}\pi$. Also, find the polar moment of inertia and the corresponding radius of gyration.

★198. CENTER OF MASS ON A PLANE CURVE

Let W be a *regular* curve (see page 395) in an xy-plane, with s as arc distance on W measured from some fixed point. Let an arc C of W be defined by

$$x = \Phi(s) \quad and \quad y = \Psi(s); \quad a \leq s \leq b. \tag{1}$$

Suppose that mass is distributed on C with $\delta(s)$ as the density at any point given by (1). We may visualize C as a material wire of negligible diameter. Then, by the definition of a density function, if m is the mass on C,

$$m = \int_a^b \delta(s)ds. \tag{2}$$

By Theorem VI on page 184, if τ is an arc of C where $\alpha \leq s \leq \alpha + \Delta s$, with mass Δm, then there exists s' such that

$$\Delta m = \int_\alpha^{\alpha+\Delta s} \delta(s)ds = \delta(s')\Delta s, \tag{3}$$

where $\alpha \leq s' \leq \alpha + \Delta s$. By a discussion similar to that for mass on an x-axis, on page 212, we obtain elements of moments of the forms

$$\Delta M_x = y\delta(s)\Delta s \quad and \quad \Delta M_y = x\delta(s)\Delta s.$$

Then,
$$M_x = \int_a^b y\delta(s)ds; \quad M_y = \int_a^b = x\delta(s)ds. \tag{4}$$

In (4), $x = \Phi(s)$ and $y = \Psi(s)$. By use of $m\bar{x} = M_y$ and $m\bar{y} = M_x$,

$$\begin{Bmatrix} \textit{center of} \\ \textit{mass} \end{Bmatrix} \qquad \bar{x} = \frac{\int_a^b x\delta(s)ds}{m} \quad and \quad \bar{y} = \frac{\int_a^b y\delta(s)ds}{m}. \tag{5}$$

If $\delta(s)$ is a constant, δ, in (5), we call $(\bar{x}, \bar{y})$ the *centroid* of C. In this case, from (2), $m = \delta L$ where L is the length of C, and (5) gives

$$(\textit{centroid}) \qquad \bar{x} = \frac{\int_a^b x\, ds}{L} \quad and \quad \bar{y} = \frac{\int_a^b y\, ds}{L}. \tag{6}$$

In (2), (4), (5), and (6), we may express ds in terms of dx, dy, or dt, where t is another parameter for C. Also, the analog of Theorem I on page 509 is true for mass on a curve C.

EXAMPLE 1. Let C be the arc of the circle $(x = a \cos t, y = a \sin t)$ in quadrant I. Mass is distributed on C with the density $\delta(x, y) = 2y$ at any point $P:(x, y)$. Find the center of mass of C.

Solution. We find $ds = a\, dt$. Then,

$$m = \int_{t=0}^{t=\pi/2} 2y\, ds = 2a^2 \int_0^{\pi/2} \sin t\, dt = 2a^2.$$

$$M_x = 2a^3 \int_0^{\pi/2} \sin^2 t\, dt = \tfrac{1}{2}\pi a^3; \quad M_y = 2a^3 \int_0^{\pi/2} \sin t \cos t\, dt = a^3.$$

Hence, from $m\bar{x} = M_y$ and $m\bar{y} = M_x$, we obtain $\bar{x} = \tfrac{1}{2}a$ and $\bar{y} = \tfrac{1}{4}\pi a$.

EXAMPLE 2. Find the centroid of the arc C of the parabola $8y = x^2$ on the interval $-4 \leq x \leq 4$.

Solution. 1. By symmetry, as seen in Figure 364, we obtain $\bar{x} = 0$.

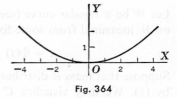

Fig. 364

2. From $8y = x^2$, with $0 \leq x \leq 4$,

$$ds = \sqrt{\frac{2+y}{y}}\, dy; \quad ds = \frac{\sqrt{16+x^2}}{4}\, dx.$$

Then,

$$L = 2\int_{x=0}^{x=4} ds = 2\int_0^4 \tfrac{1}{4}\sqrt{16+x^2}\, dx = 9.18.$$

From (6),

$$L\bar{y} = 2\int_{y=0}^{y=2} y\, ds$$

$$= 2\int_0^2 y\sqrt{\frac{2+y}{y}}\, dy = 6.72.$$

Thus, $\bar{y} = 6.72/9.18 = .73$.

★EXERCISE 156

An arc of a curve in an xy-plane is defined by the given xy-equation or parametric equations. Find the center of mass if mass is distributed on the arc with the assigned density $\delta(x, y)$ at any point (x, y).

1. The semicircle of $(x = a \cos t, y = a \sin t)$ where $0 \leq t \leq \pi$; $\delta(x, y) = 3y$.
2. Find the centroid of the arc in Problem 1.
3. The arch of the cycloid $[x = a(t - \sin t), y = a(1 - \cos t)]$ for $0 \leq t \leq 2\pi$, with $\delta(x, y) = 2y$.
4. Find the centroid of the arc, in quadrant I, of the hypocycloid
$$(x = a \cos^3 t, y = a \sin^3 t).$$
5. Find the centroid of the whole curve $r = a(1 - \cos \theta)$.
6. Find the centroid of the arc of $y^3 = x^2$ where $-8 \leq x \leq 8$.

★199. NEWTONIAN ATTRACTION *

Newton's law of attraction states that each of two mass particles with masses † m_1 and m_2, respectively, attracts the other with a force $\mathbf{F}$, a vector, whose magnitude is $|\mathbf{F}| = km_1m_2/\rho^2$, where ρ is the distance between the masses and k is a positive constant of proportionality depending on the physical units employed. Now, let mass be spread over a region R in an xy-plane with the density of mass $\delta(x, y)$ at any point (x, y) in R. We shall define the force $\mathbf{F}$ exerted by the mass of R on a mass particle μ at $Q:(a, b)$, outside of R in the plane.

Let σ be a partition of R having the norm d_σ, and representative subregion T, as in Figure 365 on page 519, where T has the area ΔA and mass Δm. By remarks

---

* We shall employ physically intuitional reasoning without some analytical details. See related problems in the chapter supplement.
† We shall use m_1 and m_2 also as *names* for the masses.

on page 489, there exists a point $P:(x, y)$ in T such that $\Delta m = \delta(x, y)\Delta A$. We shall accept the fact that the mass Δm exerts a force $\Delta\mathbf{F}$ on μ as if all of Δm were concentrated at some (unknown) point * in T. As an approximation, let

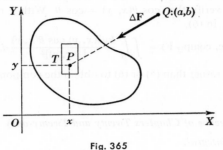

Fig. 365

Δm be concentrated at $P:(x, y)$ in T. Let $\rho(x, y) = |\overrightarrow{QP}|$, and let τ be the unit vector with the direction of $\overrightarrow{QP}$. From (4) on page 424,

$$\tau = \frac{x - a}{\rho(x, y)}\mathbf{i} + \frac{y - b}{\rho(x, y)}\mathbf{j}. \tag{1}$$

Then $\Delta\mathbf{F}$ has the direction of τ, with

$$|\Delta\mathbf{F}| = \frac{k\mu\delta(x, y)\Delta A}{[\rho(x, y)]^2}.$$

Hence, $$\Delta\mathbf{F} = \frac{k\mu\delta(x, y)}{[\rho(x, y)]^3}[(x - a)\mathbf{i} + (y - b)\mathbf{j}]\Delta A. \tag{2}$$

In Figure 365, $\Delta\mathbf{F}$ is based at Q. Let $\mathbf{F}_\sigma = \sum\Delta\mathbf{F}$, or

$$\mathbf{F}_\sigma = \mathbf{i}\left\{\sum\frac{k\mu\delta(x, y)(x - a)}{[\rho(x, y)]^3}\Delta A\right\} + \mathbf{j}\left\{\sum\frac{k\mu\delta(x, y)(y - b)}{[\rho(x, y)]^3}\Delta A\right\}, \tag{3}$$

where each sum extends over all of the subregions T of σ. We define the force, $\mathbf{F}$, exerted on μ by the mass of R as follows:

$$\mathbf{F} = \lim_{d_\sigma \to 0}\mathbf{F}_\sigma = g_x\mathbf{i} + g_y\mathbf{j}, \tag{4}$$

if the limit exists. Each scalar component on the right in (3) is an approximating sum for a double integral over R. Hence, from (3) and (4),

$$g_x = \int\int_R\frac{k\mu\delta(x, y)(x - a)}{[\rho(x, y)]^3}dA; \quad g_y = \int\int_R\frac{k\mu\delta(x, y)(y - b)}{[\rho(x, y)]^3}dA. \tag{5}$$

In using (5), if possible we employ polar coordinates $[r, \theta]$ with $Q:(a, b)$ as the pole. Then $\rho(x, y) = r$, $[(x - a)/\rho(x, y)] = \cos\theta$, $[(y - b)/\rho(x, y)] = \sin\theta$, and $\delta(x, y)$ is replaced by $\delta(r, \theta)$. Hence, from (5),

$$g_x = \int\int_R\frac{k\mu\delta(r, \theta)\cos\theta}{r^2}dA; \quad g_y = \int\int_R\frac{k\mu\delta(r, \theta)\sin\theta}{r^2}dA. \tag{6}$$

* Its exact location would not affect our final result.

Note 1. Let **U** be any unit vector, and think of the direction of **U** as the positive direction on the x-axis of an xy-system associated with an rθ-system in (6). Then g_x is the scalar component of **F** in the arbitrary direction of **U**. Let $θ(x, y)$ be the angle made by $\overrightarrow{QP}$ and **U**. For any point $P:(x, y)$, we have $0 \leqq θ(x, y) \leqq π$ whereas $0 \leqq θ < 2π$ in (6), but the student may verify that $\cos θ(x, y) = \cos θ$. With r replaced by $ρ(x, y)$, we finally obtain, from g_x in (6),

$$\text{(sc. comp}_U \text{ F)} = \int\int_R \frac{kμδ(x, y) \cos θ(x, y)}{[ρ(x, y)]^2} \, dA. \tag{7}$$

Sometimes, we use (7) rather than (5) or (6) to obtain the component of **F** in an arbitrary direction.

EXERCISE 157   (*Review of Chapters Twenty and Twenty-one*)

Compute the iterated integral.

1. $\int_0^{π/2} \int_2^{2(1+\sin θ)} r \cos θ \, dr \, dθ$.   **2.** $\int_0^{π/2} \int_{2\cos θ}^{4/(1+\cos θ)} r^2 \sin θ \, dr \, dθ$.

3. Find the area of the region bounded by the curves $y = x^2 + 5$ and $y = 2x^2 - 4$. Express the result by use of iterated integrals in two ways. Integrate one form.

Use a double integral to find the area of the region in the xy-plane bounded by the curves.

4. The curves $xy = 1$ and $x^2y = 1$ from $x = 1$ to $x = 3$.

5. The loci $y^2 = 4x - 4$, and $y = 2x - 6$.

6. Find the mass of the region where $x \geqq 0$ bounded by $x^2 - y^2 = 8$ and $x^2 + y^2 = 16$, if the density at any point (x, y) is $δ(x, y) = 2x$.

Find the volume of the region in space with the given boundaries.

7. The surfaces $y^2 = 3x$, $z = 0$, $x = 3$, and $z = x^2 + 3y^2$.

8. The surfaces $4y = x^2 + z^2$, $x = 0$, $y = 0$, $z = 4$, and $2x = z$.

Find the area of the region R in an rθ-plane, and the mass of R if the density at the point $[r, θ]$ *is* $δ(r, θ)$.

9. R is bounded by the upper semicircle of the circle $r = 1$ and by that part of the curve $r = 1 + \sin θ$ which is above the polar axis; $δ(r, θ) = 3| \cos θ |$.

10. R is inside the curve $r^2 = 2 \cos 2θ$ and outside the circle $r = 1$ in quadrant III; $δ(r, θ) = kr^2$.

11. By use of cylindrical coordinates, find the volume of the region in space above the rθ-plane within the surface $x^2 + y^2 = 8y$, and below the surface $4z = x^2 + y^2$.

Find the center of mass of the lamina in the xy-plane with the given boundaries, and density $δ(x, y)$ *at any point* (x, y).

12. Bounded by the loci $4y^3 = x^2$ and $y = 1$; $δ(x, y) = 5y$.

13. Bounded on the left by the curve $x^2 - 4x + y^2 = 0$ and on the right by the circle $x^2 + y^2 = 4$; $δ(x, y) = 2| y |$.

If mass is distributed over the plane region having the specified boundaries, with the density $δ(x, y)$ *at any point* (x, y), *obtain* I_x, I_y, *and* I_0.

14. The y-axis and the curve $x = 4y - y^2$; $δ$ a constant.

15. The axes and the curve $4x^2 + 25y^2 = 100$, with $x \geqq 0$ and $y \geqq 0$; $δ$ a constant.

16. Find the moments of inertia I_x and I_y, and the radius of gyration with respect to the x-axis for the mass in Problem 12.

Find the rectangular coordinates of the center of mass of the lamina with the specified boundaries, by integration using polar coordinates.

17. The smaller segment bounded by the circle $r = 4 \sin \theta$ and $\theta = \frac{1}{3}\pi$; the density is a constant, δ. (Thus, the *centroid* is called for.)

18. The smaller segment bounded by the curve $r = 2a$ and the line $r \cos \theta = a$. The density at any point is proportional to its distance from the polar axis, and $a > 0$.

19. Mass is spread over the region R bounded by the upper semicircle of the curve $r = a \cos \theta$, where $a > 0$, and the polar axis. The density of mass at any point is proportional to its distance from the polar axis. Find the moment of inertia and radius of gyration of the mass of R with respect to the polar axis.

20. Find the polar moment of inertia, and the corresponding radius of gyration, for a homogeneous distribution of mass over the region bounded by the curve $r = \cos 2\theta$.

21. By subtracting a certain moment of inertia, find the polar moment of inertia of a mass distributed homogeneously over the region inside the circle $x^2 + y^2 = 16$ and outside the square whose sides are on the lines $x = \pm 2$ and $y = \pm 2$.

★SUPPLEMENT FOR CHAPTER TWENTY-ONE

In Problems 22–23, k is a positive constant and $\delta(x, y)$ is the density of mass at point (x, y) in the xy-system of coordinates associated with the rθ-system of polar coordinates.

22. R is the region inside the cardioid $r = 4(1 + \sin \theta)$ and outside the parabola

$$r = \frac{3}{1 - \sin \theta},$$

to the right of the $\frac{1}{2}\pi$-line. Find I_0 for the mass of R if $\delta(x, y) = kx$.

23. R is the region between the inner loop and the outer part of the limaçon with the equation $r = 2 + 4 \cos \theta$. Find I_0 for the mass of R if $\delta(x, y) = k|y|$.

24. In a vertical plane, a region R with area A is immersed in fluid weighing w pounds per cubic unit. Prove that the force exerted on R by fluid pressure is equal to that force which would be exerted on a horizontal plane region with area A immersed in the fluid at the level of the centroid of R.

25. Mass is spread over the region bounded by the ellipse, in polar coordinates,

$$r = \frac{3}{3 + \cos \theta}.$$

The mass density at any point P is proportional to the distance of P from the polar axis. Find the polar moment of inertia of this mass, and the corresponding radius of gyration.

26. Let R be *any* region with area A in a plane. By use of double integrals, prove the theorem of Pappus in Problem 29, page 220. Use increment reasoning, and recall the volume of the solid obtained by revolving a rectangular region about an axis parallel to a side, as in Figure 239 on page 359.

27. Let C be a regular plane curve not intersecting a certain line L in the plane. Prove the theorem of Pappus which states that the area of the surface generated by revolving C about L is equal to the length of C multiplied by the circumference of the circle described by the centroid of C.

28. Mass is spread over the region R bounded by a semicircle and its bounding diameter. Find the magnitude of the attraction of this mass on a mass μ at the intersection of the axis of symmetry of the region and the circle, extended, if the mass density at any point varies as its distance from μ.

In some parts of the remaining problems, it will be necessary to develop special formulas by increment reasoning, as in Section 199.

29. In a plane, mass is spread uniformly over a semicircular ring with inner radius c and outer radius d. Find the magnitude of the attraction of this mass on a particle of mass μ at the center of the circles which form the boundaries of the ring.

30. Find the attraction of a straight wire, of uniform density and of length h, on a mass μ at a point in the line of the wire and b units distant from one of its end points.

31. Let C be a curve $[x = \phi(t), y = \psi(t)]$, as on page 517, with $a \leq t \leq b$. Mass is spread on C with $\delta(x, y)$ as the density at point (x, y). Let F be the force exerted by the mass of C on a mass μ at a point Q; U is an arbitrary unit vector in the plane of C; $\rho(x, y)$ and $\theta(x, y)$ have meanings as in Section 199. Prove that

$$(\text{sc. comp}_U \, \mathbf{F}) = \int_{t=a}^{t=b} \frac{k\mu\delta(x, y) \cos \theta(x, y)}{[\rho(x, y)]^2} \, ds.$$

32. Mass is spread uniformly on a semicircular wire, C, of negligible cross-section and radius a. Find the magnitude of the attraction of this mass on a mass μ if it is (1) at the center of the circle; (2) at the point where the axis of symmetry of C intersects the circle, extended.

33. Mass is spread over a region R bounded by a circle C of radius a, with the mass density at any point P proportional to the distance of P from a fixed diameter of C. Find the attraction of this mass on a mass μ on the diameter at a distance b from the center of C, where $b > a$.

34. Mass is spread uniformly over a circular disk. A particle of mass μ is located h units from the disk on the line perpendicular to the disk at its center. Find the magnitude of the attraction of the disk on the particle.

35. By use of (6) on page 508, prove that the location of the center of mass of a plane region R is independent of the location of the origin or directions of the axes for rectangular coordinates in the plane. It is advisable to consider translation of axes and rotation of axes separately.

36–37. In Problems 1–2, respectively, express the iterated integral, *first*, as $\iint_R f(r, \theta)dA$, a double integral in a plane where r and θ are interpreted as polar coordinates, and with $f(r, \theta)$ explicitly specified; *second*, as $\iint_R g(r, \theta)dA$, with r and θ interpreted as rectangular coordinates, and $g(r, \theta)$ explicitly specified. In each case, sketch R. Then, express each integral by use of one or two iterated integrals with the order of integration interchanged; work from each of the two figures for the problem, to verify that the same result is obtained in each case.

CHAPTER TWENTY–TWO

Triple Integrals

200. THE THREE–DIMENSIONAL DEFINITE INTEGRAL

Let F be a function of three independent variables where the domain of F includes all points (x, y, z) of a region W in an xyz-system of rectangular coordinates. We propose defining the integral of $F(x, y, z)$ over W, where W is illustrated in Figure 366. Suppose that the values of x, y, and z for points in W form the following intervals:

$$a \leqq x \leqq b; \quad c \leqq y \leqq d; \quad g \leqq z \leqq q. \tag{1}$$

Thus, W is included in the parallelepiped U (meaning *the region bounded by the*

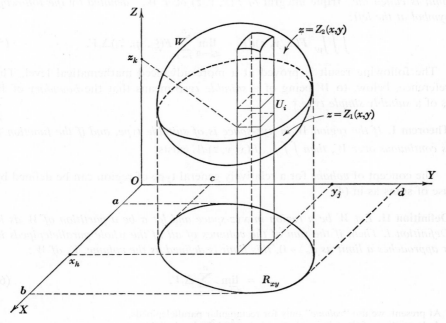

Fig. 366

523

parallelepiped) with faces in the planes $x = a$, $x = b$, $y = c$, etc. Our procedure now will parallel the introduction of the concept of a double integral, with *parallelepipeds* replacing *rectangles* as they entered for the case of a double integral.

Form partitions, separately, of the x-interval, the y-interval, and the z-interval of (1), with the following typical subintervals:

$$x_{h-1} \leqq x \leqq x_h; \quad y_{j-1} \leqq y \leqq y_j; \quad z_{k-1} \leqq z \leqq z_k. \tag{2}$$

Construct planes perpendicular to the x-axis at x_h, to the y-axis at y_j, and to the z-axis at z_k, as in Figure 366, for all values of h, j, and k. These planes superimpose a grid of parallelepipeds on W, and divide it into subregions, to create a partition σ of W. We define the norm, d_σ, of σ as the maximum of the diameters of the subregions of the grid for σ. In Figure 366, the points of W project to form the region R_{xy} in the xy-plane. Suppose that just n of the subregions in σ consist of entire parallelepipeds,

(*parallelepipeds in σ*) $U_1, U_2, \cdots, U_i, \cdots, U_n.$ \tag{3}

Then, we define a definite integral in three-space as follows.

Definition 1. *Let σ be any partition of W. In each whole parallelepiped U_i in σ, select a point (ξ_i, η_i, ζ_i) arbitrarily, and let*

$$S_\sigma = \sum_{i=1}^{n} F(\xi_i, \eta_i, \zeta_i)\Delta_i V, \tag{4}$$

*where $\Delta_i V$ is the volume * of U_i. Then, if S_σ approaches a limit as $d_\sigma \to 0$, this limit is called the "**triple integral** of $F(x, y, z)$ over W," denoted by the following symbol at the left:*

$$\iiint_W F(x, y, z)dV = \lim_{d_\sigma \to 0} \sum_{i=1}^{n} F(\xi_i, \eta_i, \zeta_i)\Delta_i V. \tag{5}$$

The following result is proved at a more advanced mathematical level. The reference, below, to W being of a *suitable type* means that the *boundary* of W is of a *suitably simple type*.†

Theorem I. *If the region W in xyz-space is of suitable type, and if the function F is continuous over W, then $\iiint_W F(x, y, z)dV$ exists.*

The concept of *volume* for a relatively general type of region can be defined by use of sums as in (4).

Definition II. *Let W be a region in xyz-space and let σ be a partition of W as in Definition I. Then, if the sum of the volumes of all of the whole parallelepipeds in σ approaches a limit as $d_\sigma \to 0$, this limit is defined as the volume, V, of W:*

$$V = \lim_{d_\sigma \to 0} \sum_{i=1}^{n} \Delta_i V. \tag{6}$$

---

* At present, we use "*volume*" only for rectangular parallelepipeds.
† A description of the admissible type is beyond the level of this text.

We notice that the right-hand side of (6) is obtained from (5) if $F(x, y, z) = 1$ at all points in W. Hence, if W is of the type mentioned in Theorem I, it follows that the volume V of W exists and is *the triple integral of* "1" *over* W, or

$$V = \int \int \int_W dV, \tag{7}$$

where "dV" means "$1 \cdot dV$" in the notation of (5). Hereafter in this text, we shall assume that any region W in space to which we refer will satisfy the condition of Theorem I, and hence has a volume. With the aid of Definition II, by use of volumes of *irregular* subregions, we obtain a new interpretation for the right-hand side of (5), as follows, where we accept the result intuitively.

Theorem II. *Let σ be a partition of a region W into subregions $\{U_i\}$ of any shape such that each U_i has a volume $\Delta_i V$, and let d_σ be the maximum of the diameters of the subregions $\{U_i\}$. Let (ξ_i, η_i, ζ_i) be an arbitrary point of U_i. Then, if a function F is continuous in W, equality (5) is true with the new meaning for the partition σ.*

Without verification, we note that triple integrals possess properties analogous to those considered for double integrals on page 485.

201. COMPUTATION OF TRIPLE INTEGRALS BY ITERATED INTEGRALS

In the following discussion, we shall assume that any integrand is continuous. Also, any region of integration, W, will be of one of the following types, or W will consist of two or more subregions of these types. The boundary functions Z_1, Z_2, Y_1, etc., in the descriptions are assumed to be differentiable, so that iterated integrals in later formulas will exist.

$(W$ *of type* I$)$
$$\begin{cases} (x, y) \text{ in region } R_{xy} \text{ in } xy\text{-plane;} \\ \quad Z_1(x, y) \leqq z \leqq Z_2(x, y). \end{cases} \tag{1}$$

$(W$ *of type* II$)$
$$\begin{cases} (y, z) \text{ in region } R_{yz} \text{ in } yz\text{-plane;} \\ \quad X_1(y, z) \leqq x \leqq X_2(y, z). \end{cases} \tag{2}$$

$(W$ *of type* III$)$
$$\begin{cases} (x, z) \text{ in region } R_{xz} \text{ in } xz\text{-plane;} \\ \quad Y_1(x, z) \leqq y \leqq Y_2(x, z). \end{cases} \tag{3}$$

The region W in Figure 366 on page 523 is of type I. In (1), R_{xy} is the projection on the xy-plane of all points in W, as seen in Figure 366. The equations $z = Z_1(x, y)$ and $z = Z_2(x, y)$ define lower and upper boundary surfaces, respectively, as in Figure 366. All of W is inside or on the cylinder formed by moving a line parallel to OZ around the boundary of R_{xy}. The following results can be proved, expressing a triple integral as a double integral of a simple integral.

$(W$ *of type* I$)$
$$\int \int \int_W F(x, y, z) dV = \int \int_{R_{xy}} \left[\int_{Z_1(x, y)}^{Z_2(x, y)} F(x, y, z) dz \right] dA_{xy}; \tag{4}$$

$(W$ *of type* II$)$
$$= \int \int_{R_{yz}} \left[\int_{X_1(y, z)}^{X_2(y, z)} F(x, y, z) dx \right] dA_{yz}; \tag{5}$$

$(W$ *of type* III$)$
$$= \int \int_{R_{xz}} \left[\int_{Y_1(x, z)}^{Y_2(x, z)} F(x, y, z) dy \right] dA_{xz}. \tag{6}$$

We may refer to (4), (5), or (6) as a form of **the fundamental theorem of integral calculus for a triple integral.** If R_{xy} in (1) is of type I as in (1) on page 487, from (4) we obtain

$$\int\int\int_W F(x, y, z)dV = \int_a^b \int_{Y_1(x)}^{Y_2(x)} \int_{Z_1(x, y)}^{Z_2(x, y)} F(x, y, z)dz\, dy\, dx. \qquad (7)$$

Suppose that a total mass m is distributed over a region W in space. Then, to state that a continuous, nonnegative function δ, whose domain is W, is the *density function* for this mass distribution means that, if U is any subregion of W, the mass Δm of U is given by

$$\Delta m = \int\int\int_U \delta(x, y, z)dV \quad and \quad m = \int\int\int_W \delta(x, y, z)dV. \qquad (8)$$

Then, we refer to $\delta(x, y, z)$ as the density of mass *at* $P{:}(x, y, z)$. If mass is spread over a region W in space, we may refer to W as a *solid*.

EXAMPLE 1. If the density of mass at $P{:}(x, y, z)$ is $\delta(x, y, z) = 2|x|$, find the mass, m, of the region W bounded by the surfaces

$$z = 8 - 3x^2 - y^2 \quad and \quad z = x^2 + 3y^2. \qquad (9)$$

Solution. 1. The values of $\delta(x, y, z)$, and the surfaces in (9), are symmetric with respect to the xz-plane and yz-plane. Hence, m is four times the mass of the part of W in the 1st octant, in Figure 367.

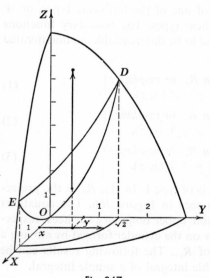

Fig. 367

2. We project W onto the xy-plane. The cylinder (see page 451), which projects the intersection of surfaces (9) onto the xy-plane, has an equation found on eliminating z by use of (9):

$$8 = 4x^2 + 4y^2, \quad or \quad x^2 + y^2 = 2. \quad (10)$$

All of W is within the cylinder (10). Surfaces (9) intersect along curve ED on cylinder (10), in Figure 367. Thus, we use (4) with R_{xy}, or simply R, as the region bounded by the x-axis, the y-axis, and the circle $x^2 + y^2 = 2$.

3. In Figure 367, the vertical arrow indicates the inner limits of integration for use in (4); the arrow in the xy-plane shows the limits for integration with respect to y. From (8) and (4), by use of (7),

$$m = 4\int\int\int_W 2x\, dV = 4\int\int_R \left[\int_{x^2+3y^2}^{8-3x^2-y^2} 2x\, dz\right] dA$$

$$= 32\int_0^{\sqrt{2}} \int_0^{\sqrt{2-x^2}} x(2 - x^2 - y^2)dy\, dx = \tfrac{256}{15}\sqrt{2}.$$

*Background * for* (4). Let W be of type I, as in Figure 368. Recall the rectangular grid used on page 524 to create a partition σ of W. The vertical planes of the grid

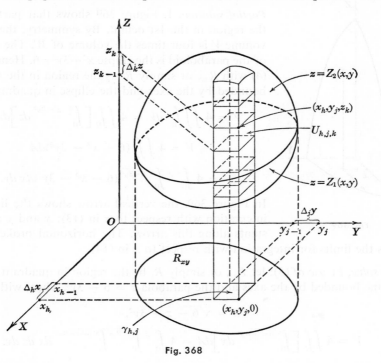

Fig. 368

superimpose a grid of rectangles on R_{xy}, and thus create a partition σ_{xy} of R_{xy}. In σ_{xy}, let $\gamma_{h,j}$ be the rectangle with sides $\Delta_h x$ and $\Delta_j y$, as shown in Figure 368. Above $\gamma_{h,j}$, there is a column of parallelepipeds of the partition σ, of type $U_{h,j,k}$ with height $\Delta_k z$ and volume $(\Delta_h x)(\Delta_j y)(\Delta_k z)$. In $U_{h,j,k}$, select (x_h, y_j, z_k) as the arbitrary point for use on the right in (4) on page 524. Then, the contribution of $U_{h,j,k}$ to S_σ in (4) on page 524 is

$$[F(x_h, y_j, z_k)\Delta_k z](\Delta_h x)(\Delta_j y). \tag{11}$$

If we first add terms (11) for all whole parallelepipeds of σ over $\gamma_{h,j}$, by summing with respect to k, then

$$S_\sigma = \sum_{(h,j)} \left[\sum_{(k)} F(x_k, y_j, z_k)\Delta_k z \right] \Delta_h x \Delta_j y. \tag{12}$$

From page 483, S_σ in (12) is in the form of an approximating sum for a double integral over R_{xy}, where *the sum with respect to k* in (12) takes the place of a value of the *integrand* for the double integral. Now, suppose that all $\Delta_h x \to 0$, $\Delta_j y \to 0$, and $\Delta_k z \to 0$. Then, it is plausible that the sum within brackets in (12) will lead to the integral of $F(x, y, z)$ with respect to z, and the sum for (h, j) in (12) will lead to a double integral over R_{xy}, as in (4).

* A proof of (4)–(6) is beyond the level of this text.

EXAMPLE 2. Obtain the volume of the region bounded below by the xy-plane and above by the surface $z = 6 - x^2 - 3y^2$.

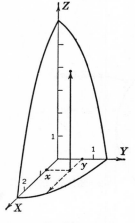

Fig. 369

Partial solution. 1. Figure 369 shows that part, W, of the region in the 1st octant. By symmetry, the desired volume V is four times the volume of W. The xy-trace of the paraboloid is the ellipse $x^2 + 3y^2 = 6$. Hence, from (4) with R_{xy}, or simply R, as the region in the xy-plane bounded by the axes and the ellipse in quadrant I,

$$V = 4 \iiint_W dV = 4 \iint_R \left[\int_0^{6-x^2-3y^2} dz \right] dA; \quad (13)$$

$$V = 4 \iint_R (6 - x^2 - 3y^2) dA$$

$$= 4 \int_0^{\sqrt{2}} \int_0^{\sqrt{6-3y^2}} (6 - x^2 - 3y^2) dx\, dy. \quad (14)$$

In Figure 369, the vertical arrow shows the limits for integration with respect to z in (13); x and y are constants along this arrow. The horizontal broken arrow shows the limits for integration with respect to x in (14).

2. *To solve, by use of* (5): let R_{yz}, or simply R, be the region in quadrant I of the yz-plane bounded by the axes and the parabola $z = 6 - 3y^2$. Then, with

$$x = \sqrt{6 - z - 3y^2},$$

$$V = 4 \iint_R \left[\int_0^{\sqrt{6-z-3y^2}} dx \right] dA = 4 \int_0^{\sqrt{2}} \int_0^{6-3y^2} \int_0^{\sqrt{6-z-3y^2}} dx\, dz\, dy. \quad (15)$$

The integration in either (14) or (15) would be rather complicated. The student is advised to complete the integration in (15).

Note 1. In (7), $Z_1(x, y)$ and $Z_2(x, y)$ can be described as the end points of the domain for z in W when x and y are fixed; $Y_1(x)$ and $Y_2(x)$ are the end points of the domain for y when x is held fast. In (7), "$dz\, dy\, dx$" can be referred to as *the differential element of volume* in rectangular coordinates, and reminds us of "$\Delta z\, \Delta y\, \Delta x$."

EXERCISE 158

Solve by use of a triple integral. Employ any symmetry for simplification. If a double integral arises which is a familiar area, its value may be used without integrating. If mass is involved, $\delta(x, y, z)$ is the density at the point (x, y, z).

1. A region W is bounded by the coordinate planes and the planes $x = 2$, $y = 3$, and $z = 1$. Find the mass of W if $\delta(x, y, z) = x^2 yz$.

2. A region W including the origin is bounded by the coordinate planes and the planes $x + 2y = 4$ and $x + y + z = 6$. Find the mass of W if $\delta(x, y, z) = 3yz$. Do not expand unnecessarily.

3. A region W is bounded by the cylinder $z^2 = 4y$, and the planes $x = 0$, $y = 1$, $z = 0$, and $2x + z = 2$. Find the volume of W and its mass if $\delta(x, y, z) = 2x$, and if W is inside the cylinder $z^2 = 4y$ with $z \geq 0$.

Express $\int\int\int_W F(x, y, z)dV$ by use of a threefold iterated integral, where W is bounded by the given surfaces.

4. The planes $z = 0$ and $z = h > 0$, and the cylinder $x^2 + y^2 = c^2$, with $c > 0$. Give two forms for the result.

5. Inside the cylinder $x^2 + y^2 = 9$ and the sphere $x^2 + y^2 + z^2 = 25$.

6. W is the smaller segment of the sphere $x^2 + y^2 + z^2 = 4$ cut off by the plane $z = 1$. Give two forms for the result.

7. Inside the surfaces $z = 6 - x^2 - y^2$ and $z^2 = x^2 + y^2$, where $z \geqq 0$.

First formulate the result as a triple integral over the region W bounded by the given surfaces. Find the volume, V, of W or its mass, m, for the given density $\delta(x, y, z)$ at any point (x, y, z), as requested.

8. For W in Problem 4, compute V, and m if $\delta(x, y, z) = 2|x|$.

9. The coordinate planes and the plane $2x + 3y + z = 6$. Compute V, and m if the density at (x, y, z) is $\delta(x, y, z) = 2 + z$.

10. The planes $x = 0$, $y = 0$, $z + 3x + 2y = 6$, and $z = 3x + y$. Compute V, and m if $\delta(x, y, z) = xy + 1$.

11. Surfaces $z = 4 - x^2 - 4y^2$ and $z = 0$. Find m if $\delta(x, y, z) = 3z|y|$.

12. Surfaces $z = 8 - y^2$ and $z = 2x^2 + y^2$. Find m if $\delta(x, y, z) = 2|zy|$.

13. Surfaces $z = 2x$ and $z = x^2 + y^2$. Find m if $\delta(x, y, z) = 2|y|$.

14. Find the volume of the sphere $x^2 + y^2 + z^2 = a^2$.

15. Find the volume of the region W in Problem 6. Integrate first with respect to x. Also, try integration first with respect to z.

16. W is bounded by the surfaces $x^2 + y^2 = 8y$, $4z = x^2 + y^2$, and $z = 0$. Find the mass of W if $\delta(x, y, z) = 2|x|$.

202. TRIPLE INTEGRALS IN CYLINDRICAL COORDINATES

In connection with an xyz-system of coordinates, let us also use the related $r\theta z$-system of cylindrical coordinates, as on page 500. Then, any function value $F(x, y, z)$ is transformed into a function value $f(r, \theta, z)$. Let W be a region consisting of all points $[r, \theta, z]$ such that

$$\left\{\begin{matrix} [r, \theta] \text{ is in a region } R \text{ in the } r\theta\text{-plane, and} \\ Z_1(r, \theta) \leq z \leq Z_2(r, \theta), \end{matrix}\right\} \tag{1}$$

where the functions Z_1 and Z_2 are differentiable in R. Then, if f is continuous in W, from (4) on page 525 we obtain

$$\int\int\int_W f(r, \theta, z)dV = \int\int_R \left[\int_{Z_1(r, \theta)}^{Z_2(r, \theta)} f(r, \theta, z)dz\right]dA, \tag{2}$$

where we omit the subscripts xy as used on page 525. When the boundary for R can be defined conveniently in the $r\theta$-system of polar coordinates, we may compute (2) by use of polar coordinates in R. For instance, if R is of type I as in (4) on page 496, we introduce "$r\,dr\,d\theta$" and obtain

$$\int\int\int_W f(r, \theta, z)dV = \int_\alpha^\beta \int_{h_1(\theta)}^{h_2(\theta)} \int_{Z_1(r, \theta)}^{Z_2(r, \theta)} rf(r, \theta, z)dz\,dr\,d\theta. \tag{3}$$

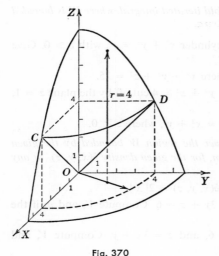

Fig. 370

EXAMPLE 1. Find the volume, V, of the region W bounded by $z = 8 - \frac{1}{4}(x^2 + y^2)$ above and by $z^2 = x^2 + y^2$ below.

Solution. 1. Change the paraboloid and cone to cylindrical coordinates:

$$z = 8 - \tfrac{1}{4}r^2 \quad and \quad z = r. \quad (4)$$

On solving system (4) with $r > 0$, we obtain $(r = 4, z = 4)$. An arc of the curve of intersection of surfaces (4) is CD in Figure 370. The cylinder projecting the curve of intersection of (4) onto the $r\theta$-plane has the equation $r = 4$; the region R for use in (2) is bounded by the circle $r = 4$ in the $r\theta$-plane, as seen from Figure 370. Part of the cylinder is shown by broken lines.

2. We use (3) with $f(r, \theta, z) = 1$:

$$V = \iiint_W dV = \iint_R \left[\int_r^{8-r^2/4} dz\right]dA = \iint_R (8 - \tfrac{1}{4}r^2 - r)dA \quad (5)$$

$$= \int_0^{\pi/2}\int_0^4 r(32 - r^2 - 4r)dr\,d\theta = \tfrac{160}{3}\pi. \quad (6)$$

Comment. In (3), $Z_1(r, \theta)$ and $Z_2(r, \theta)$ are the end points of the domain for z in W when r and θ are held fast, as indicated for (5) by the vertical arrow in Figure 370. Then, $h_1(\theta)$ and $h_2(\theta)$ of (3) are, respectively, the least and the greatest values of r when θ is held fast, as indicated for (6) by the horizontal arrow in Figure 370.

Note 1. We derived (3) from (2) on the basis of knowledge of double integrals. Instead, we could have proceeded directly from (5) on page 524, by use of a partition σ of W formed by a set of cylinders $r = r_h$, on the domain for r, and a set of planes $\theta = \theta_j$ and $z = z_k$ on the domains for θ and z. In σ, a regular subregion, to replace the typical parallelepiped in Definition I, would have the appearance of the subregion CE in Figure 371; the height of CE is Δz. The base CD of CE, or the projection KH of CD on the xy-plane, has the same shape as region $BCDE$ of Figure 344 on page 497. Thus, the area of CD is of the form $r'\Delta r\Delta\theta$. Hence, the volume ΔV of elementary region CE is given by

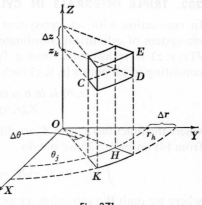

Fig. 371

$$\Delta V = r'\Delta r\Delta\theta\Delta z, \quad where \quad r' = r_h + \tfrac{1}{2}\Delta r. \quad (7)$$

Then, details similar to those involved for (11) on page 527 would lead to (3). We refer to "$r\,dz\,dr\,d\theta$" in (3) as the differential *element of volume in cylindrical coordinates;* this element recalls the volume $r'\Delta r\Delta\theta\Delta z$ of region CE in Figure 371.

ILLUSTRATION 1. Suppose that a mass m is distributed over the region of Example 1 with the density $\delta(x, y, z) = 3(x^2 + y^2)$ at any point (x, y, z). Then,

$$m = \iiint_W 3(x^2 + y^2)dV.$$

To compute m by use of (2), we first use

$$x = r \cos \theta \quad and \quad y = r \sin \theta, \quad or \quad x^2 + y^2 = r^2,$$

and obtain limits of integration as in (5) and (6):

$$m = \iiint_W 3r^2 \, dV = 4 \int_0^{\pi/2} \int_0^4 \int_r^{8 - r^2/4} 3r^3 \, dz \, dr \, d\theta.$$

EXERCISE 159

A region W is bounded by the given surfaces. Formulate the requested volume, V, or mass, m, of W as a triple integral. Then compute by use of an iterated integral in cylindrical coordinates. If mass is involved, the density at any point is represented by $\delta(r, \theta, z)$. We shall always take $r \geqq 0$ in cylindrical coordinates. Any constant a is positive.

1. Surfaces $x^2 + y^2 = 16$, $z = 0$, and $z = 5$. Find m if $\delta(r, \theta, z) = 4z$.
2. Surfaces $z = 0$ and $x^2 + y^2 + z^2 = a^2$ where $z \geqq 0$. Find m if $\delta(r, \theta, z) = 4z$.
3. Surfaces $z = a$, $x^2 + y^2 = a^2$, and $x^2 + y^2 + z^2 = 5a^2$, with $a \leqq z \leqq a\sqrt{5}$ in W. Find V.
4. Compute the volume of a sphere of radius a.
5. Cylinders $r = a$ and $z = a^2 - x^2$, and the $r\theta$-plane. Find V, and m if $\delta(r, \theta, z) = 2r$.
6. Compute the volume for the region in Problem 7, page 529.
7. Surfaces $z = 12 - x^2 - y^2$ and $z = 8$. Find V.
8. W is the smaller segment of the sphere $x^2 + y^2 + z^2 = 4$ cut off by the plane $z = 1$. Find V.
9. Surfaces $r = 4 \sin \theta$, $z = 0$, and $2z = x^2 + y^2$. Find m if $\delta(r, \theta, z) = 2r$.
10. Surfaces $z = 0$, $z = 4 - x^2$, and $z = 4 - y^2$, with $z \geqq 0$. Find m if the density at point $[r, \theta, z]$ is $\delta(r, \theta, z) = 2r$.
11. W is bounded by the half-cone $z = 4 - \sqrt{x^2 + y^2}$ and the xy-plane, inside the cylinder $r = 2 \cos \theta$. Find V, and m if $\delta(r, \theta, z) = 3x$.

203. MOMENTS AND CENTERS OF MASS IN SPACE

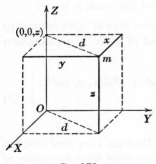

Fig. 372

Assume that a mass m is at point (x, y, z) in an xyz-system of coordinates, as in Figure 372. Then, the *moment* of m with respect to a coordinate plane is defined as the product of m and the directed distance of m from the plane. Let these moments with respect to the yz-plane, xz-plane, and xy-plane, respectively, be M_{yz}, M_{xz}, and M_{xy}:

$$M_{yz} = mx; \quad M_{xz} = my; \quad M_{xy} = mz. \quad (1)$$

Then, as in the case of moments about coordinate axes in a plane, first we could discuss the moments M_{yz}, M_{xz}, and M_{xy} for a discrete distribution of n

masses $\{m_i\}$ at points (x_i, y_i, z_i) and define the corresponding center of mass. We shall omit such details.

Suppose, now, that mass is distributed over a region W in space, with $\delta(x, y, z)$ as the density of mass at the point (x, y, z), where δ is continuous in W. Let U be any subregion of W with volume ΔV and mass Δm. From the three-dimensional analog of (2) on page 489, there exists a point (x', y', z') in U such that we have $\Delta m = \delta(x', y', z')\Delta V$. If Δm is considered as concentrated at an arbitrary point (x'', y'', z'') in U, the resulting moment, ΔM_{yz}, of Δm about the yz-plane finally becomes $\Delta M_{yz} = x''\delta(x', y', z')\Delta V$. With this as a basis, we could present details similar to those on page 508 for moments in a plane, with triple integrals replacing double integrals. Finally, we obtain

$$M_{yz} = \iiint_W x\delta(x, y, z)dV; \quad M_{xz} = \iiint_W y\delta(x, y, z)dV;$$
$$M_{xy} = \iiint_W z\delta(x, y, z)dV. \tag{2}$$

The *center of mass* for the mass distribution over W is defined as that point $(\bar{x}, \bar{y}, \bar{z})$ where the total mass, m, in W should be concentrated in order for m to have the same moments as in (2). Thus, $m\bar{x} = M_{yz}$, etc.,

$$\bar{x} = \frac{\iiint_W x\delta(x, y, z)dV}{m}, \quad \bar{y} = \frac{\iiint_W y\delta(x, y, z)dV}{m}, \quad \text{and}$$
$$\bar{z} = \frac{\iiint_W z\delta(x, y, z)dV}{m}, \quad \text{with} \quad m = \iiint_W \delta(x, y, z)dV. \tag{3}$$

If $\delta(x, y, z)$ is a constant, then $(\bar{x}, \bar{y}, \bar{z})$ is called the **centroid** of W. In this case, $\delta(x, y, z)$ divides out from each numerator and denominator in (3). For instance, the x-coordinate of the centroid is found to be

$$\bar{x} = \frac{\iiint_W x\,dV}{V}, \quad \text{where} \quad V = \iiint_W dV. \tag{4}$$

Note 1. The perpendicular from a point (x, y, z) to the z-axis meets it at the point $(0, 0, z)$, as in Figure 372 on page 531. Hence, the distance, d, between (x, y, z) and the z-axis is the distance between this point and $(0, 0, z)$, or $d = \sqrt{x^2 + y^2}$. Similarly, the distance between (x, y, z) and the x-axis is $\sqrt{y^2 + z^2}$, and the y-axis is $\sqrt{x^2 + z^2}$.

Let I_x, I_y, and I_z be the moments of inertia of the mass over W with respect to the corresponding coordinate axes. Then, with the aid of Note 1, a discussion similar to that involved for (6) on page 512 leads to

$$I_x = \iiint_W (y^2 + z^2)\delta(x, y, z)dV; \quad I_y = \iiint_W (x^2 + z^2)\delta(x, y, z)dV;$$
$$I_z = \iiint_W (x^2 + y^2)\delta(x, y, z)dV. \tag{5}$$

Note 2. By reasoning similar to that involved in proving Theorem I on page 509, the following fact can be established: *If a region W in three-dimensional space has a plane of symmetry, then the centroid of W lies in this plane.*

EXAMPLE 1. If the density is a constant, find the center of mass of the solid W bounded by the xy-plane and the upper hemisphere of the sphere

$$x^2 + y^2 + z^2 = a^2,$$

shown in Figure 373 for the 1st octant.

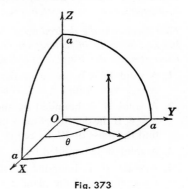

Solution. 1. The center of mass (or, the *centroid,* since the density is a constant) lies in both the xz-plane and the yz-plane, because W is symmetric to each of these planes. Hence, $(\bar{x}, \bar{y}, \bar{z})$ lies on the z-axis; or, $\bar{x} = \bar{y} = 0$. From (3) with $\delta(x, y, z)$ as a constant, or from the $\bar{z}$-form for (4),

$$\bar{z} = \frac{\iiint_W z \, dV}{V}, \quad \text{where} \quad V = \tfrac{2}{3}\pi a^3.$$

Fig. 373

2. We decide to use cylindrical coordinates. The hemisphere has the equation $z = \sqrt{a^2 - (x^2 + y^2)}$, or $z = \sqrt{a^2 - r^2}$. Hence,

$$\iiint_W z \, dV = \int_0^{2\pi}\int_0^a\int_0^{\sqrt{a^2-r^2}} rz \, dz \, dr \, d\theta = \tfrac{1}{4}\pi a^4. \tag{6}$$

Thus, $\bar{z} = (\tfrac{1}{4}\pi a^4)/(\tfrac{2}{3}\pi a^3) = \tfrac{3}{8}a$. The center of mass is $(0, 0, \tfrac{3}{8}a)$.

EXAMPLE 2. The altitude of a solid right circular cone (elementary sense) is 8 units, and the radius of its base is 6 units. If the mass density is a constant, δ, find the moment of inertia of the cone about its axis.

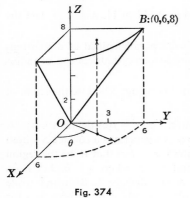

Fig. 374

Solution. Place the cone with the vertex at the origin and the axis of the cone along the positive part of the z-axis in an xyz-system, as in Figure 374. The surface of the cone is generated by revolving OB about the z-axis, where the equation of OB is $z = \tfrac{4}{3}y$. Hence, as on page 450, the cone has the equation

$$z^2 = \tfrac{16}{9}(x^2 + y^2), \quad \text{or} \quad z = \tfrac{4}{3}r$$

in cylindrical coordinates. From (5), the desired result is

$$I_z = \iiint_W (x^2 + y^2)\delta \, dV,$$

where W is the region bounded by the cone. The points in W project vertically to form the region R in the xy-plane bounded by the circle $x^2 + y^2 = 36$, or $r = 6$ in polar coordinates. Then, with dA replaced by $r \, dr \, d\theta$,

$$I_z = \delta \iint_R \left(\int_{4r/3}^8 r^2 \, dz\right)dA = \delta \int_0^{2\pi}\int_0^6\int_{4r/3}^8 r^3 \, dz \, dr \, d\theta = \tfrac{5184}{5}\pi\delta.$$

Note 3. It can be proved that the location of the center of mass for W is independent of the positions of the coordinate planes. Also, if W is subject to the attraction of gravity, in physics it is found that the center of mass of W coincides with its center of gravity.

EXERCISE 160

In finding a centroid by use of (4) *on page* 532, *and similar formulas for* $\bar{y}$ *and* $\bar{z}$, V *may be evaluated without integration if possible.*

First formulate the desired result by use of triple integrals. Compute by use of threefold iterated integrals in rectangular or cylindrical coordinates, as convenient. The density of mass at any point $P:(x, y, z)$ *is* $\delta(x, y, z)$, *or* $\delta(r, \theta, z)$ *when transformed.*

1. A solid W is bounded by the coordinate planes of the xyz-system and the planes $x = 2$, $y = 3$, and $z = 5$. If $\delta(x, y, z) = 2xy$, find the center of mass of W, and I_x.

2. A solid W is bounded by the cylinder $x^2 + y^2 = 16$, and the planes $z = 0$ and $z = 6$. If the density of mass at any point P is twice the distance of P from the z-axis, find the mass of W, its center of mass, and I_z.

3. A solid W is bounded by $x^2 + y^2 + z^2 = a^2$; $\delta(x, y, z) = 2\sqrt{x^2 + y^2}$. Find I_z.

4. A solid W is bounded by the $r\theta$-plane in cylindrical coordinates, the cylinder $r = 2 \sin \theta$, and the plane $z = y$. With $\delta(r, \theta, z) = 3r$, find the rectangular coordinates of the center of mass for W.

5. A solid W of uniform density is bounded below by the xy-plane and above by the cylinders $x^2 + z^2 = a^2$ and $y^2 + z^2 = a^2$. Find the center of mass for W, and I_z.

6. A solid W with uniform density is bounded by the cone $y^2 = 4x^2 + 4z^2$ and the plane $y = 2$. Find (a) the centroid of W, and (b) I_y.

   Hint. It is useful to introduce cylindrical coordinates, with the xz-plane becoming the $r\theta$-plane, and the y-coordinate unaltered.

7. A solid W is bounded by the paraboloid $x^2 + z^2 = 4y$ and the plane $y = 4$. Find (a) the centroid of W, and (b) I_y.

8. Find the center of mass of the solid W described in Problem 11, page 529. Use the result of that problem and symmetry.

9. Find the moment of inertia of a homogeneous solid parallelepiped of dimensions g, h, and k, about an edge of length g; of a homogeneous cylindrical rod of radius h and length k, about the cylinder's axis.

10. Find the center of mass of the solid W of Problem 13 on page 529. Use the result of that problem.

11. Consider an xyz-system of rectangular coordinates. Let $y = f(z)$ define a curve C in the yz-plane. Then, revolution of C about the z-axis generates a surface S whose equation in an $r\theta z$-system of cylindrical coordinates is $r = f(z)$. Let W be the region in space bounded by S and the planes $z = a$ and $z = b$, where $a < b$. Let mass be distributed uniformly over W, with the constant density δ. By using triple integrals, obtain expressions involving just simple integrals with respect to z for the volume of W; the coordinate $\bar{z}$ for W; I_z for W. (Use the order "$dr \, d\theta \, dz$.")

Apply Problem 11, *or any other method, to obtain the moment of inertia about the* z-*axis for the homogeneous solid bounded by the given surface of revolution.*

12. The sphere $x^2 + y^2 + z^2 = a^2$.

13. The cone $z^2 = 4x^2 + 4y^2$, between $z = 0$ and $z = h$, where $h > 0$.

14. The cylinder $x^2 + y^2 = a^2$, between $z = 0$ and $z = h$, where $h > 0$.

15. Find I_z for the homogeneous solid bounded by the surface obtained on revolving the curve $y = 2x - x^2$ about the x-axis.

204. SPHERICAL COORDINATES

Consider an *xyz*-system of rectangular coordinates, as in Figure 375. Then, we define corresponding *spherical* (or, *geographical*) *coordinates* $\{r, \theta, \phi\}$ for a point P as follows: *r is the distance* $|\overrightarrow{OP}|$; θ *is the angle from OX to* $\overrightarrow{OP'}$ *where P' is the projection of P on the xy-plane*; ϕ *is the angle from OZ to* $\overrightarrow{OP}$. For any point P,

$$r \geqq 0; \quad 0 \leqq \theta < 2\pi; \quad 0 \leqq \phi \leqq \pi.$$

We call r the *radial distance* of P. With a geographical background, we may call θ the *longitude* of P and ϕ its *colatitude*. From Figure 375, if (x, y, z) and $\{r, \theta, \phi\}$ are the corresponding coordinates for a point P, we obtain

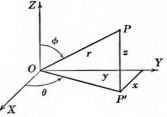

Fig. 375

$$r \sin \phi = |\overrightarrow{OP'}|, \text{ and}$$

$$r^2 = x^2 + y^2 + z^2; \quad x = r \sin \phi \cos \theta; \tag{1}$$

$$y = r \sin \phi \sin \theta; \quad z = r \cos \phi. \tag{2}$$

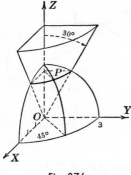

Fig. 376

Note 1. If h, α, and β are given constants, the locus on a spherical coordinate system of the equation

$$\left.\begin{array}{l} r = h \text{ is a sphere of radius } h, \text{ center } O; \\ \theta = \alpha \text{ is a half-plane through } OZ; \\ \phi = \beta \text{ is a half-cone with axis } OZ. \end{array}\right\} \tag{3}$$

Point $P:\{r = h, \theta = \alpha, \phi = \beta\}$ is the intersection of the surfaces described in (3).

ILLUSTRATION 1. $P:\{3, \frac{1}{4}\pi, \frac{1}{6}\pi\}$ is shown in Figure 376 as the intersection of the sphere $r = 3$, the half-plane $\theta = \frac{1}{4}\pi$, and the half-cone $\phi = \frac{1}{6}\pi$. When calculus is not involved, we might express θ and ϕ in degree measure.

205. TRIPLE INTEGRALS IN SPHERICAL COORDINATES

Let W be a region in an $r\theta\phi$-system of spherical coordinates, and assume that the function $f(r, \theta, \phi)$ is continuous in W, where the values of r, θ, and ϕ form the intervals

$$a \leqq r \leqq b, \quad \alpha \leqq \theta \leqq \beta, \quad \text{and} \quad \gamma \leqq \phi \leqq \eta. \tag{1}$$

We shall express $\int\int\int_W f(r, \theta, \phi)dV$ as an iterated integral with respect to r, θ, and ϕ. A complete demonstration of the results is beyond the scope of this text. Consider a subregion, U, to be called a *regular subregion*, bounded by parts of

1. *two spheres* $r = r_0$ *and* $r = r_0 + \Delta r$,

2. *two half-planes* $\theta = \theta_0$ *and* $\theta = \theta_0 + \Delta\theta$, *and*

3. *two half-cones* $\phi = \phi_0$ *and* $\phi = \phi_0 + \Delta\phi$.

In Figure 377, C is the point $\{r_0, \theta_0, \phi_0\}$, and U is the region CH, with six faces, like a parallelepiped. At any corner of U, the three edges (two curves and a line) are mutually perpendicular. In Figure 377, $|\overline{KC}| = r_0 \sin \phi_0$,

$$\angle CKD = \Delta\theta \quad \textit{and hence} \quad \widehat{CD} = r_0 \sin \phi_0 \, \Delta\theta;$$

$$\angle DOE = \Delta\phi \quad \textit{and hence} \quad \widehat{DE} = r_0\Delta\phi.$$

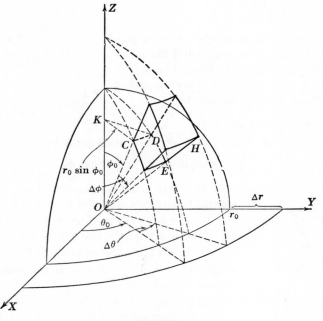

Fig. 377

Also, $|\overline{EH}| = \Delta r$. Then, as an approximation to the volume ΔV of U, take

$$\Delta V = (\widehat{CD})(\widehat{DE})(\overline{EH}), \quad or \quad \Delta V = r_0^2 \sin \phi_0 \, \Delta r\Delta\theta\Delta\phi. \tag{2}$$

Now, construct a set of h concentric spheres of type $r = r_0$ where r_0 varies from $r_0 = a$ to $r_0 = b$, a set of k half-planes of type $\theta = \theta_0$ where θ_0 varies from $\theta_0 = \alpha$ to $\theta_0 = \beta$, and s half-cones of type $\phi = \phi_0$ where ϕ_0 varies from $\phi_0 = \gamma$ to $\phi_0 = \eta$. These surfaces create a partition, σ, of W where the regular subregions of W form a set $\{U\}$, with the typical U shown in Figure 377. We shall assume that all nonregular subregions of W which are in σ can be *neglected* as we proceed. Let d_σ be the maximum of the diameters of the regular subregions formed by the mesh of surfaces which created σ. Let $\{r, \theta, \phi\}$ be the coordinates at a corner, C, of U. Then, from (2), by use of (5) and Theorem II on pages 524 and 525,

$$\iiint_W f(r, \theta, \phi)dV = \lim_{d_\sigma \to 0} \sum_{(all, \, for \, \sigma)} f(r, \theta, \phi)\Delta V$$

$$= \lim_{(\Delta r, \Delta\theta, \Delta\phi) \to (0,0,0)} \sum_{(all, \, for \, \sigma)} f(r, \theta, \phi)r^2 \sin \phi \, \Delta r\Delta\theta\Delta\phi. \tag{3}$$

On applying the usual procedure, we may express (3) as an iterated integral, with the possibility of six different orders for the integrations, when W has a convenient boundary. For instance, we may obtain

$$\iiint_W f(r, \theta, \phi)dV = \int_\gamma^\eta \int_{\theta_1(\phi)}^{\theta_2(\phi)} \int_{r_1(\theta, \phi)}^{r_2(\theta, \phi)} r^2 \sin \phi \, dr \, d\theta \, d\phi. \qquad (4)$$

In (4), W has the following nature: for points $\{r, \theta, \phi\}$ in W with θ and ϕ fixed temporarily, $r_1(\theta, \phi)$ and $r_2(\theta, \phi)$ are the least and greatest values of r; then, with ϕ fixed, $\theta_1(\phi)$ and $\theta_2(\phi)$ are the least and greatest values of θ for points in W; γ and η are the end points of the interval for ϕ in W. In (4), with (2) as a background, we refer to "$r^2 \sin \phi \, dr \, d\theta \, d\phi$" as the *differential element of volume in spherical coordinates.*

EXAMPLE 1. A region W is bounded below by the cone $\phi = \frac{1}{6}\pi$ and above by the plane $z = a > 0$. Find the mass, m, of W if the density at any point $P:\{r, \theta, \phi\}$ is $\delta(r, \theta, \phi) = r \cos \phi$.

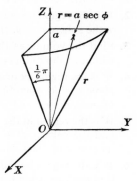

Solution. From $z=a$, we find $r \cos \phi=a$, or $r=a \sec \phi$. The straight arrow in Figure 378 indicates the domain for r, with fixed θ and ϕ.

$$m = \iiint_W \delta(r, \theta, \phi)dV$$

$$= \int_0^{\pi/6} \int_0^{2\pi} \int_0^{a \sec \phi} (r \cos \phi)r^2 \sin \phi \, dr \, d\theta \, d\phi$$

$$= \tfrac{1}{4}a^4 \int_0^{\pi/6} \int_0^{2\pi} \cos^{-3} \phi \sin \phi \, d\theta \, d\phi = \tfrac{1}{12}\pi a^4.$$

Fig. 378

EXAMPLE 2. A region W is bounded below by the plane $z = 4$ and above by the sphere $x^2 + y^2 + z^2 = 25$. Mass is distributed over W with the density at point (x, y, z) inversely proportional to the distance from the origin. Find the center of mass.

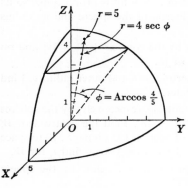

Fig. 379

Solution. 1. The $r\theta\phi$-equations for the surfaces are $r = 4 \sec \phi$ and $r = 5$; $\delta(r, \theta, \phi) = kr^{-1}$, where $k > 0$. By symmetry, the center of mass $(\bar{x}, \bar{y}, \bar{z})$ is on the z-axis, so that only $\bar{z}$ is unknown. From (3) on page 532, with

$$m = \iiint_W \delta(r, \theta, \phi)dV, \text{ then}$$

$$\bar{z} = \iiint_W kr^{-1}z \, dV / m. \qquad (5)$$

2. For fixed (ϕ, θ), $4 \sec \phi \leq r \leq 5$, as is shown by an arrow in Figure 379. For fixed θ, the domain for ϕ is $0 \leq \phi \leq \text{Arccos } \tfrac{4}{5}$.

$$\iiint_W kr^{-1}z \, dV = \int_0^{2\pi} \int_0^{\text{Arccos } (4/5)} \int_{4 \sec \phi}^5 kr^{-1}(r \cos \phi)r^2 \sin \phi \, dr \, d\phi \, d\theta = \tfrac{13}{3}k\pi.$$

Similarly, we find $m = k\pi$. Hence, from (5), $\bar{z} = 4\tfrac{1}{3}$.

Note 2. Observe that all results formulated as triple integrals in Section 203 on page 531 apply immediately in connection with spherical coordinates, with (x, y, z) first expressed in terms of $\{r, \theta, \phi\}$ by use of (1) and (2) in Section 204 on page 535. In any problem, the result should first be formulated by use of *triple integrals*. Then, we select, for W, that system of coordinates which appears most convenient for computation by means of iterated integrals.

EXERCISE 161

Formulate by use of triple integrals. Compute by use of spherical coordinates. If mass is involved, δ is the density function. Relations (1) and (2) of Section 204 on page 535 between (x, y, z) and (r, θ, ϕ) apply.

1. Find the volume of a sphere of radius a, and the mass if $\delta(r, \theta, \phi) = |xy|$.

2. W is the region whose outer boundary is the sphere $r = 2a$ and whose inner boundary is the sphere $r = a$. If $\delta(r, \theta, \phi) = 3r^2$, find the mass of W.

3. Find the volume of the region bounded by a right circular cone (elementary sense) with a as the radius of the base and α as the half-angle at the vertex.

4. W is the region bounded above by the sphere $x^2 + y^2 + z^2 = 4h^2$ and below by the plane $z = h$, where $h > 0$. Find (*a*) the volume of W, and (*b*) its mass and center of mass if $\delta(r, \theta, \phi) = 2r$.

5. W is the region in the 1st octant bounded by the coordinate planes of the xyz-system and the sphere $x^2 + y^2 + z^2 = a^2$. If mass is distributed uniformly over W, find its center of mass. Notice any symmetry, to simplify.

6. W is the region bounded by the sphere $r = a$ and the half-cone $\phi = \alpha$, where we have $0 < \alpha < \frac{1}{2}\pi$. Find (*a*) the volume of W, and (*b*) its center of mass, if mass is spread over W with uniform density.

7. W is the region bounded by the sphere $r = a$ and the half-cones $\phi = \frac{1}{3}\pi$ and $\phi = \frac{1}{4}\pi$. Mass is spread over W with the density $\delta(r, \theta, \phi) = 2z$. Find (*a*) the mass of W, and (*b*) its center of mass.

8. In a solid sphere of radius a, the density of mass at any point is proportional to its distance from the center. Find the moment of inertia of the sphere and its radius of gyration about any diameter.

9. A homogeneous solid W is bounded on the left by the cone $x^2 + z^2 = 3y^2$ and on the right by the plane $y = 4$. Find the centroid of W.

10. A homogeneous solid spherical shell has the inner radius h and outer radius a. Find the moment of inertia of the shell about a diameter.

11. A homogeneous solid W is bounded, inside and outside, respectively, by the spheres $x^2 + y^2 + (z - a)^2 = a^2$ and $x^2 + y^2 + (z - 2a)^2 = 4a^2$. Find the centroid of W first by integration, and second by an extension of Section 195 on page 510 to space of three dimensions. (Find the $r\theta\phi$-equations of the spheres.) Also, find I_z for W.

12. W is the region bounded above by the sphere $r = 2$ and below by the sphere $r = 4 \cos \phi$. Find the volume of W.

13. In Problem 12, find the center of mass of W if $\delta(r, \theta, \phi) = 3r$.

14. Sphere A of diameter h is tangent internally at a point P to sphere B of diameter g, where $h < g$. Mass is spread over the region W bounded outside by B and inside by A, with the density at any point proportional to its distance from P. Find the mass of W.

EXERCISE 162 (*Review of Chapter Twenty-two*)

Each problem refers to a region W with the given boundaries. Where mass is involved, δ is the density function. Use any desired coordinates unless otherwise required.

1. W is bounded by the surfaces $z = 6 - 3x^2$, $z = 2 + x^2 + 2y^2$, $x = 0$, and $y = 0$, where $x \geqq 0$ and $y \geqq 0$. Express $\iiint_W F(x, y, z)dV$ as a three-fold iterated integral.

2. W is bounded by the surfaces $z = 4 - x^2$, $x^2 + y^2 = 4$, and $z = 0$. Find the mass of W if $\delta(x, y, z) = z|xy|$.

3. W is bounded by the surfaces $x^2 + z^2 = 4(y - 1)$ and $y = 2$. Find the volume of W. Use a new type of cylindrical coordinates.

4. W is bounded by the surfaces $z = 8 - y^2$ and $z = 2x^2 + y^2$. Compute the volume of W by use of cylindrical coordinates.

5. W is bounded by the planes $z = 1$ and $z + y = 2$, and the cylinder $r = \sin \theta$, in cylindrical coordinates. Find the volume of W, and its mass if $\delta(r, \theta, z) = 2y$, by use of cylindrical coordinates.

6. A solid W of uniform density is bounded by the coordinate planes and the plane $x + y + z = 4$. Find the centroid of W. Use symmetry to simplify the integration.

7. Mass is distributed with uniform density over the region W of Problem 7 on page 529. Find the centroid of W.

8. W is bounded below by the xy-plane and above by the ellipsoid $4x^2 + 2y^2 + z^2 = 8$. If $\delta(x, y, z) = 2|xy|$, find the center of mass of W.

9. Find the center of mass of the upper half of the solid W in Problem 2 on page 538.

10. Find the moment of inertia I_z for the region W in Problem 7 on page 538.

11. W is bounded above by the sphere $r = 4$ and below by the half-cone $\phi = \frac{1}{3}\pi$, in spherical coordinates. Find (*a*) the volume of W, and (*b*) its center of mass if mass is spread over W with uniform density.

12. A homogeneous solid hemispherical shell has the inner radius h and outer radius k. Find the moment of inertia of the shell about its axis of symmetry.

13. A homogeneous solid, W, is bounded below by the cone $x^2 + y^2 = z^2$ and above by the plane $z = 3$. Find the centroid of W.

14. A region W in an $r\theta\phi$-system of spherical coordinates is bounded above by the sphere $r = 2 \cos \phi$ and below by the sphere $r = 1$. If mass is spread over W with the density at any point inversely proportional to the distance from the origin, find the mass and the center of mass.

★SUPPLEMENT FOR CHAPTER TWENTY-TWO

15. Each of the following iterated integrals is the value of a triple integral over a certain region W in an xyz-system of rectangular coordinates, and in an $r\theta\phi$-system of spherical coordinates, respectively. In each case, write the corresponding triple integral and describe the bounding surfaces of W. Also, express the second integral as an iterated integral in cylindrical coordinates. Assume that $a > 0$.

$$\int_{-2}^{2} \int_{-3\sqrt{4-z^2}/2}^{3\sqrt{4-z^2}/2} \int_{2x^2+6z^2}^{36-2x^2-3z^2} F(x, y, z)dy\,dx\,dz;$$

$$\int_{0}^{2\pi} \int_{a}^{2a} \int_{0}^{\text{Arcsin }(a/r)} r^2\, F(r, \theta, \phi)d\phi\,dr\,d\theta.$$

Note 1. Let mass be spread over a region W in xyz-space with $\delta(x, y, z)$ as the density of mass at $P:(x, y, z)$. If a mass of magnitude μ is at $Q:(a, b, c)$ outside * of W, the mass of W attracts μ with a force $\mathbf{F} = g_x\mathbf{i} + g_y\mathbf{j} + g_z\mathbf{k}$, which we may base at Q. Let

$$\rho(x, y, z) = |\overrightarrow{QP}|.$$

Then, if $\mathbf{U}$ is *any* unit vector, and $\theta(x, y, z)$ is the angle made by $\mathbf{U}$ and $\overrightarrow{QP}$, by the method which led to (7) on page 520 we obtain

$$(\text{sc. comp}_{\mathbf{U}} \mathbf{F}) = \iiint_W \frac{k\mu\,\delta(x, y, z)\cos\theta(x, y, z)}{[\rho(x, y, z)]^2}\,dV. \tag{1}$$

In particular, we may apply (1) with $\mathbf{U}$ as $\mathbf{i}$, $\mathbf{j}$, and $\mathbf{k}$, in turn to obtain g_x, g_y, and g_z, respectively. Let an $r\theta\phi$-system of spherical coordinates be introduced as on page 535, with Q at the origin of the related xyz-system. Then, with $\mathbf{U} = \mathbf{k}$ in (1), $\theta(x, y, z)$ becomes ϕ, and $\rho(x, y, z)$ becomes r, for the point $P:\{r, \theta, \phi\}$. With $\delta(x, y, z)$ replaced by $\delta(r, \theta, \phi)$, from (1) we then obtain

$$g_z = \iiint_W \frac{k\mu\,\delta(r, \theta, \phi)\cos\phi}{r^2}\,dV. \tag{2}$$

If W and the values of δ are symmetric with respect to the xz-plane and the yz-plane, then $g_x = g_y = 0$, and $|g_z| = |\mathbf{F}|$.

16. Mass is spread uniformly over a solid right circular cone (single nappe) of height c and semi-vertex-angle τ. Find the magnitude of the attraction of this mass on a mass μ at the cone's vertex. Technically, the resulting integral is improper because $r = 0$ at the vertex. However, this feature will cause negligible disturbance.

17. Mass is spread over the smaller segment of a sphere of radius 5 which is cut off by a plane 4 units from the center. The density of mass at any point is proportional to the distance of the point from the axis of symmetry of the segment. Find the magnitude of the attraction of the segment on a mass μ at the center of the sphere.

18. Mass is spread uniformly over a solid right circular cylinder of radius a and altitude h. Find the attraction of this mass on a mass μ which is c units distant from the cylinder on its axis of symmetry.

19. Two spheres of radii r_1 and r_2, $r_1 < r_2$, are tangent internally. Mass is spread over the region W between the spheres with the density at any point proportional to the square of the distance of the point from the point of tangency. Find the attraction of this mass on a mass μ at the point of tangency.

20. Mass is spread uniformly over a solid hemisphere. A mass μ is at the point where the axis of symmetry of the hemisphere meets the surface of the sphere, extended. Find the attraction which the hemisphere exerts on μ.

* In some cases, we may allow Q to be on the boundary of W.

CHAPTER TWENTY-THREE

Infinite Series

206. CONVERGENT AND DIVERGENT SEQUENCES

From page 113, recall that a *sequence S* is a *function* whose domain, *D*, is a set of positive integers. We assume that *D* consists of all integers, 1, 2, 3, $\cdots$, unless otherwise stated. Then, the *set of values* of the function *S*, or the range of the function *S*, is the set of numbers, called *terms*,

$$S_1, S_2, \cdots, S_n, \cdots,$$ (1)

in which we refer to S_n as the *n*th *term*, or the *general term* of the sequence. We may describe (1) as "*the sequence S*," or as "*the sequence* $\{S_n\}$." The sequence *S* is said to **converge,** or *to have a limit, L*, or *to converge to L*, in case there exists $\lim_{n \to \infty} S_n = L$ where *L* is finite. If a sequence is *not convergent*, it is said to be **divergent.** The student should review the definition of $\lim_{n \to \infty} S_n$ on page 114.

ILLUSTRATION 1. If $S_n = \dfrac{3n^2 + 2n - 3}{7n^2 + 5n - 4}$, we obtain the limit of S_n as $n \to \infty$ by first dividing the numerator and denominator of S_n by the *highest power of n in the*

denominator:
$$\lim_{n \to \infty} S_n = \lim_{n \to \infty} \frac{3 + \dfrac{2}{n} - \dfrac{3}{n^2}}{7 + \dfrac{5}{n} - \dfrac{4}{n^2}} = \frac{3 + 0 + 0}{7 + 0 + 0} = \frac{3}{7}.$$

Suppose that S_n assumes an indeterminate form as $n \to \infty$. Then, to obtain $\lim_{n \to \infty} S_n$, first we may allow *n* to be a *continuous* variable with $1 \leqq n < \infty$, and apply L'Hospital's rule from page 258. If $S_n \to L$ as $n \to \infty$ when *n* is a continuous variable, then $S_n \to L$ as $n \to \infty$ with *n* assuming only positive integral values.

ILLUSTRATION 2. The fraction $(3n^2 + 5)/(2n + 7)$ tends to the indeterminate form ∞ / ∞ as $n \to \infty$. Hence, on differentiating the numerator for a new numerator and the denominator for a new denominator, by the method of page 258 we obtain

$$\lim_{n \to \infty} \frac{3n^2 + 5}{2n + 7} = \lim_{n \to \infty} \frac{6n}{2} = + \infty.$$

Similarly, we obtain
$$\lim_{n \to \infty} \frac{\ln n}{n} = \lim_{n \to \infty} \frac{\dfrac{1}{n}}{1} = \lim_{n \to \infty} \frac{1}{n} = 0.$$

541

Note 1. In the future, wherever a sequence $\{S_n\}$ occurs, if we apply L'Hospital's rule of page 258, it will be understood that, temporarily, we are acting as if n is a continuous variable; the result is valid when the domain of n is all positive integers.

To state that a sequence $\{S_n\}$ is *nondecreasing* means that $S_n \leqq S_{n+1}$ for all values of n, or S_n *does not decrease if n increases.* To state that $\{S_n\}$ is *nonincreasing* means that $S_{n+1} \leqq S_n$ for all values of n.

ILLUSTRATION 3. Let S_n be represented as a point on a number scale. Then, the terms S_1, S_2, $\cdots$ of a nondecreasing sequence are illustrated in Figure 380. As n increases, S_n may move to the right but not to the left on the scale.

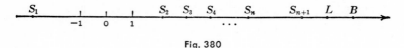

Fig. 380

Theorem I. *If a sequence $\{S_n\}$ is* **bounded and nondecreasing,** *then the sequence converges to its* **least upper bound.*** *That is, if there exists a number B such that, for all values of n,*

$$S_n \leqq B \quad and \quad S_n \leqq S_{n+1}, \tag{2}$$

then there exists a number $L \leqq B$ such that

$$S_n \leqq L \text{ for all } n, \quad and \quad \lim_{n \to \infty} S_n = L. \tag{3}$$

Proof. 1. By Theorem I on page 121, the sequence has a least upper bound $L \leqq B$. Then, $S_n \leqq L$ for all values of n.

2. Let ϵ be an arbitrarily assigned positive number, as small as we please. Then $(L - \epsilon)$ is *not* an upper bound for $\{S_n\}$, since L is the *least* upper bound. Hence, there exists an integer k such that $\qquad L - \epsilon < S_k \leqq L. \tag{4}$

Moreover, since $S_n \leqq S_{n+1}$ for all values of n, we have

$$L - \epsilon < S_k \leqq S_{k+1} \leqq S_{k+2} \cdots \leqq L.$$

Or, if $n \geqq k$, then $L - \epsilon < S_n \leqq L$, as in Figure 381. Hence, $|S_n - L| < \epsilon$ for all n sufficiently large. Therefore, by Definition III on page 114, $S_n \to L$ as $n \to \infty$.

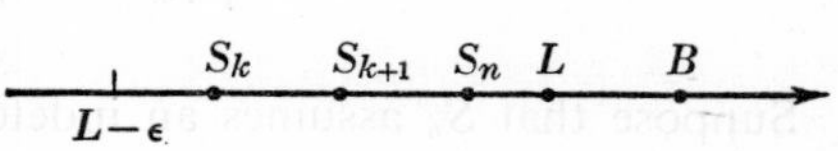

Fig. 381

ILLUSTRATION 4. If $S_n = 3 - \dfrac{1}{2^n}$, then $S_n < 3$. We verify that

$$S_1 = 3 - \tfrac{1}{2} = \tfrac{5}{2}, \quad S_2 = \tfrac{11}{4}, \quad S_3 = \tfrac{23}{8}, \cdots,$$

where S_n increases as n increases, because $1/2^n$ decreases. Or, $S_n < S_{n+1}$ for all values of n. Hence, by Theorem I, S_n has a limit as $n \to \infty$. We find $\lim_{n \to \infty} S_n = 3$.

By reversing inequalities in details of the proof of Theorem I, and referring to *lower* bounds instead of *upper* bounds, we could prove the following result; the details will be omitted.

---

* Recall the discussion of bounds on page 121.

Theorem II. *If a sequence* $\{S_n\}$ *is* **bounded and nonincreasing,** *then the sequence converges to its greatest lower bound.*

If a *nondecreasing sequence* $\{S_n\}$ *is* **not bounded,** *then* $S_n \rightarrow +\infty$ *as* $n \rightarrow \infty$. Hence, Theorem I justifies the following result.

Theorem III. *A nondecreasing sequence* $\{S_n\}$ *converges if and only if the sequence is bounded; otherwise,* $S_n \rightarrow \infty$ *as* $n \rightarrow \infty$.

EXERCISE 163

Evaluate the limit. Use differentiation if desirable.

1. $\displaystyle\lim_{n\to\infty} \frac{3n+2}{2-5n}$.

2. $\displaystyle\lim_{n\to\infty} \frac{2n+n^3}{3n^3+n^2}$.

3. $\displaystyle\lim_{n\to\infty} \frac{n-2n^2}{2+5n}$.

4. $\displaystyle\lim_{n\to\infty} \frac{\ln n}{n^3}$.

5. $\displaystyle\lim_{n\to\infty} \frac{e^n}{\ln 2n}$.

6. $\displaystyle\lim_{n\to\infty} \frac{\ln n}{3n+5}$.

7. $\displaystyle\lim_{n\to\infty} \frac{n^2}{\ln n}$.

8. $\displaystyle\lim_{n\to\infty} \frac{10^n}{e^n+4}$.

9. $\displaystyle\lim_{n\to\infty} \frac{3^n+3^2}{2(3^n)+5}$.

10. $\displaystyle\lim_{n\to\infty} \cos n\pi$.

11. $\displaystyle\lim_{n\to\infty} [2+5(-1)^n]$.

12. $\displaystyle\lim_{n\to\infty} (\sin n\pi)/n$.

Is the sequence convergent or divergent? If convergent, find its limit.

13. $\frac{1}{2}, \frac{2}{3}, \frac{3}{4}, \frac{4}{5}, \cdots$.

14. $\frac{2}{1}, -\frac{3}{2}, \frac{4}{3}, -\frac{5}{4}, \cdots$.

15. $1, -\frac{1}{2}, \frac{1}{4}, -\frac{1}{8}, \cdots$.

16. $2, 4, 6, 8, \cdots$.

207. INFINITE SERIES

If $u_1, u_2, \cdots, u_n, \cdots$ is an infinite sequence, then the symbol

$$u_1 + u_2 + u_3 + \cdots + u_n + \cdots \tag{1}$$

is referred to as an *infinite series.* * We abbreviate (1) by writing $\sum_{n=1}^{\infty} u_n$, which is read "*the sum of* u_n *from* $n=1$ *to infinity.*" However, this phraseology does not assign a *value* to the series, because no meaning has been given to the sum of infinitely many numbers. We shall introduce the concept of a *value* for an infinite series. For this purpose, in $\sum_{n=1}^{\infty} u_n$, let

$$S_1 = u_1, \quad S_2 = u_1 + u_2, \text{ etc.}, \quad S_n = u_1 + u_2 + \cdots + u_n = \sum_{k=1}^{n} u_k, \tag{2}$$

where we call S_n the nth **partial sum.**

Definition I. *To say that an infinite series* **converges,** *or that* **it is convergent,** *means that the sum of the first n terms has a limit as* $n \rightarrow \infty$, *and then this limit is called the* **sum** *of the series.*

That is, to say that a series $\sum_{n=1}^{\infty} u_n$ converges, means that *the sequence of partial sums* $\{S_n\}$ *converges.* If $\sigma = \lim_{n\to\infty} S_n$, then σ is the sum of the series, or its *value,* and we say that the series *converges to* σ. We may use "$\sum_{n=1}^{\infty} u_n$" not only

* A sum $u_1 + u_2 + \cdots + u_k$ is called a *finite series.* Unless otherwise stated, any reference to a *series* will mean an *infinite series.*

as a symbol for the series, but also for its sum, if the series converges, and write

$$\sum_{n=1}^{\infty} u_n = \sigma = \lim_{n\to\infty} S_n. \tag{3}$$

Notice that the sum of an infinite series is *not a sum in the ordinary sense*, but is *the limit of an ordinary sum of n terms as n → ∞*.

Definition II. *If an infinite series does not converge, it is said to* **diverge,** *or to be* **divergent.**

Note 1. Let S_n be the sum of the first n terms of an arithmetic progression with first term a and common difference d:

$$S_n = a + (a + d) + (a + 2d) + \cdots + [a + (n - 1)d].$$

We recall that

$$S_n = \tfrac{1}{2}n[2a + (n - 1)d]. \tag{4}$$

Note 2. Let S_n be the sum of the first n terms of a geometric progression with first term a and common ratio r:

$$S_n = a + ar + ar^2 + \cdots + ar^{n-1}.$$

We recall that

$$S_n = \frac{a - ar^n}{1 - r} = \frac{a}{1 - r} - \frac{ar^n}{1 - r}. \tag{5}$$

ILLUSTRATION 1. We call the following series an *infinite geometric series*, because the terms form a geometric progression:

$$1 + \frac{1}{2} + \frac{1}{4} + \cdots + \frac{1}{2^{n-1}} + \cdots. \tag{6}$$

In (6), we use (5) with $a = 1$ and $r = \tfrac{1}{2}$. Then,

$$S_n = \frac{1 - 2^{-n}}{1 - \frac{1}{2}} = 2 - \frac{1}{2^{n-1}}; \quad \lim_{n\to\infty} S_n = 2 - 0 = 2.$$

Thus, series (6) *converges* to the sum 2.

ILLUSTRATION 2. In the infinite geometric series

$$1 + 2 + 4 + \cdots + 2^{n-1} + \cdots, \tag{7}$$

we obtain

$$S_n = \frac{1 - 2^n}{1 - 2} = 2^n - 1. \tag{8}$$

From (8), $S_n \to +\infty$ as $n \to \infty$. Hence, (7) *diverges*.

ILLUSTRATION 3. We call $2 + 4 + 6 + \cdots + 2n + \cdots$ an *infinite arithmetic series*. From (4) with $a = 2$ and $d = 2$,

$$S_n = \tfrac{1}{2}n(2 + 2n) = n(n + 1). \tag{9}$$

From (9), $S_n \to +\infty$ as $n \to \infty$. Hence, the given series is *divergent*.

ILLUSTRATION 4. With the series $1 - 1 + 1 - 1 + \cdots$, we obtain

$$S_1 = 1, \ S_2 = 0, \ S_3 = 1, \ \cdots,$$

where S_n is alternately 1 and 0. Hence, S_n does *not* have a limit as $n \to \infty$, and the given series is *divergent*.

EXAMPLE 1. The series below is called the **harmonic series** since the reciprocals of the terms form an arithmetic progression. Prove that the series diverges.

$$1 + \frac{1}{2} + \frac{1}{3} + \cdots + \frac{1}{n} + \cdots. \tag{10}$$

Solution. 1. Consider the following inequalities, where all terms of the series (10) occur in turn on the left:

$$1 + \frac{1}{2} > \frac{1}{2}; \tag{11}$$

$$\frac{1}{3} + \frac{1}{4} > \frac{1}{4} + \frac{1}{4} = \frac{1}{2}; \tag{12}$$

$$\frac{1}{5} + \frac{1}{6} + \frac{1}{7} + \frac{1}{8} > \frac{1}{8} + \frac{1}{8} + \frac{1}{8} + \frac{1}{8} = \frac{1}{2}; \tag{13}$$

$$\frac{1}{9} + \frac{1}{10} + \cdots + \frac{1}{16} > \frac{1}{16} + \frac{1}{16} + \cdots + \frac{1}{16} = \frac{1}{2}; \tag{14}$$

. . . . *etc.* . . . .,

where the sum of the terms on the left in each line exceeds $\frac{1}{2}$.

2. Let S_n be the sum of the first n terms in (10). Then, if $n > 2$,

$$S_n = 1 + \frac{1}{2} + \cdots + \frac{1}{n} > \frac{1}{2} + \frac{1}{2} + \cdots + \frac{1}{2}, \tag{15}$$

where we include $\frac{1}{2}$ from each right-hand side in those inequalities (11), (12), $\cdots$ *preceding* the line where $1/n$ occurs on the left. If n is large enough, the right-hand side in (15) will be as large as we please. Hence, $S_n \to \infty$ as $n \to \infty$, and the harmonic series diverges.

Theorem IV. *If* $\sum_{n=1}^{\infty} u_n$ *converges, then the* n*th term,* u_n*, approaches zero as* $n \to \infty$. *Or,*

a necessary condition for convergence *is that* $u_n \to 0$ **as** $n \to \infty$. (16)

Proof. 1. For the u-series, we have

$$S_{n-1} = u_1 + u_2 + \cdots + u_{n-1} \quad and \quad S_n = u_1 + u_2 + \cdots + u_{n-1} + u_n;$$

$$u_n = S_n - S_{n-1}. \tag{17}$$

2. By hypothesis, the u-series converges, with a certain sum σ. Thus, $S_n \to \sigma$ and $S_{n-1} \to \sigma$ as $n \to \infty$. Therefore, from (17),

$$\lim_{n \to \infty} u_n = \lim_{n \to \infty} S_n - \lim_{n \to \infty} S_{n-1} = \sigma - \sigma = 0.$$

ILLUSTRATION 5. In Illustration 1, $\sum_{n=1}^{\infty} \frac{1}{2^{n-1}}$ converges. Also, the nth term approaches zero as $n \to \infty$.

Theorem V. *In a series* $\sum_{n=1}^{\infty} u_n$, **if the** n**th term does not approach zero as** $n \to \infty$, **then the series diverges.**

Proof (*indirect*). Assume that the conclusion of the theorem is *false*, or that the series *converges*. Then, we should have $u_n \to 0$ as $n \to \infty$. But, by hypothesis, this is *not true*. Hence, we have a *contradiction*, which eliminates the assumption that the series *converges*. Therefore, it *diverges*.

EXAMPLE 2. Prove that the series $\sum_{n=1}^{\infty} \dfrac{2n + 1}{3n + 2}$ diverges.

Solution. $\lim\limits_{n \to \infty} \dfrac{2n + 1}{3n + 2} = \dfrac{2}{3} \neq 0$. Hence, the series diverges.

ILLUSTRATION 6. $\sum_{n=1}^{\infty} 1/n$ diverges, although $(1/n) \to 0$ as $n \to \infty$. This proves that "$u_n \to 0$ *as* $n \to \infty$" is *not sufficient* to imply convergence for $\sum_{n=1}^{\infty} u_n$.

208. INFINITE GEOMETRIC SERIES

Suppose that $a \neq 0$ in the infinite geometric series

$$a + ar + ar^2 + \cdots + ar^{n-1} + \cdots. \tag{1}$$

Then, if $r \neq 1$,
$$S_n = \frac{a - ar^n}{1 - r} = \frac{a}{1 - r} - \frac{ar^n}{1 - r}. \tag{2}$$

If $|r| < 1$, then $ar^n \to 0$ as $n \to \infty$, and $\qquad \lim\limits_{n \to \infty} S_n = \dfrac{a}{1 - r}, \tag{3}$

or (1) converges, with the sum $a/(1 - r)$. If $|r| \geq 1$, then $|ar^{n-1}| \geq |a| > 0$, and thus ar^{n-1} does *not* approach zero as $n \to \infty$. Hence, by Theorem V, series (1) diverges if $|r| \geq 1$.

Summary. $\sum_{n=1}^{\infty} ar^{n-1}$ *converges if* $|r| < 1$ *and diverges if* $|r| \geq 1$.

ILLUSTRATION 1. The repeating decimal $3.\dot{2}\dot{7}$, or $3.272727 \cdots$, is defined as

$$3 + .27 + .0027 + .000027 + \cdots. \tag{4}$$

In (4), after the term 3, we have an infinite geometric series. From (3),

$$3.272727 \cdots = 3 + \frac{.27}{1 - .01} = 3 + \frac{.27}{.99} = 3 + \frac{3}{11} = \frac{36}{11}.$$

Similarly, *any endless repeating decimal is a symbol for a rational number.*

EXERCISE 164

Write the nth term, if it is not given for the series. Obtain S_n, and $\lim_{n \to \infty} S_n$ if convenient. Prove that the series converges, or that it diverges.

1. $1 + 3^{-1} + 3^{-2} + \cdots$.

2. $5 - 5(2^{-1}) + 5(2^{-2}) - 5(2^{-3}) + \cdots$.

3. $2 + 2(3) + 2(3^2) + \cdots$.

4. $1 - 4 + 4^2 - 4^3 + \cdots$.

5. $1 + 3 + 5 + \cdots$.

6. $2 - 4 + 6 - 8 + \cdots$.

7. $40 + 4 + .4 + .04 + \cdots$.

8. $4 + 7 + 11 + \cdots$.

9. $.\dot{2}$.

10. $.\dot{8}\dot{3}$.

11. $.\dot{2}\dot{1}$.

12. $.\dot{3}4\dot{5}$.

13. $\frac{2}{3} + \frac{3}{4} + \frac{4}{5} + \cdots$.

14. $3 + 5 + 7 + \cdots$.

15. $1 - 2 + 3 - 4 + \cdots$.

16. $1 + 6 + 6^2 + \cdots$.

17. $\sum_{n=1}^{\infty} \dfrac{3n + 5}{n + 1}$.

18. $\sum_{n=1}^{\infty} \dfrac{2^n(3n)}{4n + 1}$.

19. $\sum_{n=1}^{\infty} \sin\left(n \cdot \dfrac{\pi}{2}\right)$.

20. $\ln \frac{1}{2} + \ln \frac{1}{3} + \ln \frac{1}{4} + \cdots$.

21. $\ln \frac{2}{1} + \ln \frac{3}{2} + \ln \frac{4}{3} + \cdots$.

209. MISCELLANEOUS THEOREMS ON CONVERGENCE AND DIVERGENCE

We meet a u-series and a v-series below with partial sums S_n and T_n, respectively.

Theorem VI. *If $\sum_{n=1}^{\infty} u_n$ and $\sum_{n=1}^{\infty} v_n$ converge, with sums σ and τ, respectively, then $\sum_{n=1}^{\infty} (u_n + v_n)$ converges, with sum $(\sigma + \tau)$.*

Proof. Let W_n be the *n*th partial sum for $\sum_{n=1}^{\infty} (u_n + v_n)$. Then, $W_n = S_n + T_n$, $S_n \to \sigma$, $T_n \to \tau$, and $W_n \to (\sigma + \tau)$ as $n \to \infty$, which proves the theorem.

Note 1. From Theorem VI,
$$\sum_{n=1}^{\infty} u_n + \sum_{n=1}^{\infty} v_n = \sum_{n=1}^{\infty} (u_n + v_n), \qquad (1)$$
when the u-series and v-series converge. Thus, because of (1), we say that *two (or more) convergent series may be added term by term.*

Theorem VII.* *If $\sum_{n=1}^{\infty} u_n$ converges, with sum σ, and if k is any constant, then $\sum_{n=1}^{\infty} ku_n$ converges, with sum $k\sigma$.*

Theorem VIII.* *If $\sum_{n=1}^{\infty} v_n$ diverges and k is any constant, not zero, then $\sum_{n=1}^{\infty} kv_n$ diverges.*

ILLUSTRATION 1. To investigate
$$\frac{1}{2} + \frac{1}{4} + \frac{1}{6} + \cdots + \frac{1}{2n} + \cdots, \qquad (2)$$

we notice that
$$\frac{1}{2n} = \frac{1}{2}\left(\frac{1}{n}\right), \qquad (3)$$

and recall that $\sum_{n=1}^{\infty} (1/n)$ diverges. Hence, by Theorem VIII with $k = \frac{1}{2}$, it follows that (2) diverges.

Theorem IX. *The convergence or divergence of a series is not altered by deleting, or inserting, a finite number of terms.*

Proof. 1. In $\sum_{n=1}^{\infty} u_n$, delete k terms with sum A, to obtain $\sum_{m=1}^{\infty} v_m$. We also look on the u-series as obtained by *inserting* k terms in the v-series.

2. Let the partial sums be $\{S_n\}$ for the u-series, and $\{T_m\}$ for the v-series. Suppose that m is so large that the original location of v_m in the u-series is beyond all deleted terms, whose sum is A. Then, T_m can be obtained by subtracting A from a corresponding partial sum, S_n, where $n = m + k$ because k terms were deleted:
$$T_m = S_n - A, \quad or \quad S_n = T_m + A. \qquad (4)$$

3. From (4), if the sequence $\{T_m\}$ converges to a limit τ, then $\{S_n\}$ converges to a limit σ where $\sigma = \tau + A$, because
$$\lim_{n \to \infty} S_n = \lim_{m \to \infty} T_m + A = \tau + A. \qquad (5)$$

Similarly, if $S_n \to \sigma$ as $n \to \infty$, then the sequence $\{T_m\}$ has a limit τ where $\tau = \sigma - A$. Thus, the u-series and the v-series *both converge if either one converges.* Hence, also, they *both diverge if either one diverges*, because we cannot have one divergent and one convergent.

* To be proved in the next exercise.

ILLUSTRATION 2. If we delete the first three terms in

$$1 + \frac{1}{2} + \frac{1}{3} + \cdots + \frac{1}{n} + \cdots, \tag{6}$$

we obtain
$$\frac{1}{4} + \frac{1}{5} + \cdots + \frac{1}{m+3} + \cdots. \tag{7}$$

Then, Theorem IX shows that (7) diverges because (6) diverges.

Consider a convergent series

$$u_1 + u_2 + \cdots + u_n + \cdots, \tag{8}$$

with partial sums $\{S_n\}$, and let σ be the sum of (8). From Theorem IX, if k is any positive integer, the series

$$u_{k+1} + u_{k+2} + \cdots + u_n + \cdots \tag{9}$$

converges because (8) converges. Let R_k be the sum of (9). Then, for any value of k, we refer to R_k as the *remainder after k terms* in (8). From (5), with R_k playing the role of τ, and $A = S_k = u_1 + \cdots + u_k$,

$$\sigma = S_k + R_k, \quad or \quad R_k = \sigma - S_k. \tag{10}$$

From (10),
$$\lim_{k \to \infty} R_k = \sigma - \lim_{k \to \infty} S_k = \sigma - \sigma = 0.$$

Thus, we have proved the following result.

Theorem X. *In a convergent series, the remainder after k terms approaches zero as $k \to \infty$.*

EXERCISE 165

We have shown that the harmonic series diverges. Then, quote a theorem or theorems to prove that the series in the problem diverges.

1. $\frac{1}{6} + \frac{1}{7} + \frac{1}{8} + \cdots$.   2. $3 + 2 + 1 + \frac{1}{2} + \frac{1}{3} + \cdots$.

3. $\frac{1}{3} + \frac{1}{6} + \frac{1}{9} + \cdots$.   4. $\frac{1}{6} + \frac{1}{8} + \frac{1}{10} + \cdots$.

5. Prove Theorem VII of page 547. Then, establish Theorem VIII of page 547 by use of an indirect proof.

210. CHARACTERISTICS OF SERIES OF NONNEGATIVE TERMS

In a series $\sum_{n=1}^{\infty} u_n$, assume that the terms are nonnegative (that is, $u_n \geqq 0$). Then, the sequence of partial sums $\{S_n\}$ for the series is *nondecreasing*, because

$$S_{n+1} = S_n + u_{n+1} \geqq S_n.$$

Hence, from Theorem III on page 543, S_n has a limit as $n \to \infty$, or the u-series converges, *if and only if the sequence $\{S_n\}$ is bounded.* These remarks, and Theorem I on page 542, prove the following result.

Theorem XI. *A series of nonnegative terms, with partial sums $\{S_n\}$, converges if and only if there exists a number B such that $S_n \leqq B$ for all values of n. Then, the sum, σ, of the series is the least upper bound of the sequence $\{S_n\}$ and*

(for all n) $S_n \leqq \sigma \leqq B.$ (1)

EXAMPLE 1. Prove that the following series is convergent if $p > 1$:

$$1 + \frac{1}{2^p} + \frac{1}{3^p} + \cdots + \frac{1}{n^p} + \cdots. \tag{2}$$

Solution. 1. The following inequalities involve all terms from (2) at the left:

$$\left.\begin{array}{l}
1 \leqq 1. \\[2mm]
\dfrac{1}{2^p} + \dfrac{1}{3^p} \leqq \dfrac{1}{2^p} + \dfrac{1}{2^p} = \dfrac{2}{2^p} = \dfrac{1}{2^{p-1}}, \\[3mm]
\dfrac{1}{4^p} + \dfrac{1}{5^p} + \dfrac{1}{6^p} + \dfrac{1}{7^p} \leqq \dfrac{1}{4^p} + \dfrac{1}{4^p} + \dfrac{1}{4^p} + \dfrac{1}{4^p} = \dfrac{4}{4^p} = \dfrac{1}{4^{p-1}} = \left(\dfrac{1}{2^{p-1}}\right)^2, \\[3mm]
\dfrac{1}{8^p} + \dfrac{1}{9^p} + \cdots + \dfrac{1}{15^p} \leqq \dfrac{8}{8^p} = \dfrac{1}{8^{p-1}} = \left(\dfrac{1}{2^3}\right)^{p-1} = \left(\dfrac{1}{2^{p-1}}\right)^3, \\[3mm]
\cdots \cdots \cdots \textit{etc.} \cdots \cdots \cdots
\end{array}\right\} \tag{3}$$

2. The terms on the right in (3) form the geometric series

$$1 + \frac{1}{2^{p-1}} + \frac{1}{(2^{p-1})^2} + \cdots, \tag{4}$$

whose ratio is $r = 1/2^{p-1}$, where $r < 1$ because $p > 1$. Hence, (4) converges. If its sum is α, the sum of any number of terms from (2) in the inequalities (3) will be at most α. Thus, if S_n is the nth partial sum of (2), $S_n \leqq \alpha$ for all values of n. Therefore, by Theorem XI, (2) converges.

211. COMPARISON TESTS FOR CONVERGENCE

To test a series for *convergence* will mean to determine whether the series *converges* or *diverges*. We refer to the following Theorems XII and XIII as *comparison tests* for convergence and divergence, respectively.

Theorem XII. *If* $\sum_{n=1}^{\infty} u_n$ *and* $\sum_{n=1}^{\infty} v_n$ *are series of positive * terms, where the u-series is known to converge, and where*

$$v_n \leqq u_n, \tag{1}$$

for all values of n, then the v-series also converges.

Proof. 1. Let
$$T_n = v_1 + v_2 + \cdots + v_n, \text{ and}$$
$$S_n = u_1 + u_2 + \cdots + u_n.$$

Then, from (1), $T_n \leqq S_n$ for all values of n. Also, the sequences $\{T_n\}$ and $\{S_n\}$ are increasing sequences.

2. By hypothesis, the sequence $\{S_n\}$ converges to a limit σ, the sum of the u-series. Hence, $S_n \leqq \sigma$ for all values of n, because $\{S_n\}$ is an increasing sequence. Then $T_n \leqq S_n \leqq \sigma$, for all values of n, or the partial sums of the v-series are *bounded*. Hence, by Theorem XI, the v-series converges.

* In Theorems XII and XIII, we may allow the terms to be *nonnegative* (positive or zero).

Theorem XIII. *If* $\sum_{n=1}^{\infty} u_n$ *and* $\sum_{n=1}^{\infty} v_n$ *are series of positive terms, where the v-series is known to diverge, and where*

$$v_n \leqq u_n, \tag{2}$$

for all values of n, then the u-series also diverges.

Proof. Suppose that (2) is true, but assume that the *u*-series *converges*. Then, by Theorem XII, the *v*-series also *converges*. This is a *contradiction*. Hence, the *u*-series cannot converge.

EXAMPLE 1. Test for convergence:

$$\frac{1}{1\cdot2\cdot3} + \frac{1}{2\cdot3\cdot4} + \frac{1}{3\cdot4\cdot5} + \cdots + \frac{1}{n(n+1)(n+2)} + \cdots. \tag{3}$$

Solution. Since $n(n+1)(n+2)$, when expanded, is of degree 3 in n, we shall compare with $\sum_{n=1}^{\infty} 1/n^3$, and we suspect that (3) converges. In (3),

$$\frac{1}{1\cdot2\cdot3} < \frac{1}{1\cdot1\cdot1} = \frac{1}{1^3}; \quad \frac{1}{2\cdot3\cdot4} < \frac{1}{2\cdot2\cdot2} = \frac{1}{2^3}; \quad \cdots \tag{4}$$

$$\frac{1}{n(n+1)(n+2)} < \frac{1}{n\cdot n\cdot n} = \frac{1}{n^3}. \tag{5}$$

We know that $\sum_{n=1}^{\infty} 1/n^3$ converges [$p = 3$ in (2) on page 549]. Hence, by Theorem XII, series (3) converges. The verification of the *general* inequality in (5) was essential.

EXAMPLE 2. Prove divergent:

$$\frac{1}{\sqrt{4}} + \frac{1}{\sqrt{5}} + \frac{1}{\sqrt{6}} + \cdots + \frac{1}{\sqrt{n+3}} + \cdots. \tag{6}$$

Solution. For a comparison series, we use

$$\frac{1}{4} + \frac{1}{5} + \frac{1}{6} + \cdots + \frac{1}{n+3} + \cdots. \tag{7}$$

By Theorem IX of page 547, (7) diverges because it is obtained on omitting three terms of the harmonic series, which diverges. Observe that

$$\frac{1}{\sqrt{4}} > \frac{1}{4}, \quad \frac{1}{\sqrt{5}} > \frac{1}{5}, \cdots, \frac{1}{\sqrt{n+3}} > \frac{1}{n+3}, \tag{8}$$

because $\sqrt{n+3} < n+3$. Hence, (6) diverges because (7) diverges.

Note 1. If (1) in Theorem XII, or (2) in Theorem XIII, is true only for all values of n *greater than some fixed integer K*, then the conclusion of the theorem remains true. This is seen by applying the theorem as originally stated to the new series obtained by *omitting the first K terms* in each given series, and recalling that this omission does not alter convergence or divergence. Also, we observe that the comparison tests apply indirectly to series where all terms are negative or zero. In such a case, first we could multiply each term by -1, which does not affect convergence or divergence, and then apply a comparison test, if possible.

EXAMPLE 3. Prove convergent:

$$\frac{5}{2\cdot3\cdot4} + \frac{7}{3\cdot4\cdot5} + \frac{9}{4\cdot5\cdot6} + \cdots + \frac{2n+3}{(n+1)(n+2)(n+3)} + \cdots. \tag{9}$$

Solution. The degree of the numerator in n is 1, and of the denominator is 3. Since $(3-1) = 2$, we work toward comparison with the series $\sum_{n=1}^{\infty} 1/n^2$, or some series related simply to it, and suspect that (9) converges. Consideration of the first two terms from (9) leads us to (10) for the nth term below, as a basis for application of a comparison test:

$$\frac{5}{2\cdot3\cdot4} < \frac{1}{1\cdot1}\cdot\frac{5}{4} < \frac{1}{1^2}\cdot2; \quad \frac{7}{3\cdot4\cdot5} < \frac{1}{2\cdot2}\cdot\frac{7}{5} < \frac{1}{2^2}\cdot2;$$

$$\frac{2n+3}{(n+1)(n+2)(n+3)} < \frac{1}{n\cdot n}\cdot\frac{2n+3}{n+3} < \frac{1}{n^2}\cdot2, \tag{10}$$

because $2n + 3 < 2(n+3) = 2n + 6$. Hence, each term in (9) is less than the corresponding term in $\sum_{n=1}^{\infty} 2/n^2$, which converges because $\sum_{n=1}^{\infty} 1/n^2$ converges [$p = 2$ in (2) on page 549]. Therefore, (9) converges.

Any series of positive terms which is known to converge, or to diverge, is eligible as a comparison series for proving the convergence or divergence, respectively, of other series. The following series are particularly useful. Sometimes, (12) is called the **hyperharmonic series.**

Convergent series for comparison:

$$a + ar + ar^2 + \cdots + ar^{n-1} + \cdots; \quad (a > 0; 0 \leqq r < 1). \tag{11}$$

$$1 + \frac{1}{2^p} + \frac{1}{3^p} + \cdots + \frac{1}{n^p} + \cdots; \quad (p > 1). \tag{12}$$

$$1 + \frac{1}{2^2} + \frac{1}{3^3} + \cdots + \frac{1}{n^n} + \cdots. \tag{13}$$

Divergent series for comparison:

$$1 + \frac{1}{2} + \frac{1}{3} + \cdots + \frac{1}{n} + \cdots. \tag{14}$$

$$a + ar + ar^2 + \cdots + ar^{n-1} + \cdots; \quad (a > 0; r \geqq 1). \tag{15}$$

Note 2. To test a series $\sum_{n=1}^{\infty} u_n$ for convergence by use of a comparison test, first it is essential to make a guess as to the convergence or divergence of the series. For this purpose, the following result may be useful.

Suppose that $u_n > 0$ and $u_n = P(n)/Q(n)$, where $P(n)$ and $Q(n)$ are polynomials in n of fixed degrees h and k, respectively. Let $k - h = \alpha$. Then, the u-series is convergent if $\alpha > 1$ and divergent if $\alpha \leqq 1$.

We shall not prove or use this result at present. However, the student may desire to refer to the result, where it applies, in deciding whether a proof of convergence or of divergence is to be attempted by the comparison test.

EXERCISE 166

Prove convergent; use the comparison test or other theorems.

1. Series (13) on page 551, by comparison with (11) where $a = \frac{1}{2}$ and $r = \frac{1}{2}$, after deleting first terms.

2. $\dfrac{1}{1 \cdot 2 \cdot 3 \cdot 4} + \dfrac{1}{2 \cdot 3 \cdot 4 \cdot 5} + \cdots + \dfrac{1}{n(n + 1)(n + 2)(n + 3)} + \cdots.$

3. $\dfrac{1}{1 \cdot 3} + \dfrac{1}{2 \cdot 3^2} + \dfrac{1}{3 \cdot 3^3} + \cdots.$ 　　　　**4.** $\dfrac{1}{2^2} + \dfrac{1}{4^2} + \dfrac{1}{6^2} + \cdots.$

5. $\dfrac{1}{3^3} + \dfrac{1}{5^3} + \dfrac{1}{7^3} + \cdots.$ 　　　　**6.** $\dfrac{1}{1 \cdot 2} + \dfrac{1}{2 \cdot 3} + \dfrac{1}{3 \cdot 4} + \cdots.$

7. $\dfrac{1}{1!} + \dfrac{1}{2!} + \dfrac{1}{3!} + \cdots.$ 　　　　**8.** $\dfrac{1}{2!} + \dfrac{1}{4!} + \dfrac{1}{6!} + \cdots.$

9. $\dfrac{1}{k + 1^2} + \dfrac{1}{k + 2^2} + \dfrac{1}{k + 3^2} + \cdots, k > 0.$

10. $\dfrac{1}{2^p} + \dfrac{1}{4^p} + \dfrac{1}{6^p} + \cdots, p > 1.$

Prove divergent by the comparison test or by other means.

11. $3 + 5 + 7 + \cdots.$ 　　　　**12.** $\dfrac{3}{1} + \dfrac{4}{2} + \dfrac{5}{3} + \cdots.$

13. $\dfrac{1}{\sqrt{1}} + \dfrac{1}{\sqrt{2}} + \dfrac{1}{\sqrt{3}} + \cdots.$ 　　**14.** $\dfrac{2}{1} + \dfrac{2^2}{2} + \dfrac{2^3}{3} + \cdots.$

15. $\dfrac{1}{1 - .1} + \dfrac{1}{1 - .01} + \dfrac{1}{1 - .001} + \cdots.$

16. $\dfrac{1}{1} + \dfrac{1}{3} + \dfrac{1}{5} + \cdots.$ 　　　　**17.** $\dfrac{1}{1^p} + \dfrac{1}{2^p} + \dfrac{1}{3^p} + \cdots, p < 1.$

Test for convergence by use of available theorems.

18. $\dfrac{1}{1 \cdot 4} + \dfrac{1}{2 \cdot 5} + \dfrac{1}{3 \cdot 6} + \cdots.$ 　　**19.** $\dfrac{1}{2 \cdot 4} + \dfrac{1}{4 \cdot 6} + \dfrac{1}{6 \cdot 8} + \cdots.$

20. $-\dfrac{1}{2 \cdot 3} - \dfrac{3}{4 \cdot 3^2} - \dfrac{5}{6 \cdot 3^3} - \cdots.$ 　　**21.** $-\dfrac{1}{\sqrt{2}} - \dfrac{1}{\sqrt{4}} - \dfrac{1}{\sqrt{6}} - \cdots.$

22. $\displaystyle\sum_{n=1}^{\infty} \dfrac{1}{(2n)^3}.$ 　**23.** $\displaystyle\sum_{n=1}^{\infty} \dfrac{1}{n + 1 - \sqrt{n}}.$ 　**24.** $\displaystyle\sum_{n=1}^{\infty} \dfrac{1}{n(2n + 1)}.$

25. $\dfrac{3}{1 \cdot 4} + \dfrac{4}{2 \cdot 5} + \dfrac{5}{3 \cdot 6} + \cdots.$ 　　**26.** $\dfrac{1}{1 \cdot 2 \cdot 3} + \dfrac{3}{2 \cdot 3 \cdot 4} + \dfrac{5}{3 \cdot 4 \cdot 5} + \cdots.$

27. $\displaystyle\sum_{n=1}^{\infty} \dfrac{1}{n^n} \dfrac{n - 1}{n + 1}.$ 　**28.** $\displaystyle\sum_{n=1}^{\infty} \dfrac{1}{(2n - 1)!}.$ 　**29.** $\displaystyle\sum_{n=1}^{\infty} \dfrac{6}{n^2 + 1}.$

30. $\displaystyle\sum_{n=1}^{\infty} \dfrac{3n + 2}{2n^3 + n}.$ 　**31.** $\displaystyle\sum_{n=1}^{\infty} \dfrac{2n^2 + n}{n^3 + 3}.$ 　**32.** $\displaystyle\sum_{n=1}^{\infty} \dfrac{n + 1}{n^2 + 5}.$

Hint for Problem 30. Show that the nth term is at most $\dfrac{5}{2}\left(\dfrac{1}{n^2}\right).$

33. $\dfrac{2}{1 \cdot 3} + \dfrac{2 \cdot 4}{1 \cdot 3 \cdot 5} + \dfrac{2 \cdot 4 \cdot 6}{1 \cdot 3 \cdot 5 \cdot 7} + \cdots.$ 　**34.** $\dfrac{2}{5} + \dfrac{2 \cdot 3}{5 \cdot 7} + \dfrac{2 \cdot 3 \cdot 4}{5 \cdot 7 \cdot 9} + \cdots.$

212. ALTERNATING SERIES

An alternating series is one whose terms alternate in sign,

$$u_1 - u_2 + u_3 - \cdots + (-1)^{n+1}u_n + \cdots, \tag{1}$$

where $u_1, u_2, \cdots, u_n, \cdots$ are all positive or all negative.

ILLUSTRATION 1. We call $1 - \frac{1}{2} + \frac{1}{3} - \frac{1}{4} + \cdots$ the **alternating harmonic series.** The following theorem proves it convergent.

Theorem XIV. *An alternating series* (1) *converges if the terms decrease in absolute value,*

$$|u_n| > |u_{n+1}|, \tag{2}$$

and if the nth term approaches zero as $n \to \infty$,

$$\lim_{n \to \infty} u_n = 0. \tag{3}$$

Proof. 1. For convenience, suppose that $u_1 > 0$. Then, (2) gives

$$u_n > u_{n+1} \quad or \quad u_n - u_{n+1} > 0. \tag{4}$$

2. The partial sum, S_{2k}, of any *even* number of terms in (1) may be written in the following two forms:

$$S_{2k} = (u_1 - u_2) + (u_3 - u_4) + \cdots + (u_{2k-1} - u_{2k}); \tag{5}$$

$$S_{2k} = u_1 - (u_2 - u_3) - \cdots - (u_{2k-2} - u_{2k-1}) - u_{2k}. \tag{6}$$

In (5) and (6), each difference within parentheses is positive, because of (4). Hence, (5) shows that $S_{2k} > 0$ and S_{2k} *increases as k increases*, while (6) shows

that $S_{2k} < u_1$, or $\qquad 0 < S_2 < S_4 < S_6 < \cdots < S_{2k} < \cdots < u_1.$

That is, S_{2k} is a *bounded, increasing sequence.* Therefore, by Theorem I on page 542, S_{2k} approaches a limit, σ, as $k \to \infty$ where $\sigma \le u_1$, and where $\sigma > 0$ because $S_{2k} > 0$. That is, $S_{2k} \to \sigma$ as $k \to \infty$ and

$$0 < \sigma \le u_1. \tag{7}$$

3. In (1), let S_{2k+1} be the sum of any *odd number* of terms. Then,

$$S_{2k+1} = S_{2k} + u_{2k+1};$$

$$\lim_{k \to \infty} S_{2k+1} = \lim_{k \to \infty} S_{2k} + \lim_{k \to \infty} u_{2k+1} = \sigma + 0 = \sigma,$$

because $u_n \to 0$ as $n \to \infty$. Therefore, S_n is as near σ as we please for all values of n, *odd or even*, which are sufficiently large. That is, $S_n \to \sigma$ as $n \to \infty$, or (1) converges, with the sum σ.

4. If $u_1 < 0$ in (1), we may first multiply all terms by -1. Then, the new series converges, by our result as just proved with $u_1 > 0$. Hence, (1) converges when $u_1 < 0$, and, in place of (7), we obtain

$$u_1 \le \sigma < 0. \tag{8}$$

From (7) and (8) we reach the following conclusion.

Corollary 1. *Under hypotheses* (2) *and* (3), *the sum* σ *of* (1) *satisfies*

$$| \sigma | \leqq | u_1 |.$$

Let R_n be the *remainder* after n terms in (1). Then, R_n is the sum of the series:

$$R_n = \pm u_{n+1} \mp u_{n+2} \pm u_{n+3} \mp \cdots, \tag{9}$$

with the upper signs if n is *even*, and the lower signs if n is *odd*. On applying Corollary 1 in (9), we obtain the following result.

Corollary 2. *Under hypotheses* (2) *and* (3), *the error of any partial sum* S_n, *as an approximation to the sum* σ, *is at most equal to the absolute value of the first neglected term:*

$$| \sigma - S_n | = | R_n | \leqq | u_{n+1} |. \tag{10}$$

Note 1. From (7) and (8), we see that the sum of an alternating series, satisfying (2) and (3), has *the same sign as the first term*, u_1.

ILLUSTRATION 2. In the series $1 - \dfrac{1}{2!} + \dfrac{1}{3!} - \cdots,$

$$u_n = \frac{1}{n!}; \quad u_{n+1} = \frac{1}{(n+1)!}; \quad \frac{1}{n!} > \frac{1}{(n+1)!}; \quad \lim_{n \to \infty} u_n = 0.$$

Thus, (2) and (3) are satisfied, and hence the series converges.

EXAMPLE 1. Test for convergence: $\dfrac{1}{2 \cdot 3} - \dfrac{2}{3 \cdot 4} + \dfrac{3}{4 \cdot 5} - \cdots.$ \hfill (11)

Solution. 1. $u_n = \dfrac{n}{(n+1)(n+2)}; \quad u_{n+1} = \dfrac{n+1}{(n+2)(n+3)}.$

$$\lim_{n \to \infty} u_n = \lim_{n \to \infty} \frac{n}{n^2 + 3n + 2} = \lim_{n \to \infty} \frac{1}{2n + 3} = 0. \qquad \text{(L'Hospital's rule)}$$

2. To verify (2), we wish to prove that

$$\frac{n}{(n+1)(n+2)} > \frac{n+1}{(n+2)(n+3)}, \tag{12}$$

which is equivalent to $n(n + 3) > (n + 1)^2$, or

$$n^2 + 3n > n^2 + 2n + 1, \quad or \quad n > 1.$$

Hence, (2) and (3) are true if $n > 1$. Therefore, with the first term omitted in (11), Theorem XIV shows that the new series converges. But, this omission does not alter convergence. Hence, (11) converges.

In Example 1, we illustrated the fact that Theorem XIV remains true if (2) and (3) are assumed *only for n sufficiently large.*

213. ABSOLUTE CONVERGENCE

The following theorem is of importance when we investigate the convergence of a series whose terms are *not* all of one sign.

Theorem XV. *A series converges if the series of the absolute values of its terms converges. That is,* $\sum_{n=1}^{\infty} u_n$ *converges if* $\sum_{n=1}^{\infty} |u_n|$ *converges.*

Proof. 1. We assume that $\sum_{n=1}^{\infty} |u_n|$ converges. Let the sum of the first n terms in $\sum_{n=1}^{\infty} u_n$ be S_n, and in $\sum_{n=1}^{\infty} |u_n|$ be T_n, and let $\tau = \lim_{n \to \infty} T_n$. Then, since the sequence $\{T_n\}$ is nondecreasing, we have $T_n \leqq \tau$ for all values of n. In S_n, let P_n be the sum of the positive terms and let $-Q_n$ be the sum of the negative terms. Then,

$$S_n = P_n - Q_n \quad and \quad T_n = P_n + Q_n. \tag{1}$$

2. Since $P_n \geqq 0$, $Q_n \geqq 0$, and $T_n \leqq \tau$, from (1) we find

$$P_n \leqq \tau; \quad Q_n \leqq \tau. \tag{2}$$

As n increases, P_n and Q_n never decrease. By (2), each of the sequences $\{P_n\}$ and $\{Q_n\}$ is bounded. Therefore, by Theorem I on page 542, these sequences have limits μ and ν, or $P_n \to \mu$ and $Q_n \to \nu$ as $n \to \infty$.

3. Since $S_n = P_n - Q_n$, we obtain

$$\lim_{n \to \infty} S_n = \lim_{n \to \infty} P_n - \lim_{n \to \infty} Q_n = \mu - \nu. \tag{3}$$

That is, $\sum_{n=1}^{\infty} u_n$ converges to the sum $(\mu - \nu)$. Incidentally, we have proved the following result.

Corollary 1. *Suppose that* $\sum_{n=1}^{\infty} |u_n|$ *converges. Then, in* $\sum_{n=1}^{\infty} u_n$, *the series formed by the positive terms and the series formed by the negative terms are convergent, with sums* μ *and* $-\nu$, *respectively, and* $\sum_{n=1}^{\infty} u_n$ *converges to* $(\mu - \nu)$.

Definition III. *A series* $\sum_{n=1}^{\infty} u_n$ *is said to* **converge absolutely**, *or to be* **absolutely convergent**, *if and only if the series of absolute values* $\sum_{n=1}^{\infty} |u_n|$ *converges.*

Definition IV. *If a series converges, but does not converge absolutely, the series is said to be* **conditionally convergent.**

We may restate Theorem XV by saying that, if a series *converges* **absolutely,** then the series *converges in the* **ordinary sense.**

ILLUSTRATION 1. The series $1 - \frac{1}{2} + \frac{1}{3} - \cdots$ is known to be convergent. The series of absolute values is $1 + \frac{1}{2} + \frac{1}{3} + \cdots$, which is divergent. Hence, the alternating harmonic series is conditionally convergent.

ILLUSTRATION 2. The series $1 - \frac{1}{2} + \frac{1}{4} - \cdots$ is absolutely convergent, because $1 + \frac{1}{2} + \frac{1}{4} \cdots$ is a convergent geometric series.

★*Note 1.* If $\sum_{n=1}^{\infty} u_n$ converges *conditionally*, it can be proved that, separately, the series of positive terms and the series of negative terms in $\sum_{n=1}^{\infty} u_n$ *diverge*. Also, it can be shown that, by rearrangement of the order of terms, a conditionally convergent series may be changed into a divergent series, or into a new convergent series with *any desired sum*. On the other hand, if the terms of an absolutely convergent series are rearranged, the new series also converges absolutely, to the same sum as the given series. See Problem 38 in the supplement for this chapter.

EXERCISE 167

Test for convergence by use of Section 212 and Theorem V on page 545.

1. $\dfrac{1}{3} - \dfrac{1}{6} + \dfrac{1}{9} - \cdots$.

2. $-\dfrac{1}{\sqrt{2}} + \dfrac{1}{\sqrt{4}} - \dfrac{1}{\sqrt{6}} + \cdots$.

3. $\dfrac{1}{\ln 2} - \dfrac{1}{\ln 3} + \dfrac{1}{\ln 4} - \cdots$.

4. $\dfrac{1}{1\cdot 2} - \dfrac{1}{2\cdot 3} + \dfrac{1}{3\cdot 4} - \cdots$.

5. $\dfrac{2}{2} - \dfrac{3}{4} + \dfrac{4}{6} - \dfrac{5}{8} + \cdots$.

6. $-\dfrac{1}{5} + \dfrac{1}{7} - \dfrac{1}{9} + \cdots$.

7. $\dfrac{2}{1} - \dfrac{3}{2} + \dfrac{4}{3} - \cdots$.

8. $\dfrac{1}{2\cdot 3} - \dfrac{1}{3\cdot 3^2} + \dfrac{1}{4\cdot 3^3} - \cdots$.

9. $\displaystyle\sum_{n=1}^{\infty} \dfrac{(-1)^{n+1}}{1 + \sqrt{n}}$.

10. $\displaystyle\sum_{n=1}^{\infty} \dfrac{(-1)^{n+1}}{2^n + 1}$.

11. $\displaystyle\sum_{n=1}^{\infty} (-1)^n \ln\dfrac{1}{n}$.

12. $\dfrac{3}{1\cdot 2} - \dfrac{4}{2\cdot 3} + \dfrac{5}{3\cdot 4} - \cdots$.

13. $\dfrac{1}{1^p} - \dfrac{1}{2^p} + \dfrac{1}{3^p} - \cdots, \ (p > 0)$.

Verify that the series converges. Then, compute the sum S_4, and find a bound for the absolute value of its error as an approximation to the sum of the series.

14. $1 - \dfrac{1}{2^3} + \dfrac{1}{3^3} - \cdots$.

15. $-1 + \dfrac{1}{\sqrt{3}} - \dfrac{1}{\sqrt{5}} + \cdots$.

State whether the series converges; diverges; converges absolutely; converges conditionally. Give justification for your conclusions.

16. $1 - \dfrac{1}{3} + \dfrac{1}{5} - \cdots$.

17. $\dfrac{1}{2} - \dfrac{1}{4} + \dfrac{1}{6} - \cdots$.

18. $2 - \dfrac{2}{5} + \dfrac{2}{5^2} - \cdots$.

19. $1 - 2 + 4 - \cdots$.

20. $1 - \dfrac{1}{2^2} + \dfrac{1}{3^2} - \cdots$.

21. $3 - \dfrac{3}{2} + \dfrac{3}{2^2} - \cdots$.

22. $1 - \dfrac{1}{\sqrt{2}} + \dfrac{1}{\sqrt{3}} - \cdots$.

23. $\dfrac{1}{2\cdot 3} - \dfrac{1}{3\cdot 4} + \dfrac{1}{4\cdot 5} - \cdots$.

24. If we are given that $\displaystyle\sum_{n=1}^{\infty} |u_n|$ diverges, we cannot state that $\displaystyle\sum_{n=1}^{\infty} u_n$ diverges. Give an example to justify this statement. Thus, there is no utility for any concept of "*absolute divergence.*"

214. RATIO TEST

In a series $\displaystyle\sum_{n=1}^{\infty} u_n$, form the ratio of the $(n+1)$th term to the nth term. Suppose that, as $n \to \infty$, the absolute value of this ratio has a limit * R, finite or possibly infinite $(R = \infty)$:

$$\lim_{n\to\infty} \left| \dfrac{u_{n+1}}{u_n} \right| = R. \qquad (1)$$

Then,   *if $R < 1$, the series converges absolutely;* (A)

if $R > 1$ or if $R = \infty$, the series diverges; (B)

if $R = 1$, no conclusion can be drawn. (C)

* We take this to imply that $u_n \neq 0$ if n is sufficiently large.

Proof of (A). 1. Let $v_n = |u_n|$, and consider $\sum_{n=1}^{\infty} v_n$. If $R < 1$, we shall prove that the v-series converges.

2. Let $r_n = v_{n+1}/v_n$. Then,

$$r_n = \frac{v_{n+1}}{v_n} = \left|\frac{u_{n+1}}{u_n}\right| \quad and \quad \lim_{n \to \infty} r_n = R < 1. \qquad (2)$$

3. Since $R < 1$, we may select ρ so that $R < \rho < 1$. Since $r_n \to R$ as $n \to \infty$, then, for all values of n which are sufficiently large, r_n will be so close to R, as in Figure 382, that

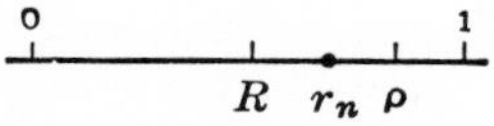

Fig. 382

$$r_n < \rho \quad or \quad \frac{v_{n+1}}{v_n} < \rho. \qquad (3)$$

Thus, there exists an integer k, sufficiently large, so that

$$v_{n+1} < \rho v_n \quad when \quad n \geq k. \qquad (4)$$

4. From (4),

when $n = k$, $\qquad\qquad v_{k+1} < \rho v_k$;

when $n = k + 1$, $\qquad v_{k+2} < \rho v_{k+1} < \rho(\rho v_k), \quad or \quad v_{k+2} < \rho^2 v_k$;

when $n = k + 2$, $\qquad v_{k+3} < \rho v_{k+2} < \rho(\rho^2 v_k), \quad or \quad v_{k+3} < \rho^3 v_k$.

Thus, below, each term in (5) is less than the corresponding term in (6):

$$v_{k+1} + v_{k+2} + v_{k+3} \cdots; \qquad (5)$$

$$\rho v_k + \rho^2 v_k + \rho^3 v_k + \cdots. \qquad (6)$$

Series (6) converges, because it is a geometric series whose ratio is $\rho < 1$. Therefore, by comparison, (5) converges. Hence, $\sum_{n=1}^{\infty} v_k$ converges, because it is obtained by adding $v_1 + \cdots + v_k$ at the beginning in (5), which does not alter its convergence. Thus, $\sum_{n=1}^{\infty} |u_n|$ converges, or $\sum_{n=1}^{\infty} u_n$ is *absolutely convergent*.

Proof of (B). Suppose that $r_n \to R > 1$ as $n \to \infty$. Then, if n is sufficiently large, r_n will be so close to R that $r_n > 1$, as in Figure 383. If $r_n \to \infty$ as $n \to \infty$, then likewise $r_n > 1$ if n is sufficiently large. Hence, if $r_n \to R > 1$ or if $r_n \to \infty$ as $n \to \infty$, there exists an integer k, sufficiently large, so that

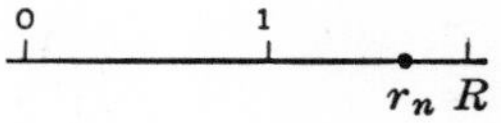

$$r_n = \frac{v_{n+1}}{v_n} > 1, \quad or \quad v_{n+1} > v_n \quad if \quad n \geq k.$$

Fig. 383

That is, if $n \geq k$, v_n increases as n increases, and hence we do *not* have $v_n \to 0$ as $n \to \infty$. Since $v_n = |u_n|$, we do *not* have $u_n \to 0$ as $n \to \infty$. Hence, by Theorem V on page 545, the u-series diverges.

Proof of (C). In the following Illustration 2, we shall exhibit a *convergent* series, and also a *divergent* series, where $R = 1$. Hence, knowledge that $R = 1$ gives no evidence about convergence or divergence. Or, the ratio test *fails if $R = 1$*.

Note 1. If we apply the ratio test to a series $\sum_{n=1}^{\infty} u_n$ where all terms are of one sign, then no mention of absolute values in the test is necessary.

ILLUSTRATION 1. In the series $\quad\dfrac{1}{2} + \dfrac{2^2}{2^2} + \dfrac{3^2}{2^3} + \cdots,$

$$u_n = \frac{n^2}{2^n}; \quad u_{n+1} = \frac{(n+1)^2}{2^{n+1}}; \quad \frac{u_{n+1}}{u_n} = \frac{1}{2}\left(\frac{n+1}{n}\right)^2;$$

$$R = \lim_{n \to \infty} \frac{1}{2}\left(1 + \frac{1}{n}\right)^2 = \frac{1}{2}(1+0)^2 = \frac{1}{2}. \tag{7}$$

Since $\frac{1}{2} < 1$, the given series converges.

ILLUSTRATION 2. For the *divergent* series $\quad 1 + \frac{1}{2} + \frac{1}{3} + \cdots,$

$$u_n = \frac{1}{n}; \quad u_{n+1} = \frac{1}{n+1}; \quad R = \lim_{n \to \infty} \frac{n}{n+1} = 1.$$

For the *convergent* series $\qquad\qquad \dfrac{1}{1^2} + \dfrac{1}{2^2} + \dfrac{1}{3^2} + \cdots,$

$$u_n = \frac{1}{n^2}; \quad u_{n+1} = \frac{1}{(n+1)^2}; \quad R = \lim_{n \to \infty}\left(\frac{n}{n+1}\right)^2 = 1.$$

ILLUSTRATION 3. In the series $\qquad\qquad \dfrac{2!}{3} - \dfrac{4!}{3^2} + \dfrac{6!}{3^3} - \cdots,$

$$|u_n| = \frac{(2n)!}{3^n}; \quad |u_{n+1}| = \frac{(2n+2)!}{3^{n+1}}; \quad \left|\frac{u_{n+1}}{u_n}\right| = \frac{(2n+1)(2n+2)}{3},$$

because $\qquad (2n+2)! = 1 \cdot 2 \cdot 3 \cdots (2n) \cdot (2n+1)(2n+2).$

$$R = \lim_{n \to \infty} \tfrac{1}{3}(2n+1)(2n+2) = +\infty. \tag{8}$$

Hence, the series diverges.

EXAMPLE 1. Test for convergence and absolute convergence:

$$\frac{3}{1 \cdot 2} - \frac{4}{2 \cdot 3} + \frac{5}{3 \cdot 4} - \cdots + \frac{(-1)^{n+1}(n+2)}{n(n+1)} + \cdots. \tag{9}$$

Solution. 1. $\qquad \left|\dfrac{u_{n+1}}{u_n}\right| = \dfrac{n(n+3)}{(n+2)^2}; \quad R = \lim_{n \to \infty} \dfrac{n^2 + 3n}{n^2 + 4n + 4} = 1.$

Hence, the ratio test fails. We proceed to use other tests.

2. The series of absolute values for (9) is

$$\frac{3}{1 \cdot 2} + \frac{4}{2 \cdot 3} + \frac{5}{3 \cdot 4} + \cdots + \frac{n+2}{n(n+1)} + \cdots, \tag{10}$$

where $\qquad\qquad \dfrac{n+2}{n(n+1)} = \dfrac{1}{n} \cdot \dfrac{n+2}{n+1} > \dfrac{1}{n},$

because $n + 2 > n + 1$. Hence, each term in (10) is greater than the corresponding term in the divergent series $\sum_{n=1}^{\infty} 1/n$. Thus, by the comparison test, (10) diverges; therefore, (9) does *not converge absolutely*. Then, we must test (9) itself.

3. By the test applicable to alternating series, we find that (9) converges. Hence, (9) is *conditionally convergent*, because it *does not converge absolutely*.

Note 2. In (1), we may use u_{n+2}/u_{n+1}, or u_n/u_{n-1}, in place of u_{n+1}/u_n. In $\sum_{n=1}^{\infty} u_n$, suppose that $|u_{n+1}/u_n| \geqq 1$ if n is sufficiently large. Then, although no limit may exist as in (1), the remarks in the proof of (B) show that the series *diverges*.

Note 3. In $\sum_{n=1}^{\infty} u_n$, suppose that $|u_{n+1}/u_n| \leq \rho < 1$ if n is sufficiently large, say $n \geq k$. Then, even when no limit exists in (1), the remarks in the proof of (*A*) show that the series converges. Under present circumstances, let $S_h = \sum_{n=1}^{h} u_n$, let R_h be the remainder after h terms, and let σ be the sum of the infinite series, with $h \geq k$. Then $\sigma = S_h + R_h$. Also, as in (5) and (6),

$$|\sigma - S_h| = |R_h| \leq |u_h|(\rho + \rho^2 + \rho^3 + \cdots). \tag{11}$$

From (11), by use of (3) on page 546 for the sum of a geometric series,

$$\left\{ \begin{array}{l} error \ of \ S_h \ as \ an \\ approximation \ to \ \sigma \end{array} \right\} = |\sigma - S_h| \leq \frac{\rho|u_h|}{1 - \rho}. \tag{12}$$

EXAMPLE 2. Find a value for h so that the partial sum S_h for the series below will give the sum, σ, of the series with an error of at most .02.

$$\sum_{n=1}^{\infty} u_n \quad where \quad u_n = \frac{n(n + 1)}{2^n}. \tag{13}$$

Solution. $\quad r_n = \dfrac{u_{n+1}}{u_n} = \dfrac{(n + 1)(n + 2)}{n(n + 1)} \cdot \dfrac{1}{2} = \dfrac{n + 2}{2n} = \dfrac{1}{2} + \dfrac{1}{n}.$ \hfill (14)

From (14), $\qquad r_n < \frac{3}{5}$ *if* $n > 10$. *Then, from* (12) *with* $\rho = \frac{3}{5}$,

if $h > 10$, $\qquad |\sigma - S_h| \leq u_h \dfrac{\frac{3}{5}}{\frac{2}{5}} = \dfrac{3}{2} \dfrac{h(h + 1)}{2^h}.$ \hfill (15)

We find that, if $h = 15$, the right-hand side of (11) is less than .02, and thus the error of S_{15} as an approximation for σ is less than .02. (The result $h = 15$ may not be the smallest value of h with the specified property.)

EXERCISE 168

Test the series for convergence by the ratio test. If it fails, test otherwise. If any alternating series converges, determine whether the convergence is conditional.

1. $\dfrac{1}{3} + \dfrac{2}{3^2} + \dfrac{3}{3^3} + \cdots.$ $\qquad$ 2. $\dfrac{4}{1} + \dfrac{4^2}{2} + \dfrac{4^3}{3} + \cdots.$

3. $\dfrac{1!}{5} + \dfrac{2!}{5^2} + \dfrac{3!}{5^3} + \cdots.$ $\qquad$ 4. $\dfrac{2}{4} - \dfrac{3}{4^2} + \dfrac{4}{4^3} - \cdots.$

5. $\dfrac{1}{2!} + \dfrac{1}{3!} + \dfrac{1}{4!} + \cdots.$ $\qquad$ 6. $\dfrac{3}{1} - \dfrac{3^2}{2^2} + \dfrac{3^3}{3^2} - \cdots.$

7. $\dfrac{4}{1!} - \dfrac{4^2}{2!} + \dfrac{4^3}{3!} - \cdots.$ $\qquad$ 8. $\dfrac{3}{2!} - \dfrac{5}{4!} + \dfrac{7}{6!} - \cdots.$

9. $\dfrac{1}{3} - \dfrac{2}{4} + \dfrac{3}{5} - \cdots.$ $\qquad$ 10. $\dfrac{1}{\sqrt[3]{1}} - \dfrac{1}{\sqrt[3]{2}} + \dfrac{1}{\sqrt[3]{3}} - \cdots.$

11. $\dfrac{1 \cdot 2}{3} - \dfrac{2 \cdot 3}{3^2} + \dfrac{3 \cdot 4}{3^3} - \cdots.$ $\qquad$ 12. $\dfrac{1}{1 \cdot 2} - \dfrac{1}{2 \cdot 3} + \dfrac{1}{3 \cdot 4} - \cdots.$

13. $\dfrac{1}{1} - \dfrac{1}{4} + \dfrac{1}{7} - \cdots.$ $\qquad$ 14. $\dfrac{2!}{\sqrt{1}} + \dfrac{4!}{\sqrt{2}} + \dfrac{6!}{\sqrt{3}} + \cdots.$

15. $\dfrac{4}{1 \cdot 2 \cdot 3} - \dfrac{5}{2 \cdot 3 \cdot 4} + \dfrac{6}{3 \cdot 4 \cdot 5} - \cdots.$ $\qquad$ 16. $\dfrac{1!}{10^2} + \dfrac{3!}{10^3} + \dfrac{5!}{10^4} + \cdots.$

17. $\displaystyle\sum_{n=1}^{\infty} (-1)^{n+1} \frac{n^3}{2^n}.$ **18.** $\displaystyle\sum_{n=1}^{\infty} \frac{n^n}{n!}.$ **19.** $\displaystyle\sum_{n=1}^{\infty} \frac{n}{\sqrt{n^2+2}}.$

20. $\displaystyle\sum_{n=1}^{\infty} (-1)^{n+1} \frac{1\cdot 3\cdot 5 \,\cdots\, (2n-1)}{4\cdot 8\cdot 12 \,\cdots\, (4n)}.$ **21.** $\displaystyle\sum_{n=1}^{\infty} \frac{(-1)^{n+1}}{\sqrt{n+2}-1}.$

22. $\displaystyle\sum_{n=1}^{\infty} (-1)^{n+1} \frac{n+\sqrt{n}}{n!}.$ **23.** $\displaystyle\sum_{n=1}^{\infty} \frac{3\cdot 6\cdot 9 \,\cdots\, (3n)}{1\cdot 3\cdot 5 \,\cdots\, (2n-1)}.$

★24–25. In Problems 11 and 22, respectively, find a value of h such that the error of the partial sum S_h as an approximation to the sum of the series is at most .001. (The requested answer is not unique.) Use (12) on page 559.

215. POWER SERIES

If the terms of a series are functions of one or more variables, it is desirable to find the values of the variables for which the series converges, or diverges. We shall study an important type of series of variable terms, called *power series*. If $c_0, c_1, c_2, \cdots$ are constants and x is a variable, then

$$c_0 + c_1 x + c_2 x^2 + \cdots + c_n x^n + \cdots \tag{1}$$

is called a *power series in* x. Similarly, if a is a constant, then

$$c_0 + c_1(x-a) + c_2(x-a)^2 + \cdots + c_n(x-a)^n + \cdots \tag{2}$$

is called a power series in $(x-a)$. Any series (1) converges if $x = 0$. In any case, it can be proved * that the values of x for which (1) converges form a single interval, possibly of length 0, about $x = 0$ as a center, called the **interval of convergence** of the series. This interval may be the whole x-axis. If the interval of convergence is of finite length, the series may converge at just one of the end points of the interval, at both end points, or at neither end point. Also, a series *converges absolutely at all values of x interior to the interval of convergence* of the series. Similar remarks apply to (2), with the center of the interval of convergence at $x = a$. The half-length of this interval is called the **radius of convergence** of the series.

Suppose that the absolute value of the quotient of successive coefficients, c_{n+1}/c_n, in (1) or (2), has a limit as $n \to \infty$, and that we are able to evaluate this limit. Then, we may find the interval of convergence of the series by the ratio test. If the interval is finite, *the ratio test always fails at the end points of the interval*. Then, the values of x at these end points must be substituted in the series, and the resulting series of constants must be examined for convergence by some test other than the ratio test.

ILLUSTRATION 1. On investigating $1 - \dfrac{x}{1!} + \dfrac{x^2}{2!} - \cdots$ by the ratio test, we find

$$R = \lim_{n\to\infty} \left| \frac{x^{n+1}}{(n+1)!} \div \frac{x^n}{n!} \right| = \lim_{n\to\infty} \left| \frac{x}{n+1} \right| = 0,$$

for any fixed x. Hence, the series converges absolutely for all values of x.

* See texts on the theory of functions of real and complex variables.

EXAMPLE 1. Test for convergence:

$$1 - \frac{x^2}{2 \cdot 2^2} + \frac{x^4}{3 \cdot 2^4} - \cdots + \frac{(-1)^n x^{2n}}{(n+1)2^{2n}} + \cdots. \tag{3}$$

Solution. 1. *Application of ratio test.* Let u_n be the term involving x^{2n}. Then,

$$|u_n| = \frac{x^{2n}}{(n+1)2^{2n}}; \quad |u_{n+1}| = \frac{x^{2n+2}}{(n+2)2^{2n+2}};$$

$$R = \lim_{n \to \infty} \left| \frac{u_{n+1}}{u_n} \right| = \frac{x^2}{4} \left(\lim_{n \to \infty} \frac{n+1}{n+2} \right) = \frac{x^2}{4} \cdot 1 = \frac{x^2}{4}. \tag{4}$$

Hence, by the ratio test, (3) *converges absolutely* if

$$\frac{x^2}{4} < 1 \quad or \quad x^2 < 4, \quad or \quad |x| < 2;$$

also, (3) diverges if

$$\frac{x^2}{4} > 1, \quad or \quad |x| > 2.$$

The ratio test fails if $\quad x^2 = 4, \quad or \quad |x| = 2, \quad or \quad x = \pm 2.$

2. *Test of the end points.* When $x = \pm 2$ in (3), we obtain the series

$$1 - \tfrac{1}{2} + \tfrac{1}{3} - \cdots,$$

which we know is conditionally convergent.

3. *Summary.* The series converges absolutely interior to the interval of convergence from $x = -2$ to $x = 2$, converges conditionally at $x = \pm 2$, and diverges if $x < -2$ and if $x > 2$, as illustrated in Figure 384.

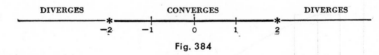

Fig. 384

EXERCISE 169

Find the interval of convergence of the series. Give a summary specifying convergence or divergence for all values of x, with absolute convergence and conditional convergence mentioned where they apply.

1. $1 + \frac{x}{2} + \frac{x^2}{3} + \cdots.$

2. $1 + \frac{x}{1!} + \frac{x^2}{2!} + \cdots.$

3. $x + 2x^2 + 3x^3 + \cdots.$

4. $1 + 2x + 2^2x^2 + \cdots.$

5. $1 - \frac{x}{2 \cdot 4} + \frac{x^2}{3 \cdot 4^2} - \cdots.$

6. $1 - \frac{3x}{\sqrt{2}} + \frac{3^2x^2}{\sqrt{3}} - \cdots.$

7. $\frac{x}{2^2 \cdot 3} + \frac{x^2}{3^2 \cdot 3^2} + \frac{x^3}{4^2 \cdot 3^3} + \cdots.$

8. $1 - \frac{x^2}{2!} + \frac{x^4}{4!} - \cdots.$

9. $\frac{x}{1!} - \frac{x^3}{3!} + \frac{x^5}{5!} - \cdots.$

10. $\frac{x(1!)}{2} + \frac{x^2(2!)}{3} + \frac{x^3(3!)}{4} + \cdots.$

11. $\frac{1}{\sqrt{1}} - \frac{x^2}{\sqrt{2}} + \frac{x^4}{\sqrt{3}} - \cdots.$

12. $\frac{1}{1^3} - \frac{2^2x^2}{3^3} + \frac{2^4x^4}{5^3} - \cdots.$

13. $1 - 3^2x^2 + 3^4x^4 - \cdots.$

14. $1 + x\sqrt{2} + x^2\sqrt{3} + \cdots.$

15. $1 - \dfrac{x-4}{3\sqrt{2}} + \dfrac{(x-4)^2}{3^2\sqrt{3}} - \dfrac{(x-4)^3}{3^3\sqrt{4}} + \cdots$.

16. $\dfrac{1}{1\cdot 2} - \dfrac{x+2}{2\cdot 3} + \dfrac{(x+2)^2}{3\cdot 4} - \dfrac{(x+2)^3}{4\cdot 5} + \cdots$.

17. $\dfrac{2}{1} + \dfrac{3}{2}\cdot\dfrac{x+1}{3} + \dfrac{4}{3}\cdot\dfrac{(x+1)^2}{3^2} + \dfrac{5}{4}\cdot\dfrac{(x+1)^3}{3^3} + \cdots$.

18. $\dfrac{2}{1}\cdot\dfrac{(x-1)^2}{3} + \dfrac{2\cdot 4}{1\cdot 3}\cdot\dfrac{(x-1)^4}{5} + \dfrac{2\cdot 4\cdot 6}{1\cdot 3\cdot 5}\cdot\dfrac{(x-1)^6}{7} + \cdots$.

19. $1 - \dfrac{1}{2}\cdot\dfrac{2}{x} + \dfrac{1}{3}\cdot\dfrac{2^2}{x^2} - \cdots$. **20.** $-\dfrac{2}{1} + \dfrac{3}{2}\cdot\dfrac{1}{3x} - \dfrac{4}{3}\cdot\dfrac{1}{3^2x^2} + \cdots$.

21. $\dfrac{3}{1\cdot 2} - \dfrac{4}{2\cdot 3}\cdot\dfrac{x}{2} + \dfrac{5}{3\cdot 4}\cdot\dfrac{x^2}{2^2} - \dfrac{6}{4\cdot 5}\cdot\dfrac{x^3}{2^3} + \cdots$.

216. INTEGRAL TEST FOR CONVERGENCE OR DIVERGENCE

The following result sometimes enables us to prove the convergence or divergence of a series of positive terms by establishing the convergence or divergence of a corresponding improper integral.

Theorem XVI. *Let* $\sum_{k=1}^{\infty} u_k$ *be a series of positive terms where* $u_k \geqq u_{k+1}$ *for all values of* k. *Suppose that there exists a function* $f(x)$, *which is defined, continuous, and decreasing* * *when* $x \geqq 1$, *and such that* $f(k) = u_k$. *Then, the u-series converges or diverges according as* $\int_1^{\infty} f(x)dx$ *converges or diverges.*

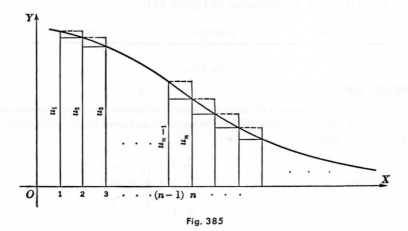

Fig. 385

Proof. 1. A graph of $y = f(x)$ is shown in Figure 385. With the interval $1 \leqq x \leqq 2$ as a base, the rectangle with a broken line at the top has the altitude u_1 and area $(u_1)\cdot(1)$ or u_1; the smaller rectangle has the altitude u_2 (linear units) and area u_2 (square units). The area of the region bounded by the lines $x = 1$ and $x = 2$, the

* Theorem XVI remains true if "*decreasing*" is changed to "*nonincreasing,*" and "$x \geqq 1$" is changed to "$x \geqq c$," where c is sufficiently large.

x-axis, and the curve $y = f(x)$, lies between the values u_1 and u_2. Similar remarks apply over each unit interval, with the larger and smaller rectangles over the interval from $x = n - 1$ to $x = n$ having the areas u_{n-1} and u_n, respectively. The area of the whole region bounded by the x-axis, the curve $y = f(x)$, and the lines $x = 1$ and $x = n$ is the integral below. Hence,

$$u_2 + u_3 + \cdots + u_n \leqq \int_1^n f(x)dx \leqq u_1 + u_2 + \cdots + u_{n-1}, \qquad (1)$$

where the expressions at the left and the right are the sums of the areas of the rectangles *under* the curve $y = f(x)$, and *above* the curve, respectively.

2. Now, assume that $\int_1^\infty f(x)dx$ converges, to a value A. That is,

$$\lim_{n \to \infty} \int_1^n f(x)dx = A; \quad also, \quad \int_1^n f(x)dx \leqq A, \qquad (2)$$

because $f(x) \geqq 0$ and thus $\int_1^n f(x)dx$ increases as n increases. From (1),

$$u_1 + u_2 + \cdots + u_n \leqq \int_1^n f(x)dx + u_1, \quad or \quad S_n \leqq A + u_1,$$

where S_n is the nth partial sum of the u-series. Thus, S_n is *bounded*, and then Theorem XI of page 548 shows that the u-series *converges*.

3. Assume, next, that $\int_1^\infty f(x)dx$ diverges. Then,

$$\int_1^n f(x)dx \to +\infty \quad as \quad n \to \infty. \qquad (3)$$

On adding u_n on the right in (1), we obtain

$$\int_1^n f(x)dx \leqq u_1 + u_2 + \cdots + u_{n-1} + u_n = S_n. \qquad (4)$$

Hence, from (3), $S_n \to +\infty$ as $n \to \infty$, or the u-series *diverges*. This completes the proof of the theorem.

EXAMPLE 1. Test for convergence: $\sum_{n=1}^\infty 1/n^3$.

Solution. Define $f(x) = \dfrac{1}{x^3}$. We verify that

$$\int_1^\infty \frac{dx}{x^3} = \lim_{h \to \infty} \int_1^h \frac{dx}{x^3} = \lim_{h \to \infty} \left[-\frac{1}{2x^2} \right]_1^h = \lim_{h \to \infty} \frac{1}{2}\left(1 - \frac{1}{h^2} \right) = \frac{1}{2},$$

or the improper integral converges. Hence the given series converges.

EXAMPLE 2. Test for convergence: $\sum_{n=2}^\infty \frac{1}{2n \ln n}$.

Solution. Let $f(x) = \dfrac{1}{x \ln x}$. Then, $f(x)$ decreases as x increases.

$$\int_2^\infty \frac{1}{x} \cdot \frac{1}{\ln x} dx = \lim_{h \to \infty} \int_2^h \frac{d(\ln x)}{\ln x} = \lim_{h \to \infty} \left[\ln (\ln x) \right]_{x=2}^{x=h} = +\infty,$$

because $\ln (\ln h) \to \infty$ as $h \to \infty$. Hence, $\int_2^\infty f(x)dx$ diverges, and therefore the given series diverges.

EXERCISE 170

Apply an integral test to prove convergence, or divergence.

1. $\displaystyle\sum_{n=1}^{\infty} \frac{1}{n^4}.$ **2.** $\displaystyle\sum_{n=1}^{\infty} \frac{1}{n}.$ **3.** $\displaystyle\sum_{n=1}^{\infty} \frac{1}{\sqrt[3]{n}}.$ **4.** $\displaystyle\sum_{n=2}^{\infty} \frac{1}{n(\ln n)^3}.$

5. $\displaystyle\sum_{n=1}^{\infty} \frac{1}{n^p}, p < 1; p > 1.$ **6.** $\displaystyle\sum_{n=1}^{\infty} \frac{n}{n^2 + 1}.$ **7.** $\displaystyle\sum_{n=1}^{\infty} \frac{1}{3n + 2}.$

8. $\displaystyle\sum_{n=1}^{\infty} \frac{1}{n^2 + 4}.$ **9.** $\displaystyle\sum_{n=1}^{\infty} \frac{1}{\sqrt{n^2 + 9}}.$ **10.** $\displaystyle\sum_{n=1}^{\infty} \frac{1}{n(n + 1)}.$

11. $\displaystyle\sum_{n=4}^{\infty} \frac{1}{n(\ln n)[\ln (\ln n)]^p}, p = 2; p > 1; p \leqq 1.$

EXERCISE 171 (*Review of Chapter Twenty-three*)

Investigate for convergence and divergence. Use more than one method if convenient.

1. $\displaystyle\sum_{n=1}^{\infty} \frac{n + 2}{2n + 3}.$ **2.** $\displaystyle\sum_{n=1}^{\infty} \cos\left(n \cdot \frac{\pi}{4}\right).$ **3.** $\displaystyle\sum_{n=1}^{\infty} \frac{(-1)^n n}{n + 2}.$

4. $\dfrac{1}{1 \cdot 4} + \dfrac{1}{2 \cdot 5} + \dfrac{1}{3 \cdot 6} + \cdots.$ **5.** $\dfrac{2}{1 \cdot 2} + \dfrac{2^2}{2 \cdot 3} + \dfrac{2^3}{3 \cdot 4} + \cdots.$

6. $\dfrac{1}{1 \cdot 2 \cdot 3} - \dfrac{1}{2 \cdot 3 \cdot 4} + \dfrac{1}{3 \cdot 4 \cdot 5} - \cdots.$ **7.** $\dfrac{3}{1 \cdot 4} + \dfrac{4}{2 \cdot 5} + \dfrac{5}{3 \cdot 6} + \cdots.$

8. $\dfrac{1!}{2} + \dfrac{2!}{3} + \dfrac{3!}{4} + \cdots.$ **9.** $\dfrac{1}{1} - \dfrac{1}{5} + \dfrac{1}{9} - \cdots.$

10. $\ln \dfrac{1}{2} + \ln \dfrac{2}{3} + \ln \dfrac{3}{4} + \cdots.$ **11.** $\dfrac{2}{1!} - \dfrac{3}{2!} + \dfrac{4}{3!} - \cdots.$

12. $\dfrac{2}{4} - \dfrac{3}{4^2} + \dfrac{4}{4^3} - \cdots.$ **13.** $\dfrac{3}{\sqrt{2}} + \dfrac{3^2}{\sqrt{3}} + \dfrac{3^3}{\sqrt{4}} + \cdots.$

14. $\displaystyle\sum_{n=1}^{\infty} \frac{n + 1}{\sqrt{n^2 + 1}}.$ **15.** $\displaystyle\sum_{n=1}^{\infty} \frac{1 \cdot 3 \cdot 5 \cdots (2n - 1)}{3 \cdot 6 \cdot 9 \cdots (3n)}.$

16. $1 + \dfrac{x}{3} + \dfrac{x^2}{5} + \cdots.$ **17.** $\dfrac{1}{2!} + \dfrac{x}{4!} + \dfrac{x^2}{6!} + \cdots.$

18. $1 + \dfrac{1}{2^2} \cdot \dfrac{x}{4} + \dfrac{1}{3^2} \cdot \dfrac{x^2}{4^2} + \cdots.$ **19.** $\dfrac{1}{1 \cdot 2} + \dfrac{2x}{2 \cdot 3} + \dfrac{2^2 x^2}{3 \cdot 4} + \cdots.$

20. $\dfrac{1}{2} + \dfrac{2}{3} \cdot 3(x - 2) + \dfrac{3}{4} \cdot 3^2(x - 2)^2 + \dfrac{4}{5} \cdot 3^3(x - 2)^3 + \cdots.$

21. $1 + \dfrac{2(x + 1)}{2!} + \dfrac{2^2(x + 1)^2}{3!} + \dfrac{2^3(x + 1)^3}{4!} + \cdots.$

22. $\displaystyle\sum_{n=1}^{\infty} \frac{\sqrt{n}}{\sqrt{n + 1} - 1}.$ **23.** $\displaystyle\sum_{n=1}^{\infty} \frac{(n + 1)^2}{n^n}.$

24. $\dfrac{1}{\ln 2} + \dfrac{3}{\ln 3} + \dfrac{5}{\ln 4} + \cdots.$ **25.** $\dfrac{e}{1^3} + \dfrac{e^2}{2^3} + \dfrac{e^3}{3^3} + \cdots.$

★26. $\dfrac{1 \cdot 3}{2 \cdot 4} \cdot \dfrac{x^2}{1} + \dfrac{3 \cdot 5}{4 \cdot 6} \cdot \dfrac{x^4}{2} + \dfrac{5 \cdot 7}{6 \cdot 8} \cdot \dfrac{x^6}{3} + \cdots.$ **★27.** $\dfrac{1}{4} \cdot \dfrac{x^2}{3} + \dfrac{1 \cdot 3}{4 \cdot 6} \cdot \dfrac{x^4}{5} + \dfrac{1 \cdot 3 \cdot 5}{4 \cdot 6 \cdot 8} \cdot \dfrac{x^6}{7} + \cdots.$

★SUPPLEMENT FOR CHAPTER TWENTY–THREE

28. Prove that $\sum_{n=1}^{\infty} \frac{(\cos nx)}{n^2}$ converges absolutely for all values of x.

29. If m has any value, prove that the following series converges if $|x| < 1$ and diverges if $|x| > 1$. Consideration of $x = \pm 1$ is not possible at our level. The series is called the **binomial series,** and its relation to $(1 + x)^m$ is discussed later.

$$1 + mx + \frac{m(m-1)x^2}{2!} + \cdots + \frac{m(m-1)(m-2)\cdots(m-n+1)}{n!} x^n + \cdots$$

30. Find the interval of convergence of the series: $\sum_{n=1}^{\infty} \frac{(x-3)^n}{2^n} \sqrt{\frac{n^n}{n!}}$.

31. Test for convergence: $\sum_{n=1}^{\infty} \frac{n(-1)^n}{(1+n^2)^{\frac{3}{2}}}$; $\sum_{n=1}^{\infty} \frac{\ln n}{1+n^{\frac{5}{2}}}$.

32. Prove that each *telescopic* series is convergent or divergent and *find its sum* if convergent. In each case, search for v_n and v_{n+1} so that $\sum_{n=1}^{\infty} u_n$ has $u_n = v_n - v_{n+1}$, and investigate S_n for the series.

$$\sum_{n=1}^{\infty} \frac{1}{(n+2)(n+3)}; \quad \sum_{n=1}^{\infty} \frac{1}{(n+1)(2n+4)}; \quad \sum_{n=2}^{\infty} \ln \frac{\ln n}{\ln(n+1)}.$$

33. If the series $P(x) = \sum_{n=0}^{\infty} a_n x^n$ converges at some point $x = x_0 \neq 0$, prove that the series converges absolutely when $|x| < |x_0|$. If $P(x)$ diverges when $x = x_0$, prove that $P(x)$ diverges when $|x| > |x_0|$. Prove that, in any case, (1) $P(x)$ converges only when $x = 0$, or (2) $P(x)$ converges for all values of x, or (3) there exists a number $R > 0$ such that $P(x)$ converges absolutely when $|x| < R$ and diverges when $|x| > R$. (The number R appears as the least upper bound of the set of all numbers $|x_0|$ such that $P(x_0)$ converges.)

Hint. For the first result, show that there exists $K > 0$ such that $|a_n x_0^n| < K$ for all values of n. Also, write $a_n x^n = a_n x_0^n (x^n/x_0^n)$.

34. With $P(x)$ as in Problem 33, prove that the series $P_1(x) = \sum_{n=1}^{\infty} n a_n x^{n-1}$ has the same radius of convergence as $P(x)$. [See the Hint for Problem 33.] We call $P_1(x)$ the *first derivative series* for $P(x)$. At a more advanced level it is proved that $P_1(x) = dP(x)/dx$ when $|x| < R$, where R is the radius of convergence of $P(x)$.

35. By definition, a *rearrangement* of a series $\sum_{n=1}^{\infty} u_n$ is a new series $\sum_{n=1}^{\infty} v_n$ where each term v_k is *some term u_h*, and where *each term u_h occurs just once in the v-series*. Prove that, if $u_n \geq 0$, then the u-series and the v-series both diverge or both converge and then have the same sum. (Recall Theorem XI, page 548.)

36. Prove the following generalized comparison tests relating to two series of positive terms, $\sum_{n=1}^{\infty} u_n$ and $\sum_{n=1}^{\infty} v_n$.

A. *If the u-series converges, and if v_n/u_n approaches a finite limit H as $n \to \infty$, then the v-series converges.*

B. *If the u-series diverges, and if v_n/u_n approaches a limit $K \neq 0$ as $n \to \infty$, where K may be finite or $+\infty$, then the v-series diverges.*

Hint. For (A), if we choose $H_1 > H$, then $(v_n/u_n) < H_1$ for large n.

37. Use the result of Problem 40 to prove the results stated in Note 2 on page 551.

38. Prove the results stated in Note 1 on page 555.

CHAPTER TWENTY–FOUR

Expansion of Functions

217. TAYLOR SERIES

Suppose that $\sum_{n=0}^{\infty} b_n(x - a)^n$ has the interval of convergence $|x - a| < R$, and let $f(x)$ represent the sum of the series. Then, by advanced methods, it can be proved that (*i*) the function f possesses continuous derivatives of all orders if $|x - a| < R$; (*ii*) for every positive integer k, the series obtained by differentiating the given series term by term, k times in succession, also has the interval of convergence $|x - a| < R$; (*iii*) the sum of the series in (*ii*) is equal to $f^{(k)}(x)$ when $|x - a| < R$. We shall use these facts in discussing the expansion of functions into power series.

EXAMPLE 1. **IF** the series on the right below converges and has $\sin x$ as its sum at all values of x on some interval $|x| < R$, find the coefficients:

$$\sin x = b_0 + b_1 x + b_2 x^2 + \cdots + b_n x^n + \cdots. \tag{1}$$

Solution. 1. From (1), on differentiating both sides, we obtain

$$\frac{d \sin x}{dx} = \cos x = b_1 + 2b_2 x + 3b_3 x^2 + \cdots + nb_n x^{n-1} + \cdots; \tag{2}$$

$$\frac{d^2 \sin x}{dx^2} = -\sin x = (2!)b_2 + 3 \cdot 2b_3 x + \cdots + n(n - 1)b_n x^{n-2} + \cdots; \tag{3}$$

$$\frac{d^3 \sin x}{dx^3} = -\cos x = (3!)b_3 + \cdots + n(n - 1)(n - 2)b_n x^{n-3} + \cdots. \tag{4}$$

2. On placing $x = 0$ in (1)–(4), we obtain $b_0 = 0$ and

$$\cos 0 = 1 = b_1; \quad 0 = b_2; \quad -1 = (3!)b_3 \quad or \quad b_3 = -(1/3!). \tag{5}$$

Since $D_x^4 \sin x = \sin x$, the successive derivatives of $\sin x$ *repeat in groups of four.* Hence, we find $b_n = 0$ if n is *even.* Since $D_x^n x^n = n!$, then $\pm 1 = (n!)b_n$ when n is *odd*, or $b_n = \pm(1/n!)$. Thus, we obtain

$$\sin x = x - \frac{x^3}{3!} + \frac{x^5}{5!} - \cdots + (-1)^{k+1} \frac{x^{2k-1}}{(2k - 1)!} + \cdots. \tag{6}$$

Theorem I. *Suppose that the function $f(x)$ possesses derivatives of all orders in its domain. Assume that there exists an infinite series in powers of $(x - a)$ which converges, and has $f(x)$ as the sum, at all values of x on some interval $|x - a| < R$. Then, when $|x - a| < R$,*

$$f(x) = f(a) + f'(a)(x - a) + \frac{f''(a)}{2!}(x - a)^2 + \cdots$$
$$+ \frac{f^{(n)}(a)}{n!}(x - a)^n + \cdots. \tag{7}$$

Proof. 1. Suppose that coefficients $\{b_n\}$ exist such that the series on the right below converges to the sum $f(x)$ when $|x - a| < R$:

$$f(x) = b_0 + b_1(x - a) + b_2(x - a)^2 + \cdots + b_n(x - a)^n + \cdots. \tag{8}$$

Then, on recalling that $d^n(x - a)^n/dx^n = n!$, we obtain

$$f'(x) = b_1 + 2b_2(x - a) + 3b_3(x - a)^2 + \cdots + nb_n(x - a)^{n-1} + \cdots;$$
$$f''(x) = (2!)b_2 + 3 \cdot 2b_3(x - a) + \cdots + n(n - 1)b_n(x - a)^{n-2} + \cdots; \text{ etc.};$$
$$f^{(n)}(x) = (n!)b_n + (n + 1)(n)(n - 1) \cdots 2b_{n+1}(x - a) + \cdots.$$

2. On placing $x = a$ above, we find

$$b_0 = f(a); \quad b_1 = f'(a); \quad b_2 = f''(a)/2!; \cdots; \quad b_n = f^{(n)}(a)/n!.$$

Hence, the series in (8) is identical with (7), which proves Theorem I.

The right-hand side of (7) is called the **Taylor series** for $f(x)$ in powers of $(x - a)$, or *Taylor's expansion* of $f(x)$ about the point $x = a$. Before (7) is of any use, we must ask, first, "*does the Taylor series in* (7) *converge on some interval* $|x - a| < R$?" If the answer to this question is "*yes*," then we shall ask, "*is $f(x)$ the sum of the series?*" Such questions will be considered later. At present, we shall assume that, *if we obtain a Taylor series for a function $f(x)$, then the sum of the series is $f(x)$ wherever the series converges*. If $a = 0$ in (7), the resulting Taylor series sometimes is called the **Maclaurin series** for $f(x)$, and has the form

$$f(x) = f(0) + f'(0)x + \frac{f''(0)}{2!}x^2 + \cdots + \frac{f^{(n)}(0)}{n!}x^n + \cdots. \tag{9}$$

EXAMPLE 2. Expand $\cos x$ in powers of $(x - \tfrac{1}{4}\pi)$.

Solution. With $f(x) = \cos x$, we calculate derivatives and substitute $x = \tfrac{1}{4}\pi$:

$$f(x) = \cos x; \quad f(\tfrac{1}{4}\pi) = \tfrac{1}{2}\sqrt{2}. \qquad f'(x) = -\sin x; \quad f'(\tfrac{1}{4}\pi) = -\tfrac{1}{2}\sqrt{2}.$$
$$f''(x) = -\cos x; \quad f''(\tfrac{1}{4}\pi) = -\tfrac{1}{2}\sqrt{2}. \qquad f'''(x) = \sin x; \quad f'''(\tfrac{1}{4}\pi) = \tfrac{1}{2}\sqrt{2}.$$
$$f^{(IV)}(x) = \cos x; \qquad f^{(IV)}(\tfrac{1}{4}\pi) = \tfrac{1}{2}\sqrt{2}. \quad \text{Etc.}$$

Since $f^{(IV)}(x) = \cos x = f(x)$, the successive derivatives at $x = \tfrac{1}{4}\pi$ repeat in groups of four each. Each coefficient in the expansion (7) will have $\tfrac{1}{2}\sqrt{2}$ as a factor. Thus, from (7), with signs of terms alternating in pairs, and $a = \tfrac{1}{4}\pi$,

$$\cos x = \frac{\sqrt{2}}{2}\left[1 - \left(x - \frac{\pi}{4}\right) - \frac{1}{2!}\left(x - \frac{\pi}{4}\right)^2 + \frac{1}{3!}\left(x - \frac{\pi}{4}\right)^3 + \cdots\right].$$

Note 1. Taylor series are named in honor of the English mathematician BROOK TAYLOR (1685–1731). Maclaurin series are named after the Scottish mathematician COLIN MACLAURIN (1698–1746).

On substituting $x = a + h$ in (7), we obtain the following form for the Taylor expansion about $x = a$:

$$f(a + h) = f(a) + hf'(a) + \frac{1}{2!} h^2 f''(a) + \cdots + \frac{1}{n!} h^n f^{(n)}(a) + \cdots. \tag{10}$$

That is, by (10), the value of $f(x)$ at $x = a + h$ is expressed in terms of $f(a)$, the derivatives of $f(x)$ at $x = a$, and the increment h by which the value $x = a + h$ differs from $x = a$.

EXAMPLE 3. Obtain the Maclaurin expansion of $(1 - x)^{-\frac{1}{3}}$.

Solution. We use (9) with $f(x) = (1 - x)^{-\frac{1}{3}}$, or (7) with $a = 0$.

$$f'(x) = +\frac{1}{3}(1 - x)^{-\frac{4}{3}} \qquad and \qquad f'(0) = \frac{1}{3};$$

$$f''(x) = \frac{1 \cdot 4}{3^2}(1 - x)^{-\frac{7}{3}} \qquad and \qquad f''(0) = \frac{1 \cdot 4}{3^2},$$

$$f'''(x) = \frac{1 \cdot 4 \cdot 7}{3^3}(1 - x)^{-\frac{10}{3}} \qquad and \qquad f'''(0) = \frac{1 \cdot 4 \cdot 7}{3^3};$$

$$\vdots \qquad\qquad\qquad\qquad \vdots$$

$$f^{(n)}(x) = \frac{1 \cdot 4 \cdot 7 \cdots (3n - 2)}{3^n}(1 - x)^{-\frac{1 + 3n}{3}} \qquad and \qquad f^{(n)}(0) = \frac{1 \cdot 4 \cdot 7 \cdots (3n - 2)}{3^n}.$$

$$(1 - x)^{-\frac{1}{3}} = 1 + \frac{1}{3}x + \frac{1 \cdot 4}{2 \cdot 3^2}x^2 + \frac{1 \cdot 4 \cdot 7}{3^3(3!)}x^3 + \cdots + \frac{1 \cdot 4 \cdots (3n - 2)}{3^n(n!)}x^n + \cdots.$$

EXAMPLE 4. How many terms in the Maclaurin series for $\sin x$ would be sufficient to obtain $\sin x$ with accuracy to six decimal places, if $|x| < .5$?

Solution. 1. By Corollary 2 on page 554, if $S_k(x)$ in (6) is used as an approximation to $\sin x$ when $|x| < .5$,

$$|error| = |\sin x - S_k(x)| < \frac{|x^{2k+1}|}{(2k + 1)!} < \frac{.5^{2k+1}}{(2k + 1)!}. \tag{11}$$

2. On the right in (11), we obtain .000002 when $k = 3$, and $5.4(10^{-9})$ when $k = 4$. Since $5.4(10^{-9}) < 5(10^{-8})$, then $S_4(x)$ gives $\sin x$ with accuracy to seven decimal places, or 4 terms are sufficient for the desired accuracy.

EXERCISE 172

Obtain the Taylor expansion of $f(x)$ about each given point. Calculate the general term of the series if convenient. In any case, obtain at least the first three nonzero terms.

1. $f(x) = \cos x$; about $x = 0$.   2. $f(x) = \sin x$; about $x = \frac{1}{4}\pi$.

3. $f(x) = e^x$; the Maclaurin series.   4. $f(x) = e^x$; about $x = 2$.

5. $f(x) = e^{-2x}$; about $x = 0$.   6. $f(x) = e^x$; about $x = a$.

7. $f(x) = 3x^4 + 2x^2 - x + 5$;   (a) about $x = 0$;   (b) about $x = -2$.

8. $f(x) = (1 - x)^{-2}$; about $x = 0$.   **9.** $f(x) = a^x$; about $x = 0$.

10. $f(x) = \ln(1 + x)$; about $x = 0$.   **11.** $f(x) = \ln(1 - x)$; about $x = 0$.

12. $\tan x$; about $x = \frac{3}{4}\pi$.   **13.** Arcsin x; about $x = 0$.

14. $\ln \sin x$; about $x = \frac{1}{2}\pi$.   **15.** $e^x \sin x$; about $x = \frac{1}{2}\pi$.

16. $\ln(2 - e^x)$; about $x = 0$.   **17.** $\sin(\frac{1}{6}\pi + x)$; about $x = 0$.

18. $(1 + x)^{\frac{3}{2}}$; about $x = 0$.   **19.** Arctan x; about $x = 0$.

20. $xe^{\sin x}$; about $x = 0$.   **21.** $\tan x$; about $x = 0$.

Obtain the Maclaurin series for the function by substituting some expression for x in a Maclaurin series previously obtained.

22. $\cos 2x$.   **23.** $\cos(-\frac{1}{2}x)$.   **24.** e^{5x}.   **25.** $\ln(1 + 2x)$.

26. $\ln(1 - 3x)$.   **27.** $\tan 3x$.   **28.** $\sin 4x$.   **29.** $(1 - x^2)^{-1}$.

30. Obtain the Maclaurin expansion of $(1 + x)^m$, where m may be any real number, and include the general term. Prove that the series converges if $|x| < 1$, and diverges if $|x| > 1$. This series is called the **binomial series.** It can be proved to converge to $(1 + x)^m$ if $|x| < 1$, for all values of m, and at $x = +1$ and $x = -1$ for certain corresponding intervals of values of m. See Problem 29 on page 565, and Problems 35–36 on page 582.

Obtain the first four nonzero terms in the Maclaurin series for each function by substituting in the binomial series.

31. $(1 - x)^{\frac{1}{3}}$.   **32.** $(1 + x^2)^{-\frac{1}{2}}$.   **33.** $(1 + x)^{-3}$.

Compute with accuracy to four decimal places by use of a Maclaurin series, and check the degree of accuracy by use of Corollary 2 on page 554, if possible.

34. $\cos .2$.   **35.** $\sin .3$.   **36.** $e^{-.4}$.   **37.** $\sin 4°$.

38. $.98^{-1}$, from $(1 + x)^{-1}$.   **39.** $\sin 32°$, from $\sin(\frac{1}{6}\pi + x)$.

40. $\ln 1.1$.   **41.** Arctan $.2$.   **42.** $1.03^{\frac{1}{2}}$.   **43.** $130^{\frac{1}{3}}$.

44. If $0 \leq x \leq .3$, how many terms in the Maclaurin expansion of $\ln(1 + x)$ would be sufficient to give $\ln(1 + x)$ accurate to 5 decimal places?

218. TAYLOR'S FORMULA

Theorem II. *Let n represent a positive integer, and assume that a function $f(x)$ is differentiable n times, with $f^{(n)}(x)$ continuous, at all values of x on some interval T including $x = a$. Then, for each point x on T, there exists a point ξ_n between * a and x such that*

$$f(x) = f(a) + f'(a)(x - a) + \frac{f''(a)}{2!}(x - a)^2 + \cdots$$
$$+ \frac{f^{(n-1)}(a)}{(n - 1)!}(x - a)^{n-1} + R_n(x), \tag{1}$$

where
$$R_n(x) = \frac{f^{(n)}(\xi_n)}{n!}(x - a)^n. \tag{2}$$

* For a proof assuming only that $f^{(n)}(x)$ *exists*, see Note 14 in the Appendix. The possibilities $\xi = a$ and $\xi = x$ in (2) are excluded by the proof on page 689.

Note 1. In (1), the first n terms on the right are the first n terms in the Taylor series for $f(x)$ in powers of $(x - a)$. Hence, in (1), even if the corresponding Taylor series should not converge, we call $R_n(x)$ *the remainder after n terms* in the Taylor series. We refer to (1) as **Taylor's formula with a remainder,** for $f(x)$ in powers of $(x - a)$, and Theorem II is called **Taylor's theorem.** Also, we call $R_n(x)$ the *error term*, when we consider the sum of the other terms on the right in (1) as an approximation to $f(x)$. The expression for $R_n(x)$ in (2) is known as *Lagrange's form* for the remainder term, in honor of the French mathematician COUNT JOSEPH LOUIS LAGRANGE (1736–1813). Other forms for $R_n(x)$ are available. We observe that the mean value theorem of page 173 is the special case of Taylor's theorem when $n = 1$, because then (1) becomes

$$f(x) = f(a) + f'(\xi_1)(x - a).$$

When $a = 0$ in (1), we obtain the Maclaurin form of Taylor's formula, and the result sometimes is referred to as **Maclaurin's formula:**

$$f(x) = f(0) + f'(0)x + \frac{f''(0)}{2!} x^2 + \cdots + \frac{f^{(n-1)}(0)}{(n-1)!} x^n + R_n(x), \qquad (3)$$

where

$$R_n(x) = \frac{f^{(n)}(\xi_n)}{n!} x^n, \qquad (4)$$

and ξ_n is some number between 0 and x. We shall prove (1) after illustrating its use in special cases.

EXAMPLE 1. Find an approximating polynomial for e^x by taking the sum of the first four terms in the Maclaurin series for e^x. Then, if $|x| < .3$, by use of Taylor's formula obtain an upper bound for the error made if the value of this polynomial is taken as an approximation to e^x.

Solution. 1. Since $d^n e^x / dx^n = e^x$, Maclaurin's series and Taylor's formula with a remainder after four terms, in powers of x, are as follows:

$$\begin{Bmatrix} \text{Maclaurin's} \\ \text{series} \end{Bmatrix} \qquad e^x = 1 + x + \frac{x^2}{2} + \frac{x^3}{6} + \cdots; \qquad (5)$$

$$\begin{Bmatrix} \text{Taylor's} \\ \text{formula} \end{Bmatrix} \qquad e^x = S_4(x) + R_4(x), \quad \text{with} \quad R_4(x) = \frac{e^\xi x^4}{4!}, \qquad (6)$$

where $S_4(x)$ is the sum of the four terms explicitly written in (5), and ξ is between 0 and x. The desired approximating polynomial is $S_4(x)$.

2. Since $e^x - S_4(x) = R_4(x)$, then $|R_4(x)|$ is the error made if $S_4(x)$ is taken as an approximate value for e^x. From (6), if $|x| < .3$,

$$|R_4(x)| < \frac{e^\xi(.3)^4}{24}, \quad \text{where} \quad |\xi| < .3.$$

Hence, $-.3 < \xi < .3$. Then $e^\xi < e^{.3}$, and thus

$$error = |R_4(x)| < \frac{e^{.3}(.3^4)}{24} = .0005 \quad (\text{by logarithms}).$$

To prove Theorem II, we shall need the following result, which is of funda-mental importance in many parts of advanced calculus.

Lemma I. (*A mean value theorem for the integral of a product.*) *Assume that the functions $g(t)$ and $h(t)$ are continuous, with $h(t)$ of one sign or zero on the interval $W : (a \leq t \leq x)$. Then, there exists a point ξ on W such that*

$$\int_a^x g(t)h(t)dt = g(\xi) \int_a^x h(t)dt. \tag{7}$$

Proof [when $h(t) \geq 0$]. Let m and M, respectively, be the absolute minimum and absolute maximum of $g(t)$ on W. Then, $m \leq g(t) \leq M$ and

(since $h(t) \geq 0$) $\qquad\qquad mh(t) \leq g(t)h(t) \leq Mh(t).$ \hfill (8)

Hence, $\qquad\qquad m\int_a^x h(t)dt \leq \int_a^x g(t)h(t)dt \leq M\int_a^x h(t)dt.$ \hfill (9)

Therefore, there exists a number μ, where $m \leq \mu \leq M$, such that

$$\int_a^x g(t)h(t)dt = \mu \int_a^x h(t)dt. \tag{10}$$

Since g is continuous, there exists a point ξ on W such that $\mu = g(\xi)$. With this expression for μ, then (10) gives (7).

Comment. To prove (7) with $h(t) \leq 0$, on the basis of the preceding proof, we first write (7) with $h(t)$ replaced by $-h(t)$, and then multiply both sides of the resulting equation by -1 to obtain (7) for $h(t) \leq 0$. If $a > x$, we prove (7) by first writing it with x and a interchanged in the limits, and then multiplying both sides by -1.

Proof of Theorem II. 1. Since all derivatives $f^{(k)}$, with $k \leq n$, are continuous, all of the following manipulations of integrals are justified. Let x have a fixed value. Then, by the fundamental theorem of integral calculus,

$$f(x) - f(a) = \int_a^x f'(t)dt. \tag{11}$$

2. In (11), integrate by parts, in the form $\int u \, dv$ with $u = f'(t)$, $dv = dt$, and $v = t - x$; then again with $dv = (x - t)dt$ and $v = -\frac{1}{2}(x - t)^2$; etc., to obtain

$$f(x) - f(a) = \left\{ (t - x)f'(t) \Big]_{t=a}^{t=x} \right\} - \int_a^x (t - x)f''(t)dt$$

$$= 0 + (x - a)f'(a) + \int_a^x (x - t)f''(t)dt \tag{12}$$

$$= (x - a)f'(a) + \frac{1}{2!}(x - a)^2 f''(a) + \frac{1}{2!}\int_a^x (x - t)^2 f'''(t)dt; \text{ etc.} \tag{13}$$

After $(n - 1)$ successive integrations, we obtain (1) with

$$R_n(x) = \frac{1}{(n - 1)!} \int_a^x (x - t)^{n-1} f^{(n)}(t)dt. \tag{14}$$

3. In (14), apply (7) with $g(t)$ as $f^{(n)}(t)$, $h(t)$ as $(x - t)^{n-1}$, and

$$\int_a^x (x - t)^{n-1} dt = -\frac{1}{n}(x - t)^n \Big]_{t=a}^{t=x} = \frac{(x - a)^n}{n}.$$

From (7), a point ξ_n exists on the interval from a to x, inclusive, such that

$$R_n = \frac{1}{(n - 1)!} \cdot \frac{1}{n}(x - a)^n f^{(n)}(\xi_n) = \frac{f^{(n)}(\xi_n)}{n!}(x - a)^n, \tag{15}$$

which proves Theorem II.

219. APPLICATIONS OF TAYLOR'S FORMULA

We now have available two distinct but related expressions:

$$\begin{Bmatrix} Taylor's \\ series \end{Bmatrix} f(x) = f(a) + f'(a)(x - a) + \cdots + \frac{f^{(n-1)}(a)}{(n - 1)!} (x - a)^{n-1} + \cdots. \quad (1)$$

$$\begin{Bmatrix} Taylor's \\ formula \end{Bmatrix} f(x) = S_n(x) + R_n(x), \quad where \quad R_n(x) = \frac{f^{(n)}(\xi_n)}{n!} (x - a)^n, \quad (2)$$

in which $S_n(x)$ is the sum of the first n terms in (1), and ξ_n is somewhere between a and x. Without questioning the equality, or convergence of the series in (1), by use of $R_n(x)$ in (2) we frequently can solve the following problem:

For any particular values of n and x, what upper bound can we specify for the error if we use $S_n(x)$ as an approximation to $f(x)$?

EXAMPLE 1. Compute ln .9 with accuracy to 5 decimal places.

Solution. 1. Let $f(x) = \ln (1 - x)$; we wish $f(.1)$. By use of (1) with $a = 0$,

$$\begin{Bmatrix} Maclaurin's \\ series \end{Bmatrix} \quad \ln (1 - x) = 0 - x - \frac{x^2}{2} - \frac{x^3}{3} - \cdots - \frac{x^n}{n} - \cdots. \quad (3)$$

In (3), $S_5(.1) = 0 - .1 - .005 - .000333 - .000025 = -.105358.$ (4)

2. We write Maclaurin's formula, (2) with $a = 0$, with a remainder after five terms:

$$\ln (1 - x) = 0 - x - \frac{x^2}{2} - \frac{x^3}{3} - \frac{x^4}{4} + R_5(x) = S_5(x) + R_5(x), \quad (5)$$

where $\dfrac{d^5 \ln (1 - x)}{dx^5} = -\dfrac{4!}{(1 - x)^5}$ and $R_5(x) = -\dfrac{x^5}{5(1 - \xi)^5}.$ (6)

With $x = .1$ in (6), we know that ξ is between 0 and .1. Hence,

$$1 - \xi > 1 - .1 = .9, \quad and \quad | R_5(.1) | < \frac{.1^5}{5(.9)^5} = .000003. \quad (7)$$

Thus, by (5), the approximation ln $.9 = S_5(.1) = -.10536$ is correct to five decimal places, because the error, in (7), is less than .000003. We kept the term 0 explicitly in (3), (4), and (5) in order to maintain the notation of (1) and (2).

EXAMPLE 2. Obtain a polynomial of degree 2 in $(x - \frac{1}{4}\pi)$ as an approximation to tan x. Then, find an upper bound for the error made if this polynomial is used to compute tan 48°.

Solution. 1. Let $f(x) = \tan x$. We expand $f(x)$ about $x = \frac{1}{4}\pi$ by use of (1) and (2).

$f'(x) = \sec^2 x;$ $f''(x) = 2 \sec^2 x \tan x;$ $f'''(x) = 2 \sec^2 x(\sec^2 x + 2 \tan^2 x);$

$$f(\tfrac{1}{4}\pi) = 1; \quad f'(\tfrac{1}{4}\pi) = 2; \quad f''(\tfrac{1}{4}\pi) = 4.$$

Taylor's series: $\tan x = 1 + 2(x - \tfrac{1}{4}\pi) + 2(x - \tfrac{1}{4}\pi)^2 + \cdots.$ (8)

Taylor's formula: $\tan x = 1 + 2(x - \tfrac{1}{4}\pi) + 2(x - \tfrac{1}{4}\pi)^2 + R_3(x),$

where $R_3(x) = \dfrac{2(1 + \tan^2 \xi)(3 \tan^2 \xi + 1)}{3!} (x - \tfrac{1}{4}\pi)^3.$ (9)

2. The desired polynomial is the sum, $S_3(x)$, of the terms given explicitly in (8). With x as the radian measure of 48°,

$$x - \tfrac{1}{4}\pi = (48 - 45)\frac{\pi}{180} = \frac{\pi}{60},$$

and ξ in (9) is the radian measure of an angle between 45° and 48°. Since $\tan \theta$ increases as θ increases from 45° to 48°, $\tan \xi < \tan 48°$ and

$$R_3(x) < \frac{2(1 + \tan^2 48°)(3 \tan^2 48° + 1)\pi^3}{6(60^3)} = .00050, \tag{10}$$

where logarithms were used to compute the fraction. That is, $\tan 48°$ is given by $S_3(x)$ with an error less than .00051.

EXERCISE 173

Solve by use of Taylor's formula.

Find an approximating polynomial for the given function by taking the sum of the indicated nonzero terms of the Taylor series in the specified powers. Then, for the given domain of values of x, obtain an upper bound for the error (to just one significant digit) if the value of this polynomial is taken as an approximation to the value of the function. Use logarithms where convenient.

1. $(1 - x)^{-1}$; in powers of x; three terms; when $|x| < .4$.
2. e^x; in powers of x; four terms; when $|x| < .2$.
3. $\ln (1 + x)$; in powers of x; four terms; when $|x| < .2$.
4. $\sin x$; the Maclaurin series; two terms; when $|x| < .1$.
5. $\cos x$; the Maclaurin series; two terms; when $|x| < .2$.
6. e^x; in powers of $(x - 3)$; three terms; when $|x - 3| < .4$.
7. $\ln x$; in powers of $(x - 2)$; three terms; when $|x - 2| < .5$.
8. $\cos x$; in powers of $(x - \tfrac{1}{4}\pi)$; two terms; if $|x - \tfrac{1}{4}\pi| < .1$.
9. $(1 + x)^{\frac{1}{2}}$; Maclaurin series; three terms; when $|x| < .5$.
10. Find a value for h so that, if $|x| < h$, the sum of the first two nonzero terms in the Maclaurin series for $\sin x$ will give the value of $\sin x$ with accuracy to four decimal places.
11. In (2) on page 572, let $x = a + h$, with ξ_n written $(a + \theta_n h)$, where $0 < \theta_n < 1$. Rewrite (2) in this notation.

220. EQUALITY OF A FUNCTION AND THE SUM OF ITS TAYLOR SERIES

Note 1. It is possible that a function $f(x)$, even of simple form, may not be represented by its Taylor series about $x = a$ even though all derivatives $f^{(n)}(x)$ are continuous at $x = a$. Thus, let

$$f(x) = e^{-1/x^2} \text{ if } x \neq 0 \quad and \quad f(0) = \lim_{x \to 0} f(x) = 0.$$

Then, $f^{(n)}(x)$ is continuous at $x = 0$. However, all terms in the Maclaurin series for $f(x)$ are 0, and $f(x)$ is not represented by the series if $x \neq 0$. A proof of this result will be suggested in Problem 38 on page 582. The fact just discussed emphasizes the importance of the following theorem.

Theorem III. *At any value of x, a necessary and sufficient condition for the Taylor series for $f(x)$ in powers of $(x - a)$ to converge to $f(x)$ is that, in Taylor's formula for $f(x)$ in powers of $(x - a)$, $R_n(x) \to 0$ as $n \to \infty$.*

Proof. 1. With $0!$ defined as 1 and $f^{(0)}(a)$ defined as $f(a)$, we have

(*Taylor's series*) $$\sum_{n=0}^{\infty} \frac{f^{(n)}(a)}{n!} (x - a)^n; \qquad (1)$$

(*Taylor's formula*) $$f(x) = S_n(x) + R_n(x), \qquad (2)$$

where $S_n(x)$ is the sum of the first n terms in (1).

2. *Proof of the necessity.* At some value of x, assume that the series in (1) converges, with $f(x)$ as the sum. Then $S_n(x) \to f(x)$ as $n \to \infty$. Hence, from (2), since $f(x)$ is a constant as n varies, there exists

$$\lim_{n \to \infty} R_n(x) = \lim_{n \to \infty} [f(x) - S_n(x)]$$
$$= f(x) - \lim_{n \to \infty} S_n(x) = f(x) - f(x) = 0.$$

3. *Proof of sufficiency.* Assume that $R_n(x) \to 0$ as $n \to \infty$. Then, from (2),

$$S_n(x) = f(x) - R_n(x); \quad \lim_{n \to \infty} S_n(x) = f(x) - 0,$$

which shows that (1) converges to $f(x)$ if "$R_n(x) \to 0$ *as* $n \to \infty$."

EXAMPLE 1. Prove that e^x is the sum of its Maclaurin series, for all x.

Solution. 1. Let $f(x) = e^x$. Then $f^{(n)}(x) = e^x$. We have

$\begin{Bmatrix} Maclaurin's \\ series\ for\ e^x \end{Bmatrix}$ $\qquad 1 + x + \dfrac{x^2}{2!} + \cdots + \dfrac{x^{n-1}}{(n-1)!} + \dfrac{x^n}{n!} + \cdots; \qquad (3)$

$\begin{Bmatrix} Taylor's \\ formula \end{Bmatrix}$ $\qquad e^x = S_n(x) + R_n(x), \quad with \quad R_n(x) = \dfrac{e^{\xi_n}}{n!} x^n, \qquad (4)$

where $S_n(x)$ is the sum of the first n-terms in (3), and ξ_n is between 0 and x.

2. *Discussion of convergence for* (3). We apply the ratio test:

$$\lim_{n \to \infty} \left| \frac{x^n}{n!} \div \frac{x^{n-1}}{(n-1)!} \right| = \lim_{n \to \infty} \left| \frac{x}{n} \right| = 0, \text{ at all values of } x.$$

Hence, (3) converges absolutely; thus, there exists a sum $S(x)$ such that

$$\lim_{n \to \infty} S_n(x) = S(x),$$

at all values of x.

3. Let x have any fixed value. Then, in (4),

$$|\xi_n| < |x|, \quad or \quad -|x| < \xi_n < |x|.$$

Hence, $\qquad e^{\xi_n} < e^{|x|} \quad and \quad |R_n(x)| < e^{|x|} \left(\left| \frac{x^n}{n!} \right| \right). \qquad (5)$

From Step 1 of the solution, $x^n/n!$ is the general term of a convergent series, and thus approaches zero as $n \to \infty$. Since $|x|$ is fixed,

$$\lim_{n \to \infty} e^{|x|} \left| \frac{x^n}{n!} \right| = e^{|x|} \lim_{n \to \infty} \left| \frac{x^n}{n!} \right| = e^{|x|} \cdot 0 = 0,$$

and thus, also, $R_n(x) \to 0$ as $n \to \infty$. Hence, by Theorem III, $e^x = S(x)$, which justifies writing

$$e^x = 1 + x + \frac{x^2}{2!} + \frac{x^3}{3!} + \cdots + \frac{x^n}{n!} + \cdots. \tag{6}$$

EXAMPLE 2. Prove that $\sin x$ is the sum of its Maclaurin series.

Solution. 1. Let $f(x) = \sin x$. Then, $f^{(n)}(x) = \sin(x + n\pi/2)$. We have

$$(Maclaurin's \ series \ for \ \sin x) \ ^* \qquad a_0 + a_1 x + \cdots + a_{n-1} x^{n-1} + \cdots; \tag{7}$$

$$\left\{ \begin{matrix} Taylor's \\ formula \end{matrix} \right\} \quad \sin x = S_n(x) + R_n(x), \quad with \quad R_n(x) = \frac{\sin(\xi_n + n\pi/2)}{n!} x^n,$$

where ξ_n is between 0 and x. Let x have any fixed value. Then,

$$\left| \sin\left(\xi_n + n\frac{\pi}{2} \right) \right| \leq 1 \quad and \quad |R_n(x)| \leq \left| \frac{x^n}{n!} \right|. \tag{8}$$

2. Since $x^n/n!$ is the general term of a convergent series (the Maclaurin series for e^x), we have $\qquad \lim_{n \to \infty} \dfrac{x^n}{n!} = 0 \quad and \ hence \quad \lim_{n \to \infty} R_n(x) = 0.$

Therefore, (7) converges and has $\sin x$ as its sum at all values of x, or

$$\sin x = x - \frac{x^3}{3!} + \frac{x^5}{5!} - \cdots + \frac{(-1)^{k+1}}{(2k-1)!} x^{2k-1} + \cdots.$$

Note 2. The method of Examples 1 and 2 applies only to a very restricted set of functions, but is of fundamental importance. At advanced levels, it is proved that any one of the elementary functions of a real variable x is represented by the Taylor series for the function in powers of $(x - a)$, on some interval $|x - a| < R$, if the function and its derivatives of all orders exist at $x = a$. Hereafter in this text, except as specified otherwise, we assume the preceding fact, with x on the interval of convergence of the Taylor series.

EXERCISE 174

Prove the specified result.

1. The Taylor's series for e^x in powers of $(x - a)$ converges to e^x at all values of x.
2. $\cos x$ is represented by its Maclaurin series at all values of x.
3. The Taylor's series for e^{2x} in powers of $(x - 1)$ represents e^{2x} at all values of x.
4. At all values of x, $\sin x$ is represented by its Taylor series in powers of $(x - \frac{1}{4}\pi)$.
5. If $0 < x \leq 1$, $\ln(1 + x)$ is represented by its Maclaurin series. (Also see the supplementary Problem 34 on page 582.)
6. Suppose that $f(x)$ possesses derivatives $f'(x)$ and $f''(x)$, and $f''(x) \geq 0$ when x is on the interval $V:(c \leq x \leq d)$. Let L be the tangent to the curve $y = f(x)$ at any point $x = a$ on V. Prove that the curve does not fall below L if x is on V. Use Taylor's formula as met on page 569. [f'' need not be continuous; see page 689.]

* Notice that the coefficients in (7) need not be known in discussing R_n.

221. APPLICATIONS OF TAYLOR'S SERIES

To obtain the Taylor expansion of a function $f(x)$ in powers of $(x - a)$, we are not limited to computation of the coefficients by the usual formula. We may employ any available method for representing $f(x)$ as a power series in $(x - a)$, because Theorem I of page 567 states that *any* series which we obtain *must be the Taylor series.*

We shall use the following properties of power series without proof. Demonstrations of the facts are met in more advanced texts.

I. *A power series may be differentiated term by term (as described in remarks on page 566), and similarly may be integrated term by term.*

II. *Suppose that $\sum_{n=0}^{\infty} a_n x^n$ and $\sum_{n=0}^{\infty} b_n x^n$ converge when $|x| < R$. Then, if $|x| < R$, the two series may be multiplied term by term, with like powers of x combined, to yield a convergent power series in x whose sum is the product of the sums of the given series.*

III. *Suppose that $f(z) = \sum_{n=0}^{\infty} a_n z^n$, which converges if $|z| < R_1$, and that $z = \sum_{k=0}^{\infty} b_k x^k$, which converges and yields $|z| < R_1$ when $|x| < R$. Then, we may substitute for z in terms of x in $f(z)$, and rearrange into a power series in x converging to $f(z)$ when $|x| < R$.*

ILLUSTRATION 1. We may obtain the Maclaurin series through the term of degree 3 for $e^x \sin x$ by termwise multiplication of the Maclaurin series for e^x and $\sin x$. Thus, we use (1) below to prove (2):

$$\sin x = x - \frac{x^3}{6} + \cdots; \quad e^x = 1 + x + \frac{x^2}{2} + \cdots; \tag{1}$$

$$e^x \sin x = x - \frac{x^3}{6} + x^2 + \frac{x^3}{2} + \cdots = x + x^2 + \frac{x^3}{3} + \cdots. \tag{2}$$

ILLUSTRATION 2. To obtain the Maclaurin series for $\cos x$, we may write

$$\int_0^x \sin x \, dx = -\cos x \Big]_0^x = 1 - \cos x.$$

Hence, $\qquad 1 - \cos x = \int_0^x \left[x - \frac{x^3}{3!} + \cdots + \frac{(-1)^{k-1} x^{2k-1}}{(2k-1)!} + \cdots \right] dx$

$$= \left[\frac{x^2}{2!} - \frac{x^4}{4!} + \cdots + \frac{(-1)^{k-1} x^{2k}}{(2k-1)!(2k)} + \cdots \right] \Big|_{x=0}^{x=x}, \; or \tag{3}$$

$$\cos x = 1 - \frac{x^2}{2!} + \frac{x^4}{4!} - \cdots + \frac{(-1)^k x^{2k}}{(2k)!} + \cdots. \tag{4}$$

ILLUSTRATION 3. From $\qquad\qquad \dfrac{1}{1+z} = 1 - z + z^2 + \cdots, \tag{5}$

with $z = x^2$, we obtain the Maclaurin series for Arctan x as follows:

$$\int_0^x \frac{dx}{1+x^2} = \text{Arctan } x = \int_0^x [1 - x^2 + x^4 - \cdots + (-1)^n x^{2n} + \cdots] dx$$

$$= x - \frac{x^3}{3} + \frac{x^5}{5} - \cdots + \frac{(-1)^n x^{2n+1}}{2n+1} + \cdots,$$

which converges when $-1 < x < 1$, because (5) converges if $-1 < z < 1$.

EXAMPLE 1. Obtain the Maclaurin series for sec x.

Solution. 1. We shall calculate sec $x = 1/\cos x$, by use of (III):

$$\sec x = \frac{1}{\cos x} = \frac{1}{1 - \dfrac{x^2}{2!} + \dfrac{x^4}{4!} - \dfrac{x^6}{6!} + \cdots} \cdot \tag{6}$$

2. Let $z = \left(\dfrac{x^2}{2!} - \dfrac{x^4}{4!} + \dfrac{x^6}{6!} - \cdots\right)$. Then, if $|z| < 1$,

$$\sec x = \frac{1}{1 - z} = 1 + z + z^2 + z^3 + \cdots . \tag{7}$$

To obtain powers of z, multiply the series for z by itself repeatedly:

$$z^2 = \frac{x^4}{4} - 2\frac{x^2}{2!}\frac{x^4}{4!} + \cdots ; \quad z^3 = \frac{x^6}{8} + \cdots .$$

Hence, from (7), $\qquad \sec x = 1 + \dfrac{x^2}{2!} - \dfrac{x^4}{4!} + \dfrac{x^6}{6!} + \dfrac{x^4}{4} - \dfrac{x^6}{4!} + \dfrac{x^6}{8} + \cdots .$

Thus, $\qquad\qquad \sec x = 1 + \dfrac{x^2}{2} + \dfrac{5x^4}{24} + \dfrac{61x^6}{720} + \cdots . \tag{8}$

In (7), the series converges if $|z| < 1$. Since $\cos x = 1 - z$, then $|z| < 1$ if $|x| < \frac{1}{2}\pi$. Hence, by (III), series (8) converges to sec x if $|x| < \frac{1}{2}\pi$.

ILLUSTRATION 4. The following integral cannot be expressed in terms of elementary functions. We expand by use of the binomial series, and then integrate term by term. The series involved converges if $|x| < 1$.

$$\int_0^{1/2} \frac{dx}{\sqrt{1 + x^3}} = \int_0^{1/2} (1 + x^3)^{-\frac{1}{2}}\, dx = \int_0^{1/2} \left(1 - \frac{x^3}{2} + \frac{1 \cdot 3}{2 \cdot 4} x^6 - \frac{1 \cdot 3 \cdot 5}{2 \cdot 4 \cdot 6} x^9 + \cdots\right) dx$$

$$= \left(x - \frac{x^4}{8} + \frac{1 \cdot 3 x^7}{2 \cdot 4 \cdot 7} - \frac{1 \cdot 3 \cdot 5 x^{10}}{2 \cdot 4 \cdot 6 \cdot 10} + \cdots\right)\Bigg]_0^{1/2}. \tag{9}$$

With $x = \frac{1}{2}$, in (9) we have a convergent alternating series with terms decreasing in absolute value, and the 4th term is approximately .00003. Hence, with an error less than .00005, from (9) we obtain .4926.

Note 1. Let $g(x) = \sum_{n=0}^{\infty} b_n x^n$, where the series converges if $|x| < R$. Then, since g possesses derivatives of all orders, g is continuous when $|x| < R$, and thus is continuous at $x = 0$. Hence, $\lim_{x \to 0} g(x) = g(0) = b_0$.

ILLUSTRATION 5. By use of Maclaurin series, instead of L'Hospital's rule,

$$\lim_{x \to 0} \frac{e^x - e^{-x}}{\sin x} = \lim_{x \to 0} \frac{\left(1 + x + \dfrac{x^2}{2!} + \cdots\right) - \left(1 - x + \dfrac{x^2}{2!} - \cdots\right)}{x - \dfrac{x^3}{3!} + \dfrac{x^5}{5!} - \cdots}$$

$$= \lim_{x \to 0} 2\frac{x + \dfrac{x^3}{3!} + \dfrac{x^5}{5!} + \cdots}{x - \dfrac{x^3}{3!} + \dfrac{x^5}{5!} + \cdots} = \lim_{x \to 0} 2\frac{1 + \dfrac{x^2}{3!} + \dfrac{x^4}{5!} + \cdots}{1 - \dfrac{x^2}{3!} + \dfrac{x^4}{5!} + \cdots} = 2. \quad \text{[By Note 2.]}$$

EXERCISE 175

Solve by use of Maclaurin or Taylor series by the methods of Section 221.

Find at least the first three nonzero terms in the Maclaurin series for the function.

1. The **hyperbolic sine** of x, or $\sinh x = \dfrac{e^x - e^{-x}}{2}$.

2. The **hyperbolic cosine** of x, or $\cosh x = \dfrac{e^x + e^{-x}}{2}$.

3. $\sin^2 x$, by use of the series (*a*) for $\cos 2x$; (*b*) for $\sin x$.

4. $\sec^2 x$, by differentiation in Problem 21 on page 569.

5. $\ln \cos x$, from $\int_0^x \tan x \, dx$.   **6.** $\ln (1 + x)$, from $\int_0^x (1 + x)^{-1} \, dx$.

7. Arcsin x, by integration.

8. $e^x \sec x$.   **9.** $(1 + x^2) \sin x$.   **10.** $\tan x \cosh x$.

11. $\sqrt{1 - \sin x}$, by first using the binomial series.

12. $\dfrac{e^{-x}}{1 + x}$.   **13.** $\dfrac{\sin x}{1 + \cos x}$.   **14.** $\dfrac{\sin x}{e^x}$.

Evaluate the limit by use of Maclaurin series appearing earlier.

15. $\lim\limits_{x \to 0} \dfrac{\sin x}{x}$.   **16.** $\lim\limits_{x \to 0} \dfrac{\ln (1 + x)}{x}$.   **17.** $\lim\limits_{x \to 0} \dfrac{\tan x - x}{x^3}$.

18. $\lim\limits_{x \to 0} \dfrac{\sin x - x}{\tan x - x}$.   **19.** $\lim\limits_{x \to 0} \dfrac{\text{Arctan } x - x}{e^x - e^{-x} - 2x}$.

Compute the integral to three decimal places by use of a series in x, with the accuracy estimated on the basis of the sizes of the terms involved.

20. $\int_0^{.5} \sqrt[3]{1 + x^2} \, dx$.   **21.** $\int_0^{.4} e^{-x^2} \, dx$.   **22.** $\int_0^1 \sqrt{4 - x^3} \, dx$.

23. $\int_0^{.2} \dfrac{e^x \, dx}{2 - x}$.   **24.** $\int_0^{.4} \dfrac{dx}{\sqrt{1 - \sin x}}$.   **25.** $\int_0^{.3} \dfrac{\cos x \, dx}{1 + x}$.

★222. COMPLEX–VALUED FUNCTIONS AND SEQUENCES

Note 1. If a and b are real numbers, and $i = \sqrt{-1}$, in algebra we define

$$|a + bi| = \sqrt{a^2 + b^2}.$$

Also, $(a + bi)$ frequently is represented as a *vector* in a **"complex plane,"** in a so-called **Argand diagram.** Thus, Figure 386 shows vectors representing $(3 + 4i)$ and $(-4 + 2i)$. With $z = a + bi$, we agree to call a the **real component** and b the **component of z in the imaginary direction.**

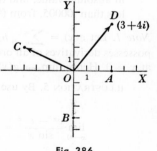

Fig. 386

Suppose that $u(x)$ and $v(x)$ represent real numbers when $\alpha \le x \le \beta$, and let $f(x) = u(x) + iv(x)$. Then, f is a **complex-valued function of the real variable x.** With $L = a + bi$ where a and b are real, we agree that the symbolism

$$\lim_{x \to c} f(x) = L \tag{1}$$

is defined in the *same words* as in Definition I on page 68. Now, think of $f(x)$ as a *vector* in the complex plane, and refer to the discussion of a *vector-valued function* $H(t)$ on page 428. With x replacing t, and with *real component* and *component in the imaginary direction* for $f(x)$ replacing *scalar components* for $H(t)$, the discussion about limits for $H(t)$ justifies the following result.

Theorem IV. *If* $f(x) = u(x) + iv(x)$, *there exists* $\lim_{x\to c} f(x)$ *if and only if there exist* $\lim_{x\to c} u(x)$ *and* $\lim_{x\to c} v(x)$, *and then*

$$\lim_{x\to c} f(x) = \lim_{x\to c} u(x) + i[\lim_{x\to c} v(x)]. \tag{2}$$

Continuity for f is defined in the same words as in Definition II on page 72 for a real-valued function. Then, as in the discussion for $H(t)$, we conclude that f is continuous at $x = c$ if and only if u and v are continuous at $x = c$. Also, Definition VI on page 79 for a derivative applies to the complex-valued function $f(x)$ without essential alteration but, again, with new significance. The discussion of $H'(t)$ on page 429, when interpreted for $f(x)$, leads to the following conclusion.

Theorem V. *If* $f(x) = u(x) + iv(x)$, *then* f *has a derivative* $f'(x)$, *at the point* x *in the domain of* f, *if and only if* u *and* v *have derivatives at* x, *and then*

$$f'(x) = u'(x) + iv'(x).$$

We may define $\int_a^b f(x)dx$ and $\int f(x)dx$ as for a real-valued function. Then

$$\int_a^b f(x)dx = \int_a^b u(x)dx + i\int_a^b v(x)dx; \tag{3}$$

$$\int f(x)dx = \int u(x)dx + i\int v(x)dx. \tag{4}$$

In (3), if $F(x)$ is such that $F'(x) = f(x)$, then $\int_a^b f(x)dx = F(b) - F(a)$.

Let $S_n = \alpha_n + i\beta_n$, where α_n and β_n are real and n is a positive integer. Then, the definition of $\lim_{n\to\infty} S_n = L$ on page 114, with $L = a + bi$, has meaning for the present sequence $\{S_n\}$, but has added significance, as applying to sequences of complex numbers. By remarks such as led to (2) in the case of the vector-valued function $H(t)$, we reach the following conclusion.

Theorem VI. *A complex-valued sequence* $\{S_n = \alpha_n + i\beta_n\}$ *converges if and only if each of the real-valued sequences* $\{\alpha_n\}$ *and* $\{\beta_n\}$ *converges, and then*

$$\lim_{n\to\infty} S_n = \lim_{n\to\infty} \alpha_n + i[\lim_{n\to\infty} \beta_n]. \tag{5}$$

Now, suppose that $w_n = u_n + iv_n$ where u_n and v_n are real, and consider $\sum_{n=1}^{\infty} w_n$. By (5), applied to partial sums of $\sum u_n$, $\sum v_n$, and $\sum w_n$, the w-series converges if and only if the u-series and v-series converge, and then

$$\sum_{n=1}^{\infty} w_n = \sum_{n=1}^{\infty} u_n + i\sum_{n=1}^{\infty} v_n. \tag{6}$$

We define *absolute convergence* and *conditional convergence* for the w-series in the same words as on page 555, and arrive at Theorem XV of page 555 for the w-series. Also, the ratio test for convergence of the w-series applies with no change in wording as compared with the discussion in Chapter 23.

ILLUSTRATION 1. Let $z = x + yi$. Consider $\sum_{n=0}^{\infty} a_n z^n$ where a_n is a complex number. Suppose that

$$\lim_{n \to \infty} \left| \frac{a_{n+1}}{a_n} \right| = \eta; \; then$$

$$\lim_{n \to \infty} \left| \frac{a_{n+1} z^{n+1}}{a_n z^n} \right| = \eta \, |z|.$$

By the ratio test, the z-series converges absolutely if

$$\eta \, |z| < 1, \quad or \quad |z| < \frac{1}{\eta} \quad when \; \eta \neq 0.$$

Thus, if we let $r = 1/\eta$, the z-series converges if $|z| < r$, that is, if z is any point interior to the *circle of convergence* $|z| = r$ in the complex plane, as in Figure 387, and diverges if z is outside this circle. For

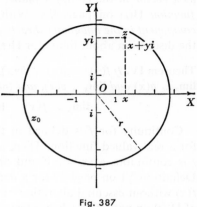

Fig. 387

points z_0 on the circle, the ratio test fails; then, advanced theory must be employed in any discussion of convergence for the z-series at $z = z_0$.

★223. THE EXPONENTIAL FUNCTION WITH AN IMAGINARY EXPONENT

The function e^u has been considered only where u is real; then

$$e^u = 1 + u + \frac{u^2}{2!} + \cdots + \frac{u^n}{n!} + \cdots. \tag{1}$$

By the ratio test, we showed that (1) converges absolutely for all real values of u. We accept the fact that the preceding application of the ratio test could be repeated to show that the series on the right in (1) converges absolutely for *all complex numbers u*. Then, for every complex number u, *we define e^u as the sum of the series at the right in* (1). By multiplication of infinite series, it can be verified that

$$e^{u_1} \cdot e^{u_2} = \left(\sum_{n=0}^{\infty} \frac{u_1^n}{n!} \right) \left(\sum_{m=0}^{\infty} \frac{u_2^m}{m!} \right) = \sum_{k=0}^{\infty} \frac{(u_1 + u_2)^k}{k!}, \quad or \quad e^{u_1} e^{u_2} = e^{u_1 + u_2}. \tag{2}$$

Theorem VII. *If x is any real number, then* $\qquad e^{ix} = \cos x + i \sin x.$ (3)

Proof. With $u = ix$ in (1), $\qquad e^{ix} = 1 + ix + \frac{i^2 x^2}{2!} + \cdots + \frac{i^n x^n}{n!} + \cdots.$ (4)

The series of even powers of x in (4) is $\quad \left(1 - \frac{x^2}{2!} + \frac{x^4}{4!} - \cdots \right)$, *or* $\cos x$. (5)

The series of odd powers of x in (4) is $\quad i \left(x - \frac{x^3}{3!} + \frac{x^3}{5!} - \cdots \right)$, *or* $i \sin x$. (6)

Let E_k, C_k, and S_k represent the sums of the first k terms in (4), (5), and (6), respectively. Then, for each value of n, there are corresponding values of h and k so that $E_n = C_h + S_k$. Since (4), (5), and (6) converge for all values of x, we have

$$e^{ix} = \lim_{n \to \infty} E_n = \lim_{h \to \infty} C_h + \lim_{k \to \infty} S_k = \cos x + i \sin x.$$

ILLUSTRATION 1. From (3),

$$e^{\pi i} = \cos \pi + i \sin \pi = -1; \quad e^{\frac{1}{2}\pi i} = \cos \tfrac{1}{2}\pi + i \sin \tfrac{1}{2}\pi = i.$$

ILLUSTRATION 2. If a and b are real numbers,

$$e^{a+bi} = e^a e^{bi} = e^a(\cos b + i \sin b).$$

Theorem VIII. *If a and b are real, and $k = a + bi$, then*

$$\frac{de^{kx}}{dx} = ke^{kx}. \tag{7}$$

Proof. $e^{kx} = e^{ax+ibx} = e^{ax}(\cos bx + i \sin bx);$

$$\frac{de^{kx}}{dx} = ae^{ax}(\cos bx + i \sin bx) + e^{ax}(-b \sin bx + bi \cos bx)$$

$$= e^{ax}(a + bi)(\cos bx + i \sin bx)$$

$$= (a + bi)e^{ax}e^{ibx} = (a + bi)e^{ax+ibx} = ke^{kx}.$$

Note 1. Sometimes (3) is referred to as **Euler's formula** for e^{ix}.

EXERCISE 176 *(Review of Chapter Twenty-four)*

Obtain the Taylor expansion of $f(x)$ about each given point. If convenient, obtain the general term of the series. In any case, obtain at least the first three nonzero terms in the expansion.

1. $f(x) = \sin 2x$; about $x = 0$.   **2.** $f(x) = (1 - x)^{-1}$; about $x = 0$.

3. $f(x) = (2x - 1)^5$; about $x = 1$; about $x = 2$.

4. Obtain the Taylor series about $x = a$ for (1) $\sin x$; (2) $\cos x$.

5. $f(x) = \ln x$; about $x = 2$; about $x = a$ where $a > 0$.

6. $\ln \cos x$; about $x = 0$.   **7.** $e^{\sin x}$; about $x = \tfrac{1}{2}\pi$.

8. $(1 - x)^{-\frac{5}{3}}$; about $x = 0$.   **9.** $\cos(\tfrac{1}{3}\pi + x)$; about $x = 0$.

Obtain the Maclaurin series for the function by substituting some expression in place of the variable in a Maclaurin series obtained previously.

10. $\cos(-\tfrac{1}{3}x)$.   **11.** e^{-3x}.   **12.** $(1 - x^3)^{-1}$.   **13.** $\ln(1 - 4x)$.

Compute with accuracy to four decimal places by use of a Maclaurin series. Either estimate the accuracy by numerical intuition or, when possible, apply Corollary 2 on page 554 to give an exact check.

14. $e^{-.2}$.   **15.** $\sin .1$.   **16.** $\ln 1.2$.   **17.** $\cos 63°$ from $\cos(\tfrac{1}{3}\pi + x)$.

18. Obtain a series for $(4 + x^3)^{\frac{1}{2}}$, or $2(1 + \tfrac{1}{4}x^3)^{\frac{1}{2}}$, by use of the binomial series.

19. Prove that the sum of the first ten terms in the Maclaurin series for e^x gives e^x correct to six decimal places if $|x| < .9$. Assume that $e < 3$.

20. If the sum of the first two nonzero terms of the Taylor series for $\sin x$ in powers of $(x - \tfrac{1}{2}\pi)$ are taken as an approximation for $\sin x$, obtain an upper bound for the error which is made (to just one significant digit) if $|x - \tfrac{1}{2}\pi| < .2$.

21. Prove that, at all values of x, $\cos x$ is represented by its Taylor series in powers of $(x - \tfrac{1}{4}\pi)$.

22. Without using any similar result already proved in this text, prove that, at all values of x, the Taylor series for e^x in powers of $(x - 2)$ represents e^x at all values of x.

23. Obtain the Maclaurin series for $\ln (1 - x)$ from $\int_0^x (1 - x)^{-1}\, dx$.

24. Obtain the Maclaurin series for $\cos^2 x$ by use of the series for $\cos x$.

25. Compute $\int_0^{.2} \ln (1 - x)dx$ to three decimal places by use of a series in powers of x, with the accuracy estimated by numerical intuition.

26. Obtain the first four nonzero terms of the Maclaurin series for $(\cos 2x)/e^x$ by use of other Maclaurin series.

★SUPPLEMENT FOR CHAPTER TWENTY–FOUR

27. Let the function $f(x) = (\sin x)/x$ be defined by the formula when $x \neq 0$, and let $f(0) = 1$. Obtain $\int_0^{.3} [(\sin x)/x]dx$ with accuracy to five decimal places.

28. By use of a series, find a solution of $\sin x = .2$ with accuracy to three decimal places.

29. If $S_k = \sum_{n=1}^{k} 1/n$, prove that $\ln (k + 1) < S_k < 1 + \ln k$.

30. If $S_k = \sum_{n=1}^{k} \dfrac{1}{n^3}$, prove that $\qquad \dfrac{1}{2} - \dfrac{1}{2(k + 1)^2} < S_k < \dfrac{3}{2} - \dfrac{1}{2k^2}$.

31. Assume that the function $f(x)$ possesses derivatives of all orders on an interval $a \leq x \leq b$. Assume that $a < c < b$ and $f'(c) = 0$, and let k be the order of the derivative of *lowest* order which is *not zero* at $x = c$. Prove that, if k is an odd integer, then f does *not* have a relative extremum at $x = c$; if k is an *even* integer, then f has a *maximum* at $x = c$ if $f^{(k)}(c) < 0$, and a *minimum* at $x = c$ if $f^{(k)}(c) > 0$. Use Taylor's theorem.

32. Apply the results of Problem 31 to test each of the following functions for maxima and minima:

$$f(x) = (x - 3)^7; \quad f(x) = (x + 2)^6; \quad f(x) = (x + 2)^4(x - 3)^3.$$

33. Apply (7) of page 571 to $R_n(x)$ in (14) on page 571, with $h(t) = 1$ and

$$g(t) = (x - t)^{n-1}f^{(n)}(t);$$

then let $\xi = a + \theta(x - a)$, with $0 \leq \theta \leq 1$. The result, below, is called *Cauchy's form* for the remainder, in honor of the French mathematician AUGUSTIN LOUIS CAUCHY (1789–1857):

$$R_n = (1 - \theta)^{n-1}(x - a)^n f^{(n)}[a + \theta(x - a)]/(n - 1)!.$$

By use of Problem 33, prove each of the following results.

34. If $-1 < x < 0$, $\ln (1 + x)$ is represented by its Maclaurin series.

35. If $|x| < 1$, $(1 - x)^{\frac{1}{2}}$ is represented by its Maclaurin series.

Hint. Prove the following inequality by use of Problem 33 if $0 < x < 1$, and $n > 1$, and a different inequality by use of the Lagrange form for R_n when $-1 < x < 0$:

$$|R_n| < \frac{1 \cdot 3 \cdots (2n - 3)}{2^n(n - 1)!} \cdot \frac{|x^n|}{(1 - x)^{\frac{1}{2}}}.$$

36. Repeat Problem 35 for $(1 - x)^m$, where m is any real number.

37. Obtain $\int_0^{.5} e^{-x^2}\, dx$ with an error of at most .0005, and prove that the maximum error is as specified.

38. First prove that $\lim_{x \to 0} e^{-x^{-2}}x^{-n} = 0$ for every positive integer n. Then, in Note 1 on page 573, prove that f and $f^{(n)}$ are continuous at $x = 0$, where all of these functions have the value *zero*. Thus, demonstrate the result stated for $f(x)$ in Note 1.

CHAPTER TWENTY–FIVE

Advanced Partial Differentiation

224. A FUNDAMENTAL INCREMENT FORMULA

Let f be a function of two independent variables where the domain of f includes an open region T of points (x, y) in an xy-system of coordinates. In the following discussion, we shall assume that any point (x, y) used as an argument for f lies in T. Let $u = f(x, y)$. Then, for any point (x_1, y_1) and increments $(\Delta x, \Delta y)$, let

$$\Delta u = f(x_1 + \Delta x, y_1 + \Delta y) - f(x_1, y_1). \tag{1}$$

Theorem I. *Suppose that f has continuous partial derivatives f_x and f_y. Let $u = f(x, y)$ and let (x_1, y_1) be a fixed point. Then, there exist variables ϵ_1 and ϵ_2, which are functions of the independent variables $(\Delta x, \Delta y)$, such that*

$$\Delta u = \frac{\partial u}{\partial x} \Delta x + \frac{\partial u}{\partial y} \Delta y + \epsilon_1 \Delta x + \epsilon_2 \Delta y, \tag{2}$$

where the derivatives are evaluated at (x_1, y_1), and

$$\epsilon_1 \to 0 \quad and \quad \epsilon_2 \to 0 \quad when \quad (\Delta x, \Delta y) \to (0, 0).$$

Proof. 1. In (1), subtract and then add $f(x_1, y_1 + \Delta y)$:

$$\left. \begin{aligned} \Delta u = [f(x_1 + \Delta x, y_1 + \Delta y) - f(x_1, y_1 + \Delta y)] \\ + [f(x_1, y_1 + \Delta y) - f(x_1, y_1)]. \end{aligned} \right\} \tag{3}$$

2. The first difference in (3) is the increment of $f(x, y_1 + \Delta y)$ as x changes from x_1 to $(x_1 + \Delta x)$. Then, by the mean value theorem of page 173, as applied to $f(x, y_1 + \Delta y)$, which is a function of x alone,

$$f(x_1 + \Delta x, y_1 + \Delta y) - f(x_1, y_1 + \Delta y) = f_x(\xi, y_1 + \Delta y)\Delta x, \tag{4}$$

where ξ is between x_1 and $(x_1 + \Delta x)$. Similarly, the second difference in (3) is the increment of $f(x_1, y)$ as y changes from y_1 to $(y_1 + \Delta y)$. Hence,

$$f(x_1, y_1 + \Delta y) - f(x_1, y_1) = f_y(x_1, \eta)\Delta y, \tag{5}$$

where η is between y_1 and $(y_1 + \Delta y)$.

* The remainder of the text deals with optional advanced content.

3. We observe $Q:(\xi, y_1 + \Delta y)$ and $R:(x_1, \eta)$ in Figure 388. If $(\Delta x, \Delta y) \to (0, 0)$, then $Q \to P$ and $R \to P$. Thus, since f_x

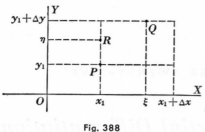

Fig. 388

and f_y are continuous at (x_1, y_1),

$$\left.\begin{array}{l} [f_x(\xi, y_1 + \Delta y) - f_x(x_1, y_1)] \to 0; \\ [f_y(x_1, \eta) - f_y(x_1, y_1)] \to 0. \end{array}\right\} \quad (6)$$

Or, if we let ϵ_1 and ϵ_2 represent the differences in (6), then

$$\left.\begin{array}{l} f_x(\xi, y_1 + \Delta y) = f_x(x_1, y_1) + \epsilon_1, \text{ and} \\ f_y(x_1, \eta) = f_y(x_1, y_1) + \epsilon_2, \end{array}\right\} \quad (7)$$

where $\epsilon_1 \to 0$ and $\epsilon_2 \to 0$ when $(\Delta x, \Delta y) \to 0$. After using (7) in (4) and (5), and then placing the results in (3), we obtain (2).

There is a formula similar to (2) for a function of any number of variables. Thus, if $u = f(x, y, z)$, we obtain

$$\Delta u = \frac{\partial u}{\partial x} \Delta x + \frac{\partial u}{\partial y} \Delta y + \frac{\partial u}{\partial z} \Delta z + \epsilon_1 \Delta x + \epsilon_2 \Delta y + \epsilon_3 \Delta z. \quad (8)$$

Note 1. Suppose that $u = f(x, y, s, t)$, where (x, y, s, t) are originally specified as independent variables. Then, we agree that u_x or $f_x(x, y, s, t)$, u_y or $f_y(x, y, s, t)$, etc. indicates the *value* of a partial derivative with respect to the variable used as a subscript when all other *original* independent variables are held fast. This agreement will hold even though, later, these variables may cease to be independent.

225. CHAIN RULE FOR DIFFERENTIATION

We shall assume that any derivative mentioned hereafter in this chapter exists and is a continuous function. Now, consider a differentiable * function $f(x, y)$, and let $u = f(x, y)$. Suppose that we place $x = g(t)$ and $y = h(t)$ in $f(x, y)$, where g and h are differentiable. Then u becomes a function of t, and we shall prove that

$$\frac{du}{dt} = u_x \frac{dx}{dt} + u_y \frac{dy}{dt} \text{; or} \quad (1)$$

$$\frac{df(x, y)}{dt} = f_x(x, y) \frac{dx}{dt} + f_y(x, y) \frac{dy}{dt}. \quad (2)$$

Proof of (2). 1. Let t have any fixed value, with x and y representing the corresponding fixed values $x = g(t)$ and $y = h(t)$. Let Δt be any nonzero increment of t, with Δx, Δy, and Δu as the corresponding increments of x, y, and u. From (2) on page 583,

$$\Delta u = f_x(x, y)\Delta x + f_y(x, y)\Delta y + \epsilon_1 \Delta x + \epsilon_2 \Delta y; \quad (3)$$

$$\frac{\Delta u}{\Delta t} = f_x(x, y) \frac{\Delta x}{\Delta t} + f_y(x, y) \frac{\Delta y}{\Delta t} + \epsilon_1 \frac{\Delta x}{\Delta t} + \epsilon_2 \frac{\Delta y}{\Delta t}. \quad (4)$$

---

* Recall that, in this text, "*differentiable*" now means that the function possesses a continuous first derivative with respect to each independent variable.

2. If $\Delta t \to 0$, then $(\Delta x, \Delta y) \to (0, 0)$ because g and h are continuous functions. If $\Delta t \to 0$ in (4) then

$$\epsilon_1 \to 0, \quad \epsilon_2 \to 0, \quad \frac{\Delta x}{\Delta t} \to \frac{dx}{dt}, \quad and \quad \frac{\Delta y}{\Delta t} \to \frac{dy}{dt}. \tag{5}$$

Hence, from (4) and (5), there exists $\dfrac{du}{dt}$, given by (2):

$$\frac{du}{dt} = \lim_{\Delta t \to 0} \frac{\Delta u}{\Delta t} = f_x(x, y)\frac{dx}{dt} + f_y(x, y)\frac{dy}{dt} + 0 \cdot \frac{dx}{dt} + 0 \cdot \frac{dy}{dt}.$$

ILLUSTRATION 1. If $u = \sin x \cos y$, $x = 3t^2$, and $y = 5t^3 + 3t$, then

$$u_x = \cos x \cos y; \quad u_y = -\sin x \sin y;$$

by (1), $\qquad \dfrac{du}{dt} = (\cos x \cos y)(6t) - (\sin x \sin y)(15t^2 + 3).$

We could have found the result without (1), as on page 471. However, (1) often is indispensable in theoretical discussions.

Note 1. As a special case, if $u = f(x, y)$ becomes merely $u = f(x)$, from (1) we obtain $du/dt = (du/dx)(dx/dt)$, which is our former result for the derivative of a composite function. Sometimes, (1) is referred to as the **chain rule,** for the case of two initially independent variables, and a single final independent variable.

A special case of (1) arises if $u = f(x, y)$ where y is a function of x, say $y = h(x)$. Then, with x in place of t in (1), and $\dfrac{dx}{dx} = 1$,

$$\frac{du}{dx} = u_x + u_y\frac{dy}{dx}, \quad or \quad \frac{df(x, y)}{dx} = f_x(x, y) + f_y(x, y)\frac{dy}{dx}, \quad or \tag{6}$$

$$\frac{du}{dx} = \left(\frac{\partial u}{\partial x}\right)_y + \left(\frac{\partial u}{\partial y}\right)_x \frac{dy}{dx}. \tag{7}$$

On the right in (7), the first term takes account of the dependence of u on x when y is considered independent of x, and the second term occurs because y is a function of x. These remarks show why du/dx in (6) sometimes is called the **total derivative** of u with respect to x.

ILLUSTRATION 2. If $u = e^{xy}\sin x$, and $y = \ln x$, then

$$\frac{\partial u}{\partial x} = e^{xy}\cos x + ye^{xy}\sin x, \quad and \quad \frac{\partial u}{\partial y} = xe^{xy}\sin x.$$

Hence, from (6), the total derivative with respect to x is

$$\frac{du}{dx} = e^{xy}\cos x + ye^{xy}\sin x + (xe^{xy}\sin x)\frac{1}{x}.$$

Similarly, as in (1), if $u = f(x, y, z)$ and x, y, and z are functions of t,

$$\frac{du}{dt} = u_x\frac{dx}{dt} + u_y\frac{dy}{dt} + u_z\frac{dz}{dt}. \tag{8}$$

If y and z are functions of x, then

$$\frac{du}{dx} = u_x + u_y\frac{dy}{dx} + u_z\frac{dz}{dx}. \tag{9}$$

Suppose, now, that $u = f(x, y)$, where $\quad x = g(s, t)$ *and* $y = h(s, t)$, $\quad$ (10)

and s and t are independent variables. Then, with s temporarily a constant, we may apply (1). Since x, y, and u are functions of two independent variables s and t, the derivatives with respect to t in (1) become partial derivatives, with s held fast, and we obtain, *without added work*,

$$\frac{\partial u}{\partial t} = u_x \frac{\partial x}{\partial t} + u_y \frac{\partial y}{\partial t}; \qquad \frac{\partial u}{\partial s} = u_x \frac{\partial x}{\partial s} + u_y \frac{\partial y}{\partial s}. \qquad (11)$$

Similarly, let u be a differentiable function of any number of independent variables, say x, y, and z. If x, y, and z are placed equal to differentiable functions of any number of independent variables, say r, s, and t, then u has a partial derivative with respect to each of these variables. Thus,

$$\frac{\partial u}{\partial t} = u_x \frac{\partial x}{\partial t} + u_y \frac{\partial y}{\partial t} + u_z \frac{\partial z}{\partial t}. \qquad (12)$$

ILLUSTRATION 3. If $u = f(x, y)$, and if we use $x = r \sin \theta$ and $y = r \cos \theta$, then

$$\frac{\partial x}{\partial r} = \sin \theta; \quad \frac{\partial x}{\partial \theta} = r \cos \theta; \quad \frac{\partial y}{\partial r} = \cos \theta; \quad \frac{\partial y}{\partial \theta} = -r \sin \theta. \qquad (13)$$

From (11), with t as r, and then t as θ,

$$\frac{\partial u}{\partial r} = u_x \sin \theta + u_y \cos \theta; \quad \frac{\partial u}{\partial \theta} = r u_x \cos \theta - r u_y \sin \theta.$$

Note 2. In formulas like (11), we may refer to (x, y) as variables of the *first class*, and to (s, t) as variables of the *second class*. Variables of the first class play two roles. First, in the evaluation of u_x and u_y, we consider x and y as independent variables. Later, x and y become dependent variables. The variables of the second class are the final independent variables.

ILLUSTRATION 4. Suppose that $u = f(x, y, s, t)$, and that x and y are differentiable functions of s and t. With x, y, s, and t as the variables of the 1st class, and s and t as the variables of the 2d class, from (12) we obtain

$$\left(\frac{\partial u}{\partial t}\right)_s = f_x(x, y, s, t) \frac{\partial x}{\partial t} + f_y(x, y, s, t) \frac{\partial y}{\partial t} + f_t(x, y, s, t), \qquad (14)$$

because s is considered as a constant in (14), and $\dfrac{\partial t}{\partial t} = 1$; or

$$\left(\frac{\partial u}{\partial t}\right)_s = u_x \frac{\partial x}{\partial t} + u_y \frac{\partial y}{\partial t} + u_t. \qquad (15)$$

Notice the confusion if we should use ambiguous "∂" notations on the right in (15), instead of the unambiguous subscript notations:

$$\frac{\partial u}{\partial t} = \frac{\partial u}{\partial x} \frac{\partial x}{\partial t} + \frac{\partial u}{\partial y} \frac{\partial y}{\partial t} + \frac{\partial u}{\partial t}, \qquad (16)$$

where $\dfrac{\partial u}{\partial t}$ appears to cancel out! In (16), $\dfrac{\partial u}{\partial t}$ on the left and on the right have different meanings, and (16) becomes intelligible only when the other independent variables are shown by subscripts:

$$\left(\frac{\partial u}{\partial t}\right)_s = \left(\frac{\partial u}{\partial x}\right)_{(y, s, t)} \left(\frac{\partial x}{\partial t}\right)_s + \left(\frac{\partial u}{\partial y}\right)_{(x, s, t)} \left(\frac{\partial y}{\partial t}\right)_s + \left(\frac{\partial u}{\partial t}\right)_{(x, y, s)}. \qquad (17)$$

We may use the chain rule to obtain formulas for ordinary or partial derivatives of solution functions defined implicitly by an equation, or a system of equations, involving two or more variables.

I. *If the variable y represents any particular function of x defined implicitly by* $F(x, y) = 0$, *then*

$$\frac{dy}{dx} = -\frac{F_x(x, y)}{F_y(x, y)}. \tag{18}$$

Proof. Let $u = F(x, y)$, where y represents a function of x defined implicitly by $F(x, y) = 0$. Then, $u = 0$ and hence $du/dx = 0$ for all values of x. We obtain du/dx by use of (6) on page 585:

$$\frac{du}{dx} = F_x(x, y) + F_y(x, y)\frac{dy}{dx} = 0, \quad or \quad \frac{dy}{dx} = -\frac{F_x(x, y)}{F_y(x, y)}.$$

II. *If the variable z represents any particular function of x and y defined implicitly by* $F(x, y, z) = 0$, *then*

$$\frac{\partial z}{\partial x} = -\frac{F_x(x, y, z)}{F_z(x, y, z)}, \quad \frac{\partial z}{\partial y} = -\frac{F_y(x, y, z)}{F_z(x, y, z)}. \tag{19}$$

Proof. To obtain $\frac{\partial z}{\partial x}$ in (19), we consider y as a constant temporarily and use (18), with y replaced by z; we find a *partial* derivative from (18) because z is a function of *two* variables. Similarly, we obtain $\frac{\partial z}{\partial y}$ in (19) by use of (18) with y replaced by z, and x replaced by y.

Formulas (18) and (19) have important theoretical applications. Also, for experience, the formulas may be used to obtain the derivatives of implicit functions in explicit equations as met on pages 471 and 472. However, the student should *continue to use the earlier methods when* (18) *and* (19) *are not specified for use.*

EXAMPLE 1. Obtain $\frac{\partial z}{\partial x}$ if $\quad z^3 + 3xz^2 - yz + xy^2 - 8x = 0$.

Solution. Let $F(x, y, z) = z^3 + 3xz^2 - yz - 8x + xy^2$. Then, by (19),

$$\frac{\partial z}{\partial x} = -\frac{3z^2 - 8 + y^2}{3z^2 + 6xz - y}.$$

EXERCISE 177

Solve each problem by use of a formula from Section 225.

Find $\frac{du}{dt}$, *without eliminating x, y, or z.*

1. $u = x^2 + 3xy + 5y^2$, when $x = 3t^3 + t$ and $y = 2t - t^2$.
2. $u = x^3 - xy^2$, when $x = 4 \sin t$ and $y = 3 \cos 2t$.
3. $u = x - y^2 - z^2$, when $x = e^t$, $y = 3 \ln t$, and $z = 4t^2$.

4. $u = \sqrt{x^2 + y^2 + z^2}$, when $x = \sin 2t$, $y = 3 \cos 2t$, and $z = 4t^3$.

Hint. Let $v = x^2 + y^2 + z^2$. Then, $u = v^{\frac{1}{2}}$ and $\dfrac{du}{dt} = \dfrac{1}{2} v^{-\frac{1}{2}} \dfrac{dv}{dt}$.

5. $u = e^z \cos y$, when $y = t \ln t$ and $z = \text{Arctan } t$.
6. $u = \ln (x - 2y + 3z)$, when $x = 3t^3$, $y = e^{2t}$, and $z = \tan t$.
7. $u = \text{Arcsin } xyz$, when $x = \sin 2t$, $y = \cos 2t$, and $z = \sec t$.
8. $u = e^{3x+4y} \ln z$, when $x = t^2 + t$, $y = t^3$, and $z = \cos t$.

Find the total derivative of u with respect to x, without eliminating y or z.

9. $u = x^3 + xy - y^3$, when $y = e^x \ln x + x$.
10. $u = \sin x + \cos y^{\frac{3}{2}}$, when $y = x^2 + 5x$.
11. $u = \sin x^2 + x \cos y^2$, when $y = \sin 2x$.
12. $u = x^3 + 4xy^3$, when $y = xe^{2x} - \ln x$.
13. $u = x^2 - xz + yz$, when $y = \cos x$ and $z = e^{-3x}$.
14. $u = \sqrt{x^2 + y^2 + z^2}$, when $y = (3x - 5)^2$ and $z = \sec x$.
15. $u = \dfrac{x + e^y}{z - e^x}$, when $y = 3 \sin x$ and $z = \ln x$.

Find $\dfrac{\partial u}{\partial s}$ and $\dfrac{\partial u}{\partial t}$ by the chain rule, without eliminating x and y.

16. $u = x^3 + 3x^2y$, where $x = te^s$ and $y = se^t$.
17. $u = x^2 - xy + y^3$, where $x = s \cos t$ and $y = st^2$.
18. $u = \sin 2x + \cos 3y$, where $x = 2s + t^2$ and $y = 3t - s^3$.
19. If $z = \sin xy$, $x = \ln \sqrt{u + v}$, and $y = \text{Arcsin } uv$, find $\dfrac{\partial z}{\partial u}$.
20. If $u = x^2y - yz^2$, $x = 2r + 3s$, $y = 4r + s$, and $z = 4 \sin rs$, find $\dfrac{\partial u}{\partial r}$.
21. If $u = x^2 + y^2 + z^2$, find $\dfrac{\partial u}{\partial r}$, $\dfrac{\partial u}{\partial \theta}$, and $\dfrac{\partial u}{\partial \phi}$ if

$$x = r \sin \phi \cos \theta, \quad y = r \sin \phi \sin \theta, \quad and \quad z = r \cos \phi.$$

22. If $u = e^{x^2y}$, $x = \text{Arcsin } \sqrt{s^2 + t^2}$, and $y = \ln st$, find $\dfrac{\partial u}{\partial s}$ and $\dfrac{\partial u}{\partial t}$.
23. If $z = \dfrac{\sin x}{1 + \cos y}$, $x = e^t + \ln t$, and $y = 5t^2$, find dz/dt.

All functions mentioned in the following problems are differentiable.

24. If $u = f(x, y, z)$, where x and z are functions of y, obtain du/dy.
25. If $v = g(x, y, u, t)$, where u and t are functions of x and y, write expressions for $\left(\dfrac{\partial v}{\partial x}\right)_y$ and $\left(\dfrac{\partial v}{\partial y}\right)_z$.
26. If u and y are functions of x, obtain $df(u, x, y)/dx$.
27. If w is a function of y, z, r, and t, and if r and t are functions of y and z, find $\left(\dfrac{\partial w}{\partial y}\right)_z$ and $\left(\dfrac{\partial w}{\partial z}\right)_y$.
28. Assume that the function $f(x, y)$ has derivatives f_x and f_y which are continuous near $(x = x_0, y = y_0)$. Prove that $f(x, y)$ is continuous at (x_0, y_0).

226. IMPLICIT DIFFERENTIATION IN GENERAL SYSTEMS

In the following theorem we shall assume that the functions $F(x, y, s, w)$ and $G(x, y, s, w)$ are differentiable and that the denominator in (2) below is not zero at any set of numbers (x, y, s, w) involved.

Theorem II. *If s and w are defined implicitly as functions of x and y by the system*

$$F(x, y, s, w) = 0 \quad and \quad G(x, y, s, w) = 0, \tag{1}$$

then
$$\frac{\partial s}{\partial x} = -\frac{\begin{vmatrix} \dfrac{\partial F}{\partial x} & \dfrac{\partial F}{\partial w} \\ \dfrac{\partial G}{\partial x} & \dfrac{\partial G}{\partial w} \end{vmatrix}}{J(x, y, s, w)} \quad and \quad \frac{\partial w}{\partial x} = -\frac{\begin{vmatrix} \dfrac{\partial F}{\partial s} & \dfrac{\partial F}{\partial x} \\ \dfrac{\partial G}{\partial s} & \dfrac{\partial G}{\partial x} \end{vmatrix}}{J(x, y, s, w)}, \tag{2}$$

where
$$J(x, y, s, w) = \begin{vmatrix} \dfrac{\partial F}{\partial s} & \dfrac{\partial F}{\partial w} \\ \dfrac{\partial G}{\partial s} & \dfrac{\partial G}{\partial w} \end{vmatrix}. \tag{3}$$

Proof of (2). On both sides of each equation in (1), differentiate with respect to x, with w and s considered as functions of x and y, and with y held fast. In this differentiation, use (12) of page 586 with $u = F(x, y, s, w)$ and t replaced by x, and then with $u = G(x, y, s, w)$:

$$\left.\begin{aligned} \frac{\partial F}{\partial x} + \frac{\partial F}{\partial s}\frac{\partial s}{\partial x} + \frac{\partial F}{\partial w}\frac{\partial w}{\partial x} = 0, \ and \\ \frac{\partial G}{\partial x} + \frac{\partial G}{\partial s}\frac{\partial s}{\partial x} + \frac{\partial G}{\partial w}\frac{\partial w}{\partial x} = 0. \end{aligned}\right\} \tag{4}$$

On solving (4) for $\dfrac{\partial s}{\partial x}$ and $\dfrac{\partial w}{\partial x}$ by use of determinants, we obtain (2). Similarly, we may obtain $\dfrac{\partial s}{\partial y}$ and $\dfrac{\partial w}{\partial y}$ from (2) by replacing $\left(\dfrac{\partial F}{\partial x}, \dfrac{\partial G}{\partial x}\right)$ by $\left(\dfrac{\partial F}{\partial y}, \dfrac{\partial G}{\partial y}\right)$.

In the denominator of (2), we meet a special case of an important type of determinant. In (3), J is called the **Jacobian** of the functions F and G with respect to s and w. Sometimes the symbol $\dfrac{\partial(F, G)}{\partial(s, w)}$ is used for a Jacobian as in (3), where use of "∂" merely is a reminder of the nature of the elements in the determinant.

ILLUSTRATION 1. If $F(x, y) = x^2 + 3xy$ and $G(x, y) = \sin xy$,

$$\frac{\partial(F, G)}{\partial(x, y)} = \begin{vmatrix} 2x + 3y & 3x \\ y \cos xy & x \cos xy \end{vmatrix} = 2x^2 \cos xy.$$

In (1) and (2), we assumed that (1) defines a unique solution for w and s as functions of x and y, near all points (x, y) which are to be considered. The theorem * justifying this assumption demands, as a hypothesis, that *the Jacobian of*

* See the *fundamental theorem on implicit functions*, in advanced texts.

F and G with respect to s and w is not zero on the domain considered for (x, y, s, w), or $J(x, y, s, w) \neq 0$ as in Theorem II. Thus, the hypothesis $J(x, y, s, w) \neq 0$, which justifies dealing with (1), also is necessary for solving (4) to arrive at (2).

Note 1. The notion of a Jacobian extends to n functions of n or more independent variables. Thus, if $F^{(1)}, \cdots, F^{(n)}$ are functions of the independent variables $(x_1, \cdots, x_n)$, the Jacobian $\dfrac{\partial(F^{(1)}, \cdots, F^{(n)})}{\partial(x_1, \cdots, x_n)}$ is defined as the determinant of order n where the element in the ith row and jth column is $\dfrac{\partial F^{(i)}(x_1, \cdots, x_n)}{\partial x_j}$.

Note 2. As a rule, special cases of (1) should be treated by the elementary method on page 473, without using (2) or similar formulas. Results such as (2) are useful in advanced discussions.

EXAMPLE 1. Find $\dfrac{\partial w}{\partial x}$ if x and y are the independent variables, and if (x, y, s, w) are related by

$$\left. \begin{array}{l} 3w^2 - 2swx + y^2 = 2s^2, \\ 2x^2 - s^3w + w^2y = 2x. \end{array} \right\} \tag{5}$$

Solution. From (2) with

$$\left. \begin{array}{l} F(x, y, s, w) = 3w^2 - 2swx + y^2 - 2s^2 = 0, \; and \\ G(x, y, s, w) = 2x^2 - s^3w + w^2y - 2x = 0, \end{array} \right\}$$

$$\frac{\partial w}{\partial x} = - \frac{\begin{vmatrix} -2wx - 4s & -2sw \\ -3s^2w & 4x - 2 \end{vmatrix}}{\begin{vmatrix} -2wx - 4s & 6w - 2sx \\ -3s^2w & -s^3 + 2wy \end{vmatrix}} = \frac{3s^3w^2 + 4wx^2 + 8sx - 2wx - 4s}{9s^2w^2 - 2s^3wx + 2s^4 - 2w^2xy - 4swy}.$$

Note 3. If (1) does not involve y, then the desired partial derivatives in (2) become ordinary derivatives $\dfrac{dw}{dx}$ and $\dfrac{ds}{dx}$, respectively.

EXAMPLE 2. If u is a function of x and y, where they occur only in the combination xy, prove that

$$x \frac{\partial u}{\partial x} - y \frac{\partial u}{\partial y} = 0. \tag{6}$$

Solution. Let $w = xy$. Then, there exists a function of a single variable, $f(w)$, such that u, w, x, and y satisfy

$$w = xy \quad and \quad u = f(w). \tag{7}$$

Consider (7) as a system of equations defining u and w as functions of x and y. From $u = f(w)$,

$$\frac{\partial u}{\partial x} = \frac{df(w)}{dw} \frac{\partial w}{\partial x} = f'(w) \frac{\partial w}{\partial x}; \quad \frac{\partial u}{\partial y} = f'(w) \frac{\partial w}{\partial y}, \; or$$

$$\frac{\partial u}{\partial x} = yf'(w); \quad \frac{\partial u}{\partial y} = xf'(w). \tag{8}$$

From (8), $x \dfrac{\partial u}{\partial x} = y \dfrac{\partial u}{\partial y}$,   *or* $x \dfrac{\partial u}{\partial x} - y \dfrac{\partial u}{\partial y} = 0.$

In connection with $F(x, y, s, w)$, sometimes $F_1(x, y, s, w)$, or also F_1 alone, is used instead of $F_x(x, y, s, w)$ for values of the partial derivative with respect to the variable in the *first place*, F_2 instead of $F_y(x, y, s, w)$, etc. Then, (2) becomes

$$\frac{\partial s}{\partial x} = - \begin{vmatrix} F_1 & F_4 \\ G_1 & G_4 \end{vmatrix} \bigg/ \begin{vmatrix} F_3 & F_4 \\ G_3 & G_4 \end{vmatrix}, \ etc.$$

227. GENERAL DEFINITION OF HOMOGENEITY

The next definition extends the elementary notion of a homogeneous function.

Definition I. *A function $f(x, y, z)$ is said to be homogeneous and of degree n in x, y, and z if and only if, for all permissible values of x, y, z, and λ,*

$$f(\lambda x, \lambda y, \lambda z) = \lambda^n f(x, y, z). \tag{1}$$

The degree n in (1) may be any real number. Definition I applies with appropriate alterations to a function of any number of variables.

ILLUSTRATION 1. The function $f(x, y, z) = 3x^3 + 4xy^2 + z^3$ is homogeneous and of degree 3 because $f(\lambda x, \lambda y, \lambda z) = 3\lambda^3 x^3 + 4\lambda^3 xy^2 + \lambda^3 z^3 = \lambda^3 f(x, y, z)$.

ILLUSTRATION 2. The function $f(x, y, z) = \sqrt{x + y - z}$ is homogeneous and of degree $\frac{1}{2}$ because, with $\lambda > 0$,

$$f(\lambda x, \lambda y, \lambda z) = \sqrt{\lambda x + \lambda y - \lambda z} = \sqrt{\lambda}\sqrt{x + y - z} = \lambda^{\frac{1}{2}} f(x, y, z).$$

Theorem III. (*Euler's theorem.*) *If a differentiable function $f(x, y, z)$ is homogeneous and of degree n, then*

$$x f_x(x, y, z) + y f_y(x, y, z) + z f_z(x, y, z) = n f(x, y, z). \tag{2}$$

Outline of proof. We can obtain (2) by differentiating both sides of (1) with respect to λ, and then placing $\lambda = 1$. (The converse can be proved.)

EXERCISE 178

1–14. Solve Problems 1–14, respectively, of Exercise 142 on page 474 by use of (2) on page 589.

Prove that the function is homogeneous and find its degree, by substituting $(\lambda x, \lambda y, \lambda z)$ for (x, y, z). Then, verify identity (2) of Section 227 for the function.

15. $f(x, y, z) = x^3 + 3xy^2 - y^3$. **16.** $f(x, y, z) = \sqrt[3]{x^2 + y^2 + z^2}$.

17. $\sin(y/x)$.   **18.** Arcsin $[x/(x + y)]$.   **19.** $z\sqrt{x^2 + y^2}$.

20. If $u = f(w)$ where $w = x - y$ and f' is continuous, prove that $u_x + u_y = 0$.

21. If $u = f(x, y, z)$, where $x = a + gt$, $y = b + ht$, $z = c + kt$, and a, b, c, g, h, and k are constants, find du/dt.

22. If $u = f(x, y)$ and if $x = r \cos \theta$ and $y = r \sin \theta$, obtain $\dfrac{\partial u}{\partial r}$ and $\dfrac{\partial u}{\partial \theta}$.

23. If u is a function of $(2x + 3y)$, prove that $3u_x = 2u_y$.

24. If u is a function of x/y, prove that $xu_x = -yu_y$.

25. If u is a function of $(x^2 + y^2)$, prove that $yu_x = xu_y$.

228. RESULTS ABOUT DIFFERENTIALS

If u is a function of the independent variables x and y, we have defined

$$du = \frac{\partial u}{\partial x}\, dx + \frac{\partial u}{\partial y}\, dy. \tag{1}$$

We proceed to establish the important result that (1) remains true even when x and y no longer are the independent variables.

Theorem IV. *Suppose that $u = f(x, y)$, where f is differentiable and x and y are differentiable functions of s and t. Then, the differential of u with respect to s and t as independent variables is given by $du = u_x\, dx + u_y\, dy$, where dx and dy are calculated with respect to s and t.*

Proof. 1. With respect to s and t as independent variables,

$$du = \frac{\partial u}{\partial s}\, ds + \frac{\partial u}{\partial t}\, dt; \quad dx = \frac{\partial x}{\partial s}\, ds + \frac{\partial x}{\partial t}\, dt; \quad dy = \frac{\partial y}{\partial s}\, ds + \frac{\partial y}{\partial t}\, dt. \tag{2}$$

2. Since $u = f(x, y)$, from (11) on page 586 we obtain

$$\frac{\partial u}{\partial s} = \frac{\partial u}{\partial x}\frac{\partial x}{\partial s} + \frac{\partial u}{\partial y}\frac{\partial y}{\partial s}; \quad \frac{\partial u}{\partial t} = \frac{\partial u}{\partial x}\frac{\partial x}{\partial t} + \frac{\partial u}{\partial y}\frac{\partial y}{\partial t}. \tag{3}$$

On using (3) in du in (2), and reordering terms, we find

$$du = \frac{\partial u}{\partial x}\left(\frac{\partial x}{\partial s}\, ds + \frac{\partial x}{\partial t}\, dt\right) + \frac{\partial u}{\partial y}\left(\frac{\partial y}{\partial s}\, ds + \frac{\partial y}{\partial t}\, dt\right). \tag{4}$$

From (2), equation (4) can be rewritten $du = u_x\, dx + u_y\, dy$.

EXAMPLE 1. Obtain du if $u = \sin x + \cos y$, where $x = \sqrt{s^2 + t^2}$ and $y = e^{st}$.

Solution. By Theorem IV, $du = \cos x\, dx - \sin y\, dy$, where

$$dx = \tfrac{1}{2}(s^2 + t^2)^{-\frac{1}{2}}(2s\, ds + 2t\, dt) \quad and \quad dy = e^{st}(s\, dt + t\, ds).$$

Thus, $\quad du = \left(\dfrac{s\cos x}{\sqrt{s^2 + t^2}} - te^{st}\sin y\right) ds - \left(se^{st}\sin y - \dfrac{t\cos x}{\sqrt{s^2 + t^2}}\right) dt. \tag{5}$

Note 1. Theorem I on page 477 is a special case of Theorem IV, with u as a function of just one variable. Theorem IV extends to the case of any number of variables.

EXAMPLE 2. Obtain dz in terms of x, y, dx, and dy if

$$z^3 + 4xyz = 5xy + 8. \tag{6}$$

Solution. Equation (6) is considered as defining z as a function of x and y. Then, the differentials of the two sides with respect to x and y as independent variables are equal. By Theorem IV, we obtain the differential of the left-hand side with respect to x and y by writing the differential with respect to x, y, and z:

$$d(z^3 + 4xyz) = d(5xy + 8), \ or$$

$$(3z^2 + 4xy)dz + 4xz\, dy + 4yz\, dx = 5y\, dx + 5x\, dy, \ or$$

$$dz = \frac{5y\, dx + 5x\, dy - 4xz\, dy - 4yz\, dx}{3z^2 + 4xy}. \tag{7}$$

EXERCISE 179

Obtain du with s and t as independent variables; do not eliminate x and y.

1. $u = x^3y + x^5y^2$, where $x = 3st^3$ and $y = \sin(s + 3t)$.

2. $u = y \sin 3x + x \cos 4y$, where $x = (s + 3t)^3$ and $y = e^s \ln t$.

3. $u = \text{Arcsin}(x + 3y)$, where $x = \sin st$ and $y = s^2e^t$.

4. $u = (x + 3y)/(2x - y)$, where $x = t + e^s$ and $y = s \ln(\ln t)$.

Find dz in terms of x, y, z, dx, and dy.

5. $3x^2 + 2yz + xz^2 = 4$.   **6.** $xy + \sin z = 7$.

7. $\tan z = x/y$.   **8.** $e^z = x^2 + y^2$.

Obtain the result without solving for z in terms of x and y.

9. If $z^2 = x^2 + y^2$, find dz when $x = 5$, $y = -12$, $dx = .1$, and $dy = -.2$.

10. If $z^2 = 3x/(2y + 1)$, find dz when $x = 3$, $y = 12$, $dx = .2$, and $dy = .3$.

11. If $e^z + xy - e^{zz} = a$, find dz when $x = 2$, $z = 1$, $y = 4$, $dx = .2$, and $dy = .3$.

The system of equations defines x and y as functions of t. Obtain dx and dy in terms of dt.

12. $xy - tx = 5$ and $x^2y^2 - ty = 4$.

13. $t^3 + tx^3 - y^3 = 0$ and $t^2 + x^2 - ty^2 = 0$.

14. $3x + t^2y + x^2 = 4$ and $4y - t^2x + t^2 = 3$.

15. If $u = g(x + kt)$, where k is a constant, prove that $\dfrac{\partial^2 u}{\partial t^2} = k^2 \dfrac{\partial^2 u}{\partial x^2}$.

16. Obtain expressions for dy/dx and dz/dx if (x, y, z) satisfy the system of equations $F(x, y, z) = 0$ and $K(x, y, z) = 0$.

17. Let $u = f(x, y)$ where f is differentiable. If $u_x = 0$ and $u_y = 0$ at all points (x, y), prove that u is a constant. In other words, if $du = 0$ for all (x, y) and all numbers (dx, dy), prove that u is a constant.

18. If $y = f(x, y)$, obtain an expression for dy/dx.

★SUPPLEMENT FOR CHAPTER TWENTY–FIVE

19. If $z = f(x, y, z)$, obtain an expression for $\partial^2 z/\partial x \partial y$.

20. If the variables x, y, and z satisfy $F(x + y - 2z, x^2 + y^2 - 2z^2) = 0$, prove that $y - x + 2(x - z)z_y + 2(z - y)z_x = 0$.

21. If $f(x, y) = \displaystyle\int_{3x^2+y^3}^{2xy} \sqrt{1 + t^3}\, dt$, calculate $f_x(x, y)$ and $f_y(x, y)$.

22. Without using general formulas from page 589, obtain expressions for $\partial u/\partial x$ and $\partial v/\partial x$ if the variables x, y, u, and v are related by the equations
$$u = f(x, y, v) \quad and \quad v = g(x, y, u).$$

23. If the functions $K(u, v, w)$, $f(x, y, z)$, $g(x, y, z)$, $h(x, y, z)$ and $\phi(x, y)$ are such that the equation $K(f(x, y, z), g(x, y, z), h(x, y, z)) = 0$ is satisfied by $z = \phi(x, y)$, obtain an expression for $\partial z/\partial y$, if all functions are differentiable.

24. In the notation of (2) on page 583, with $du = u_x\, dx + u_y\, dy$, prove that
$$\lim_{(\Delta x, \Delta y) \to (0, 0)} \frac{|\Delta u - du|}{|\Delta x| + |\Delta y|} = 0, \tag{1}$$

Equation (1) frequently is taken as the defining property of du.

CHAPTER TWENTY–SIX

Envelopes, Space Curves, and Surfaces

229. ENVELOPE OF A FAMILY OF CURVES

Let a family of curves be defined by

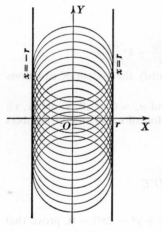

Fig. 389

$$f(x, y, t) = 0, \tag{1}$$

where t is a parameter. For each value of t, a curve of the family is determined as the graph of (1) in the xy-plane. For any family (1), suppose that f possesses continuous partial derivatives f_x, f_y, and f_t.

ILLUSTRATION 1. If β is a parameter, the equation

$$x^2 + (y - \beta)^2 = r^2, \tag{2}$$

where r is a constant, defines a family of circles with radius r. Curves of this family are in Figure 389.

We define *an* **envelope** of a family (1) as a curve E such that

I. *each curve C of the family is tangent to E at some point of C;*

II. *through each point P of E, there passes a curve of the family tangent to E.*

For a given family (1), the set of all curves E (if any exist) satisfying (I) and (II) will be called THE envelope of the family.

ILLUSTRATION 2. In Figure 389, each of the lines $x = r$ and $x = -r$ is an envelope for family (2). THE envelope consists of these lines.

ILLUSTRATION 3. Suppose that, in an xy-plane, a projectile is shot from the origin with an initial speed of v_0 feet per second, at an angle of elevation t. Under idealized conditions, the trajectory of the projectile has the equation

$$y = -\frac{gx^2}{2v_0^2 \cos^2 t} + x \tan t, \tag{3}$$

where $g = 32$, approximately. If v_0 is a constant and t varies, the family of parabolas

594

(3) has an envelope, whose equation, as obtained later, is

$$y = \frac{v_0^2}{2g} - \frac{gx^2}{2v_0^2}.$$

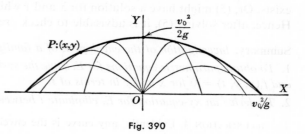

Fig. 390

Figure 390 shows the envelope and curves of family (3).

Let E be an envelope for (1), as in Figure 390. Then, for each value of t, there is a corresponding point $P:(x, y)$ on E at which E is tangent to the curve C given by (1), and each point of E is obtained in this way. Thus, if $P:(x, y)$ is on E, then x and y are functions of t, or E can be considered in parametric form with t as the parameter,

$$x = g(t) \quad and \quad y = h(t). \tag{4}$$

Theorem I. IF *a family of curves* $f(x, y, t) = 0$ *has an envelope* E, *then the parametric equations for* E *in terms of* t *satisfy*

$$f(x, y, t) = 0 \quad and \quad f_t(x, y, t) = 0. \tag{5}$$

Proof. 1. Suppose that an envelope (4) exists. Then, for each value of t, (4) gives a point on the graph of (1), or (1) is satisfied by $x = g(t)$ and $y = h(t)$:

$$f[g(t), h(t), t] = 0. \tag{6}$$

2. Let $u = f(x, y, t)$ with $x = g(t)$ and $y = h(t)$. Then, by (6), $u = 0$ for all values of t and thus $du/dt = 0$. From (9) on page 585,

$$\frac{du}{dt} = f_x(x, y, t)\frac{dx}{dt} + f_y(x, y, t)\frac{dy}{dt} + f_t(x, y, t) = 0, \text{ or}$$

$$f_x(x, y, t)g'(t) + f_y(x, y, t)h'(t) + f_t(x, y, t) = 0. \tag{7}$$

3. *With* t *fixed*, the slope at $P:(x, y)$ on curve C of family (1) is equal to dy/dx, obtained on differentiating with respect to x in (1):

$$f_x(x, y, t) + f_y(x, y, t)\frac{dy}{dx} = 0, \quad or \quad \frac{dy}{dx} = -\frac{f_x(x, y, t)}{f_y(x, y, t)}. \tag{8}$$

At $P:(x, y)$ on E, from (4), $\dfrac{dy}{dx} = \dfrac{h'(t)dt}{g'(t)dt} = \dfrac{h'(t)}{g'(t)}. \tag{9}$

Since C and E have the same slope at P, from (8) and (9) we obtain

$$-\frac{f_x(x, y, t)}{f_y(x, y, t)} = \frac{h'(t)}{g'(t)}, \quad or \quad f_x(x, y, t)g'(t) + f_y(x, y, t)h'(t) = 0. \tag{10}$$

When (10) is used, (7) becomes simply $f_t(x, y, t) = 0$. Thus, from (6) and (7), $x = g(t)$ and $y = h(t)$ satisfy the equations in (5).

Note 1. In (8) of the proof, we assumed that the tangent at P on the envelope is not vertical, so that dy/dx exists. In case this is not true, we could use dx/dy in (8). Also, in (4), we assumed that g and h possess continuous derivatives.

For a particular case, equations (5) might be inconsistent; then, no envelope exists. Or, (5) might have a solution for x and y which does not give an envelope. Hence, after solving (5), it is advisable to check graphically.

Summary. *Investigation of the envelope E of a family $f(x, y, t) = 0$.*

1. *To obtain parametric equations for E, solve the system consisting of $f(x, y, t) = 0$ and $f_t(x, y, t) = 0$ for x and y in terms of t.*

2. *To derive an xy-equation for E, eliminate t between equations* (5).

ILLUSTRATION 4. Evidently, any curve is the envelope of its tangent lines.

ILLUSTRATION 5. For (2), where β is the parameter, (5) becomes

$$x^2 + (y - \beta)^2 = r^2 \quad and \quad -2(y - \beta) = 0. \tag{11}$$

On using $y - \beta = 0$, equations (11) give $x^2 = r^2$. Thus, the envelope consists of the lines $x = r$ and $x = -r$, as verified in Figure 389, page 595.

EXAMPLE 1. Obtain the envelope of the family of all lines at a fixed distance p from the origin in an xy-plane.

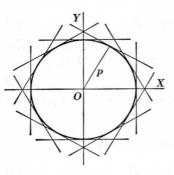

Fig. 391

Solution. 1. For any line of the family, let ω be the angle from the positive direction of the x-axis to a ray from the origin perpendicular to the line. Then, by use of the normal form for the equation of a line from (14) on page 427, with ω as a parameter, the equation for the family is

$$x \cos \omega + y \sin \omega - p = 0. \tag{12}$$

Differentiate partially with respect to the parameter ω in (12):

$$-x \sin \omega + y \cos \omega = 0. \tag{13}$$

2. To derive parametric equations for the envelope, solve (12) and (13) for x and y in terms of ω, and obtain $x = p \cos \omega$ and $y = p \sin \omega$. To find an xy-equation for the envelope, eliminate ω by squaring and adding; this gives $x^2 + y^2 = p^2$. In Figure 391, we verify that this circle is the envelope.

On page 403, we saw that the *normal* at any point on a given curve C, as in Figure 267 on page 404, is *tangent to the evolute of C*. Then, since *the evolute is the envelope of its own tangents*, we reach the following conclusion.

The evolute of a curve C is the envelope of the normals of C. $\qquad$ (14)

EXAMPLE 2. Find the evolute of the curve $\qquad\qquad x^2 = 4y.$ $\qquad$ (15)

Solution. 1. *To obtain an equation for the family of normals to* (15). From (15), $y' = \tfrac{1}{2}x$. Let $P:(x_1, y_1)$ be any point on (15). Then, the normal to (15) at P has the slope $-2/x_1$, and the equation

$$(y - y_1) = -\frac{2}{x_1}(x - x_1), \quad or \quad x_1 y - x_1 y_1 = -2x + 2x_1. \tag{16}$$

From (15), $x_1^2 = 4y_1$ or $y_1 = \frac{1}{4}x_1^2$. On substituting $y_1 = \frac{1}{4}x_1^2$ in (16) we obtain an equation for the family of normals with x_1 as the parameter:

$$8x + 4x_1y - x_1^3 - 8x_1 = 0. \tag{17}$$

2. *To obtain the envelope of* (17). For (17), equations (5), with t as x_1, become

$$4y - 3x_1^2 - 8 = 0 \quad and \quad 8x + 4x_1y - x_1^3 - 8x_1 = 0. \tag{18}$$

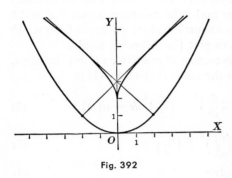

Fig. 392

From (18), we find

$$y = \tfrac{3}{4}x_1^2 + 2 \quad and \quad x = -\tfrac{1}{4}x_1^3. \tag{19}$$

Thus, (19) gives the parametric equations of the evolute of (15) in terms of x_1 as the parameter. From (19),

$$x_1^6 = \tfrac{64}{27}(y - 2)^3 \quad and \quad x_1^6 = 16x^2. \tag{20}$$

Hence, on eliminating x_1 by use of (20), we obtain $4(y - 2)^3 = 27x^2$ as the xy-equation of the evolute. Graphs of (15) and (20) are shown in Figure 392, with three normals for (15).

EXERCISE 180

All curves are in the xy-plane. Any letter other than x or y is a variable parameter, except where the letter is stated to be a constant.

Find an xy-equation for the envelope of the family.

1. $(x - t)^2 + y^2 = r^2$; r is a constant.
2. $x^2 + (y - 2t)^2 = t^2$.
3. $(x - \alpha)^2 + (y + \alpha)^2 = \alpha^2$.
4. $ky = k^2x + p$; p is a constant.
5. $y = 5x + t$.
6. $3m^2x - 3y = 2m^3$.
7. $x^2 = 4t(y - t)$.
8. $8x + m^2y = 16m$.
9. $4(x - t)^2 + (2y - t)^2 = t^2$.
10. The envelope of (3), page 594.
11. $ty = x + t^3$.
12. $x - y \sin \theta = k \cos \theta$, where k is a constant.

Obtain an equation for the tangent to the curve at an arbitrary point (x_1, y_1). *From this equation, find the envelope of the family of tangents.*

13. $y^2 = 8x - 16$.
14. $x^2 = 2y + 6$.
15. $y = x^3$.
16. The ellipse with the parametric equations $[x = a \cos \theta, y = b \sin \theta]$.
17. Find an equation for the curve whose family of tangents is

$$bx - ay \sin \theta = ab \sec \theta - ab \sin \theta \tan \theta, \text{ where } a \text{ and } b \text{ are constants.}$$

Find an xy-equation, or parametric equations, for the evolute of the curve by obtaining the envelope of its normals.

18–20. The given curves in Problems 13, 14, and 16, respectively.

21. Find the envelope of the family of lines where, on any line, the length of the segment between the coordinate axes is a constant, k (and is defined as equal to k at quadrantal positions).

230. SPACE CURVES IN PARAMETRIC FORM

In an xyz-system of coordinates, consider a curve C defined by

$$x = f(t), \quad y = g(t), \quad and \quad z = h(t), \tag{1}$$

where the domain for t is an interval, finite or infinite. An arc of C is defined as the set of points obtained for the values of t on some interval $a \leq t \leq b$. The definition of arc length for a plane curve, on page 387, applies with no essential alteration to a space curve (1). We continue under the assumption that f, g, and h have continuous derivatives. Then, the discussion for plane curves in Chapter 16 could be repeated with negligible changes to give the following results.

Every arc of (1) has length. If distance s is measured positive on C as t increases, with $s = 0$ at $t = a$, then the distance s to the point P given by (1) is

$$s = \int_{t=a}^{t} ds = \int_{a}^{t} \sqrt{\left(\frac{dx}{dt}\right)^2 + \left(\frac{dy}{dt}\right)^2 + \left(\frac{dz}{dt}\right)^2}\, dt = w(t); \tag{2}$$

$$\frac{ds}{dt} = \sqrt{\left(\frac{dx}{dt}\right)^2 + \left(\frac{dy}{dt}\right)^2 + \left(\frac{dz}{dt}\right)^2}; \tag{3}$$

$$(ds)^2 = (dx)^2 + (dy)^2 + (dz)^2. \tag{4}$$

A curve C will be called a *regular curve* in case it has a parametric representation (1) where $f'(t)$, $g'(t)$, and $h'(t)$ are continuous and

$$[f'(t)]^2 + [g'(t)]^2 + [h'(t)]^2 \neq 0 \tag{5}$$

at all values of t. On a regular curve, with s as the parameter,

$$\left(\frac{dx}{ds}\right)^2 + \left(\frac{dy}{ds}\right)^2 + \left(\frac{dz}{ds}\right)^2 = 1. \tag{6}$$

EXAMPLE 1. Find the length of arc, L, from $t = 0$ to $t = \frac{1}{2}\sqrt{3}$ on the curve $x = 2t^2 + t$, $y = 2t^2 - 2t$, and $z = t^2 + 2t$.

Solution. $\quad dx = (4t + 1)dt; \quad dy = (4t - 2)dt; \quad dz = (2t + 2)dt.$

$$(ds)^2 = [(4t + 1)^2 + (4t - 2)^2 + (2t + 2)^2](dt)^2 = (36t^2 + 9)(dt)^2.$$

$$L = \int_{0}^{t=\sqrt{3}/2} ds = 3\int_{0}^{\sqrt{3}/2} \sqrt{4t^2 + 1}\, dt = \frac{3}{2}\int_{0}^{\sqrt{3}/2} \sqrt{(2t)^2 + 1}(2\, dt) = 3.59.$$

For a regular curve (1), let $P{:}(x_0, y_0, z_0)$ and $Q{:}(x_0 + \Delta x, y_0 + \Delta y, z_0 + \Delta z)$ correspond to $t = t_0$ and $t = t_0 + \Delta t$, respectively, as in Figure 393 on page 599. Then, we shall prove that, at P, there is a tangent line PT with the direction

$$\left\{ \begin{array}{l} \text{tangent at } P, \\ \text{direction numbers} \end{array} \right\} \qquad \left(\frac{dx}{dt}\right)_P : \left(\frac{dy}{dt}\right)_P : \left(\frac{dz}{dt}\right)_P, \tag{7}$$

where the subscript P indicates evaluation at $t = t_0$, which gives P in (1).

Proof of (7). From (8) on page 420, PQ has the direction numbers $\Delta x : \Delta y : \Delta z$. With $\Delta t \neq 0$, we may divide by Δt and obtain

$$(\text{direction numbers for } PQ) \qquad \frac{\Delta x}{\Delta t} : \frac{\Delta y}{\Delta t} : \frac{\Delta z}{\Delta t}. \tag{8}$$

As $\Delta t \to 0$, the quotients in (8) have as limits the corresponding numbers in (7), where not all derivatives can be zero, because of (5). Hence, we may use (7) as direction numbers for a direction. Let PT in Figure 393 be the line through P with

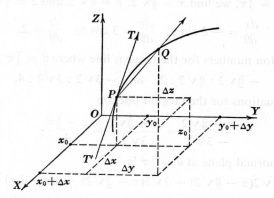

Fig. 393

direction numbers (7). As $\Delta t \to 0$, each direction number of PQ has, as a limit, the corresponding direction number of PT. Therefore, we infer that the direction cosines for either direction on PQ have as limits the corresponding direction cosines for a direction on PT, and thus the smallest nonnegative angle between PQ and PT approaches zero as $\Delta t \to 0$. Hence, we refer to PT as the *limiting position* of PQ as $\Delta t \to 0$ and call PT the **tangent line** to C at P.

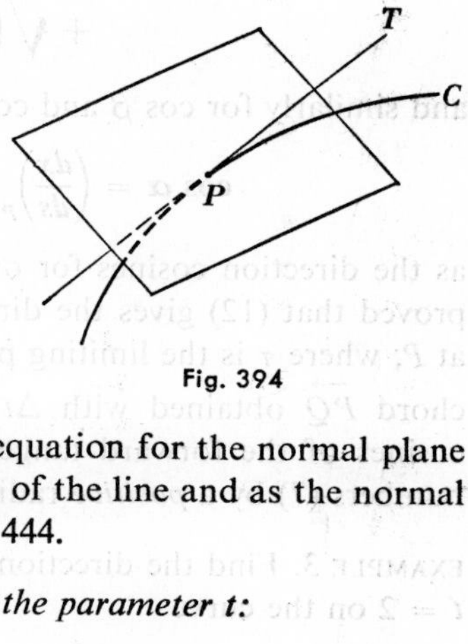

Definition I. *At any point P on a space curve, the plane perpendicular to the tangent line at P is called the* **normal plane** *for C at P.*

A normal plane for a curve is illustrated in Figure 394.

Fig. 394

To write equations for the tangent line and an equation for the normal plane for a regular curve (1) at P, use (7) as the direction of the line and as the normal direction for the plane. Also, recall pages 438 and 444.

Summary. *At* $P:(x_0, y_0, z_0)$ *on a regular curve, with the parameter t:*

1. *The tangent line has the equations*

$$\frac{x - x_0}{\left(\dfrac{dx}{dt}\right)_P} = \frac{y - y_0}{\left(\dfrac{dy}{dt}\right)_P} = \frac{z - z_0}{\left(\dfrac{dz}{dt}\right)_P}. \tag{9}$$

2. *The normal plane has the equation*

$$\left(\frac{dx}{dt}\right)_P (x - x_0) + \left(\frac{dy}{dt}\right)_P (y - y_0) + \left(\frac{dz}{dt}\right)_P (z - z_0) = 0. \tag{10}$$

EXAMPLE 2. Obtain the tangent line and normal plane where $\theta = \frac{1}{4}\pi$ on the helix

$$x = 3\cos\theta, \quad y = 3\sin\theta, \quad z = 2\theta.$$

Solution. With $\theta = \frac{1}{4}\pi$, we find $x = \frac{3}{2}\sqrt{2}$, $y = \frac{3}{2}\sqrt{2}$, and $z = \frac{1}{2}\pi$.

$$\frac{dx}{d\theta} = -3\sin\theta; \quad \frac{dy}{d\theta} = 3\cos\theta; \quad \frac{dz}{d\theta} = 2.$$

From (7), direction numbers for the tangent line where $\theta = \frac{1}{4}\pi$ are

$$-\tfrac{3}{2}\sqrt{2} : \tfrac{3}{2}\sqrt{2} : 2, \quad or \quad -3\sqrt{2} : 3\sqrt{2} : 4.$$

Then, by (9), equations for the tangent line are

$$\frac{x - \frac{3}{2}\sqrt{2}}{-3\sqrt{2}} = \frac{y - \frac{3}{2}\sqrt{2}}{3\sqrt{2}} = \frac{z - \frac{1}{2}\pi}{4}.$$

From (10), the normal plane at $\theta = \frac{1}{4}\pi$ is

$$-3\sqrt{2}(x - \tfrac{3}{2}\sqrt{2}) + 3\sqrt{2}(y - \tfrac{3}{2}\sqrt{2}) + 4(z - \tfrac{1}{2}\pi) = 0.$$

Let (α, β, γ) be the direction angles for a direction along the tangent line at P determined by (7). All derivatives will be evaluated at P. Then, from (7), and (5) on page 420, one value for $\cos\alpha$ is

$$\cos\alpha = \frac{\dfrac{dx}{dt}}{+\sqrt{\left(\dfrac{dx}{dt}\right)^2 + \left(\dfrac{dy}{dt}\right)^2 + \left(\dfrac{dz}{dt}\right)^2}} = \frac{\dfrac{dx}{dt}}{\dfrac{ds}{dt}} = \frac{dx}{ds}, \tag{11}$$

and similarly for $\cos\beta$ and $\cos\gamma$. Thus, we arrive at

$$\cos\alpha = \left(\frac{dx}{ds}\right)_P, \quad \cos\beta = \left(\frac{dy}{ds}\right)_P, \quad \cos\gamma = \left(\frac{dz}{ds}\right)_P, \tag{12}$$

as the direction cosines for one of the directions on the tangent line. It can be proved that (12) gives the direction cosines of the *forward tangent ray*, τ, to C at P, where τ is the limiting position as $\Delta t \to 0$ of the ray $K(\Delta t)$ on the forward chord $\overrightarrow{PQ}$ obtained with $\Delta t > 0$.* It can be remembered that the direction cosines of the forward tangent in (12) are obtained on dividing the direction numbers (7) by a *positive* radical.

EXAMPLE 3. Find the direction cosines of the forward tangent at the point where $t = 2$ on the curve

$$x = 3t - 2, \quad y = t^2 + t^3, \quad z = 4t - 3t^2. \tag{13}$$

Solution. From (13): $\dfrac{dx}{dt} = 3$, $\dfrac{dy}{dt} = 2t + 3t^2$, $\dfrac{dz}{dt} = 4 - 6t$. From (7) at $t = 2$, direction numbers for the tangent line are $3 : (4 + 12) : (4 - 12)$, or $3 : 16 : -8$. The cosines for the forward tangent are $\cos\alpha = 3/\sqrt{329}$, etc.

---

* The student who has studied Section 161 on page 429 may prove these facts about (12) in Problem 34 on page 613. The proof will parallel the corresponding proof relating to a plane curve in Section 161.

EXERCISE 181

Find the length of the curve between the specified points.

1. $x = 3t + 2$, $y = 1 - 2t$, $z = 4t + 3$; from $t = 1$ to $t = 5$.
2. $x = 3t + 1$, $y = 4t - 2$, $z = t^2 + 3$; from $t = 0$ to $t = 3$.
3. $x = t + 3$, $y = 3t^2 + 4$, $z = t - 2$; from $t = -1$ to $t = 2$.
4. The helix: $x = 3 \cos t$, $y = 3 \sin t$, $z = 4t$; from $t = 0$ to $t = 4\pi$.
5. $x = 2 \cos t$, $y = 2 \sin t$, $z = 3t$; from $t = 0$ to $t = 3$.
6. Find the length of the curve of intersection of the surfaces $z = x^2 + y^2$ and $y = x$ between $(0, 0, 0)$ and $(2, 2, 8)$. Use page 598 with x as the parameter in place of t.
7. Find the length of the curve of intersection of the surfaces $x + z = 6$ and $x^2 = 4y$ between $(0, 0, 6)$ and $(4, 4, 2)$.

Find equations for the tangent line and an equation for the normal plane for the curve. Also, find the direction cosines of the forward tangent at the point.

8. $x = 3t - 2$, $y = 2t^2 + t$, $z = 1 - 4t^3$; when $t = 2$.
9. $x = t^2 - t$, $y = t - t^{\frac{1}{2}}$, $z = 2t^2 - t$; when $t = 4$.
10. $x = 3t + t^2$, $y = 3t + 4t^3$, $z = 3t - t^2$; when $t = -1$.
11. $x = 3t + t^2$, $y = e^{2t}$, $z = 2e^{-t}$; when $t = 0$.
12. $x = \sin 2t$, $y = \cos 2t$; $z = \tan t$; when $t = \frac{1}{6}\pi$.
13. $x = t^2 - 2$, $y = 3t + 4$, $z = 3t^3 - t^2$; at the point $(-1, 7, 2)$.

14. A coil spring forms a cylindrical helix ($x = a \cos t$, $y = a \sin t$, $z = kt$), where the radius of the cylinder is $4''$. The coil makes 3 turns per inch along the coil's axis. The length of the axis is $10''$. Find the length of the spring.

15. Show that the following curves (A) and (B) intersect at right angles at $(3, 2, 1)$:
    (A) $x = 3 - 2t$, $y = 2e^t - 2 \sin t$, $z = e^{2t}$;
    (B) $x = 2\tau + 5$, $y = \tau^3 + \tau + 4$, $z = 2 - \tau^2$.

16. Find the cosine of the angle made by the normal to the plane $x + y + z = 0$ and the tangent to the curve ($x = -2t$, $y = -t^2$, $z = t^3$) at each point where the plane and curve intersect.

231. MOTION OF A PARTICLE IN SPACE

Note 1. For thorough appreciation of the discussion in this section, the student should have studied Supplementary Sections 160–162 in Chapter 17. If this was not done, (4) and (5) in the present section may be taken simply as *definitions* of the *velocity* and *acceleration*. Then, we may refer to * $(\dot{x}, \dot{y}, \dot{z})$ simply as the *time rates of change* of the coordinates, and as the *scalar components* of the *velocity* **V**. Also, $(\ddot{x}, \ddot{y}, \ddot{z})$ then are the scalar components of the *acceleration* **A**.

Let the position of a moving particle σ in space at any time t be specified by

$$x = f(t), \quad y = g(t), \quad and \quad z = h(t), \tag{1}$$

where (1) defines a regular curve C, with the positive direction for arc distance on

* We use $\dot{x}$ for $\dfrac{dx}{dt}$ and $\ddot{x}$ for $\dfrac{d^2x}{dt^2}$.

C as the direction in which t increases. Let $\mathbf{H}(t)$ be the vector from the origin to the position $P:(x, y, z)$ of σ given by (1). Then, by use of the position vector $\mathbf{H}(t)$ for σ, the path C of the motion is defined by

$$\mathbf{W} = \mathbf{H}(t), \text{ where}$$

$$\mathbf{W} = x\mathbf{i} + y\mathbf{j} + z\mathbf{k} \quad and \quad \mathbf{H}(t) = \mathbf{i}f(t) + \mathbf{j}g(t) + \mathbf{k}h(t). \tag{2}$$

We define the **velocity** (vector), $\mathbf{V}$, and **acceleration** (vector), $\mathbf{A}$, for σ at time t by

$$\mathbf{V} = \frac{d\mathbf{W}}{dt} \quad and \quad \mathbf{A} = \frac{d\mathbf{V}}{dt}. \tag{3}$$

The speed v of σ at time t is defined by $v = |\mathbf{V}|$. From (2) and (3),

$$\mathbf{V} = \dot{x}\mathbf{i} + \dot{y}\mathbf{j} + \dot{z}\mathbf{k} \quad and \quad \mathbf{A} = \ddot{x}\mathbf{i} + \ddot{y}\mathbf{j} + \ddot{z}\mathbf{k}; \tag{4}$$

$$v = |\mathbf{V}| = \sqrt{\dot{x}^2 + \dot{y}^2 + \dot{z}^2} = \frac{ds}{dt}. \tag{5}$$

From (4), since $\qquad \dfrac{dx}{dt} = \dfrac{dx}{ds}\dfrac{ds}{dt}, \quad \dfrac{dy}{dt} = \dfrac{dy}{ds}\dfrac{ds}{dt}, \text{ etc.,}$

$$\mathbf{V} = \frac{ds}{dt}\left(\mathbf{i}\frac{dx}{ds} + \mathbf{j}\frac{dy}{ds} + \mathbf{k}\frac{dz}{ds}\right), \quad or \quad \mathbf{V} = v\mathbf{U}(s), \tag{6}$$

where we verify from (6) on page 598 that $\mathbf{U}(s)$ is the **unit tangent vector** in the direction of the forward tangent at $P:(x, y, z)$ on C. Thus, the velocity $\mathbf{V}$ is directed along the *forward tangent,* or the instantaneous motion of the particle σ at P is in this direction, with speed ds/dt, or v. Then, from (6), the direction cosines of $\mathbf{V}$ are given by (12) on page 600. A study of the acceleration vector $\mathbf{A}$, such as was made for motion in a plane on page 433, introduces features of the differential geometry of a space curve which are beyond the scope of this text.

EXERCISE 182

The velocity $\mathbf{V}$ of a moving particle has the given scalar components at a certain instant. Find the speed, and the direction cosines of $\mathbf{V}$. Also, in a coordinate system, draw a vector from any convenient point to represent $\mathbf{V}$ to scale.

1. $\dot{x} = 3; \dot{y} = 6; \dot{z} = -2.$ 2. $\dot{x} = -6; \dot{y} = 2; \dot{z} = 9.$

The motion of a particle is determined by the equations, where t is the time. Find the speed, and the direction cosines of the velocity.

3. $x = 3t + 2, y = 2t + 4, z = -3t + 1$; when $t = 2.$
4. $x = e^{-t}, y = e^{-t}\cos t, z = 3t$; when $t = 0.$
5. $x = 3t^2 - 2, y = 3t + 5, z = t - t^3$; when $t = 3.$
6. $x = 2\sin 2t, y = 3\cos 2t, z = \sin t$; when $t = \frac{1}{4}\pi.$
7. $x = 2t\sin t, y = 2t\cos t, z = 4t$; when $t = 2\pi.$

8-9. Find the scalar components of the acceleration in the x-, y-, and z-directions in Problems 4 and 5, respectively.

10. A particle σ moves on the curve of intersection of the surfaces $x = 4y^2$ and $z = 2y^2$. The scalar component along the y-axis of the velocity is a constant, 2 units per second. When $y = 2$, find the speed of σ and the direction cosines of $\mathbf{V}$.

232. NORMAL LINE AND TANGENT PLANE TO A SURFACE

Assume that the function $F(x, y, z)$ is differentiable and

$$[F_x(x, y, z)]^2 + [F_y(x, y, z)]^2 + [F_z(x, y, z)]^2 \neq 0 \tag{1}$$

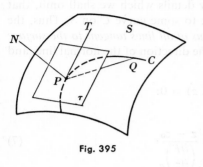

Fig. 395

in that part of the domain of F with which we shall be concerned. Let $P:(x_0, y_0, z_0)$ be any point on the surface S with the equation $F(x, y, z) = 0$. Let C be any regular curve * on S through P, as in Figure 395, where C has the parametric equations

$$x = f(t), \quad y = g(t), \quad and \quad z = h(t), \tag{2}$$

with $(x = x_0, y = y_0, z = z_0)$ at $t = t_0$. From (7) on page 598, the tangent line PT to C at P has the direction numbers

$$f'(t_0) : g'(t_0) : h'(t_0). \tag{3}$$

Definition II. *A line l is a tangent line to a surface S at a point P if and only if l is tangent at P to a curve C on S.*

In Figure 395, secant PQ of the surface S is drawn through P and Q on the curve C passing through P. Then, as $Q \to P$ along C, PQ tends to the limiting position PT, which is a tangent to S at P.

Theorem II. *All tangent lines at $P:(x_0, y_0, z_0)$ on a surface, S, with the equation $F(x, y, z) = 0$ are perpendicular to the direction*

$$F_x(x_0, y_0, z_0) : F_y(x_0, y_0, z_0) : F_z(x_0, y_0, z_0). \tag{4}$$

Proof. 1. Let PT be the tangent at P to a curve C on S, and let $u = F(x, y, z)$. Let C be defined by (2). Then, by use of (2) along C, u becomes a function of t and $u = 0$ at all values of t because C is on S. Hence, $du/dt = 0$. By the chain rule,

$$\frac{du}{dt} = F_x(x, y, z)\frac{dx}{dt} + F_y(x, y, z)\frac{dy}{dt} + F_z(x, y, z)\frac{dz}{dt} = 0. \tag{5}$$

2. In (5), place $t = t_0$. Then, $x = x_0, y = y_0, z = z_0,$

$$\frac{dx}{dt} = f'(t_0), \quad \frac{dy}{dt} = g'(t_0), \quad \frac{dz}{dt} = h'(t_0), \quad and$$

$$F_x(x_0, y_0, z_0)f'(t_0) + F_y(x_0, y_0, z_0)g'(t_0) + F_z(x_0, y_0, z_0)h'(t_0) = 0. \tag{6}$$

By (10) on page 420, equation (6) states that the tangent line PT, with direction numbers (3), is *perpendicular to the direction* (4).

Definition III. *The line PN, with the direction (4), which is perpendicular to all tangent lines for a surface S at P is called the* **normal line,** *and the direction (4) of PN is called the* **normal direction** *for S at P.*

* We omit proof that, under proper conditions at $P:(x_0, y_0, z_0)$, there exist families of curves (2) through P lying on S.

Definition IV. *The* **tangent plane** *for a surface $F(x, y, z) = 0$ at a point P is the plane τ through P perpendicular to the normal PN.*

From Theorem II, all tangent lines for the surface S at P lie in the tangent plane τ at P. Conversely, it can be shown, by details which we shall omit, that any line l through P in the plane τ is tangent to some curve C on S. Thus, the tangent plane at P may be described as *the locus of all lines tangent to the surface at P.* In the following summary, we use (4) as the direction of the normal line, and as the normal direction for the tangent plane.

Summary. *At $P:(x_0, y_0, z_0)$ on a surface $F(x, y, z) = 0$:*

1. *The normal line has the equations* *

$$\frac{x - x_0}{\left(\dfrac{\partial F}{\partial x}\right)_P} = \frac{y - y_0}{\left(\dfrac{\partial F}{\partial y}\right)_P} = \frac{z - z_0}{\left(\dfrac{\partial F}{\partial z}\right)_P}. \tag{7}$$

2. *The tangent plane has the equation*

$$\left(\frac{\partial F}{\partial x}\right)_P (x - x_0) + \left(\frac{\partial F}{\partial y}\right)_P (y - y_0) + \left(\frac{\partial F}{\partial z}\right)_P (z - z_0) = 0. \tag{8}$$

If a surface S has the equation $z = f(x, y)$, we may rewrite the equation in the standard form

$$F(x, y, z) = 0, \quad \text{where} \quad F(x, y, z) = f(x, y) - z.$$

Then $\dfrac{\partial F}{\partial x} = \dfrac{\partial f}{\partial x}, \dfrac{\partial F}{\partial y} = \dfrac{\partial f}{\partial y}, \dfrac{\partial F}{\partial z} = -1$, and the normal direction (4) becomes

$$f_x(x_0, y_0) : f_y(x_0, y_0) : -1. \tag{9}$$

Equations (7) and (8) can be written by use of (9) instead of (4).

EXAMPLE 1. Obtain equations for the normal line, and an equation for the tangent plane at $(2, -3, 5)$ on the surface

$$z = 4x^2 + y^2 - 20. \tag{10}$$

Solution. Write (10) in the standard form $F(x, y, z) = 0$, or

$$4x^2 + y^2 - 20 - z = 0, \quad \text{with} \quad F(x, y, z) = 4x^2 + y^2 - 20 - z.$$

Then $\dfrac{\partial F}{\partial x} = 8x, \dfrac{\partial F}{\partial y} = 2y,$ and $\dfrac{\partial F}{\partial z} = -1,$ and

$$F_x(2, -3, 5) = 16; \quad F_y(2, -3, 5) = -6; \quad F_z(2, -3, 5) = -1.$$

Hence, from (7) and (8),

the normal line is $$\frac{x - 2}{16} = \frac{y + 3}{-6} = \frac{z - 5}{-1};$$

the tangent plane is $$16(x - 2) - 6(y + 3) - (z - 5) = 0.$$

---

* We use the subscript P to indicate that the derivatives are evaluated at $(x = x_0, y = y_0, z = z_0)$. Usual qualifications are implied if any denominator in (7) is zero.

Suppose that the domain of a function $f(x, y)$ is an open region, R, of points in the xy-plane, where f is differentiable. In R, let C be a curve with the equation $f(x, y) = 0$, where $f_x^2(x, y) + f_y^2(x, y) \neq 0$ on C. We may think of C as the xy-trace of the cylinder S in xyz-space with the equation $f(x, y) = 0$, as in Figure 396.

Then, the tangent line PT to C at a point $P{:}(x_0, y_0, 0)$ is the xy-trace of the tangent plane τ for S at P, and τ is perpendicular to the xy-plane. The normal direction PN for the plane τ also is the direction of the normal to the curve C at P. Then, with $F_z(x, y, z) = 0$ and $z_0 = 0$ in (4), (7), and (8), we obtain the following results, where there is no need for us to mention a z-coordinate.

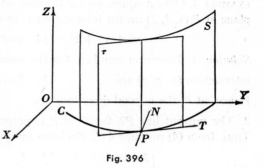

Fig. 396

Theorem III. At $P{:}(x_0, y_0)$ on a curve $f(x, y) = 0$ in the xy-plane, the normal has

the direction numbers $\qquad\qquad f_x(x_0, y_0) : f_y(x_0, y_0);$ \hfill (11)

the normal line is $\qquad\qquad \dfrac{x - x_0}{f_x(x_0, y_0)} = \dfrac{y - y_0}{f_y(x_0, y_0)};$ \hfill (12)

the tangent line is $\qquad f_x(x_0, y_0)(x - x_0) + f_y(x_0, y_0)(y - y_0) = 0.$ \hfill (13)

EXAMPLE 2. Obtain direction cosines for the normal, and equations for the tangent and the normal, at $P{:}(2, -3)$ on the curve in the xy-plane given by

$$x^2 + 4xy + 3y^2 - 6x + 5 = 0. \tag{14}$$

Solution. 1. With $f(x, y) = x^2 + 4xy + 3y^2 - 6x + 5$,

$$f_x(x, y) = 2x + 4y - 6; \quad f_y(x, y) = 4x + 6y. \tag{15}$$

At $P{:}(2, -3)$, from Theorem III, the normal has the direction numbers $-14 : -10$, or $7 : 5$. Hence, direction cosines for the normal are

$$\cos \alpha = \frac{7}{\sqrt{74}} \ \text{ and } \ \cos \beta = \frac{5}{\sqrt{74}}; \ \text{ or } \ \cos \alpha = -\frac{7}{\sqrt{74}} \ \text{ and } \ \cos \beta = -\frac{5}{\sqrt{74}}.$$

2. From (12), (13), and (15), we obtain

(the normal) $\qquad\qquad \dfrac{x - 2}{-14} = \dfrac{y + 3}{-10}, \ \text{ or } \ 5x - 7y = 31;$

(the tangent) $\qquad 7(x - 2) + 5(y + 3) = 0, \ \text{ or } \ 7x + 5y = -1.$

Suppose that the functions $F(x, y, z)$ and $G(x, y, z)$ are differentiable. Let C be the curve * defined as the intersection of the surfaces

$$F(x, y, z) = 0 \quad and \quad G(x, y, z) = 0. \tag{16}$$

At $P{:}(x_0, y_0, z_0)$ on C, the tangent line PT for C will lie in the tangent plane at

---

* We assume that hypotheses are satisfied which make C a regular curve.

P for each of the surfaces in (16). Hence, *PT* is *the intersection of the tangent planes.*
Direction numbers for *PT* can be found from the fact that *PT* is perpendicular
to the normals at *P* for the two surfaces. An exception arises *when the surfaces
have the same normal direction at P*, and hence, **by definition, are tangent at P.**

EXAMPLE 3. Obtain equations for the tangent line and an equation for the normal
plane at $P:(1, 3, 2)$ on the intersection C of the surfaces

$$x^2 + y^2 + z^2 = 14 \quad and \quad 4x^2 + y^2 = 13. \tag{17}$$

Solution. 1. Direction numbers for the normals of the surfaces at any point of

intersection (x, y, z) are $\qquad 2x : 2y : 2z \quad and \quad 8x : 2y : 0. \tag{18}$

Hence, at *P*, the normal directions are $\qquad 1 : 3 : 2 \quad and \quad 4 : 3 : 0. \tag{19}$

2. The tangent line *PT* for *C* at *P* is perpendicular to both directions in (19).
Thus, from (4) on page 442, direction numbers for *PT* are

$$\begin{vmatrix} 3 & 2 \\ 3 & 0 \end{vmatrix} : \begin{vmatrix} 2 & 1 \\ 0 & 4 \end{vmatrix} : \begin{vmatrix} 1 & 3 \\ 4 & 3 \end{vmatrix}, \quad or \quad -6 : 8 : -9,$$

and *PT* has the equations $\qquad \dfrac{x-1}{-6} = \dfrac{y-3}{8} = \dfrac{z-2}{-9}.$

The normal plane for *C* at *P* has the normal direction $-6 : 8 : -9$, and hence
the equation $-6(x-1) + 8(y-3) - 9(z-2) = 0.$

EXERCISE 183

Find equations for the normal line, and an equation for the tangent plane for the surface.

1. $x^2 + y^2 + z^2 = 121$, at $(2, -6, 9)$.   **2.** $3x^2 + y^2 + 4z^2 = 20$, at $(0, -2, 2)$.

3. $x^2 - 3y^2 + 4z^2 = 28$, at $(2, -2, 3)$.   **4.** $4y^2 - x^2 = 20$, at $(4, -3, 5)$.

5. $z = 4x^2 - y^2$, at $(2, -3, 7)$.   **6.** $z = x^2 - xy - y^2$, at $(3, 2, -1)$.

7. $xz^2 + xy^3 - y^2z = 19$, at $(2, -1, -3)$.

8. $x^{\frac{2}{3}} + y^{\frac{2}{3}} + z^{\frac{2}{3}} = 9$, at $(8, -8, 1)$.   **9.** $z = 3x/(2y - x)$, at $(2, 3, \frac{3}{2})$.

10. Prove that the normal to the sphere $x^2 + y^2 + z^2 = a^2$ at any point passes through
the center of the sphere.

*Obtain direction cosines for the normal at each given point on the curve in the xy-plane
having the given equation. Write equations for the tangent and normal at the point.*

11. $x^2 + 2xy - y^2 = -1$; at $(2, -1)$.

12. $4x^2 + 9y^2 - 36 = 0$; at $(0, 2)$ and at $(3, 0)$.

13. $2 \cos x \sin y - 4 \sin x \cos y = 3$; at $(\frac{1}{4}\pi, \frac{3}{4}\pi)$.

*Find equations for the tangent line and the normal plane at P on the intersection of the
surfaces having the given equations, or prove that the surfaces are tangent at P.*

14. $x^2 + y^2 + z^2 = 81$, $x^2 + z^2 = 17$; at $P:(4, 8, 1)$.

15. $2z = 1 + x^2 + y^2$, $z^2 = x^2 + y^2$; at $P:(0, 1, 1)$.

16. $x^2 + 3y^2 + 2z^2 = 49$, $y^2 - 2x^2 + z^2 = 10$; at $P:(-2, 3, -3)$.

17. $x^2 + 3z^2 - 4y = 25$, $3x - 2y + z = 13$; at $P:(3, -1, 2)$.

18. $z^2 = x^2 + y^2$, $y^2 = x^2 + z^2$; at $P:(0, 1, 1)$.

Obtain an equation for the tangent plane for the surface at the point (x_1, y_1, z_1), and simplify.

19. $2z = x^2 + 4y^2$. **20.** $\dfrac{x^2}{a^2} + \dfrac{y^2}{b^2} + \dfrac{z^2}{c^2} = 1$. **21.** $2az = \dfrac{x^2}{a^2} - \dfrac{y^2}{b^2}$.

Note 1. Two surfaces S and T are said to intersect orthogonally at P if the normals (or, tangent planes) of S and T at P are perpendicular. The angle of intersection, θ, of a curve C and a surface S at any point of intersection, P, is defined as the acute angle made by the tangent to C and the tangent plane of S, at P. Or, θ is the *complement* of the angle between the normal of S and the tangent to C, at P.

Determine whether the surfaces intersect orthogonally, or are tangent.

22. $x^2 + z^2 = a^2$ and $y^2 + z^2 = a^2$, at $(a, a, 0)$.

23. $x^2 - 2y^2 + z^2 = 6$ and $4x - 2y^2 + z^2 = 10$, at $(2, 1, -2)$.

24. Find the sine of the angle of intersection at $(2, -1, 1)$ of the surface with the equation $x^2 + 4y^2 + z^2 = 9$ and the curve defined by
$$x = 2 - 3t, \quad y = -1 + 4t, \quad and \quad z = 1 - 2t.$$

25. Let $P:(x_0, y_0, z_0)$ be a point on the surface $z = f(x, y)$, where f is a differentiable function. Then, at $(x = x_0, y = y_0)$, with arbitrary increments $dx = \Delta x$ and $dy = \Delta y$, we have $dz = f_x(x_0, y_0)\Delta x + f_y(x_0, y_0)\Delta y$. Prove that dz is equal to the increment of the value of z on the tangent plane to the surface at P corresponding to a change from $(x = x_0, y = y_0)$ to $(x = x_0 + \Delta x, y = y_0 + \Delta y)$.

233. A RELATION BETWEEN AREAS ON TWO INTERSECTING PLANES

Let L_1 be a first plane BCE, visualized as horizontal, and L_2 be a second plane ACE intersecting L_1, to form a dihedral angle whose measure is an acute angle θ. In Figure 397, AC and BC are perpendicular to CE, so that $\angle BCA = \theta$; CN_1 and CN_2 are normals to L_1 and L_2, so that also $\angle N_1CN_2 = \theta$. Let T_2 be a rectangle

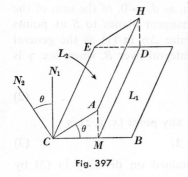

Fig. 397

with area K_2 in L_2, where one side is parallel to CE, and let T_1 with area K_1 be the vertical projection of T_2 on L_1. To obtain a relation between K_1 and K_2, we may think of moving T_2 in L_2 to a position where one side of T_2 is on CE so that T_2 is $ACEH$ and T_1 is $MCED$ in Figure 397. From right triangle MCA, where $\angle MCA = \theta$, we have $|\overline{CM}| = |\overline{CA}| \cos \theta$. Hence,

$$K_1 = |\overline{CM}| \cdot |\overline{CE}| = |\overline{CA}| \cdot |\overline{CE}| \cos \theta, \text{ or}$$

$$K_1 = K_2 \cos \theta. \tag{1}$$

Now, let R_2 be any region in L_2, with area A_2, and let R_1, with area A_1, be the perpendicular projection of R_2 on L_1. Then, by Definition II on page 483, A_2 can be expressed as the limit of a sum of areas of rectangles, which we may take of type T_2 as met above. Also, we may express A_1 as the limit of the sum of the areas of the corresponding rectangles T_1. Since (1) holds for each pair, T_1 and T_2, a similar relation holds for A_1 and A_2, or

$$A_1 = A_2 \cos \theta. \tag{2}$$

234. AREA OF A GENERAL SURFACE

We propose defining the notion of *area* for a surface S in an xyz-system of rectangular coordinates, where S is the locus of an equation $z = f(x, y)$ corresponding to points (x, y) in a region R of the xy-plane. We assume that f_x and f_y are continuous in R.

Let σ be any partition of R into subregions $\{T\}$, where the representative region T has the area ΔA, as in Figure 398. Construct a cylinder formed by moving a vertical line through all boundary points of T; this cylinder cuts out a piece T' of S. Now, choose arbitrarily a point $C:(x', y', 0)$ in T, and erect a vertical line at C to meet S at $Q:(x', y', z')$, where $z' = f(x', y')$. At Q, construct the tangent plane ϕ for S. The cylinder with T as a base cuts a plane region T'' from ϕ. Let $\Delta\eta$ be the area of T''; we visualize T'' as a desirable approximation to T', which is on S. Let γ be the angle, with $0 \leqq \gamma < \tfrac{1}{2}\pi$, between the normal QN to S and a vertical line at Q. Then, γ also is the measure of an angle between the xy-plane and the tangent plane ϕ. We observe that T'' projects into T on the xy-plane. Hence, by (2) on page 607, $\Delta\eta \cos \gamma = \Delta A$. Or, on dividing by $\cos \gamma$, we obtain

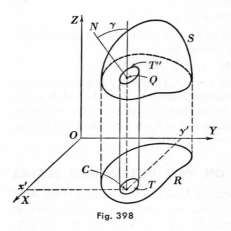

Fig. 398

$$\Delta\eta = \sec \gamma \, \Delta A. \tag{1}$$

Let d_σ be the maximum of the diameters of all subregions $\{T\}$ of the partition σ. Then, we *define* the area, η, of S to be the limit, as $d_\sigma \to 0$, of the sum of the areas $\{\Delta\eta\}$ of all regions * $\{T''\}$ cut from the tangent planes to S at points corresponding to the subregions $\{T\}$. We recognize $\Delta\eta$ in (1) as the general element of an approximating sum for a double integral over R, where $\sec \gamma$ is known as a function of x and y. Hence, from (1),

$$\eta = \iint_R \sec \gamma \, dA. \tag{2}$$

From (9), page 604, the normal direction for S at any point (x, y, z) is

$$f_x(x, y) : f_y(x, y) : -1. \tag{3}$$

Direction cosines for the normal then are obtained on dividing in (3) by $\pm \sqrt{1 + f_x^2(x, y) + f_y^2(x, y)}$. Since $0 \leqq \gamma < \tfrac{1}{2}\pi$, we must have $\cos \gamma > 0$. Hence, to obtain $\cos \gamma$, we divide in (3) by the negative of the radical:

$$\cos \gamma = \frac{1}{\sqrt{1 + f_x^2(x, y) + f_y^2(x, y)}}; \quad \sec \gamma = \sqrt{1 + f_x^2(x, y) + f_y^2(x, y)}. \tag{4}$$

---

* It would seem more natural to take areas of elementary quadrilaterals or triangles inscribed in S. For a proof that such a definition would lead to *unnatural* results, see Problem 36 on page 614.

From (2) and (4), with $\frac{\partial z}{\partial x} = f_x(x, y)$ and $\frac{\partial z}{\partial y} = f_y(x, y)$,

$$\eta = \iint_R \sqrt{1 + \left(\frac{\partial z}{\partial x}\right)^2 + \left(\frac{\partial z}{\partial y}\right)^2}\, dA. \tag{5}$$

In obtaining (5), S was projected orthogonally (perpendicularly) on the xy-plane to obtain R. Similarly, if it is desirable to project S into a region R on the xz-plane, or on the yz-plane, we obtain, respectively,

$$\eta = \iint_R \sec \beta\, dA = \iint_R \sqrt{1 + \left(\frac{\partial y}{\partial x}\right)^2 + \left(\frac{\partial y}{\partial z}\right)^2}\, dA, \text{ and} \tag{6}$$

$$\eta = \iint_R \sec \alpha\, dA = \iint_R \sqrt{1 + \left(\frac{\partial x}{\partial y}\right)^2 + \left(\frac{\partial x}{\partial z}\right)^2}\, dA. \tag{7}$$

In (6), R is a region in the xz-plane, and the integrand should be expressed in terms of x and z alone. In (7), R is a region in the yz-plane.

If the surface S is defined by $F(x, y, z) = 0$, then (2) may be more desirable than (5). Direction numbers for the normal to S now are

$$F_x(x, y, z) : F_y(x, y, z) : F_z(x, y, z), \tag{8}$$

and hence we obtain

$$\cos \gamma = \frac{\pm F_z(x, y, z)}{\sqrt{F_x^2(x, y, z) + F_y^2(x, y, z) + F_z^2(x, y, z)}},$$

with $\pm$ chosen to make $\cos \gamma > 0$.

EXAMPLE 1. Find the area of that part of the sphere $x^2 + y^2 + z^2 = a^2$ which is cut out by the cylinder $x^2 + y^2 = ax$, where $a > 0$.

Solution. 1. The desired area η is four times the area of that part, S, of the sphere cut out by the cylinder in the first octant, as in Figure 399. S projects into the region R in the xy-plane bounded by the x-axis and $x^2 + y^2 = ax$.

2. From (8), direction numbers for the normal to the sphere at $P:(x, y, z)$ are $2x : 2y : 2z$. Hence, with $z > 0$ and $\sec \gamma > 0$

$$\sec \gamma = \frac{\sqrt{x^2 + y^2 + z^2}}{z} = \frac{a}{\sqrt{a^2 - x^2 - y^2}}.$$

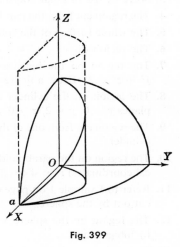

Fig. 399

Then, from (2),

$$\eta = 4a \int_0^a \int_0^{\sqrt{ax - x^2}} \frac{dy\, dx}{\sqrt{a^2 - x^2 - y^2}} = 4a \int_0^a \text{Arcsin} \sqrt{\frac{x}{a + x}}\, dx = 2a^2(\pi - 2).$$

In the calculation, we used integration by parts and substituted $u = \sqrt{x}$. Simpler details arise if cylindrical coordinates are used.

EXAMPLE 2. Obtain the area of that part, S, of the paraboloid $z = 4 - x^2 - y^2$ which is above the xy-plane.

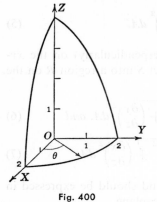

Fig. 400

Solution. 1. In Figure 400, S projects into the region R bounded by the circle $x^2 + y^2 = 4$ in the xy-plane. From (5),

$$\eta = \iint_R \sqrt{1 + 4x^2 + 4y^2} \, dA. \qquad (9)$$

2. We compute (9) by use of polar coordinates, because of the presence of $(x^2 + y^2)$. Then, with $x^2 + y^2 = r^2$, and $r \, dr \, d\theta$ as the element of area,

$$\eta = \int_0^{2\pi} \int_0^2 r\sqrt{1 + 4r^2} \, dr \, d\theta$$

$$= 2\pi(\tfrac{1}{12})(1 + 4r^2)^{\frac{3}{2}} \Big]_0^2 = \tfrac{1}{6}\pi(17\sqrt{17} - 1).$$

EXERCISE 184

Find the area of the specified region on the given surface. Use any method of integration, except where otherwise specified.

1. The region on the plane $3x - 2y + 3z = 6$ above the rectangular region on the xy-plane bounded by the lines $x = 0$, $x = 3$, $y = 0$, and $y = 2$.

2. The region on the cone $z^2 = 4x^2 + 4y^2$ above the rectangular region of Problem 1.

3. Solve by use of polar coordinates in Example 1 on page 609.

4. The region cut from the paraboloid $z = 4a^2 - x^2 - y^2$ by the cylinder $x^2 + y^2 = a^2$.

5. The whole surface of the sphere $x^2 + y^2 + z^2 = a^2$.

6. The region on $x^2 + y^2 = 4$ included between the xy-plane and the plane $z = 3y$.

7. The region on the hyperbolic paraboloid $x = y^2 - z^2$ cut out by the cylinder $y^2 + z^2 = 2$. (Draw a figure with the x-axis vertical.)

8. The region on the cylinder $x^2 + y^2 = 16$ cut out by the column bounded by the planes $y = 0$, $y = 2$, $z = 0$, and $z = 2$.

9. The region cut from one of the cylinders $x^2 + y^2 = a^2$ and $x^2 + z^2 = a^2$ by the other cylinder.

10. The region on the paraboloid $4z = 4 - x^2 - y^2$ cut out by the cylinder (in cylindrical coordinates) $r^2 = 4 \cos 2\theta$.

11. Refer to Example 1 on page 609. Find the area of that part of the cylinder which is cut out by the sphere.

12. The region on the sphere $x^2 + y^2 + z^2 = 2ay$ cut out by the cone $y^2 = x^2 + z^2$, by integration.

13. The region on the paraboloid $x^2 + z^2 = 8y$ cut out by the cylinder $x^2 = 2y$ and the plane $y = 6$.

14. In Problem 13, the region on the cylinder cut out by the paraboloid and the plane $y = 6$.

15. Find the curved surface area of a cylinder of radius a and altitude h by use of a double integral.

★235. LINE AND SURFACE INTEGRALS *

In space, let C be a regular curve $x = f(t),\ y = g(t),\ and\ z = h(t),$ (1)

where the domain for t is an interval $I = \{a \leqq t \leqq b\}$. Assume that the function $K(x, y, z)$ is continuous in an open set of points R including C. Then, to define *the line integral* of K on C, in symbols, $\int_C K(x, y, z)ds$, we commence by forming a partition σ of the interval I, as on page 177, with the typical subinterval τ_i of length $\Delta_i t$, and $\Delta_i s$ as the arc length of the corresponding piece ω_i of C. Let $P:(x_i, y_i, z_i)$ be an arbitrarily chosen point on ω_i. Then, we define

$$\int_C K(x, y, z)ds = \lim_{\text{all } \Delta_i t \to 0} \sum K(x_i, y_i, z_i)\ \Delta_i s. \tag{2}$$

With $s = w(t)$ from page 598, and $\Delta s_i = w'(\eta_i)\Delta_i t$ where η_i is on τ_i, reasoning like that on page 393 leads to the result

$$\int_C K(x, y, z)ds = \int_a^b K(f(t), g(t), h(t))\frac{ds}{dt}\ dt. \tag{3}$$

Similarly, we introduce integrals $\int_C K(x, y, z)dx$, $\int_C K(x, y, z)dy$, and $\int_C K(x, y, z)dz$, whose definitions would be obtained from (2) on replacing $\Delta_i s$ on the right by $\Delta_i x$, $\Delta_i y$, and $\Delta_i z$, respectively. For these integrals, in place of ds/dt in (3), we would have dx/dt or $f'(t)$, etc. To compute a line integral of any one of the preceding types on C, it is essential first to establish a parametric form for C.

By typical increment reasoning, the student may verify the results of the following Illustrations 1 and 2 dealing with a mass m spread over a curve C, as in (1), with the density $\delta(t)$ at any point. To evaluate any integral, it would be necessary to express its integrand as a function of a suitable parameter, indicated as t in (1), which might be x, y, z, or s.

ILLUSTRATION 1. The total mass of C is $\int_C \delta(t)ds$.

ILLUSTRATION 2. Suppose that a mass of magnitude μ is at a point Q, not on C, and **F** is the force with which the mass of C attracts μ. Let **U** be a unit vector with an arbitrary direction. Then, with k as a physical constant of proportionality, and θ and ρ having the meanings met on page 540,

$$(\text{sc. comp}_\mathbf{U}\ \mathbf{F}) = \int_C \frac{k\mu\ \delta(t)\cos\theta(x, y, z)ds}{[\rho(x, y, z)]^2}. \tag{4}$$

Let a surface S be defined by $z = f(x, y)$, where f is a differentiable function. Assume that the function $K(x, y, z)$ is defined and continuous in an open region including S. Then, with $\Delta\eta = (\sec\gamma)\Delta A$ as on page 608, and a basic increment of type $K(x, y, z)\Delta\eta$, where $P:(x, y, z)$ is on S, we are led to consider the surface integral of $K(x, y, z)$ over S, in symbols, $\iint_S K(x, y, z)d\eta$. Intuitional reasoning leads to the following result:

$$\iint_S K(x, y, z)d\eta = \iint_R K(x, y, z)\sec\gamma\ dA, \tag{5}$$

where R is a region in the xy-plane as on page 608. Other forms such as (5), (6), and (7) on page 608 can be written in place of (5) above.

* Related problems will occur in the supplement for the chapter.

EXERCISE 185 (*Review of Chapters Twenty-five and Twenty-six*)

Assume that any desired derivative exists and is continuous.

Find du/dt without eliminating x, y, or z.

1. $u = \ln(x - 5y + 3z)$, when $x = 3t^3$, $y = e^{-2t}$, and $z = \sec t$.

2. $u = \text{Arctan } xyz$, when $x = \sin 2t$, $y = \tan 2t$, and $z = \sec t$.

Find the total derivative of u with respect to x without eliminating y or z.

3. $u = x^2 - 4xy^3$, when $y = x \ln x - e^x$.

4. $u = x^2 + xz - yz$, when $y = \sin x$ and $z = e^{-3x}$.

Solve by use of the chain rule.

5. Find $\dfrac{\partial u}{\partial s}$ and $\dfrac{\partial u}{\partial t}$ if $u = \text{Arcsin}(2x + y)$, where $x = t^2 \ln s$ and $y = se^t$.

6. If $z = \cos uvw$, $u = s + e^t$, $v = \ln t + e^s$, and $w = e^s + e^{2t}$, find $\dfrac{\partial z}{\partial t}$.

7. If $z = \dfrac{\sin x}{1 + \cos y}$, $x = e^t + \tan t$, and $y = 5t^2$, find dz/dt.

8. If u and t are functions of x and y, and $g(u, v) = h(x, y, v, t)$, where g and h are differentiable functions, obtain expressions for $\left(\dfrac{\partial v}{\partial x}\right)_y$ and $\left(\dfrac{\partial v}{\partial y}\right)_x$.

Find an xy-equation for the envelope of the family of curves in the xy-plane, where t is a parameter.

9. $x^2 = t^2(y - t)$. **10.** $3x \sin t + 2y \cos t = 3$.

11. For the curve $y^2 + 4y = 2x$, obtain an equation for the tangent at an arbitrary point (x_1, y_1). Then, from this equation, find the envelope of the family of tangents.

12. Find equations for the tangent line and an equation for the normal plane at $t = \frac{1}{4}\pi$ for the curve defined parametrically by $x = 2 \cos t$, $y = 2 \sin t$, and $z = 4t$. Also, find the direction cosines of a direction on the tangent.

13. Find the length of the curve $(x = 4 \cos^2 t, y = 4 \sin^2 t, z = 2 \cos 2t)$ between the points where $t = 0$ and $t = \frac{1}{2}\pi$.

14. By obtaining the envelope of the family of normals, find an xy-equation, or parametric equations for the evolute of the curve $3y - x^2 = 12$.

15. Find equations for the normal line, and an equation for the tangent plane to the surface $z = \sin xy + \tan(x + 2y)$ at the point $(0, \frac{1}{8}\pi, 1)$.

16. Obtain and simplify an equation for the tangent plane at point (x, y, z) on the surface $x^2 + y^2 + z^2 = a^2$.

17. Determine whether the surfaces intersect orthogonally or are tangent:
$$4x^2 + 9y^2 + 2z^2 = 33 \quad and \quad 4x^2 - 8y^2 + z^2 = 12, \quad at \quad (2, -1, 2).$$

Find the area of the specified region on the surface.

18. The region on the plane $2x + 2y + 3z = 6$ cut out by the cylinder $x^2 + y^2 = 4$.

19. The region cut from the sphere $x^2 + y^2 + z^2 = 8a^2$ by the cone $x^2 + y^2 = z^2$.

20. The region on the cylinder $z^2 = y$ cut out by the cylinder $x^2 = 3y$ and the plane $y = \frac{15}{4}$.

21–22. Solve Problems 19–20, respectively, on page 474 by use of (2) on page 589.

★SUPPLEMENT FOR CHAPTER TWENTY–SIX

23. Find the envelope of the family of ellipses $b^2x^2 + a^2y^2 = a^2b^2$ where the sum of the semi-axes is equal to a constant, k.

24. Find the envelope of the family of circles through the origin which have their centers on $y^2 - x^2 = k^2$, where k is a constant. Finally, show that the envelope is a lemniscate.

25. Prove that the "*conical helix*" with the parametric equations

$$x = 2t \sin t, \quad y = 2t \cos t, \quad and \quad z = 3t$$

lies on a cone. Find the arc length from $(0, 0, 0)$ to the point where $t = \sqrt{3}$.

26. A particle moves downward on the curve with the equations

$$4 - z = y^2 - x^2 \quad and \quad x + z = 2.$$

The speed in the z-direction is 3 units per second. Find the scalar components of the velocity of the particle, its speed, and the direction cosines of the direction of the motion when $(x = 1, y = 2, z = 1)$.

27. By integration, find the area of the curved surface of a right circular cone of one nappe with altitude h and base-radius a.

28. Mass is spread on the curve C defined by

$$x = \tfrac{3}{2}\sqrt{2} \cos t, \quad y = 3 \sin t, \quad and \quad z = \tfrac{3}{2}\sqrt{2} \cos t,$$

where $(0 \leq t \leq 2\pi)$, with the density at any point P proportional to the undirected distance of P from the xy-plane. (a) Prove that C is a plane curve. (b) Find the mass on C. (c) Find the scalar components in the directions of $\mathbf{i}, \mathbf{j}$, and $\mathbf{k}$ of the attraction which the mass of C exerts on a mass μ at $(0, 3, 0)$. (d) Find the *average with respect to arc length*, or *mean value* with respect to s, of the distance of the points of C from P:$(0, 3, 0)$. [Compare with (36) on page 405.]

29. Compute the following integrals along the arc C of the parabola $[y = z^2, x = 2]$, from $(2, 4, -2)$ to $(2, 1, 1)$:

$$\int_C (y^2 + xyz)dy; \quad \int_C (z^2 - xy - z)dz.$$

30. Compute $\int_C \dfrac{x^2y^2ds}{(x^2 + y^2)^2}$, where C is the circle $x^2 + y^2 = 4$ in the xy-plane traced in (a) the clockwise direction; (b) the counterclockwise direction.

31. Compute $\int_C (xy + xz + yz)ds$, where C is the curve consisting of the quadrant of the circle $[x^2 + z^2 = 1, y = 0]$ from $(0, 0, 1)$ to $(1, 0, 0)$, the quadrant of the circle $[x^2 + y^2 = 1, z = 0]$ from $(1, 0, 0)$ to $(0, 1, 0)$, and the straight line segment from $(0, 1, 0)$ to $(0, 0, 1)$.

32. Mass is spread uniformly over the surface of a hemisphere with radius h. (a) Find the moment of inertia of this mass with respect to a diameter of the base of the hemisphere. (b) Find the magnitude of the attraction exerted by this mass on a mass of magnitude μ at the center of the sphere. (c) Find the attraction of the mass of the hemispherical lamina on a mass μ at the point where the axis of symmetry of the hemisphere would meet the sphere if it were extended.

33. Mass is spread uniformly over the surface, S, of the paraboloid $2z = 2 - x^2 - y^2$ which is above the xy-plane. Find the centroid of S.

34. Prove the facts about the forward tangent stated in the footnote on page 600.

Note 1. To appreciate why we use the somewhat unnatural definition of surface area on page 608, other definitions should be investigated. This is the objective of Problems 35 and 36 where a second definition for surface area is involved. The surface to be considered is a right circular cylinder of altitude w and base-radius a, to be referred to as a *solid* with two circular bases. If its curved surface is cut along a ruling and is spread out, the surface becomes a rectangle with area $2\pi aw$. Hence, a general definition of surface area is *not desirable* if, when applied to the cylinder, the definition *does not yield* $2\pi aw$. This result was obtained in Problem 15 on page 610 by the definition in Section 234, but will *not* be obtained with a new definition in the following Problem 36.

35. Let a cylinder of altitude h and base-radius a be placed with one base in the xy-plane and with the equation $x^2 + y^2 = a^2$ for the curved surface. For any assigned positive integer n, divide the circumferences of the lower and upper bases into n equal arcs by the points with cylindrical coordinates $\left\{ a, \dfrac{2\pi k}{n}, 0 \right\}$ on the lower base and $\left\{ a, \dfrac{(2k + 1)\pi}{n}, h \right\}$ on the upper base, for $k = 0, 1, 2, \cdots, (n - 1)$. Join each of these points to its two neighbors on the circumference involved, and to each of the two nearest division points on the opposite circumference. Prove that the sum of the area of the $2n$ triangles thus inscribed in the curved surface is

$$2an \sin (\pi/n)\sqrt{h^2 + a^2[1 - \cos (\pi/n)]^2}.$$

36. Let w be the altitude and a be the base radius of a right circular cylinder. For any assigned positive integers m and n, cut the cylinder into m cylinders each of altitude w/m, and proceed with each of these cylinders as in Problem 35, alternating the choice $2\pi k/n$ and $(2k + 1)\pi/n$ from base to base, for any assigned positive integer n. Thus, for any m and n, we have $2mn$ isosceles triangles inscribed in the surface of the cylinder. Let $T_{m,n}$ be the sum of the areas of these triangles. Show that

$$T_{m,n} = 2an \sin (\pi/n)\sqrt{w^2 + a^2m^2 [1 - \cos (\pi/n)]^2}; \quad \lim_{m \to \infty} T_{m,n} = \infty;$$

$$\lim_{n \to \infty} T_{m,n} = 2\pi aw; \quad \lim_{n \to \infty} T_{n^2,n} = 2\pi a\sqrt{w^2 + a^2(\pi^4/4)}.$$

Note 2. Thus, there does *not* exist a limit for $T_{m,n}$ as the number, mn, of inscribed triangles becomes infinite without restriction. Hence, a seemingly sensible definition of surface area as the limit of the sum of the areas of elementary inscribed polygons (*triangles* in our case) is not desirable. The example considered in Problem 36 is due to H. A. Schwarz, published in the *Gesammelte Mathematische Abhandlungen*, Volume 2, page 390, 1890.

CHAPTER TWENTY–SEVEN

Applications of Partial Derivatives

236. LEVEL CURVES AND LEVEL SURFACES

Consider a function $f(x, y)$ whose domain is some region R in the xy-plane. If u_0 is a number on the range of f, the locus of points (x, y) where $u_0 = f(x, y)$ is called a **level curve** for f. Through any point (x_0, y_0) where $f(x, y)$ is defined, there passes *just one level curve $u_0 = f(x, y)$, where $u_0 = f(x_0, y_0)$.* Thus, corresponding to the function f, there is a *family of level curves for f* with the equation $u = f(x, y)$, where we now look upon u as a variable parameter whose domain consists of all values of $f(x, y)$. A chart showing a collection of these level curves, as in Figure 401, gives impressions about how u varies when the point (x, y) moves in the xy-plane. Also, such a chart gives indications about the surface with the equation $u = f(x, y)$, in xyu-space, just as a contour map gives information about elevations on the earth. A level curve $u_0 = f(x, y)$ is *the vertical projection on the xy-plane of the curve of intersection of the surface $u = f(x, y)$ and the plane $u = u_0$.*

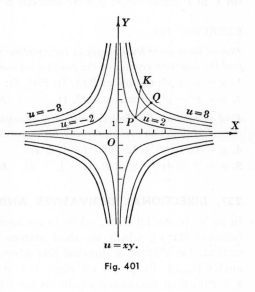

ILLUSTRATION 1. Suppose that $f(x, y) = xy$. Then, the level curves for f have the equation $u = xy$, where u is a parameter. If $u = 0$, we have $0 = xy$, whose graph consists of the coordinate axes. If $u_0 \neq 0$, the level curve $u_0 = xy$ is a hyperbola. Some level curves are shown in Figure 401. With $x = 2$ and $y = 3$, we obtain $u = 6$. Hence, the level curve $xy = 6$ passes through the point $(2, 3)$.

$$u = xy.$$

Fig. 401

Similarly, corresponding to a function $f(x, y, z)$, there exists a family of *level surfaces for f* in *xyz*-space. An equation for this family is $u = f(x, y, z)$, where the domain of the variable parameter u is the range of values of f.

ILLUSTRATION 2. For the function $f(x, y, z) = x^2 + y^2 + z^2$, the level surfaces are the spheres $u = x^2 + y^2 + z^2$ whose centers are at the origin.

ILLUSTRATION 3. In physics, the notion of a *potential function* $f(x, y, z)$ proves important in the investigation of forces (see Illustration 1 on page 621). Then, the level surfaces $u = f(x, y, z)$ are the associated *equipotential surfaces*.

Note 1. Suppose that u is a constant and consider the graph, C, of $u = f(x, y)$, or $f(x, y) - u = 0$, in an *xy*-plane. From page 605, recall that, at any point $P:(x, y)$ on C, the line PN normal to C has the direction numbers $f_x(x, y) : f_y(x, y)$. They determine one pair of direction angles (α_N, β_N) where

$$\cos \alpha_N = \frac{f_x(x, y)}{\sqrt{f_x^2(x, y) + f_y^2(x, y)}} \quad and \quad \cos \beta_N = \frac{f_y(x, y)}{\sqrt{f_x^2(x, y) + f_y^2(x, y)}}, \tag{1}$$

and a second direction (α, β) where $\cos \alpha = -\cos \alpha_N$ and $\cos \beta = -\cos \beta_N$. We shall call the direction (α_N, β_N), defined by (1), the **positive normal direction** for the graph of $f(x, y) = u$ at $P:(x, y)$. The direction opposite to (α_N, β_N) will be called the **negative normal direction**. Similar terminology will apply to a surface $u = f(x, y, z)$.

EXAMPLE 1. If $f(x, y) = 3x^2 - 2y - 5$, find an equation for the level curve, C, for f passing through $P:(2, -3)$. Also, find the direction cosines for the positive normal direction at P on C.

Solution. 1. Since $f(2, -3) = 13$, C has the equation $3x^2 - 2y - 5 = 13$.

2. Direction numbers for the normal to C at P are $f_x(2, -3) : f_y(2, -3)$, or $12 : -2$, or $6 : -1$. Hence, direction cosines for the positive normal direction for C at P are $\cos \alpha = \frac{6}{37}\sqrt{37}$ and $\cos \beta = -\frac{1}{37}\sqrt{37}$.

EXERCISE 186

Plot at least three level curves in the xy-plane for the function f, where $u = f(x, y)$. Also, find the direction cosines of the positive normal direction for the level curve for f at P.

1. $u = x^2 + y^2$; normal at $P:(4, 3)$; $P:(0, 5)$; $P:(5, -12)$.

2. $u = x^2 - y^2$; normal at $P:(2, 1)$.   **3.** $u = ye^x$; normal at $P:(0, 3)$.

Find an equation for the level surface S through P for the function f, where $u = f(x, y, z)$. Also, find direction cosines for a direction normal to S at P.

4. $u = 4x^2 - y^2 + 3z^2$; at $P:(-1, 2, 1)$.

5. $u = x^2 + 4y^2 - z$; at $P:(1, -\frac{1}{2}, -3)$.   **6.** $u = xyz$; at $P:(2, -3, 1)$.

237. DIRECTIONAL DERIVATIVES AND THE GRADIENT IN A PLANE

In an *xy*-plane, let $P:(x_0, y_0)$ be in an open set, R, of points in the domain of a function $f(x, y)$, which we shall assume to be differentiable throughout this section. Let PM be a directed line whose positive direction has the direction angles (α, β). From (1) on page 443, if $W:(x, y)$ is any point on PM, and $s = PW$, then parametric equations for PM are

$$x = x_0 + s \cos \alpha \quad and \quad y = y_0 + s \cos \beta. \tag{1}$$

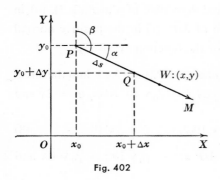

Fig. 402

If we use (1) in $u = f(x, y)$, then u is a function of s and the domain of u consists of the values of $f(x, y)$ along PM. Let $u_0 = f(x_0, y_0)$. If we move a distance Δs from P along PM to $Q:(x_0 + \Delta x, y_0 + \Delta y)$, as in Figure 402, then $\Delta s = \overline{PQ}$ and u_0 takes on an increment Δu, where

$$\Delta u = f(x_0 + \Delta x, y_0 + \Delta y) - f(x_0, y_0). \quad (2)$$

We notice that $\lim_{\Delta s \to 0} \Delta u / \Delta s = du/ds$, if the limit exists. In such a case, du/ds is given a name as follows.

Definition I. *If $u = f(x, y)$, the **directional derivative** of u, or $f(x, y)$, at $P:(x_0, y_0)$ in a direction* * *(α, β) is the rate of change of u with respect to distance, s, in the direction (α, β) at $s = 0$.*

We shall represent the derivative in Definition I by

$$D_{\alpha,\beta}\, u \mid_P \quad or \quad D_{\alpha,\beta}\, f(x, y) \mid_P, \quad or\ simply \quad \frac{du}{ds}\bigg|_P. \quad (3)$$

Then, $\qquad D_{\alpha,\beta}\, u \mid_P = \lim_{\Delta s \to 0} \frac{\Delta u}{\Delta s} = \lim_{\Delta s \to 0} \frac{f(x_0 + \Delta x, y_0 + \Delta y) - f(x_0, y_0)}{\Delta s}. \quad (4)$

If the direction (α, β) is the positive direction on the x-axis, Δs becomes Δx, the numerator in (4) becomes $f(x_0 + \Delta x, y_0) - f(x_0, y_0)$, and $D_{\alpha,\beta}\, u$ becomes $\dfrac{\partial u}{\partial x}$.

Similarly, the directional derivative in the positive y-direction is $\dfrac{\partial u}{\partial y}$. Thus, a directional derivative is a generalization of a partial derivative.

Theorem I. *At $P:(x_0, y_0)$, if $u = f(x, y)$ then*

$$D_{\alpha,\beta}\, u \mid_P = f_x(x_0, y_0) \cos \alpha + f_y(x_0, y_0) \cos \beta, \ or \quad (5)$$

$$D_{\alpha,\beta}\, u \mid_P = \frac{\partial u}{\partial x} \cos \alpha + \frac{\partial u}{\partial y} \cos \beta. \quad (6)$$

Proof. If $W:(x, y)$ is on PM, as in Figure 402, and (x, y) are given by (1), then $s = \overline{PW}$ and u, or $f(x, y)$, is a function of s. By use of the chain rule of page 584,

$$\frac{du}{ds} = \frac{df(x, y)}{ds} = \frac{\partial f(x, y)}{\partial x} \frac{dx}{ds} + \frac{\partial f(x, y)}{\partial y} \frac{dy}{ds}. \quad (7)$$

From (1), $dx/ds = \cos \alpha$ and $dy/ds = \cos \beta$. Hence, (4) and (7) give

$$D_{\alpha,\beta}\, u \bigg|_P = \frac{du}{ds}\bigg|_{(s=0)} = f_x(x_0, y_0) \cos \alpha + f_y(x_0, y_0) \cos \beta.$$

---

* Use of the two direction angles (α, β) and corresponding direction cosines makes the development in a plane parallel to that occurring later in space. Also, this avoids various details and possibly imperfect attempts at generality in proofs which occur if a single direction angle ϕ is used, and then its sine and cosine are met later in (5).

EXAMPLE 1. If $u = x^2 + y^2$, find the directional derivative of u at P:(2, 3), (a) in the direction of M:(5, 4); (b) in the direction of $\overrightarrow{MP}$; (c) in the positive normal direction $\overrightarrow{PN}$ for the level curve through P for the function $(x^2 + y^2)$.

Solution. 1. From (5), page 424, direction numbers for $\overrightarrow{PM}$ are 3 : 1, and the direction cosines for $\overrightarrow{PM}$ are $\cos \alpha = \frac{3}{10}\sqrt{10}$ and $\cos \beta = \frac{1}{10}\sqrt{10}$. Also, $u_x = 2x$ and $u_y = 2y$. Then, from (6)

$$D_{\alpha,\beta} u \mid_{(2, 3)} = \frac{3}{10}\sqrt{10}(2x) + \frac{1}{10}\sqrt{10}(2y) \mid_{(2, 3)} = \frac{9}{5}\sqrt{10}. \tag{8}$$

2. Since $\overrightarrow{MP} = -\overrightarrow{PM}$, direction cosines for $\overrightarrow{MP}$ are $-\frac{3}{10}\sqrt{10} : -\frac{1}{10}\sqrt{10}$, and

$$D_{\overrightarrow{MP}} u \mid_{(2, 3)} = -\frac{9}{5}\sqrt{10},$$

where the subscript $\overrightarrow{MP}$ illustrates another method for indicating the direction.

3. The level curve, C, through P is a circle, $u_0 = x^2 + y^2$, shown in Figure 403; we shall not need u_0. From Note 1 on page 616, direction numbers for the normal PN to C are $2x : 2y$, or $2 : 3$ at P:(2, 3). The direction cosines of the positive normal direction on PN are $\cos \alpha_N = \frac{2}{13}\sqrt{13}$ and $\cos \beta_N = \frac{3}{13}\sqrt{13}$, and

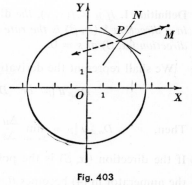

$$D_{\alpha_N,\beta_N} u \mid_{(2, 3)} = \frac{2(2x) + 3(2y)}{\sqrt{13}} \bigg|_{(2, 3)} = 2\sqrt{13}.$$

Fig. 403

Thus, $f(x, y)$ *increases* if (x, y) moves from (2, 3) in the direction (α_N, β_N).

Hereafter in this section, assume that

$$f_x^2(x, y) + f_y^2(x, y) \neq 0 \tag{9}$$

at each point P:(x, y) involved. Then, on using (cos α_N, cos β_N) from page 616 in (5), at any point P:(x, y) we obtain

$$D_{\alpha_N,\beta_N} u = \sqrt{f_x^2(x, y) + f_y^2(x, y)}. \tag{10}$$

Definition II. *The* **gradient** *of u, or of $f(x, y)$, at any point P:(x, y) is the* **vector** *having the direction angles (α_N, β_N) and the magnitude $D_{\alpha_N,\beta_N} u$.*

We write "**grad** u" for "*the gradient of u.*" In Example 1, we found that $|$ **grad** $u | = 2\sqrt{13}$.

Theorem II. *Let $u = f(x, y)$. Then, at P:(x, y),*

$$\textbf{grad } u = f_x(x, y)\textbf{i} + f_y(x, y)\textbf{j}. \tag{11}$$

Proof. Let the unit vector in the positive normal direction be **V**. Then,

$$\textbf{V} = \textbf{i} \cos \alpha_N + \textbf{j} \cos \beta_N.$$

Hence, by Definition II, (1) on page 616, and (10),

$$\textbf{grad } u = \sqrt{f_x^2(x, y) + f_y^2(x, y)} \ \textbf{V} = f_x(x, y)\textbf{i} + f_y(x, y)\textbf{j}.$$

Note 1. From page 420, recall that, if **V** and **W** are vectors,

$$\mathbf{V} \cdot \mathbf{W} = | \mathbf{V} | \cdot | \mathbf{W} | \cos \theta = | \mathbf{V} | \cdot (\text{sc. comp}_{\mathbf{V}} \mathbf{W}), \qquad (12)$$

where θ is the angle made by **V** and **W**. If $| \mathbf{V} | = 1$, then $(\text{sc. comp}_{\mathbf{V}} \mathbf{W}) = \mathbf{V} \cdot \mathbf{W}$.

Theorem III. *With $u = f(x, y)$, $D_{\alpha, \beta} u$ at $P:(x, y)$ is the scalar component of* **grad** u *in the direction (α, β). Or,*

$$D_{\alpha, \beta} u = | \text{grad } u | \cos \theta = \sqrt{f_x^2(x, y) + f_y^2(x, y)} \, \cos \theta, \qquad (13)$$

where θ is the angle made by the direction (α, β) with the positive normal direction (α_N, β_N) at P for the level curve of f through P.

Proof. Let $\mathbf{V} = \mathbf{i} \cos \alpha + \mathbf{j} \cos \beta$, the unit vector in the direction (α, β). Then, with **grad** u from (11), by use of Note 1 and (8) on page 424 we obtain

$$[\text{sc. comp}_{\mathbf{V}} (\text{grad } u)] = (\text{grad } u) \cdot \mathbf{V} = f_x(x, y) \cos \alpha + f_y(x, y) \cos \beta, \quad (14)$$

which is $D_{\alpha, \beta} u$ as in (5). Also, by use of (12) with $| \mathbf{V} | = 1$ and $\mathbf{W} = \text{grad } u$,

$$[\text{sc. comp}_{\mathbf{V}} (\text{grad } u)] = | \text{grad } u | \cos \theta,$$

where $| \text{grad } u | = \sqrt{f_x^2(x, y) + f_y^2(x, y)}$. Hence, (13) has been proved.

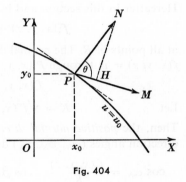

Fig. 404

ILLUSTRATION 1. In Figure 404, $\overrightarrow{PN}$ represents **grad** u for a case $u = f(x, y)$ at $P:(x_0, y_0)$, and the value of the directed line segment PH is $D_{\alpha, \beta} u$ at P in the direction of PM. Figure 404 shows the level curve for f through P.

Since $\cos \theta = 1$ at $\theta = 0$ and $\cos \theta = -1$ at $\theta = \pi$, from (13) we have justified the following statements.

I. *At $P:(x, y)$, the maximum of $D_{\alpha, \beta} u$, or $D_{\alpha, \beta} f(x, y)$, for all possible choices of (α, β) is $\sqrt{f_x^2(x, y) + f_y^2(x, y)}$, which is attained when $(\alpha = \alpha_N, \beta = \beta_N)$. The minimum $- \sqrt{f_x^2(x, y) + f_y^2(x, y)}$ of $D_{\alpha, \beta} u$ occurs when the direction (α, β) is the negative normal direction for C at P.*

II. **Grad** u *at $P:(x, y)$ can be defined as that vector whose magnitude is the maximum of $D_{\alpha, \beta} u$ at P, and whose direction is the positive normal direction (α_N, β_N).*

Note 2. The maximum property of the derivative in the normal direction corresponds to intuitions associated with a chart like Figure 401 on page 615. In that figure, a displacement Δs from P to Q along the normal causes a change $\Delta u = 8 - 2 = 6$, whereas a larger displacement Δs from P to K is necessary to cause the same change $\Delta u = 6$.

Note 3. If the domain of a function $f(x, y)$ is a region R, and $P:(x, y)$ is any point in R, let $u = f(x, y) = F(P)$. The number $F(P)$ is *independent of the coordinate system* used to describe $f(x, y)$. We refer to F as a **scalar point function**, whose domain is R. Sometimes, we say that F establishes a **scalar field** over R. Since F could be used in defining the level curve, C, for f through P, the positive normal direction, any directional derivative, and **grad** u at P, each of these is *independent of the coordinate system* used in R.

Note 4. Since $D_{\alpha_N,\beta_N} u = \sqrt{f_x^2(x, y) + f_y^2(x, y)}$, then $f(x, y)$ *increases* at a maximum rate if $P{:}(x, y)$ moves in the direction (α_N, β_N) from an initial position, and *decreases* at a maximum rate if P moves in the negative normal direction. These features account for naming the direction (α_N, β_N), and its opposite, the directions of **steepest ascent** and **steepest descent**, respectively, for $f(x, y)$.

238. DIRECTIONAL DERIVATIVES AND THE GRADIENT IN SPACE

Suppose that the domain of a function $f(x, y, z)$ is an open region R in xyz-space, and let $u = f(x, y, z)$. Then, in connection with u, or $f(x, y, z)$, space analogs exist corresponding to each main feature of the preceding section. In particular, with all derivatives calculated at $P{:}(x, y, z)$,

$$D_{\alpha,\beta,\gamma}\, u = \frac{\partial u}{\partial x}\cos\alpha + \frac{\partial u}{\partial y}\cos\beta + \frac{\partial u}{\partial z}\cos\gamma;\ or \tag{1}$$

$$D_{\alpha,\beta,\gamma}\, f(x, y, z) = f_x(x, y, z)\cos\alpha + f_y(x, y, z)\cos\beta + f_z(x, y, z)\cos\gamma. \tag{2}$$

Hereafter in this section and its applications, assume that

$$f_x^2(x, y, z) + f_y^2(x, y, z) + f_z^2(x, y, z) \neq 0 \tag{3}$$

at all points of R. The normal direction for the level surface, S, with the equation $f(x, y, z) = u$, through $P{:}(x, y, z)$ has the direction numbers

$$f_x(x, y, z) : f_y(x, y, z) : f_z(x, y, z).$$

Let
$$K = \sqrt{f_x^2(x, y, z) + f_y^2(x, y, z) + f_z^2(x, y, z)}. \tag{4}$$

Then, the *positive normal direction* for S at P is defined as the direction with direction angles $(\alpha_N, \beta_N, \gamma_N)$ determined by

$$\cos\alpha_N = \frac{f_x(x, y, z)}{K}, \quad \cos\beta_N = \frac{f_y(x, y, z)}{K}, \quad and \quad \cos\gamma_N = \frac{f_z(x, y, z)}{K}. \tag{5}$$

At $P{:}(x, y, z)$, we find that $D_{\alpha,\beta,\gamma} u$ attains its maximum, K, when the direction (α, β, γ) is the positive normal direction $(\alpha_N, \beta_N, \gamma_N)$, and attains its minimum, $-K$, in the opposite direction. We define **grad** $f(x, y, z)$ as the **vector** whose magnitude is the maximum of $D_{\alpha,\beta,\gamma} u$ at P, and direction is $(\alpha_N, \beta_N, \gamma_N)$. Then,

$$\textbf{grad } u = \textbf{grad } f(x, y, z) = f_x(x, y, z)\textbf{i} + f_y(x, y, z)\textbf{j} + f_z(x, y, z)\textbf{k}.$$

Also, for any (α, β, γ), at P we obtain

$$D_{\alpha,\beta,\gamma}\, u = |\, \textbf{grad } u\, |\cos\theta, \tag{6}$$

where θ is the angle made by the directions $(\alpha_N, \beta_N, \gamma_N)$ and (α, β, γ). In an exercise, the student may desire to prove the preceding facts.

ILLUSTRATION 1. Let a particle of mass μ be located at $P{:}(a, b, c)$ in xyz-space, and let a mass of magnitude 1 be at $Q{:}(x, y, z)$. Let **V** be the unit vector with the direction of $\overrightarrow{QP}$. Direction cosines for $\overrightarrow{QP}$ and **V** are

$$\left(\cos\alpha = \frac{a - x}{\rho}, \quad \cos\beta = \frac{b - y}{\rho}, \quad \cos\gamma = \frac{c - z}{\rho}\right), \tag{7}$$

where
$$\rho = \sqrt{(x - a)^2 + (y - b)^2 + (z - c)^2}, \tag{8}$$

and $V = i \cos \alpha + j \cos \beta + k \cos \gamma$. Newton's law of gravitational attraction states that μ attracts the unit mass at Q with a force F having the direction of $\overrightarrow{QP}$ and the magnitude $k\mu/\rho^2$, where k is a factor of proportionality depending on the physical units employed. Thus, $F = k\mu V/\rho^2$. Now, let $\phi(x, y, z) = k\mu/\rho$. Then, we find that

$$\mathbf{grad} \ \phi(x, y, z) = \frac{k}{\rho^2}\left(\frac{a-x}{\rho}\mathbf{i} + \frac{b-y}{\rho}\mathbf{j} + \frac{c-z}{\rho}\mathbf{k}\right) = \frac{k\mu}{\rho^2}\mathbf{V} = \mathbf{F}. \qquad (9)$$

On account of (9), the function ϕ is called the **Newtonian potential** of the mass μ at $P:(a, b, c)$. Any level surface S for ϕ has an equation $u = \phi(x, y, z)$, and is called an **equipotential surface**. At any point $Q:(x, y, z)$ on S, the force vector F is normal to S, by our previous results about gradients. The student may verify that any equipotential surface has an equation of the form $\rho = c$, a constant, and thus is a sphere with P as the center. The student should verify (9).

EXERCISE 187

Direction angles are indicated by (α, β) or (α, β, γ).

With $u = f(x, y)$, or $u = f(x, y, z)$, find the directional derivative of u at P in each specified direction. Draw a figure. The problem refers wholly to the xy-plane if z is not mentioned.

1. $f(x, y) = x^2 + y^2$, at $P:(4, 3)$ with $\alpha = 30°$ and $\beta = 60°$; with $\alpha = 150°$ and β acute; with $\beta = 135°$ and $\alpha > 90°$; in the positive direction of the x-axis, and then in its negative direction; in the direction from P to $M:(9, 15)$; in each direction along the normal to the level curve of f through P. Specify the maximum and minimum for $D_{\alpha,\beta} u \,|_P$, and $(\cos \alpha, \cos \beta)$ in each case.

2. Repeat Problem 1 for $u = x^2 - y^2$ at $P:(2, 1)$, with $M:(5, 5)$.

3. $f(x, y) = x^2 + 2xy - y^2$, at $P:(2, -3)$: in a direction (a) with the direction numbers $3 : -4$; (b) with $\alpha = 45°$ and $\beta > 90°$; (c) upward in the xy-plane along a line with inclination $120°$; (d) downward along that line; (e) toward $M:(7, 9)$.

4. Find the derivative of $(\ln y)(\sin x)$ at $(\frac{1}{6}\pi, e)$ in (a) a downward direction which makes an angle of $30°$ with the positive direction on the x-axis; (b) an upward direction along a line with inclination $135°$.

*Find **grad** u and the direction cosines of **grad** u at the given point.*

5. $u = 4x^2 + y^2$, at $(-2, 3)$.   6. $u = e^{xy}$, at $(-3, 2)$.

*Find the derivatives of u at P in the specified directions. Also, find **grad** u at P.*

7. $u = x^2 + y^2 + z^2$, at $P:(3, -1, 2)$: (a) in a direction having the direction numbers $4 : 4 : 7$; (b) in the direction of $M:(11, 3, 3)$; (c) in the positive normal direction at P for the level surface $u = x^2 + y^2 + z^2$ through P.

8. $u = x^2 - 2y + z$, at $P:(-2, 1, 3)$: (a) in the direction of $M:(4, 7, 10)$; (b) in the positive and negative normal directions at P for the level surface $u = x^2 - 2y + z$ through P.

9. $u = xyz$, at $(4, -2, 3)$: in the direction of $M:(10, 4, 10)$.

10. $u = x^2 - 4yz + z^2$, at $P:(1, -2, 3)$: (a) in the direction of $M:(3, 4, -6)$; (b) in those directions in which $D_{\alpha,\beta,\gamma} u$ has its maximum and minimum values.

★11. The surface $z = xy - y^2$ is cut by the plane $4x = 3y$ in a curve C. At $(3, 4, -4)$ on C, find the absolute value of the rate of change of z on C with respect to change in horizontal distance.

239. TAYLOR'S THEOREM FOR A FUNCTION OF TWO VARIABLES

Suppose that the domain of a function $f(x, y)$ includes the region R inside some circle in the xy-plane, and that f has continuous derivatives of all orders to be involved. If $P:(x_0, y_0)$ and $Q:(x_0 + h, y_0 + k)$ are two points in R, from (10) on page 444 we obtain the following parametric equations for the line PQ:

$$x = x_0 + ht \quad and \quad y = y_0 + kt. \tag{1}$$

With t on the interval $0 \le t \le 1$, the point P_1 obtained from (1) is on segment PQ, as in Figure 405, with P obtained at $t = 0$ and Q at $t = 1$; hence, P_1 is in R. We shall use (1) only with $0 \le t \le 1$. Now, define a function $G(t)$ with the domain $0 \le t \le 1$ by the equation $G(t) = f(x, y)$, with x and y given by (1). Then, the results of Chapter 24 concerning Taylor series and Taylor's formula for functions of a single variable can be extended to the function $f(x, y)$ by applying the previous results to $G(t)$ for a particular value of t.

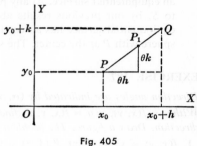

Fig. 405

With $G(t) = f(x, y)$, where $x = x_0 + ht$ and $y = y_0 + kt$, by use of the chain rule on page 584, with $dx/dt = h$ and $dy/dt = k$,

$$G'(t) = \frac{df(x, y)}{dt} = \frac{\partial f}{\partial x}\frac{dx}{dt} + \frac{\partial f}{\partial y}\frac{dy}{dt} = h\frac{\partial f}{\partial x} + k\frac{\partial f}{\partial y}; \; or \tag{2}$$

$$G'(t) = hf_x(x, y) + kf_y(x, y); \tag{3}$$

$$G''(t) = h\left(\frac{\partial f_x}{\partial x}\frac{dx}{dt} + \frac{\partial f_x}{\partial y}\frac{dy}{dt}\right) + k\left(\frac{\partial f_y}{\partial x}\frac{dx}{dt} + \frac{\partial f_y}{\partial y}\frac{dy}{dt}\right), \; or$$

$$G''(t) = h^2\frac{\partial^2 f}{\partial x^2} + 2hk\frac{\partial^2 f}{\partial x\partial y} + k^2\frac{\partial^2 f}{\partial y^2}. \tag{4}$$

By use of a *"differentiation operator,"* we may write (4) as follows:

$$G''(t) = \left(h\frac{\partial}{\partial x} + k\frac{\partial}{\partial y}\right)^2 f(x, y)\, \bigg|_{(x_0+ht,\, y_0+kt)}, \tag{5}$$

which we obtain by writing, first, as if *numbers* were involved,

$$\left(h\frac{\partial}{\partial x} + k\frac{\partial}{\partial y}\right)^2 = h^2\frac{\partial^2}{\partial x^2} + 2hk\frac{\partial^2}{\partial x\partial y} + k^2\frac{\partial^2}{\partial y^2}. \tag{6}$$

Then we *"operate"* on $f(x, y)$ with the right-hand side of (6) to obtain the right-hand side of (4). Finally, we indicate, by the subscript in (5), that the derivatives [as in (4)] are to have the arguments $(x = x_0 + ht, y = y_0 + kt)$. Similarly,

$$G^{(n)}(t) = \left(h\frac{\partial}{\partial x} + k\frac{\partial}{\partial y}\right)^n f(x, y)\, \bigg|_{(x_0+ht,\, y_0+kt)}, \tag{7}$$

where we read "*h times the partial derivative with respect to x, plus k times the partial derivative with respect to y, operating n times on $f(x, y)$.*"

ILLUSTRATION 1. To check (7) for $n = 3$, we use (4) and write

$$G'''(t) = \frac{\partial}{\partial x}[G''(t)]\frac{dx}{dt} + \frac{\partial}{\partial y}[G''(t)]\frac{dy}{dt} = h\left[h^2\frac{\partial^3 f}{\partial x^3} + 2hk\frac{\partial^3 f}{\partial x^2 \partial y} + k^2\frac{\partial^3 f}{\partial x \partial y^2}\right] + etc. \quad (8)$$

If $t = 0$ in (1), then $x = x_0$ and $y = y_0$. Hence, from (2) and (7),

$$G'(0) = hf_x(x_0, y_0) + kf_y(x_0, y_0); \quad G^{(n)}(0) = \left(h\frac{\partial}{\partial x} + k\frac{\partial}{\partial y}\right)^n f(x_0, y_0), \quad (9)$$

where we write "$f(x_0, y_0)$" in place of $f(x, y)|_{(x_0, y_0)}$ as in (7). We may apply Maclaurin's formula (3) of page 570 to $G(t)$. Then, for fixed t and n, there exists a number θ such that $0 < \theta < 1$, and

$$G(t) = G(0) + tG'(0) + \frac{t^2}{2!}G''(0) + \cdots + \frac{t^{n-1}}{(n-1)!}G^{(n-1)}(0) + R_n, \quad (10)$$

where $$R_n = \frac{t^n}{n!}G^{(n)}(\theta). \quad (11)$$

When $t = \theta$, equations (1) give $(x = x_0 + \theta h, y = y_0 + \theta k)$. This point is indicated as P_1 in Figure 405, and hereafter will be described simply as *a properly chosen point* $P_1:(x_1, y_1)$ *between* (x_0, y_0) *and* $(x_0 + th, y_0 + tk)$, where "*between*" means "*on the line segment between the given points.*"

In (1), if $t = 0$ then $(x = x_0, y = y_0)$ and $G(0) = f(x_0, y_0)$. If $t = 1$, then $(x = x_0 + h, y = y_0 + k)$ and $G(1) = f(x_0 + h, y_0 + k)$. Hence, from (10) with $t = 1$ and $n = 1$, and (3),

$$f(x_0 + h, y_0 + k) = f(x_0, y_0) + hf_x(x_1, y_1) + kf_y(x_1, y_1), \quad (12)$$

which is referred to as the *mean value theorem* for f. If n is any positive integer, when $t = 1$ in (10) we obtain Taylor's formula for $f(x, y)$ with a remainder after n terms. In particular, when $n = 2$, there exists a point (x_1, y_1) between (x_0, y_0) and $(x_0 + h, y_0 + k)$ such that

$$f(x_0 + h, y_0 + k) = f(x_0, y_0) + hf_x(x_0, y_0) + kf_y(x_0, y_0) + R_2, \quad (13)$$

where $$R_2 = \frac{1}{2!}[h^2 f_{xx}(x, y) + 2hk f_{xy}(x, y) + k^2 f_{yy}(x, y)]_{(x=x_1, y=y_1)}. \quad (14)$$

The Maclaurin series for $G(t)$ is

$$G(t) = G(0) + tG'(0) + \frac{t^2}{2!}G''(0) + \cdots + \frac{t^n}{n!}G^{(n)}(0) + \cdots. \quad (15)$$

When $t = 1$, equation (15) becomes

$$\left.\begin{array}{l} f(x_0 + h, y_0 + k) = f(x_0, y_0) + [hf_x(x_0, y_0) + kf_y(x_0, y_0)] + \cdots \\ \quad + \frac{1}{n!}\left(h\frac{\partial}{\partial x} + k\frac{\partial}{\partial y}\right)^n f(x_0, y_0) + \cdots. \end{array}\right\} \quad (16)$$

In (16), we may change the notation by using $x = x_0 + h$ and $y = y_0 + k$; $h = x - x_0$ and $k = y - y_0$. Then, (16) becomes

$$f(x, y) = f(x_0, y_0) + \sum_{n=1}^{\infty}\frac{1}{n!}\left[(x - x_0)\frac{\partial}{\partial x} + (y - y_0)\frac{\partial}{\partial y}\right]^n f(x_0, y_0), \quad (17)$$

which is referred to as the **Taylor series** *for $f(x, y)$ in powers of $(x - x_0)$ and* $(y - y_0)$. The series on the right in (17) converges, with $f(x, y)$ as the sum of the series, if and only if $R_n \to 0$ as $n \to \infty$, where R_n is given by (11) with $t = 1$, $h = x - x_0$, and $k = y - y_0$. In any application of (17) in this text, no discussion of R_n will be expected. If $x_0 = y_0 = 0$ in (17), the result is called the **Maclaurin series** for $f(x, y)$. Results similar to those just exhibited for $f(x, y)$ are available for a function of any number of variables, $f(x, y, z, w, \cdots)$.

EXAMPLE 1. If $f(x, y) = \sin xy + \sin x$, obtain the Taylor series for $f(x, y)$ in powers of $(x - \frac{1}{2}\pi)$ and y, through terms of degree 2.

Solution. We shall use (17) with $(x_0 = \frac{1}{2}\pi, y_0 = 0)$. We have

$$\frac{\partial f}{\partial x} = y \cos xy + \cos x; \quad \frac{\partial f}{\partial y} = x \cos xy; \quad \frac{\partial^2 f}{\partial x^2} = -y^2 \sin xy - \sin x; \left.\begin{matrix} \\ \\ \\ \\ \end{matrix}\right\} \quad (18)$$

$$\frac{\partial^2 f}{\partial x \partial y} = \cos xy - xy \sin xy; \quad \frac{\partial^2 f}{\partial y^2} = -x^2 \sin xy.$$

When $(x = \frac{1}{2}\pi, y = 0)$, we obtain $f(\frac{1}{2}\pi, 0) = 1$; the derivatives in (18), in the listed order, become $(0, \frac{1}{2}\pi, -1, 1, 0)$, and (17) gives

$$f(x, y) = 1 + \frac{1}{2}\pi y + \frac{1}{2!}\left[-\left(x - \frac{1}{2}\pi\right)^2 + 2y\left(x - \frac{1}{2}\pi\right)\right] + \cdots. \quad (19)$$

Comment. Series (19) could be used to compute approximate values for $f(x, y)$ if x is near $\frac{1}{2}\pi$ and y is near 0. The explicit terms on the right in (19) form a polynomial of degree 2 as an approximation to $f(x, y)$.

EXERCISE 188

Find the specified Taylor series by use of Section 239.

1. Expand $f(x, y) = \sin x + \cos xy$, (a) through the terms of degree 2 in powers of $(x - \frac{1}{2}\pi)$ and $(y - 1)$; (b) through the terms of degree 4 in powers of x and y.

2. Expand $(e^{xy} + \sin y)$ in powers of x and y through the terms of the third degree.

3. Expand $e^x \sin y$ in powers of x and y through the terms of the third degree, (a) by use of (17) on page 623; (b) by use of the Maclaurin series for e^x and $\sin y$, and then by multiplication of these series.

4. Expand $\sin(x + y)$ in powers of x and y through the terms of the third degree, (a) by use of (17) on page 623; (b) by use of the series for $\sin z$.

5. Expand $x^4 + 3x^3y + y^4$ in powers of $(x - 2)$ and $(y + 1)$.

By use of the first few terms in the Maclaurin series for the function on the left, show that it is approximately equal to the given expression if x and y are small. This assumes that the sum of any neglected terms of the series would be negligible when x and y are small.

6. $e^{-x} \sin y = y - xy$, approximately.

7. $e^y \ln(1 + x) = x + xy - \dfrac{x^2}{2}$, approximately.

8. Expand $e^{\frac{\ln y}{x}}$ in powers of $(x + 2)$ and $(y - 1)$, through the terms of degree 2.

9. Write out explicitly all terms for which $n = 3$ in (17) on page 623.

240. EXTREMA FOR FUNCTIONS OF TWO VARIABLES

To state that a function $f(x, y)$ has a relative maximum or a relative minimum at a point (x_0, y_0) in the domain of f means that the following conditions, respectively, are satisfied at all points (x, y) sufficiently near (x_0, y_0):

For a maximum: $\qquad\qquad f(x, y) \leqq f(x_0, y_0).$ (1)

For a minimum: $\qquad\qquad f(x, y) \geqq f(x_0, y_0).$ (2)

Hereafter, we assume that f possesses continuous derivatives f_x and f_y.

Theorem IV. *If f has a relative extremum at an **interior point*** (x_0, y_0) *of the domain of f, it is necessary that*

$$f_x(x_0, y_0) = 0 \quad and \quad f_y(x_0, y_0) = 0.$$ (3)

Proof. Suppose that f has a relative maximum at (x_0, y_0). From (1) with $y = y_0$, we obtain $f(x, y_0) \leqq f(x_0, y_0)$, which shows that the function ϕ defined by $\phi(x) = f(x, y_0)$ has a relative maximum at the interior point $x = x_0$ of an interval on the domain of ϕ. We notice that $\phi'(x) = f_x(x, y_0)$. Hence, because of the necessary condition on page 124 for a relative maximum of ϕ, we have

$$\phi'(x_0) = 0, \quad or \quad f_x(x_0, y_0) = 0.$$

Also, from (1) with $x = x_0$, the function of y alone with values $f(x_0, y)$ has a relative maximum at $y = y_0$, so that $f_y(x_0, y_0) = 0$. Similarly, we may prove that (3) is true when f has a relative minimum at (x_0, y_0).

Note 1. Until specified later, let *extremum* mean *relative extremum.*

In an *xyz*-system of coordinates, let T be the surface with the equation $z = f(x, y)$, as in Figure 406. Then, if f has a maximum at (x_0, y_0), the corresponding point $P:(x_0, y_0, z_0)$ on T is *as high as*, or *higher than* all points on T near P. Similarly, a minimum for f corresponds to a low point on the surface T. From page 604, an equation for the tangent plane, τ, at any point $P:(x_0, y_0, z_0)$ on T is

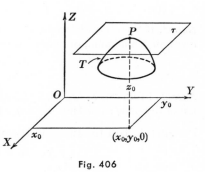

Fig. 406

$$f_x(x_0, y_0)(x - x_0) + f_y(x_0, y_0)(y - y_0) - (z - z_0) = 0.$$ (4)

Hence, from (3) and (4), if f has a maximum or a minimum at (x_0, y_0), the tangent plane τ at $P:(x_0, y_0, z_0)$ on the surface $z = f(x, y)$ is the horizontal plane $z = z_0$.

Note 2. A result corresponding to Theorem IV can be proved for functions of more than two independent variables. Thus, if a function $f(x, y, z)$ has a maximum or a minimum at an interior point (x_0, y_0, z_0) of the domain of f, it is *necessary* that

$$f_x(x_0, y_0, z_0) = 0, \quad f_y(x_0, y_0, z_0) = 0, \quad and \quad f_z(x_0, y_0, z_0) = 0.$$

---

* This stipulation is essential because, in the proof, we shall use Theorem III on page 124 where it was assumed that x_0 is an *interior point* of an *interval* of the domain of f.

Problem 10 on page 631 will show that equations (3) are *not sufficient conditions* to imply a maximum or a minimum. The following tests present one set of sufficient conditions. It is assumed that f has continuous derivatives f_x, f_y, f_{xx}, f_{xy}, and f_{yy}. A proof of the tests is beyond the scope of this text.

Summary. *Test for a maximum or a minimum of a function $f(x, y)$ at an* **interior point** *of the domain of f.*

I. *Solve the necessary conditions $f_x(x, y) = 0$ and $f_y(x, y) = 0$ to find all critical pairs $(x = x_0, y = y_0)$.*

II. *The function $f(x, y)$ has a relative extremum at (x_0, y_0) in case*

$$[f_{xy}(x_0, y_0)]^2 - f_{xx}(x_0, y_0)f_{yy}(x_0, y_0) < 0. \tag{5}$$

Then,   *a maximum occurs if $f_{xx}(x_0, y_0) < 0$;*   (6)

a minimum occurs if $f_{xx}(x_0, y_0) > 0$.   (7)

III. *No extremum occurs if "< 0" is changed to "> 0" in (5).*

Conditions (6) and (7) can be made plausible by returning to Theorem IV. In the notation of its proof, $\phi''(x) = f_{xx}(x, y_0)$. Then, sufficient conditions for a minimum of ϕ at $x = x_0$ are $\phi'(x_0) = 0$ and $\phi''(x_0) > 0$, or $f_x(x_0, y_0) = 0$ and $f_{xx}(x_0, y_0) > 0$, which appears as (7). In using (5), we shall let

$$H(x, y) = [f_{xy}(x, y)]^2 - f_{xx}(x, y)f_{yy}(x, y).$$

Condition (5) arises by consideration of R_2 in (13) on page 623, which becomes

$$f(x_0 + h, y_0 + k) - f(x_0, y_0) = R_2 \quad when \quad f_x(x_0, y_0) = f_y(x_0, y_0) = 0.$$

Note 3. If "< 0" is replaced by "$= 0$" in (5), it can be shown that f may have a maximum, or a minimum, or neither at (x_0, y_0). If we let $z = f(x, y)$, (5) becomes

$$\left(\frac{\partial^2 z}{\partial x\, \partial y}\right)^2 - \frac{\partial^2 z}{\partial x^2} \cdot \frac{\partial^2 z}{\partial y^2} < 0. \tag{8}$$

Note 4. From (5), $f_{xy}^2(x_0, y_0) < f_{xx}(x_0, y_0)f_{yy}(x_0, y_0)$, and hence $f_{xx}(x_0, y_0)$ and $f_{yy}(x_0, y_0)$ are of the same sign. Thus, f_{yy} could be used in place of f_{xx} in (6) and (7).

EXAMPLE 1. Test the function $f(x, y)$ for maxima and minima:

$$f(x, y) = x^3 + y^3 - 3xy + 15. \tag{9}$$

Solution. 1. *Necessary conditions.* From (I) of the Summary,

$$f_x(x, y) = 3x^2 - 3y = 0 \quad and \quad f_y(x, y) = 3y^2 - 3x = 0. \tag{10}$$

From system (10), $y = x^2$ and $x = y^2$. Hence, $x = x^4$, which has the solutions $x = 0$ and $x = 1$. Then, (10) has the solutions $(x = 0, y = 0)$ and $(x = 1, y = 1)$.

2. From (9), $f_{xx}(x, y) = 6x$; $f_{yy}(x, y) = 6y$; $f_{xy}(x, y) = -3$. At $(x = 0, y = 0)$, these derivatives have the values 0, 0, and -3, respectively. Hence, from (5), $H(0, 0) = 9 - 0 > 0$. Therefore, f has neither a maximum nor a minimum at $(x = 0, y = 0)$. At $(x = 1, y = 1)$, $H(1, 1) = 9 - (6)(6) = -27 < 0$. Hence, there is an extremum at $(x = 1, y = 1)$. Since $f_{xx}(1, 1) = 6 > 0$, this extremum is a minimum, and the relative minimum value of f is $f(1, 1) = 14$.

EXAMPLE 2. A rectangular box is inscribed in the sphere

$$x^2 + y^2 + z^2 = 49. \tag{11}$$

Find the dimensions for absolute maximum volume.

Solution. 1. Let V be the volume of that eighth of the box represented in Figure 407, where the corner $P:(x, y, z)$ is on the sphere. We have

$$V = xyz, \quad \text{with the constraint * } \quad x^2 + y^2 + z^2 = 49. \tag{12}$$

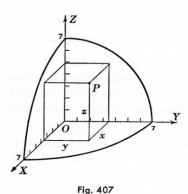

Fig. 407

2. In (12), consider z as a function of (x, y) defined implicitly by the equation of constraint. Then, V is a function of (x, y), where the domain for (x, y) consists of all points in the region R of the xy-plane bounded by the circle $x^2 + y^2 = 49$. If (x, y) is on the boundary of R, then $V = 0$. Hence, any point (x, y) at which V has an *absolute maximum* (and, therefore, also a *relative maximum*) will be an *interior point* of R. Thus, necessary conditions for a maximum are

$$\frac{\partial V}{\partial x} = 0 \quad \text{and} \quad \frac{\partial V}{\partial y} = 0. \tag{13}$$

By the chain rule of page 584, from $V = xyz$,

$$\frac{\partial V}{\partial x} = yz + xy \frac{\partial z}{\partial x} \quad \text{and} \quad \frac{\partial V}{\partial y} = xz + xy \frac{\partial z}{\partial y}. \tag{14}$$

On differentiating in $x^2 + y^2 + z^2 = 49$ with respect to x, with y held fast, and then with respect to y, with x held fast, we obtain

$$2x + 2z \frac{\partial z}{\partial x} = 0 \quad \text{or} \quad \frac{\partial z}{\partial x} = -\frac{x}{z}; \quad \frac{\partial z}{\partial y} = -\frac{y}{z}. \tag{15}$$

By use of (15) in (14), from (13) we arrive at

$$yz - \frac{x^2 y}{z} = 0 \quad \text{and} \quad xz - \frac{xy^2}{z} = 0, \text{ or}$$

$$y(z^2 - x^2) = 0 \quad \text{and} \quad x(z^2 - y^2) = 0. \tag{16}$$

From (16), since $x \neq 0$ and $y \neq 0$ for maximum volume, $z^2 = x^2$ and $z^2 = y^2$, or $x^2 = y^2 = z^2$. Hence, if there is a maximum for V, we have $x = y = z$.

3. The preceding details show that there is *just one* possible set of dimensions for a maximum volume. The geometrical setting convinces us that a maximum exists. Hence, without applying the sufficient conditions (5) and (6), we conclude that V has a maximum when $x = y = z$, and the box is a cube. From (11), $3x^2 = 49$ or $x = \frac{7}{3}\sqrt{3}$; the side of the maximum cube is $\frac{14}{3}\sqrt{3}$.

Note 5. Added discussion about extrema is given as supplementary content in the next section. Exercise 189 on page 631 can be taken up immediately.

* Or, "*side condition.*"

★241. LAGRANGE MULTIPLIERS; ABSOLUTE EXTREMA *

Assume that the functions $f(x, y)$ and $g(x, y)$ have some region R as a common domain, that f and g are differentiable, and that $g_x^2(x, y) + g_y^2(x, y) \neq 0$ in R. We wish to investigate the following problem:

$$\left\{ \begin{array}{l} \textit{To obtain } (x, y) \textit{ so that } f(x, y) \textit{ will be a relative ex-} \\ \textit{tremum for } f \textit{ subject to the constraint } g(x, y) = 0. \end{array} \right\} \tag{1}$$

We considered special cases of (1) in Section 47 on page 144. The following theorem, in a very simple fashion, produces conditions (*necessary conditions*) which (x, y) must satisfy if (1) is true. The method involves a so-called **Lagrange multiplier** and extends easily to cases where more than two variables are involved.

Theorem V. *Let* $u(x, y, \lambda) = f(x, y) + \lambda g(x, y)$, *where* λ *is a new variable to be eliminated later. Then, if* (x, y) *are treated* **as if they are independent variables** (*contrary to fact*), *and if the necessary conditions* (3) *for an extremum on page* 625 *are written for* u, *elimination of* λ *between these equations produces a necessary condition for* (x, y) *to satisfy* (1).

Proof. 1. *First*, we obtain a necessary condition on (x, y) by applying the previously justified method of page 145 to the general problem (1). Let $W = f(x, y)$, assume that $g_y(x, y) \neq 0$, and consider y as a function of x defined implicitly by $g(x, y) = 0$. We differentiate with respect to x, with y as an implicit function of x, in $g(x, y) = 0$ and $W = f(x, y)$. Then, as necessary conditions on (x, y), we obtain

$$g_x(x, y) + g_y(x, y) \frac{dy}{dx} = 0 \quad \textit{and} \quad \frac{dW}{dx} = f_x(x, y) + f_y(x, y) \frac{dy}{dx} = 0.$$

Hence, $$f_x(x, y) - \frac{f_y(x, y) g_x(x, y)}{g_y(x, y)} = 0, \textit{ or}$$

$$f_x(x, y) g_y(x, y) - f_y(x, y) g_x(x, y) = 0. \tag{2}$$

We also obtain (2) if we assume that $g_x(x, y) \neq 0$ and treat x as a function of y. Then, necessary conditions on (x, y) to satisfy (1) consist of

$$g(x, y) = 0 \quad \textit{and} \quad f_x(x, y) g_y(x, y) - f_y(x, y) g_x(x, y) = 0. \tag{3}$$

2. *Second*, we apply (3) of page 625 to $u(x, y, \lambda)$ with no theoretical basis for this action. There is obtained

$$u_x(x, y, \lambda) = 0, \textit{ or} \qquad\qquad f_x(x, y) + \lambda g_x(x, y) = 0, \textit{ and} \tag{4}$$

$$u_y(x, y, \lambda) = 0, \textit{ or} \qquad\qquad f_y(x, y) + \lambda g_y(x, y) = 0. \tag{5}$$

Assume that $g_x(x, y) \neq 0$. Then, on solving for λ in (4) and substituting the result in (5), we verify that (2) is obtained. Similarly, we obtain (2) if $g_y(x, y) \neq 0$. Thus, with no theoretical basis for our present manipulation,† we obtain a condition, (2), which is known to be necessary for an extremum in (1). Then, we join $g(x, y) = 0$ and obtain (3) as a system where any solution (x_0, y_0) is a critical point for consideration of (1).

---

* Related problems will occur in the chapter supplement.
† A different approach involving $u(x, y, \lambda)$ leads to (2) by logical steps.

EXAMPLE 1. Solve Example 1 on page 145 by use of Theorem I.

Solution. We have

$$g(x, y) = \frac{V}{\pi} - x^2y = 0, \quad and \quad f(x, y) = xy + x^2.$$

Hence, we introduce $u(x, y, \lambda) = xy + x^2 + \lambda \left(\frac{V}{\pi} - x^2y \right)$. From (4) and (5),

$$y + 2x - 2\lambda xy = 0 \quad and \quad x - \lambda x^2 = 0. \tag{6}$$

From (6), $$\lambda = \frac{1}{x} \quad and \quad y + 2x - 2 \left(\frac{1}{x} \right) xy = 0, \text{ or}$$

$$y + 2x - 2y = 0, \quad or \quad y = 2x. \tag{7}$$

This is the preliminary result obtained as a necessary condition in (8) on page 145. The student is referred there for final discussion of the problem.

Note 1. To obtain necessary conditions on (x, y, z) for an extremum of $f(x, y, z)$ subject to a side condition, or restraint, $g(x, y, z) = 0$, we would introduce

$$u = f(x, y, z) + \lambda g(x, y, z),$$

write $(u_x = 0, u_y = 0, u_z = 0)$, and use these along with $g(x, y, z) = 0$ to obtain a system of three equations in (x, y, z) not involving λ. The method of Lagrange multipliers was introduced by the great French mathematician, JOSEPH LOUIS LAGRANGE (1736–1813).

Suppose that the domain of a function $f(x, y)$ is a closed region R in the xy-plane, and that f_x and f_y exist and are continuous in R. Then, by Note 2 on page 466, f has an absolute maximum, M, and an absolute minimum, m, in R. To find M and m, we first recall that f has a *relative* extremum at any point where f attains an *absolute* extremum. Hence, to obtain M and m, sometimes we may proceed as follows, without recourse to the Summary of Section 240.

I. By use of Theorem IV, page 625, find each critical point (x_0, y_0) *interior* to R where f *might* have a relative maximum or minimum.

II. Separately, investigate f for relative maxima and minima *on each piece* * *of the boundary of R*, perhaps by considering the values of a related function of a single variable. Let the typical critical point thus obtained be (x_1, y_1).

III. Calculate $f(x_0, y_0)$ and $f(x_1, y_1)$ for all critical points. Then, the maximum and minimum of these function values are M and m, respectively.

EXAMPLE 2. Find the absolute maximum, M, and minimum, m, for the function $f(x, y) = 2x^2 + y^2 - 2xy - 4x + 3$ in the closed triangular region R bounded by the lines $y = 0$, $x = 3$, and $y = 2x$, as in Figure 408 on page 630.

Solution. 1. $$f_x(x, y) = 4x - 2y - 4; \quad f_y(x, y) = 2y - 2x.$$

On solving the system $(4x - 2y - 4 = 0 \quad and \quad 2y - 2x = 0)$, we obtain $P_1 : (x = 2, y = 2)$. By Theorem I, there *might* be an extremum, relative or absolute, at P_1.

---

* It may be convenient to consider the boundary in pieces, instead of as a whole.

2. Consider points on the *boundary segment OB* of *R*, where $y = 2x$ and $f(x, y) = 2x^2 - 4x + 3 = \phi(x)$. Since $\phi'(x) = 4x - 4$, we find $x = 1$ as the only number *interior* to the interval $I = \{0 \leqq x \leqq 3\}$ where ϕ might have an extremum. Then, $y = 2$, and the possible point for an extremum of *f* is P_2:(1, 2), in Figure 408. Also, ϕ might have an extremum at an *end point*, $x = 0$ or $x = 3$, of *I*. If $x = 0$ then $y = 0$; if $x = 3$ then $y = 6$. Hence, other possible points for extrema of *f* are P_3:(0, 0) and P_4:(3, 6) which is *B* in Figure 408.

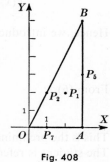

Fig. 408

3. Similarly, on the boundary segments *OA* and *AB*, other possible points for extrema of *f* are P_5:(3, 3), P_6:(3, 0), and P_7:(1, 0). To find *M* and *m*, we compute $f(x, y)$ at $P_1, \cdots, P_7$, obtaining $(-1, 1, 3, 9, 0, 9, 1)$. Hence, $M = 9$, attained at P_4:(3, 6) and P_6:(3, 0); $m = -1$, attained at P_1:(2, 2).

★242. THE OPERATOR DEL, ∇

Let a differentiation-vector ∇, read **"del,"** be defined by

$$\nabla = \left(\mathbf{i}\,\frac{\partial}{\partial x} + \mathbf{j}\,\frac{\partial}{\partial y} + \mathbf{k}\,\frac{\partial}{\partial z}\right).$$

Then, with an obvious meaning, we may write

$$\nabla f(x, y, z) = \left(\mathbf{i}\,\frac{\partial f}{\partial x} + \mathbf{j}\,\frac{\partial f}{\partial y} + \mathbf{k}\,\frac{\partial f}{\partial z}\right).$$

If $u = f(x, y, z)$, we note that $\qquad \nabla u = \nabla f(x, y, z) = \textbf{grad } u.$

The operator ∇ is used frequently in other applications of partial differentiation and vectors in both pure and applied mathematics. Thus, by definition, with ∇ acting formally like a vector

$$\nabla^2 u = (\nabla \cdot \nabla)u = \frac{\partial^2 u}{\partial x^2} + \frac{\partial^2 u}{\partial y^2} + \frac{\partial^2 u}{\partial z^2},$$

and $\nabla^2 u$ is called the **"Laplacian of *u*,"** because of connection with Laplace's differential equation $\nabla^2 u = 0$. If $V = f(x, y, z)\mathbf{i} + g(x, y, z)\mathbf{j} + h(x, y, z)\mathbf{k}$, the **"divergence of V,"** denoted by **"div V,"** is defined as the symbolic dot product

$$\nabla \cdot V = \left(\mathbf{i}\,\frac{\partial}{\partial x} + \mathbf{j}\,\frac{\partial}{\partial y} + \mathbf{k}\,\frac{\partial}{\partial z}\right) \cdot V = \frac{\partial f}{\partial x} + \frac{\partial g}{\partial y} + \frac{\partial h}{\partial z}.$$

The **"curl of V"** denoted by **"curl V"** is defined as the symbolic cross product

$$\nabla \times V = \begin{vmatrix} \mathbf{i} & \mathbf{j} & \mathbf{k} \\ \dfrac{\partial}{\partial x} & \dfrac{\partial}{\partial y} & \dfrac{\partial}{\partial z} \\ f(x, y, z) & g(x, y, z) & h(x, y, z) \end{vmatrix}$$

$$= \mathbf{i}\left(\frac{\partial h}{\partial y} - \frac{\partial g}{\partial z}\right) + \mathbf{j}\left(\frac{\partial f}{\partial z} - \frac{\partial h}{\partial x}\right) + \mathbf{k}\left(\frac{\partial g}{\partial x} - \frac{\partial f}{\partial y}\right).$$

EXERCISE 189

Test the function for maxima and minima.

1. $2xy - x^2 - 2y^2 + 3x + 4$.   **2.** $8x^3 + y^3 - 12xy + 8$.

3. $2x^2 + y^2 - 2xy - 4x + 3$.   **4.** $x^4 - 4xy + 2y^2 - 5$.

5. $13x^2 + 16xy + 7y^2 + 10x + 2y - 5$.

6. $4x^2 - 16x - 3y^2 - 6y + 8$.   **7.** $3xy + 4x^2 - 2y^2 - 5x - 7y + 3$.

8. $\cos(x + y) - 2x^2 - 2y^2 + 8x - 8y + 4xy$, if $0 < x < \frac{1}{2}\pi$ and $0 < y < \frac{1}{2}\pi$.

9. $z = \frac{1}{4}xy - \frac{1}{2x} - \frac{1}{y} + 7$.   **10.** $z = \frac{y^2}{9} - \frac{x^2}{25}$.

Note 1. In Problem 10, consider the xz-trace and yz-trace of the hyperbolic paraboloid $z = f(x, y)$, as in Figure 314 on page 454. The saddle point of the surface, with $z = 0$, is obtained when $x = y = 0$. The traces show that z is less than zero, and also greater than zero in every neighborhood of $(x = 0, y = 0)$ in the xy-plane, however small this neighborhood may be. Hence, conditions (3) on page 625 are not sufficient conditions for a maximum or a minimum.

11. A rectangular bin with a capacity of 4000 cubic feet is to have an open top. Find the dimensions to minimize the material used for the bin.

12. Find the volume of the rectangular parallelepiped of maximum volume which can be inscribed in the ellipsoid $4x^2 + y^2 + 4z^2 = 12$.

By calculus, find the point Q on the plane which is nearest P, and $|\overline{QP}|$.

13. Plane, $2x - 6y + 3z = -22$; P:(3, −3, 1).

14. Plane, $3x + 2y + 3z = 5$; P:(2, 3, 5).

15. By calculus, find the shortest distance between the lines

$$\frac{x-1}{2} = \frac{y-3}{1} = \frac{z+7}{2} \quad and \quad \frac{x+3}{3} = \frac{y+4}{-1} = \frac{z-5}{1}.$$

★SUPPLEMENT FOR CHAPTER TWENTY–SEVEN

16. By use of calculus, find the shortest distance between the point (x_0, y_0, z_0) and the plane $x \cos \alpha + y \cos \beta + z \cos \gamma = p$, where $\cos \alpha$, $\cos \beta$, and $\cos \gamma$ are direction cosines for a direction normal to the plane. Do not use page 456.

17. Let (x_i, y_i, z_i), with $i = 1, 2, \cdots, n$, be a given set of n triples of numbers, where

$$\sum_{i=1}^{n} x_i = \sum_{i=1}^{n} y_i = \sum_{i=1}^{n} z_i = 0; \qquad \sum (x_i - \lambda y_i)^2 \neq 0 \text{ for any } \lambda.$$

We seek numbers (a, b, c) so that, if $Z = ax + by + c$ is used to compute Z_i when $(x = x_i, y = y_i)$, the set $(Z_1, Z_2, \cdots, Z_n)$ will give the *best approximation* to $(z_1, z_2, \cdots, z_n)$ in the *sense of least squares*, where *"best"* is defined by stating that

$$f(a, b, c) = \sum_{i=1}^{n} (z_i - Z_i)^2 = \sum_{i=1}^{n} (z_i - ax_i - by_i - c)^2$$

is a *minimum*. Obtain equations for (a, b, c) which form a set of necessary conditions for the minimum, and solve these equations. (Simple reasoning shows that f has no upper bound.) The preceding results (and other similar results) are fundamental in the theory of multiple regression in statistics.

18–25. Solve Problems 1, 2, 3, 4, 6, 7, 8, and 11, respectively, of Exercise 42 on page 146 by use of a Lagrange multiplier. Give added verbal reasoning to demonstrate that the necessary conditions lead to the solution of the problem.

26. We search for (x, y, z) so that $f(x, y, z)$ is an extremum for f subject to the constraint $g(x, y, z) = 0$. Let $u = f(x, y, z) + \lambda g(x, y, z)$ and assume that $g_z(x, y, z) \neq 0$. Prove that the Lagrange method, as outlined in Note 1 on page 629, leads to equations which are necessary conditions on (x, y, z) for $f(x, y, z)$ to be an extremum.

27–29. Apply Problem 26 to solve Problems 11, 12, and 13, respectively.

30. Let S and T be the surfaces $g(x, y, z) = 0$ and $f(x, y, z) = h$, respectively, where h is a relative extremum of f which is attained at $P:(x_1, y_1, z_1)$ on S. If

$$g_x^2(x, y, z) + g_y^2(x, y, z) + g_z^2(x, y, z) \neq 0, \; and$$

$$f_x^2(x, y, z) + f_y^2(x, y, z) + f_z^2(x, y, z) \neq 0$$

at all points involved, prove that S and T are tangent at P_1.

31. If a plane triangle is such that the product of the sines of its angles is a maximum, prove that the triangle is equilateral.

32. For a given perimeter, prove that the triangle of maximum area is equilateral.

33. Find the absolute maximum and absolute minimum of the function $f(x, y) = xy^2 - x^2y - 3y$ in the closed region R defined by $(|x| \leq 3, |y| \leq 3)$.

34. Find the absolute extrema of the function $f(x, y) = xy - 2x^{-1} - 4y^{-1}$ in the rectangle in the xy-plane where $(\frac{1}{2} \leq x \leq 5, -3 \leq y \leq -1)$.

35. Find the absolute extrema of the function $(x^2 + 2y^2 - 2xy - 3x - 4)$ in the closed region bounded by the lines $x = 0$, $y = 2$, and $4y = x$.

36. Assume that the functions $f(x, y)$ and $F(x, y)$ have an open region R as a common domain, are continuously differentiable, and are such that $df(x, y) = dF(x, y)$ at all points of R. Prove that there exists a constant C such that $f(x, y) = F(x, y) + C$ at all points of R. The function G of page 622 may be useful. Assume that any two points of R can be connected by a path C in R consisting of joined line segments.

37. Let the function $f(x, y, z)$ be differentiable in an open region R, with $P:(x_0, y_0, z_0)$ in R and $f(x_0, y_0, z_0) = \epsilon$. Let $Q:(x_1, y_1, z_1)$ be defined by

$$\overrightarrow{PQ} = -\frac{\epsilon}{|\operatorname{grad} u|} \cdot \frac{\operatorname{grad} u}{|\operatorname{grad} u|} = -\frac{\epsilon \operatorname{grad} u}{|\operatorname{grad} u|^2}, \tag{1}$$

where $u = f(x, y, z)$ and $\operatorname{grad} u$ is evaluated at P. Let (α, β, γ) be the direction angles of $\operatorname{grad} u$ at P. Prove that, if $D_{\alpha,\beta,\gamma} u$ is a constant (which in general is *not* true) on PQ, then $f(x_1, y_1, z_1) = 0$.

Note 1. In (1), with O as the origin, let $\overrightarrow{OQ} = \overrightarrow{OP} + \mathbf{V}$, where

$$(x_1 = x_0 + \Delta x, \; y_1 = y_0 + \Delta y, \; z_1 = z_0 + \Delta z), \quad and \quad \mathbf{V} = \mathbf{i}\Delta x + \mathbf{j}\Delta y + \mathbf{k}\Delta z.$$

Then, $\mathbf{V} = \overrightarrow{PQ}$, and $\mathbf{V}$ is called the **gradient correction** (in the direction of *steepest descent*) for P as an approximation to a solution point for $f(x, y, z) = 0$. Gradient corrections are used in various methods for the solution of equations by iterative processes, with modern digital computers.

38. If $f(x, y, z) = ax + by + cz + d$, prove that Q of (1) is the orthogonal projection of P onto the plane $f(x, y, z) = 0$.

39. If $f(x, y) = 4x^2 + 9y^2 - 36$ and $P:(2, 4)$ is used in (1), find Q, and $f(x_1, y_1)$.

40. If $f(x, y) = ax^2 + 2bxy + cy^2 + 2dx + 2ey + g$, prove that Q of (1) is at one-half of the distance from P to the *polar line* of P with respect to the conic $f(x, y) = 0$. Verify this fact in Problem 39. See Problem 24 on page 327.

CHAPTER TWENTY–EIGHT

Hyperbolic Functions

243. DEFINITION OF THE HYPERBOLIC FUNCTIONS

Certain combinations of exponential functions arise so frequently that it proves convenient to introduce a related group of new functions, called the hyperbolic functions. Their names are as follows, with abbreviations in boldface type:

$$
\begin{aligned}
&\textit{hyperbolic sine,} \quad \textbf{sinh;} \quad \textit{hyperbolic cosine,} \quad \textbf{cosh;} \\
&\textit{hyperbolic tangent,} \quad \textbf{tanh;} \quad \textit{hyperbolic cotangent,} \quad \textbf{coth;} \\
&\textit{hyperbolic secant,} \quad \textbf{sech;} \quad \textit{hyperbolic cosecant,} \quad \textbf{csch.}
\end{aligned}
\tag{1}
$$

The values of sinh and cosh are defined by

$$
\sinh x = \frac{e^x - e^{-x}}{2}; \quad \cosh x = \frac{e^x + e^{-x}}{2}.
\tag{2}
$$

The values of the other hyperbolic functions are defined in terms of sinh x and cosh x:

$$
\tanh x = \frac{\sinh x}{\cosh x}; \quad \coth x = \frac{1}{\tanh x} = \frac{\cosh x}{\sinh x};
\tag{3}
$$

$$
\operatorname{sech} x = \frac{1}{\cosh x}; \quad \operatorname{csch} x = \frac{1}{\sinh x}.
\tag{4}
$$

We note a formal similarity between (3) and (4) and fundamental identities for trigonometric functions. Thus, it is not surprising that, in analogy with formulas of trigonometry, a long list of identities for hyperbolic functions can be established. First, the following identity (5) can be proved by inserting (2) on the left. Identities (6) are established by dividing on both sides of (5) by sinh x, and cosh x, in turn.

$$
\cosh^2 x - \sinh^2 x = 1.
\tag{5}
$$

$$
1 - \tanh^2 x = \operatorname{sech}^2 x; \quad \coth^2 x - 1 = \operatorname{csch}^2 x.
\tag{6}
$$

Then, various identities paralleling formulas from trigonometry, with certain changes in signs, can be established for hyperbolic functions on the basis of (2)–(6). These identities have very limited applications and will be considered only in problems of the next exercise.

633

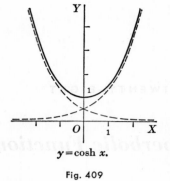

$y = \cosh x.$

Fig. 409

ILLUSTRATION 1. The full-line curve in Figure 409 is a graph of $y = \cosh x$. We find

$$\cosh x - \tfrac{1}{2}e^x = \tfrac{1}{2}e^{-x}; \ hence$$

$$\lim_{x \to \infty} (\cosh x - \tfrac{1}{2}e^x) = 0. \tag{7}$$

Similarly, $\quad \lim_{x \to -\infty} (\cosh x - \tfrac{1}{2}e^{-x}) = 0. \tag{8}$

The graphs of $y = \tfrac{1}{2}e^{-x}$ and $y = \tfrac{1}{2}e^x$ are shown by broken-line curves in Figure 409. From (7) and (8), the graph of $y = \cosh x$ has the graphs of $y = \tfrac{1}{2}e^x$ and $y = \tfrac{1}{2}e^{-x}$ as *asymptotic curves*. Similarly, the graph of $y = \sinh x$, in Figure 410, has the asymptotic curves $y = \tfrac{1}{2}e^x$ and $y = -\tfrac{1}{2}e^{-x}$.

ILLUSTRATION 2. From (2), $\sinh(-x) = -\sinh x$ and $\cosh(-x) = \cosh x$. Thus, $\cosh x$ is called an *even* function of x. Since $\sinh x$ changes sign if x is replaced by $-x$, $\sinh x$ is called an *odd* function of x. From Table V, we obtain

$$\sinh .6 = .6367; \quad hence \quad \sinh(-.6) = -.6367.$$

ILLUSTRATION 3. If $a > 0$, the graph of

$$y = a \cosh \frac{x}{a}, \quad or \quad y = \frac{a}{2}\left(e^{\frac{x}{a}} + e^{-\frac{x}{a}}\right)$$

is called a **catenary** (see page 713).

ILLUSTRATION 4. From (2),

$$\frac{d \sinh x}{dx} = \frac{e^x + e^{-x}}{2} = \cosh x;$$

$$\frac{d \cosh x}{dx} = \frac{e^x - e^{-x}}{2} = \sinh x.$$

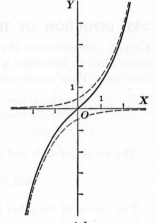

$y = \sinh x.$

Fig. 410

ILLUSTRATION 5. From (2) and (3), $\qquad \tanh x = \dfrac{e^x - e^{-x}}{e^x + e^{-x}}.$

A graph of $y = \tanh x$ is shown in Figure 411. We verify that $\tanh x \to 1$ as $x \to \infty$, and $\tanh x \to -1$ when $x \to -\infty$. From (3) and Illustration 4,

$$\frac{d \tanh x}{dx} = \frac{\cosh^2 x - \sinh^2 x}{\cosh^2 x} = \frac{1}{\cosh^2 x} = \operatorname{sech}^2 x.$$

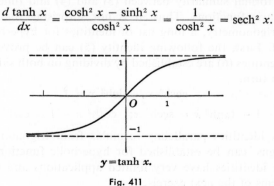

$y = \tanh x.$

Fig. 411

Similarly, derivatives of the other hyperbolic functions can be found by use of (3)–(6). Then, from these derivatives, we obtain corresponding differentials and indefinite integrals. Only those formulas relating to sinh x and cosh x will be of importance for us later. In the following formulas, u represents any differentiable function of x, and (VII) of page 98 was used.

$$\frac{d \sinh u}{dx} = \cosh u \frac{du}{dx}, \quad or \quad d \sinh u = \cosh u \, du. \tag{9}$$

$$\frac{d \cosh u}{dx} = \sinh u \frac{du}{dx}, \quad or \quad d \cosh u = \sinh u \, du. \tag{10}$$

$$\int \sinh u \, du = \cosh u + C. \tag{11}$$

$$\int \cosh u \, du = \sinh u + C. \tag{12}$$

EXERCISE 190

1. Obtain expressions in terms of e^x and e^{-x} for coth x, sech x, and csch x.

Investigate the graph of the function by use of calculus, determining the domains for x and y, any horizontal or vertical asymptotes, extrema, and inflection points. Use Table V.

2. $y = \sinh x$.   **3.** $y = \cosh x$.   **4.** $y = \tanh x$.   **5.** $y = \coth x$.

Find the function value by interpolation in Table V.

6. sinh .273.   **7.** cosh .784.   **8.** cosh 2.13.   **9.** sinh 1.67.

Prove the identity.

10. $\sinh (x + y) = \sinh x \cosh y + \cosh x \sinh y$.

11. $\cosh (x + y) = \cosh x \cosh y + \sinh x \sinh y$.

12. $\sinh 2x = 2 \sinh x \cosh x$.   **13.** $\cosh 2x = \cosh^2 x + \sinh^2 x$.

14. $\sinh^2 x = \frac{1}{2}(\cosh 2x - 1); \cosh^2 x = \frac{1}{2}(\cosh 2x + 1)$.

Find the derivative of the function whose values are defined.

15. $\sinh 3x$.   **16.** $\cosh x^3$.   **17.** $\tanh 4x$.

18. $\coth x$.   **19.** $\tanh \frac{1}{3}x$.   **20.** $\cosh^2 2x$.

Evaluate the limit or integral.

21. $\lim\limits_{x \to 0} \dfrac{\sinh x}{x}$.   **22.** $\lim\limits_{x \to 0} \dfrac{\cosh x - 1}{x}$.   **23.** $\lim\limits_{x \to 0} \dfrac{x}{\tanh x}$.

24. $\int \sinh 4x \, dx$.   **25.** $\int \cosh 2x \, dx$.   **26.** $\int x \sinh x \, dx$.

27. $\int x \cosh 3x \, dx$.   **28.** $\int \cosh x \sinh x \, dx$.

29. $\int \cosh^2 x \, dx$.   **30.** $\int \cosh^3 x \, dx$.

31. $\int \sinh^2 x \cosh^3 x \, dx$.   **32.** $\int \sinh^2 x \, dx$.

33. Find the derivatives of sech x and csch x.

Verify the Maclaurin series for the function.

34. $\sinh x = x + \dfrac{x^3}{3!} + \dfrac{x^3}{5!} + \cdots$.   **35.** $\cosh x = 1 + \dfrac{x^2}{2!} + \dfrac{x^4}{4!} + \cdots$.

244. INVERSE HYPERBOLIC FUNCTIONS

On the graph of $y = \sinh x$ in Figure 410 on page 634, observe that y increases as x increases. Hence, from page 104, the equation $y = \sinh x$ defines x as a function of y, where this inverse of the function sinh will be called the **inverse hyperbolic sine,** denoted by $\sinh^{-1}$. It will be convenient to interchange the preceding roles of x and y; then, $\sinh^{-1} x$ is defined by the statement

$$y = \sinh^{-1} x \quad \text{is equivalent to} \quad x = \sinh y. \tag{1}$$

The graph of $y = \sinh^{-1} x$ in Figure 412 is the graph of $x = \sinh y$. The domain of the function $\sinh^{-1}$ is $-\infty < x < \infty$; the range of $\sinh^{-1}$ is $-\infty < y < \infty$.

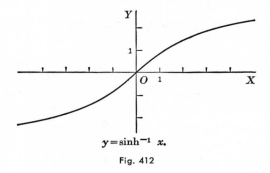

$$y = \sinh^{-1} x.$$

Fig. 412

On the graph of $y = \cosh x$ in Figure 409 on page 634, for each value of $y > 1$ there are *two values of x*, and hence the equation $y = \cosh x$ does *not* define x as a function (single-valued) of y. Therefore, to obtain an inverse (single-valued) of the function cosh, we use the restriction $x \geq 0$ in $y = \cosh x$. With the roles of x and y interchanged, Figure 413 shows the graph of $x = \cosh y$, with $y \geq 0$. The symmetrical part of the graph, where $y \leq 0$, is not to be used, and is shown lightly as a broken curve. In Figure 413, x increases as y increases and, from page 104, the equation $x = \cosh y$ defines y as a function of x, where this function will be called the **inverse hyperbolic cosine,** denoted by $\cosh^{-1}$. Thus, the inverse function's value, $\cosh^{-1} x$, is defined by the statement

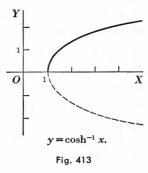

$$y = \cosh^{-1} x.$$

Fig. 413

$$(y \geq 0) \qquad y = \cosh^{-1} x \quad \text{is equivalent to} \quad x = \cosh y. \tag{2}$$

With $y = \cosh^{-1} x$, the domain of $\cosh^{-1}$ is $1 \leq x < \infty$, and the range is $0 \leq y < \infty$.

★*Note 1.* Occasionally, $\cosh^{-1}$ (with *small c*) is defined as a *two-valued function*, contrary to the best current usage restricting "*function*" to mean "*single-valued function.*" In such a case, Cosh^{-1} is met with the meaning adopted in (2) for $\cosh^{-1} x$ as in this text, and is called the *principal value* of $\cosh^{-1} x$. No possibility of a "*two-valued*" meaning arises for $\sinh^{-1} x$ and $\tanh^{-1} x$.

ILLUSTRATION 1. To obtain $v = \cosh^{-1} 1.1945$, write $\cosh v = 1.1945$. In Table V, $\cosh .61 = 1.1919$ and $\cosh .62 = 1.1984$. By interpolation,

$$v = \cosh^{-1} 1.1945 = .61 + \tfrac{2}{5}(.01) = .614.$$

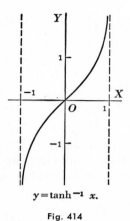

$y = \tanh^{-1} x.$

Fig. 414

A graph of $x = \tanh y$ is in Figure 414. Then, the inverse of tanh is denoted by $\tanh^{-1}$, and $\tanh^{-1} x$ is defined by the statement

$$x = \tanh y \quad \text{is equivalent to} \quad y = \tanh^{-1} x. \qquad (3)$$

With $y = \tanh^{-1} x$, the domain of the function $\tanh^{-1}$ is $-1 < x < 1$, and the range is $-\infty < y < \infty$.

Our major interest in presenting hyperbolic functions is to arrive where inverse hyperbolic functions may be used as a substitute for logarithmic forms in the evaluation of certain types of indefinite integrals. For this purpose, the following results (4) and (5) are essential. We also list (6) in case it should be desired to use $\tanh^{-1}$ or $\coth^{-1}$ in integration, which is not essential.

$(-\infty < x < \infty)$ $\qquad\qquad \sinh^{-1} x = \ln (x + \sqrt{x^2 + 1}).$ $\qquad\qquad (4)$

$(x \geqq 1)$ $\qquad\qquad\qquad \cosh^{-1} x = \ln (x + \sqrt{x^2 - 1}).$ $\qquad\qquad (5)$

$(-1 < x < 1)$ $\qquad\qquad \tanh^{-1} x = \dfrac{1}{2} \ln \dfrac{1 + x}{1 - x}.$ $\qquad\qquad (6)$

Proof of (4). From (1), if $y = \sinh^{-1} x$ then $x = \sinh y$, or

$$x = \tfrac{1}{2}(e^y - e^{-y}), \quad \text{or} \quad e^{2y} - 2xe^y - 1 = 0. \qquad (7)$$

In (7), let $u = e^y$. Then, $\qquad\qquad\qquad u^2 - 2xu - 1 = 0.$

Hence, by the quadratic formula, $\qquad u = e^y = x \pm \sqrt{x^2 + 1}. \qquad (8)$

In (8), we must use $+ \sqrt{x^2 + 1}$ because $e^y > 0$. Thus,

$$e^y = x + \sqrt{x^2 + 1} \quad \text{and} \quad y = \ln (x + \sqrt{x^2 + 1}) = \sinh^{-1} x.$$

Proof of (5). From (2) with $y \geq 0$, if $y = \cosh^{-1} x$ then $x = \cosh y$, or

$$x = \frac{e^y + e^{-y}}{2}; \quad \text{or} \quad e^{2y} - 2xe^y + 1 = 0; \qquad (9)$$

by the quadratic formula, $\qquad\qquad e^y = x \pm \sqrt{x^2 - 1}. \qquad (10)$

Since $y \geq 0$, we must choose the sign, $\pm$, in (10) which makes $e^y \geq 1$. We verify that $(x + \sqrt{x^2 - 1}) > 1$ if $x > 1$. Also,

$$(x + \sqrt{x^2 - 1})(x - \sqrt{x^2 - 1}) = x^2 - x^2 + 1 = 1.$$

Hence, if $x > 1$, $\qquad\qquad\qquad x - \sqrt{x^2 - 1} < 1.$

Therefore, in (10) we must choose $+ \sqrt{x^2 - 1}$, or

$$e^y = x + \sqrt{x^2 - 1}; \quad y = \ln (x + \sqrt{x^2 - 1}), \text{ or}$$

$$\cosh^{-1} x = \ln (x + \sqrt{x^2 - 1}), \quad \text{with} \quad x \geq 1. \qquad (11)$$

The student will have an opportunity to prove (6) later. By differentiation on the right in (4)–(6), we obtain

$$\frac{d \sinh^{-1} x}{dx} = \frac{1}{\sqrt{1 + x^2}}; \qquad \frac{d \cosh^{-1} x}{dx} = \frac{1}{\sqrt{x^2 - 1}}; \qquad (12)$$

$$\frac{d \tanh^{-1} x}{dx} = \frac{1}{1 - x^2}. \qquad (13)$$

Proof of (12) *for* $\sinh^{-1} x$. Let $f(x) = \sinh^{-1} x$. Then, from (4),

$$f'(x) = \frac{1}{x + \sqrt{x^2 + 1}} \left(1 + \frac{x}{\sqrt{x^2 + 1}}\right) = \frac{1}{\sqrt{x^2 + 1}}.$$

Proofs of the other formulas in (12)–(13) will be requested later. From (12)–(13), corresponding formulas are obtained for derivatives, differentials, and indefinite integrals, as follows, where $a > 0$ and u is any continuously differentiable function of x. We use (VII) on page 98 below.

$$\frac{d \sinh^{-1} u}{dx} = \frac{1}{\sqrt{1 + u^2}} \frac{du}{dx}, \quad or \quad d \sinh^{-1} u = \frac{du}{\sqrt{1 + u^2}}. \qquad (14)$$

$$\frac{d \cosh^{-1} u}{dx} = \frac{1}{\sqrt{u^2 - 1}} \frac{du}{dx}, \quad or \quad d \cosh^{-1} u = \frac{du}{\sqrt{u^2 - 1}}. \qquad (15)$$

$$\frac{d \tanh^{-1} u}{du} = \frac{1}{1 - u^2} \frac{du}{dx}, \quad or \quad d \tanh^{-1} u = \frac{du}{1 - u^2}. \qquad (16)$$

$$\int \frac{du}{\sqrt{a^2 + u^2}} = \sinh^{-1} \frac{u}{a} + C. \qquad (17)$$

$(u > a)$
$$\int \frac{du}{\sqrt{u^2 - a^2}} = \cosh^{-1} \frac{u}{a} + C. \qquad (18)$$

$(u < -a)$
$$= -\cosh^{-1} \left|\frac{u}{a}\right| + C. \qquad (19)$$

Proof of (14)–(16). If u is a differentiable function of x, and $f(u) = \sinh^{-1} u$, then

$$\frac{df(u)}{dx} = \frac{df(u)}{du} \cdot \frac{du}{dx} = \frac{1}{\sqrt{1 + u^2}} \frac{du}{dx}; \quad df(u) = \frac{du}{\sqrt{1 + u^2}}.$$

Similarly, the other results in (14)–(16) are obtained.

Proof of (18)–(19). 1. In (18) with $u > a$, let $u = av$. Then, $v > 1$ and, from (15) with a constant of integration omitted,

$$\int \frac{du}{\sqrt{u^2 - a^2}} = \int \frac{a \, dv}{a \sqrt{v^2 - 1}} = \int \frac{dv}{\sqrt{v^2 - 1}} = \cosh^{-1} v = \cosh^{-1} \frac{u}{a}.$$

2. To prove (19), let $u = -w$. Then, by use of (18),

$$\int \frac{du}{\sqrt{u^2 - a^2}} = -\int \frac{dw}{\sqrt{w^2 - a^2}} = -\cosh^{-1} \frac{w}{a} = -\cosh \left|\frac{u}{a}\right|,$$

because $w = |u|$. The student may prove (17).

ILLUSTRATION 2. $\qquad \displaystyle\int_5^6 \frac{dx}{\sqrt{x^2-9}} = \cosh^{-1}\frac{x}{3}\Big]_5^6 = .23.$ $\qquad$ (Table V)

ILLUSTRATION 3. To evaluate the following integral, use (19):

$$I = \int_{-6}^{-5} \frac{dx}{\sqrt{x^2-9}} = -\cosh^{-1}\left|\frac{x}{3}\right|\Big]_{-6}^{-5} = -(\cosh^{-1}1.6667 - \cosh^{-1}2) = .23.$$

When an extensive table of values of the hyperbolic functions is available, (17)–(19) sometimes are more convenient than the corresponding logarithmic formula (46) in Table VII, for computing definite integrals.

By use of (17), and (46) on page 704 for $\sqrt{u^2+a^2}$, we justify the remark about $\sinh^{-1}(u/a)$ in Note 6 on page 703, where $a > 0$ by a general agreement. The remark about $\sinh^{-1}|a/u|$ in that note is proved by substituting $x = a/|u|$ in (4) on page 637.

EXAMPLE 1. Prove that, if $a > 0$,

(when $u \geqq a$) $\qquad \ln|u + \sqrt{u^2-a^2}| = \cosh^{-1}\left|\frac{u}{a}\right| + \ln a;$ $\qquad$ (20)

(when $u \leqq -a$) $\qquad\qquad\qquad = -\cosh^{-1}\left|\frac{u}{a}\right| + \ln a.$ $\qquad$ (21)

Solution. 1. We verify that $(u + \sqrt{u^2-a^2})$ is positive or negative according as $u > a$ or $u < -a$. Hence, the absolute value signs are redundant if $u \geqq a$, in (20), but are essential in (21).

2. Assume that $u \geqq a$. Then, from (5),

$$\ln(u + \sqrt{u^2-a^2}) = \ln a\left(\frac{u}{a} + \sqrt{\left(\frac{u}{a}\right)^2 - 1}\right) = \ln a + \cosh^{-1}\frac{u}{a}. \qquad (22)$$

3. Assume that $u \leqq -a$, and let $w = -u = |u|$. Then,

$$\ln|u + \sqrt{u^2-a^2}| = \ln|-w + \sqrt{w^2-a^2}|.$$

We find $\qquad -w + \sqrt{w^2-a^2} = \dfrac{(\sqrt{w^2-a^2} - w)(\sqrt{w^2-a^2} + w)}{\sqrt{w^2-a^2} + w}$

$$= \frac{-a^2}{\sqrt{w^2-a^2} + w}.$$

Thus, we obtain

$$\ln|-w + \sqrt{w^2-a^2}| = \ln\frac{a^2}{\sqrt{w^2-a^2} + w}$$

$$= 2\ln a - \ln(\sqrt{w^2-a^2} + w)$$

[from (22)] $\qquad = 2\ln a - \cosh^{-1}\frac{w}{a} - \ln a = \ln a - \cosh^{-1}\left|\frac{u}{a}\right|.$

Notice that the right-hand side in (20) or (21) is a hyperbolic term *plus a constant*. Thus, the hyperbolic term may be used in place of the left-hand side, in the formula for any indefinite integral mentioned in Note 6 on page 703.

245. GEOMETRIC INTERPRETATION OF HYPERBOLIC FUNCTIONS

ILLUSTRATION 1. Let α be any angle and let $x = \cos \alpha$. For simplicity, assume that

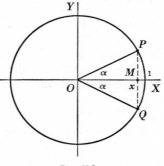

Fig. 415

$0 < \alpha < \frac{1}{2}\pi$. The circle in Figure 415 is a graph of $x^2 + y^2 = 1$. In Figure 415, construct $\angle XOP = \alpha$ and $\angle QOX = \alpha$, and let P have the coordinates (x, y). Then $OM = \cos \alpha = x$. The area, A, of the sector QOP of the circle is given by $\frac{1}{2}r^2(2\alpha)$, with $r = 1$, or

$$A = \alpha = \text{Cos}^{-1} x, \tag{1}$$

where we use $\text{Cos}^{-1} x$ in place of Arccos x.

ILLUSTRATION 2. Figure 416 shows a branch of the equilateral hyperbola $x^2 - y^2 = 1$. For any value of $x \geqq 1$, locate the corresponding points $P{:}(x, y)$ and $Q{:}(x, -y)$ on the hyperbola; let A be the area of the ruled sector OPQ. Then, by subtracting the area of the region bounded by the hyperbola and PQ, from the area of $\triangle OPQ$, we obtain

$$A = (\overline{OM})(\overline{MP}) - 2\int_1^x y \, dx$$

$$= x\sqrt{x^2 - 1} - 2\int_1^x \sqrt{x^2 - 1} \, dx.$$

Fig. 416

By use of the hyperbolic form for (41) in Table VII,

$$2\int_1^x \sqrt{x^2 - 1} \, dx = x\sqrt{x^2 - 1} - \cosh^{-1} x, \text{ and hence}$$

$$A = \cosh^{-1} x. \tag{2}$$

Let A be any number, to be interpreted as *the measure of an angle*, or *area* in Figure 415, and as the measure of *an area* in Figure 416. In either case, let x be the abscissa of the corresponding point P determined by A. Then, from (1), we may define $\text{Cos}^{-1} x$ by the relation $A = \text{Cos}^{-1} x$, or define $\cos A$ by the relation $x = \cos A$. From (2), similarly, we may define $\cosh^{-1} x$, or $\cosh A$, by the relation $A = \cosh^{-1} x$, or $x = \cosh A$. Although these definitions would be inconvenient, the similarity of the geometric backgrounds in Figures 415 and 416 justifies the similarities of the notations for trigonometric and hyperbolic functions. Also, we are led to anticipate the analogies which we have observed between properties of the two types of functions.

The preceding geometric backgrounds justify the names *circular functions* and *hyperbolic functions*, as previously applied.

Recall Euler's formula, (3) on page 580. Then, since $\cos(-x) = \cos x$ and $\sin(-x) = -\sin x$, we obtain the useful expression

$$e^{-ix} = \cos(-x) + i\sin(-x), \text{ or}$$

$$e^{-ix} = \cos x - i\sin x. \tag{3}$$

Also,
$$e^{ix} = \cos x + i\sin x. \tag{4}$$

Hence, on adding and then subtracting, we find

$$\cos x = \frac{1}{2}(e^{ix} + e^{-ix}); \qquad \sin x = \frac{1}{2i}(e^{ix} - e^{-ix}).$$

Thus, as another feature of similarity between circular and hyperbolic functions, $\cos x$ and $\sin x$ are expressible in terms of the exponentials e^{ix} and e^{-ix} by formulas which resemble (2) of page 633 for $\cosh x$ and $\sinh x$.

Note 1. Parametric equations for the circle $x^2 + y^2 = a^2$ are $x = a\cos t$ and $y = a\sin t$. The student may show that, analogously, parametric equations for the equilateral hyperbola $x^2 - y^2 = a^2$ are $x = a\cosh t$ and $y = a\sinh t$.

EXERCISE 191

1–20. Solve Problems 1–20, respectively, in Exercise 87 on page 288 by use of inverse hyperbolic forms for the indefinite integrals.

★21. Graph $y = \coth x$. Then, define $\coth^{-1} x$ and graph $y = \coth^{-1} x$.

★22. Prove (6) on page 637, and a corresponding formula for $\coth^{-1} x$.

★23. Prove formulas (25_1) and (25_2) in Table VII.

★Evaluate the integrals by use of (25_1) and (25_2) in Table VII.

24–37. Problems 1–14, respectively, in Exercise 85 on page 283.

★SUPPLEMENT FOR CHAPTER TWENTY–EIGHT

38. Find the centroid of (1) the arc of the catenary in Figure 27 on page 713 from $x = -a$ to $x = a$; (2) the region bounded by the catenary, the x-axis, and the lines $x = a$ and $x = -a$.

Assume that the function $f(x)$ has a continuous derivative, not identically zero, and that $f(x) \geqq 0$ for all values of x. In each of Problems 39–40, prove that, if f has the stated property, then the graph of $y = f(x)$ is a catenary (in standard form if the axes are chosen so that $y' = 0$ when $x = 0$).

39. *Given property:* the area of the region R bounded by the curve $y = f(x)$, the x-axis, and any two lines $x = x_1$ and $x = x_2$ is proportional to the arc length of the curve between $x = x_1$ and $x = x_2$. (Think of $x_2 = x$ as a variable.) Give explicit attention to any ambiguous sign.

40. *Given property:* If R represents the region of Problem 39, the volume of the solid obtained by revolving R about the x-axis is proportional to the curved area of the surface of the solid.

CHAPTER TWENTY-NINE

Differential Equations

246. REVIEW OF PREVIOUS RELATED CONTENT *

A *differential equation* in certain independent and related dependent variables is an equation involving at least one of the derivatives of the dependent variables. If there is just *one* independent variable, any derivative is an *ordinary derivative* and the equation is called an *ordinary differential equation*. Otherwise, the derivatives are *partial derivatives*, and the equation is called a *partial differential equation*.

ILLUSTRATION 1. The first equation below is an ordinary differential equation. The second equation is a partial differential equation.

$$x\frac{d^2y}{dx^2} - 3\frac{dy}{dx} - \cos x \sin y = 8x; \quad \frac{\partial^2 u}{\partial x^2} + \frac{\partial^2 u}{\partial y^2} = u \sin (x + y).$$

Hereafter, we shall consider only *ordinary* differential equations. Then, a single differential equation in an independent variable x, and one dependent variable y, usually determines a *family of functions*, where the values of any one of these functions are represented by y. Similarly, a system of n differential equations, with x as the independent variable, and n dependent variables, usually determines a family of *sets of n functions*, whose values are represented by the dependent variables. In this chapter, we shall treat only special cases of a *single* differential equation in two variables.

In a differential equation for y as a function of x, suppose that each side of the equation is a polynomial in the derivatives of y, with x possibly involved in coefficients. Then, the **degree** of the equation is defined as the exponent of the *highest power* of the derivative of *highest order* which occurs in the equation. We recall that the *order* of this derivative is called the **order** of the equation. Our discussion will be restricted mainly to differential equations of the first degree.

ILLUSTRATION 2. The following equation of the 3d order is of degree 4:

$$\left(\frac{d^3y}{dx^3}\right)^4 + 3y^5 \left(\frac{d^2y}{dx^2}\right)^6 - 2x \left(\frac{dy}{dx}\right)^5 = 8x.$$

* The student should review pages 202–207 and 290–298.

Note 1. In any differential equation with which we shall deal, we shall assume that any function involved is continuous in its arguments.

The **general solution** of a differential equation of order n is a solution involving n *arbitrary constants.* *To solve* a differential equation means to find its general solution, unless otherwise specified. To solve a differential equation, with certain initial conditions on the variables, means to find a particular case of the general solution satisfying the conditions.

A differential equation of the first order and first degree, defining y as a function of x, is of the form

$$P(x, y) + Q(x, y)\frac{dy}{dx} = 0. \tag{1}$$

We may write (1) in the form

$$Q(x, y) + P(x, y)\frac{dx}{dy} = 0, \tag{2}$$

where we think of the equation as defining x as a function of y. Or, we may write (1) in the differential form

$$P(x, y)dx + Q(x, y)dy = 0. \tag{3}$$

In (3), there is no visible commitment to choice of x or of y as the independent variable. If (3) is equivalent to

$$f(x)dx = g(y)dy, \tag{4}$$

we say that (3) is of **separable type**; in (4), we state that the **variables have been separated.** On page 294, we showed that the general solution of (4) is

$$\int f(x)dx = \int g(y)dy + C, \tag{5}$$

where $\int f(x)dx$ and $\int g(y)dy$ represent any particular indefinite integrals of the integrands. Also, on page 295, we obtained the following equation defining a *particular solution* of (4) for y as a function of x, or for x as a function of y, satisfying the initial conditions $x = a$ when $y = \alpha$:

$$\int_a^x f(t)dt = \int_\alpha^y g(u)du. \tag{6}$$

EXAMPLE 1. Obtain the solution of $x^2 \, dy + y^3 \, dx = 0$ satisfying the initial conditions $x = 2$ when $y = -1$.

Solution. 1. To separate the variables, divide by $x^2 y^3$:

$$\frac{dy}{y^3} = -\frac{dx}{x^2}. \tag{7}$$

2. By use of (6), the desired solution of (7) is

$$\int_{-1}^y \frac{du}{u^3} = -\int_2^x \frac{dt}{t^2}, \quad or \quad -\frac{1}{2u^2}\Big]_{-1}^y = \frac{1}{t}\Big]_2^x, \quad or$$

$$\frac{1}{2} - \frac{1}{2y^2} = \frac{1}{x} - \frac{1}{2}, \quad or \quad 2xy^2 - x = 2y^2.$$

EXAMPLE 2. Solve: $\qquad\qquad\qquad y' = x \cos 2x.$ $\qquad\qquad$ (8)

Solution. From (8), $dy = x \cos 2x\,dx$, which is a simple illustration of (4) with $g(y) = 1$. The general solution of (8) is obtained from (5):

$$\int dy = \int x \cos 2x\,dx + C, \quad or \quad y = \tfrac{1}{2}x \sin 2x + \tfrac{1}{4} \cos 2x + C. \qquad (9)$$

On the right-hand side, we integrated by parts:

$$\int x(\cos 2x\,dx) = \tfrac{1}{2}x \sin 2x - \tfrac{1}{2} \int \sin 2x = \tfrac{1}{2}x \sin 2x + \tfrac{1}{4} \cos 2x + C.$$

On page 291, we observed that, to solve an equation of the form $y^{(n)} = f(x)$, or $\dfrac{d^n y}{dx^n} = f(x)$, we may perform n successive integrations, each of which introduces a constant of integration.

EXAMPLE 3. Solve: $\qquad\qquad\qquad \dfrac{d^3 y}{dx^3} = \sin 3x - 2e^{-x}.$ $\qquad\qquad$ (10)

Solution. 1. Let $q = y''$. Then $\qquad\qquad \dfrac{dq}{dx} = \sin 3x - 2e^{-x}$, *or*

$$dq = (\sin 3x - 2e^{-x})dx; \quad \int dq = \int (\sin 3x - 2e^{-x})dx + C_1, \text{ or}$$

$$q = y'' = -\tfrac{1}{3}\cos 3x + 2e^{-x} + C_1.$$

2. Let $p = y'$. Then $\dfrac{dp}{dx} = y''$ *and*

$$\int dp = \int (-\tfrac{1}{3}\cos 3x + 2e^{-x} + C_1)dx + C_2, \text{ or}$$

$$p = -\tfrac{1}{9}\sin 3x - 2e^{-x} + C_1 x + C_2 = \dfrac{dy}{dx}.$$

Hence, $\qquad\qquad \int dy = \int (-\tfrac{1}{9}\sin 3x - 2e^{-x} + C_1 x + C_2)dx + C_3, \text{ or}$

$$y = \tfrac{1}{27}\cos 3x + 2e^{-x} + \tfrac{1}{2}C_1 x^2 + C_2 x + C_3.$$

Consider a differential equation of the first order, as in (1) or (3). We have seen that the general solution of the equation is of the form $f(x, y, c) = 0$, where c is an arbitrary constant. The equation $f(x, y, c) = 0$ is the equation of a *family of curves*, and we refer to the given equation, (1), or (3), as *the differential equation of the family*. This feature was mentioned on page 291. Conversely, suppose that we are given the equation $h(x, y, c) = 0$ of a family of curves. Then, we may obtain a differential equation for the family by differentiating in $h(x, y, c) = 0$ with respect to x, or y, and then eliminating c by use of the resulting equation and $h(x, y, c) = 0$. For review about this matter, the student should recall Example 1 on page 292.

EXERCISE 192

Verify the given solution of the differential equation.

1. $y'(x + y) + y = x$; solution, $y^2 + 2xy - x^2 = c$, where c is a constant.
2. $y'' = 9y$; solution, $y = c_1 e^{3x} + c_2 e^{-3x}$, where c_1 and c_2 are constants.

Find the general solution of the equation, or the particular solution satisfying the initial conditions. Obtain a solution not involving logarithms where convenient.

3. $\dfrac{d^2u}{dx^2} = 2e^x + \sin 2x.$
4. $\dfrac{d^3s}{dt^3} = e^{2t} + 6t.$

5. $(1 + 2y)dx + (1 + 2x)dy = 0.$
6. $2y(3 + x)dy = (1 + y^2)dx.$

7. $\sqrt{2 - x^2}\, dy = \sqrt{1 - y^2}\, dx;\ y = \frac{1}{2}$ when $x = 1.$

8. $(1 + x^2)y' = x(4 + y^2);\ x = 1$ when $y = 2.$

9. $y\, dx + x\, dy = 0;$ find the general solution in a form not involving logarithms; obtain the particular solutions passing through the points $(-2, 3)$ and $(2, 4)$, and sketch the graphs of these solutions.

Find an exponential form for the solution of the differential equation.

10. $\dfrac{dy}{dt} = 4y;\ y = 4$ when $t = 2.$
11. $\dfrac{ds}{dt} = -3s;\ s = 6$ when $t = -3.$

12. In the motion of a particle on an s-axis, the acceleration, a, at any time t seconds is given by $a = 3t + 2.$ If $s = 2$ and the velocity $v = -3$ at $t = 3$, find the equation of motion. (No vectors are employed for this rectilinear motion.)

Find a differential equation for the given family of curves, where c and k are parameters.

13. $x^2 - 5x = 2y^2 + c.$
14. $x^2 = 3cy.$
15. $s = c \cos (3t - k).$

16. Find the equation of the curve in the xy-plane through the point $(-2, 4)$ if the slope of the curve at any point (x, y) is $2x/3y^2.$

17. Without solving the equation $x^5 \sqrt[3]{y^3 + 7}\, dy = y^2\sqrt{20 + x^4}\, dx$, find the slope of that solution of the equation passing through the point $(x = 2, y = 1).$

18. In a cylindrical tank, let h be the height of the surface of the fluid above the center of an orifice through which the fluid is being discharged. Then, $dh/dt = -K\sqrt{h}$, where K is a positive constant depending on the physical situation and the units for t and h. (a) If $h = h_1$ when $t = t_1$, solve for h as a function of t by use of (4) on page 643. (b) If, besides, $h = h_2$ when $t = t_2$, express $(t_2 - t_1)$ in terms of h_1 and $h_2.$

19. A certain radioactive substance has a half-life of 2 years. (a) If a mass on hand today consists of h atoms of the substance, how many atoms will remain at the end of t years? (b) When will only 20% of the atoms remain? See Example 2 on page 298.

20. The half-life of strontium–90 is 28 years. How long will it take for 80% of a given mass of the element to decay?

247. HOMOGENEOUS EQUATIONS

To state that a differential equation of the first degree in x and y of the form

$$P(x, y)dx + Q(x, y)dy = 0 \qquad (1)$$

is of the **homogeneous type** means that the functions $P(x, y)$ and $Q(x, y)$ are homogeneous * and of the same degree. Then, we shall find that, if the variables are changed to (x, v) by the substitution $y = vx$, the new equation is of the *separable type* in (x, v). Thus, the following method of solution for a homogeneous equation (1) is available.

* As defined on page 591. The degree is not necessarily an integer.

1. *Substitute $y = vx$, to obtain a new equation, which always is of the separable type, in x and v.*

2. *Solve the equation in x and v, and then substitute $v = y/x$.*

In substituting $y = vx$ in (1), we replace dy by use of

$$dy = v\,dx + x\,dv. \tag{2}$$

Before solving (1) by use of $y = vx$, we may prefer to write, first,

$$\frac{dy}{dx} = -\frac{P(x, y)}{Q(x, y)}, \quad \text{and then use} \quad \frac{dy}{dx} = v + x\,\frac{dv}{dx}. \tag{3}$$

EXAMPLE 1. Solve: $\qquad\qquad (2xy + y^2)dx - x^2\,dy = 0. \tag{4}$

Solution. 1. The functions $(2xy + y^2)$ and $-x^2$ are homogeneous, of degree 2. Hence, we substitute $y = vx$ and use (2):

$$(2vx^2 + v^2x^2)dx - x^2(v\,dx + x\,dv) = 0.$$

Divide both sides by x^2, to obtain an equation of separable type:

$$(v^2 + v)dx - x\,dv = 0, \quad or \quad \frac{dx}{x} - \frac{dv}{v(v + 1)} = 0. \tag{5}$$

2. With $C > 0$, the general solution of (5) is

$$\int \frac{dx}{x} - \int \frac{dv}{v(v + 1)} = \ln C; \; or \tag{6}$$

$$\ln|x| - \ln|v| + \ln|v + 1| = \ln C; \; or$$

$$\ln\left|\frac{x(v + 1)}{v}\right| = \ln C; \quad or \quad \left|\frac{x(v + 1)}{v}\right| = C; \; or \tag{7}$$

$$\frac{x(v + 1)}{v} = K, \tag{8}$$

where K is an arbitrary constant, positive or negative. On substituting $v = y/x$ in (8), we obtain the general solution of (4): $\qquad x(x + y) = Ky$.

EXERCISE 193

Solve the equation by the method of Section 247, if applicable.

1. $2y\,dx - x\,dy = 0.$ **2.** $2xy\,dy = (3y^2 - x^2)dx.$ **3.** $x\,dy = -(4x + y)dx.$

4. $\dfrac{dy}{dx} = \dfrac{x^3y}{x^4 - y^4}.$ **5.** $\dfrac{ds}{dt} = \dfrac{s + 4t}{4s + t}.$ **6.** $w\,\dfrac{du}{dw} = u + w.$

7. $(x^2 + 3xy + y^2)dx - x^2\,dy = 0.$ **8.** $(2x + 3y)dx + (2y - 3x)dy = 0.$

9. $(y + 4x)dx + (x + y)dy = 0.$ **10.** $(4x + 3y)dx + (3x - y)dy = 0.$

11. $(6x + 5y)dx + (3y + 5x)dy = 0.$ **12.** $x\,dy + \left(x\cos\dfrac{y}{x}\right)dx = y\,dx.$

13. $(4y + 3x)dy - (3y + 4x)dx = 0.$

Find the particular solution of the equation satisfying the initial conditions.

14. $2x\,dy = (3y - 2x)dx; \; y = 0$ when $x = 1.$

15. $(2x - y)dx + (4y - x)dy = 0; \; y = 2$ when $x = -1.$

248. EXACT DIFFERENTIAL EQUATIONS

An expression $P(x, y)dx + Q(x, y)dy$ is called an **exact differential** * if and only if there exists a function $f(x, y)$ such that, if $u = f(x, y)$, then

$$du = P(x, y)dx + Q(x, y)dy. \tag{1}$$

ILLUSTRATION 1. The expression $x\,dy + y\,dx$ is an exact differential because $d(xy) = x\,dy + y\,dx$.

Hereafter, we shall assume that the functions P and Q in (1) have continuous first partial derivatives with respect to x and y.

Theorem I. *A necessary and sufficient condition for $P(x, y)dx + Q(x, y)dy$ to be an exact differential is that*

$$\frac{\partial P}{\partial y} = \frac{\partial Q}{\partial x}. \tag{2}$$

Proof of the necessity. We assume that there exists a differentiable function $f(x, y)$ such that, if $u = f(x, y)$, then (1) is true. We recall

$$du = \frac{\partial u}{\partial x}\,dx + \frac{\partial u}{\partial y}\,dy. \tag{3}$$

Then, from (1) and (3),

$$\frac{\partial u}{\partial x} = P(x, y) \quad and \quad \frac{\partial u}{\partial y} = Q(x, y). \tag{4}$$

Hence,

$$\frac{\partial^2 u}{\partial y\,\partial x} = \frac{\partial}{\partial y}\left(\frac{\partial u}{\partial x}\right) = \frac{\partial P}{\partial y}; \quad \frac{\partial^2 u}{\partial x\,\partial y} = \frac{\partial}{\partial x}\left(\frac{\partial u}{\partial y}\right) = \frac{\partial Q}{\partial x}. \tag{5}$$

Since $\dfrac{\partial^2 u}{\partial x\,\partial y} = \dfrac{\partial^2 u}{\partial y\,\partial x}$, we have proved (2).

Note 1. To establish the *sufficiency* of (2) in Theorem I, we would take (2) as an hypothesis and then prove that $f(x, y)$ exists so that, if $u = f(x, y)$, then (1) is true. The proof is found in Note 12 of the Appendix. Our later method for use of (2) essentially verifies the sufficiency in each application.

ILLUSTRATION 2. We find $(6x + 5y - y \cos xy)dx + (5x - x \cos xy)dy$ to be an exact differential because

$$\frac{\partial(6x + 5y - y \cos xy)}{\partial y} = 5 - \cos xy + xy \sin xy = \frac{\partial(5x - x \cos xy)}{\partial x}.$$

To state that a differential equation

$$P(x, y)dx + Q(x, y)dy = 0 \tag{6}$$

is **exact** means that its left-hand side is an **exact differential.** Hence, a necessary and sufficient condition for (6) to be exact is that (2) is true.

Theorem II. *If the equation $P(x, y)dx + Q(x, y)dy = 0$ is exact, it has the general solution $f(x, y) = C$, where C is an arbitrary constant and f is any function of two independent variables such that*

$$df(x, y) = P(x, y)dx + Q(x, y)dy. \tag{7}$$

---

* Also called a *perfect differential*, or simply a *differential*.

Proof. 1. From (7), $f_x(x, y) = P(x, y)$ *and* $f_y(x, y) = Q(x, y)$.

2. Let (6) be written $P(x, y) + Q(x, y)y' = 0$. Then, if $y = \psi(x)$ satisfies (6),

$$P(x, \psi(x)) + Q(x, \psi(x))\psi'(x) = f_x(x, \psi(x)) + f_y(x, \psi(x))\psi'(x) = 0. \qquad (8)$$

By the chain rule, if $y = \psi(x)$, on account of (8) we obtain

$$\frac{df(x, y)}{dx} = f_x(x, y) + f_y(x, y)\frac{dy}{dx} = f_x(x, \psi(x)) + f_y(x, \psi(x))\psi'(x) = 0. \qquad (9)$$

Or, if $y = \psi(x)$ satisfies (6), then $f(x, y) = C$ for some value of C.

3. Conversely, suppose that $y = \psi(x)$ satisfies $f(x, y) = C$ for some value of C. Then, again by the chain rule, we obtain (9), which can be rewritten

$$P(x, y) + Q(x, y)\frac{dy}{dx} = 0, \quad with \quad y = \psi(x). \qquad (10)$$

That is, $y = \psi(x)$ satisfies (6).

4. Hence, the set of all solutions $y = \psi(x)$ of (6) is the set of all solutions of $f(x, y) = C$ for y as a function of x, where C is an arbitrary constant, and thus Theorem II has been proved.

EXAMPLE 1. Solve $(9x^2 + 2y^2)dx + (4xy + 15y^2)dy = 0.$ \qquad (11)

Solution. 1. The equation is exact: $\dfrac{\partial(9x^2 + 2y^2)}{\partial y} = 4y = \dfrac{\partial(4xy + 15y^2)}{\partial x}.$

2. We seek $f(x, y)$ so that (11) will become $df(x, y) = 0$, or

$$f_x(x, y)dx + f_y(x, y)dy = (9x^2 + 2y^2)dx + (4xy + 15y^2)dy. \qquad (12)$$

3. From (12), $f_x(x, y)dx = (9x^2 + 2y^2)dx.$ \qquad (13)

With y considered as a constant temporarily, we integrate on both sides of (13), recognizing that the constant of integration may be of the form $\phi(y)$. With any indefinite integral representing any particular one of the possible expressions,

$$\int f_x(x, y)dx = \int (9x^2 + 2y^2)dx + \phi(y), \; or$$

$$f(x, y) = 3x^3 + 2xy^2 + \phi(y), \qquad (14)$$

where ϕ must possess a continuous derivative ϕ' because of the relation of ϕ to the other terms in (14).

4. From (12) and then (14),

$$f_y(x, y) = 4xy + 15y^2 = 4xy + \phi'(y), \; and \; hence$$

$$\phi'(y) = 15y^2; \quad \phi(y) = \int 15y^2 \, dy = 5y^3, \qquad (15)$$

where we omit a constant of integration because we are interested only in finding a particular function f. From (14) and (15), $f(x, y) = 3x^3 + 2xy^2 + 5y^3$. Hence, by Theorem II, the solution of (10) is

$$3x^3 + 2xy^2 + 5y^3 = C, \qquad (16)$$

where C is an arbitrary constant. As a brief check on (16), we compute the differential of both sides and verify that (11) is obtained.

Summary. *Solution of an exact equation $P(x, y)dx + Q(x, y)dy = 0$.*

1. *Search for $f(x, y)$ so that $df(x, y) = P(x, y)dx + Q(x, y)dy$, or*

$$f_x(x, y)dx + f_y(x, y)dy = P(x, y)dx + Q(x, y)dy.$$

2. *Let $\int P(x, y)dx = H(x, y)$. From $\int f_x(x, y)dx = \int P(x, y)dx$,*

$$f(x, y) = \int P(x, y)dx + \phi(y) = H(x, y) + \phi(y). \qquad (17)$$

3. *From $f_y(x, y) = Q(x, y) = H_y(x, y) + \phi'(y)$, obtain $\phi'(y)$.*

Then, $\phi(y) = \int \phi'(y)dy$ and (17) gives $f(x, y)$.

4. *The general solution is * $f(x, y) = C$. Check by calculating $df(x, y)$.*

Note 1. In the Summary, each symbol for an indefinite integral may be taken as any particular one of the possible forms, without an arbitrary constant.

Without using the test for exactness, we may show that a differential equation is exact, and obtain its solution, *by recognizing combinations of terms which form exact differentials.* In doing this, recall exact differentials from page 252, and note that *a sum of exact differentials is an exact differential.*

ILLUSTRATION 3. Any term $f(x)dx$ or $g(y)dy$ is an exact differential, because

$$f(x)dx = d\left[\int f(x)dx\right] \quad \text{and} \quad g(y)dy = d\left[\int g(y)dy\right].$$

Thus, any equation $f(x)dx + g(y)dy = 0$, where the variables are separated, is exact and is of the form $du = 0$ where $\qquad u = \int f(x)dx + \int g(y)dy$; the general solution is $\int f(x)dx + \int g(y)dy = C$, as on page 643.

ILLUSTRATION 4. We decide that the equation

$$(y + 2e^{2x+y})dx + (x + e^{2x+y})dy = x \, dx \qquad (18)$$

is exact, because we may group terms to obtain

$$(y \, dx + x \, dy) + e^{2x+y}(2 \, dx + dy) = x \, dx; \quad \text{or} \quad du + dv = dw,$$

where $\qquad u = xy, \quad v = e^{2x+y}, \quad \text{and} \quad w = \int x \, dx = \tfrac{1}{2}x^2.$

Hence, the general solution of (18) is $u + v = w + C$, or $xy + e^{2x+y} = \tfrac{1}{2}x^2 + C$.

A function $g(x, y)$ is called an **integrating factor** for (6) if it becomes exact after both sides are multiplied by $g(x, y)$. It can be proved † that any equation (6) has an unlimited number of integrating factors.

ILLUSTRATION 5. By the usual test, the equation $x \, dy - y \, dx = 0$ is not exact. If both sides are multiplied by $1/x^2$, we obtain

$$\frac{x \, dy - y \, dx}{x^2} = 0, \quad \text{or} \quad d\left(\frac{y}{x}\right) = 0, \qquad (19)$$

which is exact. Hence, $1/x^2$ is an integrating factor for $x \, dy - y \, dx = 0$; its solution, as obtained from (19), is $x^{-1}y = C$, or $y = Cx$. Another integrating factor is $1/xy$.

---

* If f and F are two possible functions here, their values differ by a constant, so that it is immaterial which function is used. See Problem 36 on page 632 concerning $f(x, y) = F(x, y) + k$.
† See page 14, *A First Course in Differential Equations*, by Rudolph E. Langer (New York: John Wiley & Sons, Inc., 1954).

EXERCISE 194

Test for exactness. Then, solve the equation if it is exact.

1. $(9x^2 + 8xy^2 + y)dx + (8x^2y + x + 4y)dy = 0.$

2. $(x - y)dx + (6y^2 - x)dy = 0.$ 3. $3x\,dx + 2x\,dy = 5y\,dy - 2y\,dx.$

4. $(6x + 5y)dx + (3y^2 - 5x)dy = 0.$

5. $(2e^{2x+3y} + y)dx + (3e^{2x+3y} + x)dy = 0.$

6. $(6x^2 + \ln y)dx + xy^{-1}\,dy = 12y^2\,dy.$

7. $(\cos y \cos x + x^{-1})dx + (y^{-1} + \sin x \sin y)dy = 0.$

8. $3 \sin x \cos x\,dx + 5 \sin y \cos y\,dy = 0.$

9. $e^{3x}\dfrac{dy}{dx} + 3ye^{3x} = 0.$ 10. $3xe^x\dfrac{dx}{dy} = \cos y.$

11. $x^{-1}e^{2y}\,dx + 2(\ln x)e^{2y}\,dy = 0.$

12. $ye^x\,dx + xye^x\,dx + y^{-1}\,dy + x^{-1}\,dx + xe^x\,dy = 0.$

13. Find the equation of a curve in the xy-plane passing through the point $(3, -1)$, if the slope of the curve at any point (x, y) is equal to $(3x + 3y)/(y - 3x)$.

Group terms into one or more exact differentials, in order to see that the equation is exact. Then, solve the equation.

14. $x^2\,dy + 2xy\,dx + xe^{xy}\,dy + ye^{xy}\,dx = 0.$

15. $\dfrac{2x\,dx}{x^2 + y^2} + \dfrac{2y\,dy}{x^2 + y^2} = x^3\,dx + y^2\,dy.$

16. $2 \cos (2x + 3y)\,dx + 3 \cos (2x + 3y)\,dy = x\,dy + y\,dx.$

Prove that the specified integrating factor makes the equation exact; then, find the general solution of the equation.

17. $x\,dy - y\,dx = 0$; integrating factor, $1/xy.$

18. $x\,dy - 2y\,dx = x^4\,dx$; integrating factor, $1/x^3.$

19. $y\,dx + dy = e^x\,dx$; integrating factor, $e^x.$

20. $dy + y \sec^2 x\,dx = \sec^2 x\,dx$; integrating factor, $e^{\tan x}.$

249. LINEAR DIFFERENTIAL EQUATIONS OF THE FIRST ORDER

A differential equation of the first order, defining y as a function of x, is said to be linear with respect to y if the equation is of the first degree in y and y' jointly. Hence, the coefficients of y and of y' in the equation are functions of x alone. If both sides of the equation are divided by the coefficient of y', the equation can be written in the standard form

$$\frac{dy}{dx} + p(x)y = q(x),\ or \tag{1}$$

$$dy + p(x)y\,dx = q(x)dx, \tag{2}$$

where we assume that the functions p and q are continuous on the domain for x. When a differential equation of the first order is written in differential form, we recognize linearity with respect to y by observing that the equation is *linear in y and dy jointly*.

ILLUSTRATION 1. The following equations are linear in y:

$$x^3 \frac{dy}{dx} + y \sin x = e^z; \quad x^2 \, dy + (\ln x)y \, dx = \cos x \, dx.$$

The following equation is linear in x, with y as the independent variable:

$$y^2 \frac{dx}{dy} + x \tan y = \cos y, \quad or \quad y^2 \, dx + x \tan y \, dy = \cos y \, dy.$$

Theorem III. *An integrating factor for* (2) *is* $e^{\int p(x)dx}$, *where* $\int p(x)dx$ *is any particular indefinite integral of* $p(x)$.

Proof. Suppose that the nonnegative function $\sigma(x)$ is an integrating factor for (2). Then, on multiplying both sides of (2) by $\sigma(x)$, we obtain the exact equation

$$\sigma(x)dy + p(x)y\sigma(x)dx = q(x)\sigma(x)dx. \tag{3}$$

The right-hand side of (3) is an exact differential if σ is continuous, because

$$q(x)\sigma(x)dx = d\big(\int q(x)\sigma(x)dx \big).$$

Hence, (3) will be exact if and only if the left-hand side is an exact differential. By Theorem I on page 647, the preceding fact will be true if

$$\frac{d\sigma(x)}{dx} = \frac{\partial}{\partial y}[p(x)y\sigma(x)], \quad or \quad \frac{d\sigma(x)}{dx} = p(x)\sigma(x). \tag{4}$$

From (4), $\dfrac{d\sigma(x)}{\sigma(x)} = p(x)dx$, or $\ln \sigma(x) = \int p(x)dx$, or $\sigma(x) = e^{\int p(x)dx}$.

Theorem IV. *The general solution of* $y' + p(x)y = q(x)$ *is*

$$ye^{\int p(x)dx} = \int q(x)e^{\int p(x)dx} \, dx + C, \tag{5}$$

where C is an arbitrary constant.

Proof. Multiply in (2) by the integrating factor $e^{\int p(x)dx}$:

$$e^{\int p(x)dx} dy + p(x)e^{\int p(x)dx} y \, dx = q(x)e^{\int p(x)dx} dx. \tag{6}$$

We verify that

$$d[ye^{\int p(x)dx}] = e^{\int p(x)dx} dy + y \, d[e^{\int p(x)dx}] = e^{\int p(x)dx} dy + ye^{\int p(x)dx} p(x)dx,$$

because $d\big[\int p(x)dx \big] = p(x)dx$. Hence, (6) becomes

$$d[ye^{\int p(x)dx}] = d\big[\int q(x)e^{\int p(x)dx} \, dx \big]. \tag{7}$$

On integrating in (7) we obtain (5).

EXAMPLE 1. Solve: $\qquad\qquad xy' - 2y = x^5.$ $\qquad\qquad$ (8)

Solution. 1. To change (8) to the form (1), divide by x: $\quad \dfrac{dy}{dx} - \dfrac{2}{x}y = x^4,$ $\quad$ (9)

where $p(x) = -2/x$ and $q(x) = x^4$. For use in (5), we obtain

$$\int p(x)dx = -2 \int \frac{dx}{x} = -2 \ln |x| = -\ln x^2 = \ln \frac{1}{x^2}; \quad e^{\int p(x)dx} = \frac{1}{x^2}.$$

2. From (5), $\quad y \cdot \dfrac{1}{x^2} = \int x^4 \cdot \dfrac{1}{x^2} dx + C,$ *or* $\dfrac{y}{x^2} = \dfrac{x^3}{3} + C,$ *or* $y = \tfrac{1}{3}x^5 + Cx^2.$

EXERCISE 195

Solve the equation by the preceding method.

1. $x\dfrac{dy}{dx} + y = x^4$.

2. $x\dfrac{dy}{dx} + 2y = -x^{-3}$.

3. $y' + y \cot x = 2 \cos x$.

4. $y' - y \tan x = 3 \cos^3 x$.

5. $\dfrac{ds}{dt} = 3s + 5$.

6. $\dfrac{dx}{dy} + 4x = e^{3y}$.

7. $x\,dy + y\,dx = e^x\,dx$.

8. $t\,ds - 2s\,dt = (t^5 + t^2)dt$.

9. $dx + x \tan y\,dy = \sec y\,dy$.

10. $dy - my\,dx = 0$.

11. $2uv\,du - 2u\,du + dv = 0$.

12. $xy' - 2y + x^3 e^{2x} - x^4 = 0$.

13. $dy + y\,dx = \cos x\,dx + \sin x\,dx$.

14. $\dfrac{ds}{dt} = \dfrac{\cos^3 t - s \sin t}{\cos t}$.

15. $\dfrac{du}{dv} = \dfrac{(v + 2)^3 - 3u}{v + 2}$.

16. $s\dfrac{dt}{ds} + t = s \cos 3s$.

17. $x\dfrac{dy}{dx} - 2y = x^4 \sin 2x$.

18. $\dfrac{dy}{dx} = (1 - y)\cos x$.

19. $\dfrac{dx}{dy} = e^y - 2x \cot 2y$.

20. $3y\,dx - x\,dy + 5x^5(\ln x)dx = 0$.

21. $3xy\,dx + x^2\,dy - \text{Arctan } x\,dx = 0$.

Find the particular solution satisfying the initial conditions.

22. $y' + 2y \cot 2x = \cos 2x + 1$; $y = 2$ when $x = \frac{1}{4}\pi$.

23. $x(2x + 1)dy = 2x(2x + 1)dx - y\,dx$; $y = 3$ when $x = 2$.

24. The differential equation specifying the current i in an electric circuit involving a constant resistance R and inductance L, due to an impressed electromotive force E, at any instant of time t, is

$$E = Ri + L\frac{di}{dt}.$$

Solve the preceding equation (*a*) if E is a constant; (*b*) if $E = k \sin \omega t$ where k and ω are constants.

250. CERTAIN TYPES OF EQUATIONS OF THE SECOND ORDER

If a differential equation of the second order defines y as a function of x, and if y is not involved explicitly in the equation, it can be written in the following form:

Type I: $F(x, y', y'') = 0,$ (1)

where F is some function of (x, y', y''). It is sometimes possible to solve (1) by commencing with the substitution $p = y'$, which changes (1) into $F(x, p, p') = 0$, a differential equation of the first order in x and p. After p, or y', is obtained as a function of x, the resulting equation of the first order is solved to obtain y as a function of x.

EXAMPLE 1. Solve: $x^2 y'' + 2xy' = 3.$ (2)

Solution. 1. Let $p = y'$. Then, $y'' = \dfrac{dp}{dx}$ and (2) becomes

$$x^2 \frac{dp}{dx} + 2xp = 3, \quad or \quad \frac{dp}{dx} + \frac{2}{x}p = \frac{3}{x^2}, \tag{3}$$

which is linear in p. By the method of Section 249, with an assumption for convenience that $x > 0$, we solve (3):

$$px^2 = 3x + C_1, \quad or \quad x^2 y' = 3x + C_1. \tag{4}$$

2. From (4), $\qquad\qquad dy = 3x^{-1}\, dx + C_1 x^{-2}\, dx. \tag{5}$

On solving (5), we obtain the general solution of (2):

$$y = \ln x^3 + K_1 x^{-1} + C_2, \tag{6}$$

where $K_1 = - C_1$, and K_1 and C_2 are arbitrary constants.

If a differential equation of the second order defines y as a function of x, and involves just y'' and y, the equation can be written as follows:

Type II: $\qquad\qquad\qquad y'' = f(y), \tag{7}$

where $f(y)$, as indicated, is a function of y alone. To solve (7), we use $y'' = dy'/dx$, and multiply both sides by $y'\, dx$. Then, since $y'\, dx = dy$,

$$y'\, dy' = f(y)y'\, dx, \quad or \quad y'\, dy' = f(y)dy, \tag{8}$$

which is of separable type, in y and y'. By solving (8) for y' in terms of y, we obtain an equation of the first order defining y as a function of x.

EXAMPLE 2. Solve: $\qquad\qquad\qquad y'' = - y^{-3}. \tag{9}$

Solution. 1. Use $y'' = dy'/dx$, and multiply by $2y'$ in (9):

$$2y' \frac{dy'}{dx} = - \frac{2y'}{y^3}, \quad or \quad 2y'\, dy' = - \frac{2\, dy}{y^3}, \tag{10}$$

because, on the right, $y'\, dx = dy$. On integrating in (10), we obtain

$$\int 2y'\, dy' = - \int \frac{2\, dy}{y^3} + c_1, \quad or \quad y'^2 = \frac{1}{y^2} + c_1.$$

2. Hence, $\qquad\qquad\qquad y'y = \pm \sqrt{1 + c_1 y^2}$, or

$$\pm \frac{y\, dy}{\sqrt{1 + c_1 y^2}} = dx; \quad \pm \int \frac{y\, dy}{\sqrt{1 + c_1 y^2}} = \int dx. \tag{11}$$

From (11), $\qquad + \frac{\sqrt{1 + c_1 y^2}}{c_1} = x + c_2 \quad or \quad - \frac{\sqrt{1 + c_1 y^2}}{c_1} = x + c_3. \tag{12}$

Either equation in (12) is a solution of (9). If we agree to take $c_2 = c_3$, then the two equations in (12) are equivalent to the single equation

$$\left(x + c_2 - \frac{\sqrt{1 + c_1 y^2}}{c_1}\right)\left(x + c_2 + \frac{\sqrt{1 + c_1 y^2}}{c_1}\right) = 0, \, or \tag{13}$$

(with $c_1 c_2 = k_1$) $\qquad\qquad 1 + c_1 y^2 = (c_1 x + k_1)^2. \tag{14}$

Comment. Sometimes, in the answers to exercises, an agreement like that used in (13) is responsible for the form of the listed answer.

EXERCISE 196

Find the general solution of the equation.

1. $y'' + y' - 3e^x = 0$.   **2.** $xy'' + 2y' = 8$.

3. $y''(x + 1) + y' = 0$.   **4.** $y'' = y' + xe^{-x}$.

5. $x\dfrac{d^2y}{dx^2} + \dfrac{dy}{dx} = x^3$.   **6.** $\dfrac{d^2s}{dt^2} = \dfrac{1}{s^3}$.   **7.** $\dfrac{d^2y}{dx^2} = -\dfrac{4}{y^3}$.

8. $\dfrac{d^2s}{dt^2} = -(s - 1)$.   **9.** $\dfrac{d^2u}{dv^2} = -4u$.   **10.** $\dfrac{d^2y}{dx^2} = -9y$.

11. $\dfrac{d^2y}{dx^2} + x = \sin 2x$.   **12.** $x\dfrac{d^2y}{dx^2} + x^3 = 4$.   **13.** $\dfrac{d^2y}{dx^2} e^x - x = 1$.

Find the solution of the differential equation satisfying the initial conditions.

14. $x\dfrac{d^2y}{dx^2} - 3\dfrac{dy}{dx} = 3x^4$; $y = 1$ and $\dfrac{dy}{dx} = 5$ when $x = 1$.

15. $\dfrac{d^2s}{dt^2} = 2s^3$; $s = 2$ and $s' = 4$ when $t = 2$.

16. A particle P moves on an s-axis with the acceleration, a, at any time t given by $a = -2s^{-2}$. If P is at $s = 4$ with the velocity $v = 1$ when $t = 0$, obtain the co-ordinate s of P at any time t.

251. ORTHOGONAL TRAJECTORIES

Note 1. In an xy-plane, a curve C will be called a **smooth curve** if it can be defined parametrically in the form $[x = \phi(t), y = \psi(t)]$ where ϕ' and ψ' exist, are continuous, and $\phi'^2(t) + \psi'^2(t) \neq 0$ at any value of t. Thus, a smooth curve has a tangent at each point and the tangent at $P:(x, y)$ on C turns continuously as P moves on C.

A curve U is called an *orthogonal trajectory* of a family F of smooth curves if U cuts each curve of F orthogonally (at right angles). Two families F and G of smooth curves are said to be *mutually orthogonal* if each curve of G is an orthogonal trajectory of F. Then, also, each curve of F is an orthogonal trajectory of G. Suppose that F is defined by

$$f(x, y, c) = 0, \qquad\qquad (1)$$

where c is a parameter, and that a curve V of F passes through each point $P:(x_0, y_0)$ in a corresponding region. Then, as a rule, there exists just one family G of orthogonal trajectories for F with the property that a curve U of G passes through each point $P:(x_0, y_0)$.

Note 2. Mutually orthogonal families of curves are of interest in applied mathematics. Thus, the curves of one family may be lines of force, curves of flow, or streamlines, while the curves of the other family are equipotential curves, level curves, or isothermal lines, respectively.

ILLUSTRATION 1. The family of circles $x^2 + y^2 = c^2$ is cut orthogonally by the straight lines $y = kx$, where c and k are parameters.

The following method for finding orthogonal trajectories is based on the fact that lines with slopes m and $-1/m$ are perpendicular.

Summary. *To find the family, G, of curves orthogonal to a family, F, of curves where an equation for F is f(x, y, c) = 0:*

1. *Derive a differential equation for F by considering y as a function of x, differentiating with respect to x in f(x, y, c) = 0, and using the result with f(x, y, c) = 0 to eliminate c.*

2. *In the differential equation for F, replace y′ by − 1/y′ to obtain a differential equation for the orthogonal family G. Then, find the general solution of this differential equation to obtain an equation for G.*

EXAMPLE 1. Obtain the family G of orthogonal trajectories for the family F defined by the following equation, where c is a parameter: $\qquad x^2 = 4cy.$ $\qquad$ (2)

Solution. 1. Parabolas of the family F defined by (2) are seen in Figure 417. To obtain a differential equation for F, differentiate with respect to x on both sides of (2), and eliminate c from the resulting equation by use of $c = x^2/4y$ from (2):

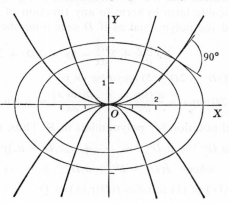

Fig. 417

$$2x = 4c\frac{dy}{dx}, \quad or \quad 2x = \frac{x^2}{y}y', \quad or \quad 2y = xy'. \qquad (3)$$

2. In (3), replace $y′$ by $- 1/y'$, where $y′$ now is the slope for an orthogonal trajectory at an arbitrary point (x, y), to obtain a differential equation for G:

$$2yy' = - x, \quad or \quad 2y\,dy + x\,dx = 0. \qquad (4)$$

The general solution of (4) is $2y^2 + x^2 = k^2$, where k^2 is an arbitrary constant. Thus, G is a family of ellipses, illustrated in Figure 417.

EXERCISE 197

If c is an arbitrary constant, find (a) the differential equation of the given family of curves and (b) an equation for the family of orthogonal trajectories of the given curves.

1. $y^2 = 4(x - c)$. $\qquad$ 2. $x^2 = 2(c - y)$. $\qquad$ 3. $x^2 + y^2 = c^2$.

4. $y = cx$. $\qquad$ 5. $4x^2 + y^2 = c^2$. $\qquad$ 6. $x^2 + cy^2 = 4$.

7. $y^2 - x^2 = c$. $\qquad$ 8. $xy = c$. $\qquad$ 9. $y = ce^x$.

252. LINEAR DIFFERENTIAL EQUATIONS AND THE OPERATOR D

A linear differential equation of order n, defining y as a function of x, can be written in the form

$$\frac{d^n y}{dx^n} + a_1 \frac{d^{n-1} y}{dx^{n-1}} + a_2 \frac{d^{n-2} y}{dx^{n-2}} + \cdots + a_{n-1} \frac{dy}{dx} + a_n y = Q, \tag{1}$$

where the variables $a_1, a_2, \cdots, a_n, Q$ are functions of x alone. If Q is 0, then (1) is said to be *homogeneous*. Hereafter, in our limited discussion of (1), we shall assume that the coefficients $a_1, a_2, \cdots, a_n$ are constants.

In dealing with (1), it is convenient to use "D," as on page 80, for differentiation with respect to x, and D^k for k successive differentiations with respect to x. If c is a constant, $(cD^k)y$ is defined by

$$(cD^k)y = cD^k y = c\frac{d^k y}{dx^k}, \tag{2}$$

with the added agreement that $(cD^0)y = cy$. Then, any polynomial in D is taken as an *operator* applicable term by term to any function of x possessing enough derivatives. We read the polynomial as if D were a number of algebra.

ILLUSTRATION 1. $\qquad 3\frac{d^2 y}{dx^2} + 2\frac{dy}{dx} - 5y = (3D^2 + 2D - 5)y,$

which we read "$(3D^2 + 2D - 5)$ *operating on* y."

$$(D^2 - 2D)\sin x = \frac{d^2(\sin x)}{dx^2} - 2\frac{d(\sin x)}{dx} = -\sin x - 2\cos x.$$

We use functional notation for polynomials in D. Thus, (1) becomes

$$(D^n + a_1 D^{n-1} + a_2 D^{n-2} + \cdots + a_{n-1} D + a_n)y = Q, \text{ or} \tag{3}$$

$$f(D)y = Q, \quad \text{where} \quad f(D) = D^n + a_1 D^{n-1} + \cdots + a_{n-1} D + a_n. \tag{4}$$

Any solution $y = y_1(x)$ of (1) satisfies $f(D)y_1(x) = Q$.

ILLUSTRATION 2. The equation $(D^2 - 5D + 6)y = e^{4x}$ has the solution $y = \frac{1}{2}e^{4x}$ because $D(\frac{1}{2}e^{4x}) = 2e^{4x}$, $D^2(\frac{1}{2}e^{4x}) = 8e^{4x}$, and thus

$$(D^2 - 5D + 6)(\frac{1}{2}e^{4x}) = 8e^{4x} - 10e^{4x} + 3e^{4x} = e^{4x}. \tag{5}$$

To indicate successive operations by polynomials in D, we write the polynomials side by side, and we call the result an *operational product*. By the properties of differentiation with respect to x,

$$D^m(D^n y) = D^n(D^m y) = D^{n+m} y. \tag{6}$$

Thus, powers of D are commutative and obey the law of exponents for multiplication. We conclude finally that, in an operational product of polynomials in D, we may act as if D is a number of algebra in formal multiplication, or factoring, before operating on any function of x.

ILLUSTRATION 3. $\qquad (D - 2)(D - 3)y = (D^2 - 5D + 6)y = y'' - 5y' + 6y.$

Since the derivative of a sum of functions is equal to the sum of their derivatives, $f(D)$ is a *linear operator* as applied to linear combinations of functions with constant coefficients. If c_1 and c_2 are constants, and y_1 and y_2 are functions of x,

$$f(D)(c_1 y_1 + c_2 y_2) = c_1 f(D) y_1 + c_2 f(D) y_2. \tag{7}$$

The following theorems are useful in solving the homogeneous equation

$$f(D)y = 0, \tag{8}$$

where $f(D)$ is defined in (4). We shall use the results only when $a_1, a_2, \cdots, a_n$ in (4) are constants, but we note that the following theorems and their proofs are unaltered when the coefficients are functions of x.

Theorem V. *If $y = y_1(x)$ is a solution of a homogeneous equation $f(D)y = 0$, and c is any constant, then $y = cy_1(x)$ is a solution.*

Proof. By hypothesis, $f(D)y_1(x) = 0$. Hence,

$$f(D)[cy_1(x)] = cf(D)y_1(x) = 0,$$

which proves that $y = cy_1(x)$ is a solution of $f(D)y = 0$.

Theorem VI. *If $y = y_1(x)$ and $y = y_2(x)$ are solutions of a homogeneous equation $f(D)y = 0$, then $y = y_1(x) + y_2(x)$ is a solution.*

Proof. By hypothesis, $f(D)y_1(x) = f(D)y_2(x) = 0$. Hence,

$$f(D)[y_1(x) + y_2(x)] = f(D)y_1(x) + f(D)y_2(x) = 0 + 0 = 0,$$

which states that $y = y_1(x) + y_2(x)$ satisfies $f(D)y = 0$.

Note 1. To say that certain functions are **linearly independent,** means that it is *impossible* to express any one of them as a linear combination of the others, with constant coefficients. If the functions are *not* linearly independent, they are said to be **linearly dependent.** Then, at least one of them can be expressed as a linear combination of the others.

Theorem VII. *If $y_1(x)$, $y_2(x)$, $\cdots$, $y_n(x)$ are n linearly independent* solutions of a homogeneous linear differential equation (8) of order n, then the general solution of the equation is*

$$y = c_1 y_1(x) + c_2 y_2(x) + \cdots + c_n y_n(x), \tag{9}$$

where $c_1, c_2, \cdots, c_n$ are arbitrary constants.

Proof. (*Written for the case $n = 2$.*) We have the solutions $y = y_1(x)$ and $y = y_2(x)$. Then, by Theorem V, $y = c_1 y_1(x)$ and $y = c_2 y_2(x)$ are solutions. Hence, by Theorem VI, the equation $f(D)y = 0$ has the solution

$$y = c_1 y_1(x) + c_2 y_2(x), \tag{10}$$

where c_1 and c_2 are arbitrary constants.

Note 2. It is interesting to observe why (10) is *not* the general solution of $f(D)y = 0$ if $y_1(x)$ and $y_2(x)$ are *linearly dependent*. In this case, we may suppose that $y_2(x) = hy_1(x)$, where h is a fixed constant, and (10) becomes

$$y = c_1 y_1(x) + c_2 h y_1(x) = (c_1 + hc_2) y_1(x), \tag{11}$$

where $c_1 + hc_2 = k$, a single arbitrary constant. Hence, (10) yields only those solutions where y is a multiple of $y_1(x)$, and (10) is not the general solution of $f(D)y = 0$.

* It is beyond our level to discuss why linear independence is essential.

EXERCISE 198

In the problems, D means d/dx. Carry out each indicated operation.

1. $D(xe^{2x})$; $D^2(xe^{2x})$; $D^3(xe^{2x})$.   **2.** De^{4x}; D^2e^{4x}; D^3e^{4x}; D^ke^{4x}.

3. De^{mx}; D^3e^{mx}; D^ke^{mx}.   **4.** $(D + 2)(x^2 + \sin 3x)$.

5. $(D - 3)\sin x$.   **6.** $(D + 5)\cos 2x$.   **7.** $(D^2 - 3)\sin 3x$.

8. $(D - 2)(D + 3)xe^{3x}$.   **9.** $(D + 3)(D - 1)e^{-2x}$.

10. $D(D - 2)\sin 3x$.   **11.** $D^2(D + 1)\cos 2x$.

12. Prove that $(D - a)[(D - b)y] = (D - b)[(D - a)y]$.

13. Write the differential equation by use of D: $4y'' + 3y' + 2y = \sin x$.

Verify the statement by substitution in the differential equation.

14. $y = e^{3x}$ is a solution of $(D^2 - 2D - 3)y = 0$.

15. $y = e^{-x} \sin 2x$ and $y = e^{-x} \cos 2x$ are solutions of $(D^2 + 2D + 5)y = 0$.

16. $y = \frac{1}{3}e^x$ is a solution of $(D^2 + 5D - 3)y = -e^x$.

253. HOMOGENEOUS CASE, REAL CHARACTERISTIC ROOTS

Consider the homogeneous linear differential equation

$$\frac{d^2y}{dx^2} + a_1 \frac{dy}{dx} + a_2y = 0, \quad or \quad f(D)y = 0, \tag{1}$$

where

$$f(D) = D^2 + a_1D + a_2, \tag{2}$$

in which a_1 and a_2 are constants. In Problem 10, page 652, we found that the linear equation of the first order $y' - my = 0$ has the solution $y = ce^{mx}$, which suggests seeking similar solutions for (1).

Theorem VIII. *The equation $f(D)y = 0$ is satisfied by $y = e^{mx}$ if and only if*

$$f(m) = 0, \quad or \quad m^2 + a_1m + a_2 = 0. \tag{3}$$

Proof. To obtain m so that $y = e^{mx}$ satisfies (1), we substitute $y = e^{mx}$, $y' = me^{mx}$, and $y'' = m^2e^{mx}$ in (1), and find

$$m^2e^{mx} + a_1me^{mx} + a_2e^{mx} = 0, \quad or \quad e^{mx}(m^2 + a_1m + a_2) = 0. \tag{4}$$

Since $e^{mx} \neq 0$ for any values of m and x, from (4) we obtain (3).

We shall call (3) the *characteristic equation* for (1). The roots of (3) will be called the *characteristic exponents* for (1). These roots may be real and distinct, real and equal, or imaginary. Theorem VII proves the following result.

Corollary 1. *If the characteristic equation has distinct real roots $m = m_1$ and $m = m_2$, then (1) has the linearly independent solutions e^{m_1x} and e^{m_2x}, and the general solution*

$$y = c_1e^{m_1x} + c_2e^{m_2x}. \tag{5}$$

ILLUSTRATION 1. The characteristic equation for

$$y'' - 3y' - 4y = 0, \quad or \quad (D^2 - 3D - 4)y = 0, \tag{6}$$

is $m^2 - 3m - 4 = 0$, whose roots are $m = 4$ and $m = -1$. Hence, the general solution of (6) is $y = c_1e^{4x} + c_2e^{-x}$.

Theorem IX. *If the characteristic equation has a double root* $m = m_1$, *then* (1) *has the solutions* $e^{m_1 x}$ *and* $xe^{m_2 x}$, *and the general solution*

$$y = e^{m_1 x}(c_1 x + c_2). \tag{7}$$

Proof. 1. By hypothesis, (3) can be written $f(m) = (m - m_1)^2 = 0$. Then, $f(D) = (D - m_1)^2$, and (1) becomes

$$(D - m_1)(D - m_1)y = 0. \tag{8}$$

2. Let $v = (D - m_1)y$. Then (8) becomes $\qquad (D - m_1)v = 0. \tag{9}$

By Problem 10 on page 652, the solution of (9) is $v = c_1 e^{m_1 x}$. Hence, from the equation $v = (D - m_1)y$,

$$(D - m_1)y = c_1 e^{m_1 x}, \quad or \quad \frac{dy}{dx} - m_1 y = c_1 e^{m_1 x}. \tag{10}$$

By use of (5) on page 651, with $p(x) = -m_1$, the solution of (10) is

$$ye^{-m_1 x} = c_1 \int e^{-m_1 x} e^{m_1 x}\, dx + c_2 = c_1 x + c_2. \tag{11}$$

On multiplying by $e^{m_1 x}$ in (11), we obtain the general solution of (1):

$$y = (c_1 x + c_2)e^{m_1 x}. \tag{12}$$

3. We obtain the particular solutions $y = xe^{m_1 x}$ and $y = e^{m_1 x}$ from (12) by using $(c_1 = 1, c_2 = 0)$ and $(c_1 = 0, c_2 = 1)$, respectively.

EXAMPLE 1. Find the particular solution of $y'' - 6y' + 9y = 0$ which satisfies the conditions $y = 2$ and $y' = -1$ when $x = 0$.

Solution. 1. The characteristic equation is $m^2 - 6m + 9 = 0$, which has the double root $m = 3$. Hence, the general solution is

$$y = e^{3x}(c_1 + c_2 x). \tag{13}$$

2. From (13), $\qquad\qquad y' = e^{3x}(3c_1 + c_2 + 3c_2 x). \tag{14}$

With $x = 0$ in (13) and (14), the initial conditions give $c_1 = 2$ and $c_2 = -7$. Thus, the particular solution is $y = e^{3x}(2 - 7x)$.

EXERCISE 199

Solve the equation. If no independent variable is visible, assume that it is x. Find any specified particular solution.

1. $\dfrac{d^2y}{dx^2} + \dfrac{dy}{dx} - 2y = 0.$

2. $\dfrac{d^2s}{dt^2} + 5\dfrac{ds}{dt} + 4s = 0.$

3. $3\dfrac{d^2u}{dv^2} + 5\dfrac{du}{dv} - 2u = 0.$

4. $\dfrac{d^2y}{dt^2} + 4\dfrac{dy}{dt} + 4y = 0.$

5. $y'' - 10y' + 25y = 0.$

6. $2y'' - 5y' + 3y = 0.$

7. $\dfrac{d^2y}{dt^2} - 9y = 0.$

8. $\dfrac{d^2s}{dt^2} = 25s.$

9. $4\dfrac{d^2u}{dv^2} = 9u.$

10. $y'' - y = 0.$

11. $y'' = 3y'.$

12. $4y'' = 9y'.$

13. $6y'' + 7y' + 2y = 0.$

14. $3y'' + 2y' - y = 0.$

15. $4s'' + s = 4s'$.   **16.** $y'' = a^2 y$.   **17.** $49y'' - 4y = 0$.

18. $4y'' + 24y' + 9y = 0$.   **19.** $a^2 y'' - 2aby' + b^2 y = 0$.

20. $y'' + y' - 6y = 0$; $y = 5$ and $y' = -5$ when $x = 0$.

21. $9y'' - 12y' + 4y = 0$; $y = -2$ and $y' = 3$ when $x = 0$.

254. CHARACTERISTIC EQUATION WITH IMAGINARY ROOTS *

Consider the equation of the second order

$$(D^2 + a_1 D + a_2)y = 0, \quad or \quad f(D)y = 0, \tag{1}$$

when the characteristic equation $f(m) = 0$ has imaginary roots $m = \alpha \pm \beta i$, where α and β are real and $\beta \neq 0$. Then, the general solution of (1) is

$$y = c_1 e^{(\alpha + i\beta)x} + c_2 e^{(\alpha - i\beta)x} = e^{\alpha x}(c_1 e^{i\beta x} + c_2 e^{-i\beta x}). \tag{2}$$

In (2), use the Euler formula (3) of page 580 to obtain

$$e^{\pm i\beta x} = \cos \beta x \pm i \sin \beta x.$$

Then, $$y = e^{\alpha x}[(c_1 + c_2) \cos \beta x + (c_1 i - c_2 i) \sin \beta x]. \tag{3}$$

If c_1 and c_2 are unequal real numbers in (3), then y has imaginary values. However, y is real-valued if we choose c_1 and c_2 so that

$$\left. \begin{array}{l} ic_1 - ic_2 = A, \text{ and} \\ c_1 + c_2 = B, \end{array} \right\} \tag{4}$$

where A and B are real. Observe that (4) has a unique solution for c_1 and c_2 if A and B are assigned arbitrarily. Then, (3) gives the real form

$$y = e^{\alpha x}(A \sin \beta x + B \cos \beta x). \tag{5}$$

From (5), we obtain the linearly independent solutions $e^{\alpha x} \sin \beta x$ and $e^{\alpha x} \cos \beta x$, by use of $(A = 1, B = 0)$ and $(A = 0, B = 1)$, respectively.

Summary. *If the characteristic equation $f(m) = 0$ has imaginary roots $m = \alpha \pm i\beta$, then $f(D)y = 0$ has the solutions $e^{\alpha x} \sin \beta x$ and $e^{\alpha x} \cos \beta x$, and hence the general solution (5).*

Note 1. If A and B are not both zero, define $H > 0$ and ω by

$$A^2 + B^2 = H^2; \quad H \cos \omega = A; \quad H \sin \omega = B. \tag{6}$$

Then, (5) becomes $y = H(\sin \beta x \cos \omega + \cos \beta x \sin \omega)e^{\alpha x}$, or

$$y = He^{\alpha x} \sin (\beta x + \omega). \tag{7}$$

Similarly, define γ and $H > 0$ by the equations

$$A^2 + B^2 = H^2; \quad -H \sin \gamma = A; \quad H \cos \gamma = B. \tag{8}$$

Then, the general solution (5) becomes

$$y = He^{\alpha x} \cos (\beta x + \gamma). \tag{9}$$

Let us allow $H = 0$ in (7) and (9) in order to obtain the solution $y = 0$ for (1). Then, either (7) or (9), as well as (5), can be taken as the general solution of (1).

---

* Recall the discussion in Section 222 on page 578 concerning calculus for complex-valued functions. Thus, Theorem VIII on page 658 is valid when m is an imaginary number.

EXAMPLE 1. Find the particular solution of

$$\frac{d^2y}{dx^2} - 4\frac{dy}{dx} + 13y = 0 \tag{10}$$

satisfying the conditions $y = 5$ and $y' = -5$ when $x = 0$.

Solution. 1. The characteristic equation $m^2 - 4m + 13 = 0$ has the solutions $m = 2 \pm 3i$. Hence, the general solution of (10) is

$$y = e^{2x}(c_1 \sin 3x + c_2 \cos 3x). \tag{11}$$

Then, $\qquad y' = e^{2x}[(2c_1 - 3c_2)\sin 3x + (2c_2 + 3c_1)\cos 3x]. \tag{12}$

2. With $x = 0$, $y = 5$, and $y' = -5$ in (11) and (12), we obtain

$$c_2 = 5 \quad and \quad 2c_2 + 3c_1 = -5.$$

Thus, $c_1 = -5$. The solution is

$$y = e^{2x}(-5 \sin 3x + 5 \cos 3x).$$

Comment. The general solution of (10) also can be written

$$y = He^{2x} \sin (3x + \omega) \quad or \quad y = He^{2x} \cos (3x + \gamma).$$

Whenever the characteristic equation for (1) has imaginary roots, we agree to use a *real form* (5), (7), or (9), for the general solution.

EXERCISE 200

Solve the equation. If no independent variable is visible, assume that it is x. Give three trigonometric forms, if they apply.

1. $\dfrac{d^2y}{dx^2} + 2\dfrac{dy}{dx} + 5y = 0.$ $\qquad$ 2. $\dfrac{d^2s}{dt^2} - 4\dfrac{ds}{dt} + 8s = 0.$

3. $(D^2 + 6D + 25)y = 0.$ $\qquad$ 4. $(4D^2 - 12D + 25)u = 0.$

5. $2y'' - 2y' + 5y = 0.$ $\qquad$ 6. $9y'' - 6y' + 10y = 0.$

7. $\dfrac{d^2s}{dt^2} + s = 0.$ $\qquad$ 8. $\dfrac{d^2u}{dv^2} + 9u = 0.$ $\qquad$ 9. $9\dfrac{d^2u}{dx^2} + 4u = 0.$

10. $6y'' - 7y' - 3y = 0.$ $\qquad$ 11. $y'' - 3y' + 3y = 0.$

12. $(D^2 + 4)y = 0.$ $\qquad$ 13. $s'' + k^2s = 0.$ $\qquad$ 14. $y'' = 49y.$

15. $2\dfrac{d^2s}{dt^2} + 5\dfrac{ds}{dt} - 12s = 0.$ $\qquad$ 16. $4\dfrac{d^2u}{dv^2} - 12\dfrac{du}{dv} + 13u = 0.$

17. $4\dfrac{d^2y}{dx^2} - 8\dfrac{dy}{dx} + 5y = 0.$ $\qquad$ 18. $4\dfrac{d^2y}{dx^2} - 25y = 0.$

Find the desired particular solution of the differential equation.

19. $\dfrac{d^2y}{dx^2} + y = 0;\ y = 2$ and $y' = -3$ when $x = 0.$

20. $(D^2 + 6D + 13)y = 0;\ y = -1$ and $y' = 2$ when $x = 0.$

21. $\dfrac{d^2s}{dt^2} + 16s = 0;\ s = 3$ and $\dfrac{ds}{dt} = 4$ when $t = \tfrac{1}{4}\pi.$

22. $y'' + 4y = 0;\ y = 3$ and $y' = -2$ when $x = \tfrac{3}{4}\pi.$

23. $u'' - 4u' + 20u = 0;\ u = 3e^{\frac{1}{2}\pi}$ and $u' = -3e^{\frac{1}{2}\pi}$ when $x = \tfrac{1}{4}\pi.$

255. NONHOMOGENEOUS LINEAR DIFFERENTIAL EQUATIONS

Consider the nonhomogeneous linear differential equation

$$f(D)y = Q(x), \tag{1}$$

of order n, defining y as a function of x, where

$$f(D) = D^n + a_1 D^{n-1} + a_2 D^{n-2} + \cdots + a_{n-1} D + a_n, \tag{2}$$

in which $a_1, a_2, \cdots, a_n$ are constants. The method of solution for (1) is based on the following result, stated for the case $n = 2$.

Theorem X. *Suppose that $P(x)$ is a particular solution of a nonhomogeneous equation $f(D)y = Q(x)$. Let $H(x, c_1, c_2)$ be the general solution of the corresponding homogeneous equation $f(D)y = 0$. Then, the general solution of $f(D)y = Q(x)$ is*

$$y = H(x, c_1, c_2) + P(x). \tag{3}$$

Proof. 1. Let $g(x)$ be *any* solution of (1), where $n = 2$. On substituting $y = P(x)$ and $y = g(x)$ in (1), we obtain

$$f(D)g(x) = Q(x) \quad and \quad f(D)P(x) = Q(x). \tag{4}$$

Hence, $\quad f(D)[g(x) - P(x)] = f(D)g(x) - f(D)P(x) = Q(x) - Q(x) = 0. \tag{5}$

Thus, (5) states that $y = [g(x) - P(x)]$ satisfies the homogeneous equation $f(D)y = 0$. Therefore, by use of proper values for the constants c_1 and c_2 in the general solution $H(x, c_1, c_2)$, we would obtain

$$g(x) - P(x) = H(x, c_1, c_2), \quad or \quad g(x) = H(x, c_1, c_2) + P(x). \tag{6}$$

2. To prove, conversely, that *any function $g(x)$ of the form* (6) *is a solution of* (1), we substitute $y = g(x)$ in $f(D)y$ on the left in (1):

$$f(D)[H(x, c_1, c_2) + P(x)] = f(D)H(x, c_1, c_2) + f(D)P(x)$$
$$= 0 + Q(x) = Q(x), \tag{7}$$

because $y = H(x, c_1, c_2)$ satisfies $f(D)y = 0$, and $y = P(x)$ satisfies (1). From (7), $y = g(x)$ satisfies (1), and thus is its general solution.

ILLUSTRATION 1. We verify that the equation $y'' - 4y = e^{3x}$ has the particular solution $y = \frac{1}{5}e^{3x}$. By Section 253, we find that the homogeneous equation $y'' - 4y = 0$ has the general solution $y = c_1 e^{2x} + c_2 e^{-2x}$. Hence, the general solution of the nonhomogeneous equation is $y = c_1 e^{2x} + c_2 e^{-2x} + \frac{1}{5}e^{3x}$.

In (3), where $H(x, c_1, c_2)$ is the general solution of the homogeneous equation, we call the function $H(x, c_1, c_2)$ the **complementary function** for the solution of the nonhomogeneous equation. To obtain its general solution,

I. *obtain a particular solution $y = P(x)$ by any device;*

II. *find the general solution $H(x, c_1, c_2)$ of the homogeneous equation $f(D)y = 0$, and then use* (3).

In the absence of advanced theory, we shall proceed as follows to obtain a particular solution $y = P(x)$ for (1), under certain circumstances. The suggestions will be stated in such a way as to apply later to equations of *any order n.*

Write $P(x)$ with undetermined coefficients in accordance with later suggestions. Then, obtain these coefficients by substituting $y = P(x)$ in (1).

Forms for $y = P(x)$ to satisfy $f(D)y = Q(x)$:

A. *When $Q(x)$ is a polynomial of degree k:*

1. If $m = 0$ is not a solution of $f(m) = 0$, use
$$P(x) = b_0 + b_1 x + b_2 x^2 + \cdots + b_k x^k. \tag{8}$$

2. If $m = 0$ is a simple root of $f(m) = 0$, use
$$P(x) = x(b_0 + b_1 x + b_2 x^2 + \cdots + b_k x^k). \tag{9}$$

B. *When $Q(x) = h e^{kx}$, where h and k are constants:*

1. Use $P(x) = b e^{kx}$ if $m = k$ is not a solution of $f(m) = 0$.

2. If $m = k$ is a simple root of $f(m) = 0$, use $\qquad P(x) = b x e^{kx}$. (10)

C. *When $Q(x) = h \cos rx + k \sin rx$, where h, k, and r are constants, and h and k are not both zero:*

1. Use * $P(x) = b_1 \cos rx + b_2 \sin rx$, if $m = ri$ is not a solution of $f(m) = 0$.

2. If $m = ri$ is a simple root of $f(m) = 0$, use
$$P(x) = x(b_1 \cos rx + b_2 \sin rx). \tag{11}$$

D. *When $Q(x)$ is a sum of terms of preceding types, use $P(x)$ as a corresponding sum of terms as suggested.*

Note 1. In (A, 2), (B, 2), and (C, 2), if m is a double root of $f(m) = 0$, use x^2 instead of x as a factor in (9), (10), (11); use x^s as a factor if m is a root of multiplicity s.

EXAMPLE 1. Solve: $\qquad \dfrac{d^2 y}{dx^2} + \dfrac{dy}{dx} - 2y = 25 - 4x - 6x^2.$ (12)

Solution. 1. *The complementary function:* The corresponding homogeneous equation is $(D^2 + D - 2)y = 0$, whose solution is $y = c_1 e^x + c_2 e^{-2x}$.

2. *The particular solution:* By (A, 1), we substitute
$$y = b_0 + b_1 x + b_2 x^2$$
in (12), and equate coefficients of corresponding powers of x on the two sides, in order to determine the unknown coefficients b_0, b_1, and b_2:

$$2b_2 + (2b_2 x + b_1) - 2(b_0 + b_1 x + b_2 x^2) = 25 - 4x - 6x^2, \, or \tag{13}$$

$$(2b_2 + b_1 - 2b_0) + x(2b_2 - 2b_1) - 2b_2 x^2 = 25 - 4x - 6x^2.$$

Thus $\qquad -2b_2 = -6; \quad 2b_2 - 2b_1 = -4; \quad 2b_2 + b_1 - 2b_0 = 25.$ (14)

From (14), $b_2 = 3$, $b_1 = 5$, and $b_0 = -7$. Hence, a particular solution of (12) is $y = 3x^2 + 5x - 7$. From (3), the general solution of (12) is

$$y = c_1 e^x + c_2 e^{-2x} + 3x^2 + 5x - 7.$$

* Even if h or k is equal to zero in (C), we use both $\sin rx$ and $\cos rx$ in (C, 1).

EXAMPLE 2. Solve: $$y'' - 4y = 2e^{3x}. \tag{15}$$

Solution. 1. The complementary function is the solution of $(D^2 - 4)y = 0$:

$$y = c_1 e^{2x} + c_2 e^{-2x}. \tag{16}$$

2. We substitute $y = be^{3x}$ in (15) to find a particular solution, and obtain

$$9be^{3x} - 4(be^{3x}) = 2e^{3x}, \quad or \quad 5be^{3x} = 2e^{3x}.$$

Hence, $b = \frac{2}{5}$ and a particular solution of (15) is $y = \frac{2}{5}e^{3x}$. From (3) and (16), the general solution of (15) is $y = c_1 e^{2x} + c_2 e^{-2x} + \frac{2}{5}e^{3x}$.

EXAMPLE 3. Solve: $$y'' - 4y = 4e^{2x}. \tag{17}$$

Solution. 1. The complementary function is specified in (16).

2. We recall from (16) that $y = e^{2x}$ is a particular solution of the homogeneous equation corresponding to (17), or $m = 2$ is a simple root of the characteristic equation $m^2 - 4 = 0$. Then, by (B, 2), we use $y = bxe^{2x}$ for a particular solution of (17). It is found that

$$D(bxe^{2x}) = 2bxe^{2x} + be^{2x}; \quad D^2(bxe^{2x}) = 4be^{2x} + 4bxe^{2x}.$$

Hence, from (17), with $y = bxe^{2x}$,

$$4bxe^{2x} + 4be^{2x} - 4bxe^{2x} = 4e^{2x}, \quad or \quad be^{2x} = e^{2x}.$$

Thus, $b = 1$ and a particular solution of (17) is $y = xe^{2x}$. Then, from (3) and (16), the general solution of (17) is $y = c_1 e^{2x} + c_2 e^{-2x} + xe^{2x}$.

EXAMPLE 4. Solve: $$y'' + 3y' = 8\cos 2x - 14 \sin 2x. \tag{18}$$

Solution. 1. The solution of $y'' + 3y' = 0$ is $y = c_1 + c_2 e^{-3x}$. Hence, the function $(c_1 + c_2 e^{-3x})$ is the complementary function for the solution of (18).

2. For a particular solution of (18), by (C, 1), we use the form

$$y = h \sin 2x + k \cos 2x. \tag{19}$$

On substituting (19) in (18), we obtain

$$(6h - 4k)\cos 2x - (4h + 6k)\sin 2x = 8 \cos 2x - 14 \sin 2x.$$

Thus, $$6h - 4k = 8 \quad and \quad 4h + 6k = 14. \tag{20}$$

We solve system (20), and obtain $h = 2$ and $k = 1$. A particular solution is $y = 2 \sin 2x + \cos 2x$, and the general solution of (18) is

$$y = c_1 + c_2 e^{-3x} + 2 \sin 2x + \cos 2x.$$

EXERCISE 201

Solve the equation. If no independent variable is visible, assume that it is x.

1. $\dfrac{d^2y}{dx^2} + \dfrac{dy}{dx} - 6y = 12x.$

2. $\dfrac{d^2s}{dt^2} - \dfrac{ds}{dt} - 2s = 16.$

3. $\dfrac{d^2y}{dx^2} - 9y = 18x - 27.$

4. $\dfrac{d^2y}{dx^2} + 4y = 12x^2 - 2.$

5. $y'' + 2y' + 5y = 25.$

6. $9y'' + 6y' + y = 2x + 7.$

7. $4\dfrac{d^2u}{dx^2} - 9u = 8 + 18x - 9x^2.$ **8.** $\dfrac{d^2z}{dy^2} + z = 6y + y^3.$

9. $2y'' + 3y' - 2y = 4e^{3x}.$ **10.** $s'' + 3s' + 2s = 3e^{2x}.$

11. $y'' - 6y' = -8e^{4x}.$ **12.** $3y'' - 2y' = -6e^{3x}.$

13. $y'' + 4y' + 5y = 29e^{\frac{1}{2}x}.$ **14.** $y'' - y = -8 \sin x.$

15. $y'' + y = 9 \cos 2x.$ **16.** $2y'' + y = 2 \sin \frac{1}{2}x.$

17. $2y'' - y' = 20 \sin 3x.$ **18.** $y'' - 6y' + 10y = 30.$

19. $y'' + 9y = 5 \sin 2x + 5 \cos 2x.$

20. $y'' - 4y' + 3y = 6 \sin 3x + 12 \cos 3x.$

21. $z'' + 3z' + 2z = 2x^2 + 14x + 14.$

22. $2y'' + y' = 6 + 2x.$ **23.** $3y'' - 2y' = 10 - 8x.$

24. $(D^2 - 25)y = 20e^{5x}.$ **25.** $(D^2 - 1)y = 4e^x.$

26. $(D^2 - 16)y = e^{4x}.$ **27.** $(D^2 + 9)y = 6 \cos 3x.$

28. $(D^2 + 4)y = 16 \sin 2x.$ **29.** $y'' - y' - 2y = -\frac{9}{2}e^{-x}.$

30. $y'' + 2y' = 6x^2 + 6x + 6.$

31. $y'' + 25y = 10 \sin 5x - 5 \cos 5x.$

32. $y'' - y = 8e^{3x} - x.$ **33.** $4y'' + y = 5e^x - 6 \sin x.$

Hint. Recall (D), page 663. In Problem 32, use $P(x) = ae^{3x} + bx + c.$

34. $9y'' - y = 10e^{\frac{1}{2}x} + 8.$ **35.** $y'' - 2y' + y = 5e^{2x} - 4.$

36. $3y'' + y' - 2y = 4e^x - 6x + 3.$

37. $2y'' + y' - y = -10 \sin x + 6.$

38. $\dfrac{d^2s}{dt^2} - 4\dfrac{ds}{dt} + 4s = 6e^{2t}.$ **39.** $(D^2 + 10D + 25)y = 3e^{-5x}.$

40. $y'' - 6y' + 9y = 27x + 27.$

Find the particular solution of the equation satisfying the conditions.

41. $3\dfrac{d^2u}{dv^2} - \dfrac{du}{dv} - 2u = 6v - 11;$ $u = 5$ and $u' = -3$ when $v = 0.$

42. $\dfrac{d^2z}{dw^2} + 49z = -25 \sin 2w;$ $z = 4$ and $z' = -2$ when $w = \pi.$

256. APPLICATIONS OF LINEAR DIFFERENTIAL EQUATIONS

In this section, when dealing with the motion of a particle on an s-axis, we shall use t, v, and a to represent the time, velocity, and acceleration, respectively.* Vectors will not be involved for v and a since the motion is in a line. Suppose that a particle P has the acceleration

$$\frac{d^2s}{dt^2} = -k^2s, \tag{1}$$

where k^2 is a positive constant, and we take $k > 0$. From Problem 13 on page 661, the general solution of (1) can be written as

$$s = H \sin (kt - \omega), \tag{2}$$

* The units will be 1 second for time and 1 foot for distance.

where H and ω are arbitrary constants, with $H \geqq 0$. With any initial conditions $s = s_0$ and $v = v_0$ at $t = t_0$, where s_0 and v_0 are not both zero, we may obtain corresponding values of H and ω so that (2) is the equation of motion for the particle. Motion governed by (1), with the equivalent relation (2), is called **simple harmonic motion.** We met this type of motion on page 249. From the characteristics of the sine function in (2), the motion is periodic with the period $2\pi/k$ seconds. The particle P oscillates between $s = -H$ and $s = H$ on the s-axis, with an interval of π/k seconds between extreme positions, as shown by the graph of (2) in Figure 418. From physics, if P has mass m, then P is acted on by a force f where

$$f = ma = m\frac{d^2s}{dt^2} = -k^2ms,$$

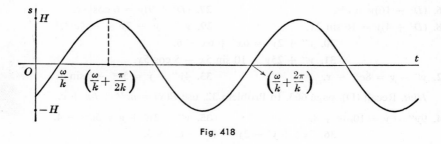

Fig. 418

whose absolute value is $k^2m\,|\,s\,|$. If we represent the force as a vector based at P on the s-axis, then the magnitude of f is $k^2m\,|\,s\,|$ and the direction of f is to the *left* if $s > 0$, and to the *right* if $s < 0$, as in Figure 419. Thus, simple harmonic motion occurs if a particle of mass m moves on a line subject to a force *proportional to the displacement of the particle from some fixed point on the line, and directed at this point.* We shall not use (2) as a formula. Any special case of (1) should be solved as in Section 254.

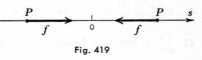

Fig. 419

EXAMPLE 1. Study the motion determined by (1) with $k^2 = 4$, if the initial conditions are $s = \frac{5}{2}\sqrt{2}$ and $v = 5\sqrt{2}$ at $t = 0$.

Solution. 1.

$$\frac{d^2s}{dt^2} = -4s, \quad or \quad s'' + 4s = 0, \tag{3}$$

whose general solution is

$$s = c_1 \cos (2t + c_2). \tag{4}$$

2. From (4),

$$v = \frac{ds}{dt} = -2c_1 \sin (2t + c_2). \tag{5}$$

From (4) and (5), with $s = \frac{5}{2}\sqrt{2}$ and $v = 5\sqrt{2}$ at $t = 0$, we obtain

$$\tfrac{5}{2}\sqrt{2} = c_1 \cos c_2; \quad 5\sqrt{2} = -2c_1 \sin c_2. \tag{6}$$

Hence,

$$\frac{\sin c_2}{\cos c_2} = \tan c_2 = -1.$$

We select $c_2 = -\frac{1}{4}\pi$. Then, (6) gives $c_1 = 5$, and (4) becomes

$$s = 5 \cos (2t - \tfrac{1}{4}\pi). \tag{7}$$

3. From (7), s is a periodic function of t with the period $2\pi/2$ or π seconds. The maximum $s = 5$ occurs when

$$\cos (2t - \tfrac{1}{4}\pi) = 1, \quad or \quad 2t - \tfrac{1}{4}\pi = 2h\pi, \quad or \quad t = \tfrac{1}{8}\pi + h\pi,$$

where h is any integer; $s = -5$ when $t = (\tfrac{1}{8}\pi + \tfrac{1}{2}\pi) + h\pi$. The particle P oscillates between 5 and -5 on the s-axis.

EXAMPLE 2. A particle P moves on an s-axis with the acceleration $a = -\frac{17}{4}s - v$. Find s in terms of t if $s = 0$ and $v = 2$ at $t = 0$.

Comment. If P has mass m, the force f acting on P is

$$f = ma = -\tfrac{17}{4}ms - mv. \tag{8}$$

The component $-mv$ resists the motion if $v \neq 0$, because $-mv$ and v have opposite signs. The force $-\frac{17}{4}ms$ alone would cause simple harmonic motion. Thus, the motion of P is the result of disturbing simple harmonic motion by a resistance proportional to the velocity, and is called a **damped harmonic motion**, or a **damped vibration**.

Solution. 1. We have
$$4 \frac{d^2s}{dt^2} + 4 \frac{ds}{dt} + 17s = 0, \tag{9}$$

whose characteristic equation is $4m^2 + 4m + 17 = 0$, with the solutions $m = -\frac{1}{2} \pm 2i$. Hence, with $H \geq 0$, the general solution of (9) is

$$s = He^{-\frac{1}{2}t} \sin (2t + \omega). \tag{10}$$

Then,
$$v = \frac{ds}{dt} = He^{-\frac{1}{2}t}[-\tfrac{1}{2} \sin (2t + \omega) + 2 \cos (2t + \omega)]. \tag{11}$$

2. On using $(s = 0, v = 2, t = 0)$ in (10) and (11), we obtain

$$H \sin \omega = 0 \quad and \quad H(-\tfrac{1}{2} \sin \omega + 2 \cos \omega) = 2. \tag{12}$$

From (12), $\sin \omega = 0$ and we select $\omega = 0$; then $2H = 2$ or $H = 1$. Hence,

$$s = e^{-\frac{1}{2}t} \sin 2t. \tag{13}$$

From (13),
$$v = \frac{ds}{dt} = \tfrac{1}{2}e^{-\frac{1}{2}t}(4 \cos 2t - \sin 2t). \tag{14}$$

3. From (14), $v = 0$ when $\sin 2t = 4 \cos 2t$, or $\tan 2t = 4$. Then, from Table IV, $2t = 1.325 + n\pi$ or $t = .663 + n(\tfrac{1}{2}\pi)$, where $n = 0, 1, 2, \cdots$. These values of t locate the successive maxima and minima of the graph of (13) in Figure 183 on page 251.

4. *The motion of P when $t \geq 0$.* In (13), $\sin 2t$ is periodic with the period $2\pi/2$ or π, but the motion is not periodic because of the factor $e^{-\frac{1}{2}t}$. However, the motion exhibits certain features periodically. Thus, from (13), $s = 0$ when $\sin 2t = 0$ or $t = 0 + n(\tfrac{1}{2}\pi)$, where $n = 0, 1, 2, \cdots$, so that P oscillates through the origin on the s-axis at intervals of $\tfrac{1}{2}\pi$ seconds. Also, from (14), P is instantaneously at rest at intervals of $\tfrac{1}{2}\pi$ seconds, when s attains a maximum or a minimum, or P arrives at an extreme point of an oscillation. The amplitudes

of these oscillations approach zero as $t \to \infty$, on account of $e^{-\frac{1}{2}t}$ in (13), because $e^{-\frac{1}{2}t} \to 0$ as $t \to \infty$. This fact causes $e^{-\frac{1}{2}t}$ to be called the **damping factor.**

Comment. If the term $- mv$ were omitted in (8), the motion would become simple harmonic and we would obtain an expression of the form $s = M \sin (kt - \gamma)$, where $k = \frac{1}{2}\sqrt{17}$. This motion is periodic with the period $2\pi/k$ or 3.048 seconds. Thus, the particle P oscillates through the origin $s = 0$, between extreme positions $s = \pm M$, at intervals of $\frac{1}{2}(3.048)$ or 1.524 seconds. In Example 2, the corresponding interval was $\frac{1}{2}\pi$ or 1.571 seconds. Thus, as compared to this simple harmonic motion, the resistance $- mv$ in (8) increases the period of the oscillations and damps their amplitudes.

If a particle P of mass m is moving with simple harmonic motion, or with a damped vibration, and if an oscillatory force is added to the force acting on P, then **"forced vibration"** occurs.

ILLUSTRATION 1. If a particle P with mass m has the acceleration

$$\frac{d^2s}{dt^2} = - k^2s + h \sin (\mu t + \gamma), \tag{15}$$

where $\mu > 0$, $k > 0$, and $h \neq 0$, then the force f acting on P is

$$f = - mk^2s + mh \sin (\mu t + \gamma). \tag{16}$$

By the method of Section 255, if $\mu \neq k$, the solution of (15) is found to be

$$s = c_1 \sin (kt + c_2) + \frac{h}{k^2 - \mu^2} \sin (\mu t + \gamma), \tag{17}$$

where c_1 and c_2 are arbitrary constants. We refer to the term involving $\sin (\mu t + \gamma)$ in (17) as a *forced vibration*, due to $mh \sin (\mu t + \gamma)$ in (16). If $c_1 \neq 0$ in (17), the motion of P is the result of superimposing the effects of two simple harmonic motions, given by the terms in (17). If $\mu = k$ in (15), its solution is found to be

$$s = c_1 \sin (kt + c_2) - \frac{h}{2k} t \cos (kt + \gamma).$$

Then, as $t \to \infty$, no upper bound exists for $|s|$. In this case, the resulting phenomenon is referred to as *resonance*.

ILLUSTRATION 2. If a particle P with mass m has the acceleration

$$(h \neq 0) \qquad \frac{d^2s}{dt^2} = - 6\frac{ds}{dt} - 10s + h \sin 3t, \tag{18}$$

where $h \neq 0$, then the force f acting on P is

$$f = ma = - 6mv - 10ms + hm \sin 3t. \tag{19}$$

The motion of P is the result of disturbing a damped vibration, as in Example 2, by the periodic force $hm \sin 3t$ in (19). The solution of (18) is

$$s = c_1e^{-3t} \sin (t + c_2) + k \sin (3t + \alpha). \tag{20}$$

In (20), k and α are fixed constants, and c_1 and c_2 are arbitrary constants. In (20), we call $k \sin (3t + \alpha)$ the forced vibration, due to $hm \sin 3t$ in (19). As $t \to \infty$ in (20), the first term on the right tends to zero, and the forced vibration becomes the dominant term. That is, as t grows large, the oscillations of P tend to give up the natural period 2π of the term $\sin (t + c_2)$, and take on the period $2\pi/3$ of the disturbing periodic force in (19). In (20), the first term is called the **transient part** of the solution, and the second term the **steady state.**

EXERCISE 202

A particle P with the coordinate s moves on the s-axis with the acceleration a. Find s in terms of t. If P oscillates, find its period. Use g = 32.

1. $a = -4s$; $s = 3$ and $v = 6\sqrt{3}$ at $t = 0$.

2. $a = -9s$; $s = -4$ and $v = -12\sqrt{3}$ at $t = \pi/3$.

3. $a = -s + 12 \sin 2t$; $s = 6$ and $v = -2$ at $t = 0$.

4. $a = -4v - 5s$; $s = 0$ and $v = 4$ at $t = 0$.

5. $a = -2v - 5s$; $s = 0$ and $v = -6$ at $t = 0$.

6. $a = -6v - 5s$; $s = 12$ and $v = 0$ at $t = 0$.

7. $a = -4v - 13s + 40 \cos t$; $s = 0$ and $v = 13$ at $t = 0$.

8. $a = -9s + 18 \sin 3t$; $s = -8$ and $v = 6$ at $t = 0$.

9. The engines of a boat stop and it continues to move in a straight line with the water resistance proportional to the velocity. Then, $a = -kv$, where $k > 0$. If $v = 20'$ per second at $t = 0$, and $k = .1$, find the distance s traveled in the next t seconds. How far will the boat go?

10. A man and parachute fall from rest under the action of gravity, with air resistance proportional to the velocity. Then, the acceleration of the man is given by $a = g - kv$, where $k > 0$. (1) If $k = \frac{1}{2}$, find the distance fallen in t seconds. (2) Find $v_0 = \lim_{t\to\infty} v$, where v_0 is called the *limiting velocity*, and is approximately the velocity at which the man hits the ground if he falls from a considerable height.

11. A spring is extended to length l and hangs in equilibrium with a body of mass m attached to the free end. We set the spring into vertical vibration by pulling downward on the body and then releasing it. Let y be the length of the spring t seconds later. Then, if $s = y - l$, it is found that $s'' = -\lambda^2 s$, where $\lambda^2 = k/m$ and k is a measure of the stiffness of the spring. Find the period of the vibration.

257. LINEAR DIFFERENTIAL EQUATIONS OF HIGHER ORDER

Let y be defined as a function of x by the equation

$$f(D)y = Q(x), \tag{1}$$

where
$$f(D) = D^n + a_1 D^{n-1} + \cdots + a_{n-1}D + a_n \tag{2}$$

and n is any positive integer. We have solved instances of (1) only where $n = 2$. A few added details of proof, which we omit, would justify extensions of our methods for any value of n. The following results become available.

Corresponding to the n roots of the characteristic equation $f(m) = 0$, obtain n particular solutions of the homogeneous equation $f(D)y = 0$ as follows:

1. *If $f(m) = 0$ has a real root $m = m_1$, of multiplicity h, there are h solutions: $e^{m_1 x}, xe^{m_1 x}, \cdots, x^{h-1}e^{m_1 x}$.*

2. *A pair of imaginary roots $m = \alpha \pm \beta i$ gives two solutions:*

$$e^{\alpha x} \sin \beta x \quad and \quad e^{\alpha x} \cos \beta x. \tag{3}$$

If the roots $m = \alpha \pm \beta i$ are repeated h times, there are 2h solutions of $f(D)y = 0$ consisting of (3) and each of these multiplied in turn by $x, x^2, \cdots, x^{h-1}$.

EXAMPLE 1. Solve: $\qquad\qquad y''' + y'' + 3y' - 5y = 60e^{3x}.$ (4)

Solution. 1. The characteristic equation for (4) is

$$m^3 + m^2 + 3m - 5 = 0,$$

whose roots are $m = 1$ and $m = -1 \pm 2i$. Hence, the complementary function for (4), or the general solution of $y''' + y'' + 3y' - 5y = 0$, is

$$y = c_1 e^x + e^{-x}(c_2 \sin 2x + c_3 \cos 2x).$$

2. To find a particular solution of (4), we try $y = ke^{3x}$ by substitution, and obtain $k = \frac{3}{2}$. Hence, the general solution of (4) is

$$y = c_1 e^x + e^{-x}(c_2 \sin 2x + c_3 \cos 2x) + \tfrac{3}{2}e^{3x}.$$

EXERCISE 203

Solve. If no independent variable is visible, assume that it is x.

1. $(D - 2)(D + 3)^2 y = 0.$ 2. $(D - 1)(D^2 + 4D + 5)y = 0.$

3. $(D - 2)^3 y = 0.$ 4. $(D - 3)(D^2 + 4)y = 0.$ 5. $(D^2 + 9)^2 y = 0.$

6. $\dfrac{d^3s}{dt^3} - 2\dfrac{d^2s}{dt^2} - 3\dfrac{ds}{dt} = 0.$ 7. $\dfrac{d^3u}{dv^3} - 2\dfrac{d^2u}{dv^2} + \dfrac{du}{dv} = 0.$

8. $\dfrac{d^3y}{dv^3} - 9\dfrac{dy}{dv} = 0.$ 9. $\dfrac{d^3s}{dx^3} = \dfrac{d^2s}{dx^2}.$ 10. $\dfrac{d^4y}{dx^4} = 16y.$

           11. $y''' - 2y'' - 5y' + 6y = 0.$

           12. $2y''' + y'' - 12y' + 9y = 0.$

13. $y''' - y = 0.$ 14. $s''' = 8s.$ 15. $16y^{\text{IV}} = 81y.$

16. $y''' + y = 365 \sin 3x.$ 17. $y''' + 8y = 5e^{4x}.$

18. $y''' + y'' - 6y' = 4x + 8.$ 19. $y^{\text{IV}} - 2y''' - 3y'' = x - 3.$

20. $y^{\text{IV}} - 81y = 2e^{3x}.$ 21. $y''' - 2y'' - 3y' = 4 \sin 2x.$

EXERCISE 204   (*Review of Chapter Twenty-nine*)

Find the general solution of the equation or the specified particular solution.

1. $(2x - y)dx + (2y - x)dy = 0.$ 2. $(3x^2 - 2xy)dx = (x^2 - 3y^2)dy.$

3. $(x + 2)(y - 1)dy = 3x(y + 3)dx.$ 4. $\sqrt{9 + x^2}\, dy = \sqrt{1 - y^2}\, dx.$

5. $xy' + y = x^4,$ by two methods.   6. $y' - 2y \tan 2x = \cos^3 2x.$

7. $\dfrac{d^2s}{dt^2} - \dfrac{ds}{dt} = 6s.$ 8. $4\dfrac{d^2u}{dv^2} + 9u = 12\dfrac{du}{dv}.$

9. $(e^y \cos x + 2xy^3) + (e^y \sin x + 3x^2y^2)\dfrac{dy}{dx} = 0.$

10. $2x(x + 1)yy' = (1 + 3x)(y^2 + 2).$ 11. $xy\, dx + (y^2 - x^2)dy = 0.$

12. $(\cos x \cos y + \sec^2 x \sin y)dx + (\tan x \cos y - \sin x \sin y)dy = 0.$

13. $\dfrac{d^2y}{dx^2} + 6\dfrac{dy}{dx} + 14y = 0.$ 14. $\dfrac{d^2s}{dt^2} + 9s = 3 \sin 4t.$

15. $\dfrac{d^3s}{dt^3} = \sin 2t.$ 16. $3\dfrac{d^2y}{dx^2} + 2\dfrac{dy}{dx} = x^2 + 4.$

17. $\dfrac{d^2y}{dx^2} = e^x + \cos x,$ with $y = 4$ and $y' = 2$ at $x = 0.$

18. $\dfrac{d^2x}{dt^2} = 25x$, with $x = 2$ and $\dfrac{dx}{dt} = -15$ when $t = 0$.

19. $2y'' + 5y' - 3y = e^{4x}$.   **20.** $y'' + 2y' + 10y = e^{2x}$.

21. $y'' - y' - 2y = 3e^{2x}$.   **22.** $y'' - 3y' = 13 \sin 2x$.

23. $\sin t\, dx + 2x \cos t\, dt - \sin t \cos t\, dt = 0$.

24. $\dfrac{d^2y}{dx^2} - 16y = 2 \sin 4x$.   **25.** $(x + 3)\dfrac{d^2y}{dx^2} - \dfrac{dy}{dx} = 0$.

26. $\dfrac{d^2y}{dx^2} = -\dfrac{1}{y^2}$ with $y = 1$ and $y' = 1$ at $x = 3$.

27. $\dfrac{d^2y}{dx^2} + 4y = 3 \sin 2x$.   **28.** $\dfrac{dy}{dx} = \dfrac{\sqrt{x^2 + 4xy + 3y^2}}{2x + 3y} + \dfrac{y}{x}$.

29. Find an equation for the orthogonal trajectories for the family of curves with the equation $(y - 3)^2 = 4k(x - 2)$, where k is the parameter.

30. The velocity dx/dt of a tri-molecular chemical reaction is given by

$$\frac{dx}{dt} = k(\alpha - x)(\beta - x)(\gamma - x),$$

where α, β, and γ are the original amounts of the three reacting substances, and x is the amount of each which has reacted in t units of time. Solve the equation for t in terms of x, if $\alpha = 3$, $\beta = 4$, and $\gamma = 1$.

31. A simple pendulum, with length l, swings in a vertical plane in a medium offering no resistance. Let θ be the angle of smallest absolute value made by the pendulum with the vertical, where θ is signed as in trigonometry. If $|\theta|$ is small, it is found that, approximately,

$$\frac{d^2\theta}{dt^2} = -k^2\theta,$$

where $k^2 = g/l$. If the pendulum is released from rest with $\theta = \alpha$ at $t = 0$, express θ as a function of t, and obtain the half-period of the pendulum.

★SUPPLEMENT FOR CHAPTER TWENTY–NINE

32. If the pendulum of Problem 31 is oscillating in a medium where the resistance is proportional to the velocity, then

$$\frac{d^2\theta}{dt^2} = -2\lambda\frac{d\theta}{dt} - k^2\theta, \tag{1}$$

where $\lambda > 0$ and $k^2 = g/l$. Find the general solution for this damped vibration if $\lambda < k$; $\lambda = k$; $\lambda > k$. If oscillatory motion occurs, what is its period? Investigate θ as $t \to \infty$ in each case.

33. A particle of mass m falls from rest in a liquid under the action of gravity. If the resistance of the liquid is proportional to the square of the velocity, the acceleration of the particle is given by $a = g - hv^2$, or $a = h(k^2 - v^2)$, where $h > 0$ and $k^2 = g/h$. Find the distance s fallen in t seconds, and the limiting velocity, as $t \to \infty$.

34. There exists a function $f(x)$ such that, if both sides of the equation

$$y(2 + x)dx + x\, dy = 0$$

are multiplied by $f(x)$, the equation becomes exact. Find a suitable function $f(x)$ and then solve the given equation.

35. A vertical tank in the form of a rectangular parallelepiped, 64 feet high, has a horizontal square cross section whose sides are 20 feet long. The tank is full of water, when a leak develops in the bottom through a hole with area A. Assume that the instantaneous rate per hour at which water leaks out, per unit surface area of the hole, is proportional to the square root of the height of the water at any instant. If 19% of the water leaks out in the first hour, show that the volume of water remaining at time t is given by $V = 25,600(1 - .1t)^2$ cubic feet.

36. A cylindrical tank with a horizontal bottom and vertical side is 81 feet high and is filled with water. A vertical slit of uniform width in the side of the tank permits leakage. Assume that the instantaneous time rate of leakage per unit surface area at any point in the slit is proportional to the square root of the height of the water above that point. With t as the time in days after the tank is filled, $\frac{4}{9}$ of the water remains when $t = 2$. Show that only $\frac{1}{9}$ of the water will be left when $t = 8$.

37. Prove that the family of orthogonal trajectories of the family of cardioids $r = a(1 - \cos \theta)$ is a family of cardioids.

38. A 100-gallon tank, A, stands above a second 100-gallon tank, B, and the tanks have a connecting common hole. Initially, A and B are filled with fresh water. Brine containing 2 pounds of salt per gallon runs into A at the rate of 3 gallons per minute and the mixture flows from A to B and then out of B at the same rate. Assume that the fluid in each tank is perfectly mixed at all times. Find the amount of salt in each of the tanks at the end of t minutes. Prove that, as $t \to \infty$, the amount in each tank approaches 200 pounds as a limit.

39. Let the function $f(x)$ be such that f' is continuous and $\neq 0$, and $f(x) \geqq 0$ on some interval $0 \leqq x \leqq b$. A surface S is formed by revolving the curve $y = f(x)$ about the x-axis. If the area of S between the planes perpendicular to the x-axis at any points x_1 and x_2 is proportional to $| x_1 - x_2 |$, find $f(x)$.

Note 1. Let $f(D)$ represent an operator polynomial with real coefficients. We define the inverse operator $1/f(D)$ by stating that

$$y = \frac{1}{f(D)} g(x) \quad \text{if and only if} \quad f(D)y = g(x).$$

40. By solving a differential equation, prove that:

$$\frac{1}{D - a} g(x) = e^{ax} \int e^{-ax} g(x) dx.$$

If $f(a) \neq 0$,

$$\frac{1}{f(D)} e^{ax} = \frac{1}{f(a)} e^{ax}.$$

If $\phi(- h^2) \neq 0$,

$$\frac{1}{\phi(D^2)} \sin hx = \frac{1}{\phi(- h^2)} \sin hx.$$

Use these results to solve Problems 10 and 33 on page 665.

Appendix

Note 1. GREEK ALPHABET

Letters		Names	Letters		Names	Letters		Names
A	α	alpha	I	ι	iota	P	ρ	rho
B	β	beta	K	κ	kappa	Σ	σ	sigma
Γ	γ	gamma	Λ	λ	lambda	T	τ	tau
Δ	δ	delta	M	μ	mu	Υ	υ	upsilon
E	ϵ	epsilon	N	ν	nu	Φ	ϕ	phi
Z	ζ	zeta	Ξ	ξ	xi	X	χ	chi
H	η	eta	O	o	omicron	Ψ	ψ	psi
Θ	θ	theta	Π	π	pi	Ω	ω	omega

Note 2. MISCELLANEOUS FORMULAS

1. *The binomial expansion* $(x + y)^n$, *where n is a positive integer.*

$$(x + y)^n = x^n + nx^{n-1}y + \frac{n(n - 1)}{2!} x^{n-2}y^2 + \cdots$$
$$+ \frac{n(n - 1)(n - 2) \cdots (n - r + 1)}{r!} x^{n-r}y^r + \cdots + nxy^{n-1} + y^n; \tag{1}$$

$$(x + y)^n = x^n + {}_nC_1 x^{n-1}y + \cdots + {}_nC_r x^{n-r}y^r + \cdots + {}_nC_{n-1}xy^{n-1} + {}_nC_n y^n, \tag{2}$$

where $\displaystyle {}_nC_r = \frac{n!}{r!(n - r)!}$.

2. *Formulas from elementary geometry.*

Circle of radius r: Area $= \pi r^2$; circumference $= 2\pi r$.

Circular sector with central angle α radians: Area $= \frac{1}{2}r^2\alpha$.

Sphere of radius r: Volume $= \frac{4}{3}\pi r^3$; (surface area) $= 4\pi r^2$.

Right circular cylinder with radius r and altitude h:

$$\text{Volume} = \pi r^2 h; \quad \text{(lateral area)} = 2\pi rh.$$

Right circular cone with altitude h, slant height s, and r as the radius of the base:

$$\text{Volume} = \frac{1}{3}\pi r^2 h; \quad \text{(lateral area)} = \pi rs.$$

Pyramid with base area A and altitude h: Volume $= \frac{1}{3}Ah$.

3. *Quadratic formula for solution of* $ax^2 + bx + c = 0$:

$$x = \frac{-b \pm \sqrt{b^2 - 4ac}}{2a}.$$

673

Note 3. INTRODUCTION TO OPERATIONS ON SETS

All sets to be mentioned will be subsets of a certain set of elements T, to be called the **universe.** Any letter which is introduced will represent a subset of T.

Definition I. *The* **complement** *of a set H is the set, H', of elements of T which are not in H.*

Although the elements of T are considered as abstract objects r, let us visualize them as points in a plane. Also, let T be thought of as all points of the plane inside or on some simple closed curve, such as C in Figure 420. Then, let H be the set of points inside or on the boundary of some curve, as in Figure 420 where H is not ruled. With the preceding representation, the complement of H is the set H' which is ruled in T. This interpretation of a set as points in a plane is extremely useful; a corresponding figure like Figure 420 sometimes is called a **Venn diagram.**

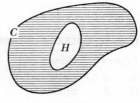

Fig. 420

> ILLUSTRATION 1. If S is the set of points covered by horizontal rulings in Figure 421, and T is the whole plane, then S' is indicated by the radial lines.

Definition II. *The* **union** *of any number of sets is the set consisting of all elements which are in one or more of the sets.*

If A and B are sets, "*the union of A and B*" is represented by "$A \cup B$." The order in which the sets are described is of no importance in Definition II. Thus, $A \cup B = B \cup A$. The "*union of three sets, A, B, and C*" is represented by

Fig. 421

"$A \cup B \cup C$," or any similar expression with the letters in any desired order. The symbol "$\cup$" may be read "*union*" wherever met.

> ILLUSTRATION 2. Let T be the set of all points in the plane in Figure 422, and let A and B represent the sets of points indicated by the vertical and horizontal rulings, respectively. Then $A \cup B$ consists of all ruled points; this set includes some points which are in *both sets*, and thus have double rulings. In general, $A \cup B$ consists of all elements in A alone, or in B alone, or in both A and B.

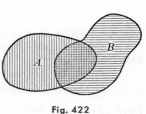

Fig. 422

Definition III. *The* **intersection** *of any number of given sets is the set of elements belonging to all of the given sets.*

If A and B are sets, "*the intersection of A and B*" is denoted by "$A \cap B$"; it consists of all elements in *both A and B*. In Figure 422, $A \cap B$ consists of all points in the doubly ruled region. To denote "*the intersection of A, B, and C*," we write "$A \cap B \cap C$," where the order of the letters is immaterial. The symbol "$\cap$" may be read "*intersection*."

Definition IV. *To say that two sets A and B are* **mutually exclusive,** *or* **disjoint,** *means that they have no element in common, or $A \cap B = \emptyset$. To say that certain sets A, B, C, $\cdots$ are mutually exclusive, means that the intersection of any two of the sets is the empty set.*

Fig. 423

ILLUSTRATION 3. In Figure 423 on page 674, A and B are mutually exclusive sets of points in the plane.

Definition V. *The* **difference** *of two sets A and B, represented by $A \setminus B$, and read "A slash B," is the set of all points of A which are not in B.*

We may refer to "$\setminus$" as a sign for *set subtraction*. It is important to notice that this operation is not so simple as subtraction of numbers in ordinary algebra.

ILLUSTRATION 4. For any set H in the basic space T, we have $H' = T \setminus H$. In Figure 424, where A is the set inside the outer curve and B is the set inside the inner curve, $A \setminus B$ is the set of points covered just by vertical rulings. If we let $W = A \setminus B$, then $A = W \cup B$, because $W \cup B$ merely replaces those points of A which were removed by subtracting B. In Figure 424, $B \setminus A = \emptyset$, because all points of B are in A; in this case, we do *not* have $B = \emptyset \cup A$ because $\emptyset \cup A = A$ and $B \neq A$.

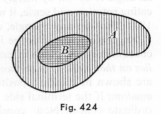

Fig. 424

The preceding operations on sets, and the concept of inclusion, $\subset$, from page 7, form the basis for the algebra of sets, with $\cup$, $\cap$, $\setminus$, and $\subset$ playing roles analogous to those of $+$, $\times$, $-$, and $\leq$ in ordinary algebra. Set algebra does not parallel ordinary algebra in many respects.

Note 4. REVIEW OF TRIGONOMETRIC FUNCTIONS OF ANGLES

Suppose that a ray or half-line, issuing from a point O in a plane, rotates about O in the plane in either a clockwise or a counterclockwise sense from an initial position OA to a terminal position OB. Then, this rotation is said to form or generate an *angle AOB* with *vertex O, initial side OA,* and *terminal side OB,* as illustrated in Figure 425. The

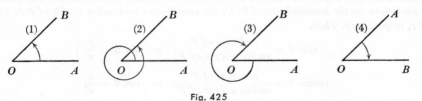

Fig. 425

measure of $\angle AOB$ is defined as a measure of the amount of rotation used in forming the angle. As a measure of rotation, one degree (1°) is defined as 1/360 of a complete revolution, one minute (1′) as 1/60 of 1°, and one second (1″) as 1/60 of 1′. Regardless of the unit of measurement, an angle is assigned *positive measure*, and is called a *positive angle*, if it is generated by **counterclockwise rotation;** the angle is assigned *negative measure*, and is called a *negative angle*, if it is generated by **clockwise rotation.** An angle can be said to have *zero measure* if the initial and terminal sides of the angle coincide. In representing an angle in a figure, we may indicate the corresponding amount of rotation by a curved arrow, as in Figure 425. We may say that an *angle* is the *configuration* resulting from a rotation as just described, or that an *angle* is an *amount of rotation* of a *ray* (a *half-line*) about its initial point. In either case, we shall refer to an angle as a *geometric entity*.

ILLUSTRATION 1. In (1) of Figure 425 on page 675, the measure of $\angle AOB$ is 45°, called the value of the angle, and we write $\angle AOB = 45°$. We do not call "45°" a *number;* "45°" abbreviates "45 *degrees.*" We also permit use of a symbol like 45° to represent the angle involved. In (2) of Figure 425, $\angle AOB = 360° + 45° = 405°$.

A positive angle is called an **acute angle** when its value lies between 0° and 90°, and an **obtuse angle** when the value lies between 90° and 180°. To state that an angle is a **quadrantal angle** means that its value is $k \cdot (90°)$ where k is some integer. If at any time an angle is shown by merely drawing two rays radiating from the vertex, without indicating rotation and sense, it will be assumed that the angle has positive measure, at most 180°. Thus, in any triangle, each angle will be considered to have a positive measure.

An angle θ is said to be in its **standard position** on an xy-system * of rectangular coordinates in a plane in case the vertex of θ is at the *origin* and the *initial side of θ lies on that half of the horizontal axis which represents positive numbers, x.* A few angles are shown in standard positions in Figure 426. An angle θ is said to be *in a certain quadrant* if the terminal side of θ falls there when θ is in its standard position on a coordinate system. Now, consider θ as a variable whose *domain* consists of *all angles.* For each angle † θ, six numbers, sine θ, cosine θ, etc. are defined as follows.

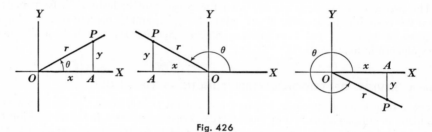

Fig. 426

Definition I. *Place angle θ in standard position on a coordinate system. Choose any point P, not the origin, on the terminal side of θ; let the coordinates and radius vector of P be (x, y) and r, respectively. Then,*

$$
\begin{aligned}
sine\ \theta &= \frac{ordinate\ of\ P}{radius\ vector\ of\ P}, &\quad or \quad & \sin \theta = \frac{y}{r}; \\[2mm]
cosine\ \theta &= \frac{abscissa\ of\ P}{radius\ vector\ of\ P}, &\quad or \quad & \cos \theta = \frac{x}{r}; \\[2mm]
tangent\ \theta &= \frac{ordinate\ of\ P}{abscissa\ of\ P}, &\quad or \quad & \tan \theta = \frac{y}{x}; \\[2mm]
cotangent\ \theta &= \frac{abscissa\ of\ P}{ordinate\ of\ P}, &\quad or \quad & \cot \theta = \frac{x}{y}; \\[2mm]
secant\ \theta &= \frac{radius\ vector\ of\ P}{abscissa\ of\ P}, &\quad or \quad & \sec \theta = \frac{r}{x}; \\[2mm]
cosecant\ \theta &= \frac{radius\ vector\ of\ P}{ordinate\ of\ P}, &\quad or \quad & \csc \theta = \frac{r}{y}.
\end{aligned}
\tag{1}
$$

* In all of this note of the Appendix, the scale units will be equal on the axes of any coordinate system, and the same unit will be used for distance in an arbitrary direction.
† With the exception of certain quadrantal angles in the case of tan θ, cot θ, sec θ, and csc θ, when some denominator becomes zero in (1).

The six functions, as defined in (1), are called the basic (direct) *trigonometric functions of angles*. We recall that tan θ and sec θ are not defined when θ is a quadrantal angle whose terminal side, in standard position, is vertical; cot θ and csc θ are not defined when the terminal side, as just mentioned, is horizontal. For instance, we write tan 90° *is infinite*, meaning that (a) tan 90° *does not exist* and (b) | tan θ | $\rightarrow \infty$ *if* $\theta \rightarrow 90°$.

Two angles are said to be **coterminal** if their terminal sides coincide when both angles are placed in their standard positions on the same coordinate system. Since Definition I involves only the terminal side of the angle, it follows that, *if two angles θ and ϕ are coterminal, each trigonometric function of θ is equal to the same function of ϕ.*

ILLUSTRATION 2. sin 30° = sin 390°, because 30° and 390° are coterminal.

Definition II. *Let θ be an angle in any quadrant, and let θ be placed in its standard position in a coordinate plane. Then, the* **reference angle** *for θ is the acute angle, α, between the terminal side of θ and the horizontal axis.*

Various reference angles are indicated in Figure 427. We recall the following useful theorem, which can be proved by use of (1) on page 676.

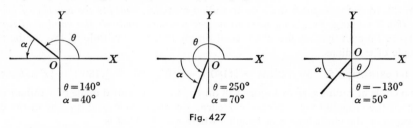

Fig. 427

Theorem I. *The value of any trigonometric function of an angle θ in any quadrant is numerically equal to the value of the same-named function of the reference angle, α, for θ. That is,*

$$\text{(any function of } \theta) = \pm \text{ (same function of reference angle } \alpha), \qquad (2)$$

with "+" or "−" according as the function of θ is positive or negative.

By Theorem I, the values of the trigonometric functions of an angle of any size can be found by use of a table of the function values for just acute angles. We disregard quadrantal angles in the preceding statement, since the trigonometric functions of a quadrantal angle are the same as the functions for 0°, 90°, 180°, or 270°.

ILLUSTRATION 3. To find tan 140°, notice that $\alpha = 40°$ in Figure 427. Also, the tangent is negative in quadrant II. Hence, from (2) and Table IV for acute angles, tan 140° = − tan 40° = − .839.

For the purposes of calculus, and in certain fields of applied mathematics, the convenient unit for angular measurement is one *radian*.

Definition III. *One* **radian** *is the measure of a positive angle which, if its vertex is at the center of a circle, intercepts on the circle an arc whose length is the radius of the circle.*

ILLUSTRATION 4. In Figure 428, $\angle BOC = (1 \text{ rad.})$.

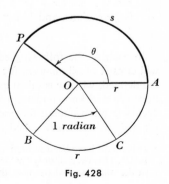

Fig. 428

Let K be the measure in radians of a complete counterclockwise rotation of OB, in Figure 428, on page 677, about O. Then, the angle K radians intercepts the whole circumference, of length $2\pi r$, and 1 radian intercepts arc BC, of length r. Hence,

$$\frac{K}{1} = \frac{2\pi r}{r}, \quad or \quad K = 2\pi. \tag{3}$$

Since the angle K radians also has the measure 360°,

$$360° = (2\pi \text{ radians}), \quad or \quad 180° = (\pi \text{ radians}). \tag{4}$$

Notice that equalities like (4) are *not equations* in the usual sense of expressing the equality of two *numbers*. Thus, (4) abbreviates (*an angle of* 360° *also has the measure* 2π *radians*), etc. On dividing both sides of 180° = (π radians) first by 180 and, second, by π, we obtain

$$1° = \frac{\pi}{180} \text{ radians} = .0174533 \text{ radian}, \text{ approximately;} \tag{5}$$

$$1 \text{ radian} = \frac{180°}{\pi} = 57.2958°, \text{ approximately.} \tag{6}$$

From (5), to change degree measure to radian measure, *multiply the number of degrees by* $\pi/180$. To change radian measure to degree measure, *multiply the number of radians by* $180/\pi$. Frequently, it is useful to recall simply that any multiple of 180° is the same multiple of π radians.

ILLUSTRATION 5. $\frac{5}{6}\pi$ radians = $\frac{5}{6}(180°)$ = 150°.   90° = $\frac{1}{2}(180°)$ = $\frac{1}{2}\pi$ *radians*.

In a circle of radius r, as in Figure 428 on page 677, a central angle of 1 radian intercepts on the circle an arc of length r. Hence, a central angle of θ radians in the circle intercepts on the circle an arc of length s where $s = \theta r$. That is

$$s = r\theta, \quad or \quad \textbf{arc} = (\textbf{radius} \times \textbf{angle, in radians}) \tag{7}$$

ILLUSTRATION 6. If $r = 25$ and $s = 75$, then $\theta = s/r = (\frac{75}{25}) = 3$, radians.

Hereafter in this Appendix and throughout the text, unless otherwise implied, if the measure of an angle is indicated, it is to be understood that *this measure is in radians*. Also, if a symbol, such as x, is referred to as an *angle*, without indication of an angular unit, or if the symbol is the argument of a trigonometric function of angles, then x represents a *number* and is taken as an abbreviated symbol for x *radians*.*

ILLUSTRATION 7. The trigonometric functions of x radians are sin x, tan x, etc. From Table IV, cos 1.02 = .52337. We note that sin $\frac{1}{3}\pi$ means the sine of $\frac{1}{3}\pi$ radians: sin $\frac{1}{3}\pi$ = $\frac{1}{2}\sqrt{3}$. The acute reference angle (see page 677) for $\frac{11}{6}\pi$ radians is $\frac{1}{6}\pi$ radians, and $\frac{11}{6}\pi$ radians is an angle in quadrant IV; hence

$$\tan \tfrac{11}{6}\pi = -\tan \tfrac{1}{6}\pi = -\tfrac{1}{3}\sqrt{3}.$$

In each of the following equations, as a rule, the domain for any variable, say x, will consist of all *numbers* for which all corresponding function values in the equation are defined, when x is taken as a symbol for the angle † "x *radians*." Each of the equations is a well-known identity from trigonometry. Whenever desired, any variable which occurs in an argument for one of the functions may be interpreted simply as a symbol for a *geometric entity* called an *angle*. The following identities are very useful.

* This might have been written $x^{(r)}$, or in some similar fashion, in analogy with a notation such as 45°. However, simply "x" is used instead of $x^{(r)}$.
† In the main part of the text, this connection with angles will be waived when desirable.

$$\csc x = \frac{1}{\sin x}; \qquad \sec x = \frac{1}{\cos x}; \qquad \cot x = \frac{1}{\tan x}; \qquad \tan x = \frac{\sin x}{\cos x}. \qquad \text{(I)}$$

$$\sin^2 x + \cos^2 x = 1; \qquad \tan^2 x + 1 = \sec^2 x; \qquad 1 + \cot^2 x = \csc^2 x. \qquad \text{(II)}$$

("+" *with* "+") $\qquad\qquad \sin (x \pm y) = \sin x \cos y \pm \cos x \sin y.$ (III)

("+" *with* "−") $\qquad\qquad \cos (x \pm y) = \cos x \cos y \mp \sin x \sin y.$ (IV)

$$\tan (x + y) = \frac{\tan x + \tan y}{1 - \tan x \tan y}; \qquad \tan (x - y) = \frac{\tan x - \tan y}{1 + \tan x \tan y}. \qquad \text{(V)}$$

$$\sin 2x = 2 \sin x \cos x. \qquad \text{(VI)}$$

$$\cos 2x = \cos^2 x - \sin^2 x = 2 \cos^2 x - 1 = 1 - 2 \sin^2 x. \qquad \text{(VII)}$$

$$2 \cos^2 x = 1 + \cos 2x; \qquad 2 \sin^2 x = 1 - \cos 2x. \qquad \text{(VIII)}$$

$$2 \cos^2 \tfrac{1}{2}x = 1 + \cos x; \qquad 2 \sin^2 \tfrac{1}{2}x = 1 - \cos x. \qquad \text{(IX)}$$

$$2 \sin x \cos y = \sin (x + y) + \sin (x - y). \qquad \text{(X)}$$

$$2 \cos x \cos y = \cos (x + y) + \cos (x - y). \qquad \text{(XI)}$$

$$2 \sin x \sin y = \cos (x - y) - \cos (x + y). \qquad \text{(XII)}$$

$$2 \cos x \sin y = \sin (x + y) - \sin (x - y). \qquad \text{(XIII)}$$

$$\sin x - \sin y = 2 \cos \tfrac{1}{2}(x + y) \sin \tfrac{1}{2}(x - y). \qquad \text{(XIV)}$$

$$\sin (-x) = - \sin x; \qquad \cos (-x) = \cos x; \qquad \tan (-x) = - \tan x. \qquad \text{(XV)}$$

$$[\textit{Any trig. function of } (x \pm 2\pi)] * = (\textit{same function of } x). \qquad \text{(XVI)}$$

$$\tan (x \pm \pi) = \tan x; \qquad \cot (x \pm \pi) = \cot x. \qquad \text{(XVII)}$$

$$[\textit{Any trig. function of } (\tfrac{1}{2}\pi - x)] = (\textit{cofunction of } x). \qquad \text{(XVIII)}$$

$$\begin{bmatrix} \textit{Any trig. function} \\ \textit{of } (\pm x + n \cdot \tfrac{1}{2}\pi) \end{bmatrix} = \begin{bmatrix} \pm \ (\textit{same function of } x),\ n \textbf{ even;} \\ \pm \ (\textit{cofunction of } x),\ n \textbf{ odd.} \end{bmatrix} \qquad \text{(XIX)}$$

An *oblique triangle* is one which has no angle equal to 90°. However, the formulas to be listed for an oblique triangle apply to a right triangle as a special case. Hence, we consider *any* triangle ABC, as in Figure 429, where α, β, and γ are the measures (with any angular unit) of the angles at A, B, and C, respectively, and a, b, and c are the lengths of the corresponding opposite sides. Also, we shall use a, b, c, α, β, and γ as symbols for the sides and angles for which these letters represent the measures. The following formulas will be useful in this text.

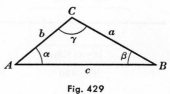

Fig. 429

Law of cosines. *In any triangle, the square of the length of any side is equal to the sum of the squares of the lengths of the other sides minus twice the product of their lengths times the cosine of the angle included by the sides. For instance,*

$$a^2 = b^2 + c^2 - 2bc \cos \alpha. \qquad \text{(8)}$$

Law of sines. *In any triangle, the lengths of the sides are proportional to the sines of the opposite angles:* $\qquad a : b : c = \sin \alpha : \sin \beta : \sin \gamma,$ *or* (9)

$$\frac{a}{\sin \alpha} = \frac{b}{\sin \beta} = \frac{c}{\sin \gamma}. \qquad \text{(10)}$$

* In (XVI)–(XIX), if we adopt the viewpoint that x is a symbol for an angle, with its measure taken in degrees, then $\tfrac{1}{2}\pi$ should be replaced by 90°. In (XIX), n is any integer.

Note 5. ANALYTIC LIMIT PROOFS

We shall employ Note 2 on page 70: "$\lim_{x \to c} f(x) = L$" *means that, for every* $\epsilon > 0$, *there exists a corresponding* $\delta > 0$ *such that*

$$if \quad 0 < |x - c| < \delta \quad then \quad |f(x) - L| < \epsilon. \tag{1}$$

The condition "$0 < |x - c|$" in (1) is not involved where f is continuous at $x = c$.

EXAMPLE 1. If $f(x) = 2x + 5$, prove that $\lim_{x \to 3} f(x) = 11$.

Solution. 1. *Suggestive details.* To apply (1), for certain values of x we should have

$$|f(x) - 11| = |2x + 5 - 11| = 2|x - 3| < \epsilon, \quad or \quad |x - 3| < \tfrac{1}{2}\epsilon. \tag{2}$$

If $\delta = \tfrac{1}{2}\epsilon$ and $|x - 3| < \delta$, we notice that (2) is true.

2. *Proof.* Let $\epsilon > 0$ be arbitrarily assigned. Define $\delta = \tfrac{1}{2}\epsilon$. If $|x - 3| < \delta$, then

$$|f(x) - 11| = 2|x - 3| < 2\delta = \epsilon; \, or,$$

$$if \quad \delta = \tfrac{1}{2}\epsilon, \quad then \quad |x - 3| < \delta \quad implies \, that \quad |f(x) - 11| < \epsilon. \tag{3}$$

Hence, by (1) we have proved that $\lim_{x \to 3} f(x) = 11$.

Note 1. From (7) on page 6, recall that, for any r and s,

$$|r + s| \leqq |r| + |s|. \tag{4}$$

Auxiliary Theorem. *If* $\eta(x) \to 0$ *and* $\gamma(x) \to 0$ *as* $x \to c$, *then*

$$(A) \, \lim_{x \to c} [\eta(x) + \gamma(x)] = 0; \quad (B) \, \lim_{x \to c} \eta(x)\gamma(x) = 0; \tag{5}$$

$$(C) \, if \, k \, is \, any \, number, \quad \lim_{x \to c} k\eta(x) = 0. \tag{6}$$

Case (A). *Suggestive details.* To apply (1) to $[\eta(x) + \gamma(x)]$ with $L = 0$, consider

$$|\eta(x) + \gamma(x)| \leqq |\eta(x)| + |\gamma(x)| < \epsilon, \tag{7}$$

which will be true if $|\eta(x)| < \tfrac{1}{2}\epsilon$ and $|\gamma(x)| < \tfrac{1}{2}\epsilon$.

Proof of (A). 1. Let $\epsilon > 0$ be arbitrarily assigned. Then, from (1) with $L = 0$ and ϵ replaced by $\tfrac{1}{2}\epsilon$, there exists $\delta_1 > 0$ applying to $\eta(x)$, and $\delta_2 > 0$ applying to $\gamma(x)$, such that

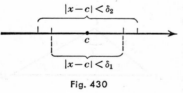

Fig. 430

$$if \quad 0 < |x - c| < \delta_1 \quad then \quad |\eta(x)| < \tfrac{1}{2}\epsilon; \tag{8}$$

$$if \quad 0 < |x - c| < \delta_2 \quad then \quad |\gamma(x)| < \tfrac{1}{2}\epsilon. \tag{9}$$

2. Designate δ as the *minimum* of δ_1 and δ_2, as illustrated in Figure 430 for a case where $\delta_1 < \delta_2$. Then, if $0 < |x - c| < \delta$, both inequalities at the right in (8) and (9) are true and hence

$$|\eta(x) + \gamma(x)| \leqq |\eta(x)| + |\gamma(x)| < \tfrac{1}{2}\epsilon + \tfrac{1}{2}\epsilon = \epsilon.$$

Therefore, by (1), $\lim_{x \to c} [\eta(x) + \gamma(x)] = 0$.

Case (B). *Suggestive details.* To apply (1) for $\eta(x)\gamma(x)$ with $L = 0$, we consider

$$|\eta(x)\gamma(x)| = |\eta(x)| \cdot |\gamma(x)| < \epsilon,$$

which will be true if $|\eta(x)| < \sqrt{\epsilon}$ and $|\gamma(x)| < \sqrt{\epsilon}$.

Proof of (B). 1. Let $\epsilon > 0$ be arbitrarily assigned. Then, from (1) with ϵ replaced by $\sqrt{\epsilon}$, there exist numbers $\delta_1 > 0$ and $\delta_2 > 0$ such that

$$if \quad 0 < |x - c| < \delta_1 \quad then \quad |\eta(x)| < \sqrt{\epsilon}; \tag{10}$$

$$if \quad 0 < |x - c| < \delta_2 \quad then \quad |\gamma(x)| < \sqrt{\epsilon}. \tag{11}$$

2. Designate δ as the minimum of δ_1 and δ_2. Then, $0 < |x - c| < \delta$ implies that both inequalities at the right in (10) and (11) are true and hence

$$|\eta(x)\gamma(x)| = |\eta(x)| \cdot |\gamma(x)| < \sqrt{\epsilon}\,\sqrt{\epsilon} = \epsilon.$$

Therefore, by (1), $\lim_{x \to c} \eta(x)\gamma(x) = 0$.

Proof of (C). The student may verify that, for any $\epsilon > 0$, there exists $\delta > 0$ such that, if $0 < |x - c| < \delta$, then

$$|\eta(x)| < \frac{\epsilon}{|k| + 1} \quad and \ hence \quad |k\eta(x)| < \frac{|k|\,\epsilon}{|k| + 1} < \epsilon,$$

which proves (C). We used $(|k| + 1)$ in the denominator to cover the special case $k = 0$ as well as $k \neq 0$.

We shall refer to Theorems I–IV of Section 23 on page 70 simply as (I)–(IV). They have the hypotheses

$$\lim_{x \to c} f(x) = L \quad and \quad \lim_{x \to c} g(x) = M. \tag{12}$$

Let $\qquad\qquad L - f(x) = \eta(x) \quad and \quad M - g(x) = \gamma(x). \tag{13}$

Then $\qquad\qquad \eta(x) \to 0 \quad and \quad \gamma(x) \to 0 \quad as \quad x \to c. \tag{14}$

Proof of (I). We have

$$(L + M) - [f(x) + g(x)] = [L - f(x)] + [M - g(x)] = \eta(x) + \gamma(x). \tag{15}$$

Hence, by (A), (14), and (15),

$$\lim_{x \to c} [f(x) + g(x) - (L + M)] = 0,$$

or $[f(x) + g(x)] \to (L + M)$ as $x \to c$.

Proof of (II). From (13), $\qquad kL - kf(x) = k[L - f(x)] = k\eta(x)$.

By use of (C), $\qquad k\eta(x) \to 0 \ as \ x \to c, \quad or \quad kf(x) \to kL \ as \ x \to c$.

Proof of (III). From (13),

$$f(x)g(x) - LM = [L - \eta(x)][M - \gamma(x)] - LM = \eta(x)\gamma(x) - L\gamma(x) - M\eta(x). \tag{16}$$

By use of (B) and (C), each term on the right in (16) has the limit 0 as $x \to c$; then, by use of (I), the right-hand side in (16) has the limit 0, or $[f(x)g(x) - LM] \to 0$ as $x \to c$. That is, $f(x)g(x) \to LM$ as $x \to c$.

(IV)$_a$. *If* $\lim_{x \to c} g(x) = M \neq 0$, *then* $\lim_{x \to c} |1/g(x)| = 1/M$.

Proof. 1. To manipulate $1/g(x)$, first we must restrict x so that $g(x) \neq 0$. Since $M \neq 0$, we may use $\epsilon = \frac{1}{2}|M|$ in (1); then there exists $\delta_1 > 0$ so that, if $0 < |x - c| < \delta_1$, we have $|g(x) - M| < \frac{1}{2}|M|$, and hence

$$|M| = |[M - g(x)] + g(x)| < |M - g(x)| + |g(x)| < \tfrac{1}{2}|M| + |g(x)|, \ or$$

$$|M| - \tfrac{1}{2}|M| < |g(x)|, \quad or \quad |g(x)| > \tfrac{1}{2}|M|. \tag{17}$$

2. With $0 < |x - c| < \delta_1$ hereafter, by (13) and (17) we obtain

$$\left|\frac{1}{g(x)} - \frac{1}{M}\right| = \frac{|M - g(x)|}{|M| \cdot |g(x)|} < \frac{|\gamma(x)|}{\frac{1}{2}|M|^2}. \tag{18}$$

Because of (C), the right-hand side of (18) has the limit 0, and hence $|1/g(x) - 1/M| \to 0$ as $x \to c$, which proves (IV)$_a$.

Proof of (IV). With $M \neq 0$, by use of (III) and (IV)$_a$ we obtain

$$\lim_{x \to c} \frac{f(x)}{g(x)} = \lim_{x \to c} f(x) \cdot \frac{1}{g(x)} = L \cdot \frac{1}{M} = \frac{L}{M}.$$

Note 6. THE DERIVATIVE OF A COMPOSITE FUNCTION

The following demonstration of Theorem I on page 98 eliminates the assumption of the previous proof that $\Delta u \neq 0$ when Δx is small.

Proof. 1. From page 98,

$$\lim_{\Delta u \to 0} \frac{\Delta y}{\Delta u} = \frac{dy}{du}; \quad \lim_{\Delta x \to 0} \frac{\Delta u}{\Delta x} = \frac{du}{dx}. \tag{1}$$

2. Define a function $\eta(\Delta u)$ by the conditions $\eta(0) = 0$ and, if $\Delta u \neq 0$,

$$\eta(\Delta u) = \frac{\Delta y}{\Delta u} - \frac{dy}{du}. \tag{2}$$

From the equality at the left in (1), $\eta(\Delta u) \to 0$ if $\Delta u \to 0$; also, by definition, $\eta(0) = 0$. Hence, $\eta(\Delta u)$ is a continuous function of Δu at $\Delta u = 0$. Since $\Delta u \to 0$ if $\Delta x \to 0$, it follows then that $\eta(\Delta u) \to 0$ as $\Delta x \to 0$.

3. From (2), if $\Delta u \neq 0$, $\qquad\qquad \Delta y = \frac{dy}{du} \cdot \Delta u + (\Delta u)\eta(\Delta u). \tag{3}$

If $\Delta u = 0$, then $\Delta y = 0$, $\eta(\Delta u) = 0$, and hence (3) remains true because each term in (3) is zero. On dividing by Δx in (3), and letting $\Delta x \to 0$, we find

$$\lim_{\Delta x \to 0} \frac{\Delta y}{\Delta x} = \frac{dy}{du}\left(\lim_{\Delta x \to 0} \frac{\Delta u}{\Delta x}\right) + \left(\lim_{\Delta x \to 0} \frac{\Delta u}{\Delta x}\right)\left(\lim_{\Delta x \to 0} \eta(\Delta u)\right), \text{ or}$$

$$\frac{dy}{dx} = \frac{dy}{du}\frac{du}{dx} + \frac{du}{dx}(0) = \frac{dy}{du} \cdot \frac{du}{dx}.$$

Note 7. REVIEW OF RADICALS AND RATIONAL EXPONENTS

If x is any real number and n is a positive integer, then x^n is defined as the product of n factors x. If $n = 0$ and $x \neq 0$, we define x^n to be 1. However, **0^0 is not defined,** for reasons which will become clear in Illustration 3 on page 241.

If x is any number and q is a positive integer, we call R a qth **root** of x in case $R^q = x$. If $x = 0$, then $R = 0$ is the only qth root of x. If $x \neq 0$, in algebra it is shown that x has just q qth roots, some or all of which may be imaginary numbers. We recall the following facts:

If $x > 0$ and q is even, then x has just two real qth roots, of opposite signs and equal absolute values.

If $x < 0$ and q is even, then all qth roots of x are imaginary.

If q is odd and $x \neq 0$, then x has just one real qth root, which is of the same sign as x.

If $x \neq 0$, we let $\sqrt[q]{x}$ represent just *that qth root of x which is real and has the same sign as x,* when such a root exists. If $x = 0$, we let $\sqrt[q]{x} = 0$. In any of these cases, we read "$\sqrt[q]{x}$" as "*the qth root of x,*" and call $\sqrt[q]{x}$ the **principal qth root** of x. If $x < 0$ and q is even, so that all qth roots are imaginary, we may use the symbol $\sqrt[q]{x}$ for a qth root, but then we merely say that it is an imaginary number, and do not earmark it as any particular root.

ILLUSTRATION 1. $\qquad \sqrt[3]{0} = 0. \qquad \sqrt[5]{32} = 2. \qquad \sqrt[5]{-32} = -2. \qquad \sqrt[4]{16} = 2.$

$\sqrt[4]{-8}$ is an imaginary number. The real 4th roots of 16 are $\pm \sqrt[4]{16}$ or ± 2.

From page 4, we recall that a **rational number** is a real number which can be expressed as the quotient of two integers, p/q. If a rational number enters as an exponent, we agree to write it in a form p/q where p and q have *no integer except ± 1 as a common* *factor.* Then, if x is any real number, $p > 0$, and $q > 0$, where q *is not even when* $x < 0$, we define $x^{\frac{p}{q}}$ as $\sqrt[q]{x^p}$, *the (real) principal* qth *root of* x^p. If $x^{\frac{p}{q}}$ ever enters discussion when $x < 0$ and q is even, we shall say merely that $x^{\frac{p}{q}}$ is imaginary. In algebra it is verified that $x^{\frac{p}{q}}$ can be written in either of two forms: $\quad x^{\frac{p}{q}} = \sqrt[q]{x^p} \quad and \quad x^{\frac{p}{q}} = (\sqrt[q]{x})^p$.

ILLUSTRATION 2. $4^{\frac{3}{2}} = \sqrt{4^3} = \sqrt{64} = 8; \quad or, \quad 4^{\frac{3}{2}} = (\sqrt{4})^3 = 2^3 = 8.$

Finally, if $-p/q$ is a *negative* rational number, where $p > 0$ and $q > 0$, and x is any number not zero, we define $x^{-\frac{p}{q}} = 1/x^{\frac{p}{q}}$, and *we do not define* $x^{-\frac{p}{q}}$ when $x = 0$.

Note 8. PROOF THAT CONTINUITY IMPLIES INTEGRABILITY

We shall employ Theorem I of page 121, Theorem II of page 122, and the theorem stated in Note 1 on page 176; we accepted all of these theorems without proof in this text. Any *extremum* to which we shall refer will be an *absolute extremum*. Also, we shall use the notation of Section 56 on page 177. All sums, $\sum$, will have $i = 1, \cdots, n$.

Proof of Theorem I *on page* 179. 1. The ith subinterval of any partition σ is a *closed* interval $T_i = \{x_{i-1} \leq x \leq x_i\}$. By Theorem II of page 122, f has a maximum M and a minimum m on $I = \{a \leq x \leq b\}$; f also has a maximum M_i and a minimum m_i for x on T_i, and there exist points η_i and γ_i on T_i such that $M_i = f(\eta_i)$ and $m_i = f(\gamma_i)$.

Let
$$\overline{S}_\sigma = \sum f(\eta_i)\Delta_i x = \sum M_i \Delta_i x; \tag{1}$$
$$\underline{S}_\sigma = \sum f(\gamma_i)\Delta_i x = \sum m_i \Delta_i x. \tag{2}$$

We shall call $\overline{S}_\sigma$ and $\underline{S}_\sigma$ the *upper* and *lower* sums, respectively, for f corresponding to σ. If S_σ is an arbitrary Riemann sum, from (3) on page 178,
$$\sum m_i \Delta_i x \leq \sum f(\xi_i)\Delta_i x \leq \sum M_i \Delta_i x, \text{ or}$$
$$\underline{S}_\sigma \leq S_\sigma \leq \overline{S}_\sigma, \tag{3}$$
because $m_i \leq f(\xi_i) \leq M_i$ for all values of i.

2. Since $m_i \leq M$, $m \leq M_i$, and $\sum \Delta_i x = b - a$, we have
$$\underline{S}_\sigma = \sum m_i \Delta_i x \leq \sum M \Delta_i x = M \sum \Delta_i x, \text{ or} \tag{4}$$
$$\underline{S}_\sigma \leq M(b - a); \quad similarly, \quad \overline{S}_\sigma \geq m(b - a). \tag{5}$$

3. Consider the sets $W = \{\underline{S}_\sigma\}$, and $V = \{\overline{S}_\sigma\}$, *for all partitions* σ. By (5), W is bounded *above* and hence has a *least upper bound*, u; V is bounded *below* and hence has a *greatest lower bound*, z. Let σ and τ be any two partitions of I; let ω be the partition formed by using all division points of both σ and τ. From (1), (2), and (3), the student may prove that
$$\underline{S}_\sigma \leq \underline{S}_\omega \leq \overline{S}_\omega \leq \overline{S}_\tau.$$

Or, *any upper sum,* $\overline{S}_\tau$, *is an upper bound for all lower sums,* W; hence $u \leq \overline{S}_\tau$. Then, u is a lower bound for $V = \{\overline{S}_\tau\}$; hence $u \leq z$, as in Figure 431. Thus, for all σ,
$$\underline{S}_\sigma \leq u \leq z \leq \overline{S}_\sigma. \tag{6}$$

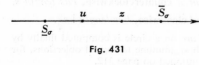

Fig. 431

4. From Note 1 on page 176, recall that f is *uniformly continuous* on I. Hence, if we assign any number $\epsilon > 0$, there exists a corresponding number $\delta_\epsilon > 0$ such that, if x_1 and x_2 are on I, and

$$if \quad |x_1 - x_2| < \delta_\epsilon \quad then \quad |f(x_1) - f(x_2)| < \frac{\epsilon}{b-a}. \tag{7}$$

5. Let σ be any partition such that $d_\sigma < \delta_\epsilon$. Then, on any subinterval T_i of σ, in (1) and (2) we have $|\eta_i - \gamma_i| \leqq d_\sigma < \delta_\epsilon$, and hence

$$[f(\eta_i) - f(\gamma_i)] < \frac{\epsilon}{b-a}, \quad or \quad (M_i - m_i) < \frac{\epsilon}{b-a};$$

$$0 \leqq \overline{S}_\sigma - \underline{S}_\sigma = \sum (M_i - m_i)\Delta_i x < \frac{\epsilon}{b-a} \sum \Delta_i x = \epsilon, \tag{8}$$

because $\sum \Delta_i x = b - a$.

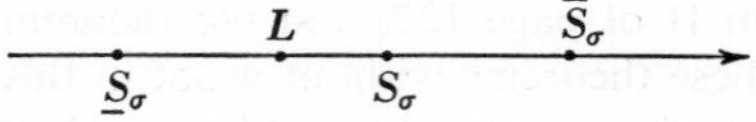

L

$\underline{S}_\sigma$ $\overline{S}_\sigma$

$\underline{S}_\sigma$ S_σ

Fig. 432

6. From (8), and (6) with $d_\sigma < \delta_\epsilon$, we have $0 \leqq z - u \leqq \epsilon$ for every $\epsilon > 0$. Since $(z - u)$ is a *constant*, the preceding statement implies that $z - u = 0$ or $z = u$; let this common value be L. Then, from (6), for every σ,

$$\underline{S}_\sigma \leqq L \leqq \overline{S}_\sigma. \tag{9}$$

7. From (3) and (9), both S_σ and L lie on an interval of numbers of length $(\overline{S}_\sigma - \underline{S}_\sigma)$, as in Figure 432. From (8), this length is less than ϵ if $d_\sigma < \delta_\epsilon$, and then $|L - S_\sigma| < \epsilon$. Thus, we have proved that, *if a positive number ϵ is assigned arbitrarily, there exists a corresponding $\delta_\epsilon > 0$ such that, if $d_\sigma < \delta_\epsilon$, then $|L - S_\sigma| < \epsilon$.* Hence, we have shown that $\lim_{d_\sigma \to 0} S_\sigma = L$, or $\int_a^b f(x)dx$ exists when f is continuous on I.

Note 9. TRIGONOMETRIC FUNCTIONS OF NUMBERS BY THE WINDING PROCESS

We propose to define outright the trigonometric functions of numbers, without any mention of angles. Then, later, we shall show how the geometric trigonometric functions of angles can be introduced as a second-stage event.

In Figure 433, a circle H of radius 1 with center at the origin is drawn in an xy-plane where a single unit is used for measuring all distances, and where this unit is the unit for length on the scales for both axes. We assume * that the notion of *length of arc* is well defined for arcs on the circle. Let s be any real number. To each value of s, we make correspond a point T_s on the circle, in Figure 433, as follows:

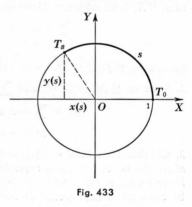

Fig. 433

If $s = 0$, T_0 is the point on the circle H with coordinates $(1, 0)$.

*If $s > 0$, T_s is on H and such that arc T_0T_s, measured **counterclockwise**, has length s.*

*If $s < 0$, T_s is on H and such that arc T_0T_s, measured **clockwise**, has length $|s|$.*

---

* Logically, this creates a defect, because the *length of arc* on a circle is computed finally by use of an *inverse trigonometric function*. Another method, immune to logical objections, for introducing sin x and cos x without using angles is mentioned on page 312.

ILLUSTRATION 1. The circle H has length 2π, since the radius is 1. Hence, if $s = \frac{1}{2}\pi$, then T_s is the point $(0, 1)$. If $s = -\frac{3}{4}\pi$, then T_s is in quadrant III, so that the line OT_s bisects the 90° angle between the axes in quadrant III; hence T_s has the coordinates $(-\frac{1}{2}\sqrt{2}, -\frac{1}{2}\sqrt{2})$.

We shall call T_s the **trigonometric point** corresponding to the number s. Let the coordinates of T_s for any value of s be denoted by $(x(s), y(s))$; thus we introduce two *functions* x and y whose domain (the *domain* of the functions) is *all real numbers* s. Then, we define the six functions sine, cosine, tangent, cotangent, secant, and cosecant by specifying that their values for any number s in their domain are as follows (except where zero denominators cause some functions to be undefined):

$$\left.\begin{array}{l} \sin s = y(s); \quad \cos s = x(s); \quad \tan s = \dfrac{y(s)}{x(s)}; \\[2ex] \csc s = \dfrac{1}{y(s)}; \quad \sec s = \dfrac{1}{x(s)}; \quad \cot s = \dfrac{x(s)}{y(s)}. \end{array}\right\} \tag{1}$$

The functions defined by (1) are called the **standard trigonometric functions of numbers.** We note that *no mention of angles* has occurred in reaching (1). On this basis, we could proceed to develop all of analytic trigonometry, again with no necessity for mentioning angles. Thus, from (1) and Figure 433, we could obtain $\sin^2 s + \cos^2 s = 1$, and all other familiar identities.

In Figure 433, construct the broken-line segment OT_s. Since the radius of the circle is 1, we verify that s is the radian measure of the directed angle with initial side OT_0 and rotation counterclockwise or clockwise from OT_0 to the terminal side OT_s according as $s > 0$ or $s < 0$. Now, let the real number s be interpreted in (1) as a symbol for the *angle* with measure s radians. Then, we could refer to the functions defined by (1) as **geometrical trigonometric functions,** whose domain consists of all angles s. It can be verified that, as now interpreted, the standard functions of numbers defined in (1) are the same as those introduced differently on page 222.

Note 1. In defining T_s in Figure 433 on page 684, essentially we *wound a real number scale around the circle.* Hence, in (1), we might choose to call $x(s)$ and $y(s)$ *winding functions.* The intimate connection of $x(s)$ and $y(s)$ with a circle, as in Figure 433, also justifies giving the alternate name **"circular functions"** to the *trigonometric functions.*

Note 10. CONCERNING L'HOSPITAL'S RULE

Theorem I. Extended law of the mean. *Assume that the functions $\phi(x)$ and $\psi(x)$ are continuous when $a \leq x \leq b$, with derivatives when $a < x < b$, $\phi(b) \neq \phi(a)$, and $\psi'(x)$ and $\phi'(x)$ never zero simultaneously when $a < x < b$. Then, there exists a number ξ between a and b such that*

$$\frac{\psi(b) - \psi(a)}{\phi(b) - \phi(a)} = \frac{\psi'(\xi)}{\phi'(\xi)}. \tag{1}$$

Proof. Define a function $h(x)$ by the equation

$$h(x) = \psi(x)[\phi(b) - \phi(a)] - \phi(x)[\psi(b) - \psi(a)] - K, \tag{2}$$

where $K = \psi(a)\phi(b) - \psi(b)\phi(a). \tag{3}$

We find $h(a) = h(b) = K - K = 0$, and $h'(x)$ exists when $a < x < b$, with

$$h'(x) = \psi'(x)[\phi(b) - \phi(a)] - \phi'(x)[\psi(b) - \psi(a)]. \tag{4}$$

Thus, h satisfies the hypotheses of Rolle's theorem on page 172. Hence, there exists a number ξ where $a < \xi < b$ and $h'(\xi) = 0$; or, from (4),

$$\psi'(\xi)[\phi(b) - \phi(a)] - \phi'(\xi)[\psi(b) - \psi(a)] = 0. \tag{5}$$

If $\phi'(\xi)$ were zero, then (5) shows that $\psi'(\xi) = 0$, which is contrary to the hypotheses of Theorem I. Hence, $\phi'(\xi) \neq 0$ and we obtain (1) on dividing by $\phi'(\xi)[\phi(b) - \phi(a)]$ in (5).

Theorem II. *Assume that the functions $\phi(t)$ and $\psi(t)$ have derivatives if $a < t < c$ (or, $c < t < a$),* with $\phi'(t) \neq 0$, $\phi(t) \neq 0$, and*

$$\phi(t) \to 0 \quad and \quad \psi(t) \to 0 \quad as \quad t \to a. \tag{6}$$

Suppose that $\psi'(t)/\phi'(t)$ has a limit λ, finite or infinite, as $t \to a$. Then

$$\lim_{t \to a} \frac{\psi(t)}{\phi(t)} = \lim_{t \to a} \frac{\psi'(t)}{\phi'(t)}. \tag{7}$$

Proof, Case 1: *finite a.* 1. Extend the domain of ϕ and ψ by defining $\phi(a) = \psi(a) = 0$. Then, ϕ and ψ are continuous on $a \leqq t < c$, and have derivatives if $a < t < c$.

2. By Theorem I, for any particular $t < c$, there exists ξ such that $a < \xi < t$ and

$$\frac{\psi(t) - \psi(a)}{\phi(t) - \phi(a)} = \frac{\psi'(\xi)}{\phi'(\xi)}, \quad or \quad \frac{\psi(t)}{\phi(t)} = \frac{\psi'(\xi)}{\phi'(\xi)}. \tag{8}$$

In (8), ξ will be as near a as we please if t is taken sufficiently near a. Hence, from (8), we obtain the result in (7):

$$\lim_{t \to a} \frac{\psi(t)}{\phi(t)} = \lim_{\xi \to a} \frac{\psi'(\xi)}{\phi'(\xi)} = \lambda.$$

Proof, Case 2: $a = +\infty$, *with t restricted to an interval $k < t < +\infty$ (or, similarly for $a = -\infty$).* 1. Let $z = t^{-1}$, or $t = z^{-1}$, and introduce

$$\Phi(z) = \phi(t) = \phi(z^{-1}) \quad and \quad \Psi(z) = \psi(t) = \psi(z^{-1}). \tag{9}$$

From (9), $\Phi'(z) = \dfrac{d\phi(t)}{dz} = \dfrac{d\phi(t)}{dt}\dfrac{dt}{dz} = -\dfrac{1}{z^2}\phi'(t)$, *or*

$$\Phi'(z) = -\frac{1}{z^2}\phi'(z^{-1}); \quad \Psi'(z) = -\frac{1}{z^2}\psi'(z^{-1}). \tag{10}$$

Hence, $\displaystyle \lim_{z \to 0+} \frac{\Psi'(z)}{\Phi'(z)} = \lim_{z \to 0+} \frac{\psi'(z^{-1})}{\phi'(z^{-1})} = \lim_{t \to +\infty} \frac{\psi'(t)}{\phi'(t)} = \lambda.$

2. From (10), $\Phi'(z) \neq 0$ because $\phi'(t) \neq 0$. Also, $\Phi(z) \to 0$ and $\Psi(z) \to 0$ as $z \to 0+$. Hence, from Case 1 as applied to $\Psi(z)/\Phi(z)$,

$$\lim_{t \to +\infty} \frac{\psi(t)}{\phi(t)} = \lim_{z \to 0+} \frac{\Psi(z)}{\Phi(z)} = \lim_{z \to 0+} \frac{\Psi'(z)}{\Phi'(z)} = \lambda,$$

which proves Theorem II with $a = +\infty$.

Theorem III. *Assume that the functions $\phi(t)$ and $\psi(t)$ have derivatives if $c < t < a$, where a is finite, with $\phi'(t) \neq 0$, $\phi(t) \neq 0$, and $\phi(t) \to +\infty$ as $t \to a$. Assume, also, that $\psi'(t)/\phi'(t)$ has a limit λ as $t \to a$. Then* (7) *is true.*

Proof, when λ is finite. Select $h > 0$ and let $\epsilon > 0$ be arbitrarily assigned. Then, there exists γ_ϵ such that $c < \gamma_\epsilon < a$ and

$$\frac{\psi'(\xi)}{\phi'(\xi)} = \lambda + g(\xi), \quad where \quad |g(\xi)| < \tfrac{1}{2}\epsilon \quad if \quad \gamma_\epsilon < \xi < a; \tag{11}$$

$$h < \phi(t) \quad if \quad \gamma_\epsilon < t. \tag{12}$$

---

* In the proof, t is restricted to whichever interval is involved.

Now select s so that $\gamma_\epsilon < s < a$, and suppose that $s < t < a$, with t so large that $\phi(s) < \phi(t)$. Then, by (1), there exists ξ such that $\gamma_\epsilon < s < \xi < t$ and

$$\frac{\psi(t) - \psi(s)}{\phi(t) - \phi(s)} = \frac{\psi'(\xi)}{\phi'(\xi)} = \lambda + g(\xi), \; or \tag{13}$$

$$\frac{\psi(t)}{\phi(t)} - \lambda = g(\xi) + \frac{\psi(s)}{\phi(t)} - \frac{[\lambda + g(\xi)]\phi(s)}{\phi(t)}. \tag{14}$$

In (14), consider s as a fixed number. Recall $| g(\xi) | < \frac{1}{2}\epsilon$ because $\gamma_\epsilon < \xi$. Then, in (14), $\psi(s)$ and $\phi(s)$ are fixed constants while $| \lambda + g(\xi) | < | \lambda | + \frac{1}{2}\epsilon$. Hence, since $\phi(t) \to \infty$ as $t \to a$, there exists $\tau_\epsilon > s > \gamma_\epsilon$ such that, if $t > \tau_\epsilon$, the sum of the absolute values of the two fractions on the right in (14) will be less than $\frac{1}{2}\epsilon$, or $| [\psi(t)/\phi(t)] - \lambda | < \epsilon$. This proves that (7) is true. Modified details would prove (7) for the case $a = \pm \infty$, or cases where $\lambda = \pm \infty$.

Note 11. EFFECTS OF PARALLEL PROJECTION IN FIGURES

The traces of the sphere $x^2 + y^2 + z^2 = 9$ are correctly indicated in Figure 434. In contrast to Figure 299 on page 436, the xz-trace and xy-trace in Figure 434 are ellipses with axes rotated slightly from the coordinate axes. The resulting bulges over the circle which is the yz-trace could be verified by computing coordinates of points on the traces. The projecting lines of the system of parallel projection, for points in *front* of the yz-plane, map the actual points of space into positions *downward* and to the left on the yz-plane. The visible (full-line) parts and hidden (broken-line) parts of the traces in Figure 434 are drawn as if three diametral planes of a solid sphere are being represented, with the remainder of the sphere evaporated. Figure 434 could be augmented by drawing the elliptical border of the shadow of the sphere as it would appear on the yz-plane under a beam of light rays parallel to the system of lines of parallel projection. However, the complicated augmented figure would have no claim to presenting the sphere *as it is seen*. Hence, for simplicity, we adopt Figure 299 as a compromise.

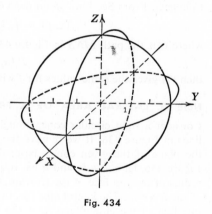

Fig. 434

Note 12. SUFFICIENT CONDITION FOR AN EXACT DIFFERENTIAL

Suppose that each of the functions $P(x, y)$ and $Q(x, y)$ is defined in a region R bounded by a rectangle, and that the derivatives P_x, P_y, Q_x, and Q_y exist and are continuous in R. We shall prove the following result.

Theorem I. *If* $P_y(x, y) = Q_x(x, y)$ *in R, then there exists a function f(x, y) such that, for all points (x, y) in R,*

$$df(x, y) = P(x, y)dx + Q(x, y)dy. \tag{1}$$

In other words, Theorem I states that "$P_y(x, y) = Q_x(x, y)$" is a sufficient condition for the right-hand side of (1) to be an *exact differential*.

Proof of Theorem I. 1. Let $M:(a, b)$ be in R. Let a function f of two variables with domain R be defined by specifying that, at any point $S:(u, v)$ in R, as shown in Figure 435,

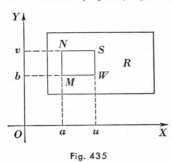

$$f(u, v) = \int_a^u P(x, v)dx + \int_b^v Q(a, y)dy; \quad then, \quad (2)$$

$$f_u(u, v) = \frac{\partial}{\partial u}\left(\int_a^u P(x, v)dx\right) + 0 = P(u, v); \quad (3)$$

$$f_v(u, v) = \frac{\partial}{\partial v}\left(\int_a^u P(x, v)dx\right) + Q(a, v). \quad (4)$$

2. By notational agreements, $\dfrac{\partial P(x, v)}{\partial v} = P_y(u, v)$. Then, by a theorem of advanced calculus which is plausible without proof, from (4) we find the derivative with respect to v by differentiating under the integral sign:

Fig. 435

$$f_v(u, v) = \int_a^u P_y(x, v)dx + Q(a, v) = \int_a^u Q_x(x, v)dx + Q(a, v), \quad (5)$$

because $P_y(x, u) = Q_x(x, v)$. From (5),

$$f_v(u, v) = Q(x, v)\Big]_{x=a}^{x=u} + Q(a, v) = Q(u, v) - Q(a, v) + Q(a, v) = Q(u, v). \quad (6)$$

3. From (3) and (6), $df(u, v) = P(u, v)du + Q(u, v)dv$, for all (u, v) in R. With (u, v) replaced by (x, y), we thus have proved (1).

Comment. From Section 235 on page 611, in (2) we find that

$$f(x, y) = \int_C [P(x, y)dx + Q(x, y)dy], \quad (7)$$

where C is the path MNS in Figure 435. Advanced theory proves that, if

$$P_y(x, y) = Q_x(x, y),$$

then (7) gives the same values for f with any reasonable choice of C in R.

Note 13. LATERAL AREA OF A FRUSTUM OF A CONE

Consider a right circular cone, thought of as a solid, and indicated partly by broken lines in Figure 436. If we remove the small cone above a plane parallel to and above the plane of the given cone's base, the remainder is called a **frustum** of a cone. In Figure 436, let r_1, r_2, k, and h be, respectively, the radius of the base of the cone, the radius of the top face of the frustum, the slant height of the cone, and the slant height of the frustum. The lateral area (or, the area of the curved surface) of a cone is equal to one half of the circumference of the base multiplied by the slant height. The lateral area, A, of the frustum is equal to the difference of the lateral areas of the given cone and the small cone which was cut off. Hence,

$$A = \pi r_1 k - \pi r_2(k - h) = \pi[k(r_1 - r_2) + r_2 h].$$

From similar triangles in Figure 436,

$$\frac{k - h}{r_2} = \frac{k}{r_1}, \quad or \quad k(r_1 - r_2) = r_1 h.$$

Hence, $\qquad A = \pi(r_1 h + r_2 h) = 2\pi h[\tfrac{1}{2}(r_1 + r_2)].$

With $r_3 = \tfrac{1}{2}(r_1 + r_2)$, which is the radius of the midsection, $A = 2\pi r_3 h$. Or, A is equal to *the slant height times the circumference, $2\pi r_3$, of the midsection of the frustum of the cone.*

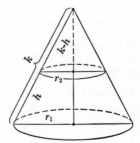

Fig. 436

Note 14. TAYLOR'S FORMULA WITH WEAKENED HYPOTHESES

Taylor's Theorem. *Suppose that the function $f(s)$ has continuous derivatives of orders $1, 2, \cdots, (n-1)$ when $a \leqq s \leqq x$ (or, $x \leqq s \leqq a$), and that $f^{(n)}(s)$ exists when $a < s < x$. Then, there exists a number ξ between a and x such that*

$$f(x) = f(a) + f'(a)(x-a) + \cdots + \frac{f^{(n-1)}(a)}{(n-1)!}(x-a)^{n-1} + R_n(x), \tag{1}$$

where

$$R_n(x) = \frac{(x-a)^n}{n!} f^{(n)}(\xi). \tag{2}$$

Proof. 1. We define R_n by (1) and wish to prove (2). Let x have a fixed value. Let s be a variable with the range $a \leqq s \leqq x$. Define a function $G(s)$ by the following equation, whose terms are suggested by the first n terms observed on the right-hand side in (1) with $a = s$:

$$f(x) = f(s) + f'(s)(x-s) + \cdots + \frac{f^{(n-1)}(s)}{(n-1)!}(x-s)^{n-1} + G(s). \tag{3}$$

We obtain $G'(s)$ by differentiating with respect to s on both sides of (3). Thus, for any integer $k > 1$,

$$\frac{d}{ds}\left[\frac{f^{(k)}(s)(x-s)^k}{k!}\right] = -\frac{f^{(k)}(s)(x-s)^{k-1}}{(k-1)!} + \frac{f^{(k+1)}(s)(x-s)^k}{k!}. \tag{4}$$

When (4) is used for each corresponding term on the right in (3), cancellation termwise occurs, and we obtain

$$G'(s) + \frac{f^{(n)}(s)}{(n-1)!}(x-s)^{n-1} = 0, \text{ or}$$

$$G'(s) = -\frac{f^{(n)}(s)(x-s)^{n-1}}{(n-1)!}. \tag{5}$$

2. In (3), on placing $s = x$ and then $s = a$, we obtain $G(x) = 0$ and $G(a) = R_n(x)$, because of (1).

3. Let $\phi(s)$ be defined by

$$\phi(s) = -\frac{(x-s)^n}{n!}. \tag{6}$$

Then, we obtain

$$\phi'(s) = \frac{(x-s)^{n-1}}{(n-1)!}. \tag{7}$$

4. Apply Theorem I of page 685 with G and ϕ as the functions appearing in the numerator and denominator, respectively, and with $s = x$ and $s = a$ as the values involved for the variable. Then, from (1) of Note 10 on page 685 and (3) above, there exists a number ξ where $a < \xi < x$, such that

$$\frac{G(x) - G(a)}{\phi(x) - \phi(a)} = \frac{G'(\xi)}{\phi'(\xi)} = \left\{-\frac{f^{(n)}(\xi)(x-\xi)^{n-1}}{(n-1)!} \div \frac{(x-\xi)^{n-1}}{(n-1)!}\right\} = -f^{(n)}(\xi). \tag{8}$$

Since $G(x) = \phi(x) = 0$, $G(a) = R_n(x)$, and $\phi(a) = -(x-a)^n/n!$, from (8) we obtain

$$\frac{G(a)}{\phi(a)} = -\frac{R_n(x)}{\dfrac{(x-a)^n}{n!}} = -f^{(n)}(\xi), \quad or \quad R_n(x) = \frac{(x-a)^n}{n!}f^{(n)}(\xi),$$

which we desired to prove.

Note 15. CONDITIONS FOR $f_{xy}(x, y) = f_{yx}(x, y)$

Assume that the domain of a function $f(x, y)$ includes some circular neighborhood, T, of the point $(x = a, y = b)$, and that all arguments (x, y) to be used for f and its derivatives are in T. Also, assume that the functions

$$f_x(x, y), \quad f_y(x, y), \quad f_{xy}(x, y) = \frac{\partial}{\partial y}\left(\frac{\partial f(x, y)}{\partial x}\right), \quad \text{and} \quad f_{yx}(x, y) = \frac{\partial}{\partial x}\left(\frac{\partial f(x, y)}{\partial y}\right)$$

exist when (x, y) is in T and are continuous at (a, b). Then, we shall prove that

$$f_{xy}(a, b) = f_{yx}(a, b); \tag{1}$$

or, *the order of the partial differentiations is immaterial.*

Proof. 1. Let $g(h)$, $\phi(x)$, and $\psi(y)$ be defined as follows:

$$g(h) = f(a + h, b + h) - f(a + h, b) - f(a, b + h) + f(a, b); \tag{2}$$

$$\phi(x) = f(x, b + h) - f(x, b); \quad \psi(y) = f(a + h, y) - f(a, y). \tag{3}$$

There exist
$$\phi'(x) = f_x(x, b + h) - f_x(x, b); \tag{4}$$

$$\psi'(y) = f_y(a + h, y) - f_y(a, y). \tag{5}$$

Moreover, $\qquad g(h) = \phi(a + h) - \phi(a) \quad and \quad g(h) = \psi(b + h) - \psi(b).$ $\qquad$ (6)

2. First, we apply the mean value theorem for functions to $\phi(x)$ in the form (6) of page 174. Thus, there exists a number θ_1 such that $0 < \theta_1 < 1$ and

$$g(h) = \phi(a + h) - \phi(a) = h\phi'(a + \theta_1 h), \text{ or}$$

$$g(h) = h[f_x(a + \theta_1 h, b + h) - f_x(a + \theta_1 h, b)]. \tag{7}$$

Then, we apply (6) of page 174 to the function of y with the values $f_x(a + \theta_1 h, y)$, whose derivative with respect to y is $f_{xy}(a + \theta_1 h, y)$. Hence, from (7), there exists $\theta_{1,2}$ such that $0 < \theta_{1,2} < 1$ and

$$g(h) = h[hf_{xy}(a + \theta_1 h, b + \theta_{1,2} h)]. \tag{8}$$

3. Similarly, on commencing with $g(h) = \psi(b + h) - \psi(b)$, by two applications of the mean value theorem, we find that there exist numbers θ_2 and $\theta_{2,1}$ between 0 and 1 such that

$$g(h) = h^2 f_{yx}(a + \theta_{2,1} h, b + \theta_2 h). \tag{9}$$

From (8) and (9), we obtain

$$f_{xy}(a + \theta_1 h, b + \theta_{1,2} h) = f_{yx}(a + \theta_{2,1} h, b + \theta_2 h). \tag{10}$$

If $h \to 0$, then $\theta_1 h \to 0$, $\theta_{1,2} h \to 0$, $\theta_{2,1} h \to 0$ and $\theta_2 h \to 0$, and the arguments of f_{xy} and f_{yx} in (10) both approach (a, b). Hence, since f_{xy} and f_{yx} are continuous at $(x = a, y = b)$, the left-hand and the right-hand sides of (10) have limits as $h \to 0$, which gives $f_{xy}(a, b) = f_{yx}(a, b)$, as we desired to prove.

Tables

I. POWERS AND ROOTS

No.	Sq.	Sq. Root	Cube	Cube Root	No.	Sq.	Sq. Root	Cube	Cube Root
1	1	1.000	1	1.000	51	2,601	7.141	132,651	3.708
2	4	1.414	8	1.260	52	2,704	7.211	140,608	3.732
3	9	1.732	27	1.442	53	2,809	7.280	148,877	3.756
4	16	2.000	64	1.587	54	2,916	7.348	157,464	3.780
5	25	2.236	125	1.710	55	3,025	7.416	166,375	3.803
6	36	2.449	216	1.817	56	3,136	7.483	175,616	3.826
7	49	2.646	343	1.913	57	3,249	7.550	185,193	3.848
8	64	2.828	512	2.000	58	3,364	7.616	195,112	3.871
9	81	3.000	729	2.080	59	3,481	7.681	205,379	3.893
10	100	3.162	1,000	2.154	60	3,600	7.746	216,000	3.915
11	121	3.317	1,331	2.224	61	3,721	7.810	226,981	3.936
12	144	3.464	1,728	2.289	62	3,844	7.874	238,328	3.958
13	169	3.606	2,197	2.351	63	3,969	7.937	250,047	3.979
14	196	3.742	2,744	2.410	64	4,096	8.000	262,144	4.000
15	225	3.873	3,375	2.466	65	4,225	8.062	274,625	4.021
16	256	4.000	4,096	2.520	66	4,356	8.124	287,496	4.041
17	289	4.123	4,913	2.571	67	4,489	8.185	300,763	4.062
18	324	4.243	5,832	2.621	68	4,624	8.246	314,432	4.082
19	361	4.359	6,859	2.668	69	4,761	8.307	328,509	4.102
20	400	4.472	8,000	2.714	70	4,900	8.367	343,000	4.121
21	441	4.583	9,261	2.759	71	5,041	8.426	357,911	4.141
22	484	4.690	10,648	2.802	72	5,184	8.485	373,248	4.160
23	529	4.796	12,167	2.844	73	5,329	8.544	389,017	4.179
24	576	4.899	13,824	2.884	74	5,476	8.602	405,224	4.198
25	625	5.000	15,625	2.924	75	5,625	8.660	421,875	4.217
26	676	5.099	17,576	2.962	76	5,776	8.718	438,976	4.236
27	729	5.196	19,683	3.000	77	5,929	8.775	456,533	4.254
28	784	5.291	21,952	3.037	78	6,084	8.832	474,552	4.273
29	841	5.385	24,389	3.072	79	6,241	8.888	493,039	4.291
30	900	5.477	27,000	3.107	80	6,400	8.944	512,000	4.309
31	961	5.568	29,791	3.141	81	6,561	9.000	531,441	4.327
32	1,024	5.657	32,768	3.175	82	6,724	9.055	551,368	4.344
33	1,089	5.745	35,937	3.208	83	6,889	9.110	571,787	4.362
34	1,156	5.831	39,304	3.240	84	7,056	9.165	592,704	4.380
35	1,225	5.916	42,875	3.271	85	7,225	9.220	614,125	4.397
36	1,296	6.000	46,656	3.302	86	7,396	9.274	636,056	4.414
37	1,369	6.083	50,653	3.332	87	7,569	9.327	658,503	4.431
38	1,444	6.164	54,872	3.362	88	7,744	9.381	681,472	4.448
39	1,521	6.245	59,319	3.391	89	7,921	9.434	704,969	4.465
40	1,600	6.325	64,000	3.420	90	8,100	9.487	729,000	4.481
41	1,681	6.403	68,921	3.448	91	8,281	9.539	753,571	4.498
42	1,764	6.481	74,088	3.476	92	8,464	9.592	778,688	4.514
43	1,849	6.557	79,507	3.503	93	8,649	9.644	804,357	4.531
44	1,936	6.633	85,184	3.530	94	8,836	9.695	830,584	4.547
45	2,025	6.708	91,125	3.557	95	9,025	9.747	857,375	4.563
46	2,116	6.782	97,336	3.583	96	9,216	9.798	884,736	4.579
47	2,209	6.856	103,823	3.609	97	9,409	9.849	912,673	4.595
48	2,304	6.928	110,592	3.634	98	9,604	9.899	941,192	4.610
49	2,401	7.000	117,649	3.659	99	9,801	9.950	970,299	4.626
50	2,500	7.071	125,000	3.684	100	10,000	10.000	1,000,000	4.642

N	0	1	2	3	4	5	6	7	8	9	Prop. Parts
10	.0000	0043	0086	0128	0170	0212	0253	0294	0334	0374	
11	.0414	0453	0492	0531	0569	0607	0645	0682	0719	0755	
12	.0792	0828	0864	0899	0934	0969	1004	1038	1072	1106	
13	.1139	1173	1206	1239	1271	1303	1335	1367	1399	1430	
14	.1461	1492	1523	1553	1584	1614	1644	1673	1703	1732	
15	.1761	1790	1818	1847	1875	1903	1931	1959	1987	2014	
16	.2041	2068	2095	2122	2148	2175	2201	2227	2253	2279	
17	.2304	2330	2355	2380	2405	2430	2455	2480	2504	2529	
18	.2553	2577	2601	2625	2648	2672	2695	2718	2742	2765	
19	.2788	2810	2833	2856	2878	2900	2923	2945	2967	2989	
20	.3010	3032	3054	3075	3096	3118	3139	3160	3181	3201	
21	.3222	3243	3263	3284	3304	3324	3345	3365	3385	3404	
22	.3424	3444	3464	3483	3502	3522	3541	3560	3579	3598	
23	.3617	3636	3655	3674	3692	3711	3729	3747	3766	3784	
24	.3802	3820	3838	3856	3874	3892	3909	3927	3945	3962	
25	.3979	3997	4014	4031	4048	4065	4082	4099	4116	4133	
26	.4150	4166	4183	4200	4216	4232	4249	4265	4281	4298	
27	.4314	4330	4346	4362	4378	4393	4409	4425	4440	4456	
28	.4472	4487	4502	4518	4533	4548	4564	4579	4594	4609	
29	.4624	4639	4654	4669	4683	4698	4713	4728	4742	4757	
30	.4771	4786	4800	4814	4829	4843	4857	4871	4886	4900	
31	.4914	4928	4942	4955	4969	4983	4997	5011	5024	5038	
32	.5051	5065	5079	5092	5105	5119	5132	5145	5159	5172	
33	.5185	5198	5211	5224	5237	5250	5263	5276	5289	5302	
34	.5315	5328	5340	5353	5366	5378	5391	5403	5416	5428	
35	.5441	5453	5465	5478	5490	5502	5514	5527	5539	5551	
36	.5563	5575	5587	5599	5611	5623	5635	5647	5658	5670	
37	.5682	5694	5705	5717	5729	5740	5752	5763	5775	5786	
38	.5798	5809	5821	5832	5843	5855	5866	5877	5888	5899	
39	.5911	5922	5933	5944	5955	5966	5977	5988	5999	6010	
40	.6021	6031	6042	6053	6064	6075	6085	6096	6107	6117	
41	.6128	6138	6149	6160	6170	6180	6191	6201	6212	6222	
42	.6232	6243	6253	6263	6274	6284	6294	6304	6314	6325	
43	.6335	6345	6355	6365	6375	6385	6395	6405	6415	6425	
44	.6435	6444	6454	6464	6474	6484	6493	6503	6513	6522	
45	.6532	6542	6551	6561	6571	6580	6590	6599	6609	6618	
46	.6628	6637	6646	6656	6665	6675	6684	6693	6702	6712	
47	.6721	6730	6739	6749	6758	6767	6776	6785	6794	6803	
48	.6812	6821	6830	6839	6848	6857	6866	6875	6884	6893	
49	.6902	6911	6920	6928	6937	6946	6955	6964	6972	6981	
50	.6990	6998	7007	7016	7024	7033	7042	7050	7059	7067	
N	0	1	2	3	4	5	6	7	8	9	

Prop. Parts (right column)

	28	27	26
1	2.8	2.7	2.6
2	5.6	5.4	5.2
3	8.4	8.1	7.8
4	11.2	10.8	10.4
5	14.0	13.5	13.0
6	16.8	16.2	15.6
7	19.6	18.9	18.2
8	22.4	21.6	20.8
9	25.2	24.3	23.4

	22	21	20
1	2.2	2.1	2.0
2	4.4	4.2	4.0
3	6.6	6.3	6.0
4	8.8	8.4	8.0
5	11.0	10.5	10.0
6	13.2	12.6	12.0
7	15.4	14.7	14.0
8	17.6	16.8	16.0
9	19.8	18.9	18.0

	16	15	14
1	1.6	1.5	1.4
2	3.2	3.0	2.8
3	4.8	4.5	4.2
4	6.4	6.0	5.6
5	8.0	7.5	7.0
6	9.6	9.0	8.4
7	11.2	10.5	9.8
8	12.8	12.0	11.2
9	14.4	13.5	12.6

	13	12	11
1	1.3	1.2	1.1
2	2.6	2.4	2.2
3	3.9	3.6	3.3
4	5.2	4.8	4.4
5	6.5	6.0	5.5
6	7.8	7.2	6.6
7	9.1	8.4	7.7
8	10.4	9.6	8.8
9	11.7	10.8	9.9

Prop. Parts (bottom)

	43	42	41	40	39		38	37	36	35	34		33	32	31	30	29	
1	4.3	4.2	4.1	4.0	3.9	1	3.8	3.7	3.6	3.5	3.4	1	3.3	3.2	3.1	3.0	2.9	1
2	8.6	8.4	8.2	8.0	7.8	2	7.6	7.4	7.2	7.0	6.8	2	6.6	6.4	6.2	6.0	5.8	2
3	12.9	12.6	12.3	12.0	11.7	3	11.4	11.1	10.8	10.5	10.2	3	9.9	9.6	9.3	9.0	8.7	3
4	17.2	16.8	16.4	16.0	15.6	4	15.2	14.8	14.4	14.0	13.6	4	13.2	12.8	12.4	12.0	11.6	4
5	21.5	21.0	20.5	20.0	19.5	5	19.0	18.5	18.0	17.5	17.0	5	16.5	16.0	15.5	15.0	14.5	5
6	25.8	25.2	24.6	24.0	23.4	6	22.8	22.2	21.6	21.0	20.4	6	19.8	19.2	18.6	18.0	17.4	6
7	30.1	29.4	28.7	28.0	27.3	7	26.6	25.9	25.2	24.5	23.8	7	23.1	22.4	21.7	21.0	20.3	7
8	34.4	33.6	32.8	32.0	31.2	8	30.4	29.6	28.8	28.0	27.2	8	26.4	25.6	24.8	24.0	23.2	8
9	38.7	37.8	36.9	36.0	35.1	9	34.2	33.3	32.4	31.5	30.6	9	29.7	28.8	27.9	27.0	26.1	9

II. FOUR–PLACE COMMON LOGARITHMS

Prop. Parts

	25	24	23
1	2.5	2.4	2.3
2	5.0	4.8	4.6
3	7.5	7.2	6.9
4	10.0	9.6	9.2
5	12.5	12.0	11.5
6	15.0	14.4	13.8
7	17.5	16.8	16.1
8	20.0	19.2	18.4
9	22.5	21.6	20.7

	19	18	17
1	1.9	1.8	1.7
2	3.8	3.6	3.4
3	5.7	5.4	5.1
4	7.6	7.2	6.8
5	9.5	9.0	8.5
6	11.4	10.8	10.2
7	13.3	12.6	11.9
8	15.2	14.4	13.6
9	17.1	16.2	15.3

	10	9
1	1.0	0.9
2	2.0	1.8
3	3.0	2.7
4	4.0	3.6
5	5.0	4.5
6	6.0	5.4
7	7.0	6.3
8	8.0	7.2
9	9.0	8.1

	8	7
1	0.8	0.7
2	1.6	1.4
3	2.4	2.1
4	3.2	2.8
5	4.0	3.5
6	4.8	4.2
7	5.6	4.9
8	6.4	5.6
9	7.2	6.3

	6	5	4
1	0.6	0.5	0.4
2	1.2	1.0	0.8
3	1.8	1.5	1.2
4	2.4	2.0	1.6
5	3.0	2.5	2.0
6	3.6	3.0	2 4
7	4.2	3.5	2.8
8	4.8	4.0	3.2
9	5.4	4.5	3.6

N	0	1	2	3	4	5	6	7	8	9
50	.6990	6998	7007	7016	7024	7033	7042	7050	7059	7067
51	.7076	7084	7093	7101	7110	7118	7126	7135	7143	7152
52	.7160	7168	7177	7185	7193	7202	7210	7218	7226	7235
53	.7243	7251	7259	7267	7275	7284	7292	7300	7308	7316
54	.7324	7332	7340	7348	7356	7364	7372	7380	7388	7396
55	.7404	7412	7419	7427	7435	7443	7451	7459	7466	7474
56	.7482	7490	7497	7505	7513	7520	7528	7536	7543	7551
57	.7559	7566	7574	7582	7589	7597	7604	7612	7619	7627
58	.7634	7642	7649	7657	7664	7672	7679	7686	7694	7701
59	.7709	7716	7723	7731	7738	7745	7752	7760	7767	7774
60	.7782	7789	7796	7803	7810	7818	7825	7832	7839	7846
61	.7853	7860	7868	7875	7882	7889	7896	7903	7910	7917
62	.7924	7931	7938	7945	7952	7959	7966	7973	7980	7987
63	.7993	8000	8007	8014	8021	8028	8035	8041	8048	8055
64	.8062	8069	8075	8082	8089	8096	8102	8109	8116	8122
65	.8129	8136	8142	8149	8156	8162	8169	8176	8182	8189
66	.8195	8202	8209	8215	8222	8228	8235	8241	8248	8254
67	.8261	8267	8274	8280	8287	8293	8299	8306	8312	8319
68	.8325	8331	8338	8344	8351	8357	8363	8370	8376	8382
69	.8388	8395	8401	8407	8414	8420	8426	8432	8439	8445
70	.8451	8457	8463	8470	8476	8482	8488	8494	8500	8506
71	.8513	8519	8525	8531	8537	8543	8549	8555	8561	8567
72	.8573	8579	8585	8591	8597	8603	8609	8615	8621	8627
73	.8633	8639	8645	8651	8657	8663	8669	8675	8681	8686
74	.8692	8698	8704	8710	8716	8722	8727	8733	8739	8745
75	.8751	8756	8762	8768	8774	8779	8785	8791	8797	8802
76	.8808	8814	8820	8825	8831	8837	8842	8848	8854	8859
77	.8865	8871	8876	8882	8887	8893	8899	8904	8910	8915
78	.8921	8927	8932	8938	8943	8949	8954	8960	8965	8971
79	.8976	8982	8987	8993	8998	9004	9009	9015	9020	9025
80	.9031	9036	9042	9047	9053	9058	9063	9069	9074	9079
81	.9085	9090	9096	9101	9106	9112	9117	9122	9128	9133
82	.9138	9143	9149	9154	9159	9165	9170	9175	9180	9186
83	.9191	9196	9201	9206	9212	9217	9222	9227	9232	9238
84	.9243	9248	9253	9258	9263	9269	9274	9279	9284	9289
85	.9294	9299	9304	9309	9315	9320	9325	9330	9335	9340
86	.9345	9350	9355	9360	9365	9370	9375	9380	9385	9390
87	.9395	9400	9405	9410	9415	9420	9425	9430	9435	9440
88	.9445	9450	9455	9460	9465	9469	9474	9479	9484	9489
89	.9494	9499	9504	9509	9513	9518	9523	9528	9533	9538
90	.9542	9547	9552	9557	9562	9566	9571	9576	9581	9586
91	.9590	9595	9600	9605	9609	9614	9619	9624	9628	9633
92	.9638	9643	9647	9652	9657	9661	9666	9671	9675	9680
93	.9685	9689	9694	9699	9703	9708	9713	9717	9722	9727
94	.9731	9736	9741	9745	9750	9754	9759	9763	9768	9773
95	.9777	9782	9786	9791	9795	9800	9805	9809	9814	9818
96	.9823	9827	9832	9836	9841	9845	9850	9854	9859	9863
97	.9868	9872	9877	9881	9886	9890	9894	9899	9903	9908
98	.9912	9917	9921	9926	9930	9934	9939	9943	9948	9952
99	.9956	9961	9965	9969	9974	9978	9983	9987	9991	9996
N	0	1	2	3	4	5	6	7	8	9

N	0	1	2	3	4	5	6	7	8	9
1.0	0.0 0000	0995	1980	2956	3922	4879	5827	6766	7696	8618
1.1	0.0 9531	*0436	*1333	*2222	*3103	*3976	*4842	*5700	*6551	*7395
1.2	0.1 8232	9062	9885	*0701	*1511	*2314	*3111	*3902	*4686	*5464
1.3	0.2 6236	7003	7763	8518	9267	*0010	*0748	*1481	*2208	*2930
1.4	0.3 3647	4359	5066	5767	6464	7156	7844	8526	9204	9878
1.5	0.4 0547	1211	1871	2527	3178	3825	4469	5108	5742	6373
1.6	0.4 7000	7623	8243	8858	9470	*0078	*0682	*1282	*1879	*2473
1.7	0.5 3063	3649	4232	4812	5389	5962	6531	7098	7661	8222
1.8	0.5 8779	9333	9884	*0432	*0977	*1519	*2058	*2594	*3127	*3658
1.9	0.6 4185	4710	5233	5752	6269	6783	7294	7803	8310	8813
2.0	0.6 9315	9813	*0310	*0804	*1295	*1784	*2271	*2755	*3237	*3716
2.1	0.7 4194	4669	5142	5612	6081	6547	7011	7473	7932	8390
2.2	0.7 8846	9299	9751	*0200	*0648	*1093	*1536	*1978	*2418	*2855
2.3	0.8 3291	3725	4157	4587	5015	5442	5866	6289	6710	7129
2.4	0.8 7547	7963	8377	8789	9200	9609	*0016	*0422	*0826	*1228
2.5	0.9 1629	2028	2426	2822	3216	3609	4001	4391	4779	5166
2.6	5551	5935	6317	6698	7078	7456	7833	8208	8582	8954
2.7	0.9 9325	9695	*0063	*0430	*0796	*1160	*1523	*1885	*2245	*2604
2.8	1.0 2962	3318	3674	4028	4380	4732	5082	5431	5779	6126
2.9	6471	6815	7158	7500	7841	8181	8519	8856	9192	9527
3.0	1.0 9861	*0194	*0526	*0856	*1186	*1514	*1841	*2168	*2493	*2817
3.1	1.1 3140	3462	3783	4103	4422	4740	5057	5373	5688	6002
3.2	6315	6627	6938	7248	7557	7865	8173	8479	8784	9089
3.3	1.1 9392	9695	9996	*0297	*0597	*0896	*1194	*1491	*1788	*2083
3.4	1.2 2378	2671	2964	3256	3547	3837	4127	4415	4703	4990
3.5	5276	5562	5846	6130	6413	6695	6976	7257	7536	7815
3.6	1.2 8093	8371	8647	8923	9198	9473	9746	*0019	*0291	*0563
3.7	1.3 0833	1103	1372	1641	1909	2176	2442	2708	2972	3237
3.8	3500	3763	4025	4286	4547	4807	5067	5325	5584	5841
3.9	6098	6354	6609	6864	7118	7372	7624	7877	8128	8379
4.0	1.3 8629	8879	9128	9377	9624	9872	*0118	*0364	*0610	*0854
4.1	1.4 1099	1342	1585	1828	2070	2311	2552	2792	3031	3270
4.2	3508	3746	3984	4220	4456	4692	4927	5161	5395	5629
4.3	5862	6094	6326	6557	6787	7018	7247	7476	7705	7933
4.4	1.4 8160	8387	8614	8840	9065	9290	9515	9739	9962	*0185
4.5	1.5 0408	0630	0851	1072	1293	1513	1732	1951	2170	2388
4.6	2606	2823	3039	3256	3471	3687	3902	4116	4330	4543
4.7	4756	4969	5181	5393	5604	5814	6025	6235	6444	6653
4.8	6862	7070	7277	7485	7691	7898	8104	8309	8515	8719
4.9	1.5 8924	9127	9331	9534	9737	9939	*0141	*0342	*0543	*0744
5.0	1.6 0944	1144	1343	1542	1741	1939	2137	2334	2531	2728
5.1	2924	3120	3315	3511	3705	3900	4094	4287	4481	4673
5.2	4866	5058	5250	5441	5632	5823	6013	6203	6393	6582
5.3	6771	6959	7147	7335	7523	7710	7896	8083	8269	8455
5.4	1.6 8640	8825	9010	9194	9378	9562	9745	9928	*0111	*0293
5.5	1.7 0475	0656	0838	1019	1199	1380	1560	1740	1919	2098
5.6	2277	2455	2633	2811	2988	3166	3342	3519	3695	3871
5.7	4047	4222	4397	4572	4746	4920	5094	5267	5440	5613
5.8	5786	5958	6130	6302	6473	6644	6815	6985	7156	7326
5.9	7495	7665	7834	8002	8171	8339	8507	8675	8842	9009
6.0	1.7 9176	9342	9509	9675	9840	*0006	*0171	*0336	*0500	*0665
N	0	1	2	3	4	5	6	7	8	9

694

III. NATURAL LOGARITHMS

N	0	1	2	3	4	5	6	7	8	9
6.0	1.7 9176	9342	9509	9675	9840	*0006	*0171	*0336	*0500	*0665
6.1	1.8 0829	0993	1156	1319	1482	1645	1808	1970	2132	2294
6.2	2455	2616	2777	2938	3098	3258	3418	3578	3737	3896
6.3	4055	4214	4372	4530	4688	4845	5003	5160	5317	5473
6.4	5630	5786	5942	6097	6253	6408	6563	6718	6872	7026
6.5	7180	7334	7487	7641	7794	7947	8099	8251	8403	8555
6.6	1.8 8707	8858	9010	9160	9311	9462	9612	9762	9912	*0061
6.7	1.9 0211	0360	0509	0658	0806	0954	1102	1250	1398	1545
6.8	1692	1839	1986	2132	2279	2425	2571	2716	2862	3007
6.9	3152	3297	3442	3586	3730	3874	4018	4162	4305	4448
7.0	4591	4734	4876	5019	5161	5303	5445	5586	5727	5869
7.1	6009	6150	6291	6431	6571	6711	6851	6991	7130	7269
7.2	7408	7547	7685	7824	7962	8100	8238	8376	8513	8650
7.3	1.9 8787	8924	9061	9198	9334	9470	9606	9742	9877	*0013
7.4	2.0 0148	0283	0418	0553	0687	0821	0956	1089	1223	1357
7.5	1490	1624	1757	1890	2022	2155	2287	2419	2551	2683
7.6	2815	2946	3078	3209	3340	3471	3601	3732	3862	3992
7.7	4122	4252	4381	4511	4640	4769	4898	5027	5156	5284
7.8	5412	5540	5668	5796	5924	6051	6179	6306	6433	6560
7.9	6686	6813	6939	7065	7191	7317	7443	7568	7694	7819
8.0	7944	8069	8194	8318	8443	8567	8691	8815	8939	9063
8.1	2.0 9186	9310	9433	9556	9679	9802	9924	*0047	*0169	*0291
8.2	2.1 0413	0535	0657	0779	0900	1021	1142	1263	1384	1505
8.3	1626	1746	1866	1986	2106	2226	2346	2465	2585	2704
8.4	2823	2942	3061	3180	3298	3417	3535	3653	3771	3889
8.5	4007	4124	4242	4359	4476	4593	4710	4827	4943	5060
8.6	5176	5292	5409	5524	5640	5756	5871	5987	6102	6217
8.7	6332	6447	6562	6677	6791	6905	7020	7134	7248	7361
8.8	7475	7589	7702	7816	7929	8042	8155	8267	8380	8493
8.9	8605	8717	8830	8942	9054	9165	9277	9389	9500	9611
9.0	2.1 9722	9834	9944	*0055	*0166	*0276	*0387	*0497	*0607	*0717
9.1	2.2 0827	0937	1047	1157	1266	1375	1485	1594	1703	1812
9.2	1920	2029	2138	2246	2354	2462	2570	2678	2786	2894
9.3	3001	3109	3216	3324	3431	3538	3645	3751	3858	3965
9.4	4071	4177	4284	4390	4496	4601	4707	4813	4918	5024
9.5	5129	5234	5339	5444	5549	5654	5759	5863	5968	6072
9.6	6176	6280	6384	6488	6592	6696	6799	6903	7006	7109
9.7	7213	7316	7419	7521	7624	7727	7829	7932	8034	8136
9.8	8238	8340	8442	8544	8646	8747	8849	8950	9051	9152
9.9	2.2 9253	9354	9455	9556	9657	9757	9858	9958	*0058	*0158
10.0	2.3 0259	0358	0458	0558	0658	0757	0857	0956	1055	1154
N	0	1	2	3	4	5	6	7	8	9

NOTE 1. The base for natural logarithms is $e = 2.71828\ 18284\ 59045 \cdots$:

$$\log_e 10 = 2.3025\ 8509. \qquad \log_{10} e = 0.4342\ 9448. \tag{1}$$

NOTE 2. If $N > 10$ or $N < 1$, then we may write $N = P \cdot 10^k$ where k is an integer and $1 \leqq P < 10$. Then, to find $\log_e N$, use the following relation with $\log_e P$ obtained from the preceding table and $\log_e 10$ obtained from (1):

$$\log_e N = \log_e (P \cdot 10^k) = \log_e P + k \log_e 10.$$

IV. TRIGONOMETRIC FUNCTIONS, WITH RADIAN MEASURE

α Rad.	Degrees in α	Sin α	Cos α	Tan α	α Rad.	Degrees in α	Sin α	Cos α	Tan α
.00	0° 00.0′	.00000	1.0000	.00000	.60	34° 22.6′	.56464	.82534	.68414
.01	0° 34.4′	.01000	.99995	.01000	.61	34° 57.0′	.57287	.81965	.69892
.02	1° 08.8′	.02000	.99980	.02000	.62	35° 31.4′	.58104	.81388	.71391
.03	1° 43.1′	.03000	.99955	.03001	.63	36° 05.8′	.58914	.80803	.72911
.04	2° 17.5′	.03999	.99920	.04002	.64	36° 40.2′	.59720	.80210	.74454
.05	2° 51.9′	.04998	.99875	.05004	.65	37° 14.5′	.60519	.79608	.76020
.06	3° 26.3′	.05996	.99820	.06007	.66	37° 48.9′	.61312	.78999	.77610
.07	4° 00.6′	.06994	.99755	.07011	.67	38° 23.3′	.62099	.78382	.79225
.08	4° 35.0′	.07991	.99680	.08017	.68	38° 57.7′	.62879	.77757	.80866
.09	5° 09.4′	.08988	.99595	.09024	.69	39° 32.0′	.63654	.77125	.82534
.10	5° 43.8′	.09983	.99500	.10033	.70	40° 06.4′	.64422	.76484	.84229
.11	6° 18.2′	.10978	.99396	.11045	.71	40° 40.8′	.65183	.75836	.85953
.12	6° 52.5′	.11971	.99281	.12058	.72	41° 15.2′	.65938	.75181	.87707
.13	7° 26.9′	.12963	.99156	.13074	.73	41° 49.6′	.66687	.74517	.89492
.14	8° 01.3′	.13954	.99022	.14092	.74	42° 23.9′	.67429	.73847	.91309
.15	8° 35.7′	.14944	.98877	.15114	.75	42° 58.3′	.68164	.73169	.93160
.16	9° 10.0′	.15932	.98723	.16138	.76	43° 32.7′	.68892	.72484	.95045
.17	9° 44.4′	.16918	.98558	.17166	.77	44° 07.1′	.69614	.71791	.96967
.18	10° 18.8′	.17903	.98384	.18197	.78	44° 41.4′	.70328	.71091	.98926
.19	10° 53.2′	.18886	.98200	.19232	.79	45° 15.8′	.71035	.70385	1.0092
.20	11° 27.5′	.19867	.98007	.20271	.80	45° 50.2′	.71736	.69671	1.0296
.21	12° 01.9′	.20846	.97803	.21314	.81	46° 24.6′	.72429	.68950	1.0505
.22	12° 36.3′	.21823	.97590	.22362	.82	46° 59.0′	.73115	.68222	1.0717
.23	13° 10.7′	.22798	.97367	.23414	.83	47° 33.3′	.73793	.67488	1.0934
.24	13° 45.1′	.23770	.97134	.24472	.84	48° 07.7′	.74464	.66746	1.1156
.25	14° 19.4′	.24740	.96891	.25534	.85	48° 42.1′	.75128	.65998	1.1383
.26	14° 53.8′	.25708	.96639	.26602	.86	49° 16.5′	.75784	.65244	1.1616
.27	15° 28.2′	.26673	.96377	.27676	.87	49° 50.8′	.76433	.64483	1.1853
.28	16° 02.6′	.27636	.96106	.28755	.88	50° 25.2′	.77074	.63715	1.2097
.29	16° 36.9′	.28595	.95824	.29841	.89	50° 59.6′	.77707	.62941	1.2346
.30	17° 11.3′	.29552	.95534	.30934	.90	51° 34.0′	.78333	.62161	1.2602
.31	17° 45.7′	.30506	.95233	.32033	.91	52° 08.3′	.78950	.61375	1.2864
.32	18° 20.1′	.31457	.94924	.33139	.92	52° 42.7′	.79560	.60582	1.3133
.33	18° 54.5′	.32404	.94604	.34252	.93	53° 17.1′	.80162	.59783	1.3409
.34	19° 28.8′	.33349	.94275	.35374	.94	53° 51.5′	.80756	.58979	1.3692
.35	20° 03.2′	.34290	.93937	.36503	.95	54° 25.9′	.81342	.58168	1.3984
.36	20° 37.6′	.35227	.93590	.37640	.96	55° 00.2′	.81919	.57352	1.4284
.37	21° 12.0′	.36162	.93233	.38786	.97	55° 34.6′	.82489	.56530	1.4592
.38	21° 46.3′	.37092	.92866	.39941	.98	56° 09.0′	.83050	.55702	1.4910
.39	22° 20.7′	.38019	.92491	.41105	.99	56° 43.4′	.83603	.54869	1.5237
.40	22° 55.1′	.38942	.92106	.42279	1.00	57° 17.7′	.84147	.54030	1.5574
.41	23° 29.5′	.39861	.91712	.43463	1.01	57° 52.1′	.84683	.53186	1.5922
.42	24° 03.9′	.40776	.91309	.44657	1.02	58° 26.5′	.85211	.52337	1.6281
.43	24° 38.2′	.41687	.90897	.45862	1.03	59° 00.9′	.85730	.51482	1.6652
.44	25° 12.6′	.42594	.90475	.47078	1.04	59° 35.3′	.86240	.50622	1.7036
.45	25° 47.0′	.43497	.90045	.48306	1.05	60° 09.6′	.86742	.49757	1.7433
.46	26° 21.4′	.44395	.89605	.49545	1.06	60° 44.0′	.87236	.48887	1.7844
.47	26° 55.7′	.45289	.89157	.50797	1.07	61° 18.4′	.87720	.48012	1.8270
.48	27° 30.1′	.46178	.88699	.52061	1.08	61° 52.8′	.88196	.47133	1.8712
.49	28° 04.5′	.47063	.88233	.53339	1.09	62° 27.1′	.88663	.46249	1.9171
.50	28° 38.9′	.47943	.87758	.54630	1.10	63° 01.5′	.89121	.45360	1.9648
.51	29° 13.3′	.48818	.87274	.55936	1.11	63° 35.9′	.89570	.44466	2.0143
.52	29° 47.6′	.49688	.86782	.57256	1.12	64° 10.3′	.90010	.43568	2.0660
.53	30° 22.0′	.50553	.86281	.58592	1.13	64° 44.7′	.90441	.42666	2.1198
.54	30° 56.4′	.51414	.85771	.59943	1.14	65° 19.0′	.90863	.41759	2.1759
.55	31° 30.8′	.52269	.85252	.61311	1.15	65° 53.4′	.91276	.40849	2.2345
.56	32° 05.1′	.53119	.84726	.62695	1.16	66° 27.8′	.91680	.39934	2.2958
.57	32° 39.5′	.53963	.84190	.64097	1.17	67° 02.2′	.92075	.39015	2.3600
.58	33° 13.9′	.54802	.83646	.65517	1.18	67° 36.5′	.92461	.38092	2.4273
.59	33° 48.3′	.55636	.83094	.66956	1.19	68° 10.9′	.92837	.37166	2.4979
.60	34° 22.6′	.56464	.82534	.68414	1.20	68° 45.3′	.93204	.36236	2.5722

IV. TRIGONOMETRIC FUNCTIONS, WITH RADIAN MEASURE

α Rad.	Degrees in α	Sin α	Cos α	Tan α	α Rad.	Degrees in α	Sin α	Cos α	Tan α
1.20	68° 45.3′	.93204	.36236	2.5722	**1.40**	80° 12.8′	.98545	.16997	5.7979
1.21	69° 19.7′	.93562	.35302	2.6503	1.41	80° 47.2′	.98710	.16010	6.1654
1.22	69° 54.1′	93910	.34365	2.7328	1.42	81° 21.6′	.98865	.15023	6.5811
1.23	70° 28.4′	.94249	.33424	2.8198	1.43	81° 56.0′	.99010	.14033	7.0555
1.24	71° 02.8′	.94578	.32480	2.9119	1.44	82° 30.4′	.99146	.13042	7.6018
1.25	71° 37.2′	.94898	.31532	3.0096	**1.45**	83° 04.7′	.99271	.12050	8.2381
1.26	72° 11.6′	.95209	.30582	3.1133	1.46	83° 39.1′	.99387	.11057	8.9886
1.27	72° 45.9′	.95510	.29628	3.2236	1.47	84° 13.5′	.99492	.10063	9.8874
1.28	73° 20.3′	.95802	.28672	3.3413	1.48	84° 47.9′	.99588	.09067	10.983
1.29	73° 54.7′	.96084	.27712	3.4672	1.49	85° 22.2′	.99674	.08071	12.350
1.30	74° 29.1′	.96356	.26750	3.6021	**1.50**	85° 56.6′	.99749	.07074	14.101
1.31	75° 03.4′	.96618	.25785	3.7471	1.51	86° 31.0′	.99815	.06076	16.428
1.32	75° 37.8′	.96872	.24818	3.9033	1.52	87° 05.4′	.99871	.05077	19.670
1.33	76° 12.2′	.97115	.23848	4.0723	1.53	87° 39.8′	.99917	.04079	24.498
1.34	76° 46.6′	.97348	.22875	4.2556	1.54	88° 14.1′	.99953	.03079	32.461
1.35	77° 21.0′	.97572	.21901	4.4552	**1.55**	88° 48.5′	.99978	.02079	48.078
1.36	77° 55.3′	.97786	.20924	4.6734	1.56	89° 22.9′	.99994	.01080	92.620
1.37	78° 29.7′	.97991	.19945	4.9131	1.57	89° 57.3′	1.0000	.00080	1255.8
1.38	79° 04.1′	.98185	.18964	5.1774	1.58	90° 31.6′	.99996	−.00920	−108.65
1.39	79° 38.5′	.98370	.17981	5.4707	1.59	91° 06.0′	.99982	−.01920	−52.067
1.40	80° 12.8′	.98545	.16997	5.7979	**1.60**	91° 40.4′	.99957	−.02920	−34.233

DEGREES IN RADIANS

1°	0.01745	16°	0.27925	31°	0.54105	46°	0.80285	61°	1.06465	76°	1.32645
2	0.03491	17	0.29671	32	0.55851	47	0.82030	62	1.08210	77	1.34390
3	0.05236	18	0.31416	33	0.57596	48	0.83776	63	1.09956	78	1.36136
4	0.06981	19	0.33161	34	0.59341	49	0.85521	64	1.11701	79	1.37881
5	0.08727	**20**	0.34907	**35**	0.61087	**50**	0.87266	**65**	1.13446	**80**	1.39626
6	0.10472	21	0.36652	36	0.62832	51	0.89012	66	1.15192	81	1.41372
7	0.12217	22	0.38397	37	0.64577	52	0.90757	67	1.16937	82	1.43117
8	0.13963	23	0.40143	38	0.66323	53	0.92502	68	1.18682	83	1.44862
9	0.15708	24	0.41888	39	0.68068	54	0.94248	69	1.20428	84	1.46608
10	0.17453	**25**	0.43633	**40**	0.69813	**55**	0.95993	**70**	1.22173	**85**	1.48353
11	0.19199	26	0.45379	41	0.71558	56	0.97738	71	1.23918	86	1.50098
12	0.20944	27	0.47124	42	0.73304	57	0.99484	72	1.25664	87	1.51844
13	0.22689	28	0.48869	43	0.75049	58	1.01229	73	1.27409	88	1.53589
14	0.24435	29	0.50615	44	0.76794	59	1.02974	74	1.29154	89	1.55334
15	0.26180	**30**	0.52360	**45**	0.78540	**60**	1.04720	**75**	1.30900	**90**	1.57080

$1° = .01745329$ rad. $\log .01745329 = 8.24187737 − 10.$

$1′ = .0002908882$ rad. $\log .0002908882 = 6.46372612 − 10.$

$1'' = .0000048481368$ rad. $\log .0000048481368 = 4.68557487 − 10.$

MINUTES IN RADIANS

1′	0.00029	11′	0.00320	21′	0.00611	31′	0.00902	41′	0.01193	51′	0.01484
2	0.00058	12	0.00349	22	0.00640	32	0.00931	42	0.01222	52	0.01513
3	0.00087	13	0.00378	23	0.00669	33	0.00960	43	0.01251	53	0.01542
4	0.00116	14	0.00407	24	0.00698	34	0.00989	44	0.01280	54	0.01571
5	0.00145	**15**	0.00436	**25**	0.00727	**35**	0.01018	**45**	0.01309	**55**	0.01600
6	0.00175	16	0.00465	26	0.00756	36	0.01047	46	0.01338	56	0.01629
7	0.00204	17	0.00495	27	0.00785	37	0.01076	47	0.01367	57	0.01658
8	0.00233	18	0.00524	28	0.00814	38	0.01105	48	0.01396	58	0.01687
9	0.00262	19	0.00553	29	0.00844	39	0.01134	49	0.01425	59	0.01716
10	0.00291	**20**	0.00582	**30**	0.00873	**40**	0.01164	**50**	0.01454	**60**	0.01745

V. EXPONENTIAL AND HYPERBOLIC FUNCTIONS

x	e^x	Sinh x	Cosh x	x	e^x	Sinh x	Cosh x
0.00	1.0000	0.0000	1.0000	0.45	1.5683	0.4653	1.1030
.01	1.0101	0.0100	1.0001	.46	1.5841	.4764	1.1077
.02	1.0202	0.0200	1.0002	.47	1.6000	.4875	1.1125
.03	1.0305	0.0300	1.0005	.48	1.6161	.4986	1.1174
.04	1.0408	0.0400	1.0008	.49	1.6323	.5098	1.1225
.05	1.0513	0.0500	1.0013	.50	1.6487	.5211	1.1276
.06	1.0618	0.0600	1.0018	.51	1.6653	.5324	1.1329
.07	1.0725	0.0701	1.0025	.52	1.6820	.5438	1.1383
.08	1.0833	0.0801	1.0032	.53	1.6989	.5552	1.1438
.09	1.0942	0.0901	1.0041	.54	1.7160	.5666	1.1494
.10	1.1052	0.1002	1.0050	.55	1.7333	.5782	1.1551
.11	1.1163	0.1102	1.0061	.56	1.7507	.5897	1.1609
.12	1.1275	0.1203	1.0072	.57	1.7683	.6014	1.1669
.13	1.1388	0.1304	1.0085	.58	1.7860	.6131	1.1730
.14	1.1503	0.1405	1.0098	.59	1.8040	.6248	1.1792
.15	1.1618	0.1506	1.0113	.60	1.8221	.6367	1.1855
.16	1.1735	0.1607	1.0128	.61	1.8404	.6485	1.1919
.17	1.1853	0.1708	1.0145	.62	1.8589	.6605	1.1984
.18	1.1972	0.1810	1.0162	.63	1.8776	.6725	1.2051
.19	1.2092	0.1911	1.0181	.64	1.8965	.6846	1.2119
.20	1.2214	0.2013	1.0201	.65	1.9155	.6967	1.2188
.21	1.2337	0.2115	1.0221	.66	1.9348	.7090	1.2258
.22	1.2461	0.2218	1.0243	.67	1.9542	.7213	1.2330
.23	1.2586	0.2320	1.0266	.68	1.9739	.7336	1.2402
.24	1.2712	0.2423	1.0289	.69	1.9937	.7461	1.2476
.25	1.2840	0.2526	1.0314	.70	2.0138	.7586	1.2552
.26	1.2969	0.2629	1.0340	.71	2.0340	.7712	1.2628
.27	1.3100	0.2733	1.0367	.72	2.0544	.7838	1.2706
.28	1.3231	0.2837	1.0395	.73	2.0751	.7966	1.2785
.29	1.3364	0.2941	1.0423	.74	2.0959	.8094	1.2865
.30	1.3499	.3045	1.0453	.75	2.1170	.8223	1.2947
.31	1.3634	.3150	1.0484	.76	2.1383	.8353	1.3030
.32	1.3771	.3255	1.0516	.77	2.1598	.8484	1.3114
.33	1.3910	.3360	1.0549	.78	2.1815	.8615	1.3199
.34	1.4049	.3466	1.0584	.79	2.2034	.8748	1.3286
.35	1.4191	.3572	1.0619	.80	2.2255	.8881	1.3374
.36	1.4333	.3678	1.0655	.81	2.2479	.9015	1.3464
.37	1.4477	.3785	1.0692	.82	2.2705	.9150	1.3555
.38	1.4623	.3892	1.0731	.83	2.2933	.9286	1.3647
.39	1.4770	.4000	1.0770	.84	2.3164	.9423	1.3740
.40	1.4918	.4108	1.0811	.85	2.3396	.9561	1.3835
.41	1.5068	.4216	1.0852	.86	2.3632	.9700	1.3932
.42	1.5220	.4325	1.0895	.87	2.3869	.9840	1.4029
.43	1.5373	.4434	1.0939	.88	2.4109	.9981	1.4128
.44	1.5527	.4543	1.0984	.89	2.4351	1.0122	1.4229

V. EXPONENTIAL AND HYPERBOLIC FUNCTIONS

x	e^x	Sinh x	Cosh x	x	e^x	Sinh x	Cosh x
.90	2.4596	1.0265	1.4331	2.75	15.643	7.7894	7.8533
.91	2.4843	1.0409	1.4434	2.80	16.445	8.1919	8.2527
.92	2.5093	1.0554	1.4539	2.85	17.288	8.6150	8.6728
.93	2.5345	1.0700	1.4645	2.90	18.174	9.0596	9.1146
.94	2.5600	1.0847	1.4753	2.95	19.106	9.5268	9.5791
.95	2.5857	1.0995	1.4862	3.00	20.086	10.018	10.068
.96	2.6117	1.1144	1.4973	3.05	21.115	10.534	10.581
.97	2.6379	1.1294	1.5085	3.10	22.198	11.076	11.122
.98	2.6645	1.1446	1.5199	3.15	23.336	11.647	11.689
.99	2.6912	1.1598	1.5314	3.20	24.533	12.246	12.287
1.00	2.7183	1.1752	1.5431	3.25	25.790	12.876	12.915
1.05	2.8577	1.2539	1.6038	3.30	27.113	13.538	13.575
1.10	3.0042	1.3356	1.6685	3.35	28.503	14.234	14.269
1.15	3.1582	1.4208	1.7374	3.40	29.964	14.965	14.999
1.20	3.3201	1.5095	1.8107	3.45	31.500	15.734	15.766
1.25	3.4903	1.6019	1.8884	3.50	33.115	16.543	16.573
1.30	3.6693	1.6984	1.9709	3.55	34.813	17.392	17.421
1.35	3.8574	1.7991	2.0583	3.60	36.598	18.286	18.313
1.40	4.0552	1.9043	2.1509	3.65	38.475	19.224	19.250
1.45	4.2631	2.0143	2.2488	3.70	40.447	20.211	20.236
1.50	4.4817	2.1293	2.3524	3.75	42.521	21.249	21.272
1.55	4.7115	2.2496	2.4619	3.80	44.701	22.339	22.362
1.60	4.9530	2.3756	2.5775	3.85	46.993	23.486	23.507
1.65	5.2070	2.5075	2.6995	3.90	49.402	24.691	24.711
1.70	5.4739	2.6456	2.8283	3.95	51.935	25.958	25.977
1.75	5.7546	2.7904	2.9642	4.00	54.598	27.290	27.308
1.80	6.0496	2.9422	3.1075	4.10	60.340	30.162	30.178
1.85	6.3598	3.1013	3.2585	4.20	66.686	33.336	33.351
1.90	6.6859	3.2682	3.4177	4.30	73.700	36.843	36.857
1.95	7.0287	3.4432	3.5855	4.40	81.451	40.719	40.732
2.00	7.3891	3.6269	3.7622	4.50	90.017	45.003	45.014
2.05	7.7679	3.8196	3.9483	4.60	99.484	49.737	49.747
2.10	8.1662	4.0219	4.1443	4.70	109.95	54.969	54.978
2.15	8.5849	4.2342	4.3507	4.80	121.51	60.751	60.759
2.20	9.0250	4.4571	4.5679	4.90	134.29	67.141	67.149
2.25	9.4877	4.6912	4.7966	5.00	148.41	74.203	74.210
2.30	9.9742	4.9370	5.0372	5.20	181.27	90.633	90.639
2.35	10.486	5.1951	5.2905	5.40	221.41	110.70	110.71
2.40	11.023	5.4662	5.5569	5.60	270.43	135.21	135.22
2.45	11.588	5.7510	5.8373	5.80	330.30	165.15	165.15
2.50	12.182	6.0502	6.1323	6.00	403.43	201.71	201.72
2.55	12.807	6.3645	6.4426	7.00	1096.6	548.32	548.32
2.60	13.464	6.6947	6.7690	8.00	2981.0	1490.5	1490.5
2.65	14.154	7.0417	7.1123	9.00	8103.1	4051.5	4051.5
2.70	14.880	7.4063	7.4735	10.00	22026.	11013.	11013.

VI. THREE–PLACE VALUES OF TRIGONOMETRIC FUNCTIONS
AND
DEGREES IN RADIAN MEASURE

Rad.	Deg.	Sin	Tan	Sec	Csc	Cot	Cos	Deg.	Rad.
.000	0°	.000	.000	1.000	——	——	1.000	90°	1.571
.017	1°	.017	.017	1.000	57.30	57.29	1.000	89°	1.553
.035	2°	.035	.035	1.001	28.65	28.64	0.999	88°	1.536
.052	3°	.052	.052	1.001	19.11	19.08	.999	87°	1.518
.070	4°	.070	.070	1.002	14.34	14.30	.998	86°	1.501
.087	5°	.087	.087	1.004	11.47	11.43	.996	85°	1.484
.105	6°	.105	.105	1.006	9.567	9.514	.995	84°	1.466
.122	7°	.122	.123	1.008	8.206	8.144	.993	83°	1.449
.140	8°	.139	.141	1.010	7.185	7.115	.990	82°	1.431
.157	9°	.156	.158	1.012	6.392	6.314	.988	81°	1.414
.175	10°	.174	.176	1.015	5.759	5.671	.985	80°	1.396
.192	11°	.191	.194	1.019	5.241	5.145	.982	79°	1.379
.209	12°	.208	.213	1.022	4.810	4.705	.978	78°	1.361
.227	13°	.225	.231	1.026	4.445	4.331	.974	77°	1.344
.244	14°	.242	.249	1.031	4.134	4.011	.970	76°	1.326
.262	15°	.259	.268	1.035	3.864	3.732	.966	75°	1.309
.279	16°	.276	.287	1.040	3.628	3.487	.961	74°	1.292
.297	17°	.292	.306	1.046	3.420	3.271	.956	73°	1.274
.314	18°	.309	.325	1.051	3.236	3.078	.951	72°	1.257
.332	19°	.326	.344	1.058	3.072	2.904	.946	71°	1.239
.349	20°	.342	.364	1.064	2.924	2.747	.940	70°	1.222
.367	21°	.358	.384	1.071	2.790	2.605	.934	69°	1.204
.384	22°	.375	.404	1.079	2.669	2.475	.927	68°	1.187
.401	23°	.391	.424	1.086	2.559	2.356	.921	67°	1.169
.419	24°	.407	.445	1.095	2.459	2.246	.914	66°	1.152
.436	25°	.423	.466	1.103	2.366	2.145	.906	65°	1.134
.454	26°	.438	.488	1.113	2.281	2.050	.899	64°	1.117
.471	27°	.454	.510	1.122	2.203	1.963	.891	63°	1.100
.489	28°	.469	.532	1.133	2.130	1.881	.883	62°	1.082
.506	29°	.485	.554	1.143	2.063	1.804	.875	61°	1.065
.524	30°	.500	.577	1.155	2.000	1.732	.866	60°	1.047
.541	31°	.515	.601	1.167	1.942	1.664	.857	59°	1.030
.559	32°	.530	.625	1.179	1.887	1.600	.848	58°	1.012
.576	33°	.545	.649	1.192	1.836	1.540	.839	57°	0.995
.593	34°	.559	.675	1.206	1.788	1.483	.829	56°	0.977
.611	35°	.574	.700	1.221	1.743	1.428	.819	55°	0.960
.628	36°	.588	.727	1.236	1.701	1.376	.809	54°	0.942
.646	37°	.602	.754	1.252	1.662	1.327	.799	53°	0.925
.663	38°	.616	.781	1.269	1.624	1.280	.788	52°	0.908
.681	39°	.629	.810	1.287	1.589	1.235	.777	51°	0.890
.698	40°	.643	.839	1.305	1.556	1.192	.766	50°	0.873
.716	41°	.656	.869	1.325	1.524	1.150	.755	49°	0.855
.733	42°	.669	.900	1.346	1.494	1.111	.743	48°	0.838
.750	43°	.682	.933	1.367	1.466	1.072	.731	47°	0.820
.768	44°	.695	0.966	1.390	1.440	1.036	.719	46°	0.803
.785	45°	.707	1.000	1.414	1.414	1.000	.707	45°	0.785
Rad.	Deg.	Cos	Cot	Csc	Sec	Tan	Sin	Deg.	Rad.

Note 1. An arbitrary constant may be added to any result.

Note 2. No formula in the table may be used with any value of the variable, or of any constant, for which the integrand on the left, or the result on the right, is imaginary or otherwise undefined.

Note 3. In each formula, u may be considered as the independent variable, or as a differentiable function of some independent variable.

Note 4. If ambiguous signs, $\pm$ or $\mp$, occur more than once in a formula, it is understood that the *upper* (*lower*) signs apply simultaneously throughout.

Note 5. Arctan u, Arcsin u, Arcsec u, and $\cosh^{-1} u$, in any formulas, represent function values on the intervals indicated below:

$$-\tfrac{1}{2}\pi \leqq \text{Arcsin } u \leqq \tfrac{1}{2}\pi; \qquad (\text{Arcsin } u < 0 \text{ if } u < 0)$$

$$-\tfrac{1}{2}\pi < \text{Arctan } u < \tfrac{1}{2}\pi; \qquad (\text{Arctan } u < 0 \text{ if } u < 0)$$

$$0 \leqq \text{Arcsec } u < \tfrac{1}{2}\pi \text{ if } u > 0; \qquad -\pi \leqq \text{Arcsec } u < -\tfrac{1}{2}\pi \text{ if } u < 0;$$

$$0 \leqq \cosh^{-1} u. \qquad (u \geqq 1 \text{ always})$$

Also, we remark that $\sinh^{-1} u$, $\tanh^{-1} u$, and $\coth^{-1} u$ are single-valued.

Integrals of Rational Functions of u and $(a + bu)$

1. $\displaystyle \int u^n\, du = \frac{u^{n+1}}{n+1}.$

2. $\displaystyle \int \frac{du}{u} = \ln |u|.$

3. $\displaystyle \int (a+bu)^n\, du = \frac{(a+bu)^{n+1}}{b(n+1)}.$

4. $\displaystyle \int \frac{du}{a+bu} = \frac{1}{b}\ln|a+bu|.$

5. $\displaystyle \int \frac{du}{u(a+bu)} = \frac{1}{a}\ln\left|\frac{u}{a+bu}\right|.$

6. $\displaystyle \int \frac{du}{u^2(a+bu)} = -\frac{1}{au} + \frac{b}{a^2}\ln\left|\frac{a+bu}{u}\right|.$

7. $\displaystyle \int \frac{du}{u(a+bu)^2} = \frac{1}{a(a+bu)} + \frac{1}{a^2}\ln\left|\frac{u}{a+bu}\right|.$

8. $\displaystyle \int \frac{du}{u^2(a+bu)^2} = -\frac{a+2bu}{a^2u(a+bu)} + \frac{2b}{a^3}\ln\left|\frac{a+bu}{u}\right|.$

9. $\displaystyle \int \frac{u\, du}{(a+bu)^2} = \frac{1}{b^2}\left(\ln|a+bu| + \frac{a}{a+bu}\right).$

10. $\displaystyle \int \frac{u\, du}{(a+bu)^3} = \frac{1}{b^2}\left[-\frac{1}{a+bu} + \frac{a}{2(a+bu)^2}\right].$

11. $\displaystyle \int \frac{u^2\, du}{(a+bu)^3} = \frac{1}{b^3}\left[\ln|a+bu| + \frac{2a}{a+bu} - \frac{a^2}{2(a+bu)^2}\right].$

12. $\displaystyle \int \frac{du}{u^m(a+bu)^n} = \frac{-1}{a(m-1)u^{m-1}(a+bu)^{n-1}} - \frac{b(m+n-2)}{a(m-1)}\int \frac{du}{u^{m-1}(a+bu)^n}.$

13. $\displaystyle \int \frac{du}{u^m(a+bu)^n} = \frac{1}{a(n-1)u^{m-1}(a+bu)^{n-1}} + \frac{(m+n-2)}{a(n-1)}\int \frac{du}{u^m(a+bu)^{n-1}}.$

Irrational Integrands Involving $(a + bu)$

14. $\displaystyle\int u\sqrt{a + bu}\, du = -\frac{2(2a - 3bu)(a + bu)^{\frac{3}{2}}}{15b^2}.$

15. $\displaystyle\int u^m\sqrt{a + bu}\, du = \frac{2u^m(a + bu)^{\frac{3}{2}}}{b(2m + 3)} - \frac{2am}{b(2m + 3)}\int u^{m-1}\sqrt{a + bu}\, du.$

16. $\displaystyle\int \frac{u\, du}{\sqrt{a + bu}} = \frac{2(bu - 2a)\sqrt{a + bu}}{3b^2}.$

17. $\displaystyle\int \frac{u^2\, du}{\sqrt{a + bu}} = \frac{2(3b^2u^2 - 4abu + 8a^2)\sqrt{a + bu}}{15b^3}.$

18. $\displaystyle\int \frac{u^m\, du}{\sqrt{a + bu}} = \frac{2u^m\sqrt{a + bu}}{b(2m + 1)} - \frac{2am}{b(2m + 1)}\int \frac{u^{m-1}\, du}{\sqrt{a + bu}}.$

19. $\displaystyle\int \frac{du}{u\sqrt{a + bu}} = \frac{1}{\sqrt{a}} \ln \left|\frac{\sqrt{a + bu} - \sqrt{a}}{\sqrt{a + bu} + \sqrt{a}}\right|,$ if $a > 0.$

20. $\displaystyle\int \frac{du}{u\sqrt{a + bu}} = \frac{2}{\sqrt{-a}} \operatorname{Arctan} \sqrt{\frac{a + bu}{-a}},$ if $a < 0.$

21. $\displaystyle\int \frac{du}{u^m\sqrt{a + bu}} = -\frac{\sqrt{a + bu}}{a(m - 1)u^{m-1}} - \frac{b(2m - 3)}{2a(m - 1)}\int \frac{du}{u^{m-1}\sqrt{a + bu}}.$

22. $\displaystyle\int \frac{\sqrt{a + bu}}{u}\, du = 2\sqrt{a + bu} + a\int \frac{du}{u\sqrt{a + bu}}.$

23. $\displaystyle\int \frac{\sqrt{a + bu}}{u^m}\, du = -\frac{(a + bu)^{\frac{3}{2}}}{a(m - 1)u^{m-1}} - \frac{b(2m - 5)}{2a(m - 1)}\int \frac{\sqrt{a + bu}\, du}{u^{m-1}}.$

Rational Forms Involving * $(a^2 \pm u^2)$

24. $\displaystyle\int \frac{du}{a^2 + u^2} = \frac{1}{a} \operatorname{Arctan} \frac{u}{a}.$ **25.** $\displaystyle\int \frac{du}{u^2 - a^2} = \frac{1}{2a} \ln \left|\frac{u - a}{u + a}\right|.$

25₁. $\displaystyle\int \frac{du}{a^2 - u^2} = \frac{1}{a} \tanh^{-1} \frac{u}{a}.$ $(u^2 < a^2)$

25₂. $\displaystyle\int \frac{du}{u^2 - a^2} = -\frac{1}{a} \coth^{-1} \frac{u}{a}.$ $(u^2 > a^2)$

26. $\displaystyle\int \frac{du}{(a^2 + u^2)^n} = \frac{u}{2(n - 1)a^2(a^2 + u^2)^{n-1}} + \frac{2n - 3}{(2n - 2)a^2}\int \frac{du}{(a^2 + u^2)^{n-1}}.$

Irrational Forms Involving $\sqrt{a^2 - u^2}$

27. $\displaystyle\int \sqrt{a^2 - u^2}\, du = \frac{u}{2}\sqrt{a^2 - u^2} + \frac{a^2}{2} \operatorname{Arcsin} \frac{u}{a}.$

28. $\displaystyle\int \frac{du}{\sqrt{a^2 - u^2}} = \operatorname{Arcsin} \frac{u}{a}.$ **29.** $\displaystyle\int \frac{du}{(a^2 - u^2)^{\frac{3}{2}}} = \frac{u}{a^2\sqrt{a^2 - u^2}}.$

30. $\displaystyle\int u^2\sqrt{a^2 - u^2}\, du = -\frac{1}{4}u(a^2 - u^2)^{\frac{3}{2}} + \frac{1}{4}a^2\int \sqrt{a^2 - u^2}\, du.$

* Wherever a constant a^2 enters, infer that $a > 0.$

31. $\displaystyle\int \frac{u^2\,du}{\sqrt{a^2-u^2}} = -\frac{u}{2}\sqrt{a^2-u^2} + \frac{a^2}{2}\,\text{Arcsin}\,\frac{u}{a}.$

32. $\displaystyle\int \frac{u^2\,du}{(a^2-u^2)^{\frac{3}{2}}} = \frac{u}{\sqrt{a^2-u^2}} - \text{Arcsin}\,\frac{u}{a}.$

33. $\displaystyle\int \frac{du}{u\sqrt{a^2-u^2}} = -\frac{1}{a}\ln\left|\frac{a+\sqrt{a^2-u^2}}{u}\right|; \qquad = -\frac{1}{a}\cosh^{-1}\frac{a}{u},\ \text{if}\ 0 < u < a.$

34. $\displaystyle\int \frac{du}{u^2\sqrt{a^2-u^2}} = -\frac{\sqrt{a^2-u^2}}{a^2 u}.$

35. $\displaystyle\int \frac{\sqrt{a^2-u^2}\,du}{u} = \sqrt{a^2-u^2} - a\ln\left|\frac{a+\sqrt{a^2-u^2}}{u}\right|;$

35'. $\displaystyle\qquad\qquad = \sqrt{a^2-u^2} - a\,\cosh^{-1}\frac{a}{u},\ \text{if}\ 0 < u < a.$

36. $\displaystyle\int \frac{\sqrt{a^2-u^2}}{u^2}\,du = -\frac{\sqrt{a^2-u^2}}{u} - \text{Arcsin}\,\frac{u}{a}.$

37. $\displaystyle\int u^m(a^2-u^2)^{\frac{n}{2}}\,du \qquad (m \geqq 0\ \ \text{or}\ \ m < 0)$

$\displaystyle\qquad = \frac{u^{m+1}(a^2-u^2)^{\frac{n}{2}}}{n+m+1} + \frac{a^2 n}{n+m+1}\int u^m(a^2-u^2)^{\frac{n}{2}-1}\,du.$

38. $\displaystyle\int u^m(a^2-u^2)^{\frac{n}{2}}\,du \qquad (n > 0\ \ \text{or}\ \ n < 0)$

$\displaystyle\qquad = -\frac{u^{m-1}(a^2-u^2)^{\frac{n}{2}+1}}{n+m+1} + \frac{a^2(m-1)}{n+m+1}\int u^{m-2}(a^2-u^2)^{\frac{n}{2}}\,du.$

39. $\displaystyle\int \frac{(a^2-u^2)^{\frac{n}{2}}}{u^m}\,du \qquad (n > 0\ \ \text{or}\ \ n < 0)$

$\displaystyle\qquad = -\frac{(a^2-u^2)^{\frac{n}{2}+1}}{a^2(m-1)u^{m-1}} + \frac{m-n-3}{a^2(m-1)}\int \frac{(a^2-u^2)^{\frac{n}{2}}}{u^{m-2}}\,du.$

40. $\displaystyle\int \frac{u^m\,du}{(a^2-u^2)^{\frac{n}{2}}} \qquad (m \geqq 0\ \ \text{or}\ \ m < 0)$

$\displaystyle\qquad = \frac{u^{m+1}}{a^2(n-2)(a^2-u^2)^{\frac{n}{2}-1}} - \frac{m-n+3}{a^2(n-2)}\int \frac{u^m\,du}{(a^2-u^2)^{\frac{n}{2}-1}}.$

Irrational Forms Involving $\sqrt{u^2 \pm a^2}$

Note 6. In any formula of the present types, by the method of proof used in Example 1, page 639, it can be shown that we may replace

$$\ln(u+\sqrt{u^2+a^2})\ \ by\ \ \sinh^{-1}\frac{u}{a}; \quad \ln\left|\frac{a+\sqrt{u^2+a^2}}{u}\right|\ \ by\ \ \sinh^{-1}\left|\frac{a}{u}\right|;$$

$$\ln|u+\sqrt{u^2-a^2}|\ \ by\ \ \begin{cases} \cosh^{-1}\dfrac{u}{a},\ if\ u \geqq a \\[2mm] -\cosh^{-1}\left|\dfrac{u}{a}\right|,\ if\ u \leqq -a \end{cases}.$$

41. $\displaystyle\int \sqrt{u^2 \pm a^2}\, du = \tfrac{1}{2}[u\sqrt{u^2 \pm a^2} \pm a^2 \ln \mid u + \sqrt{u^2 \pm a^2}\mid].$

42. $\displaystyle\int u^2\sqrt{u^2 \pm a^2}\, du = \tfrac{1}{8}u(2u^2 \pm a^2)\sqrt{u^2 \pm a^2} - \tfrac{1}{8}a^4 \ln \mid u + \sqrt{u^2 \pm a^2}\mid.$

43. $\displaystyle\int \frac{\sqrt{u^2 + a^2}}{u}\, du = \sqrt{u^2 + a^2} - a \ln \left| \frac{a + \sqrt{u^2 + a^2}}{u}\right|.$

44. $\displaystyle\int \frac{\sqrt{u^2 - a^2}}{u}\, du = \sqrt{u^2 - a^2} - a \operatorname{Arcsec} \frac{u}{a}.$

45. $\displaystyle\int \frac{\sqrt{u^2 \pm a^2}}{u^2}\, du = - \frac{\sqrt{u^2 \pm a^2}}{u} + \ln \mid u + \sqrt{u^2 \pm a^2}\mid.$

46. $\displaystyle\int \frac{du}{\sqrt{u^2 \pm a^2}} = \ln \mid u + \sqrt{u^2 \pm a^2}\mid.$ **46$_1$.** $\displaystyle\int \frac{du}{\sqrt{u^2 + a^2}} = \sinh^{-1} \frac{u}{a}.$

46$_2$. $\displaystyle\int \frac{du}{\sqrt{u^2 - a^2}} = \cosh^{-1}\frac{u}{a}, \ (u > a);\qquad = - \cosh^{-1}\left|\frac{u}{a}\right|, \ (u < -a).$

47. $\displaystyle\int \frac{du}{u\sqrt{u^2 - a^2}} = \frac{1}{a}\operatorname{Arcsec}\frac{u}{a}.$ **48.** $\displaystyle\int \frac{du}{u\sqrt{u^2 + a^2}} = \frac{1}{a}\ln\left|\frac{u}{a + \sqrt{u^2 + a^2}}\right|.$

49. $\displaystyle\int \frac{u^2\, du}{\sqrt{u^2 \pm a^2}} = \frac{1}{2}\left(u\sqrt{u^2 \pm a^2} \mp a^2 \ln \mid u + \sqrt{u^2 \pm a^2}\mid\right).$

50. $\displaystyle\int \frac{du}{u^2\sqrt{u^2 \pm a^2}} = \mp \frac{\sqrt{u^2 \pm a^2}}{a^2 u}.$ **51.** $\displaystyle\int \frac{du}{(u^2 \pm a^2)^{\frac{3}{2}}} = \frac{\pm u}{a^2\sqrt{u^2 \pm a^2}}.$

52. $\displaystyle\int \frac{u^2\, du}{(u^2 \pm a^2)^{\frac{3}{2}}} = \frac{-u}{\sqrt{u^2 \pm a^2}} + \ln \mid u + \sqrt{u^2 \pm a^2}\mid.$

53. $\displaystyle\int u^m(u^2 \pm a^2)^{\frac{n}{2}}\, du \qquad (n > 0 \ \text{ or } \ n < 0)$

$$= \frac{u^{m-1}(u^2 \pm a^2)^{\frac{n}{2}+1}}{n + m + 1} \mp \frac{a^2(m - 1)}{n + m + 1} \int u^{m-2}(u^2 \pm a^2)^{\frac{n}{2}}\, du.$$

54. $\displaystyle\int \frac{(u^2 \pm a^2)^{\frac{n}{2}}\, du}{u^m} \qquad (n > 0 \ \text{ or } \ n < 0)$

$$= \frac{\mp (u^2 \pm a^2)^{\frac{n}{2}+1}}{a^2(m - 1)u^{m-1}} \mp \frac{m - n - 3}{a^2(m - 1)} \int \frac{(u^2 \pm a^2)^{\frac{n}{2}}}{u^{m-2}}\, du.$$

55. $\displaystyle\int \frac{u^m\, du}{(u^2 \pm a^2)^{\frac{n}{2}}} \qquad (m \geqq 0 \ \text{ or } \ m < 0)$

$$= \frac{\pm u^{m+1}}{a^2(n - 2)(u^2 \pm a^2)^{\frac{n}{2}-1}} \mp \frac{m - n + 3}{a^2(n - 2)} \int \frac{u^m\, du}{(u^2 \pm a^2)^{\frac{n}{2}-1}}.$$

56. $\displaystyle\int u^m(u^2 \pm a^2)^{\frac{n}{2}}\, du \qquad (m \geqq 0 \ \text{ or } \ m < 0)$

$$= \frac{(u^2 \pm a^2)^{\frac{n}{2}}u^{m+1}}{n + m + 1} \pm \frac{a^2 n}{n + m + 1} \int u^m(u^2 \pm a^2)^{\frac{n}{2}-1}\, du.$$

Note 7. $\sqrt{2au + u^2} = \sqrt{(u + a)^2 - a^2}$; $\sqrt{2au - u^2} = \sqrt{a^2 - (u - a)^2}$.

57. $\displaystyle\int (2au + u^2)^{\frac{n}{2}}\, du.$ Use $\displaystyle\int (v^2 - a^2)^{\frac{n}{2}}\, dv$ with $v = u + a$.

58. $\displaystyle\int (2au - u^2)^{\frac{n}{2}}\, du.$ Use $\displaystyle\int (a^2 - v^2)^{\frac{n}{2}}\, dv$ with $v = u - a$.

59. $\displaystyle\int \sqrt{2au - u^2}\, du = \frac{u - a}{2}\sqrt{2au - u^2} + \frac{a^2}{2}\,\text{Arcsin}\,\frac{u - a}{a}.$

60. $\displaystyle\int \sqrt{2au + u^2}\, du = \frac{u + a}{2}\sqrt{2au + u^2} - \frac{a^2}{2}\,\ln|u + a + \sqrt{2au + u^2}|.$

61. $\displaystyle\int u\sqrt{2au + u^2}\, du = \frac{2u^2 + au - 3a^2}{6}\sqrt{2au + u^2} + \frac{a^3}{2}\ln|u + a + \sqrt{2au + u^2}|.$

62. $\displaystyle\int u\sqrt{2au - u^2}\, du = \frac{2u^2 - au - 3a^2}{6}\sqrt{2au - u^2} + \frac{a^3}{2}\,\text{Arcsin}\,\frac{u - a}{a}.$

63. $\displaystyle\int \frac{du}{\sqrt{2au - u^2}} = \text{Arcsin}\,\frac{u - a}{a}.$

64. $\displaystyle\int \frac{du}{\sqrt{2au + u^2}} = \ln|u + a + \sqrt{u^2 + 2au}|.$

65. $\displaystyle\int \frac{u\,du}{\sqrt{2au - u^2}} = -\sqrt{2au - u^2} + a\,\text{Arcsin}\,\frac{u - a}{a}.$

66. $\displaystyle\int \frac{u\,du}{\sqrt{2au + u^2}} = \sqrt{2au + u^2} - a\ln|u + a + \sqrt{2au + u^2}|.$

67. $\displaystyle\int \frac{u^n\,du}{\sqrt{2au - u^2}} = -\frac{u^{n-1}\sqrt{2au - u^2}}{n} + \frac{a(2n - 1)}{n}\int \frac{u^{n-1}\,du}{\sqrt{2au - u^2}}.$

68. $\displaystyle\int \frac{du}{u^n\sqrt{2au - u^2}} = \frac{\sqrt{2au - u^2}}{a(1 - 2n)u^n} + \frac{n - 1}{(2n - 1)a}\int \frac{du}{u^{n-1}\sqrt{2au - u^2}}.$

69. $\displaystyle\int u^n\sqrt{2au - u^2}\, du = -\frac{u^{n-1}(2au - u^2)^{\frac{3}{2}}}{n + 2} + \frac{(2n + 1)a}{n + 2}\int u^{n-1}\sqrt{2au - u^2}\, du.$

70. $\displaystyle\int \frac{\sqrt{2au - u^2}}{u^n}\, du = \frac{(2au - u^2)^{\frac{3}{2}}}{a(3 - 2n)u^n} + \frac{n - 3}{(2n - 3)a}\int \frac{\sqrt{2au - u^2}}{u^{n-1}}\, du.$

Forms Involving $f(u) = a + bu \pm cu^2,\ c > 0$

Note 8. By completing a square with the terms in u, $f(u)$ assumes the form $\pm c(A^2 + v^2)$, $\pm c(v^2 - A^2)$, or $\pm cv^2$, with $v = u \pm \dfrac{b}{2c}$. Then, substitution of $v = (2cu \pm b)/2c$ gives an integrand $F(v)$ involving $(A^2 \pm v^2)$, $(v^2 - A^2)$, or v^2.

Note 9. Any radicand $(4ac + b^2)$ is assumed to be positive.

71. $\displaystyle\int \frac{du}{a + bu - cu^2} = \frac{1}{\sqrt{b^2 + 4ac}}\ln\left|\frac{\sqrt{b^2 + 4ac} - b + 2cu}{\sqrt{b^2 + 4ac} + b - 2cu}\right|.$

72. $\displaystyle\int \frac{du}{\sqrt{a + bu + cu^2}} = \frac{1}{\sqrt{c}}\ln|2cu + b + 2\sqrt{c}\sqrt{a + bu + cu^2}|.$

73. $\displaystyle\int \frac{du}{\sqrt{a + bu - cu^2}} = \frac{1}{\sqrt{c}}\ \text{Arcsin}\ \frac{2cu - b}{\sqrt{b^2 + 4ac}}.$

74. $\displaystyle\int \frac{du}{(a + bu \pm cu^2)^{\frac{3}{2}}} = \frac{2(\pm\, 2cu + b)}{(\pm\, 4ac - b^2)\sqrt{a + bu \pm cu^2}}.$

75. $\displaystyle\int \sqrt{a + bu + cu^2}\ du = \frac{2cu + b}{4c}\ \sqrt{a + bu + cu^2}$
$$- \frac{b^2 - 4ac}{8c^{\frac{3}{2}}} \ln\,|\,2cu + b + 2\sqrt{c}\sqrt{a + bu + cu^2}\,|.$$

76. $\displaystyle\int \sqrt{a + bu - cu^2}\ du = \frac{2cu - b}{4c}\ \sqrt{a + bu - cu^2}$
$$+\ \frac{b^2 + 4ac}{8c^{\frac{3}{2}}}\ \text{Arcsin}\ \frac{2cu - b}{\sqrt{b^2 + 4ac}}.$$

77. $\displaystyle\int \frac{u\ du}{\sqrt{a + bu + cu^2}} = \frac{\sqrt{a + bu + cu^2}}{c}$
$$-\ \frac{b}{2c^{\frac{3}{2}}} \ln\,|\,2cu + b + 2\sqrt{c}\sqrt{a + bu + cu^2}\,|.$$

78. $\displaystyle\int \frac{u\ du}{\sqrt{a + bu - cu^2}} = -\ \frac{\sqrt{a + bu - cu^2}}{c} + \frac{b}{2c^{\frac{3}{2}}}\ \text{Arcsin}\ \frac{2cu - b}{\sqrt{b^2 + 4ac}}.$

79. $\displaystyle\int u\ \sqrt{a + bu \pm cu^2}\ du = \frac{(a + bu \pm cu^2)^{\frac{3}{2}}}{\pm\, 3c} \mp \frac{b}{2c}\int \sqrt{a + bu \pm cu^2}\ du.$

Binomial Reduction Formulas

$$\int u^m(a + bu^n)^p\,du\colon \qquad (m\ \text{and}\ p,\ \text{positive or negative})$$

80.
$$= \frac{u^{m-n+1}(a + bu^n)^{p+1}}{b(np + m + 1)} - \frac{a(m - n + 1)}{b(np + m + 1)}\int u^{m-n}(a + bu^n)^p\ du.$$

81.
$$= \frac{u^{m+1}(a + bu^n)^p}{np + m + 1} + \frac{npa}{np + m + 1}\int u^m(a + bu^n)^{p-1}\ du.$$

82.
$$= \frac{u^{m+1}(a + bu^n)^{p+1}}{a(m + 1)} - \frac{b(np + n + m + 1)}{a(m + 1)}\int u^{m+n}(a + bu^n)^p\ du.$$

83.
$$= -\frac{u^{m+1}(a + bu^n)^{p+1}}{na(p + 1)} + \frac{np + n + m + 1}{na(p + 1)}\int u^m(a + bu^n)^{p+1}\ du.$$

Trigonometric Forms

Note 10. Hereafter, any constant a, b, h, k may have any real value, subject to Note 2 and other specified conditions.

84. $\displaystyle\int \sin u\ du = \cos u.$ **85.** $\displaystyle\int \cos u\ du = -\sin u.$

86. $\displaystyle\int \tan u\ du = -\ln\,|\cos u\,| = \ln\,|\sec u\,|.$

87. $\displaystyle\int \cot u\ du = \ln\,|\sin u\,|.$ **88.** $\displaystyle\int \sec u\ du = \ln\,|\sec u + \tan u\,|.$

89. $\displaystyle\int \csc u\ du = \ln\,|\csc u - \cot u\,| = \ln\left|\tan \frac{u}{2}\right|.$

90. $\int \sec^2 u \, du = \tan u.$ **91.** $\int \csc^2 u \, du = -\cot u.$

92. $\int \sec u \tan u \, du = \sec u.$ **93.** $\int \csc u \cot u \, du = -\csc u.$

94. $\int \sin^2 au \, du = \dfrac{1}{2} u - \dfrac{1}{4a} \sin 2au.$ **95.** $\int \cos^2 au \, du = \dfrac{1}{2} u + \dfrac{1}{4a} \sin 2au.$

96. $\int \sin hu \sin ku \, du = -\dfrac{\sin (k+h)u}{2(k+h)} + \dfrac{\sin (k-h)u}{2(k-h)}.$

97. $\int \cos hu \cos ku \, du = \dfrac{\sin (k+h)u}{2(k+h)} + \dfrac{\sin (k-h)u}{2(k-h)}.$

98. $\int \sin hu \cos ku \, du = -\dfrac{\cos (k+h)u}{2(k+h)} - \dfrac{\cos (k-h)u}{2(k-h)}.$

99. $\int \dfrac{du}{a + b \cos u} = \dfrac{2}{\sqrt{a^2 - b^2}} \text{Arctan} \dfrac{\sqrt{a^2 - b^2} \tan \frac{1}{2}u}{a + b};$ $(0 < b, \ a^2 > b^2)$

$\qquad\quad = \dfrac{1}{\sqrt{b^2 - a^2}} \ln \left| \dfrac{a + b + \sqrt{b^2 - a^2} \tan \frac{1}{2}u}{a + b - \sqrt{b^2 - a^2} \tan \frac{1}{2}u} \right|.$ $(0 < a, \ b^2 > a^2)$

100. $\int \dfrac{du}{a + b \sin u} = \dfrac{2}{\sqrt{a^2 - b^2}} \text{Arctan} \dfrac{a \tan \frac{1}{2}u + b}{\sqrt{a^2 - b^2}};$ $(0 < a, \ a^2 > b^2)$

$\qquad\quad = \dfrac{1}{\sqrt{b^2 - a^2}} \ln \left| \dfrac{a \tan \frac{1}{2}u + b - \sqrt{b^2 - a^2}}{a \tan \frac{1}{2}u + b + \sqrt{b^2 - a^2}} \right|.$ $(0 < a, \ b^2 > a^2)$

101. $\int \dfrac{du}{a \sin u + b \cos u} = \dfrac{1}{\sqrt{a^2 + b^2}} \ln | \csc (u + \alpha) - \cot (u + \alpha) |. \quad \left(\tan \alpha = \dfrac{b}{a}\right)$

102. $\int \sec^3 u \, du = \dfrac{1}{2} \left[\sec u \tan u + \ln | \sec u + \tan u | \right].$

103. $\int \csc^3 u \, du = -\dfrac{1}{2} \left[\cot u \csc u - \ln | \csc u - \cot u | \right].$

104. $\int \text{Arcsin } u \, du = u \, \text{Arcsin } u + \sqrt{1 - u^2}.$

105. $\int \text{Arctan } u \, du = u \, \text{Arctan } u - \ln \sqrt{1 + u^2}.$

Trigonometric Reduction Formulas

106. $\int \sin^n u \, du = -\dfrac{\sin^{n-1} u \cos u}{n} + \dfrac{n-1}{n} \int \sin^{n-2} u \, du.$

107. $\int \cos^n u \, du = \dfrac{\cos^{n-1} u \sin u}{n} + \dfrac{n-1}{n} \int \cos^{n-2} u \, du.$

108. $\int \sec^n u \, du = \dfrac{\tan u \sec^{n-2} u}{n-1} + \dfrac{n-2}{n-1} \int \sec^{n-2} u \, du.$

109. $\int \csc^n u \, du = -\dfrac{\cot u \csc^{n-2} u}{n-1} + \dfrac{n-2}{n-1} \int \csc^{n-2} u \, du.$

110. $\int \tan^n u \, du = \dfrac{\tan^{n-1} u}{n-1} - \int \tan^{n-2} u \, du.$

111. $\int \cot^n u \, du = -\dfrac{\cot^{n-1} u}{n-1} - \int \cot^{n-2} u \, du.$

$$\int \cos^m u \sin^n u \, du: \qquad (m \text{ and } n, \text{ positive or negative})$$

112. $\qquad = \dfrac{\cos^{m-1} u \sin^{n+1} u}{m+n} + \dfrac{m-1}{m+n} \int \cos^{m-2} u \sin^n u \, du.$

113. $\qquad = -\dfrac{\sin^{n-1} u \cos^{m+1} u}{m+n} + \dfrac{n-1}{m+n} \int \cos^m u \sin^{n-2} u \, du.$

114. $\qquad = -\dfrac{\sin^{n+1} u \cos^{m+1} u}{m+1} + \dfrac{m+n+2}{m+1} \int \cos^{m+2} u \sin^n u \, du.$

115. $\qquad = \dfrac{\sin^{n+1} u \cos^{m+1} u}{n+1} + \dfrac{m+n+2}{n+1} \int \cos^m u \sin^{n+2} u \, du.$

116. $\int u^n \sin au \, du = -\dfrac{u^n \cos au}{a} + \dfrac{n}{a} \int u^{n-1} \cos au \, du.$

117. $\int u^n \cos au \, du = \dfrac{u^n \sin au}{a} - \dfrac{n}{a} \int u^{n-1} \sin au \, du.$

Exponential and Logarithmic Forms

118. $\int e^u \, du = e^u.$ **119.** $\int a^u \, du = \dfrac{a^u}{\ln a}.$

120. $\int u^n e^{au} \, du = \dfrac{u^n e^{au}}{a} - \dfrac{n}{a} \int u^{n-1} e^{au} \, du.$

121. $\int \dfrac{e^{au}}{u^n} \, du = -\dfrac{e^{au}}{(n-1)u^{n-1}} + \dfrac{a}{n-1} \int \dfrac{e^{au} \, du}{u^{n-1}}.$

122. $\int \ln u \, du = u \ln u - u.$ **123.** $\int u^n \ln u \, du = \dfrac{u^{n+1} \ln u}{n+1} - \dfrac{u^{n+1}}{(n+1)^2}.$

124. $\int u^m \ln^n u \, du = \dfrac{u^{m+1} \ln^n u}{m+1} - \dfrac{n}{m+1} \int u^m \ln^{n-1} u \, du.$

125. $\int e^{au} \sin nu \, du = \dfrac{e^{au}(a \sin nu - n \cos nu)}{a^2 + n^2}.$

126. $\int e^{au} \cos nu \, du = \dfrac{e^{au}(n \sin nu + a \cos nu)}{a^2 + n^2}.$

Forms Involving Hyperbolic Functions

127. $\int \sinh u \, du = \cosh u.$ **128.** $\int \cosh u \, du = \sinh u.$

129. $\int \tanh u \, du = \ln \cosh u.$ **130.** $\int \coth u \, du = \ln | \sinh u |.$

131. $\int \operatorname{sech} u \, du = \text{Arctan} (\sinh u).$ **132.** $\int \operatorname{csch} u \, du = \ln \left| \tanh \dfrac{1}{2} u \right|.$

133. $\int \operatorname{sech}^2 u \, du = \tanh u.$ **134.** $\int \operatorname{csch}^2 u \, du = -\coth u.$

135. $\int \operatorname{sech} u \tanh u = -\operatorname{sech} u.$ **136.** $\int \operatorname{csch} u \coth u = -\operatorname{csch} u.$

708

VIII. CURVES FOR REFERENCE

1. SINE FUNCTION

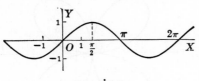

$$y = \sin x$$

2. COSINE FUNCTION

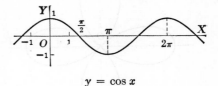

$$y = \cos x$$

3. TANGENT FUNCTION

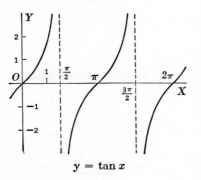

$$y = \tan x$$

4. SECANT FUNCTION

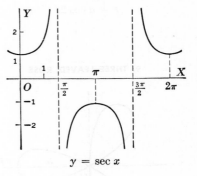

$$y = \sec x$$

INVERSE TRIGONOMETRIC FUNCTIONS

Note 1. See pages 234 and 236 for graphs of the following equations:

$$y = \text{Arcsin } x; \quad y = \text{Arctan } x.$$

5. SEMICUBICAL PARABOLA

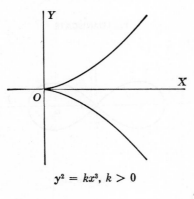

$$y^2 = kx^3, \ k > 0$$

6. EQUILATERAL HYPERBOLA

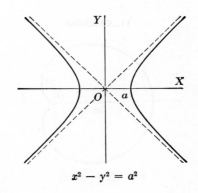

$$x^2 - y^2 = a^2$$

709

7. FOUR–LEAVED ROSE

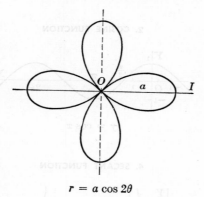

$$r = a \cos 2\theta$$

8. FOUR–LEAVED ROSE

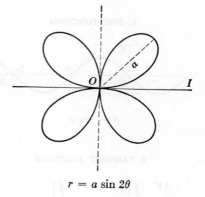

$$r = a \sin 2\theta$$

9. THREE–LEAVED ROSE

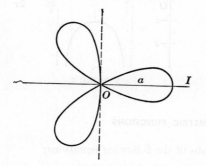

$$r = a \cos 3\theta$$

10. THREE–LEAVED ROSE

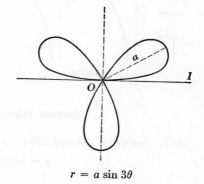

$$r = a \sin 3\theta$$

11. CARDIOID

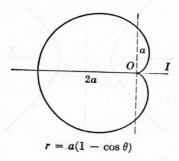

$$r = a(1 - \cos \theta)$$

12. LEMNISCATE

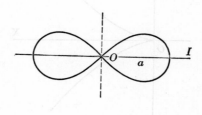

$$r^2 = a^2 \cos 2\theta$$

710

13. LIMAÇON

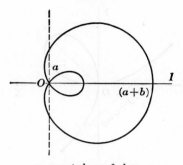

$$r = a + b\cos\theta,\ b > a$$

14. LIMAÇON

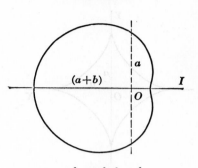

$$r = a - b\cos\theta,\ 0 < b < a$$

15. KAPPA CURVE

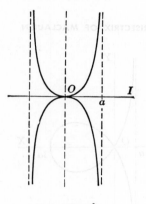

$$r = a\tan\theta$$

16. PARABOLA

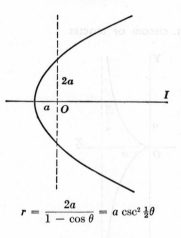

$$r = \frac{2a}{1 - \cos\theta} = a\csc^2\tfrac{1}{2}\theta$$

17. EXPONENTIAL FUNCTION

18. LOGARITHM FUNCTION

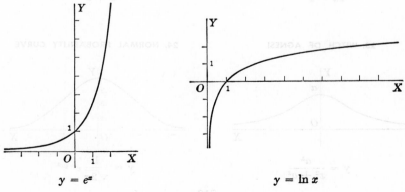

$$y = e^x \qquad\qquad\qquad y = \ln x$$

19. HYPOCYCLOID OF FOUR CUSPS

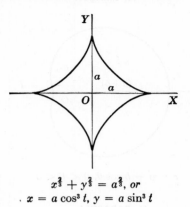

$$x^{\frac{2}{3}} + y^{\frac{2}{3}} = a^{\frac{2}{3}}, \text{ or}$$
$$x = a \cos^3 t, \ y = a \sin^3 t$$

20. FOLIUM OF DESCARTES

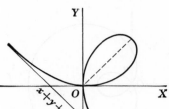

$$x^3 + y^3 = 3axy$$

21. CISSOID OF DIOCLES

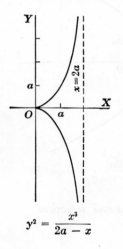

$$y^2 = \frac{x^3}{2a - x}$$

22. TRISECTRIX OF MACLAURIN

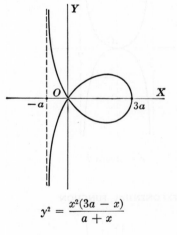

$$y^2 = \frac{x^2(3a - x)}{a + x}$$

23. WITCH OF AGNESI

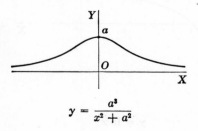

$$y = \frac{a^3}{x^2 + a^2}$$

24. NORMAL PROBABILITY CURVE

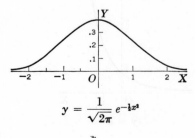

$$y = \frac{1}{\sqrt{2\pi}} \, e^{-\frac{1}{2}x^2}$$

25. CYCLOID

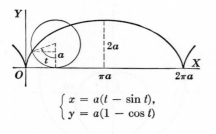

$$\begin{cases} x = a(t - \sin t), \\ y = a(1 - \cos t) \end{cases}$$

26. CONCHOID OF NICOMEDES

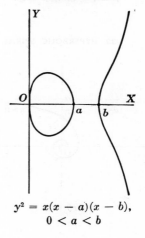

$$\boldsymbol{r} = h \csc \theta + b,$$
$$b > h > 0$$

27. CATENARY

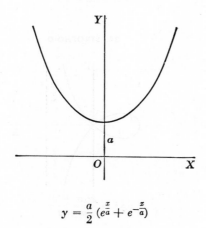

$$y = \frac{a}{2} \left(e^{\frac{x}{a}} + e^{-\frac{x}{a}} \right)$$

28. BIPARTITE CUBIC

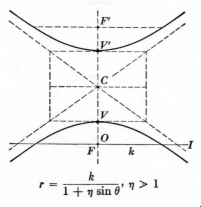

$$y^2 = x(x - a)(x - b),$$
$$0 < a < b$$

29. HYPERBOLA

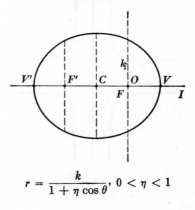

$$r = \frac{k}{1 + \eta \sin \theta}, \; \eta > 1$$

30. ELLIPSE

$$r = \frac{k}{1 + \eta \cos \theta}, \; 0 < \eta < 1$$

31. LOGARITHMIC SPIRAL

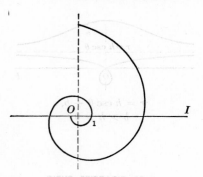

$$r = e^{a\theta}, \text{ or } \ln r = a\theta$$

32. SPIRAL OF ARCHIMEDES

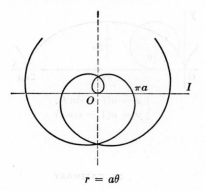

$$r = a\theta$$

33. HYPERBOLIC SPIRAL

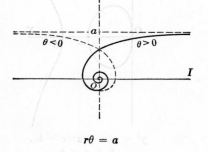

$$r\theta = a$$

34. STROPHOID

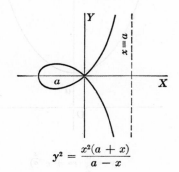

$$y^2 = \frac{x^2(a + x)}{a - x}$$

35. CRUCIFORM CURVE

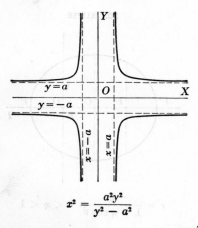

$$x^2 = \frac{a^2 y^2}{y^2 - a^2}$$

36. TWO–LEAVED ROSE

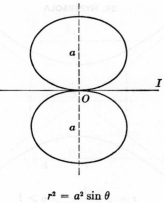

$$r^2 = a^2 \sin\theta$$

714

Answers to Exercises

Note. Answers to most of the odd-numbered problems are given here. Answers to even-numbered problems are furnished in a separate pamphlet, when ordered by the instructor. To encourage self-criticism by superior students, no answers are given for problems in chapter supplements, beyond the results indicated in the text for certain problems.

Exercise 1.   Page 6

1. 3.   **3.** 2.   **5.** 8.

Exercise 2.   Page 10

1. 4, $-$ 2.   **3.** $-1 \pm i$.   **5.** $-2 \leqq x \leqq 2$.   **7.** $x < \frac{33}{2}$.   **9.** $x > -\frac{12}{7}$.
11. All x such that $-6 < x < -2$.   **13.** All x such that $-4 < x < -2$.
15. All x such that $x < -4$ or $x > 2$.
17. $\{1, 2, 3\}$, $\{3, 5, 6\}$, etc., or 20 subsets in all.

Exercise 3.   Page 13

1. $(-5, -1)$.   **3.** $y = -3$.   **5.** A line parallel to x-axis, 4 units below.
7. $M:(-2, 0)$; $N:(0, 4)$.   **9.** $M:(8, 0)$; $N:(0, -7)$.   **11.** $\overline{AB} = -6$.   **13.** $|\overline{AB}| = 7$.
15. $\overline{AB} = y_2 - y_1$.   **17.** 13.   **19.** 13.   **21.** $\sqrt{65}$ **23.** 6.

Exercise 4.   Page 16

1. 3.271.   **3.** -1.   **5.** 1.   **7.** 71.6°.   **9.** 116.6°.   **11.** $\frac{7}{5}$.   **13.** 3.   **15.** -4.

Exercise 6.   Page 23

1. $R = \{16, 9, 4, 1, 0\}$; $F = \{(-4, 16), (-3, 9), (-2, 4), (-1, 1), (0, 0), (1, 1),$ $(2, 4),$ etc.$\}$.
7. 7.   **9.** -1.   **11.** 25.   **13.** 3525.   **15.** $32c^4 - 12c^2$.   **17.** 12.
19. $3b^2 + 2a - ab$.   **21.** $175; 9; -\frac{7}{3}; 2x^3 - 1; x^3 + 6x + 7$.
23. $k^3 + 6k^2 + 12k + 8; 8x^3; x^3 - 9x^2 + 27x - 27$.
25. $H(3) = 17$; $K(-1) = 4$; $Q(2) = 1$. Domain of Q is all $x \neq -5$. $M(3) = 81$.

Exercise 7.   Page 25

1. $y = \frac{1}{3}(6 - 2x)$; $x = \frac{1}{2}(6 - 3y)$.   **3.** $y = \frac{1}{2}(x^2 - 5)$; $x = \pm \sqrt{5 + 2y}$.
5. $y = \pm \sqrt{4x^2 - 1}$; $x = \pm \frac{1}{2}\sqrt{1 + y^2}$.   **9.** $y = \frac{3}{2}x^2$.   **11.** $y = x^2 - x + 3$.

Exercise 8.   Page 29

1. $y = -5$.   **3.** $y = 3x + 2$.   **5.** $3x + 2y = 6$.   **7.** $y = -\frac{2}{3}x + 4$.
9. $y = \frac{1}{3}\sqrt{3}x + 2$.   **11.** $y = x + 3$.   **13.** $y = 5x - 14$.   **15.** $4y + x = 3$.
17. $x = 5$.   **19.** $x - y = -4$.   **21.** $x - 3y = -11$.   **23.** $x = -1$.
25. $6x + y = -3$.   **27.** $y = -\sqrt{3}x + 6$.   **29.** $y = -x + 5$.
31. $2x - y = -11$; $x + 2y = 12$.   **33.** $2x - y = 1$.   **35.** $y = -\frac{2}{3}x + 2$.
37. $y = \frac{5}{12}x - \frac{1}{2}$.   **39.** $y = \frac{6}{5}x + 2$.

Exercise 9.   Page 32

1. $y = 3x - 10$; $3y + x + 10 = 0$.   **3.** $3y = 4x + 15$; $3x + 4y = 20$.
5. $y = 0$; $x = 0$.   **11.** x-int., $-C/A$; y-int., $-C/B$.   **13.** 82.9°.
15. 40.6°.   **17.** 90°.   **19.** 45°.   **21.** $\frac{4}{3}$; -3.   **23.** 60.2°; 81.9°; 37.9°.
25. 31.0°; 47.7°; 101.3°.

Exercise 10.   Page 34

1. $x = 2 + 6t$, $y = 4 + 6t$; (5, 7); (4, 6) and (6, 8).
3. $x = -8 + 6t$, $y = -3 + 6t$; $(-5, 0)$; $(-6, -1)$ and $(-4, 1)$.
5. $x = -10 + 6t$, $y = -2 + 7t$; $(-7, \frac{3}{2})$; $(-8, \frac{1}{3})$ and $(-6, \frac{8}{3})$.
7. $(\frac{7}{2}, \frac{11}{2})$, (5, 7), $(\frac{13}{2}, \frac{17}{2})$.   **9.** $(21, -14)$.   **11.** (6, 11).   **13.** (5, 9).
15. $\left(\dfrac{k_1 x_2 + k_2 x_1}{k_1 + k_2}, \dfrac{k_1 y_2 + k_2 y_1}{k_1 + k_2} \right)$.

Exercise 11.   Page 36

1. $(-\frac{2}{3}, -\frac{5}{3})$.   **3.** $(-\frac{8}{3}, 3)$.   **5.** Inconsistent.   **7.** $g = -4$; $h = -6$.
9. $g = -12$; $h = \frac{1}{2}$.   **11.** $(x = 1, y = -2)$.   **13.** $x = ky + 4$.
15. $y + 4 = m(x - 2)$.   **17.** $2x + y = k$.   **19.** $5x - 3y + 4 = 0$.

Exercise 13.   Page 44

1. $(x - 3)^2 + (y - 4)^2 = 4$.   **3.** $(x - 3)^2 + (y + 2)^2 = 16$.   **5.** $x^2 + y^2 = 16$.
7. $x^2 + 4x + y^2 = 0$.   **9.** $x^2 + y^2 - 2bx = 0$.   **11.** (3, 2); 4.
13. $(-3, 2)$; $\sqrt{10}$.   **15.** (3, 0); $2\sqrt{5}$.   **17.** Point circle, $(-3, 2)$.
19. Imag. circle.   **21.** $x^2 \pm 8x + y^2 + 6y + 9 = 0$.
23. $x^2 + 10x + y^2 - 8y + 37 = 0$.   **25.** $x^2 - 4x + y^2 + 6y = 4$.
27. $x^2 + y^2 - 2x - 4y = 8$.   **29.** $(x - 15)^2 + (y + 3)^2 = 225$.
31. $3x^2 + 3y^2 - 16x - 10y = 12$; $(-1, 1)$ and $(2, -2)$.

Exercise 14.   Page 49

1. $y^2 = 16x$.   **3.** Line $y = 0$.   **5.** Line $x = 0$.   **7.** Line $y = 0$.
9. Line $x = 0$.   **11.** Line $y = 0$.   **13.** Line $y = 0$.   **15.** Line $x = 0$.
17. Line $y = 0$.   **19.** $y^2 + 6x = 0$, or $x^2 + 6y = 0$.
21. $x^2 = 2y$ or $y^2 = -54x$.   **23.** Focus $(0, -\frac{3}{4})$.   **25.** Focus $(-\frac{5}{2}, 0)$.

Exercise 15.   Page 53

1. $9x^2 + 16y^2 = 144$; $16x^2 + 9y^2 = 144$.

15. $\dfrac{x^2}{36} + \dfrac{y^2}{25} = 1$.   **17.** $\dfrac{x^2}{4} + y^2 = 1$.

19. $\dfrac{x^2}{36} + \dfrac{y^2}{20} = 1$.   **21.** $\dfrac{x^2}{9} + \dfrac{y^2}{5} = 1$.

Exercise 16.   Page 56

1. $3x = \pm 4y$.   **3.** $15y = \pm 8x$.   **5.** $2y = \pm x$.   **7.** $y\sqrt{3} = \pm x$.
9. $3x = \pm y\sqrt{7}$.   **11.** $3x = \pm 2y$.   **19.** $25x^2 - 16y^2 = 400$.
21. $39y^2 - 25x^2 = 975$.   **23.** $16y^2 - 9x^2 = 144$.

Exercise 17.   Page 59

11. (c) $x'^2 + y'^2 = 1$.   **13.** $9y^2 - 25x^2 = 225$.   **15.** $144y^2 - 25x^2 = 3600$.

Exercise 18.   Page 64

1. $(1, 3)$; $(-6, 2)$; $(-3, -6)$; $(-2, -4)$.   **3.** $y'^2 = 4x'$.
9. Vertex $(2, 4)$; $y'^2 = 6x'$.   **11.** Center $(-3, 0)$; $4x'^2 + 9y'^2 = 36$.
13. Vertex $(2, 3)$.   **15.** Asymptotes, $5x - 10 = \pm 2(y + 4)$.
17. Imaginary locus.   **19.** Center $(0, \frac{1}{2})$; $x'^2 + 4y'^2 = 0$.
21. Asymptotes, $5(x + 2) = \pm 2(y + 5)$.
27. $4x^2 - 16x + 9y^2 + 90y + 232 = 0$.   **29.** $(y - 5)^2 = 8(x - 1)$.
31. $(y - 8)^2 - 48(x - 5)^2 = 16$.   **33.** $(x - 2)^2 = -8(y + 4)$, equal units.

Exercise 19.   Page 65

1. $(2, 2)$; $(\frac{7}{3}, \frac{10}{3})$ and $(\frac{5}{3}, \frac{2}{3})$; $P:(\frac{3}{2}, 0)$.   **3.** 14; 13; -11.   **5.** $68x - 17y = 23$.
7. $h = \frac{8}{3}$; $k = \frac{9}{4}$.   **9.** $71.0°$; $159.8°$.   **13.** $81.9°$.   **17.** Vertex $(-6, 2)$.
19. Vertex $(0, 0)$.   **21.** Vertex $(0, 0)$.   **23.** Center $(0, 0)$.   **25.** Vertex $(1, 2)$.
27. Center $(2, -1)$.   **29.** Center $(2, -4)$.   **31.** $4(x' + 1)^2 - 5(y' - 2)^2 = 20$.
33. $x^2 + 4y^2 = 16$.   **35.** $4(y - 3)^2 - 9(x - 2)^2 = 36$.   **37.** $y^2 = -6x + 21$.
39. $7(y + 4)^2 - 9(x - 2)^2 = 63$.

Exercise 20.   Page 72

1. 4.   **3.** $2\sqrt{2}$.   **5.** 0.   **7.** $\frac{11}{4}$.   **9.** $\frac{5}{2}$.   **11.** $\frac{3}{4}$.

Exercise 21.   Page 75

1. $\frac{7}{18}$.   **3.** $1 - \sqrt{2}$.   **5.** -3.

Exercise 22.   Page 79

1. Av. rates: 2.5; 2.1; 1.9; 2.01; 1.99. Inst. rate: 2. $y = 2x - 12$.   **3.** 12.
5. In ft. per sec.: (a) 96; 80; 32.   (b) $(60.8, 67.2)$; $(62.4, 65.6)$; $(63.84, 64.16)$.   (c) 64.
7. $23'$ and $17'$ p.s.   **9.** $14'$ p.s.

Exercise 23.   Page 82

1. $f'(x) = 6x + 4$; -8.   **3.** $D_x y = 2x - 1$; -7.   **5.** $f'(z) = -3/z^2$.
7. $f'(x) = 2 - 3x^2$.   **9.** $g'(w) = -\dfrac{4}{(2w + 3)^2}$.   **11.** $y' = \dfrac{1}{(2x + 1)^2}$.
13. $y' = \dfrac{3}{2\sqrt{3x - 1}}$.   **15.** $-2x$; -8.

Exercise 24.   Page 86

Note. All velocities or speeds are in feet per second.
1. $D_x y = 2x - 6$; $2x + y = -1$; $2x - y = 13$.
3. $y' = -4x + 4$; $y = -1$; $12x + y = 29$. Slope 5 at $x = -\frac{1}{4}$.
5. $v = -32t + 64$; -32; 32; $|v| = 32$ at $t = 1$ and $t = 3$.
7. $v = 16t + 4$; 52; 4.

Exercise 25.   Page 90

1. $\dfrac{dy}{dx} = 2$; $dy = .8$; $dy = .02$.   **3.** $\dfrac{dy}{dx} = 3kx^2$; $dy = 4.8k$; $dy = .12k$.   **5.** 2 sq. in.
7. 8π cu. in.

Exercise 26.   Page 95

1. $6x + 15x^2$.   **3.** $3 + 5z^4 - 8z^7$.   **5.** $-3 - 5x + \frac{7}{2}x^2 - \frac{1}{2}x^3$.
7. $28z^3 - 9z^2 + \frac{1}{3}z$.   **9.** $4t^2 - \frac{4}{3}t + 6$.   **11.** $-5 - \frac{3}{4}x + 9x^8$.

13. $6x^2 + 6x + 6$. **15.** $4x^3 - 20x^4 + 4x - 24x^2$. **17.** $-16z^3 + 3z^2 + 24z - 3$.
19. $8t^3 - 9t^2 - 28t + 15$. **21.** At $(2, 5)$; $y = 3x - 3$.
23. Stationary at $t = 2$ and $t = 4$. **25.** \$180 per unit.

Exercise 27. Page 100

1. $\dfrac{9}{(2x + 5)^2}$. **3.** $\dfrac{42x - 15x^2 - 10}{(5x - 7)^2}$. **5.** $-6(2z + 4)^{-2}$.

7. $-12x^{-4}$. **9.** $\frac{8}{3}y^{\frac{1}{3}}$. **11.** $-\frac{14}{3}y^{-\frac{5}{3}}$. **13.** $-\frac{24}{5}x^{-4}$.

15. $-\frac{5}{4}x^{-\frac{3}{2}}$. **17.** $24(3x^2 + 2x)^{11}(3x + 1)$.

19. $5(3x - 2x^{-4})^4(3 + 8x^{-5})$. **21.** $-3(t^{-1} - 2t^4)^2(t^{-2} + 8t^3)$.

23. $5x(2x^2 + 1)^{\frac{1}{4}}$. **25.** $\frac{3}{5}(y + 3y^2)^{-\frac{2}{5}}(1 + 6y)$.

27. $3s/\sqrt{3s^2 + 5}$. **29.** $-9(2x + 5)^{-\frac{5}{2}}$. **31.** $-(3t + 5)^{-\frac{4}{3}}$.

33. $(2t^3 - t^4)^4(t^2 + 5t)^2(180t^3 - 73t^4 - 26t^5)$. **35.** $-2(z - 1)^{-\frac{3}{2}}(3z + 1)^{-\frac{1}{2}}$.

37. $4(x + 3)^3(4x^2 + 5)^{-5}(5 - 24x - 4x^2)$. **39.** $\dfrac{(2x - 3x^2)^2(30 - 106x + 60x^2)}{(5 - 4x)^2}$.

41. $\frac{1}{2}(18x^2 - 8 - 5x^4)(x^3 - 2x)^{-\frac{1}{2}}(4 - x^2)^{-\frac{1}{2}}$. **43.** $\frac{1}{6}s^{-\frac{1}{2}}(s^{\frac{1}{2}} - a^{\frac{1}{2}})^{-\frac{2}{3}}$.

Exercise 28. Page 103

1. $3x^2y + x^3y'$. **3.** $3y^2y' + y^3$. **5.** $-x^{-2}y^{-2}(y + xy')$.

7. $\frac{1}{2}(x - y^2)^{-\frac{1}{2}}(1 - 2yy')$. **9.** $y' = -x^2/y^2$. **11.** $y' = -(1 + y)/x$.

13. $4x/9y$. **15.** $(x + y)/(y - x)$. **17.** $-2xy/(x^2 + 3y^2)$.

19. $(xy^2 - 4x)/(4y - x^2y)$. **21.** $-2\sqrt{y}/3\sqrt{x}$.

23. $(5 - 6r^3t)/(2r + 9r^2t^2)$. **25.** $9y/4x$.

27. $(y - x)/(x + y)$. **29.** $3x - 5y = 34$. **31.** Slopes: $-\frac{7}{9}$; $\frac{62}{45}$.

33. $\dfrac{4(x + 3y^2) - 6(2x + 5y)^2}{15(2x + 5y)^2 - 24y(x + 3y^2)}$.

Exercise 29. Page 107

1. $f(x) = x^5$ and $g(y) = y^{\frac{1}{5}}$, with $-\infty < x < \infty$ and $-\infty < y < \infty$.

$\dfrac{dy}{dx} = 5x^4$; $\dfrac{dx}{dy} = \frac{1}{5}x^{-4}$.

3. $f(x) = \sqrt{4 - x}$ and $g(y) = 4 - y^2$; $x \leqq 4$ and $y \geqq 0$. $\left.\begin{array}{l}\end{array}\right\}$ $\dfrac{dx}{dy} = -2y$; $\dfrac{dy}{dx} = -\dfrac{1}{2y}$.

Or, $f(x) = -\sqrt{4 - x}$ and $g(y) = 4 - y^2$; $x \leqq 4$ and $y \leqq 0$.

5. $\dfrac{dy}{dx} = \dfrac{6x - y}{x - 3y^2}$; $\dfrac{dx}{dy} = \dfrac{x - 3y^2}{6x - y}$. **7.** $\dfrac{dx}{dy} = \dfrac{4y^2}{3x}$, etc. **9.** $\dfrac{dy}{dx} = -\dfrac{x}{4y}$, etc.

11. $\dfrac{dx}{dy} = -\sqrt{\dfrac{x}{y}}$; $\dfrac{dy}{dx} = -\sqrt{\dfrac{y}{x}}$. **13.** $60x^3 - 12x$; $180x^2 - 12$; $360x$.

15. $30x^4 - 12x^2 - 6x$; $120x^3 - 24x - 6$; $360x^2 - 24$.

17. $-2/(s - 1)^3$. **19.** $g''(t) = \frac{35}{2}t^{\frac{3}{2}} + \frac{2}{3}t^{-\frac{5}{3}}$. **21.** $120t^{-7} - 18t^{-4}$.

23. $168(2t - 3)^5$. **25.** $\frac{4}{9}(15 - 2s^2)(2s^2 + 5)^{-\frac{5}{3}}$. **27.** $1296(2t - 1)^2(5t - 1)$.

29. $-a^2/y^3$. **31.** $y'' = -a^2/y^3$. **33.** $y'' = -6/25y^3$.

35. $y'' = -b^4/a^2y^3$. **37.** $y'' = a^{\frac{1}{2}}/2x^{\frac{3}{2}}$.

39. At $(2, 1)$: $y' = -1$; $y'' = -\frac{12}{5}$. At $(2, -\frac{3}{7})$: $y' = \frac{9}{7}$; $y'' = \frac{84}{35}$.

41. $\dfrac{d^2x}{dy^2} = -\dfrac{a^2}{x^3}$. **43.** $\dfrac{d^2x}{dy^2} = \dfrac{a^2}{x^3}$.

Exercise 30. Page 108

3. 30; 14. **5.** $y' = 2x - 2$. **7.** $-(1 - 2x)^{-\frac{1}{2}}$.

9. $v = -16t + 64$; rising, $t < 4$; falling, $t > 4$; stationary, $t = 4$.

11. $-15/x^4$. **13.** $4(2x - 5x^3)^3(2 - 15x^2)$. **15.** $\frac{2}{3}(1 + t)(2t + t^2)^{-\frac{2}{3}}$.

17. $\frac{6}{5}(1 + y)(2y + y^2)^{-\frac{2}{5}}$. **19.** $2(x - 1)(2x + 3)^3(6x - 1)$. **21.** $z(1 - z^2)^{-\frac{3}{2}}$.

23. $4(x + 2)^3(1 + 4x + x^2)(1 - x^2)^{-5}$. **25.** $\dfrac{dy}{dx} = \dfrac{y}{y - x}; \dfrac{dx}{dy} = \dfrac{y - x}{y}$.

27. $5x + 4y = 14$. **29.** $D_x^2 y = -\frac{256}{81}y^{-3}$.

31. $\dfrac{dy}{dx} = f'(u)(9x^2 + 1)$, where $u = 3x^3 + x$.

Exercise 31. Page 112

1. $0; +\infty$. **3.** $0; +\infty; -\infty$. **5.** $\frac{4}{5}$. **7.** $-\frac{1}{2}$. **9.** $-\infty$. **11.** 0. **13.** $+\infty$.
15. $-\infty; +\infty$; no limit; no limit. **19.** $-\infty$.

Exercise 32. Page 115

1. $2 + 4(n - 1)$. **3.** $3(-2)^{n-1}$. **13.** $\frac{1}{3}$. **15.** $-\frac{2}{3}$. **17.** $+\infty$. **19.** $\frac{3}{2}$.

Exercise 33. Page 120

1. $\dfrac{dy}{dx} = 2x - 4$; at $x = 3$, tangent $2x - y = 3$ and normal $x + 2y = 9$.

3. $\dfrac{dy}{dx} = \dfrac{1}{2y + 6}$. Tangent, $x - 4y = -5$; normal, $4x + y = -37$.

5. $\dfrac{dy}{dx} = -\dfrac{x}{4y}$. At $(2, 1)$, $x + 2y = 4$ and $2x - y = 3$. At $(2, -1)$, $x - 2y = 4$ and
$2x + y = 3$.

7. $\dfrac{dy}{dx} = \frac{3}{8}x^2; \dfrac{dx}{dy} = \dfrac{8}{3x^2}$. **9.** $\dfrac{dx}{dy} = 4y^3$. **11.** $\dfrac{dx}{dy} = \dfrac{8 - 4y}{x + 3}$. **13.** $54.0°$.

17. $b^2xx_1 + a^2yy_1 = a^2b^2$. **19.** $yy_1 = p(x + x_1)$.

Exercise 34. Page 122

1. (l.u.b.) = max. = 1; (g.l.b.) = 0; no min.

3. (g.l.b.) = min. = -1; (l.u.b.) = max. = 1.

5. With $D = \{all\ x > 1\}$: (g.l.b.) = 0; no max. or min.; not bdd. above.
With $D = \{2 \leqq x < \infty\}$: (g.l.b.) = 0; (l.u.b.) = max. = 1; no min.

7. With $D = \{all\ x\}$: (g.l.b.) = min. = 0; not bdd. above.
With $D = \{all\ |\ x\ | < 4\}$: (g.l.b.) = min. = 0; (l.u.b.) = 4; no max.
With $D = \{all\ |\ x\ | \leqq 4\}$: (g.l.b.) = min. = 0; (l.u.b.) = max. = 4.

9. (l.u.b.) = max. = 1; (g.l.b.) = min. = -1.

Exercise 35. Page 127

1. Min. 0 at $x = 0$. **3.** No extrema. **5.** Max. 2 at $x = 2$.
7. Max. 12 at $x = 1$; min. -15 at $x = -2$.
9. Max. 3 at $y = -1$; min. -24 at $y = 2$.
11. Max. 0 at $x = 0$; min. $-\frac{108}{3125}$ at $x = \frac{2}{5}$. **13.** Min. -27 at $y = 1$.
15. Max. 10; min. 1. **17.** Max. $\frac{295}{2}$; min. $-\frac{73}{2}$.

Exercise 36. Page 131

19. Min. at $x = a$; max. at $x = \frac{1}{7}(3a + 4b)$.

Exercise 39. Page 137

1. 64. **3.** Decr., 3π sq. in. p.m.; decr., $\frac{5}{4}\pi$ cu. in. p.m.
5. Decr., $32\frac{1}{7}$ ft. p.m. **7.** $1.25'$ p.s.

9. Decr., 2.77 mi. p.h.; at end 3.2 h.   **11.** Decr., 12.6 cu. ft. p.m.; .373′ p.m.
13. Decr., .110 amp. p.s.   **15.** .239′ p.s.   **17.** Incr., .0354′ p.s.
19. Decr., 2.5 sq. in. p.m.   **21.** .2$\frac{2}{3}$ ohms p.s.   **23.** $\frac{du}{dt} = (\frac{1}{2}xt^{-\frac{1}{2}} + 2ty + 2z)/u$.
25. 7(4⁸).

Exercise 40.   Page 140

Note. Velocity is in feet p.s.; acceleration is in feet per second per second.
  1. $v = 138$, $a = 90$.   **3.** $v = 0$, $a = -4$; $v = 69$, $a = 50$.
  5. Max. at $t = 8$; $v > 0$ if $t < 8$; v decr. for all t; speed incr. when $t > 8$.
  7. Max. at $t = 0$; $v < 0$ if $t > 0$; speed incr. for all $t > 0$.
  9. Max. at $t = 6$; $v > 0$ if $t < 6$; speed incr. if $t > 6$.
 11. v incr. if $t > 0$; speed incr. if $t > 1$.
 13. v incr. if $t > 2$; speed incr. if $1 < t < 2$, or $t > 3$.   **15.** (α) 18; (β) 22$\frac{1}{2}$.

Exercise 41.   Page 142

  1. In yd., 75 × 50.   **3.** Side, $(5 - \frac{5}{3}\sqrt{3})$ in.   **5.** In ft., $\frac{2}{3}\sqrt{3}$ by $\frac{2}{3}\sqrt{6}$.
  7. In ft., $8\sqrt{2}$ by $8\sqrt{2}$.   **9.** 4′ × 4′ × 2′.   **11.** In ft., $10\sqrt{5}$.
 13. 20″ × 20″ × 40″.   **15.** 10″.   **17.** (1, 2).
 19. Base-rad., $\frac{1}{2}r\sqrt{2}$; alt., $r\sqrt{2}$.   **21.** Alt., $4r$; base-rad., $r\sqrt{2}$.
 23. $x = \sqrt{C/b}$.   **25.** $x = \frac{9}{4}$.

Exercise 42.   Page 146

  1. $\frac{1}{2}r\sqrt{2}$ by $r\sqrt{2}$.   **3.** Box is a cube.   **5.** A square in both cases.
  7. Box is a cube.
  9. $2a/b$, where a is the base-rad. and b is the alt. of the cone.
 11. Alt. is $\sqrt{2}$ times base-rad.   **13.** $\frac{1}{2}\sqrt{2}$.   **15.** Cube in each case.
 17. $16\sqrt{3}$ sq. in.   **19.** 5″.

Exercise 44.   Page 153

  1. $dy = 1$; $\Delta y = 1.125$.   **3.** $(6x^2 + 10x)dx$.   **5.** $-20(3 - 5x)^3 dx$.
  7. $\dfrac{2x + 1}{2\sqrt{x^2 + x}} dx$.   **9.** $(3x + 2)(45x - 8)dx$.   **11.** $\frac{1}{2}x^{-\frac{1}{2}}\sqrt{3} dx$.
 13. $-10(2x + 3)^{-2} dx$.   **15.** $\frac{2}{21}(2x + 4)^{-\frac{2}{3}} dx$.   **17.** $\dfrac{16x^2 + 24x - 16}{(4x + 3)^2} dx$.
 19. $\dfrac{4x^2 - 1}{3x^2} dx$.   **21.** $dy = \dfrac{(6x^2 + 3y - 2x)dx}{1 - 3x}$.
 23. $dy = \dfrac{(3 - 2x)dx}{4y + 1}$.

Exercise 45.   Page 156

  1. $.9\pi$ cu. in.   **3.** 60π cu. in.   **5.** 6 sq. in.; 6%.   **7.** 2%.
  9. .016″.   **11.** $7\frac{1}{14}$.   **13.** $5\frac{1}{15}$.   **15.** $2\pi r\, dr$.   **17.** 10%.
 21. $1 + \frac{1}{3}y$.   **23.** $1 - \frac{1}{2}y$.

Exercise 46.   Page 160

  1. $x = 2 + 3t$, $y = 5 + 2t$.   **3.** $x = -2 + 3t$, $y = -4 + 9t$.   **5.** $3y + 2x = 7$.
  7. $25x^2 + 4y^2 = 100$.   **9.** $4(x + 1)^2 + (y - 3)^2 = 16$.   **11.** $x^3 = 5x^2 - y^2$.
 13. (4, 0); (0, 3).   **15.** $(-\frac{1}{2}t - \frac{3}{4})$; $\frac{1}{8}$.   **17.** $\dfrac{dy}{dx} = \dfrac{t}{t - 1}$; $\dfrac{d^2y}{dx^2} = \dfrac{1}{2(t - 1)^3}$.

19. $\dfrac{dy}{dx} = 2t; \dfrac{d^2y}{dx^2} = \dfrac{4}{t}$.

21. $y' = \dfrac{2t}{8 + 3t^2}; y'' = \dfrac{32 - 12t^2}{(8 + 3t^2)^3}$.

23. $7x + 6y = 19$.

25. $y' = \dfrac{v_0 \sin \alpha - gt}{v_0 \cos \alpha}; y = \dfrac{v_0^2 \sin^2 \alpha}{2g}$.

Exercise 47. Page 162

13. $x = \dfrac{a(3 - t^2)}{1 + t^2}, y = \dfrac{at(3 - t^2)}{1 + t^2}$.

Exercise 48. Page 169

1. $|\mathbf{A}| = 5; |\mathbf{B}| = \sqrt{193}; |\mathbf{A} + \mathbf{B}| = 4\sqrt{17}$. **3.** $\sqrt{13}; \sqrt{37}; 3\sqrt{10}$.
5. $v = 3\sqrt{26}; a = 2\sqrt{37}$. **7.** $v = \sqrt{85}; a = 2\sqrt{10}$. **9.** $v = 1; a = 2\sqrt{2}; \frac{1}{2}\sqrt{2}$.
11. $v = 4\sqrt{241}, a = 32$; speed 100; min. at $t = \frac{5}{2}$.
13. At $(-4, 2)$, $(v_x = 10, v_y = -10)$; at $(4, 2)$, $(v_x = 10, v_y = 10)$.
15. (a) $v_x = -12, v_y = 18$; (b) at $15\sqrt{2}$ ft. p.s.
17. $(v_x = 8, v_y = 0)$; $(v_y = -8, v_x = 0)$.
19. $v_x = -9, a_x = -36, v = \sqrt{97}, a = 12\sqrt{10}$. **21.** $\frac{5}{16}$ ft. p.s.

Exercise 49. Page 170

1. $y = 15x + 45, x + 15y = 223; 2y + 24x = 9, 24y - 2x = 253$.
3. $71.6°$ at each point. **5.** Min. -11; max. 4.
7. Min. at $x = -3$. **9.** Min. at $x = 5$, vert. tgt.; a cusp.
13. $-.232''$ p.s.; 1.35 sq. in. p.s.
15. Tgt. $x + 6y = 0$; normal $y = 6x; \dfrac{d^2y}{dx^2} = \dfrac{t^2 - 3t + 3}{18(2t - t^2)^3}$.
17. $\frac{9}{2}(2 + 3t)^{\frac{1}{2}} dt$. **19.** $\frac{200}{3}\pi$ cu. ft. **21.** 11.6 cu. ft., or 1.15%.
23. $x = 2 + 6t, y = 3 + t$. **25.** $v = 3\sqrt{65}; a = 2\sqrt{65}$.
29. $15' \times 15' \times 5'$. **31.** Equal.

Exercise 50. Page 175

1. $\xi = 4$. **3.** $\xi = 1$.

Exercise 51. Page 181

1. 3.3125. **3.** 7.35. **5.** 1.78. **7.** 10.75.

Exercise 52. Page 183

1. $\frac{25}{2}h$. **3.** b^3. **5.** $\frac{1}{3}(b^3 - a^3)$.

Exercise 53. Page 188

1. $\frac{2}{5}x^5$. **3.** $-\frac{5}{2}x^{-2}$. **5.** $\frac{1}{2}x^6 - \frac{2}{3}x^3 - \frac{4}{3}x^{\frac{3}{2}} + 6x$. **7.** 56. **9.** -80.
11. $8\frac{1}{4}$. **13.** 52. **15.** $\frac{9}{2}$. **17.** $10\frac{2}{3}$. **19.** $4; 5\frac{3}{4}$. **21.** $\frac{2}{3}$.

Exercise 54. Page 192

3. $\frac{1}{6}x^6 + c$. **5.** $\frac{1}{10}(x + 2)^{10} + c$. **7.** $-\dfrac{1}{4x^2} + c$.
9. $-\frac{4}{3}x^{-\frac{1}{4}} + c$. **11.** $-\frac{1}{3}(3 + t)^{-3} + c$. **13.** $-\frac{1}{16}(3 - 4x)^4 + c$.
15. $\frac{1}{4}(3y - 2)^{\frac{4}{3}} + c$. **17.** $\frac{14}{9}$. **19.** $\frac{1}{24}(y^3 - 3)^8 + c$. **21.** $\frac{2 \cdot 6}{1 \cdot 5}$.
23. $-\frac{1}{12}(3u + 2)^{-4} + c$. **25.** $-\frac{2}{5}(3 - 5z)^{\frac{1}{2}} + c$. **27.** $\frac{1}{3}(2\sqrt{2} - 8)$.
29. $3 - \sqrt{6}$. **31.** 32.75. **33.** $\frac{243}{4}$.

Exercise 55.   Page 195

1. 18.   **3.** $\frac{9}{2}$.   **5.** 9.   **7.** $\frac{8}{3}$.   **9.** 36.
11. $85\frac{1}{3}$.   **13.** $\frac{24}{5}$.   **15.** $\frac{8}{15}$.   **17.** 2.   **19.** 16.

Exercise 56.   Page 198

3. $125\pi/12$.   **5.** $512\pi/15$.   **7.** $81\pi/10$.   **9.** $128\pi/7$·
11. 16π; $\frac{128}{3}\pi\sqrt{2}$.   **13.** $\pi/3$.   **15.** $32\pi a^3/105$.   **17.** $\frac{1}{3}\pi b^2 h$.

Exercise 57.   Page 201

1. 8250 ft.-lb.   **3.** $2.232(10^6)$ ft.-lb.   **5.** 67.5 ft.-lb.; 1.875 ft.-lb.
7. $-\frac{2}{3}km_1 m_2$; $\frac{1}{4}km_1 m_2$.   **9.** $5.760\ (10^7)$ ft.-lb.

Exercise 58.   Page 205

3. $y = 2x^2 + 7x - 19$.   **5.** $s = \frac{3}{2}t^2 - 5t + 1$.   **7.** $y = \frac{1}{2}x^3 - x^2 - 18x + 60$.
9. $u = -\frac{1}{6}t^4 + \frac{5}{2}t^2 + \frac{7}{3}t + 4$.   **11.** $s = \frac{1}{4}t^4 + \frac{5}{6}t^3 + c_1 t^2 + c_2 t + c_3$.
13. $y = -3x^2 - 12x - 7$.   **15.** $y = 4x^{-1}$.
17. $f(x) = \frac{3}{2}x^2 - x - 3$.   **19.** $y = x^3 - \frac{5}{2}x^2 + 7$.

Exercise 59.   Page 207

1. $s = \frac{3}{2}t^2 + 4t + 2$.   **3.** $s = -\frac{1}{6}t^3 + 3t + 2$.   **5.** $s = \frac{1}{2}(t^3 + t^2 + t - 3)$.
7. $s = \frac{1}{4}t^4 + t^3 - 22t + 35$.   **9.** $s = t^3 + \frac{3}{2}t^2 + 3t - 2$.   **11.** 10 sec.; $400'$ p.s.
13. 20 sec. later.   **15.** At end 6 sec.; $72'$ upward.

Exercise 60.   Page 213

1. $\frac{67}{13}$.   **3.** $(\frac{19}{14}, \frac{25}{7})$.   **5.** 70; 14; $\bar{x} = \frac{107}{21}$.   **7.** $\frac{104}{3}$; $\frac{13}{3}$; $\bar{x} = \frac{363}{65}$.   **9.** 28; 7; $\bar{x} = \frac{18}{7}$.

Exercise 61.   Page 216

1. $(\frac{8}{3}, \frac{2}{3})$.   **3.** $(1, \frac{2}{5})$.   **5.** $(\frac{24}{5}, \frac{3}{2})$.   **7.** $(0, 8/3\pi)$.   **9.** $(0, 4b/3\pi)$.
11. On radius $\perp$ to diam., at distance $4a/3\pi$.   **13.** $(\frac{4}{3}, \frac{2}{3})$.

Exercise 62.   Page 218

1. $\bar{x} = 3$.   **3.** $\bar{y} = \frac{8}{3}$.   **5.** $\bar{x} = \frac{3}{2}$.   **7.** $\bar{y} = \frac{7}{4}$.   **9.** $\bar{x} = \frac{7}{2}$.   **11.** $\bar{x} = \frac{9}{4}$.

Exercise 63.   Page 219

1. $\xi = \frac{5}{2}$.   **3.** 3.78.   **5.** $11\frac{5}{6}$.   **7.** $-\frac{1}{9}(2 - x)^9 + c$.
9. $\frac{1}{6}(4x + 7)^{\frac{3}{2}} + c$.   **11.** $\frac{1}{72}(4t^3 + 1)^6 + c$.
13. $-(4 - x^2)^{\frac{1}{2}} + c$.   **15.** $3t^3 + 6t - t^{-1} + c$.
17. $\frac{2}{15}$.   **19.** 24π.   **21.** $64\frac{64}{135}\pi$.
23. $f(x) = 2x^2 - 2x - 5$.   **25.** $t^3 + t^2 - 14t + 15$.
27. Mass $= 12$; av. dens. is 3; $\bar{x} = \frac{17}{9}$.

Exercise 64.   Page 224

3. .98545.   **5.** $-$.39934.   **7.** $g(1) = .017$; $S(1) = .84147$.

Exercise 65.   Page 228

1. $5\cos 5x$.   **3.** $4\sec^2 4t$.   **5.** $-\frac{3}{2}\csc \frac{3}{2}t \cot \frac{3}{2}t$.   **7.** $-5\cot^4 z \csc^2 z$.
9. $\frac{\cos x}{2\sqrt{\sin x}}$·   **11.** $-\frac{\sin 2x}{2\sqrt{\cos^3 2x}}$ **13.** $-\frac{12\cos 4x}{\sin^4 4x}$·   **15.** $\frac{\sin \sqrt{x}}{2\sqrt{x}\cos^2 \sqrt{x}}$
17. $(4x + 1)\cos(2x^2 + x)$.   **19.** $-14\csc^2(2 + 7x)\cot(2 + 7x)$.

21. $\dfrac{(6 - 4x)\sin (2x - 3)^2}{\sqrt{\cos (2x - 3)^2}}.$ **23.** $x^2(3 \sin x + x \cos x).$

25. $4 \cos^2 x \cos 4x - 2 \cos x \sin 4x \sin x.$

27. $(3 + 4x)[8 \sec^2 x + (6 + 8x)\sec^2 x \tan x].$ **29.** $\dfrac{2 \sin x}{(1 + \cos x)^2}.$

31. $\dfrac{3(4x^2 - x)\sin 6x - (8x - 1)\sin^2 3x}{(4x^2 - x)^2}.$

33. $\dfrac{t^2[(2 + \cos^2 t)(t \sec^2 t + 3 \tan t) + 2t \sin^2 t]}{(2 + \cos^2 t)^2}.$

35. $\dfrac{1}{x} \sin \dfrac{1}{x} + \cos \dfrac{1}{x}.$ **37.** $\dfrac{3}{(2 - x)^2} \cos \dfrac{x + 1}{2 - x}.$

39. $\frac{1}{4} - \frac{5}{12}\pi\sqrt{3}.$ **41.** $\frac{8}{3}.$ **43.** $2 \cos x - x \sin x.$

45. $\dfrac{\cos x}{3 - \sin y}.$ **47.** $\dfrac{1 - \cos (x + 3y)}{3 \cos (x + 3y)}.$ **49.** $\dfrac{2x \sec^2 (x^2 - y)}{\sec^2 (x^2 - y) + \csc^2 y}.$

Exercise 66. Page 230

13. $70.5°.$
15. Rel. min. 0 at $x = 0$; rel. max. 0 at $x = 2\pi$; abs. max. $\frac{3}{2}\sqrt{3}$ at $x = \frac{1}{3}\pi$; abs. min. $-\frac{3}{2}\sqrt{3}$ at $x = \frac{5}{3}\pi$.
17. Rel. min. 4 at $x = 0$; rel. max. 4 at $x = 2\pi$; abs. min. -5 at $x = 3.785$; abs. max. 5 at $x = .643$.
19. Abs. max. is 4; abs. min. is $-\frac{9}{4}$.

Exercise 67. Page 232

1. $\frac{3}{2}\sqrt{3} - .5.$ **3.** $\frac{1525}{9}\pi$ yd. p.s. **5.** $\frac{4}{9}\pi a^3\sqrt{3}.$ **7.** $\frac{9}{170}$ rad. p.s. **9.** $10\sqrt{5}.$
11. $60°.$ **13.** $17.7'.$ **15.** $.1144''$ p.m. **17.** Incr., $\frac{1}{82}$ rad. p.s.
19. Incr., $.04758$ rad. p.m.

Exercise 68. Page 236

11. $.25.$ **13.** $-\frac{1}{6}\pi.$ **15.** $-\frac{1}{3}\pi.$ **21.** $-1.06.$ **27.** $\frac{1}{2}\sqrt{3}.$ **29.** $-\frac{4}{3}.$
33. $\frac{2}{5}\sqrt{6}.$ **35.** sin, $-\frac{3}{5}$; cos, $\frac{4}{5}$; etc.
37. $\sin (y + z) = \frac{1}{10}(3 - 4\sqrt{3});$ $\cos (y + z) = \frac{1}{10}(4 + 3\sqrt{3});$ $\sin 2y = \frac{24}{25};$ $\cos 2y = \frac{7}{25}.$

Exercise 69. Page 239

1. $\dfrac{4}{\sqrt{1 - 16x^2}}.$ **3.** $\dfrac{3}{1 + (3x + 2)^2}.$ **5.** $\dfrac{2 \tan x \sec^2 x}{\sqrt{1 - \tan^4 x}}.$

7. $3x^2.$ **9.** $\dfrac{-2x^{-3}}{1 + x^{-4}}.$ **11.** $\dfrac{1}{\sqrt{a^2 - x^2}}.$ **13.** $\dfrac{1}{a^2 + x^2}.$

15. $-\dfrac{2}{t^3} \operatorname{Arcsin} t + \dfrac{1}{t^2\sqrt{1 - t^2}}.$ **17.** $3 \cos 3x \operatorname{Arcsin} \sqrt{x} + \dfrac{\sin 3x}{2\sqrt{x - x^2}}.$

19. $\sqrt{a^2 - x^2}.$ **21.** $\left(3x^2 - \dfrac{1}{\sqrt{1 - x^2}}\right)(1 + y^2).$ **23.** $-\dfrac{1 + [1 + (x + 2y)^2]\cos x}{2 + [1 + (x + 2y)^2]\sin y}.$

25. $\dfrac{-128x}{(1 + 16x^2)^2}.$ **29.** 948.6 yd.

Exercise 70. Page 244

11. $e^3.$ **13.** $e.$

Exercise 71. Page 246

1. $\dfrac{5}{3 + 5x}$. **3.** $\dfrac{2z + 2}{z^2 + 2z}$. **5.** $-\dfrac{\log_a e}{\sin x \cos x}$. **7.** $3 \tan 3x$.

9. $(\log_a e)/(x \ln x)$. **11.** $3x^{-1}$. **13.** $\dfrac{4}{1 + 2x}$. **15.** $\dfrac{2 \log_{10} e}{\sin x \cos x}$.

17. $\dfrac{12 [\ln (1 - 4x)]^2}{4x - 1}$. **19.** $\dfrac{3}{2(3x - 1)\sqrt{\ln (3x - 1)}}$.

21. $\dfrac{3x^2}{4x^3 - 4}$. **23.** $\dfrac{-2}{125x(\ln x)^3}$. **25.** $\dfrac{\ln \sin x}{x} + \cot x \ln 2x$.

27. $\dfrac{4x - 15x^2 - 5}{(1 + x^2)(2 - 5x)}$. **29.** $\dfrac{22z^3 - 6z^2 + 30}{(3 + z^3)(2z - 1)}$.

31. $3 \sec^2 x \cot x + 4 \cot 2x - 3 \tan 3x$. **33.** $\dfrac{\cot x}{2} + \dfrac{\sin x}{3(1 - \cos x)}$.

35. $-\dfrac{6}{x(\ln x)^3}$. **37.** $\dfrac{\cos x \ln \cos x + \sin x \tan x}{(\ln \cos x)^2}$.

39. $\dfrac{(\cot x)\ln \cos x + (\tan x)\ln \sin x}{(\ln \cos x)^2}$. **41.** $\dfrac{5}{2(3 + x)(x - 2)}$.

43. $\dfrac{9 - 18 \ln (3x - 1)}{(3x - 1)^3}$. **45.** $.09658$. **47.** $-y/x$.

49. $\dfrac{2(4x^3 + 6x^2y + 6y + 3x)}{3x}$. **51.** $(22x + 23)(2 + x)^2(2x - 3)^7$.

53. $\dfrac{(27 + 3x)(2 + x)^2}{(1 - 3x)^5}$. **55.** $\dfrac{7}{2\sqrt{2x - 1}(3x + 2)^{\frac{3}{2}}}$. **57.** $\dfrac{24x - 38}{15(1 - 3x)^{\frac{4}{5}}(2 + 4x)^{\frac{4}{3}}}$.

59. $\dfrac{(-1)^{n+1}(n - 1)!}{x^n}$. **61.** $\dfrac{(-1)^{n+1}(n - 1)!}{(1 + x)^n}$.

Exercise 72. Page 249

1. $4e^{4x}$. **3.** $-(\csc^2 x)e^{\cot x}$. **5.** $-2e^{-2x}$. **7.** $4a^{4t} \ln a$.

9. $\dfrac{2 \ln x}{x} e^{(\ln x)^2}$. **11.** $(3 - 2x)e^{3x - x^2}$. **13.** $3e^{-x3}(x^2 - x^5)$.

15. $e^x \cos e^x$. **17.** $\dfrac{2e^{2t}}{\sqrt{1 - e^{4t}}}$. **19.** $\dfrac{1 - 3x \ln x}{xe^{3x}}$. **21.** $\dfrac{\sqrt{2x} \cos x - \sin x}{\sqrt{2x}e^{\sqrt{2x}}}$.

23. $\dfrac{e^{2x}(1 + 2x)}{1 + x^2e^{4x}}$. **25.** $-e^{-2t}(5 \sin 5t + 2 \cos 5t)$. **27.** $\dfrac{-6e^{-x}}{(e^x - e^{-2x})^2}$.

29. $5(3x + e^{-2x})^4(3 - 2e^{-2x})$. **31.** $\dfrac{e^x(2x + 2x \ln x + 1)}{2x\sqrt{1 + \ln x}}$. **33.** $\dfrac{y^2}{1 - ye^{-y} - xy}$.

35. $x^{x^2+1}(2 \ln x + 1)$. **37.** $x^{\cos x - 1}[\cos x - x(\ln x)\sin x]$. **39.** $e^x; \, xe^x + ne^x$.

Exercise 73. Page 251

1. v: 6, 0, -6, 0, 6. a: 0, -12, 0, 12, 0. Period is π sec.
3. v: $4\sqrt{3}$, $-4\sqrt{3}$, 0, $4\sqrt{3}$, 0. a: -8, -8, 16, -8, 16. Period is π sec.
5. v: 6, 6, -6, -6. a: 12, -12, -12, 12. Period is π sec.

Exercise 74. Page 254

1. $4e^{4x} dx$. **3.** $2 \sec^2 2x \, dx$. **5.** $(\cos x)e^{\sin x} dx$.

7. $\dfrac{dx}{x \ln x}$. **9.** $-\tan y \, dy$. **11.** $\dfrac{3 \, dy}{1 + 9y^2}$.

13. $e^x(3 \cos 3x + \sin 3x)dx.$

15. $e^{-2x}\left(-2 \ln x + \dfrac{1}{x}\right)dx.$

17. $\dfrac{dx}{(1 + x^2) \text{ Arctan } x}.$

19. $a^t[(\ln a)(\ln \sin t) + \cos t]dt.$

21. $\dfrac{-2\, dt}{(\sin t - \cos t)^2}.$ **23.** .52'.   **25.** .6%; .9%.   **27.** $1\frac{1}{2}\%$.

Exercise 75.   Page 257

1. $-\frac{2}{3}\tan \theta$; $-\frac{2}{9}\sec^3 \theta$.   **3.** $\tan t$; $\frac{1}{2}\sec^3 t$.   **5.** $x + y = \frac{3}{2}\pi$; $y = x - 2 + \frac{3}{2}\pi$.
7. $9(x - 2)^2 + 25(y + 1)^2 = 225.$ **9.** $x^{\frac{2}{3}} + y^{\frac{2}{3}} = 3^{\frac{2}{3}}.$ **13.** $v = 3$; $a = 3$.
15. $v = 2\sqrt{2}$; $a = 2$.   **17.** $x^2 + y^2 = k^2$; $a = h^2 k$.

Exercise 76.   Page 260

1. 0.   **3.** $+ \infty$.   **5.** 0.   **7.** 0.   **9.** 1.   **11.** 0.
13. -1.   **15.** $+ \infty$.   **17.** $- \infty$.   **19.** $- \infty$.   **21.** $+ \infty$.   **23.** 0.
25. -2.   **27.** $\frac{1}{2}$.   **29.** 1.   **31.** $\frac{1}{12}$.   **33.** $- \infty$.   **35.** $\frac{1}{2}$.
37. $\frac{1}{4}$.   **39.** 1.   **41.** 0.   **43.** -3.   **45.** 1.   **47.** $-\frac{1}{2}$.
49. $\frac{2}{3}$.   **51.** $- \infty$.   **53.** $\frac{1}{5}$.   **55.** 0.   **57.** -1.

Exercise 77.   Page 263

1. 0.   **3.** 0.   **5.** 2.   **7.** 1.   **9.** 0.   **11.** $\frac{3}{2}$.   **13.** $- \infty$.
15. 1.   **17.** 1.   **19.** e^{-6}.   **21.** 0.   **23.** 1.   **25.** $e^{-2/\pi}$.   **27.** $\frac{1}{2}$.
29. 0.   **31.** -1.   **33.** 2.   **35.** e^3.   **37.** $\sec^2 \alpha$.   **39.** $- \infty$.
41. $- \infty$.   **43.** 0.

Exercise 78.   Page 267

1. 1.27; 4.73.   **3.** 1.15.   **5.** 3.18; -1.86; .68.   **7.** 5.70.   **9.** -2.72.
11. 636°.

Exercise 79.   Page 267

1. $(9x^2 - 1)\sin 2(3x^3 - x).$ **3.** $\dfrac{2 \cos 2x}{1 + \sin^2 2x}.$ **5.** $3e^{3x} \sec e^{3x} \tan e^{3x}.$

7. $\dfrac{2e^{2t}}{\sqrt{1 - e^{4t}}}.$ **9.** $e^{3x}(3 \sin 4x + 4 \cos 4x).$ **11.** $-12e^{3 \cos 4x} \sin 4x.$

13. $\sin \dfrac{3}{x} - \dfrac{3}{x}\cos \dfrac{3}{x}.$ **15.** $\dfrac{\sin t - 1 - t(\ln t)\cos t}{t(\sin t - 1)^2}.$

17. $-2 \cot x - 3 \tan x.$ **19.** $\dfrac{2}{(2z - 3)\sqrt{\ln (2z - 3)^2}}.$ **21.** $\dfrac{2}{x\sqrt{1 - 4(\ln x)^2}}.$

23. $y' = \dfrac{1}{x(2y - e^y)}.$ **25.** $y' = \dfrac{\cos (x + y) - \sec^2 (x + 2y)}{2 \sec^2 (x + 2y) - \cos (x + y)}.$

27. $(\ln x)^{\cos x - 1}\left\{\dfrac{\cos x}{x} - (\sin x)(\ln x)[\ln (\ln x)]\right\}.$ **29.** 6.

31. $\dfrac{12x}{2x^2 + 5} + \dfrac{10 \cos 2x}{\sin 2x - 1}.$ **33.** $\dfrac{2\{1 - [\ln (\ln x)](\ln x + 1)\}}{x^2(\ln x)^2}.$

35. Min. at $x = \pi$.   **37.** Max. at $x = 2.747$; min. at $x = 5.888$.
39. Max. at $x = \frac{1}{4}\pi$ and $x = \frac{5}{4}\pi$.   **41.** Incr., 1.15° p.s.

43. $e^{-2x}\left[\dfrac{1}{x \ln x} - 2 \ln (\ln x)\right] dx.$ **45.** $10^{2x}[2(\ln 10)\cot 3x - 3 \csc^2 3x] dx.$

47. No limit, because $\lim_{x \to 0+} \csc 2x = + \infty$ and $\lim_{x \to 0-} \csc 2x = - \infty$.

49. $-\infty$.   **51.** $+\infty$.   **53.** $+\infty$.
55. $y = x + \frac{1}{2}\pi\sqrt{2}$; $x + y = 2\sqrt{2}$; downward.
57. Decr. $.0709h$ atoms p.h.; $.0142h$ atom.

Exercise 80.   Page 274

1. $-\frac{1}{15}x^{-3} + c$.
3. $-\frac{1}{4}t^{-2} - \frac{5}{6}t^{-1} + c$.
5. $\frac{1}{16}(x^2 + 2x - 3)^8 + c$.
7. $-\frac{1}{5}\cos 5x + c$.
9. $3 \sin \frac{1}{3}x + c$.
11. $\frac{1}{2} - \frac{1}{4}\sqrt{2}$.
13. $-\dfrac{1}{a}\cot au + c$.
15. $2 \tan \frac{1}{2}x + c$.
17. $\frac{1}{7}\sin^7 x + c$.
19. $\frac{1}{4}\tan^4 x + c$.
21. $-\frac{1}{10}\cos^5 2x + c$.
23. $\frac{1}{14}(3 + 2 \tan y)^7 + c$.
25. $\frac{1}{3}\sin x^3 + c$.
27. $2 \tan 2y + c$.
29. $\frac{1}{4}\cos^{-4} x + c$.
31. $\frac{1}{2}\sqrt{2t^2 - 4t} + c$.
33. $\frac{1}{5}(\ln 3)^5$.
35. $\frac{3}{2}(2 + \tan t)^{\frac{2}{3}} + c$.
37. $\frac{1}{2}(\text{Arcsin } x)^2 + c$.
39. $\frac{39}{4}$.
41. $\frac{1}{3}(3 + e^{-x})^{-3} + c$.
43. 2.   **45.** 2.   **47.** π.

Exercise 81.   Page 275

1. $\frac{1}{3}e^{3x} + c$.
3. $\dfrac{1}{\ln 10}10^x + c$.
5. $\frac{1}{5}e^{2+5x} + c$.
7. $\dfrac{a^x e^x}{1 + \ln a} + c$.
9. $-\frac{1}{4}e^{3-4t} + c$.
11. $-\frac{1}{3}e^{-x^3} + c$.
13. $-8e^{-\frac{1}{2}x} + c$.
15. $-\dfrac{3}{\sqrt[3]{e^t}} + c$.
17. $\frac{1}{4}x^4 + c$.
19. $-e^{\frac{1}{x}} + c$.
21. $\frac{2}{3}e^{x\sqrt{x}} + c$.
23. $\frac{1}{2}e^{\sin 2y} + c$.
25. $e^{-1} - 1$.
27. $\dfrac{e^{2az}}{2a} + 2x - \dfrac{e^{-2az}}{2a} + c$.
29. $\frac{1}{6}(3 + 4e^z)^{\frac{3}{2}} + c$.
31. $\dfrac{1}{6(2 - 3e^u)^2} + c$.
33. $-e^{\cos^2 y} + c$.
35. $1 - e^{-3}$.
37. $a^2(e^{\frac{1}{2}} - e^{-\frac{1}{2}})$.
39. $\frac{1}{2}\pi(1 - e^{-6})$.

Exercise 82.   Page 277

1. 1.25276.
3. $\ln(1 + x^2) + c$.
5. $-.54930$.
7. $-\frac{1}{2}\ln|1 - 2\tan x| + c$.
9. $\frac{1}{4}\ln|1 + 4\sec t| + c$.
11. $x^2 - x + \frac{3}{2}\ln|2x + 1| + c$.
13. 1.43508.
15. $-\frac{1}{2}\ln|1 + 2\cot y| + c$.
17. $\ln|2 + \ln y| + c$.
19. $-\frac{1}{2}\ln(1 + \cos^2 u) + c$.
21. $-\frac{1}{2}e^{-2x} + e^{-x} - \ln(1 + e^{-x}) + c$.
23. $\frac{1}{2}\ln|\text{Arcsin } 2u| + c$.
25. 6.438.
27. .432.

Exercise 83.   Page 279

Note. Hereafter, as a rule, additive constants of integration will not be included with answers for indefinite integration. However, the student should continue to include such constants in his solutions.

1. $\frac{1}{2}\ln|\sec 2x|$.
3. $4 \ln|\sin \frac{1}{4}x|$.
5. $-\frac{1}{4}\cot 4t$.
7. $\ln|\csc v - \cot v|$.
9. $\frac{1}{3}\sin 3v$.
11. $2 \sec \frac{1}{2}x$.
13. $a^{-1}\ln|\sec ax + \tan ax|$.
15. $\frac{1}{2}x + \frac{1}{4}\sin 2x$.
17. $\frac{1}{2}x + \frac{1}{12}\sin 6x$.
19. $-u - \cot u$.
21. $\frac{7}{12}\pi - \frac{1}{4}(2 + \sqrt{3})$.
23. $\frac{1}{4}\tan 4u - u$.
25. $2 \tan y - 2 \sec y - y$.
27. $\frac{1}{3}\ln|4 + 3\tan t|$.
29. $-\cos(3x + x^2)$.
31. $\ln(3 - 2\sqrt{2})$.
33. $\ln|\sec e^x|$.
35. $-\frac{1}{3}\ln|\csc x^3|$.
37. $\cos e^{-x}$.
39. 1.03973.
41. $\frac{1}{2}\pi^2$.
43. $\pi(\sqrt{3} - \frac{1}{3}\pi)$.

Exercise 84. Page 281

1. $\frac{1}{2}$ Arctan $\frac{1}{2}x$. 3. $\frac{1}{5}$ Arcsin $\frac{5}{3}x$. 5. $-\frac{1}{3}$ Arcsin $\frac{3}{4}y$. 7. $\frac{1}{3}\pi$. 9. $\frac{5}{12}\pi$. 11. $-\frac{1}{4}\pi$.
13. .125. 15. $\frac{1}{14}$ Arctan $(\frac{2}{7}\sin\theta)$. 17. $\frac{1}{9}$ Arctan $\frac{1}{3}x^3$. 19. $\frac{1}{4}$ Arctan $\frac{1}{2}x^2$.
21. $2x - \frac{23}{5}$ Arctan $\frac{2}{5}x$. 23. Arcsin (ln u). 25. Arcsin $\frac{1}{2}(2 + x)$.
27. $\frac{1}{30}$ Arctan $\frac{5}{3}(2x + 3)$.. 29. $\frac{1}{3}\pi$. 31. $\frac{7}{12}\pi$. 33. .785.

Exercise 85. Page 283

1. $\frac{1}{4}\ln\left|\dfrac{u - 2}{u + 2}\right|$. 3. $\frac{1}{24}\ln\left|\dfrac{4z - 3}{4z + 3}\right|$. 5. $-.20118$. 7. .02939.

9. $\frac{1}{30}\sqrt{5}\ln\left|\dfrac{3e^x - \sqrt{5}}{3e^x + \sqrt{4}}\right|$. 11. $\frac{1}{18}\ln\left|\dfrac{x^3 - 3}{x^3 + 3}\right|$.

13. $\frac{1}{12}\ln\left|\dfrac{1 + 3x}{3 - 3x}\right|$. 15. $\frac{1}{6}\ln\left|\dfrac{\tan x - 3}{\tan x + 3}\right|$.

Exercise 86. Page 286

1. $\frac{2}{5}(2 + x)^{\frac{5}{2}} - \frac{4}{3}(2 + x)^{\frac{3}{2}}$. 3. $\frac{3}{28}(1 + 2x)^{\frac{7}{3}} - \frac{3}{16}(1 + 2x)^{\frac{4}{3}}$.
5. $-\frac{2}{3}(1 - 3x)^{\frac{1}{2}} + \frac{4}{9}(1 - 3x)^{\frac{3}{2}}$. 7. $\frac{1}{24}(3 + 4u)^{\frac{3}{2}} - \frac{3}{8}(3 + 4u)^{\frac{1}{2}}$.
9. $\frac{3}{20}(5 + 2x)^{\frac{5}{3}} - \frac{15}{8}(5 + 2x)^{\frac{2}{3}}$. 11. $-\frac{9}{5}(3 - x)^{\frac{5}{3}} + \frac{9}{8}(3 - x)^{\frac{8}{3}}$.
13. $\frac{1}{2}(1 + 4x)^{\frac{1}{2}} - (1 + 4x)^{-\frac{1}{2}}$. 15. $-\frac{644}{5}$. 17. $\frac{516}{5}$. 19. $\frac{2350}{9}\sqrt{5}$.

Exercise 87. Page 288

1. $\ln(x + \sqrt{x^2 + 4})$. 3. $\ln(z + \sqrt{z^2 + 16})$. 5. $\frac{1}{3}\ln(3t + \sqrt{9t^2 + 25})$.
7. $\frac{1}{3}\ln|3t + \sqrt{9t^2 - 121}|$. 9. $\frac{1}{6}\ln(6y + \sqrt{36y^2 + 1})$.
11. $\ln(\tan t + \sqrt{\tan^2 t + 9})$. 13. $\frac{1}{2}\ln(\sin 2x + \sqrt{16 + \sin^2 2x})$.
15. .874. 17. .218. 19. .303. 21. .188; .111.

Exercise 88. Page 290

1. $\frac{1}{2}$ Arctan $\frac{1}{2}(x + 3)$. 3. $\frac{1}{4}\ln\left|\dfrac{3 + x}{1 - x}\right|$. 5. Arcsin $\frac{1}{5}(x + 4)$.

7. No real value for any x. 9. $\frac{1}{4}$ Arctan $\frac{1}{2}(2t - 1)$. 11. $\dfrac{\sqrt{2}}{12}\ln\left|\dfrac{3u + 1 - \sqrt{2}}{3u + 1 + \sqrt{2}}\right|$.

13. $\frac{1}{8}\ln\left|\dfrac{3v - 3}{3v + 5}\right|$. 15. $\frac{1}{2}\sqrt{2}$ Arcsin $\frac{1}{3}(4x - 1)$. 17. $\frac{1}{4}\ln\left|\dfrac{x - 1}{x}\right|$.
19. $\frac{1}{2}\ln|2x - 1 + \sqrt{4x^2 - 4x + 10}|$. 21. $\frac{1}{3}\sqrt{3}\ln(3t + 1 + \sqrt{9t^2 + 6t + 6})$.
23. $\frac{3}{2}$ Arctan $\frac{1}{2}x + \ln(4 + x^2)$. 25. 5 Arcsin $\frac{1}{3}t - 3(9 - t^2)^{\frac{1}{2}}$.
27. $\frac{3}{8}\ln\left|\dfrac{4 + z}{4 - z}\right| + 2\ln|16 - z^2|$. 29. $-3\ln|x^2 + 4x - 5| + \frac{5}{2}\ln\left|\dfrac{x - 1}{x + 5}\right|$.
31. $-8\sqrt{7 + 6x - x^2} + 29$ Arcsin $\frac{1}{4}(x - 3)$. 33. No real value for the radical.
35. $\sqrt{9t^2 + 12t + 3} + \frac{10}{3}\ln|3t + 2 + \sqrt{9t^2 + 12t + 3}|$. 37. $\frac{1}{2}\ln\left|\dfrac{\tan x + 1}{\tan x + 3}\right|$.

Exercise 89. Page 292

3. $s = \cos t + 2 - \frac{1}{2}\sqrt{2}$. 5. $y = -\frac{3}{4}\cos 2x - 3x + 2 + \frac{3}{4}\pi$.
7. $u = -2\sin x - 3\cos x + c_1 x + c_2$. 9. $y = \frac{1}{8}\cos 2x + k_1 x^2 + k_2 x + k_3$.
11. $y' = -x$. 13. $x + 4yy' = 0$. 15. $y^2 - xyy' = 4$. 17. $y + xy' = 0$.
21. $s = k\sin(t\sqrt{5} - \alpha)$; $s = c_1\sin t\sqrt{5} + c_2\cos t\sqrt{5}$.
23. $s = 8\cos 5t$. 25. $s = -\frac{5}{2}\sqrt{2}(\sin 3t + \cos 3t)$.
27. $s = \sin 2t + 4$.

Exercise 90.   Page 296

1. $\ln |x| + \ln |y| = c$; $xy = k$; $xy = -6$; $xy = 8$.

3. $\frac{2}{3}(2 + x)^{\frac{3}{2}} = \frac{3}{4}y^{\frac{4}{3}} + c$.   **5.** $s = -e^{-t} + e^t + c$.

7. $y^2 = cx$.   **9.** $1 + x^2 = c(3 + y)$.   **11.** $3x^3 + cx^3y = y$.

13. $\csc y - \cot y = c(\csc x - \cot x)$.   **15.** $\frac{1}{3}y^3 + \ln |\cos y| - \cos x = c$.

17. $x^2 - 4y^2 = 9$.   **19.** $x^2(y + 3) = 8$.   **21.** $x = 2y$.

23. $y^3 + 1 = c(x^3 + 1)$.   **25.** Arctan $\frac{1}{2}y = \sqrt{2}$ Arctan $\frac{1}{2}x\sqrt{2} + c$.

27. $4x^2 + 9y^2 = 160$.   **29.** $(x - 3)(2y + 1) = 3$.

Exercise 91.   Page 298

1. $x_0 e^{-.23105t}$; 5.21 yr.   **3.** 5.27 hr.   **5.** $i = 30e^{-54.161t}$; .1053 sec.

7. $p = 760e^{-.1186h}$, with h in kilometers; at $h = 1.99$.   **9.** $\beta v - x = (\beta v - 30)e^{-\frac{k}{v}t}$.

11. 1.30 (10^4) years.

Exercise 92.   Page 303

1. $e^x(x - 1)$.   **3.** $x \sin x + \cos x$.   **5.** $-e^{-x}(x + 1)$.

7. $\frac{1}{24}\pi(3\sqrt{2} - 4) + \frac{1}{2}(\sqrt{3} - \sqrt{2})$.   **9.** $\frac{1}{4}x^2(2 \ln x - 1)$.   **11.** $\frac{1}{9}x^3(3 \ln x - 1)$.

13. $x^{n+1}[(n + 1)\ln x - 1]/(n + 1)^2$.   **15.** $\frac{1}{2}x^2 \sin 2x + \frac{1}{2}x \cos 2x - \frac{1}{4}\sin 2x$.

17. x Arcsin $3x + \frac{1}{3}\sqrt{1 - 9x^2}$.   **19.** $2 \ln 2 - \pi$.

21. $\frac{1}{2}x^2$ Arccot $2x + \frac{1}{4}x + \frac{1}{8}$ Arccot $2x$.

23. $-x^3 \cos x + 3x^2 \sin x + 6x \cos x - 6 \sin x$.

25. x Arcsin $2x + \frac{1}{2}(1 - 4x^2)^{\frac{1}{2}}$.   **27.** $-\dfrac{x \cos kx}{k} + \dfrac{\sin kx}{k^2}$.

29. $\dfrac{xa^x}{\ln a} - \dfrac{a^x}{(\ln a)^2}$.   **31.** $-e^{-2x}(\frac{1}{2}x^2 + \frac{1}{2}x + \frac{1}{4})$.

33. $x^2(4 + x^2)^{\frac{1}{2}} - \frac{2}{3}(4 + x^2)^{\frac{3}{2}}$.   **35.** $2x^{\frac{1}{2}}$ Arcsin $\sqrt{x} + 2(1 - x)^{\frac{1}{2}}$.

37. $-\dfrac{\ln x}{x + 2} + \frac{1}{2}\ln \left|\dfrac{x}{x + 2}\right|$.   **39.** $\sqrt{1 + x^2}$ Arctan $x - \ln |x + \sqrt{1 + x^2}|$.

41. $2\sqrt{x}$ Arccot $\sqrt{x} + \ln |1 + x|$.   **43.** $\dfrac{e^x(\sin 3x - 3 \cos 3x)}{10}$.

45. $\dfrac{e^{-2x}(-2 \sin x - \cos x)}{5}$.   **47.** $\dfrac{6e^{\frac{1}{2}x}(3 \cos \frac{1}{3}x + 2 \sin \frac{1}{3}x)}{13}$.

49. $(e^2 + 1)$; $\pi(2e^2 - 2)$.   **51.** π; $(\frac{1}{6}\pi^4 - \frac{1}{4}\pi^2)$.

Exercise 93.   Page 305

1. $\frac{1}{4}\sin^4 x$.   **3.** $\frac{1}{2}\sec^2 x$.   **5.** $-\frac{1}{3}\cos^3 x + \frac{1}{5}\cos^5 x$.   **7.** $-\frac{3}{4}\cos \frac{2}{3}x$.

9. $-\dfrac{1}{h}\cos hx + \dfrac{1}{3h}\cos^3 hx$.   **11.** $\frac{1}{2}x - \frac{1}{12}\sin 6x$.   **13.** $\sin x - \frac{1}{3}\sin^3 x$.

15. $\frac{3}{8}x - \frac{1}{4}\sin 2x + \frac{1}{32}\sin 4x$.   **17.** $-\cos x + \frac{1}{3}\sec^3 x - 2 \sec x$.

19. $\frac{1}{8}x - \frac{1}{32}\sin 4x$.   **21.** $\frac{1}{320}\sin^5 2x + \frac{3}{256}x - \frac{1}{256}\sin 4x + \frac{1}{2048}\sin 8x$.

23. $-\frac{1}{96}\sin^3 4x + \frac{1}{16}x - \frac{1}{128}\sin 8x$.   **25.** $-\frac{1}{12}\cos 6x + \frac{1}{4}\cos 2x$.

27. $\frac{1}{4}\sin 2x + \frac{1}{20}\sin 10x$.   **29.** $\frac{1}{8}\tan^4 2x$.

31. $-\frac{1}{2}\cot x$.   **33.** $-\cot \frac{1}{2}z$.

35. $\pm\frac{1}{4}\sqrt{2} \ln |\csc 2x - \cot 2x|$, where "+" applies if $\sin 2x > 0$.

37. $4\sqrt{2}$.   **39.** $4\sqrt{2}$ (radical not always $\sqrt{2} \cos \frac{1}{2}x$).

41. $\dfrac{1}{3 \sin x \cos^3 x} - \frac{8}{3}\cot 2x$.

Exercise 94.   Page 307

1. $\frac{1}{2}\tan 2x - x$.

3. $-\frac{1}{2}\cot^2 y - \ln|\sin y|$.

5. $\frac{1}{4}\tan^4 x - \frac{1}{2}\tan^2 x + \ln|\sec x|$.

7. $-\frac{1}{2}\cot^4 \frac{1}{2}x + \cot^2 \frac{1}{2}x + 2\ln|\sin \frac{1}{2}x|$.

9. $-\cot x - \frac{2}{3}\cot^3 x - \frac{1}{5}\cot^5 x$.

11. $\frac{1}{3}\tan 3x + \frac{1}{9}\tan^3 3x$.

13. $\frac{1}{3}\tan^3 t + \frac{1}{5}\tan^5 t$.

15. $-\frac{1}{8}\cot^4 2t - \frac{1}{4}\cot^2 2t$.

17. $\frac{1}{5}\sec^5 \theta - \frac{1}{3}\sec^3 \theta$.

19. $-\frac{1}{18}\cot^9 2x - \frac{1}{7}\cot^7 2x - \frac{1}{10}\cot^5 2x$.

21. $-\cot x + \tan x$.

23. $\frac{1}{8}\tan^4 2x + \frac{1}{4}\tan^2 2x$.

25. $-\cot^2 \frac{1}{2}x$.

27. $\frac{1}{5}\tan^5 x$.

29. $\sec x + \ln|\csc x - \cot x|$.

31. $-\frac{1}{6}\cot^3 2x - \frac{1}{2}\cot 2x$.

33. $\frac{2}{5}\sec^{\frac{5}{2}} x - 2\sec^{\frac{1}{2}} x$.

35. $\frac{1}{4}\sec 2x \tan 2x + \frac{1}{4}\ln|\sec 2x + \tan 2x|$.

37. $2\sin \frac{1}{2}x - \frac{2}{3}\sin^3 \frac{1}{2}x$.

39. $-\frac{1}{2}x \cot 2x - \frac{1}{6}x \cot^3 2x + \frac{1}{6}\ln|\sin 2x| - \frac{1}{24}\cot^2 2x$.

41. $\frac{1}{3}z \sec^3 z - \frac{1}{6}\sec z \tan z - \frac{1}{6}\ln|\sec z + \tan z|$.

Exercise 95.   Page 310

1. $\dfrac{x}{9\sqrt{9 - x^2}}$.

3. $\sqrt{x^2 - 9} - 3\,\text{Arctan}\,\frac{1}{3}\sqrt{x^2 - 9}$.

5. $\frac{1}{3}\ln\left|\dfrac{\sqrt{9 + 4y^2} - 3}{2y}\right|$.

7. $\ln\left|\dfrac{1 - \sqrt{1 - 9y^2}}{3y}\right|$.

9. See (31), Table VII, to check.

11. $-\frac{5}{3} + \frac{3}{4}\sqrt{6}$.

13. $\frac{1}{54}\text{Arctan}\,\dfrac{x}{3} + \dfrac{x}{18(9 + x^2)}$.

15. Special case of (50) in Table VII.

17. $\frac{4}{3}\sqrt{3} - \frac{1}{2}\pi$.

19. $\frac{1}{2}x\sqrt{a^2 + 9x^2} + \frac{1}{6}a^2 \ln (3x + \sqrt{a^2 + 9x^2})$.

21. See (27), Table VII.

23. $-\dfrac{3}{8(9 + 4x^2)} + \dfrac{5}{108}\text{Arctan}\,\dfrac{2x}{3} + \dfrac{5x}{18(9 + 4x^2)}$.

25. $\dfrac{x + 2}{9\sqrt{5 - x^2 - 4x}}$.

27. $\dfrac{\tan t}{4\sqrt{4 - \tan^2 t}}$.

29. $-a^2(a^2 - u^2)^{\frac{1}{2}} + \frac{1}{3}(a^2 - u^2)^{\frac{3}{2}}$.

31. $\frac{1}{3}\text{Arctan}\,\frac{1}{3}\sqrt{y^2 - 4y - 5}$.

33. $\frac{1}{2}(x - a)\sqrt{x^2 - 2ax} - \frac{1}{2}a^2 \ln|x - a + \sqrt{x^2 - 2ax}|$.

35. 6π.

Exercise 96.   Page 311

3. $\frac{3}{10}x^{\frac{10}{3}}$.

5. $\frac{1}{5}\ln|4 + 5v|$.

7. $-4x^{-1} + 8x^{-\frac{1}{2}} + \ln|x|$.

9. $-\frac{1}{4}\cos x$.

11. $\dfrac{10^{4z}}{4\ln 10}$.

13. $\tan (1 + x)$.

15. $\sqrt{2}$.

17. $\frac{3}{4}\pi$.

19. $\frac{1}{12}(e^{2x} + 3)^6$.

21. $\frac{2}{3}(e^8 - e^{-1})$.

23. $\frac{1}{5}x^{10} + \frac{3}{5}x^5$.

25. $\frac{1}{42}\ln\left|\dfrac{7 + 3x}{7 - 3x}\right|$.

27. $\frac{7}{120}\pi$.

29. $\frac{2}{49}\sqrt{4 + 9x^2} - \frac{3}{7}\ln|7x + \sqrt{4 + 49x^2}|$.

31. $\frac{2}{5}$.

33. $2x + \frac{3}{2}\ln (x^2 + 16) - 8\,\text{Arctan}\,\frac{1}{4}x$.

35. $\frac{1}{4}\ln|7x - 3 - 2x^2| + \frac{9}{4}\ln\left|\dfrac{2x - 1}{2x - 6}\right|$.

37. $11{,}996/135$.

39. $x \sin x + \cos x$.

41. $x\,\text{Arcsin}\,2x + \frac{1}{2}\sqrt{1 - 4x^2}$.

43. $\frac{1}{5}e^{2x}(2\sin x - \cos x)$.

45. $\frac{3}{8}x - \frac{1}{8}\sin 4x + \frac{1}{64}\sin 8x$.

47. $\frac{1}{5}\tan^5 x + \frac{1}{7}\tan^7 x$.

49. $\frac{1}{3}\tan^3 x + \frac{1}{5}\tan^5 x$.

51. $\ln|u + \sqrt{u^2 - 9}| - \dfrac{\sqrt{u^2 - 9}}{u}$.

53. $\frac{5}{24}\pi - \frac{1}{4} - \frac{1}{8}\sqrt{3}$.

55. $\dfrac{-6x - 5}{\sqrt{4x^2 + 4x + 2}}$.

57. $y = \frac{1}{8}\cos 2x + k_1 x^2 + k_2 x + k_3$.

59. $x^2(y + 3) = 36$.

Exercise 97.   Page 314

1. $3; \frac{17}{5}; 2$.   **3.** $\frac{99}{17}; \frac{61}{17}$.   **5.** $\frac{18}{13}$.   **7.** Area 10.

Exercise 98.   Page 317

1. $\eta = \frac{1}{5}\sqrt{21}$; directrices, $x = \pm\frac{50}{21}\sqrt{21}$.   **3.** $\eta = 1$; directrix, $x = 2$.
5. $\eta = \frac{13}{5}$; directrices, $y = \pm\frac{25}{13}$.   **7.** $4x^2 + 3y^2 = 108$.
9. $5x^2 + 9y^2 + 10x - 18y - 166 = 0$.   **11.** $x^2 - 8y^2 - 4x + 24y + 4 = 0$.
13. $19x^2 + 16y^2 + 4xy + 116x - 152y + 496 = 0$.   **15.** $8x^2 + 9y^2 = 288$.
17. $9x^2 + 5y^2 = 180$.   **19.** $3x^2 - y^2 = 3$.

Exercise 99.   Page 320

1. $x'^2 + 4y'^2 = 16$.   **3.** $x'^2 - y'^2 = -9$.   **5.** $y'^2 - 4x'^2 = 4$.
7. $y'^2 = 9$.   **9.** $x'^2 + 2y'^2 = 2$.

Exercise 100.   Page 324

Note. Nonessential variations in method would give an answer with x'' and y'' interchanged, and possibly with the sign of any linear term changed.

1. $4x''^2 + y''^2 = 4$.   **3.** $y''^2 = 2x''$.   **5.** $y''^2 = -2x''$.
7. $x''^2 - y''^2 + 4 = 0$.   **9.** $4x''^2 - y''^2 = 0$.

Exercise 101.   Page 326

1. $y^2 = 2x$.   **3.** $8x^2 + y^2 = 1$.   **5.** $100x^2 + 36y^2 = 225$.
7. With the points as $(\pm c, 0)$ and k as the given constant, $2x^2 + 2y^2 = k - 2c^2$.
9. $y = 2$.   **11.** $a^2my + b^2x = 0$.   **13.** $3x^2 + 2y^2 = 35$.
15. $x^2 + 2xy + y^2 = 6$; $x^2 - 2xy + y^2 = 2$.

Exercise 102.   Page 332

1. $(-\frac{3}{2}, \frac{3}{2}\sqrt{3})$.   **3.** $(0, 1)$.   **5.** $(-\frac{3}{2}\sqrt{2}, -\frac{3}{2}\sqrt{2})$.   **7.** $(\sqrt{2}, -\sqrt{2})$.
9. $[\sqrt{2}, \frac{1}{4}\pi]$.   **11.** $[2, -\frac{1}{3}\pi]$.   **13.** $[4, \frac{11}{6}\pi]$; $[4, -\frac{1}{6}\pi]$.
15. $[5, 3.79]$.   **17.** $x^2 + y^2 = 16$.   **19.** $x = 3$.
21. $x^2 + y^2 = 6y$.   **23.** $x^2 + y^2 + 2y = 0$.
25. $x^2 = 4 + 4y$.   **27.** $3x^2 + 4y^2 - 8x = 16$.   **29.** $r \cos \theta = 5$.

Exercise 103.   Page 336

17. $r = -2 \cos \hat{\theta}$.   **19.** $r \sin \hat{\theta} = -2$.
21. $r = 2(1 + \cos \hat{\theta})$; $r = 2(1 + \sin \hat{\theta})$.

Exercise 105.   Page 341

1. $x = 6 \cos^2 \theta$, $y = 3 \sin 2\theta$; slope 0.
3. $x = 2 \cos 3\theta \cos \theta$, $y = 2 \cos 3\theta \sin \theta$; slope $-\frac{1}{3}\sqrt{3}$.   **5.** Slope 0.
7. Slope $\sqrt{3}$.   **9.** Slope -3.   **15.** Arctan $2\sqrt{3}$.   **17.** $\frac{1}{2}\pi$.

Exercise 106.   Page 342

1. $\dfrac{dr}{dt} = -2 \sin \theta$; $v_x = -2 \sin 2\theta$; $v_y = 2 \cos 2\theta$; $a_x = -2 \cos 2\theta$; $a_y = -2 \sin 2\theta$.

3. $\dfrac{dr}{dt} = \frac{1}{2} \cos \theta$; $v_x = \frac{1}{2}(\cos 2\theta - \sin \theta)$; $v_y = \frac{1}{2}(\cos \theta + \sin 2\theta)$;

   $a_x = -\frac{1}{8}(2 \sin 2\theta + \cos \theta)$; $a_y = \frac{1}{8}(2 \cos 2\theta - \sin \theta)$.

5. $\frac{dr}{dt} = -\frac{1}{10}\sin\theta$; $v_x = -\frac{1}{10}(3\sin\theta + \sin 2\theta)$; $v_y = \frac{1}{10}(3\cos\theta + \cos 2\theta)$;

$a_x = -\frac{1}{100}(3\cos\theta + 2\cos 2\theta)$; $a_y = -\frac{1}{100}(3\sin\theta + 2\sin 2\theta)$.

Exercise 107.   Page 346

1. 12.   **3.** 2.1589.   **5.** $\frac{937}{12}$.   **7.** $\frac{1}{2}$.   **9.** $\frac{32}{15}\sqrt{2}$.
11. 1.555.   **13.** $\frac{3}{8}\pi a^2$.   **15.** $2\pi a^2$.   **17.** $\frac{192}{5}\sqrt{3}$.

Exercise 108.   Page 348

1. $\frac{3}{2}\pi$.   **3.** π.   **5.** $\frac{3}{2}\pi a^2$.   **7.** $\frac{3}{8}\pi$.   **9.** 2.   **11.** 6.
13. $\frac{1}{6}\pi^3 k^2$.   **15.** $2a^2/3\pi$.   **17.** $\frac{4}{3}\pi - \sqrt{3}$.   **19.** $\frac{7}{24}\pi - \frac{1}{2}\sqrt{3}$.
21. $\sqrt{3} - \frac{1}{3}\pi$.   **23.** $\frac{5}{24}\pi - \frac{1}{4}\sqrt{3}$.

Exercise 109.   Page 351

1. $\frac{1}{3}$.   **3.** Div.   **5.** Div.   **7.** $\frac{1}{8}\pi$.   **9.** 2.   **11.** .464.   **13.** Div.
15. Div.   **17.** $\frac{1}{4}\pi$.   **19.** Div.   **21.** 1.   **23.** 1.   **25.** $1/\pi$.

Exercise 110.   Page 354

1. $2\sqrt{2}$.   **3.** Div.   **5.** $3\sqrt[3]{5}$.   **7.** 2.   **9.** $\frac{1}{6}\pi$.   **11.** Div.   **13.** Div.
15. 1.09861.   **17.** $1/(1-k)$.   **19.** Div.   **21.** $\frac{2}{3}\pi$.   **23.** $a^2(\frac{1}{6}\pi + \frac{1}{8}\sqrt{3})$.
25. Div.   **27.** $\frac{2}{9}\pi$.

Exercise 111.   Page 356

1. 96.   **3.** 144π; 2304; $288\sqrt{3}$.   **5.** $3\sqrt{3}$; $\frac{3}{2}\pi$; $\frac{3}{2}\pi$.   **7.** 288.
9. $\frac{3}{2}\pi$.   **11.** $5\pi r^2$.   **13.** $\frac{125}{9}\pi$ cu. ft.   **15.** $\frac{16}{3}$; 8; does not exist.

Exercise 112.   Page 360

1. $\frac{256}{5}\pi$.   **3.** $\frac{16}{15}\pi$; $\frac{136}{15}\pi$.   **5.** $(259\frac{1}{5})\pi$.   **7.** $\frac{9}{2}\pi$; $\frac{48}{7}\pi$; $\frac{96}{35}\pi$.
9. $\frac{108}{5}\pi$ **11.** $\pi[\frac{8}{3}\pi + 8\ln(2-\sqrt{3}) + 2\sqrt{3}]$.   **13.** $\frac{32}{105}\pi a^3$.   **15.** $\frac{5}{12}\pi$.
17. $\frac{1}{5}\pi$.   **19.** $\pi(\frac{1}{2}\ln 3 - \frac{13}{24})$.

Exercise 113.   Page 363

1. 120π; 140π.   **3.** 216π; 360π.   **5.** $6\pi e^4$.   **7.** $\frac{4}{3}\pi(125 - 10\sqrt{10})$.   **9.** $2h\pi^2 a^3$.
11. $\frac{13}{5}\pi$.   **13.** (a) $\frac{256}{15}\pi\sqrt{2}$; (b) 8π.   **15.** $2\pi^2 a^3$.   **17.** $\frac{2}{3}\pi^2 a^3$.

Exercise 114.   Page 365

1. $1.984(10^5)$ ft.-lb.   **3.** $\frac{1}{9}(6,348,800)\pi$ ft.-lb.
5. $2.24(10^6)\pi$ ft.-lb.   **7.** 30,000 ft.-lb.

9. (a) $m = \frac{7}{6}\pi$, $\bar{x} = -\frac{6\ln 2}{7\pi}$; (b) $m = \pi$, no $\bar{x}$; (c) $m = 2\pi$, no $\bar{x}$.

11. $(\frac{1}{2}\pi, \frac{1}{8}\pi)$.   **13.** $(\frac{1}{2}\pi, \frac{5}{8}\pi)$.

Exercise 115.   Page 372

1. $\ln(x-4)^4 | 2x+1 |^{-\frac{3}{2}}$.   **3.** 1.28093.   **5.** -1.46274.
7. $2x + \ln | (x-2)^3(x+2)^5 |$.   **9.** $\ln | x-1 | - 2(x-1)^{-1} - (x-1)^{-2}$.
11. $\frac{7}{81}$.   **13.** $\ln | (x-1)^2(x-2)^3 | - (x-1)^{-1}$.
15. $\frac{1}{2}x^2 + 2x + 3\ln | x | - (x-3)^{-1}$.
17. $\ln(x-1)^{-2}(3x+2)^{-\frac{2}{3}} - 3(x-1)^{-1} - \frac{1}{3}(3x+2)^{-1}$.
19. $t = \frac{1}{4}\ln\frac{2(3-x)}{3(2-x)}$.

Exercise 116.   Page 375

1. $\ln | (x + 1)(x^2 + 3) | + \sqrt{3}$ Arctan $\frac{1}{3}x\sqrt{3}$.

3. $\ln (2x - 5)^2(x^2 + 2)^{-\frac{1}{2}} + \frac{3}{2}\sqrt{2}$ Arctan $\frac{1}{2}x\sqrt{2}$.

5. $\ln | (x - 2)^3(x^2 + 2x + 4)^{\frac{1}{2}} | - \frac{2}{3}\sqrt{3}$ Arctan $\frac{1}{3}\sqrt{3}(x + 1)$.

7. $\ln (2x^2 + 3)^{\frac{1}{2}}(x^2 + 5)^{\frac{3}{2}} + \frac{1}{6}\sqrt{6}$ Arctan $\frac{1}{3}x\sqrt{6}$.

9. $\frac{5}{54}$ Arctan $\frac{x}{3} + \frac{5x - 36}{18(9 + x^2)}$.
         11. $\frac{y}{18(4y^2 + 9)} + \frac{1}{108}$ Arctan $\frac{2y}{3}$.

13. $(x^2 + 2)^{-1} + \ln (2 + x^2)^{\frac{1}{2}} + \frac{1}{2}\sqrt{2}$ Arctan $\frac{1}{2}x\sqrt{2}$.

15. $3 \ln | x - 1 | + \dfrac{9x - 2}{2(x^2 + 3)} + \dfrac{3}{2}\sqrt{3}$ Arctan $\dfrac{x}{\sqrt{3}}$.
     17. $3.2189 - \frac{1}{4}\pi$.

19. $.2027$.
    21. $\frac{1}{3} \ln \left| \dfrac{x - 3}{x + 3} \right| - \frac{1}{2}\sqrt{6}$ Arctan $x\sqrt{\frac{2}{3}}$.

Exercise 117.   Page 376

1. $\frac{1}{4} \ln \left| \dfrac{2 + \tan \frac{1}{2}y}{2 - \tan \frac{1}{2}y} \right|$.
      3. $\dfrac{2}{1 - \tan \frac{1}{2}x}$.
      5. $\frac{2}{5}$ Arctan $\frac{1}{5}$.

7. $\frac{1}{6} \ln | \tan \frac{3}{2}x | - \frac{1}{12} \tan^2 \frac{3}{2}x$.
  9. $\frac{2}{3}\sqrt{3} \ln (1 + \sqrt{3})$.
  11. $\frac{1}{8}\sqrt{2} \ln \left| \dfrac{\tan x + \sqrt{2}}{\tan x - \sqrt{2}} \right|$.

13. $\frac{1}{3} \ln 2$.
    15. $- \frac{1}{2}$ Arctan $(\tan \frac{1}{2}z) + \frac{5}{6}$ Arctan $(3 \tan \frac{1}{2}z)$.
    17. $\dfrac{- 4}{5 + \tan \frac{1}{4}x}$.

Exercise 118.   Page 379

1. $2x^{\frac{1}{2}} - 6x^{\frac{1}{3}} + 24x^{\frac{1}{6}} - 48 \ln (x^{\frac{1}{6}} + 2)$.
  3. $\frac{1}{3}(9 + x^2)^{\frac{3}{2}} - 9(9 + x^2)^{\frac{1}{2}}$.

5. $\frac{2}{3}x^{\frac{3}{2}} + 8x^{\frac{1}{2}} + 4 \ln \left| \dfrac{\sqrt{x} - 1}{\sqrt{x} + 1} \right|$.
    7. $3 - 3 \ln \frac{4}{3}$.

9. $\frac{2}{9}(4 + x^3)^{\frac{3}{2}} - \frac{8}{3}(4 + x^3)^{\frac{1}{2}}$.
     11. $- \frac{1}{7}(1 + x^4)^{\frac{7}{4}}x^{-7}$.

13. $2\sqrt{2x} + 2\sqrt{x + 4} + 4\sqrt{2} \ln \left| \dfrac{\sqrt{x} - 2(\sqrt{x + 4} - 2\sqrt{2})}{x - 4} \right|$.

15. $x + \sqrt{1 + e^{2x}} - \ln (1 + \sqrt{1 + e^{2x}})$.
  17. 3 Arcsin $\frac{1}{3}(x - 1) + \sqrt{8 + 2x - x^2}$.

19. $\dfrac{4\sqrt{1 + 4x^2}}{x} - \dfrac{(1 + 4x^2)^{\frac{3}{2}}}{3x^3}$.

Exercise 119.   Page 383

1. 9.03; exactly 9, the true value, by Simpson's rule (why?).

3. 3.69; 3.68.
         5. 1.401; 1.402.

Exercise 120.   Page 384

11. $[x = 2(\cos \theta)(1 + \cos \theta), y = 2(\sin \theta)(1 + \cos \theta)]$. Slope, $\frac{1}{2}\sqrt{2}(2 - \sqrt{2})$.
    Hor. at $\theta = \frac{1}{3}\pi$, π (by a special argument), and $\frac{5}{3}\pi$.   Ver. at $\theta = 0$, $\frac{2}{3}\pi$, and $\frac{4}{3}\pi$.

13. $\frac{37}{12}$.   **15.** $4\pi - 3\sqrt{3}$.   **17.** $\frac{8}{3}$.   **19.** $2\sqrt{3}$.   **21.** Div.   **23.** $\frac{3}{40}\pi$.   **25.** Div.

27. $- 1$.   **29.** (a) $\pi(\pi - 2)$; (b) $\pi[2 + \pi - 4\sqrt{2} \ln (1 + \sqrt{2})]$.   **31.** $\frac{7}{12}\pi$.

33. $4.200(10^7)$ ft.-lb.   **35.** $\ln [(x^2 + 1)(4x^2 + 7)^{-\frac{1}{8}}] + \frac{1}{7}\sqrt{7}$ Arctan $\frac{2}{7}x\sqrt{7}$.   **37.** $\ln 2$.

39. $\frac{1}{18} \ln \dfrac{| \sqrt[3]{27 + y^3} - 3 |^2}{| (27 + y^3)^{\frac{2}{3}} + 3(27 + y^3)^{\frac{1}{3}} + 9 |} + \dfrac{1}{3\sqrt{3}}$ Arctan $\dfrac{2\sqrt[3]{27 + y^3} + 3}{3\sqrt{3}} + c$.

41. Trap., 1.4672; Simp., 1.4627.

Exercise 121.   Page 390

1. $20\sqrt{10} - 2$.　　**3.** $\frac{1}{4}[6\sqrt{37} + \ln(6 + \sqrt{37})]$.　　**5.** $2\sqrt{2} + 2\ln(1 + \sqrt{2})$.
7. $a(e - e^{-1})$.　　**9.** $6a$.　　**11.** $12\sqrt{3}$.　　**13.** $\frac{14}{3}$.　　**15.** $\frac{1}{2}[\sqrt{2} + \ln(1 + \sqrt{2})]$.
17. $\sqrt{2}(e - e^{-1})$.

Exercise 122.   Page 392

1. $2\pi a$.　　**3.** $8a$.　　**5.** $\pi a\sqrt{2}$.　　**7.** $\sqrt{1 + k^2}(e^k - 1)/k$.

9. $2a(\sqrt{7} - 2) + 2a\sqrt{3}\ln\dfrac{4 + 2\sqrt{3}}{\sqrt{3} + \sqrt{7}}$.

Exercise 123.   Page 394

1. $\frac{1}{27}\pi(145\sqrt{145} - 1)$.　　**5.** $4\pi^2 ab$.　　**7.** $4\pi a^2$.　　**9.** $19\pi/3$.　　**11.** $12\pi a^2/5$.
13. $64\pi a^2/3$.　　**15.** $4\pi[\sqrt{2} + \ln(1 + \sqrt{2})]$.
17. $\pi[32\sqrt{17} - 16 - 8\sqrt{2}\ln(4 + \sqrt{14}) + 8\sqrt{2}\ln(2 + \sqrt{2})]$.
19. $7424\pi/1215$.　　**21.** $4\pi^2 a^2$.　　**23.** $\frac{1}{3}\pi(30\sqrt{5} - 34)$.

Exercise 124.   Page 400

1. $\frac{1}{2}$; 2.　　**3.** $\frac{3}{100}\sqrt{10}$; $\frac{10}{3}\sqrt{10}$.　　**5.** 1; 1.　　**7.** $\frac{1}{4}\sqrt{2}$; $2\sqrt{2}$.　　**9.** $\frac{4}{25}\sqrt{5}$; $\frac{5}{4}\sqrt{5}$.
11. $\frac{3}{4}, \frac{4}{3}$; $\frac{2}{9}, \frac{9}{2}$.　　**13.** $\frac{1}{50}\sqrt{5}$; $10\sqrt{5}$.　　**15.** $K = \frac{4}{25}\sqrt{10}$; $R = \frac{5}{8}\sqrt{10}$.
17. $\frac{1}{9}\sqrt{3}$; $3\sqrt{3}$.　　**19.** $(\frac{1}{2}\sqrt{2}, -\frac{1}{2}\ln 2)$.

21. On $-\frac{1}{2}\pi < x < \frac{5}{2}\pi$, max. at $\frac{1}{2}\pi$ and $\frac{3}{2}\pi$.　　**23.** $\dfrac{|p|^{\frac{1}{2}}}{|p + 2x_1|^{\frac{3}{2}}}$.

25. $\dfrac{1}{|3a\sin t_1 \cos t_1|}$.　　**29.** $K = 0$; R undefined.

31. $K = \dfrac{3}{4h}$, $R = \dfrac{4h}{3}$; $K = \dfrac{3}{2h}$, $R = \dfrac{2h}{3}$.

Exercise 125.   Page 404

Note. The values of K will be omitted. Just R is given.
1. $(2, 2)$; 2.　　**3.** $(\frac{28}{3}, 12)$; $\frac{10}{3}\sqrt{10}$.　　**5.** $(1, 1)$; 1.　　**7.** $(3, -2)$; $2\sqrt{2}$.
9. $[\frac{1}{4}\pi - \frac{5}{2}, \frac{9}{4}]$; $\frac{5}{4}\sqrt{5}$.　　**11.** $(\frac{5}{3}, 0)$, $\frac{4}{3}$; $(0, -\frac{5}{2})$, $\frac{9}{2}$.　　**13.** $(10, -16)$; $10\sqrt{5}$.
15. $(-\frac{3}{4}\sqrt{2}, \frac{3}{8}\sqrt{2})$, $R = \frac{5}{8}\sqrt{10}$; $(0, -\frac{3}{2})$, $R = \frac{1}{2}$.　　**17.** $(-2\sqrt{2}, 3)$; $3\sqrt{3}$.
19. $\alpha = -4x^3$, $\beta = \frac{1}{2} + 3x^2$; $27\alpha^2 = 2(2\beta - 1)^3$.　　**21.** $8(\alpha - p)^3 = 27p\beta^2$.
23. $(3\alpha)^{\frac{2}{3}} + (2\beta)^{\frac{2}{3}} = 5^{\frac{2}{3}}$.　　**25.** $27\alpha^2 = 4(\beta - 4)^3$.
27. $(a\alpha)^{\frac{2}{3}} - (b\beta)^{\frac{2}{3}} = (a^2 + b^2)^{\frac{2}{3}}$.　　**29.** $\alpha = a(\theta + \sin\theta)$, $\beta = a(\cos\theta - 1)$, a cycloid.

Exercise 126.   Page 408

1. $\sqrt{29}$.　　**3.** 3.　　**5.** 5.　　**7.** $\sqrt{29}$.　　**9.** $3\sqrt{5}$.　　**11.** 3.　　**13.** $\sqrt{14}$.

Exercise 127.   Page 413

1. $2\mathbf{i} + 3\mathbf{j} + 4\mathbf{k}$; $\frac{2}{29}\mathbf{i}\sqrt{29} + \frac{3}{29}\mathbf{j}\sqrt{29} + \frac{4}{29}\mathbf{k}\sqrt{29}$.
3. $-2\mathbf{i} - \mathbf{j} + 2\mathbf{k}$; $-\frac{2}{3}\mathbf{i} - \frac{1}{3}\mathbf{j} + \frac{2}{3}\mathbf{k}$.　　**5.** $-3\mathbf{i} + 4\mathbf{j}$; $-\frac{3}{5}\mathbf{i} + \frac{4}{5}\mathbf{j}$.
7. $2\mathbf{i} - 5\mathbf{j}$; $\frac{1}{29}\sqrt{29}(2\mathbf{i} - 5\mathbf{j})$.　　**9.** $2\mathbf{i} + 4\mathbf{j} + 5\mathbf{k}$; $\frac{1}{15}\sqrt{5}(2\mathbf{i} + 4\mathbf{j} + 5\mathbf{k})$.
11. $-2\mathbf{i} + 2\mathbf{j} + \mathbf{k}$; $-\frac{2}{3}\mathbf{i} + \frac{2}{3}\mathbf{j} + \frac{1}{3}\mathbf{k}$.　　**13.** $2\mathbf{i} + 3\mathbf{j} - \mathbf{k}$; $\frac{1}{14}\sqrt{14}(2\mathbf{i} + 3\mathbf{j} - \mathbf{k})$.
25. $\mathbf{Z} = -\frac{7}{2}\mathbf{i} + \mathbf{j}$.　　**27.** $\frac{1}{29}\sqrt{29}(-5\mathbf{i} - 2\mathbf{j})$.

Exercise 128. Page 418

1. $U = \frac{3}{7}i - \frac{2}{7}j + \frac{6}{7}k$, cosines $(\frac{3}{7}, -\frac{2}{7}, \frac{6}{7})$; $-U = -\frac{3}{7}i + \frac{2}{7}j - \frac{6}{7}k$.

3. $U = \frac{6}{11}i - \frac{9}{11}j + \frac{2}{11}k$, cosines $(\frac{6}{11}, -\frac{9}{11}, \frac{2}{11})$; etc.

5. $U = \frac{1}{2}\sqrt{2}(-i - j)$, with $(\alpha = 135°, \beta = 135°)$; for $-U$, $(\alpha = 45°, \beta = 45°)$.

7. $U = \frac{1}{2}i\sqrt{3} + \frac{1}{2}j$, with $(\alpha = 30°, \beta = 60°)$; for $-U$, $(\alpha = 150°, \beta = 120°)$.

9. $(\frac{2}{3}, \frac{2}{3}, -\frac{1}{3})$.   11. For x-axis, $(0°, 90°, 90°)$.

13. $\cos \beta = \pm \frac{1}{2}$, and $\beta = 60°$ or $120°$.   15. Impossible data.

17. $U = \frac{1}{2}i\sqrt{3} + \frac{1}{2}j$, with $\beta = 60°$; or $U = \frac{1}{2}i\sqrt{3} - \frac{1}{2}j$, with $\beta = 120°$.

19. $U = \frac{1}{2}\sqrt{2}(-i - j)$, with $\alpha = 135°$; or $U = \frac{1}{2}\sqrt{2}(i - j)$, with $\alpha = 45°$.

21. $U = \frac{1}{2}i + \frac{1}{2}j\sqrt{3}$, with $\beta = 30°$; or $U = \frac{1}{2}i - \frac{1}{2}j\sqrt{3}$, with $\beta = 150°$.

23. $U = .6i + .8j$, with $\beta = 36.9°$; or $U = .6i - .8j$, with $\beta = 143.1°$.

25. $2/\sqrt{30}$.   27. $23/\sqrt{13}\sqrt{41}$.

Exercise 129. Page 421

1. $(\pm \frac{3}{7}, \pm \frac{2}{7}, \mp \frac{6}{7})$, where upper signs, and lower signs, apply together.

3. $(\pm \frac{6}{11}, \mp \frac{9}{11}, \mp \frac{2}{11})$.   5. $(\mp \frac{10}{15}, \pm \frac{11}{15}, \mp \frac{2}{15})$.

7. $-3 : 5 : -6$; for $\overrightarrow{P_1P_2}$, $\left(-\dfrac{3}{\sqrt{70}}, \dfrac{5}{\sqrt{70}}, -\dfrac{6}{\sqrt{70}}\right)$.

9. $3 : -2 : 4$; for $\overrightarrow{P_1P_2}$, $\left(\dfrac{3}{\sqrt{29}}, -\dfrac{2}{\sqrt{29}}, \dfrac{4}{\sqrt{29}}\right)$.

11. For $\overrightarrow{P_1P_2}$, $\left(-\dfrac{2}{\sqrt{94}}, \dfrac{3}{\sqrt{94}}, \dfrac{9}{\sqrt{94}}\right)$.   19. $\pm \frac{11}{29}$; $67.8°$ and $112.2°$.

Exercise 130. Page 427

1. $V \cdot W = 4$; $\frac{4}{3}$; $\frac{4}{3}(\frac{2}{3}i - \frac{2}{3}j - \frac{1}{3}k)$.   3. 12; $2\sqrt{2}$; $2(i + j)$.

5. 3; $\frac{3}{17}\sqrt{17}$; $\frac{3}{17}(4i - j)$.   7. -9; $-\frac{9}{10}\sqrt{10}$; $\frac{9}{10}(-3i + j)$.

11. $-\frac{5}{13}x + \frac{12}{13}y - 13 = 0$.   13. $\frac{1}{2}\sqrt{2}x + \frac{1}{2}\sqrt{2}y - \frac{5}{4}\sqrt{2} = 0$; $\frac{5}{4}(i + j)$; $(\frac{5}{4}, \frac{5}{4})$.

15. $-\frac{1}{2}x - \frac{1}{2}\sqrt{3}y - 2 = 0$; $(-i - j\sqrt{3})$; $(-1, -\sqrt{3})$.

17. $-\frac{1}{2}x + \frac{1}{2}\sqrt{3}y = 0$; $(-\frac{1}{2}i + \frac{1}{2}j\sqrt{3})$; $(-\frac{1}{2}, \frac{1}{2}\sqrt{3})$.

19. $-x - \frac{17}{4} = 0$; $-\frac{17}{4}i$; $(-\frac{17}{4}, 0)$.   21. $-\frac{73}{17}$; $-\frac{48}{17}$.   23. Dis. $= \frac{11}{10}$.

27. $x + 4y + 17 = 0$.   29. $y = 4x$.   31. $8x + 8y = 7$; $4x - 4y + 13 = 0$.

Exercise 131. Page 434

1. C is a circle. $V = 15(-i \sin 3t + j \cos 3t)$; $A = -9W$; $v = 15$; $N = N_1 = i$; $a_T = 0$; $a_N = 45$; magnitude $= 45m$.

3. Path, $27y^2 = 4x^3$; $V = (6t)i + (6t^2)j$; $A = 6i + (12t)j$; $v = 6\sqrt{2}$;

$N = -\dfrac{i}{\sqrt{2}} + \dfrac{j}{\sqrt{2}} = N_1$; $a_T = 9\sqrt{2}$; $a_N = 3\sqrt{2}$; magnitude $= 3m\sqrt{2}$.

5. Path, $27y^2 = 4x^3$; $V = (6t)i - (6t^2)j$; $A = 6i - (12t)j$; $v = 6\sqrt{2}$; $N = \dfrac{i}{\sqrt{2}} + \dfrac{j}{\sqrt{2}}$;

$N_1 = -N$; $a_T = 9\sqrt{2}$; $a_N = -3\sqrt{2}$: magnitude $= 3m\sqrt{2}$.

Exercise 132. Page 439

13. $3x - y + 4z = -3$.   15. $2z - y + 2 = 0$.

17. $4x - y = 5$.   19. $2x - 3y + z + 11 = 0$.   21. $y = -1$.

Exercise 133.   Page 443

11. $79.0°$.

17. $x - y = -1; 2y + 3z = 6; 2x + 3z = 4$.

19. $(\frac{3}{2}, 1, 0)$; no other points.

21. $(0, 4, 3); (4, 0, -3); (2, 2, 0)$.

23. $-6 : 4 : 7$; cosines $\left(\dfrac{-6}{\pm\sqrt{101}}, \dfrac{4}{\pm\sqrt{101}}, \dfrac{7}{\pm\sqrt{101}}\right)$.

25. $6 : 19 : 4$, etc.

27. $-10 : -6 : 7$, etc.

29. $-14 : 22 : 3$.

31. $-14x + 22y + 3z = 27$.

Exercise 134.   Page 446

3. $4x + 3y = 12; y = 4z - 4$.

5. $(x = 2, y = 4 + 4t, z = 2 + 3t); (x = 2$ and $3y - 4z = 4)$.

7. $(x = -1 + 2t, y = 2 - 3t, z = 3 + t); \dfrac{x+1}{2} = \dfrac{y-2}{-3} = \dfrac{z-3}{1};$

$(2y + 3x = 1$ and $y + 3z = 11)$.

9. $(x = -t, y = -1 - 2t, z = 3 + 2t); \dfrac{x}{-1} = \dfrac{y+1}{-2} = \dfrac{z-3}{2};$

$(2x - y = 1$ and $y + z = 2)$.

11. $(x = -1, y = -t, z = -3 + 3t); (x = -1$ and $3y + z = -3)$.

13. $(x = -3 + 3t, y = 1, z = -3t); (y = 1$ and $x + z = -3)$.

15. $(x = 2 + 3t, y = -1 + 2t, z = 3 + 5t)$; etc.

17. $\dfrac{x-2}{2} = \dfrac{y+1}{2} = \dfrac{z-3}{-1}$; etc.

19. $(x = 2 - 3t, y = -1 - 2t, z = 2 + 5t)$; etc.

21. $(4, 7, -1)$.

23. Point $(\frac{2}{3}, -5, -\frac{1}{2})$; dir. $8 : 18 : -15$. The point is not unique.

25. Point $(\frac{2}{5}, -\frac{3}{4}, \frac{1}{2})$; dir. $-3 : 0 : 10$.

27. Point $(\frac{1}{2}, 3, 0)$; dir. $-3 : 4 : -2$.

29. Point $(\frac{1}{2}, \frac{9}{4}, 0)$; dir. $0 : 3 : 4$.

31. $(y + 4x = 7$ and $z = 0)$.

Exercise 135.   Page 451

1. $(x - 2)^2 + (y - 5)^2 + (z - 7)^2 = 4$.

3. $(-1, 3, 0); \sqrt{15}$.

17. $25x^2 + 9y^2 + 25z^2 = 225$.

19. $x^2 + y^2 = 6z$.

21. $x^2 = 9y^2 + 9z^2$.

23. $4x^2 + 4y^2 - 9z^2 = 36$.

25. A paraboloid of revolution obtained by revolution about the y-axis.

27. Axis of revolution is x-axis.

29. Axis of revolution is y-axis.

Exercise 137.   Page 456

1. $x^2 + y^2 = 9$.

3. $x + y = 3$.

Exercise 138.   Page 462

1. $2x - y + z = -1$.

3. $-\frac{5}{3}$.

5. $\frac{8}{7}$.

7. $x - 5y + 4z = 64; 13x - 23y - 32z = 34$.

9. $3i + j + 7k; 17; 17$.

Exercise 139.   Page 468

1. $u_x = 6xy + 12x^2y; u_y = 3x^2 + 4x^3$.

3. $w_x = 3e^{3x+2y}; w_y = 2e^{3x+2y}$.

5. $w_x = (6x + 3y)(x^2 + xy)^2; w_y = 3x(x^2 + xy)^2$.

7. $f_x(x, y) = 9x(3x^2 - 2y)^{\frac{1}{2}}; f_y(x, y) = -3(3x^2 - 2y)^{\frac{1}{2}}$.

9. $f_x(x, y) = 4y\cos 4xy; f_y(x, y) = 4x\cos 4xy$.

11. $G_x(x, z) = -2ze^{-2z} + e^{-3z}; G_z(x, z) = e^{-2z} - 3xe^{-3z}$.

13. $H_x(x, y) = 8(4x - 5y)\sec^2(4x - 5y)^2; H_y(x, y) = 10(5y - 4x)\sec^2(4x - 5y)^2$.

15. $g_x(x, z) = \dfrac{2(4x + 3z)10^{2z} \ln 10 - 4(10^{2z})}{(4x + 3z)^2}$; $g_z(x, z) = \dfrac{-3(10^{2z})}{(4x + 3z)^2}$.

17. With respect to x, y, and z: $e^y x^{-1}$; $e^y \ln x + e^z y^{-1}$; $e^z \ln y$.

19. 25; 42.   **21.** -36.   **23.** 8; 4.

Exercise 140.   Page 470

1. $u_{xx} = 6xy^4$; $u_{yy} = 12x^3y^2$; $u_{xy} = 12x^2y^3$.

3. $u_{xx} = -4x^2y^2 \sin x^2y + 2y \cos x^2y$; $u_{yy} = -x^4 \sin x^2y$;
$u_{xy} = 2x \cos x^2y - 2x^3y \sin x^2y$.

5. $w_{xx} = e^x \ln y$; $w_{xy} = e^x y^{-1}$; $w_{yy} = -e^x y^{-2}$.

7. $f_{xx}(x, y) = 6x + 8y$; $f_{yy}(x, y) = -6y$; $f_{xy}(x, y) = 8x$.

9. $g_{xx}(x, y) = -\dfrac{y^2}{(x^2 - y^2)^{\frac{3}{2}}}$; $g_{xy}(x, y) = \dfrac{xy}{(x^2 - y^2)^{\frac{3}{2}}}$; $g_{yy}(x, y) = -\dfrac{x^2}{(x^2 - y^2)^{\frac{3}{2}}}$.

11. $g_{xx}(x, y, z) = -y^2z^2 \cos xyz$; $g_{zz}(x, y, z) = -y \sin xyz - xy^2z \cos xyz$; etc.

Note. We shall use F as the function symbol where no symbol is given in the problem.

13. $F_{xx}(x, y) = \dfrac{-2xy}{(x^2 + y^2)^2}$; $F_{xy}(x, y) = \dfrac{x^2 - y^2}{(x^2 + y^2)^2}$; $F_{yy}(x, y) = \dfrac{2xy}{(x^2 + y^2)^2}$.

15. $F_{yy}(x, y, z) = -4 \cos (x + 2y - 3z)$; $F_{yz}(x, y, z) = 6 \cos (x + 2y - 3z)$; etc.

17. $z_{xxy} = 4(\cos x^2y^2)(y - 2x^4y^5) - 20x^2y^3 \sin x^2y^2$; etc.   **19.** $-e^x \sin y$.

Exercise 141.   Page 472

1. $z_x = -\dfrac{x}{z}$; $z_y = -\dfrac{4y}{z}$.   **3.** $z_x = -e^{x-z}$; $z_y = -e^{y-z}$.

5. $z_x = -1$; $z_y = \frac{4}{3}$.   **7.** $z_x = -\frac{27}{41}$; $z_y = \frac{30}{41}$.

9. $z_x = -x^{-\frac{1}{3}}z^{\frac{1}{3}}$; $z_y = -y^{-\frac{1}{3}}z^{\frac{1}{3}}$.   **11.** $z_x = \dfrac{1 - xy^2}{xe^z}$; $z_y = -2xye^{-z}$.

13. $z_x = \dfrac{\cos x \cos z}{\sin x \sin z - \cos y \cos z + 1}$; $z_y = \dfrac{-\sin y \sin z}{\sin x \sin z - \cos y \cos z + 1}$.

15. $z_x = \dfrac{e^{z^2+x}(1 + x)}{2ye^{2z-y} - 2xze^{x+z^2}}$; $z_y = \dfrac{e^{2z-y}(1 - y)}{2xze^{x+z^2} - 2ye^{2z-y}}$.

17. $z_x = \dfrac{2}{3(2x + z)e^{y-3z} - 1}$; $z_y = \dfrac{(2x + z)e^{y-3z}}{3(2x + z)e^{y-3z} - 1}$.

19. $z_x = \dfrac{4 \sec^2 (2x - x^2)}{D}$; $z_y = \dfrac{2y \csc^2 (y^2 - 2z)}{D}$;
$D = 4z \sec^2 (2x - z^2) + 2 \csc^2 (y^2 - 2z)$.

21. $z_x = \dfrac{e^x - 2e^y - 2e^z}{D}$; $z_y = \dfrac{e^y(2x + 5z + 5yz) + 5ze^z}{-D}$;
$D = 2e^{2z} + (2x + 5yz + 5y)e^z + 5ye^y$.   **23.** $\frac{12}{27}$.

Exercise 142.   Page 474

1. $y' = -\frac{9}{19}$; $z' = -\frac{13}{19}$.   **3.** $y' = \dfrac{x - 6z}{4z - y}$; $z' = \dfrac{2x - 3y}{4z - y}$.

5. $y' = \dfrac{6z - 2z^2 - xy - 2x^2}{4yz + x^2}$; $z' = \dfrac{4xy + 2y^2 + 3x - xz}{4yz + x^2}$.

7. $u_x = -11$; $v_y = -1$.   **9.** $u_x = \dfrac{1}{2u - 1}$; $v_y = \dfrac{u}{2uv - v}$.

11. $u_x = -\dfrac{u + 2u^2v}{x + 4uvx}$; $v_y = -\dfrac{v + 2uv^2}{y + 4uvy}$.

13. $u_x = \cos v$; $v_y = u^{-1} \cos v$.   **15.** $\dfrac{\partial x}{\partial u} = \tfrac{1}{3}$; $\dfrac{\partial y}{\partial v} = \tfrac{11}{3}$.

17. $\dfrac{\partial x}{\partial u} = 2u$; $\dfrac{\partial y}{\partial v} = 2v$.   **19.** $\dfrac{3 \sin x - 2z \cos x}{4yz - 6}$.   **21.** $\left(\dfrac{\partial u}{\partial x}\right)_v = \dfrac{3 + 2xy}{y - 2u}$.

Exercise 143.   Page 478

1. $du = 15x^2\,dx + 6xy^3\,dx + 9x^2y^2\,dy$.   **3.** $dv = \cos x \cos y\,dx - \sin x \sin y\,dy$.

5. $du = \dfrac{(\ln y)(\ln z)}{x}\,dx + \dfrac{(\ln x)(\ln z)}{y}\,dy + \dfrac{(\ln x)(\ln y)}{z}\,dz$.

7. $(2xy^4 + 9x^2)dx + 4x^2y^3\,dy$.   **9.** $e^{4x^2+y^2}(8x\,dx + 2y\,dy)$.

11. $4(x^2 + 3y + z^2)^3(2x\,dx + 3\,dy + 2z\,dz)$.   **13.** $\dfrac{x\,dx + y\,dy + z\,dz}{\sqrt{x^2 + y^2 + z^2}}$.

15. $e^y(z^2\,dx + xz^2\,dy + 2xz\,dz)$.   **17.** $\dfrac{2(\cos 2x)(1 + \cos y)dx + \sin 2x \sin y\,dy}{(1 + \cos y)^2}$.

19. $\dfrac{2x\,dx + 2y\,dy}{3(x^2 + y^2)}$.   **21.** $\dfrac{y^{-1}\,dx - xy^{-2}\,dy}{1 + x^2y^{-2}}$.

Exercise 144.   Page 479

1. 45π cu. in.; 9%, or 45π cu. in.   **3.** 300π cu. in.; 1.8%.

5. $.434''$ and $.452''$.   **7.** $.29°$.   **9.** 1.18 lb.; 18%.

11. $dz = 3.8$; $\Delta z = 3.97$.   **13.** $.22$.   **15.** p decr. by $\tfrac{1}{4}$ lb., or by $\tfrac{1}{2}\%$.

Exercise 145.   Page 485

1. 69 sq. units.

Exercise 146.   Page 486

1. $\tfrac{27}{2}$.   **3.** $\tfrac{1}{4}e^8 - \tfrac{5}{4}e^2$.   **5.** $\tfrac{38}{3}a^3 - 5a^2$.   **7.** $-\tfrac{8}{21}$.

9. $\tfrac{7}{96}\pi$.   **11.** $-\tfrac{1}{2}\pi$.   **13.** $\tfrac{1}{4}\sqrt{3} - \tfrac{1}{12}\pi$.

Exercise 147.   Page 490

1. $\displaystyle\int_0^3 \int_{\frac{1}{3}x^2}^{\sqrt{3x}} F(x, y)dy\,dx$; $\displaystyle\int_0^3 \int_{\frac{1}{3}y^2}^{\sqrt{3y}} F(x, y)dx\,dy$.

3. $\displaystyle\int_0^{\frac{1}{4}\pi} \int_{\sin x}^{\cos x} F(x, y)dy\,dx$; $\displaystyle\int_0^{\frac{1}{2}\sqrt{2}} \int_0^{\text{Arcsin } y} F(x, y)dx\,dy + \int_{\frac{1}{2}\sqrt{2}}^1 \int_0^{\text{Arccos } y} F(x, y)dx\,dy$.

5. $\tfrac{16}{3}$.   **9.** $\tfrac{568}{3}$.   **11.** 4.   **13.** $e^3 - 1$.   **15.** $\tfrac{1}{2} - \tfrac{1}{2}e^{-1}$.

17. $\tfrac{16}{3}$.   **19.** $\tfrac{22}{33}k$.   **21.** $\tfrac{1}{25} \ln 2$.   **23.** $\tfrac{211}{5}$.   **25.** πab.

29. $\displaystyle\int_{e^{-1}}^1 \int_{-1}^{\ln y} F(x, y)dx\,dy + \int_1^e \int_{-1}^{-\ln y} F(x, y)dx\,dy$.

Exercise 148.   Page 495

1. $\tfrac{1}{2}$.   **3.** $\tfrac{27}{2}$.   **5.** $\tfrac{22}{3}$.   **7.** $\tfrac{32}{21}$.

9. 36.   **11.** $\tfrac{3}{4}\pi k^4$.   **13.** 32.   **15.** $\tfrac{16}{3}a^3$.

Exercise 149.   Page 499

1. $\displaystyle\int_{-\frac{1}{6}\pi}^{\frac{1}{6}\pi} \int_{3 \sec \theta}^{4 \cos \theta} rf(r, \theta)dr\,d\theta$.

3. $\displaystyle\int_0^{\frac{1}{6}\pi} \int_0^{2 \sec \theta} rf(r, \theta)dr\,d\theta$; $\displaystyle\int_0^2 \int_0^{\frac{1}{6}\pi} rf(r, \theta)d\theta\,dr + \int_2^{\frac{4}{3}\sqrt{3}} \int_{\text{Arccos } (2/r)}^{\frac{1}{6}\pi} rf(r, \theta)d\theta\,dr$.

7. $\tfrac{640}{3}\pi$.   **9.** $\tfrac{19}{2}$.   **11.** $(\pi + 8)$; $\tfrac{16}{3}k$.   **13.** $\tfrac{16}{15}$.   **15.** $\tfrac{1}{48}ku^3\sqrt{3}(4 + 3 \ln 3)$.

Exercise 150.   Page 501

3. $\frac{2}{3}\pi a^3(8 - 3\sqrt{3})$.   **5.** $\frac{9}{4}$.   **7.** $\frac{4}{3}\pi$.   **9.** $\frac{3}{4}\pi a^4$.   **11.** $\frac{10}{3}$.

Exercise 151.   Page 504

Note. The weight of a cubic foot of liquid is represented by w.

1. $400w$ lb.   **3.** $(179\frac{2}{3})w$ lb.   **5.** $(1866\frac{2}{3})w$ lb.   **7.** $\frac{5000}{3}w$ lb.   **9.** $56\pi w$ lb.

Exercise 153.   Page 511

13. $(\frac{1}{3}a, \frac{1}{3}b)$.   **15.** $(1, \frac{1}{8}\pi)$.   **17.** $(\frac{3}{2}, 2)$.   **19.** $(2, 1)$; $(\frac{7}{3}, \frac{2}{3})$.

21. $(-\frac{1}{7}, 0)$.   **23.** $(0, \frac{5}{2})$.   **25.** $(\frac{146}{51}, \frac{53}{51})$.   **27.** $(0, 4b/3\pi)$.

Exercise 154.   Page 514

1. (a) $I = \frac{1}{3}mh^2$, $k = \frac{1}{3}h\sqrt{3}$; (b) $I = \frac{1}{6}mh^2$, $k = \frac{1}{6}h\sqrt{6}$.

3. (a) $\frac{1}{3}m(h^2 + k^2)$; (b) $\frac{1}{3}mk^2$. Radii of gyra., $\frac{1}{3}\sqrt{3(h^2 + k^2)}$; $\frac{1}{3}k\sqrt{3}$.

5. $I_x = \frac{16}{3}\delta$; $I_y = \frac{64}{3}\delta$; $I_o = \frac{10}{3}m$; $k = \frac{1}{3}\sqrt{30}$.

7. $I_x = \frac{6}{7}\delta$; $I_y = \frac{18}{5}\delta$.   **9.** $I_x = 54$, $I_y = \frac{144}{5}$.

11. (a) $I_x = \frac{48}{5}$, $I_y = \frac{176}{5}$; (b) $I_x = \frac{32}{3}$, $I_y = 96$.

13. $I_x = \frac{1}{8}\pi ab^3\delta$, $I_y = \frac{1}{8}\pi a^3 b\delta$.   **15.** $\frac{1}{4}\pi\delta(a^3b + ab^3)$.   **17.** 36δ.

Exercise 155.   Page 516

1. $(\frac{1}{2}a, 2a/3\pi)$.   **3.** $(\frac{8}{3}, \frac{4}{3}\sqrt{3})$.   **5.** $\left(-\dfrac{3(5\pi + 16)}{2(3\pi + 8)}, 0\right)$.   **7.** $(\frac{3}{5}a, \frac{9}{40}a)$.

9. (a) $I_O = \frac{1}{2}h^2m$, $k = \frac{1}{2}h\sqrt{2}$; (b) $I_O = \frac{3}{5}h^2m$, $k = \frac{1}{5}h\sqrt{15}$.

11. $\frac{1}{3}(3\pi + 8)\delta$; $I_O = \frac{1}{2}m\pi$; $k = \frac{1}{2}\sqrt{2\pi}$.

Exercise 156.   Page 518

1. $(0, \frac{1}{4}\pi a)$.   **3.** $(\pi a, \frac{3}{2}a)$.   **5.** $(-\frac{4}{5}a, 0)$.

Exercise 157.   Page 520

1. $\frac{8}{3}$.   **3.** 36.   **5.** 9.   **7.** $3888/35$.   **9.** Area $= \frac{1}{4}\pi - 2$; mass $= 4$.

11. 96π.   **13.** $(1, 0)$.   **15.** $I_x = \frac{5}{2}\pi\delta$; $I_y = \frac{125}{8}\pi\delta$.

17. $\left(\dfrac{9}{4\pi - 3\sqrt{3}}, \dfrac{8\pi - 9\sqrt{3}}{4\pi - 3\sqrt{3}}\right)$.   **19.** $I_x = \frac{1}{10}a^2m$; $k = \frac{1}{10}a\sqrt{10}$.   **21.** $\frac{128}{3}(3\pi - 1)\delta$.

Exercise 158.   Page 528

1. 6.   **3.** $V = \frac{5}{6}$, $m = \frac{3}{5}$.   **5.** $\displaystyle\int_{-3}^{3}\int_{-\sqrt{9-x^2}}^{\sqrt{9-x^2}}\int_{-\sqrt{25-x^2-y^2}}^{\sqrt{25-x^2-y^2}} F(x, y, z)\,dz\,dy\,dx$.

7. $\displaystyle\int_{-2}^{2}\int_{-\sqrt{4-x^2}}^{\sqrt{4-x^2}}\int_{\sqrt{x^2+y^2}}^{6-x^2-y^2} F(x, y, z)\,dz\,dy\,dx$; etc.   **9.** $V = 6$; $m = 21$.   **11.** $512/35$.

13. $16/15$.   **15.** $5\pi/3$.

Exercise 159.   Page 531

1. 800π.   **3.** $\frac{1}{3}\pi a^3(10\sqrt{5} - 19)$.   **5.** $\frac{3}{4}\pi a^4$, $m = \frac{14}{15}\pi a^5$.

7. 8π.   **9.** $16,384/75$.   **11.** $V = 4\pi - \frac{32}{9}$, $m = 12\pi - \frac{64}{5}$.

Exercise 160.   Page 534

1. $(\frac{4}{3}, 2, \frac{5}{2})$; $I_x = 1155$.   **3.** $\frac{1}{3}\pi^2 a^6$.   **5.** $(0, 0, \frac{3}{8}a)$; $I_z = 64a^5\delta/45$.

7. $(0, \frac{8}{3}, 0)$; $I_y = 512\pi\delta/3$.   **9.** $\frac{1}{3}m(h^2 + k^2)$; $\frac{1}{2}mh^2$.

11. $V = \pi\int_a^b y^2\,dz$; $\bar{z} = \left[\pi\int_a^b y^2 z\,dz\right]/V$; $I_z = \frac{1}{2}\pi\delta\int_a^b y^4\,dz$.

13. $\frac{1}{160}\pi h^5\delta$.   **15.** $2^7\pi\delta/315$.

Exercise 161. Page 538

1. $m = \frac{8}{15}a^5$.   **3.** $\frac{1}{3}\pi a^2 h$, where $h = a \cot \alpha$.   **5.** $(\frac{3}{8}a, \frac{3}{8}a, \frac{3}{8}a)$.
7. $m = \frac{1}{8}\pi a^4$; $\bar{z} = \frac{4}{15}a(2\sqrt{2} - 1)$.   **9.** $\bar{y} = 3$.
11. $\bar{z} = \frac{15}{7}a$; $I_z = \frac{248}{15}\pi a^5 = \frac{62}{35}a^2 m$.   **13.** $\bar{z} = \frac{23}{21}$.

Exercise 162. Page 539

1. $\displaystyle\int_0^{\sqrt{2}} \int_0^{\frac{1}{2}\sqrt{4-2y^2}} \int_{2+x^2+2y^2}^{6-3x^2} F(x, y, z)\,dz\,dx\,dy$.

3. 2π.   **5.** $V = \pi/8$; $m = 3\pi/32$.   **7.** $(0, 0, \frac{23}{8})$.
9. $\bar{z} = 315a/372$.   **11.** $V = 64\pi/3$; $\bar{z} = \frac{9}{4}$.   **13.** $\bar{z} = \frac{9}{4}$.

Exercise 163. Page 543

1. $-\frac{3}{5}$.   **3.** $-\infty$.   **5.** $+\infty$.   **7.** $+\infty$.   **9.** $\frac{1}{2}$.
11. No limit.   **13.** Converges to 1.   **15.** Converges to 0.

Exercise 166. Page 552

Note. Hereafter in this chapter, C and D abbreviate converges and diverges, respectively.

19. *C.*   **21.** *D.*   **23.** *D.*   **25.** *D.*   **27.** *C.*   **29.** *C.*   **31.** *D.*   **33.** *D.*

Exercise 167. Page 556

1. *C.*   **3.** *C.*   **5.** *D.*   **7.** *D.*   **9.** *C.*   **11.** *D.*   **13.** *C.*
15. $S_4 = -.49190$; $|\text{error}| < \frac{1}{3}$.

Exercise 168. Page 559

1. *C.*   **3.** *D.*   **5.** *C.*   **7.** *C.*   **9.** *D.*   **11.** *C* absolutely.   **13.** *C* conditionally.
15. *C* absolutely.   **17.** *C* absolutely.   **19.** *D.*   **21.** *C* conditionally.   **23.** *D.*

Exercise 169. Page 561

Note. The series diverges except where otherwise specified.

1. *C* absolutely, $|x| < 1$; *C* conditionally, $x = -1$.   **3.** *C* absolutely, $|x| < 1$.
5. *C* absolutely, $|x| < 4$; *C* conditionally, $x = 4$.   **7.** *C* absolutely, $|x| \leq 3$.
9. *C* absolutely, all values of x.
11. *C* absolutely, $|x| < 1$; *C* conditionally, $x = \pm 1$.   **13.** *C* absolutely, $|x| < \frac{1}{3}$.
15. *C* absolutely, $1 < x < 7$; *C* conditionally, $x = 7$.
17. *C* absolutely, $-4 < x < 2$.
19. *C* absolutely, $|x| > 2$; *C* conditionally, $x = 2$.
21. *C* absolutely, $|x| < 2$; *C* conditionally, $x = 2$.

Exercise 170. Page 564

1. *C.*   **3.** *D.*   **5.** *D* if $p < 1$; *C* if $p > 1$.
7. *D.*   **9.** *D.*   **11.** *C* if $p > 1$; *D* if $p \leq 1$.

Exercise 171. Page 564

1. *D.*   **3.** *D.*   **5.** *D.*   **7.** *D.*   **9.** *C* conditionally.
11. *C* absolutely.   **13.** *D.*   **15.** *C.*   **17.** *C* absolutely, all values of x.
19. *C* absolutely, $|x| \leq \frac{1}{2}$.   **21.** *C* absolutely, all values of x.
23. *C.*   **25.** *D.*   **27.** *C* absolutely, $|x| \leq 1$.

Exercise 172.   Page 568

Note. Recall that we have defined $0! = 1$.

1. $\sum_{n=0}^{\infty} \dfrac{(-1)^n x^{2n}}{(2n)!}$.
     3. $\sum_{n=0}^{\infty} \dfrac{x^n}{n!}$.
     5. $\sum_{n=0}^{\infty} (-1)^n \dfrac{2^n}{n!} x^n$.

7. $5 - x + 2x^2 + 3x^4$; $63 - 105(x + 2) + 74(x + 2)^2 - 24(x + 2)^3 + 3(x + 2)^4$.

9. $\sum_{n=0}^{\infty} \dfrac{(\ln a)^n}{n!} x^n$.
     11. $\sum_{n=1}^{\infty} -\dfrac{x^n}{n}$.
     13. $x + \frac{1}{6}x^3 + \frac{3}{40}x^5$.

15. $e^{\frac{1}{2}\pi}[1 + (x - \frac{1}{2}\pi) - \frac{1}{3}(x - \frac{1}{2}\pi)^3]$.
     17. $\frac{1}{2} + \frac{1}{2}\sqrt{3}x - \frac{1}{4}x^2$.
     19. $x - \frac{1}{3}x^3 + \frac{1}{5}x^5$.

21. $x + \frac{1}{3}x^3 + \frac{2}{15}x^5$.
     23. $\sum_{k=0}^{\infty} (-1)^k \dfrac{x^{2k}}{(2k)! 2^{2k}}$.
     25. $\sum_{n=1}^{\infty} (-1)^{n+1} \dfrac{2^n x^n}{n}$.

27. $3x + 9x^3 + \frac{162}{5}x^5$.
     29. $\sum_{n=0}^{\infty} x^{2n}$.
     31. $1 - \frac{1}{3}x - \frac{1}{9}x^2 - \frac{5}{81}x^3$.

33. $1 - 3x + 6x^2 - 10x^3$.
     35. $.2955$.
     37. $.0698$.

39. $.5299$.
     41. $.1974$.
     43. 5.0658.

Exercise 173.   Page 573

1. $1 + x + x^2$; $|\,\text{error}\,| < .5$.
     3. $x - \frac{1}{2}x^2 + \frac{1}{3}x^3 - \frac{1}{4}x^4$; $|\,\text{error}\,| < .0002$.

5. $1 - \frac{1}{2}x^2$; $|\,\text{error}\,| < .0003$.
     7. $\ln 2 + \frac{1}{2}(x - 2) - \frac{1}{8}(x - 2)^2$; $|\,\text{error}\,| < .01$.

9. $1 + \frac{1}{2}x - \frac{1}{8}x^2$; $|\,\text{error}\,| < .04$.

11. $f(a + h) = f(a) + hf'(a) + \dfrac{1}{2!} h^2 f''(a) + \cdots$; $R_n(x) = \dfrac{h^n f^{(n)}(a + \theta_n h)}{n!}$.

Exercise 175.   Page 578

1. $\sum_{n=1}^{\infty} \dfrac{x^{2n-1}}{(2n-1)!}$.
     3. $\sum_{k=1}^{\infty} (-1)^{k+1} \dfrac{2^{2k-1} x^{2k}}{(2k)!}$.

5. $-\frac{1}{2}x^2 - \frac{1}{12}x^4 - \frac{1}{45}x^6$.
     7. $x + \frac{1}{6}x^3 + \frac{3}{40}x^5$.
     9. $x + \frac{5}{6}x^3 - \frac{19}{120}x^5$.

11. $1 - \frac{1}{2}x - \frac{1}{8}x^2$.
     13. $\frac{1}{2}x + \frac{1}{24}x^3 + \frac{1}{240}x^5$.
     15. 1.
     17. $\frac{1}{3}$.

19. -1.
     21. $.380$.
     23. $.117$.
     25. $.259$.

Exercise 176.   Page 581

1. $\sum_{n=1}^{\infty} \dfrac{(-1)^{n+1} 2^{2n-1} x^{2n-1}}{(2n-1)!}$.

3. $1 + 10(x - 1) + 40(x - 1)^2 + 80(x - 1)^3 + 80(x - 1)^4 + 32(x - 1)^5$;
     $243 + 810(x - 2) + 1080(x - 2)^2 + 720(x - 2)^3 + 240(x - 2)^4 + 32(x - 2)^5$.

5. $\ln a + \sum_{n=1}^{\infty} \dfrac{(-1)^{n-1}}{na^n} (x - a)^n$.
     7. $e[1 - \frac{1}{2}(x - \frac{1}{2}\pi)^2 + \frac{1}{6}(x - \frac{1}{2}\pi)^4]$.

9. $\frac{1}{2} - \frac{1}{2}x\sqrt{3} - \frac{1}{4}x^2$.
     11. $\sum_{n=0}^{\infty} \dfrac{(-1)^n 3^n x^n}{n!}$.
     13. $\sum_{n=1}^{\infty} -\dfrac{4^n x^n}{n}$.

15. $.0998$.
     17. $.454$.
     23. $\sum_{n=1}^{\infty} -\dfrac{x^n}{n}$.
     25. $-.0215$.

Exercise 177.   Page 587

1. $(2x + 3y)(9t^2 + 1) + (3x + 10y)(2 - 2t)$.
     3. $e^t - 6yt^{-1} - 17tz$.

5. $e^z(\cos y)(1 + t^2)^{-1} - e^z(\sin y)(\ln t + 1)$.

7. $\dfrac{2yz \cos 2t - 2xz \sin 2t + xy(\sec t)\tan t}{\sqrt{1 - x^2 y^2 z^2}}$.

9. $3x^2 + y + (x - 3y^2)(e^z \ln x + e^z x^{-1} + 1)$.

11. $2x \cos x^2 + \cos y^2 - 4xy(\sin y^2) \cos 2x$.

13. $2x - z - 3(y - x)e^{-3z} - z \sin x$.

15. $\dfrac{(z - e^z)(1 + 3e^y \cos x) - (x + e^y)(x^{-1} - e^z)}{(z - e^z)^2}.$

17. $(2x - y)\cos t + (3y^2 - x)t^2;\ s(y - 2x)\sin t + 2st(3y^2 - x).$

19. $(\cos xy)\left[\dfrac{y}{2(u + v)} + \dfrac{vx}{\sqrt{1 - u^2 v^2}}\right].$

21. $\dfrac{\partial u}{\partial r} = 2x \sin \phi \cos \theta + 2y \sin \phi \sin \theta + 2z \cos \phi;$

$\dfrac{\partial u}{\partial \theta} = -2rx \sin \phi \sin \theta + 2ry \sin \phi \cos \theta;$ etc.

23. $\dfrac{(e^t + t^{-1})\cos x}{1 + \cos y} + \dfrac{10t \sin x \sin y}{(1 + \cos y)^2}.$ **27.** $\left(\dfrac{\partial w}{\partial y}\right)_z = w_y + w_r \dfrac{\partial r}{\partial y} + w_t \dfrac{\partial t}{\partial y},$ etc.

Exercise 178.   Page 591

15. Degree 3.   **17.** Degree 0.   **19.** Degree 2.   **21.** $\dfrac{du}{dt} = gf_x + hf_y + kf_z.$

Exercise 179.   Page 593

1. $(3x^2y + 5x^4y^2)(3t^3\,ds + 9st^2\,dt) + (x^3 + 2x^5y)[\cos(s + 3t)](ds + 3\,dt).$

3. $\dfrac{(\cos st)(t\,ds + s\,dt) + 3e^t(s^2\,dt + 2s\,ds)}{\sqrt{1 - (x + 3y)^2}}.$ **5.** $-\dfrac{6x\,dx + 2z\,dy + z^2\,dx}{2y + 2xz}.$

7. $(\cos^2 z)(y\,dx - x\,dy)/y^2.$ **9.** $\pm \tfrac{29}{130}.$ **11.** $\dfrac{.2e^2 - 1.4}{e - 2e^2}.$

13. $dx = \dfrac{(3y^3 - 6ty + 6t^3 + 2tx^3)dt}{-6t^2x^2 + 6xy};$ $dy = \dfrac{(3tx^2y^2 - 6t^2x^2 + 6t^2x + 2x^4)dt}{-6t^2x^2y + 6xy^2}.$

Exercise 180.   Page 597

1. $y = \pm r,$ or $y^2 = r^2.$ **3.** $x = 0$ and $y = 0,$ or $xy = 0.$ **5.** No envelope.
7. $x^2 = y^2.$ **9.** $3y^2 - 4xy = 0.$ **11.** $27x^2 = 4y^3.$ **13.** $y^2 = 8x - 16.$
15. $y = x^3.$ **17.** $b^2x^2 - a^2y^2 = a^2b^2.$ **19.** $27x^2 = 8(y + 2)^3.$ **21.** $x^{\frac{2}{3}} + y^{\frac{2}{3}} = k^{\frac{2}{3}}.$

Exercise 181.   Page 601

1. $4\sqrt{29}.$ **3.** $\sqrt{146} + \tfrac{1}{2}\sqrt{38} + \tfrac{1}{6}\ln(12 + \sqrt{146}) - \tfrac{1}{6}\ln(\sqrt{38} - 6).$
5. $3\sqrt{13}.$ **7.** $2\sqrt{6} + 2\ln(4 + 2\sqrt{6}) - \ln 8.$

9. $\dfrac{x - 12}{28} = \dfrac{y - 2}{3} = \dfrac{z - 28}{60};\ 28(x - 12) + 3(y - 2) + 60(z - 28) = 0;$
$(28/\sqrt{4393},$ etc.$).$

11. $\dfrac{x}{3} = \dfrac{y - 1}{2} = \dfrac{z - 2}{-2};\ 3x + 2(y - 1) - 2(z - 2) = 0;\ (3/\sqrt{17},\ 2\sqrt{17},\ -2\sqrt{17}).$

13. $\dfrac{x + 1}{2} = \dfrac{y - 7}{3} = \dfrac{z - 2}{7};\ 2(x + 1) + 3(y - 7) + 7(z - 2) = 0;$
$(\tfrac{1}{31}\sqrt{62},\ \tfrac{3}{62}\sqrt{62},\ \tfrac{7}{62}\sqrt{62}).$

Exercise 182.   Page 602

1. $v = 7;\ \tfrac{3}{7} : \tfrac{6}{7} : -\tfrac{2}{7}.$ **3.** $v = \sqrt{22};\ \tfrac{3}{22}\sqrt{22} : \tfrac{1}{11}\sqrt{22} : -\tfrac{3}{22}\sqrt{22}.$
5. $v = \sqrt{1009};\ \tfrac{18}{1009}\sqrt{1009} : \tfrac{3}{1009}\sqrt{1009} : -\tfrac{26}{1009}\sqrt{1009}.$
7. $v = 2\sqrt{4\pi^2 + 5};\ \dfrac{2\pi}{\sqrt{4\pi^2 + 5}} : \dfrac{1}{\sqrt{4\pi^2 + 5}} : \dfrac{2}{\sqrt{4\pi^2 + 5}}.$ **9.** $6, 0, -18.$

Exercise 183. Page 606

1. $\dfrac{x-2}{2}=\dfrac{y+6}{-6}=\dfrac{z-9}{9}$; $2(x-2)-6(y+6)+9(z-9)=0$.

3. $\dfrac{x-2}{1}=\dfrac{y+2}{3}=\dfrac{z-3}{6}$; $x-2+3(y+2)+6(z-3)=0$.

5. $\dfrac{x-2}{16}=\dfrac{y+3}{6}=\dfrac{z-7}{-1}$; $16(x-2)+6(y+3)-(z-7)=0$.

7. $\dfrac{x-2}{8}=\dfrac{z+3}{-13}$ and $y=-1$; $8(x-2)-13(z+3)=0$.

9. $\dfrac{x-2}{-9}=\dfrac{y-3}{6}=\dfrac{z-\frac{3}{2}}{8}$; $-9(x-2)+6(y-3)+8(z-\tfrac{3}{2})=0$.

11. $\tfrac{1}{10}\sqrt{10}:\tfrac{3}{10}\sqrt{10}$; normal, $\dfrac{x-2}{1}=\dfrac{y+1}{3}$; tangent, $(x-2)+3(y+1)=0$.

13. $\tfrac{1}{2}\sqrt{2}:\tfrac{1}{2}\sqrt{2}$. Normal, $\dfrac{x-\frac{1}{4}\pi}{1}=\dfrac{y-\frac{3}{4}\pi}{1}$; tangent, $x-\tfrac{1}{4}\pi=\tfrac{3}{4}\pi-y$.

15. Tangent.   **17.** $\dfrac{x-3}{2}=\dfrac{y+1}{3}$ and $z=2$; $2(x-3)+3(y+1)=0$.

19. $z+z_1=xx_1+4yy_1$.   **21.** $a(z+z_1)=\dfrac{xx_1}{a^2}-\dfrac{yy_1}{b^2}$.

Exercise 184. Page 610

1. $2\sqrt{22}$.   **3.** $2a^2(\pi-2)$.   **5.** $4\pi a^2$.   **7.** $13\pi/3$.

9. $8a^2$.   **11.** $4a^2$.   **13.** $224\pi/9$.   **15.** $2\pi ah$.

Exercise 185. Page 612

1. $\dfrac{9t^2+10e^{-2t}+3\sec t\tan t}{x-5y+3z}$.   **3.** $2x-4y^3-12xy^2(1+\ln x-e^z)$.

5. $\dfrac{2t^2s^{-1}+e^t}{\sqrt{1-(2x+y)^2}}$; $\dfrac{4t\ln s+se^t}{\sqrt{1-(2x+y)^2}}$.

7. $\dfrac{(e^t+\sec^2 t)\cos x}{1+\cos y}+\dfrac{10t\sin x\sin y}{(1+\cos y)^2}$.

9. $27x^2=4y^3$.   **11.** $y^2+4y=2x$.   **13.** $4\sqrt{3}$.

15. $\dfrac{x}{\frac{1}{8}\pi+2}=\dfrac{y-\frac{1}{8}\pi}{4}=\dfrac{z-1}{-1}$; $(\tfrac{1}{8}\pi+2)x+4(y-\tfrac{1}{8}\pi)-(z-1)=0$.

19. $16\pi a^2(2-\sqrt{2})$.

Exercise 186. Page 616

1. $\tfrac{4}{5}:\tfrac{3}{5}$; $0:1$; $\tfrac{5}{13}:-\tfrac{12}{13}$.   **3.** $\tfrac{3}{10}\sqrt{10}:\tfrac{1}{10}\sqrt{10}$.

5. $\tfrac{2}{21}\sqrt{21}:-\tfrac{4}{21}\sqrt{21}:-\tfrac{1}{21}\sqrt{21}$; $x^2+4y^2-z=5$.

Exercise 187. Page 621

1. $(3+4\sqrt{3})$; $(3-4\sqrt{3})$; $-7\sqrt{2}$; 8; -8; $\tfrac{112}{13}$; ± 10.

Max., 10, with $(\cos\alpha=\tfrac{4}{5},\ \cos\beta=\tfrac{3}{5})$;

min., -10, with $(\cos\alpha=-\tfrac{4}{5},\ \cos\beta=-\tfrac{3}{5})$.

3. $\pm\tfrac{46}{5}$; $-6\sqrt{2}$; $(5\sqrt{3}+1)$; $(-1-5\sqrt{3})$; $\tfrac{110}{13}$; max. $2\sqrt{26}$, direction $-\dfrac{1}{\sqrt{26}}:\dfrac{5}{\sqrt{26}}$; min. $-2\sqrt{26}$ in opposite direction.

5. $-16\mathbf{i} + 6\mathbf{j}$; $(\cos \alpha = -\frac{8}{73}\sqrt{73}, \cos \beta = \frac{3}{73}\sqrt{73})$.

7. $\pm\frac{44}{9}$; $\frac{44}{9}$; $2\sqrt{14}$; $(6\mathbf{i} - 2\mathbf{j} + 4\mathbf{k})$.

9. $-\frac{20}{11}$; $(-6\mathbf{i} + 12\mathbf{j} - 8\mathbf{k})$.   **11.** $\frac{8}{5}$.

Exercise 188.   Page 624

1. $1 - (x - \frac{1}{2}\pi) - \frac{1}{2}\pi(y - 1) - \frac{1}{2}(x - \frac{1}{2}\pi)^2 - (x - \frac{1}{2}\pi)(y - 1)$;
$1 + x - \frac{1}{6}x^3 - \frac{1}{2}x^2y^2$.

3. $y + xy + \frac{1}{2}x^2y - \frac{1}{6}y^3$.

5. $-7 - 4(x - 2) + 20(y + 1) + 6(x - 2)^2 + 36(x - 2)(y + 1) + 6(y + 1)^2$
$+ 5(x - 2)^3 + 18(x - 2)^2(y + 1) - 4(y + 1)^3$
$+ (x - 2)^4 + 3(x - 2)^3(y + 1) + (y + 1)^4$.

Exercise 189.   Page 631

1. Max. $(3, \frac{3}{2})$.   **3.** Min. $(2, 2)$.   **5.** Min. $(-1, 1)$.

7. None at $(1, -1)$.   **9.** Min. $(-1, -2)$.   **11.** Base $20' \times 20'$; height $10'$.

13. 7; nearest point, $(1, 3, -2)$.   **15.** $10\sqrt{2}$.

Exercise 190.   Page 635

1. $\coth x = \dfrac{e^x + e^{-x}}{e^x - e^{-x}}$; $\operatorname{sech} x = \dfrac{2}{e^x + e^{-x}}$; $\operatorname{csch} x = \dfrac{2}{e^x - e^{-x}}$.

7. 1.3234.   **9.** 2.563.   **15.** $3 \cosh 3x$.   **17.** $4 \operatorname{sech}^2 4x$.

19. $\frac{1}{3} \operatorname{sech}^2 \frac{1}{3}x$.   **21.** 1.   **23.** 1.   **25.** $\frac{1}{2} \sinh 2x$.

27. $\frac{1}{3}x \sinh 3x - \frac{1}{9} \cosh 3x$.   **29.** $\frac{1}{4} \sin 2x + \frac{1}{2}x$.   **31.** $\frac{1}{3} \sinh^3 x + \frac{1}{5} \sinh^5 x$.

33. $\dfrac{d \operatorname{sech} x}{dx} = - \operatorname{sech} x \tanh x$; $\dfrac{d \operatorname{csch} x}{dx} = - \operatorname{csch} x \coth x$.

Exercise 191.   Page 641

1. $\sinh^{-1} \frac{1}{2}x$.   **3.** $\sinh^{-1} \frac{1}{4}z$.   **5.** $\frac{1}{3} \sinh^{-1} \frac{3}{5}t$.

7. $\frac{1}{3} \cosh^{-1} \frac{3}{11}t$ if $t > \frac{11}{3}$; $- \frac{1}{3} \cosh^{-1} \frac{3}{11}|t|$ if $t < -\frac{11}{3}$.   **9.** $\frac{1}{6} \sinh^{-1} 6y$.

11. $\sinh^{-1} (\frac{1}{3} \tan t)$.   **13.** $\frac{1}{2} \sinh^{-1} (\frac{1}{4} \sin 2x)$.

15. $\cosh^{-1} \frac{5}{2} - \cosh^{-1} \frac{5}{4}$. Obtain the decimal value by use of Table V and compare with the result in Exercise 87. Table V is too brief to give extended accuracy.

17. $\cosh^{-1} 2 - \cosh^{-1} \frac{5}{3}$.   **19.** $\cosh^{-1} \frac{5}{3} - \cosh^{-1} \frac{4}{3}$.

25. $\frac{1}{3} \tanh^{-1} \frac{1}{3}t$, if $t^2 < 9$.   **27.** $\frac{1}{15} \tanh^{-1} \frac{3}{5}x$.   **29.** $\frac{1}{6}(\coth^{-1} 4 - \coth^{-1} 2)$

31. $- \frac{1}{15} \tanh^{-1} \frac{3}{5}$.   **33.** $\dfrac{1}{4\sqrt{7}} \tanh^{-1} \dfrac{2y^2}{\sqrt{7}}$, if $2y^2 < \sqrt{7}$.

35. $\frac{1}{9} \tanh^{-1} \frac{2}{3}y^{\frac{3}{2}}$, if $2y^{\frac{3}{2}} < 3$.   **37.** $- \frac{1}{20} \coth^{-1} \frac{2}{5}(2x + 3)$, if $4(2x + 3)^2 > 25$.

Exercise 192.   Page 644

3. $u = 2e^x - \frac{1}{4} \sin 2x + c_1 x + c_2$.   **5.** $(1 + 2x)(1 + 2y) = c$.

7. Arcsin $y -$ Arcsin $\frac{1}{2}x\sqrt{2} = -\frac{1}{12}\pi$.

9. $xy = c$, where $c \neq 0$; $xy = -6$; $xy = 8$.   **11.** $s = 6e^{-3(t+3)}$.

13. $2x - 5 = 4yy'$.   **15.** $s'' = -9s$.   **17.** $y' = \frac{3}{32}$.   **19.** $he^{-.34658t}$; 4.642 yr.

Exercise 193.   Page 646

1. $x^2 = ky$.   **3.** $xy + 2x^2 = c$.   **5.** $(t - s)^5(s + t)^3 = c$.   **7.** $x = ce^{-x/(x+y)}$.

9. $y^2 + 2xy + 4x^2 = c$.   **11.** $6x^2 + 10xy + 3y^2 = c$.

13. $(y - x)^7(x + y) = c$.   **15.** $x^2 - xy + 2y^2 = 11$.

Exercise 194.   Page 650

1. $3x^3 + 4x^2y^2 + xy + 2y^2 = c.$ **3.** $3x^2 + 4xy - 5y^2 = c.$ **5.** $e^{2x+3y} + xy = c.$
7. Not exact.   **9.** $ye^{3x} = c.$ **11.** $e^{2y} \ln x = c.$ **13.** $3x^2 + 6xy - y^2 = 8.$
15. $x^2 + y^2 = ke^{\frac{1}{4}x^4 + \frac{1}{3}y^3}.$ **17.** $y = cx.$ **19.** $2ye^x = e^{2x} + c.$

Exercise 195.   Page 652

Note. For simplicity in the remaining answers, if a function enters in the argument of a logarithm, we shall assume that the function is positive-valued, and omit inserting absolute value bars.

1. $5xy = x^5 + c.$ **3.** $y \sin x = \sin^2 x + c.$ **5.** $3s = -5 + ce^{3t}.$
7. $xy = e^x + c.$ **9.** $x = \sin y + c \cos y.$ **11.** $ve^{u^2} = e^{u^2} + c.$
13. $ye^x = e^x \sin x + c.$ **15.** $6u(v + 2)^3 = (v + 2)^6 + c.$
17. $4y = x^2 \sin 2x - 2x^3 \cos 2x + cx^2.$ **19.** $5x \sin 2y = e^y (\sin 2y - 2 \cos 2y) + c.$
21. $2x^3y = x^2 \operatorname{Arctan} x - x + \operatorname{Arctan} x + c.$
23. $2xy = 2x(2x + 1) - (2x + 1) \ln (2x + 1) + (\ln 5 - \frac{8}{5})(2x + 1).$

Exercise 196.   Page 654

1. $y = c_1e^{-x} + \frac{3}{2}e^x + c_2.$ **3.** $x = c_2e^{y/c_1} - 1.$
5. $y = \frac{1}{16}x^4 + c_1 \ln x + c_2.$ **7.** $c_1y^2 = (c_1x + c_2)^2 - 4.$
9. $u = c \sin (2v + \alpha).$ **11.** $y = -\frac{1}{6}x^3 - \frac{1}{4} \sin 2x + c_1x + c_2.$
13. $y = 3e^{-x} + xe^{-x} + c_1x + c_2.$ **15.** $s^{-1} = \frac{5}{2} - t.$

Exercise 197.   Page 655

1. $yy' = 2; y = ce^{-\frac{1}{2}x}.$ **3.** $x \, dx + y \, dy = 0; y = cx.$
5. $4x + yy' = 0; y^4 = cx.$ **7.** $yy' = x; xy = k.$
9. $y' = y; y^2 = c - 2x.$

Exercise 198.   Page 658

1. $2xe^{2x} + e^{2x}; 4e^{2x} + 4xe^{2x}; 12e^{2x} + 8xe^{2x}.$ **3.** $D^k e^{mx} = m^k e^{mx}.$
5. $\cos x - 3 \sin x.$ **7.** $-12 \sin 3x.$
9. $-3e^{-2x}.$ **11.** $8 \sin 2x - 4 \cos 2x.$

Exercise 199.   Page 659

1. $y = c_1e^x + c_2e^{-2x}.$ **3.** $u = c_1e^{-2v} + c_2e^{\frac{1}{3}v}.$ **5.** $y = c_1xe^{5x} + c_2e^{5x}.$
7. $y = c_1e^{3t} + c_2e^{-3t}.$ **9.** $u = c_1e^{\frac{3}{2}v} + c_2e^{-\frac{3}{2}v}.$ **11.** $y = c_1 + c_2e^{3x}.$
13. $y = c_1e^{-\frac{1}{2}x} + c_2e^{-\frac{2}{3}x}.$ **15.** $y = c_1xe^{\frac{1}{2}x} + c_2e^{\frac{1}{2}x}.$ **17.** $y = c_1e^{\frac{2}{7}x} + c_2e^{-\frac{2}{7}x}.$
19. $y = c_1xe^{\frac{b}{a}x} + c_2e^{\frac{b}{a}x}.$ **21.** $y = -2e^{\frac{2}{3}x} + \frac{13}{3}xe^{\frac{2}{3}x}.$

Exercise 200.   Page 661

1. $y = e^{-x}(c_1 \cos 2x + c_2 \sin 2x),$ or $y = ke^{-x} \sin (2x + \alpha),$ etc.
3. $y = e^{-3x}(c_1 \cos 4x + c_2 \sin 4x),$ or $y = ke^{-3x} \cos (4x + \alpha),$ etc.
5. $y = e^{\frac{1}{2}x}(c_1 \cos \frac{3}{2}x + c_2 \sin \frac{3}{2}x).$ **7.** $s = c_1 \cos t + c_2 \sin t.$
9. $u = c_1 \cos \frac{2}{3}x + c_2 \sin \frac{2}{3}x.$ **11.** $y = e^{\frac{3}{2}x}[c_1 \cos \frac{1}{2}x\sqrt{3} + c_2 \sin \frac{1}{2}x\sqrt{3}].$
13. $s = c \cos (kt + \alpha),$ etc.   **15.** $s = c_1e^{-4t} + c_2e^{\frac{3}{2}t}.$
17. $y = ce^x \cos (\frac{1}{2}x + \alpha),$ etc.   **19.** $y = 2 \cos x - 3 \sin x.$
21. $y = -3 \cos 4t - \sin 4t.$ **23.** $u = e^{2x}(-3 \cos 4x + \frac{9}{4} \sin 4x).$

Exercise 201. Page 664

1. $y = c_1 e^{2x} + c_2 e^{-3x} - \frac{1}{3} - 2x$.   **3.** $y = c_1 e^{3x} + c_2 e^{-3x} - 2x + 3$.

5. $y = e^{-x}(c_1 \cos 2x + c_2 \sin 2x) + 5$.   **7.** $u = c_1 e^{\frac{3}{2}x} + c_2 e^{-\frac{3}{2}x} - 2x + x^2$.

9. $y = c_1 e^{\frac{1}{2}x} + c_2 e^{-2x} + \frac{4}{25} e^{3x}$.   **11.** $y = c_1 + c_2 e^{6x} + e^{4x}$.

13. $y = e^{-2x}(c_1 \cos x + c_2 \sin x) + 4e^{\frac{1}{2}x}$.   **15.** $y = c_1 \sin x + c_2 \cos x - 3 \cos 2x$.

17. $y = c_1 + c_2 e^{\frac{1}{2}x} - \frac{120}{111} \sin 3x + \frac{20}{111} \cos 3x$.

19. $y = c_1 \cos 3x + c_2 \sin 3x + \sin 2x + \cos 2x$.   **21.** $y = c_1 e^{-x} + c_2 e^{-2x} + x^2 + 4x$.

23. $y = c_1 + c_2 e^{\frac{2}{3}x} + x + 2x^2$.   **25.** $y = c_1 e^x + c_2 e^{-x} + 2xe^x$.

27. $y = c_1 \cos 3x + c_2 \sin 3x + x \sin 3x$.   **29.** $y = c_1 e^{2x} + c_2 e^{-x} + \frac{3}{2} xe^{-x}$.

31. $y = c_1 \cos 5x + c_2 \sin 5x - x \cos 5x - \frac{1}{2}x \sin 5x$.

33. $y = c_1 \cos \frac{1}{2}x + c_2 \sin \frac{1}{2}x + e^x + 2 \sin x$.   **35.** $y = c_1 e^x + c_2 xe^x + 5e^{2x} - 4$.

37. $y = c_1 e^{-x} + c_2 e^{\frac{1}{2}x} - 6 + 3 \sin x + \cos x$.

39. $y = c_1 e^{-5x} + c_2 xe^{-5x} + \frac{3}{2} x^2 e^{-5x}$.   **41.** $u = -\frac{4}{5} e^v - \frac{6}{5} e^{-\frac{2}{3}v} - 3v + 7$.

Exercise 202. Page 669

1. $s = 6 \sin (2t + \frac{1}{6}\pi)$; period π.   **3.** $s = 6 \sin t + 6 \cos t - 4 \sin 2t$; period π.

5. $s = -3e^{-t} \sin 2t$.   **7.** $s = e^{-2t}(-3 \cos 3t + 2 \sin 3t) + \sin t + 3 \cos t$.

9. $s = 200 - 200e^{-.1t}$; will go 200′, or $s \to 200$ as $t \to \infty$.   **11.** $2\pi/\lambda$.

Exercise 203. Page 670

1. $y = c_1 e^{2x} + e^{-3x}(c_2 + c_3 x)$.   **3.** $y = e^{2x}(c_1 + c_2 x + c_3 x^2)$.

5. $y = (\cos 3x)(c_1 + c_2 x) + (\sin 3x)(c_3 + c_4 x)$.   **7.** $u = c_1 + e^v(c_2 + c_3 v)$.

9. $s = c_1 + c_2 x + c_3 e^x$.   **11.** $y = c_1 e^x + c_2 e^{3x} + c_3 e^{-2x}$.

13. $y = c_1 e^x + e^{-\frac{1}{2}x}(c_2 \cos \frac{1}{2}x\sqrt{3} + c_3 \sin \frac{1}{2}x\sqrt{3})$.

15. $y = c_1 e^{\frac{3}{2}x} + c_2 e^{-\frac{3}{2}x} + c_3 \cos \frac{3}{2}x + c_4 \sin \frac{3}{2}x$.

17. $y = c_1 e^{-2x} + e^x(c_2 \cos x\sqrt{3} + c_3 \sin x\sqrt{3}) + \frac{5}{72} e^{4x}$.

19. $y = c_1 + c_2 x + c_3 e^{3x} + c_4 e^{-x} - \frac{1}{18}x^3 + \frac{11}{18}x^2$.

21. $y = c_1 + c_2 e^{3x} + c_3 e^{-x} + \frac{8}{65} \sin 2x + \frac{14}{65} \cos 2x$.

Exercise 204. Page 670

1. $x^2 - xy + y^2 = c$.   **3.** $\ln (x + 2)^6 - \ln (y + 3)^4 + y - 3x = c$.

5. $5xy = x^5 + c$.   **7.** $s = c_1 e^{3t} + c_2 e^{-2t}$.   **9.** $e^y \sin x + x^2 y^3 = c$.   **11.** $y = ce^{-\frac{x^2}{2y^2}}$.

13. $y = e^{-3x}(c_1 \cos x\sqrt{5} + c_2 \sin x\sqrt{5})$.   **15.** $s = \frac{1}{8} \cos 2t + c_1 t^2 + c_2 t + c_3$.

17. $y = e^x - \cos x + x + 4$.   **19.** $y = c_1 e^{-3x} + c_2 e^{\frac{1}{2}x} + \frac{1}{49} e^{4x}$.

21. $y = c_1 e^{2x} + c_2 e^{-x} + xe^{2x}$.   **23.** $3x \sin^2 t = \sin^3 t + c$.   **25.** $y = c_1 x^2 + 6c_1 x + c_2$.

27. $y = c_1 \cos 2x + c_2 \sin 2x - \frac{3}{4}x \cos 2x$.   **29.** $(y - 3)^2 + 2(x - 2)^2 = k$.

31. $\theta = \alpha \cos kt$; half-period π/k.

Index

(Numbers refer to pages.)

$$\Delta u = (x + dx)(y + dy) - xy$$